Notation:

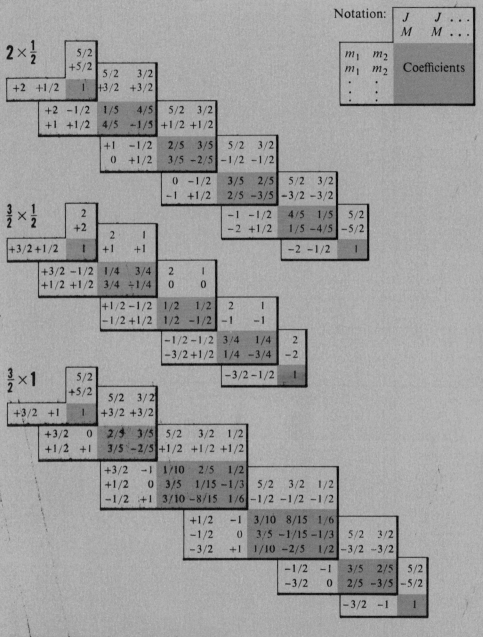

		J	J ...
		M	M ...
m_1	m_2	Coefficients	
m_1	m_2		
⋮	⋮		

$2 \times \frac{1}{2}$

m_1	m_2	J = 5/2, M = +5/2
+2	+1/2	1

m_1	m_2	J = 5/2, M = +3/2	J = 3/2, M = +3/2
+2	−1/2	1/5	4/5
+1	+1/2	4/5	−1/5

m_1	m_2	J = 5/2, M = +1/2	J = 3/2, M = +1/2
+1	−1/2	2/5	3/5
0	+1/2	3/5	−2/5

m_1	m_2	J = 5/2, M = −1/2	J = 3/2, M = −1/2
0	−1/2	3/5	2/5
−1	+1/2	2/5	−3/5

m_1	m_2	J = 5/2, M = −3/2	J = 3/2, M = −3/2
−1	−1/2	4/5	1/5
−2	+1/2	1/5	−4/5

m_1	m_2	J = 5/2, M = −5/2
−2	−1/2	1

$\frac{3}{2} \times \frac{1}{2}$

m_1	m_2	J = 2, M = +2
+3/2	+1/2	1

m_1	m_2	J = 2, M = +1	J = 1, M = +1
+3/2	−1/2	1/4	3/4
+1/2	+1/2	3/4	−1/4

m_1	m_2	J = 2, M = 0	J = 1, M = 0
+1/2	−1/2	1/2	1/2
−1/2	+1/2	1/2	−1/2

m_1	m_2	J = 2, M = −1	J = 1, M = −1
−1/2	−1/2	3/4	1/4
−3/2	+1/2	1/4	−3/4

m_1	m_2	J = 2, M = −2
−3/2	−1/2	1

$\frac{3}{2} \times 1$

m_1	m_2	J = 5/2, M = +5/2
+3/2	+1	1

m_1	m_2	J = 5/2, M = +3/2	J = 3/2, M = +3/2
+3/2	0	2/5	3/5
+1/2	+1	3/5	−2/5

m_1	m_2	J = 5/2, M = +1/2	J = 3/2, M = +1/2	J = 1/2, M = +1/2
+3/2	−1	1/10	2/5	1/2
+1/2	0	3/5	1/15	−1/3
−1/2	+1	3/10	−8/15	1/6

m_1	m_2	J = 5/2, M = −1/2	J = 3/2, M = −1/2	J = 1/2, M = −1/2
+1/2	−1	3/10	8/15	1/6
−1/2	0	3/5	−1/15	−1/3
−3/2	+1	1/10	−2/5	1/2

m_1	m_2	J = 5/2, M = −3/2	J = 3/2, M = −3/2
−1/2	−1	3/5	2/5
−3/2	0	2/5	−3/5

m_1	m_2	J = 5/2, M = −5/2
−3/2	−1	1

$$\langle j_1 j_2 m_1 m_2 | j_1 j_2 J M\rangle$$
$$= (-1)^{J-j_1-j_2} \langle j_2 j_1 m_2 m_1 | j_2 j_1 J M\rangle$$

Models of Elementary Particles

A BLAISDELL BOOK IN THE PURE AND APPLIED SCIENCES

MODELS OF ELEMENTARY PARTICLES

Bernard T. Feld

Massachusetts Institute of Technology

Blaisdell Publishing Company
A Division of Ginn and Company

Waltham, Massachusetts • Toronto • London

Library of Congress Catalog Card Number: 71–80431
Printed in the United States of America.

Preface

This book has been over ten years in the writing. It originated in a continuing series of courses on various aspects of particle and high-energy physics, given by the author at MIT, at CERN, and at Saclay and the École Polytechnique, starting in 1955. These courses have been aimed primarily at experimentalists, in an attempt to provide the necessary theoretical bases for the understanding and interpretation of experimental observations; but they have also had very much in mind the complementary need of the theorist to maintain constant and meaningful contact with the rapid accumulation of new experimental information. In essence, I have tried to provide a framework within which all physicists interested in particle and high-energy phenomena could try to "understand" what was going on.

In a field that has evolved as rapidly as this one, since the discovery by Occhialini and Powell of the π-meson in 1947, all attempts at summarizing the status of the field have been rendered obsolete almost as rapidly as they could be committed to print; indeed, the author has accumulated a number of volumes of notes which, if useful at the time, have been very rapidly outdistanced by new developments and discoveries.

However, over the years, I have tried to evolve an approach to the consideration of particle and high-energy phenomena which, it has been my hope, may be largely invariant to the vicissitudes of the specific phenomena to which it can be applied. Unfortunately, however, in addition to the obsolescence that arises inevitably from the accumulation of new experimental discoveries and theoretical inventions, any given approach is subject to an obsolescence deriving from changes in the "style" that, at any given time, dominates the theoretical framework within which observed phenomena are evaluated. Considering that a large part of high-energy "theory" is concerned with the extraction of the consequences of known invariance and conservation principles in a variety of experimental situations, the stylistic framework in which phenomena are viewed is very largely a matter of taste. Nevertheless, I am acutely aware that, to many of the younger practitioners in the field, my approach may well be regarded as excessively "short-haired." For these deficiencies I have only the excuse of age, but I have attempted to compensate for them in the final chapter.

Some years ago, at a social gathering, the attractive young wife of a European colleague exclaimed, on being introduced to me: "Oh, are you the Feld of *Feld Theorie?*" Flattered though I was, it was not until the spring of 1967 that I was able to accumulate the confidence (or foolhardiness) required to prepare for publication, this, my version of *Feld Theorie.*

So many volumes relating to this field — monographs, textbooks, lecture notes, conference proceedings, etc. — have appeared in recent years that to list them would require more space than can be justified; the interested reader will find them in overwhelming number on the shelves of any up-to-date physics reading room. Many of these volumes are referred to in the text in connection with specific applications.

For those interested in how the subject was approached in the (not-so-distant) past by some of the great master innovators, I recommend especially the following, still illuminating, volumes: W. Pauli, *Meson Theory of Nuclear Forces*, Interscience Publishers, New York (1946); G. Wentzel, *The Quantum Theory of Fields,* Interscience Publishers, New York (1949); E. Fermi, *Elementary Particles,* Yale University Press, New Haven (1951); and B. Rossi, *High Energy Particles,* Prentice-Hall, New York (1952).

For the beginning student, or the nonspecialist in the field, who has not yet accumulated the basic vocabulary or become acquainted with the variegated classifications of particle zoology, I recommend the reading of one or more of the following "popular" accounts: K. W. Ford, *The World of Elementary Particles,* Blaisdell Publishing Co., Waltham, Mass. (1963); V. F. Weisskopf, *Physics Today, 16:* 26 (1963); L. M. Brown, *Physics Today, 19:* 44 (1966); and S. F. Tuan, *Physics Today, 21:* 31 (1968).

As the reader gets into the subject, he may wish to pursue certain aspects more deeply. For this purpose, references are provided in footnotes at appropriate places in the text. In addition, there are the aforementioned recent monographs, lecture notes, etc. Beyond these, the reader should refer to the volumes of *Annual Review of Nuclear Science* (Stanford University Press), each of which has at least one excellent review article on some branch of the subject, to the frequent Supplements to the journal of the Italian Physical Society, *Il Nuovo Cimento,* and to the relatively new review journals, *Comments on Nuclear and Particle Physics* and *Physics.*

It is almost impossible to list all those to whom I am indebted for help, in one form or another, in the long process of preparation of this work. I am beholden to a large number of former students, not only for aid in the preparation of notes on earlier versions of this material, but for the intellectual stimulation that comes from having to justify new ideas and approaches to lively and questioning minds; among these students, I cannot fail to record special thanks to R. Gomez, P. C. Stein, G. Costa, B. Maglic, P. C. M. Yock, and H. C. Pradhan. Some of the material for the book was developed during periods when I was a guest at CERN in Geneva, in Paris at the École Polytechnique, and at the Atomic Energy Center in Saclay. I am most especially in the debt of Professors L. Leprince-Ringuet, F. Muller, A. Berthelot, and A. Rogozinski, for having provided the atmosphere in which this work could be effectively started and carried a long way toward completion.

A number of colleagues were kind enough to read and comment on some portions of the earlier drafts — particularly Professors H. J. Lubatti and A. H. Rosenfeld. Some problems were very kindly provided by Professors L. S. Osborne, L. Rosenson, and K. Tsipis. It is also a pleasure to record my thanks to Professor Gordon L. Kane for a critical, yet sympathetic reading of the entire work, and for his many useful suggestions for its improvement, and to Jane Zoba for repeated patient and skillful typing of the manuscript.

Finally, I would like to take this opportunity to express my profound indebtedness to two outstanding physicists — superb teachers and great men who, by their example and by their patient and friendly guidance, provided a scientific and human standard worthy of emulation by any aspiring physicist:

To the late

Enrico Fermi
and
Leo Szilard

I humbly dedicate this book.

B. T. Feld

Cambridge, Massachusetts
December 21, 1968

Contents

PART I
Phenomenological Approach

PART III

Unitary Symmetry and Quark Models

PART I

Phenomenological Approach

1

Basic Considerations

Ever since Becquerel's discovery of radioactivity, almost three-quarters of a century ago, the mysteries of the structure of the atom have been steadily peeled away, one after the other, like the layers of an onion, until it can now be asserted that what remains to be done for the understanding of atomic structure is more technical than conceptual: The application of known laws of interaction and motion to a finite number of possible combinations of electrons, protons, and neutrons that make up the atoms and whose properties, individually and collectively, determine the chemical laws of atomic combination, the physical laws of the behavior of matter in bulk, and the interactions among atomic nuclei in the so-called low-energy range of nuclear phenomena.

But even more profound than the increased knowledge of the detailed structure of the atom has been the revolution in our concepts of the nature of matter and radiation, of energy in its many forms and transformations. The discovery of relativity brought with it the inextricable mixing of space and time, of momentum, energy, and matter; and the quantum theory swept away the belief in the causal behavior of nature and abolished the distinction between particle and wave.

The study of radioactivity implied that the atom is not immutable, and Rutherford and the Curies demonstrated that the elements can be transmuted by artificial means. Pauli and Fermi proved that some of the processes of radioactivity involve the creation of matter waves in a new form — the neutrino. Then Dirac, through a brilliant mixture of mathematical deduction and physical insight, introduced the concept of antimatter, and the possibility of its materialization out of radiant energy alone. Yukawa took the final step of abolishing completely the distinction between matter and radiation; all was in the field, latently present and indeed necessary to account for the forces between particles, and requiring only the appropriate physical circumstances to become manifest in observable form.

At first, physicists had available only the sources provided by nature — the radiations from naturally radioactive nuclei — as a means of probing into the inner structure of the atomic nucleus; and it is remarkable indeed how far they were able to proceed with these *ad hoc* tools. But it was not long before laboratory sources were devised that were capable of controlled acceleration of nuclear projectiles, so that the structure of nuclei could be systematically and efficiently unraveled. Still, the energies available in these devices, while sufficient for investigations into the atomic nucleus, were not great enough for the next step: probing into the structure of the nucleonic particles themselves — the protons and neutrons that make up atomic nuclei. Fortunately, at the same time that the magnificent insight of Yukawa provided the first convincing clue to the possibility of observation of new forms of matter, the mesons that serve as the quanta for transmission of the nuclear force field, and indicated that the realm of energies necessary to achieve their materialization was in the hundreds of millions of electron volts, a source of projectiles in this energy range was already conveniently available through the study of cosmic rays. So it was that the mesons of Yukawa were discovered in cosmic radiation (as Anderson had discovered the positron, or antielectron, in the preceding decade), and the ingenious experiments pioneered by Occhialini and Powell, utilizing photographic emulsion techniques, were able to deduce their main characteristics and properties.

However, advanced accelerator technology did not lag far behind and soon provided the requisite energies and the instrumentation adequate for the controlled and systematic elucidation of these new forms of particles and for the systematic study of the many new forms of unstable particles that began to be uncovered in the exploration of this fecund realm of elementary particle spectroscopy.

What has emerged in the ever deepening investigation of the elementary particles and their variety of states and interactions is still far from being adequately understood or explained. In addition to the vast accumulation of information about the detailed properties of these particles and their modes of interaction and decay, there is a growing insight into how to approach their study, into how they should be regarded and correlated — in short, a new theoretical framework into which we may eventually hope to fit the facts and from which, in due time, will emerge a "theory" adequate to correlate all the observations and to predict and fit whatever new facts continuing investigations are certain to uncover.

This theoretical framework has a number of essential elements. Perhaps the most important may be described by the simple statement of Feynman: All particles are equally elementary. However, owing to the nature of the force fields governing their interactions, the different states of the elementary particles have different energies, or masses. A state of higher energy, or mass, will decay into lower mass states provided it can do so through the emission of other elementary particles without violating any of the laws of conservation or selection. Thus, some of the elementary particles have a relatively transitory existence, while others are relatively stable, for example, the neutron and proton [1] which, being unable to decay, form the nuclei of the stable atoms.

Nevertheless, as will be seen in this work, it is frequently convenient and even fruitful to develop models of the elementary particles in which some of them figure as the building blocks out of which the others are constructed. (All particles are equally elementary, but some appear to be more elementary than others.) The usefulness of such models notwithstanding, it must always be borne in mind that they serve only as convenient simplifications for the as yet incompletely understood laws governing the dynamical interactions among the various states of matter in its elementary forms. It must further be remembered that these assumed building blocks, while resembling in their characteristics some of the observed particle states, are generally to be regarded as fictitious and probably unobservable mathematical constructs designed to represent in a physically envisageable manner the consequences of an as yet poorly understood theory.

On the other hand, the successes of such models are probably not entirely accidental. Rather, they may be taken as an indication of one of the underlying features of the contemporary view of the elementary particles — that each state must be regarded as being composed of appropriate combinations of all the others. Thus, the description of any one of the elementary particles involves a kind of "bootstrap" operation, in which the description of its structure requires a knowledge of the interactions of combinations of all the others. The utility of a given model depends on the dominance of one or just a few of the combinations of constituents in the determination of the particular properties under consideration.

One of the important elements of the modern view of elementary particles is the clear distinction among the different types of interactions that govern their behavior. Thus, we recognize a hierarchy of interactions, four in number, with the major member — the forces that bind together the particles in the nucleus and also account for the variety of nucleonic states — referred to as the "strong" interactions. The elementary particle states determined by the strong interactions are collectively referred to as the *hadrons;* they are subdivided into nucleonic-type particles, or *baryons* — which, having half-integral spin, obey the Fermi–Dirac statistics — and the *integral-spin mesons* — which behave in the manner of the particles devised by Yukawa to act as the transmitters of the nuclear force field. Next in order of strength in the hierarchy is the electromagnetic interaction, mediated by the photons, whose nature is very adequately described by the laws of quantum electrodynamics, the quantum extension of Maxwell's classical laws of electromagnetism. The third type of force field is that which governs the β decay of nuclei, but which is recognized to be of a much more universal character, governing the decay of all those elementary particle states energetically incapable of strong hadron emission or prohibited by strong or

[1] Indeed, the proton is "absolutely" stable, with a lifetime greater than 10^{28} yr [F. Reines, C. L. Cowen, Jr., and M. Goldhaber, *Phys. Rev., 96:* 1157 (1954)]. The neutron is unstable against β decay in its free state, with a mean life of 1000 sec. However, inside nuclear matter containing the appropriate proportion of protons and neutrons, it is stabilized by the nuclear binding force.

electromagnetic interaction selection rules from decaying to lower hadronic states. These "weak" interactions give rise to the creation of the neutrino, and have a form distinctively different from that of the strong interactions, while being at the same time intimately related to them. Finally, there is the gravitational force field, a *tensor* interaction (that is, one whose quanta carry spin 2) which determines the behavior of matter in bulk — the motion of the planets, for example — but whose relation to the other interactions among the elementary particles is not understood at this time.

But perhaps the major aspect of the contemporary revolution in the conception of the elementary particles lies in the realization of the correspondence between the laws of conservation and selection among the elementary particle interactions and the basic symmetries inherent in the structure of the universe — symmetries and invariance properties that are frequently geometrical in their origin. Relativity is basically an expression of such invariance-symmetry principles. For example, the inability of observers to distinguish between different frames of reference in uniform relative motion leads to the Lorentz transformations, and the conservation of mass-energy (the invariance of the length of 4-vectors). The invariance of the laws of nature to the choice of origin of the coordinate system used in their description has as a consequence the law of conservation of momentum, while the law of conservation of energy follows from the invariance of the laws of nature with respect to the choice of origin of the time axis. Invariance under rotation of the coordinate system about an arbitrary space axis implies the conservation of angular momentum; equivalence of right- and left-handed coordinate systems leads to the conservation of parity; and, in a strange and subtle fashion, the assumption of the invariance of natural laws with respect to the direction of the time axis (time-reversal invariance), together with the geometrical invariances noted above, gives rise to the equivalence of particle and antiparticle systems (charge-conjugation invariance).

Other important relationships that can be derived among the elementary particles and their interactions are more mathematical or analytical than geometrical in their origin. Thus, for example, the quantum expression of the concept of causality — that no signal can be transmitted with a speed greater than that of light — leads to a set of relations among the amplitudes of the wave functions describing observable systems (the dispersion relations) that are of wide and significant applicability. The connections between the statistical behavior of identical particles (that is, Fermi–Dirac versus Bose–Einstein statistics) and their spin may be deduced from the quantum-mechanical commutation rules. The analytical continuation of the mathematical description of angular momentum into the complex plane gives rise to the concept of *Regge poles* and to relations governing the dependence of the scattering of elementary particles on energy. Such relations, and others, are basic to the conceptual approach to contemporary elementary particle theory.

But what is probably the most exciting aspect of recent developments in elementary particle physics is the recognition of the correspondence between the observed particle states and the elements of certain mathematical groups (generally, the Lie groups). These relationships have permitted the correlation and prediction of connections between the observed static properties of most of the known particle states and the prediction of a number of the particles most recently discovered, as well as connections among some dynamical aspects of their interactions. These group properties lie at the basis of the models of the elementary particles that are currently proving to be so fruitful and that are the main subject of this work.

1.1 Yukawa Theory

Yukawa[2] introduced the concept of the meson as the carrier (quantum) of the nuclear field. According to this approach, the basic interaction between nucleons, $\mathfrak{N}$ ($\mathfrak{N}$ = proton P or neutron N), can be thought of as arising from the spontaneous emission and absorption of π-mesons,

$$\mathfrak{N} \rightleftharpoons \mathfrak{N} + \pi, \tag{1}$$

in analogy to the electromagnetic case, in which the exchange of photons gives rise to the electromagnetic field,

$$e \rightleftharpoons e + \gamma. \tag{2}$$

Pursuing the analogy between the photon and the meson fields, we may define a *meson potential,* φ, which represents the amplitude of the meson field; $\varphi\varphi^*(\mathbf{r}, t)$ is the probability of finding a meson at the position $\mathbf{r}$ at the time t. At the same time, in the quantized version of meson field theory, φ^* and φ are, respectively, meson creation and destruction operators which, when acting on an appropriate (nucleon) source function, lead to the emission and absorption of π-mesons by the source. The meson potential φ is assumed to obey Laplace's equation, modified, however, to take into account the finite rest mass, μ, of the meson. In the absence of sources, φ is given by the (free) field equation

$$(\Box^2 - \kappa^2)\varphi = \left(\nabla^2 - \frac{1}{c^2}\frac{\partial^2}{\partial t^2} - \kappa^2\right)\varphi = 0. \tag{3}$$

Equation (3) has plane-wave solutions

$$\varphi = e^{i(\mathbf{k}\cdot\mathbf{r} - \omega t)}, \tag{4}$$

where $\mathbf{k}$ and ω are, respectively, the wave number and frequency of the meson plane wave. Substitution into Equation (3) gives

$$k^2 + \kappa^2 = \frac{\omega^2}{c^2}. \tag{5}$$

Invoking the De Broglie relationships between wave number and momentum,

$$\hbar k = p, \tag{5a}$$

and between frequency and particle energy,

$$\hbar\omega = E, \tag{5b}$$

[2] H. Yukawa, *Proc. Phys.-Math. Soc.* (Japan), *17:* 48 (1935).

we note that Equation (5) becomes

$$p^2 + \hbar^2\kappa^2 = \frac{E^2}{c^2}. \tag{5$'$}$$

Thus, κ is related to the meson mass

$$\hbar^2\kappa^2 = \mu^2 c^2, \tag{5c}$$

the inverse of κ being the pion Compton wavelength

$$\kappa^{-1} = \frac{\hbar}{\mu c}. \tag{5c$'$}$$

According to the Yukawa theory, the meson field is generated by nucleonic sources. We consider the Poisson equation corresponding to a static, point nucleon source at the origin,

$$\nabla^2\varphi - \kappa^2\varphi = -4\pi g\ \delta(\mathbf{r} = 0), \tag{6}$$

where g is the interaction strength, analogous for the nucleonic field to the electron charge e, whose magnitude determines the strength of the electromagnetic interaction.[3] Solution of Equation (6) gives, for the meson potential,

$$\varphi = g\,\frac{e^{-\kappa r}}{r}. \tag{6a}$$

Note that, in contrast to the "infinite" range of the electrostatic $(1/r)$ potential, the Yukawa field has the finite range

$$R = \kappa^{-1} = \frac{\hbar}{\mu c} \tag{6b}$$

inversely proportional to the meson mass. Qualitatively, the finite range of the Yukawa potential may be understood in terms of Heisenberg's uncertainty principle, $\Delta x \Delta p \gtrsim \hbar$, by associating the range with the uncertainty in position of an emitted (virtual) meson, $\Delta x \approx R$, which, owing to its finite mass, carries the corresponding momentum uncertainty[4] $\Delta p \approx \mu c$.

The static potential energy of interaction of the meson field [Equation (6a)] with a second nucleon, whose position density is $\rho'(\mathbf{r})$, is

$$V = -g\int \rho'(\mathbf{r})\ \varphi(\mathbf{r})\ d\mathbf{r}. \tag{7}$$

Taking $\rho'(\mathbf{r}) = \delta(\mathbf{r})$, we have

$$V = -g^2\,\frac{e^{-\kappa r}}{r}, \tag{7a}$$

---

[3] The dimensionless constant $g^2/\hbar c \approx 0.1$–1 is the analogue, for the Yukawa field, of the fine structure constant $\alpha = e^2/\hbar c = \frac{1}{137}$ which characterizes the strength of the Maxwell field.

[4] Alternatively, the uncertainty relationships may be interpreted in terms of the inability to specify the system's energy, $\Delta E \approx \mu c^2$, associated with the time, $\Delta t \approx R/c$, required for the process of virtual emission and reabsorption of the meson, through the canonical relationship $\Delta E\ \Delta t \gtrsim \hbar$.

which is the standard Yukawa interaction between two nucleons corresponding to the exchange of a *scalar* meson. We may rewrite Equation (7a) as follows:

$$V(r) = -g^2\kappa \frac{e^{-\kappa r}}{\kappa r} = -\left(\frac{g^2}{\hbar c}\right)(\mu c^2)\mathcal{Y}(\kappa r). \tag{7a$'$}$$

In this form, we observe clearly the main characteristics of the Yukawa interaction: it is attractive; its depth, measured in terms of the meson rest energy μc^2, is determined by the value of the dimensionless coupling $g^2/\hbar c$; its spatial dependence $\mathcal{Y}(\kappa r) = e^{-\kappa r}/\kappa r$ falls off exponentially with $r > R = \kappa^{-1}$.

However, the mesons most abundantly observed in nature, the π-mesons, or pions, which act as the carriers of the strong nucleonic interactions, exhibit two features that are at variance with those expected for the quanta of the scalar meson field described above: first, in addition to the neutral variety, the π^0, two other, charged members are observed: the π^+ and π^-. In fact, the three pions π^+, π^0, π^- behave like an isotopic triplet, in the sense that their interactions with nucleons exhibit the property of "charge independence" or, more accurately, isotopic invariance, a property we shall discuss in greater detail in a following section.

In addition, the π-mesons can be demonstrated to be *pseudoscalar,* which is to say that they have spin 0 but negative intrinsic parity. Thus, in contrast to the simple behavior described by Equation (6), which corresponds to the emission and absorption of mesons in an S state (orbital angular momentum $l = 0$), the π-mesons are observed to be emitted and absorbed preferentially in a P state ($l = 1$). The field-theoretic description of this characteristic requires a modified Poisson equation of the form

$$\Box^2\varphi - \kappa^2\varphi = -\frac{4\pi f}{\kappa}(\boldsymbol{\sigma}\cdot\boldsymbol{\nabla})\rho(\mathbf{r}, t, \mathbf{s}), \tag{8a}$$

in which $\boldsymbol{\sigma}$ is the Pauli vector representing the spin $\frac{1}{2}$ state of the nucleonic source. Since the right-hand side of Equation (8a) has negative parity, owing to the negative parity of the gradient operator $\boldsymbol{\nabla}$, the meson field operator φ must correspondingly behave as a pseudoscalar, i.e., a particle of spin 0^-,

$$\varphi(-r) = -\varphi(r). \tag{8b}$$

Since the operator $\boldsymbol{\sigma}\cdot\boldsymbol{\nabla}$ acts on the spin of the nucleon, as well as on the space coordinates, the nucleon density function must contain an appropriate component representing the state of its spin, $\mathbf{s}$:

$$\rho(\mathbf{r}, t, \mathbf{s}) = \rho(\mathbf{r}, t)\chi(\mathbf{s}). \tag{8c}$$

In particular, the nucleon having spin $\frac{1}{2}$, the spin function $\chi(\mathbf{s})$ has, with respect to an arbitrary spin axis, two eigenstates, α and β, representing, respectively, the values $+\frac{1}{2}$ and $-\frac{1}{2}$ of the z component of the spin.

The static (time-independent) solution of Equation (8a) is

$$\begin{aligned}\varphi &= \frac{f}{\kappa}\int \frac{e^{-\kappa|\mathbf{r}-\mathbf{r}'|}}{|\mathbf{r}-\mathbf{r}'|}(\boldsymbol{\sigma}\cdot\boldsymbol{\nabla}')\rho(\mathbf{r}',\mathbf{s})\,d\mathbf{r}' \\ &= \frac{f}{\kappa}\int \boldsymbol{\sigma}\rho(\mathbf{r}',\mathbf{s})\cdot\boldsymbol{\nabla}'\frac{e^{-\kappa|\mathbf{r}-\mathbf{r}'|}}{|\mathbf{r}-\mathbf{r}'|}\,d\mathbf{r}', \end{aligned} \tag{9}$$

which, for the case of a point nucleon,

$$\rho(\mathbf{r},\mathbf{s}) = \delta(\mathbf{r}=0)\chi(\mathbf{s}), \tag{10a}$$

becomes

$$\begin{aligned}\varphi &= f\boldsymbol{\sigma}\chi(\mathbf{s})\cdot\nabla\frac{e^{-\kappa r}}{\kappa r} \\ &= -f\kappa\boldsymbol{\sigma}\chi(\mathbf{s})\cdot\mathbf{r}_0\mathcal{Y}'(\kappa r),\end{aligned} \tag{10b}$$

where $\mathbf{r}_0$ is a unit vector. In Equation (10b) the spatial dependence is given by the modified (P-wave) Yukawa function

$$\mathcal{Y}'(\kappa r) = -\frac{1}{\kappa}\frac{d}{dr}\left(\frac{e^{-\kappa r}}{\kappa r}\right) = (1+\kappa r)\frac{e^{-\kappa r}}{\kappa^2 r^2}, \tag{10c}$$

which, for $\kappa r \gg 1$, reduces to the ordinary Yukawa function

$$\mathcal{Y}'(\kappa r \gg 1) \rightarrow \frac{e^{-\kappa r}}{\kappa r} = \mathcal{Y}(\kappa r). \tag{10d}$$

In this case, the potential energy between two point nucleons becomes ($\mathbf{r}=\mathbf{r}_1-\mathbf{r}_2$)

$$\begin{aligned}V(r_1,r_2) &= -f\int \rho'(\mathbf{r}_2,\mathbf{s}_2)\varphi(\mathbf{r},\mathbf{s}_1)\,d\mathbf{r} \\ &= \frac{f^2}{\kappa^2}(\boldsymbol{\sigma}_1\cdot\boldsymbol{\nabla}_1)(\boldsymbol{\sigma}_2\cdot\boldsymbol{\nabla}_2)\chi_1(\mathbf{s}_1)\chi_2(\mathbf{s}_2)\frac{e^{-\kappa r}}{r} \\ &= \frac{f^2\kappa}{3}\left\{S_{12}\left(\frac{3}{\kappa^2 r^2}+\frac{3}{\kappa r}+1\right)+\boldsymbol{\sigma}_1\cdot\boldsymbol{\sigma}_2\right\}\chi_1(\mathbf{s}_1)\chi_2(\mathbf{s}_2)\mathcal{Y}(\kappa r),\end{aligned} \tag{11}$$

where S_{12} is the tensor force operator,

$$S_{12} = 3(\boldsymbol{\sigma}_1\cdot\mathbf{r}_0)(\boldsymbol{\sigma}_2\cdot\mathbf{r}_0) - \boldsymbol{\sigma}_1\cdot\boldsymbol{\sigma}_2 . \tag{11a}$$

Thus, in the case of the pseudoscalar meson field, the nucleon-nucleon potential is not only spin-dependent but, according to the properties of S_{12}, becomes noncentral as well.

Returning to the expression for the pion field, Equation (10b), we note that its *angular dependence* may be determined by consideration of the effect of the $\boldsymbol{\sigma}\cdot\boldsymbol{\nabla}$ operator,

$$\boldsymbol{\sigma}\cdot\boldsymbol{\nabla} = \tfrac{1}{2}\sigma_+\nabla_- + \tfrac{1}{2}\sigma_-\nabla_+ + \sigma_z\nabla_z, \tag{12}$$

with

$$\sigma_\pm = \sigma_x \pm i\sigma_y, \tag{12a}$$

$$\nabla_\pm = \frac{\partial}{\partial x} \pm i\frac{\partial}{\partial y}. \tag{12b}$$

In Equation (12), $\boldsymbol{\sigma}$ is the three-component Pauli spin operator represented by the 2×2 matrices

$$\sigma_x = \begin{pmatrix} 0 & 1 \\ 1 & 0 \end{pmatrix}, \qquad \sigma_y = \begin{pmatrix} 0 & -\mathrm{i} \\ \mathrm{i} & 0 \end{pmatrix}, \qquad \sigma_z = \begin{pmatrix} 1 & 0 \\ 0 & -1 \end{pmatrix}. \tag{12c}$$

Let α represent the $m = \frac{1}{2}$ (spin-up) nucleon state $\chi(\alpha) = \begin{Bmatrix} 1 \\ 0 \end{Bmatrix}$, and β the spin-down, $\chi(\beta) = \begin{Bmatrix} 0 \\ 1 \end{Bmatrix}$. We may consider simultaneously the effect of both possibilities,

$$(\boldsymbol{\sigma} \cdot \boldsymbol{\nabla}) \begin{Bmatrix} \alpha \\ \beta \end{Bmatrix} \frac{e^{-\kappa r}}{\kappa r} = \begin{Bmatrix} -\beta \sin\theta\, e^{i\varphi} - \alpha \cos\theta \\ -\alpha \sin\theta\, e^{-i\varphi} + \beta \cos\theta \end{Bmatrix} \kappa \mathcal{Y}'(\kappa r), \tag{13a}$$

whence

$$\varphi = f\kappa \begin{Bmatrix} \sqrt{\tfrac{2}{3}}\, \beta Y_1^1(\theta,\varphi) - \sqrt{\tfrac{1}{3}}\, \alpha Y_1^0(\theta,\varphi) \\ -\sqrt{\tfrac{2}{3}}\, \alpha Y_1^{-1}(\theta,\varphi) + \sqrt{\tfrac{1}{3}}\, \beta Y_1^0(\theta,\varphi) \end{Bmatrix} \mathcal{Y}'(\kappa r). \tag{13b}$$

The upper and lower parts in the braces $\begin{Bmatrix} P_{1/2,1/2} \\ P_{1/2,-1/2} \end{Bmatrix}$ represent a spin $\frac{1}{2}$ nucleon combined with an $l = 1$ pion into a $P_{1/2}$ state with $m = +\frac{1}{2}$ and $-\frac{1}{2}$, respectively.

Equation (13b) describes the spatial distribution of the meson field resulting from a spin $\frac{1}{2}$ nucleon source, but there is still no provision made for the possibility of different pion charge states; in fact, the field represented by Equation (13b) corresponds to emission of neutral pseudoscalar mesons only — i.e., the π^0 — in processes like

$$P \rightleftharpoons P + \pi^0, \tag{14a}$$

$$N \rightleftharpoons N + \pi^0. \tag{14b}$$

For the true pion field, on the other hand, in addition to the emission of neutral pions, we have the possibility of charged pion emission

$$P \rightleftharpoons N + \pi^+, \tag{14c}$$

$$N \rightleftharpoons P + \pi^-. \tag{14d}$$

To describe reactions (14a)–(14d) in a charge-independent (that is, isotopically invariant) manner, we represent the two states of the nucleon as a dichotomic variable or spinor $\begin{Bmatrix} p \\ n \end{Bmatrix}$ in a fictitious charge space

$$P = \begin{Bmatrix} 1 \\ 0 \end{Bmatrix}, \qquad N = \begin{Bmatrix} 0 \\ 1 \end{Bmatrix}, \tag{15a}$$

and construct an isotopic-spin operator $\boldsymbol{\tau}$ in complete analogy to the Pauli spin operator $\boldsymbol{\sigma}$ [Equations (12a) and (12c)], such that the combinations $\tau_\pm$ change N to P and vice versa, while τ_z distinguishes between the two charge states (eigenvalues $\tau_z = \pm\frac{1}{2}$) of the nucleon $\mathfrak{N}$ of isotopic spin $t = \frac{1}{2}$. The pion, on the other hand, having three eigenvalues of the charge, is represented by a vector in charge space (isotopic spin $t=1$), and the meson field must accordingly be a three-component vector field $\boldsymbol{\varphi}$. Correspondingly, the source term in Equation (8a) must be modified to become

$$\frac{-4\pi f}{\kappa}\boldsymbol{\tau}(\boldsymbol{\sigma}\cdot\boldsymbol{\nabla})\rho(\mathbf{r},t,\mathbf{s},\boldsymbol{\tau}), \tag{15b}$$

with

$$\rho(\mathbf{r},t,\mathbf{s},\boldsymbol{\tau})=\rho(\mathbf{r},t)\chi(\mathbf{s})\begin{Bmatrix}p\\n\end{Bmatrix}, \tag{15c}$$

and the modified static solution of Equation (8a) becomes

$$\boldsymbol{\varphi}=-f\kappa\boldsymbol{\tau}\begin{Bmatrix}p\\n\end{Bmatrix}\boldsymbol{\sigma}\chi(\mathbf{s})\cdot\mathbf{r}_0\,\mathcal{Y}'(\kappa r). \tag{15d}$$

In order to investigate the *charge distribution* in the pion field, we must associate the components of the meson field amplitude $\boldsymbol{\varphi}$ with the meson creation operators

$$\phi^*=\sqrt{\tfrac{1}{2}}\,(\varphi_x+i\varphi_y), \tag{16a}$$

which creates a (−) π^+,

$$\phi=\sqrt{\tfrac{1}{2}}\,(\varphi_x-i\varphi_y), \tag{16b}$$

which creates a π^-, and

$$\phi_3=\varphi_z, \tag{16c}$$

which creates a π^0. The pion charge state is now projected out as follows:

$$\boldsymbol{\phi}\cdot\boldsymbol{\varphi}=f\kappa\begin{Bmatrix}P_{1/2,1/2}\\P_{1/2,-1/2}\end{Bmatrix}\mathcal{Y}'(\kappa r)\boldsymbol{\tau}\cdot\boldsymbol{\phi}\begin{Bmatrix}p\\n\end{Bmatrix}, \tag{17}$$

with

$$\begin{aligned}\boldsymbol{\tau}\cdot\boldsymbol{\phi}&=\sqrt{2}\,\tau_+\phi+\sqrt{2}\,\tau_-\phi^*+\tau_3\phi_3\\&=\sqrt{2}\,\tau_+\pi^--\sqrt{2}\,\tau_-\pi^++\tau_3\pi^0,\end{aligned} \tag{17a}$$

giving, finally,

$$\boldsymbol{\phi}\cdot\boldsymbol{\varphi}=f\kappa\begin{Bmatrix}P_{1/2,1/2}\\P_{1/2,-1/2}\end{Bmatrix}\begin{Bmatrix}-\sqrt{2}\,n\pi^++p\pi^0\\\sqrt{2}\,p\pi^--n\pi^0\end{Bmatrix}\mathcal{Y}'(\kappa r), \tag{17b}$$

as a complete description of the Yukawa process. We note that the second brace $\begin{Bmatrix}(\mathfrak{N}\pi)_{1/2,1/2}\\(\mathfrak{N}\pi)_{1/2,-1/2}\end{Bmatrix}$ describes the charge combination of a nucleon ($t=\frac{1}{2}$) and a pion ($t=1$) combined in the isotopic spin $t=\frac{1}{2}$ state.

To summarize: the Yukawa reaction leads to the emission by a nucleon of a pion in a $P_{1/2}$ state ($l=1$) and in a (charge) state of total isotopic spin $t=\frac{1}{2}$. We may conveniently abbreviate it as follows:

$$\begin{Bmatrix} p \\ n \end{Bmatrix} \begin{Bmatrix} \alpha \\ \beta \end{Bmatrix} \begin{matrix} \rightarrow \\ \leftarrow \end{matrix} \begin{Bmatrix} -\sqrt{2}\, n\pi^+ + p\pi^0 \\ \sqrt{2}\, p\pi^- - n\pi^0 \end{Bmatrix} \begin{Bmatrix} \sqrt{2}\, \beta Y_1^1 - \alpha Y_1^0 \\ -\sqrt{2}\, \alpha Y_1^{-1} + \beta Y_1^0 \end{Bmatrix}, \tag{18}$$

from which we may obtain the appropriate combination for any given initial state by the product of the corresponding elements on the right in Equation (18), for example,

$$P_{-1/2} \rightleftharpoons 2n\alpha\pi^+ Y_1^{-1} - \sqrt{2}\, n\beta\pi^+ Y_1^0 - \sqrt{2}\, p\alpha\pi^0 Y_1^{-1} + p\beta\pi^0 Y_1^0, \tag{18a}$$

and so forth. That is, a real (physical) proton in the spin state $m = -\frac{1}{2}$ is, as a result of the Yukawa pion emission process, composed of the combination of an $m = \frac{1}{2}$ neutron with a P-wave π^+ in the $m_l = -1$ state; of an $m = -\frac{1}{2}$ neutron and π^+ with $m_l = 0$; of an $m = \frac{1}{2}$ proton and π^0 with $m_l = -1$; and of an $m = -\frac{1}{2}$ proton and π^0 with $m_l = 0$. The relative probabilities and phases are given by the coefficients of the corresponding terms in Equation (18a).

Given the Poisson equation corresponding to the pion field, with the appropriate nucleon source term, it is possible to compute the amplitude for the scattering of mesons by physical nucleons. This computation, however, is more complicated than in the analogous case of the scattering of photons by, say, electrons, owing to the considerably larger value of the mesonic coupling constant (g or f) than the electron charge e, with the consequence that conventional perturbation-theoretic techniques, which work so well in the electromagnetic case, cannot be reliably applied to the meson-nucleon scattering problem.

We may, nevertheless, deduce some of the qualitative features of meson-nucleon scattering, especially at low energy, through use of the perturbation approach, or simply by taking advantage of the analogy between the meson and the photon fields. Consider, for example, the scalar meson field, Equation (6). In the case of the scattering of long-wavelength photons by free electrons of mass m (Thompson scattering) the cross section is

$$\sigma_{\mathrm{Th}} = \frac{8\pi}{3}\left(\frac{e^2}{mc^2}\right)^2 = \frac{8\pi}{3}\left(\frac{e^2}{\hbar c}\right)^2\left(\frac{\hbar}{mc}\right)^2. \tag{19a}$$

For the analogous slow meson scattering by nucleons, mass M, the cross section will be[5]

$$\sigma_{\mathrm{sc}} = 4\pi\left(\frac{g^2}{Mc^2}\right)^2 = 4\pi\left(\frac{g^2}{\hbar c}\right)^2\left(\frac{\hbar}{Mc}\right)^2 \cong 200\ \mu\text{b (microbarns)},^6 \tag{19b}$$

where we have assumed $(g^2/\hbar c) \approx 0.2$. This cross section is of an order of magnitude smaller than the low-energy ($p_\pi \ll \mu c$) pion-nucleon scattering cross section; besides, Equation (19b) is energy independent while, in contrast, the π–$\mathfrak{N}$ scattering cross section rises rapidly with increasing pion momentum, roughly in proportion to p_π^4.

These discrepancies between the predictions of the scalar theory and the

[5] The factor $8\pi/3 = \frac{2}{3} \cdot 4\pi$ in the Thompson scattering formula arises from the fact that the photon has only two polarization states rather than the three states of polarization corresponding to a normal (finite rest mass) particle of spin 1.

[6] 1 barn = 1 b = $10^{-24}\ \mathrm{cm}^2$.

observed scattering disappear in the consideration of field theories involving pseudoscalar charged mesons, as a consequence of both the spin dependence [Equation (8a)] and the isotopic-spin dependence [Equation (15b)] of the nucleon-source term in the Poisson equation that governs the emission and absorption of pseudoscalar charged mesons. The latter has the effect that the scattering of charged mesons can result from an isotopic spin-flip process, analogous to the magnetic scattering of photons by a source with an anomalous magnetic moment of $\sim e\hbar/\mu c$, with the consequence that the amplitude for meson scattering now involves the pion mass μ rather than the nucleon mass M. In other words, scattering requires that the incident pion wave excite only the pion cloud, rather than the nucleon core itself. Thus the scattering cross section for charged scalar mesons becomes[7]

$$\sigma_{\text{sc}} \cong 4\pi\left(\frac{g^2}{\mu c^2}\right)^2 = 4\pi\left(\frac{g^2}{\hbar c}\right)^2\left(\frac{\hbar}{\mu c}\right)^2 \approx 10 \text{ mb (millibarns)}. \tag{19c}$$

In addition, the effect of the $(\boldsymbol{\sigma} \cdot \boldsymbol{\nabla})$ factor in the meson source term (the pseudoscalar nature of the meson field) is to introduce a typical P-wave dependence into the meson-scattering cross section which, still for $p_\pi \ll \mu c$, finally results in[8]

$$\sigma_{\text{sc}}(\pi\text{–}\mathfrak{N}) \cong 4\pi\left(\frac{f^2}{\hbar c}\right)^2\left(\frac{\hbar}{\mu c}\right)^2\left(\frac{\mu c^2}{E_\pi}\right)^2\left(\frac{p_\pi}{\mu c}\right)^4. \tag{19d}$$

Equation (19d) implies that low-energy pion-nucleon scattering is dominated by the P-wave amplitude, which indeed it is. However, there is also observed a small amount of S-wave π–$\mathfrak{N}$ scattering [which, of course, dominates as $p_\pi \to 0$; see Equations (19e) and (19e′)], whose phase shifts have the interesting property

$$a_{0,1} + 2a_{0,3} \cong 0, \tag{20a}$$

$$a_{0,1} - a_{0,3} \cong 0.27\left(\frac{\hbar}{\mu c}\right), \tag{20b}$$

where $a_{0,1}$ and $a_{0,3}$ are, respectively, the $l=0$ scattering lengths in the isospin $\frac{1}{2}$ and $\frac{3}{2}$ states. Although small S-wave scattering terms are expected to arise from the finite mass of the nucleon, as a result of the nucleon recoil term (pro-

---

[7] More accurately, $4\pi(g^2/\hbar c)^2(\hbar/\mu c)^2(\mu c^2/E_\pi)^2$, the last factor arising from the "normalization" factor $(\hbar c/2\omega_\pi V)$ of the incident meson plane-wave. At low meson energies, $E_\pi = \hbar\omega_\pi \approx \mu c^2$.

[8] Generally, in terms of the scattering phase shifts, δ_l,

$$\sigma_{\text{sc}} = \frac{4\pi}{k^2}\sum_l (2l+1)\sin^2\delta_l, \tag{19e}$$

with

$$\delta_l \cong a_l k^{2l+1}. \tag{19e'}$$

For $\hbar k \ll \mu c$, the momentum dependences of Equations (19c) and (19d) follow for $l=0$ and 1, respectively.

portional to $\mu/M \approx \frac{1}{7}$) a perturbation (Born approximation) computation, starting with Equation (15b), fails to yield even roughly the observed values [Equations (20a) and (20b)]. However, this computation when done correctly is a difficult and complex one, and recent applications of more sophisticated techniques — dispersion relations, current algebra, and so on — especially taking into account the possibility of ρ-meson exchange in π–$\mathfrak{N}$ scattering, have demonstrated that the S-wave phase shifts can be reasonably explained.[9]

At the opposite extreme of very high incident pion momenta, $p_\pi \gg \mu c$, we expect inelastic processes to dominate owing to the strength of the interaction. The result will be a typical diffraction type of elastic scattering with, however, the size of the diffracting object being characterized by the dimensions of the pion cloud around the nucleon, which is the pion Compton wavelength, $\hbar/\mu c \simeq 1.4 \times 10^{-13}$ cm $= 1.4$ f (fermis). High-energy phenomena are discussed in Chapter 11.

It is in the intermediate energy range that the complications of the strong coupling render the field-theoretic computations most difficult and suspect. Indeed, the complexity of the actual situation is evident from the observation that, in the range of pion momenta[10] up to $\sim$ 1–2 GeV/c, the pion-nucleon scattering cross section exhibits a number of resonances. Of these, the lowest, at a total *cm* energy[11] of 1238 MeV, plays a dominant role in all low-energy pion-nucleon phenomena. It has total angular momentum $j = \frac{3}{2}^+$ (i.e., resonant pion-nucleon scattering in the $P_{3/2}$ state) and total isotopic spin $t = \frac{3}{2}$ [i.e., four charge states (+2, +1, 0, −1), the highest and lowest being, respectively, pure π^+P and π^-N combinations, while the states of charge +1 and 0 are the appropriate combinations of pions and nucleons, orthogonal to the $t = \frac{1}{2}$ charge combinations shown in Equation (18)]. That it should be this state, frequently referred to as the (3, 3) nucleon isobar, $\mathfrak{N}^*(3,3)$ or $\mathfrak{N}^*(1238)$ or Δ, which dominates the low-energy pion-nucleon interaction, can be understood in rough, qualitative fashion as follows: According to Equation (18), the state of nucleon core plus virtual pion, which may be thought of as giving a crude first-approximation representation of the physical nucleon, is one in which the pion cloud is in a $P_{1/2}$ state with respect to the nucleon core, the total isospin of the system being $t = \frac{1}{2}$. Now, suppose we attempt to add a second pion to this system in the state of maximum binding to the nucleon core; this second pion will also prefer to be added in the $P_{1/2}$, $t = \frac{1}{2}$ state, *with respect to the core.* Thus, both the orbital angular momentum vector and the isotopic-spin vector (in charge space) of the two pions — the original and the added — will tend to be aligned with each other, and both opposite to the core spin and isospin. Clearly, the state just described is predominantly the $P_{3/2}$, $t = \frac{3}{2}$ combination of the incident (scattered) pion plus physical nucleon.

---

[9] See contributions by J. J. Sakurai and others in *Proceedings of the Conference on π–$\mathfrak{N}$ Scattering*, University of California, Irvine (December 1967).

[10] We adopt the metric system notation, i.e., GeV for billion electron volts (BeV in the United States and the United Kingdom).

[11] *cm* = center-of-mass, or baryocentric, system; *lab* = laboratory coordinate system.

The expectations of such crude physical arguments are borne out by the more reliable field-theoretic computational techniques developed by Chew and Low and others.[12]

PROBLEM

Consider a model of the physical nucleon (P, N) as a Dirac nucleon core (p, n) with a bound pion (π^+, π^0, π^-) in the $P_{1/2}$ state with isospin $\frac{1}{2}$. Now add a second pion in a state $l = 1$, so that the system has total angular momentum J and isospin T. By projecting out the various states of core plus second pion, show that the state $J = \frac{3}{2}$, $T = \frac{3}{2}$ contains the largest proportion of $j = \frac{1}{2}$, $t = \frac{1}{2}$ for the core-π_2 system. (Assume $\mu/M_{\text{core}} \approx 0$.)

1.2 Emission and Absorption of Real Mesons

We may pursue even further the analogy between Yukawa's field-theoretic description of the nucleon field and the well-known properties of the emission and absorption of quanta of the electromagnetic field. Classically, the power radiated by an oscillating dipole of frequency ω and amplitude R is given by

$$-\frac{dW}{dt} = \frac{4}{3}\frac{e^2}{c^3}\left(\overline{\frac{d^2r}{dt^2}}\right)^2 = \frac{2}{3}\frac{e^2}{c^3}R^2\omega^4. \tag{21}$$

This expression can be recast to describe the rate of emission of electromagnetic quanta:

$$\lambda_\gamma = -\frac{1}{\hbar\omega}\frac{dW}{dt} = \frac{2}{3}\left(\frac{e^2}{\hbar c}\right)\left(\frac{c}{R}\right)\left(\frac{\omega R}{c}\right)^3. \tag{22}$$

The expression for λ_π, the rate of pion emission by an excited nucleonic field (in, say, the process $\mathfrak{N}^* \rightarrow \mathfrak{N} + \pi$), can be written down in direct analogy to Equation (22). Thus, $e^2/\hbar c \rightarrow f^2/\hbar c$, the dimensionless strength constant of the meson field; $(c/R)^{-1}$, the characteristic time of the electromagnetic system, becomes $(\kappa c)^{-1} = \hbar/\mu c^2 \simeq 5 \times 10^{-24}$ sec for nucleonic systems. Finally, the factor $(\omega R/c)^3 = (R/\lambda\!\!\!^-)^3$ is actually a special case, for dipole emission, of the general $(R/\lambda\!\!\!^-)^{2l+1}$ dependence of photon emission on the multipolarity (orbital angular momentum) of the radiation for the case of long-wavelength ($\lambda\!\!\!^- \gg R$) radiation; we may substitute for this the factor $\rho(\eta) \cdot v_l(\eta)$ in which $\eta = R/\lambda\!\!\!^- = p/\hbar\kappa = p/\mu c$; $\rho(\eta) \sim \eta$ is a factor arising from the phase-space density, while $v_l(\eta)$ is the angular momentum barrier penetration factor

$$v_l(\eta \ll 1) \simeq \frac{\eta^{2l}}{[1 \cdot 3 \cdots (2l-1)]^2}, \tag{23a}$$

$$v_l(\eta \gg l) \simeq 1. \tag{23b}$$

[12] G. F. Chew and F. E. Low, *Phys. Rev., 101:* 1570 (1955); E. Fermi, *Suppl. Nuovo Cimento, 2:* 17 (1955); G. C. Wick, *Rev. Mod. Phys., 27:* 339 (1955); G. Costa and B. T. Feld, *Ann. Phys., 9:* 354 (1960).

Putting together all the components, and combining all numerical factors into a single effective coupling constant $\xi(f^2/\hbar c) = \bar{f}^2/\hbar c \lesssim 1$, we obtain

$$\lambda_\pi = \left(\frac{\bar{f}^2}{\hbar c}\right) \kappa c \, \rho(\eta) \, \nu_l(\eta). \tag{24}$$

Thus, typical widths for excited nucleonic systems with $\eta \gtrsim 1$, $\rho(\eta) \sim \nu_l(\eta) \sim 1$ would be $\Gamma_\pi = \hbar\lambda_\pi \approx \mu c^2 = 137$ MeV, which is indeed what one finds.

The same factors that determine the decay of excited systems also determine the inverse (absorption) process $\pi + \mathfrak{N} \rightarrow \mathfrak{N}^*$. Generally, we may relate the decay and its inverse through the relation

$$\lambda_\pi = nv\sigma_\pi, \tag{25}$$

in which σ_π is the cross section for pion absorption at the velocity v corresponding to the excitation energy, while $n \simeq 3\kappa^3/4\pi$ is the density of pions in the excited state. Thus

$$\begin{aligned} \sigma_\pi &\approx \left(\frac{\bar{f}^2}{\hbar c}\right)\left(\frac{c}{v}\right) \rho(\eta) \, \nu_l(\eta) \cdot \pi \left(\frac{\hbar}{\mu c}\right)^2 \\ &\approx \pi \left(\frac{\hbar}{\mu c}\right)^2 \cong 60 \text{ mb} \end{aligned} \tag{26}$$

for the typical case.

Characteristically, the cross sections for the production of K-mesons and "strange" baryons (Y) are smaller than Equation (26) by a factor of ~ 10, indicating field coupling strengths of the same order as for the pion field. On the other hand, the decays of the "strange" particles, e.g., $K \rightarrow 2\pi$, $Y \rightarrow \mathfrak{N} + \pi$, with lifetimes of $\sim 10^{-10}$ sec, are slower by a factor of $\sim 10^{13}$ than anticipated from Equation (24) on the assumption that these particles are simply excited mesonic or nucleonic states. Of course, it was exactly this paradox that led Pais (Rochester Conference, 1950) to propose the hypothesis of associated production — requiring that the new K-mesons and hyperons (Y) be produced in pairs, through a Yukawa reaction of the form

$$\mathfrak{N} \rightleftharpoons Y + K. \tag{27}$$

The K being too heavy, however, the decay $Y \rightarrow \mathfrak{N} + K$ is not possible, and the individual decay of these particles is energetically possible only through pion emission. This is not, however, a permitted strong interaction, rendering the particles metastable, with correspondingly long lifetimes. This concept was formalized by Gell-Mann and Nishijima through the introduction of a single new additive quantum number, the strangeness, with values $S = \pm 1$, associated with the new particles ($S = 0$ for the old) and with the new requirement of conservation of total S in any strong (production) interaction. Decays of the strange particles into nucleons and pions require $\Delta S = \pm 1$, and are therefore forbidden and can proceed only through some "weak" process that violates strangeness conservation.

PROBLEM

Consider a spectrum of excited nucleonic states with spin values $j = \frac{1}{2}, \frac{3}{2}, \frac{5}{2}, \ldots$, and masses (energies) that increase monotonically according to the expression

$$m^2 \cong m_0^2 j + A,$$

with $m_0 \approx \mu$. (This is not an unreasonable approximation for the energies of the excited nucleonic states according to the Regge hypothesis. See Chapters 11 and 16.) Consider a state with $j \gg 1$. By comparing the rate of decay, through one-pion emission, to the next lowest state ($j \to j-1$, $l_\pi \approx 1$) with the rate of one-pion emission to the ground state ($l_\pi \approx j + \frac{1}{2}$), show:

(a) that decay by a "cascade" process may be expected to dominate over direct decay to a low-lying level;
(b) that the level widths are expected to decrease with increasing j, like $j^{-1/2}$.

Note: for $n \gg 1$, the factorial function $(n!!)^2 = [1 \cdot 3 \cdots (2n-1)]^2 \approx (2n)!$ may be approximated by Stirling's formula.

2

Classification of Particles and Resonant States

As noted in our introduction to Chapter 1, the elementary particles may be classified according to the interactions of which they partake: the hadrons — baryons and mesons — constitute the set of particles that participate in the strong interactions; in addition, the electromagnetic interactions introduce the photon, carrier of the electromagnetic field; the weak interactions bring in the leptons, which are *not* involved in the strong interactions (the leptons do, however, have electromagnetic interactions by virtue of their charges and magnetic moments); finally, there is the graviton, the little-understood carrier of the gravitational field. In this chapter, we discuss the properties of the observed particles with reference to this hierarchy of interactions.

2.1 Strongly Interacting Particles

The classification due to Gell-Mann and Nishijima is based on the observed connection, for nucleons and mesons, between a particle's charge Q (in units of the electron charge $|e|$), its isotopic spin, and its baryon or nucleon number B ($B = 1, 0, -1$ for nucleons, mesons, and antinucleons, respectively):

$$Q = t_3 + \frac{B}{2}. \tag{1}$$

With each of the groups of new, strange hyperons ($B = 1$) and K-mesons ($B = 0$), Gell-Mann and Nishijima associated a value of the "strangeness" quantum number S, such that

$$Q = t_3 + \frac{B}{2} + \frac{S}{2}. \tag{2}$$

Among the quantum numbers involved in Equation (2), just two, the charge Q and the baryon number B, are, as far as is now known, absolutely conserved. That is, the total charge $\Sigma_i Q_i$ and total baryon number $\Sigma_i B_i$ remain constant in all interactions among particles and systems of particles. In the strong and electromagnetic interactions, the total "strangeness" $\Sigma_i S_i$ is conserved as well; this has the consequence, through Equation (2), that $t_3 = \Sigma_i t_{3i}$ is also conserved.

In addition, for the strong interactions (and only for these) the total isotopic spin $\mathbf{t} = \Sigma_i \mathbf{t}_i$ is conserved. This property of isotopic invariance of the strong interactions is sometimes referred to as "charge independence."[1] The consequences in nuclear physics of the charge independence of the forces among nucleons are well known. Thus, for example, the energy levels of the light nuclei all belong to definite isotopic-spin multiplets, the members of a given multiplet (isobars) all having the same values of the spin and parity, and essentially the same energy (mass), differing among themselves only in the value of the charge or t_3; a typical example is the Li^7–Be^7 ground state doublet. Charge independence also leads to definite selection rules among possible nuclear reactions. Thus, for example, the reaction $D + \alpha \rightarrow Li^6$ can proceed only through those states of Li^6 with $t = 0$, owing to the isotopic-singlet ($t = 0$) character of both the deuteron and the α-particle.

In the domain of elementary particles and their interactions, isotopic-spin invariance is of crucial importance. Thus, we have previously noted that the charge-independent character of the Yukawa reaction between pions and nucleons (manifested in the requirement that the virtual pion, in the reaction $\mathfrak{N} \rightleftharpoons \mathfrak{N} + \pi$, should combine with the nucleon into a state of total isotopic spin $t = \frac{1}{2}$, where $\mathbf{t} = \mathbf{t}_{\mathfrak{N}} + \mathbf{t}_{\pi}$) gives rise to those special combinations of charges previously described in Section 1.1.[2]

In the electromagnetic interactions, while Q, B, S, and hence t_3 are all conserved, the total isotopic spin, $\mathbf{t}$, is no longer constant, the electromagnetic interactions being manifestly charge dependent. Using a geometrical analogy, one may consider the strong interactions as being describable as scalars in isotopic-spin space, while electromagnetic interactions have the properties of vectors (that is, they depend on the choice of axes). On this basis, we may obtain the specific form of the violation of isotopic-spin conservation brought about by the electromagnetic interactions, that is, the selection rule $\Delta t = 0, \pm 1$. Alter-

---

[1] Charge independence is a special case of isotopic invariance in which the amplitude for the interaction of two particles in a state of definite spatial symmetry is independent of the particle charges. More generally, isotopic invariance specifies that the interaction amplitude depends only on the value of the total isotopic spin, t, and not on the value of t_3, which specifies the charge state. In the case of the nucleon-nucleon interaction, charge independence is equivalent to isotopic invariance, but this is a consequence of the nucleon isotopic spin of $\frac{1}{2}$.

[2] To each set of the same elementary particles of multiplicity n but varying charge (e.g., π^+, π^0, π^-) is assigned a value of the isotopic spin t, such that $n = 2t + 1$; thus, $t_{\mathfrak{N}} = \frac{1}{2}$ and $t_{\pi} = 1$. The isotopic spins may then be treated as vectors with properties strictly analogous to those of angular momentum vectors in ordinary space. Thus, the length is given by $|t| = \sqrt{t(t+1)}$; $t_z = t_3$, associated with the charge according to Equation (2), takes on $2t + 1$ integral or half-integral values in unit steps $t \geq t_3 \geq -t$; the operators $t_{\pm} = t_x \pm it_y$ serve as charge raising or lowering operators. The combination of isotopic-spin vectors $\mathbf{t} = \Sigma \mathbf{t}_i$ involves the Clebsch-Gordan coefficients, etc. Isospin invariance is equivalent to the invariance of $\mathbf{t}$ with respect to rotations in "charge space."

natively, we may think of the photon, the quantum of the electromagnetic field, as carrying both isotopic spin 0 and isotopic spin 1.

The strongly interacting elementary particles (hadrons) may be classified according to the values of their intrinsic quantum numbers,[3] B, S, t, the spin and intrinsic parity, $j^{\pm}$, and total rest energy (mass). A given particle is completely identified by the specification of the values of the whole set of its quantum numbers, and no two particles have identical sets, although occasionally two particles may differ by only one number. Thus, there are two particles with $B = 1$, $S = 0$ ($\mathcal{Y} = 1$), $t = \frac{1}{2}$, $j = \frac{1}{2}^+$: the nucleon ($M = 938$ MeV) and one of the low-lying nucleon isobars, $\mathfrak{N}^*(M \cong 1470) = \mathfrak{N}^*_{1/2}(1470)$. A few other examples of particles apparently differing only in their mass may be found among the mesons.

The known elementary particles are listed in Table 2.1.[4] Broadly speaking, aside from the photon, these are divided into the baryons (hadrons with $B = 1$), the mesons (hadrons with $B = 0$), and leptons (to which we shall return later).

2.1.1 Baryons

We are most familiar with the nucleons that, having strangeness $S = 0$ (or $\mathcal{Y} = 1$), have, according to Equation (2), half-integral isotopic spin (the charge Q only takes on integral values). For $t = \frac{1}{2}$, $t_3 = \pm\frac{1}{2}$, giving $Q = 1$ (proton) or 0 (neutron). For $t > \frac{1}{2}$, some members of the corresponding nucleonic multiplet are multiply charged, as in the case of $t = \frac{3}{2}$ with $Q = 2, 1, 0, -1$, of which there are a number of clearly established examples among the resonant states.

Baryons with $S \neq 0$ are called *hyperons*. So far, all the well-established hyperons have $S < 0$. For $S = -1$ ($\mathcal{Y} = 0$), two types are known: Y_0 or Λ^* with $t = 0$, $Q = 0$, of which the prototype is the Λ_0; and Y_1 or Σ^*, $t = 1$, with $Q = 1, 0, -1$, e.g., the $\Sigma^{+,0,-}$ triplet. Hyperons with $S = -2$ ($\mathcal{Y} = -1$) have half-integral isotopic spin. With $t = \frac{1}{2}$, we have $Q = 0, -1$, of which the prototype is the $\Xi_{1/2}$ doublet. No $S = -2$ hyperons have as yet been observed with $t > \frac{1}{2}$. Finally, for $S = -3$ ($\mathcal{Y} = -2$), the only known member is the Ω_0^-, a $t = 0$ singlet.

Considering the existence of the $t = \frac{3}{2}$ nucleonic ($S = 0$) multiplet, with its doubly charged member, there may be no special significance to the fact that no multiply charged hyperons that are stable against strong decay have as yet been discovered. However, even assuming that there is some basic reason to exclude such hyperons, the Gell-Mann–Nishijima classification has room for another singly charged isotopic singlet, with positive strangeness $S = 1$ ($\mathcal{Y} = 2$), a Z_0^+. Some experimental evidence has been reported for such a particle, but its existence remains in doubt.

One of the major tasks of any model of the elementary particles is, of course, to explain why the known baryon multiplets — and only these — are found in nature.

---

[3] It is frequently convenient to substitute, for the strangeness, an alternative number, the hypercharge $\mathcal{Y}$, defined as $\mathcal{Y} = (B + S)$. Equation (2) then becomes $Q = t_3 + \mathcal{Y}/2$.

[4] This table is a recent version of the collection prepared and continuously revised by a group at the Lawrence Radiation Laboratory, University of California, Berkeley, under the leadership of A. H. Rosenfeld. The tables are issued as report number UCRL-8030.

Table 2.1 Properties of Particles and Resonant States

Table S: STABLE PARTICLES. January, 1969.
(Closing date for data: November 1, 1968)

From Review of Particle Properties, UCRL-8030.

N. Barash-Schmidt, G. Conforto, A. Barbaro-Galtieri, L. R. Price, Matts Roos, A. H. Rosenfeld, Paul Söding, C. G. Wohl

Quantities in italics have changed by more than one (old) standard deviation since January, 1968.

STABLES

Particle	$I^G(J^P)C$	Mass (MeV)	Mass difference (MeV)	Mean life (sec) $c\tau$(cm)	Mass^2 (GeV)^2	Decays: Partial mode	Decays: Fraction	Q(MeV) ‡	p or p_{max} (MeV/c)	Partial Rates (sec^{-1})
γ	$0, 1(1^-)^-$	0 ($<2.\times10^{-21}$ MeV)		stable	0	stable				
ν	ν_e $J=\frac{1}{2}$	0(<0.2 keV)		stable	0	stable				
	ν_μ	0(<1.6 MeV)								
e	$J=\frac{1}{2}$	0.511006 ±.000002		stable ($>2\times10^{21}$y)	0.000	stable	μ_e = 1.001159557 ±.000000030 $\frac{e\hbar}{2m_e c}$			
μ	$J=\frac{1}{2}$	105.659 ±.002		2.1983×10^{-6}	0.011	$e\nu\bar{\nu}$	100	105	53	
				±.0008		$e\gamma\gamma$	(<1.6)10^{-5}	105	53	
				$c\tau = 6.592\times10^4$		3e	(<1.3)10^{-7}	104	53	
	μ_μ = 1.00116614 ±.00000031 $\frac{e\hbar}{2m_\mu c}$		-33.920 ±.013			$e\gamma$	(<6)10^{-9}	105	53	
$\pi^\pm$	1 (0^-)	139.578 ±.013		2.604×10^{-8}	0.019	$\mu\nu$	100 %	34	30	
				±.007, S=2.3*		$e\nu$	(1.24±0.03)10^{-4}	139	70	
				$c\tau$ = 781		$\mu\nu\gamma$	e(1.24±0.25)10^{-4}	34	30	
			4.6041 ±.0037	$(\tau^+-\tau^-)/\bar{\tau}$ = (0.09±0.07) %		$\pi^0 e\nu$	(1.02±0.07)10^{-8}	4	5	
				(test of CPT)		$e\nu\gamma$	e(3.0 ±0.5)10^{-8}	139	70	
π^0	$1^-(0^-)^+$	134.975		c 0.89×10^{-16}	0.018	$\gamma\gamma$	(98.83±0.04)%	135	67	
				±.18, S=1.6*		γe^+e^-	(1.17±0.04)%	134	67	
				$c\tau = 2.67\times10^{-6}$		$\gamma\gamma\gamma$	(< 5)10^{-6}	135	67	
						$e^+e^-e^+e^-$	b(3.47)10^{-5}	133	67	
$K^\pm$	$\frac{1}{2}(0^-)$	493.82 ±0.11		1.235×10^{-8}	0.244	$\mu\nu$	(63.65±0.29)% S = 1.1*	388	236	(51.54±0.30)10^6 S = 1.2*
				±.004 S = 1.8*		$\pi\pi^0$	(21.03±0.30)% S = 1.2*	219	205	(17.03±0.26)10^6 S = 1.2*
				$c\tau$ = 370		$\pi\pi^-\pi^+$	(5.57±0.04)% S = 1.2*	75	126	(4.52±0.03)10^6 S = 1.1*
				$(\tau^+-\tau^-)/\bar{\tau}$=(.09±.12)%		$\pi\pi^0\pi^0$	(1.70±0.05)%	84	133	(1.38±0.04)10^6
				(test of CPT)		$\mu\pi^0\nu$	(*3.18 ± 0.14*)% S = 2.4*	253	215	(*2.58 ± 0.11*)10^6 S = 2.4*
				S=1.3*		$e\pi^0\nu$	(4.86±0.07)% S = 1.2*	358	228	(3.93±0.06)10^6 S = 1.2*
						$\pi\pi^\mp e^\pm\nu$	(3.4 ±0.3)10^{-5}	214	203	
			-3.94 ±0.13			$\pi\pi^\pm e^\mp\nu$	(<7)10^{-7}	214	203	
						$\pi\pi^\mp\mu^\pm\nu$	(1.0 ±0.5)10^{-5}	109	151	
						$\pi\pi^\pm\mu^\mp\nu$	(<3)10^{-6}	109	151	
						$e\nu$	(1.24±0.40)10^{-5}	493	247	
						$\pi\pi^0\gamma$	e(2.2 ±0.7)10^{-4}	219	205	
						$\pi\pi^+\pi^-\gamma$	e(10 ±4)10^{-5}	75	126	
						$\pi e\nu\gamma$	e(6 ±4)10^{-4}	354	227	
						πe^+e^-	(<1.1)10^{-6}	353	227	
						$\pi\mu^+\mu^-$	(<2.4)10^{-6}	143	172	
						$\pi\gamma\gamma$	(<1.1)10^{-4}	354	227	
K^0	$\frac{1}{2}(0^-)$	497.76 ±0.16		50% K_{short}, 50% K_{long}						
K^0_S	$\frac{1}{2}(0^-)$	S = 1.5*		0.862×10^{-10}	0.248	$\pi^+\pi^-$	(68.4 ±1.1)%	219	206	(0.794±0.013)10^{10}
			$-0.469\times\frac{1}{\tau_S}$ ±.015	±.006 S=1.2*		$\pi^0\pi^0$	(31.6 ±1.1)%	228	209	(0.367±0.013)10^{10}
				$c\tau$ = 2.59						
K^0_L	$\frac{1}{2}(0^-)$			5.38×10^{-8}	0.248	$\pi^0\pi^0\pi^0$	(*21.5 ± 0.7*)% S=1.2*	93	139	(*4.00 ± 0.20*)10^6 S=1.3*
				±.20		$\pi^+\pi^-\pi^0$	(*12.7 ± 0.3*)% S=1.1*	84	133	(2.36 ±0.10)10^6 S=1.4*
				$c\tau$ = 1614		$\pi\mu\nu$	(28.1 ±0.8)%	253	216	(5.22 ±0.25)10^6 S=1.3*
				S = 1.7*		$\pi e\nu$	(*37.7 ± 0.9*)%	358	229	(*7.01 ± 0.30*)10^6 S=1.4*
						$\pi^+\pi^-$	(*0.157 ± 0.004*)%	219	206	(0.029±0.001) 10^6
						c) $\pi^0\pi^0$	still uncertain	228	209	
						$\pi^+\pi^-\gamma$	e(< 0.4)10^{-3}	219	206	
						$\gamma\gamma$	(5.2 ±0.5)10^{-4}	498	249	
						$e\mu$	(< 0.6)10^{-5}	392	238	
						$\mu^+\mu^-$	(< 1.5)10^{-6}	286	225	
						e^+e^-	(< 1.7)10^{-5}	497	249	

General Atomic and Nuclear Constants [a]

N	$= 6.02252\times10^{23}$ mole^{-1} (based on $A_C 12 = 12$)
c	$= 2.997925\times10^{10}$ cm sec^{-1}
e	$= 4.80298\times10^{-10}$ esu $= 1.60210\times10^{-19}$ coulomb
1 MeV	$= 1.60210\times10^{-6}$ erg
$\hbar$	$= 6.5819\times10^{-22}$ MeV sec
	$= 1.05449\times10^{-27}$ erg sec
$\hbar c$	$= 1.9732\times10^{-11}$ MeV cm = 197.32 MeV fermi
$k_{Boltzmn}$	$= 8.6171\times10^{-11}$ MeV/° = 1 eV/11605°K
α	$= e^2/\hbar c$ = 1/137.0388
m_e	= 0.511006 MeV/c^2 = 1/1836.10 m_p
m_p	= 938.256 MeV/c^2 = 1836.10 m_e = 6.721 $m_{\pi^\pm}$
	= 1.00727663 m_1 (where m_1 = 1 amu = $\frac{1}{12} m_C 12$ = 931.478 MeV/c^2)
r_e	$= e^2/m_e c^2$ = 2.81777 fermi (1 fermi = 10^{-13} cm)
$\lambda\!\!\!^{-}_e$	$= \hbar/m_e c = r_e\alpha^{-1} = 3.86144\times10^{-11}$ cm
a_∞ Bohr	$= \hbar^2/m_e e^2 = r_e\alpha^{-2}$ = 0.529167 A (1 A = 10^{-8} cm)
$\sigma_{Thomson}$	$= \frac{8}{3}\pi r_e^2 = 0.66516\times10^{-24}$ cm^2 = 0.66516 barn
μ_{Bohr}	$= e\hbar/2m_e c = 0.578817\times10^{-14}$ Mev gauss^{-1}
μ_{nucl}	$= e\hbar/2m_p c = 3.1524\times10^{-18}$ Mev gauss^{-1}

$\frac{1}{2}\omega_{cyclotron}$ (rad sec^{-1} gauss^{-1})

$= e/2m_e c = 8.79404\times10^6$

$= e/2m_p c = 4.7895\times10^3$

(continued on other sheet)

[a] Based mainly on E. R. Cohen and J. W. M. DuMond, Rev. Mod. Phys. 37, 537 (1965). Note that recent fine structure and ac Josephson effect measurements currently indicate that α is ~20 ppm larger than the value given above. The corresponding readjustment of the fundamental constants will increase e by 60 ppm, $\hbar$ by 100 ppm, m_e by 60 ppm, and decrease N by 60 ppm. For a preliminary analysis see W. H. Parker, B. N. Taylor, and D. N. Langenberg, Phys. Rev. Lett. 18, 287 (1967).

CP violation parameters

$$\eta_{+-\,(00)} = \frac{A(K_L \to \pi^{+(0)}\pi^{-(0)})}{A(K_S \to \pi^{+(0)}\pi^{-(0)})} = |\eta_{+-\,(00)}|\, e^{i\Phi_{+-\,(00)}}$$

$|\eta_{+-}| = (1.92\pm0.04)\times10^{-3}$

$\Phi_{+-} = (50\pm8)°$

$|\eta_{00}|$ still uncertain, see data listings for published values

												Decay Parameters†			
											Magnetic Moment ($e\hbar/2m_pc$)	Measured α	Measured Φ(degree)	Derived γ	Derived Δ(degree)
η	$0^+(0^-)^+$	548.8 ±0.6		$\Gamma=(2.63\pm.64)$keV	Neutral decays 71.1%	$\gamma\gamma$	(38.1 ± 2.3)%	S=1.3*	549	274					
						$\pi^0\gamma\gamma$	(2.5 ± 2.8)%		414	258					
						$3\pi^0$	(29.4 ±2.8)%	(c)	144	179					
					Charged decays 28.9%	$\pi^+\pi^-\pi^0$	(23.3 ±1.1)%	S=1.2*	135	174					
						$\pi^+\pi^-\gamma$	(5.5 ±0.5)%		269	236					
						$\pi^0e^+e^-$	(< 0.01)%		413	258					
						$\pi^+\pi^-e^+e^-$	(0.1 ±0.1)%		268	236					
p	$\frac{1}{2}(\frac{1}{2}^+)$	938.256 ±0.005	-1.2933 ±.0001	stable ($>2\times10^{28}$ y)	0.880						2.792763 ±.000030				
n	$\frac{1}{2}(\frac{1}{2}^+)$	939.550 ±0.005		c$(0.932\pm0.014)10^3$ $c\tau=2.80\times10^{13}$	0.882	$pe^-\nu$	100 %		1	1	-1.913148 ±.000066	$\frac{g_A}{g_V}=-1.231\pm.010$†			$\delta=(176.1\pm6.4)°$†
Λ	$0(\frac{1}{2}^+)$	1115.60 ±0.08 S=1.3*		2.51×10^{-10} ±.03 S=1.3* $c\tau$ = 7.54	1.245	$p\pi^-$	(65.3 ±1.2)%		38	100	-0.73 ±.16 S=1.2*	0.646±0.016	(-6.3±3.5)°	0.76	(7.5±3.9)°
						$n\pi^0$	(34.7)%		41	104		0.71 ±0.18			
						$pe\nu$	(0.85±0.08)10^{-3}	S=1.3*	177	163		For $\Lambda\to pe\nu$, $\frac{g_A}{g_V}=-0.97^{+0.14}_{-0.22}$†			
						$p\mu\nu$	(1.35±0.60)10^{-4}		72	131					
Σ^+	$1(\frac{1}{2}^+)$	1189.40 ±0.19 S=1.7*	-7.92 ±.13	0.810×10^{-10} ±.013 $c\tau$ = 2.43	1.412	$p\pi^0$	(52.8 ±1.5)%		116	189	2.5 ±.5	-.955±0.070 ← S=1.1*			
						$n\pi^+$	(47.2)%		110	185		+.018±0.039	(161±21)°	-0.95	$(-88^{+175}_{-2})°$
						$p\gamma$	(1.9 ±0.5)10^{-3}		251	225					
						$n\pi^+\gamma$	e(0.9 ±0.3)10^{-4}		110	185					
						$\Lambda e^+\nu$	(2.11±0.45)10^{-5}		73	72					
				$\frac{\Gamma(\Sigma^+\to\ell^+n\nu)}{\Gamma(\Sigma^-\to\ell^-n\nu)}=<.04$ ←		$n\mu^+\nu$	(< 0.36)10^{-4}		144	202					
						$ne^+\nu$	(< 0.19)10^{-4}		249	224					
Σ^0	$1(\frac{1}{2}^+)$	1192.46 ±0.12 S=1.2*	-4.86 ±.07	$<1.0\times10^{-14}$ $c\tau<3\times10^{-4}$	1.422	$\Lambda\gamma$	100 %		77	75					
						Λe^+e^-	b(5.45)10^{-3}								
Σ^-	$1(\frac{1}{2}^+)$	1197.32 ±0.11 S=1.3*		1.64×10^{-10} ±.06 S=2.4* $c\tau$ = 4.92	1.434	$n\pi^-$	100 %		118	193		-.06 ±0.05 S=1.6*	(4±17)°	1.0	$(230^{+31}_{-125})°$
						$ne^-\nu$	(1.08±0.05)10^{-3}		257	230		For $\Sigma^-\to ne^-\nu$, $g_A/g_V=0.28\pm0.16$†			
						$n\mu^-\nu$	(0.48 ± 0.06)10^{-3}		152	210					
						$\Lambda e^-\nu$	(0.60±0.06)10^{-4}		81	79		For $\Sigma^-\to\Lambda e\nu$, $g_V/g_A=0.3\pm0.3$†			
						$n\pi^-\gamma$	e(<1)10^{-3}		118	193					
Ξ^0	$\frac{1}{2}(\frac{1}{2}^+)$§	1314.7 ±0.7	-6.6 ±.7	3.03×10^{-10} ±.18 $c\tau$ = 9.10	1.728	$\Lambda\pi^0$	100 %		64	135		-.35±0.08	(25±21)° S=1.3*	0.85	$(229\pm^{+14}_{-38})°$
						$p\pi^-$	(< 0.9)10^{-3}		237	299					
						$pe^-\nu$	(< 1.3)10^{-3}		376	323					
						$\Sigma^+e^-\nu$	(< 1.5)10^{-3}		125	119					
						$\Sigma^-e^+\nu$	(< 1.5)10^{-3}		117	112					
						$\Sigma^+\mu^-\nu$	(< 1.5)10^{-3}		20	64					
						$\Sigma^-\mu^+\nu$	(< 1.5)10^{-3}		12	49					
						$p\mu^-\nu$	(< 1.3)10^{-3}		271	309					
Ξ^-	$\frac{1}{2}(\frac{1}{2}^+)$§	1321.25 ±0.18		1.66×10^{-10} ±.04 S=1.1* $c\tau$ = 4.98	1.746	$\Lambda\pi^-$	100 %		66	139		-.41 ±.04	(-3±9)° S=1.3*	0.90	(172±18)°
						$\Lambda e^-\nu$	d(0.67±0.23)10^{-3}		205	190					
						$\Sigma^0e^-\nu$	(<0.5)10^{-3}		128	122					
						$\Lambda\mu^-\nu$	(<1.3)10^{-3}		100	163					
						$\Sigma^0\mu^-\nu$	(<0.5)%		23	70					
						$n\pi^-$	(<1.1)10^{-3}		242	303					
						$ne^-\nu$	(<1.0)%		381	327					
Ω^-	$0(\frac{3}{2}^+)$§	1672.4±.6 S=1.1*		$1.3^{+0.4}_{-0.3}\times10^{-10}$ $c\tau$ = 3.9	2.797	$\Xi^0\pi^-$	8 events seen		217	293					
						$\Xi^-\pi^0$	3 events seen		216	289					
						ΛK^-	13 events seen		63	210					

†The definition of these quantities is as follows: [for more details on sign convention, see text]

$\alpha=\frac{2|s||p|\cos\Delta}{|s|^2+|p|^2}$; $\beta=\sqrt{1-\alpha^2}\sin\Phi$

$\beta=\frac{-2|s||p|\sin\Delta}{|s|^2+|p|^2}$; $\gamma=\sqrt{1-\alpha^2}\cos\Phi$

g_A/g_V defined by: $\langle B_f|\gamma_\lambda(g_V-g_A\gamma_5)|B_i\rangle$

δ defined by: $g_A/g_V=|g_A/g_V|e^{i\delta}$

* S = Scale factor = $\sqrt{\chi^2/(N-1)}$ where N ≈ number of experiments. S should be ≈ 1. If S > 1, we have enlarged the error of the mean, δx, i.e., δx→S δx. This new convention is still inadequate, since if S > 1, the real uncertainty is probably even greater than Sδx. See text of January 1967 edition.

‡ In decays with more than two bodies, P_{max} is the maximum momentum that any particle can have. § Predicted from SU(3).

b. Theoretical value, see also data card listings. d. Assumes rate for $\Xi^-\to\Sigma^0e^-\nu$ small compared with $\Xi^-\to\Lambda e^-\nu$.

c. See note in data card listings.

e. See date card listings for energy limits used in measuring this branching ratio.

STABLES

STABLES STABLES STABLES STABLES STABLES STABLES STABLES

Table 2.1 (continued)

MESONS January, 1969

Change in Notation. The subscript N stands for "normal spin-parity series" ($J^P=0^+, 1^-, 2^+, \ldots$), A for "abnormal" ($J^P=0^-, 1^+, 2^-, \ldots$).

Quantities in italics have changed by more than one (old) standard deviation since January, 1968.

Particle	Symbol (J^P)	$I^G(J^P)C_n$ (underline: estab.; ? = guess)	Mass M (MeV)	Width Γ (MeV)	M^2 ± Γ M (GeV)^2 (a)	Partial decay modes: Mode	Fraction %	Q (MeV)	p or p_{max} (b) (MeV/c)
$\pi^\pm(140)$ $\pi^0(135)$ →	$\pi(0^-)$	$1^-(0^-)+$	139.58 134.97	7.2 eV ±1.2 eV	0.019483 0.018217	See Table S			
$\eta(549)$ →	$\eta(0^-)$	$0^+(0^-)+$	548.8 ±0.6	2.63 keV ±.64 keV	0.301 ±.000	all neutral $\pi^+\pi^-\pi^0+\pi^+\pi^-\gamma$	71 29	} See Table S	
ρ (765)	$\rho(1^-)$	$1^+(1^-)-$	765 (c) ±10	125 (c) ±20	0.585 ±.095	$\pi\pi$	≈ 100	491	359
						$\pi^\pm\pi^+\pi^-\pi^0$	< 0.2	212	247
						$\pi^+\pi^-\pi^+\pi^-$	< 0.15	212	247
						$\pi^\pm\gamma$	< 0.4	630	372
						$\eta\pi^\pm$	< 0.8	82	146
						e^+e^-	.0061±.0005 (d)	769	385
						$\mu^+\mu^-$	.0066±.0015 (e)	559	370
$\omega(783)$	$\phi'(1^-)$	$0^-(1^-)-$	783.4 ±0.7 S=2.0*	12.6 ±1.1	0.614 ±.010	$\pi^+\pi^-\pi^0$	≈ 90	369	328
						$\pi^+\pi^-$	seen (f)	504	366
						$\pi^0\gamma$	9.3±0.8	648	380
						η+ neutral	< 1.5	234	199
						$\pi^+\pi^-\gamma$	< 5	504	366
						$\pi^0\pi^0\gamma$	< 1	513	368
						e^+e^-	0.0068±.0022(g)	782	392
						$\mu^+\mu^-$	< 0.10	572	377
						$\pi^0\mu^+\mu^-$	< 0.2	437	350
$\eta'(958)$ or X^0	$\eta'(0^-)$	$0^+(0^-)+$	958.3 ±0.8	< 4	0.918 <.004	$\eta\pi\pi$	71 ± 4	131	232
		$J^P = 2^-$ not yet excluded				$\pi^+\pi^-\gamma$(incl. $\rho^0\gamma$)	22 ± 3	958	479
See note (h), on name η'.						$\gamma\gamma$	6.2 ± 3.1 (s)		
						for upper limits see footnote (i)			
$\delta(962)$	?( ) These two could be related, see listings	≥1 ( )	962 ±5	< 5	0.927 <.005	$\eta\pi$ possibly seen		278	306
→ $\pi_N(1016)$ → $K\bar{K}$	$\pi(0^+)$	$1^-(0^+)+$	1016 ±10	~25 } if res.	1.032 ±.025	$K^\pm K^0$	only mode seen	24	110
						$\eta\pi$	< 80	328	342
Resonance, virtual bound state, or antibound state, still not distinguished.									
$\phi(1019)$	$\phi(1^-)$	$0^-(1^-)-$	1019.5 ±0.6 S = 1.5*	3.7 ±0.6	1.039 ±.004	K^+K^-	47.6 ± 1.8	32	126
						K_LK_S	*32.8 ± 1.9 S = 1.5**	24	109
						$\pi^+\pi^-\pi^0$ (incl. $\rho\pi$)	*19.6 ± 2.3 S = 1.5**	605	462
						e^+e^-	0.036±.006	1018	510
						$\mu^+\mu^-$	$0.035^{+.035}_{-.018}$	808	499
						for upper limits see footnote (j)			
$\eta_{0+}(1070)$ → K_SK_S	$\eta(0^+)$	$0^+(0^+)+$ if res.	1070§ ±20§ S = 2.3*	~ 80 (?) see note (k)	1.14 ±.09	$\pi\pi$	< 65	793	516
Resonance or scattering length both possible.						$K\bar{K}$	> 35	76	198
A1(1070)	$\pi(1^+)$	$1^-(1^+)+$	1070§ ±20§	80§ ±35§	1.14 ±.09	3π see note (ℓ)	≈ 100	651	488
Existence still in doubt ←		($J^P = 2^-$ not yet excluded)				$K\bar{K}$	< 0.25[$G=(-1)^{\ell+I}$ forbids this]		
B(1220)	$\rho(A)$?	$1^+(1^+)-$	1221 ±16 S=1.2*	123 ±16 S=1.3*	1.46 ±.14	$\omega\pi$	≈ 100	297	339
						$\pi\pi$	< 30 } suggests	950	600
						$K\bar{K}$	< 2 } $J^P \neq 3^-, 5^-, \ldots$	240	360
$J^P = 2^+, 3^-, \ldots$ still poss.						for other upper limits see footnote (m)			
$K^+(494)$ $K^0(498)$ →	$K(0^-)$	$1/2(0^-)$	493.82 497.76		0.244 0.248	See Table S			
$K^*(890)$ ⇉	$K(1^-)$	$1/2(1^-)$	891.4 ±0.6	49.7 ±1.1 (for charged K^*)	0.797 ±.044	$K\pi$	≈ 100	259	289
$m_0 - m_\pm = 6.3 \pm 4.1$						$K\pi\pi$	< 0.2	120	216
$K_A(1240)$ or C	$K(A)$	$1/2(1^+)$	≈ 1240	≈ 60	1.54 ±.07	Q-Region } $K\pi\pi$ dominant. See footnote (r).			
Not well established (footnote (r)). $J^P=2^-$ not yet ruled out completely									
⇈ $K_A(1320)$	$K(A)$	$1/2(1^+)$	≈ 1330	≈ 70	1.77 ±.09				
$J^P = 2^-$ not yet completely ruled out.									
$K_N(1420)$	$K(2^+)$	$1/2(2^+)$	*1422* ±4 S=1.3*	90 ±6	2.022 ±.128	$K\pi$	51 ± 5	787	615
						$K^*\pi$	33 ± 3	388	413
						$K\rho$	11 ± 4 } S = 1.5*	156	318
						$K\omega$	3.4± 1.2	143	304
→ $J^P = 3^-$ still possible.						$K\eta$	2.0± 1.1	378	482
$K_A(1780)$ or L	$K(A)$?	$1/2(A)$?	1775 ±12 S=1.3*	72 ±26 S=1.4*	3.17 ±.13	$K\pi$	< *6*	1167	825
						$K^*\pi$	34 ± 12	772	670
						$K_N(1420)\pi$	19 ± 15	245	317
						$K\rho$	11 ± 9	532	632
						Remaining $K\pi\pi$	*28 ± 13*	1032	807
→ $J^P = 1^+, 2^-, 3^+$ favored						$K\omega$	*8 ± 5*	519	624
						Upper limits; $K\eta < 1\%$, $K^*\eta < 5$; $K\phi < 5$.			

f(1260)	η'(2+)	$0^+(2^+)+$	1264 ±10§	145§ ±25§ S=2.7*	1.57 ±.15	ππ	large	984	616
						$2\pi^+2\pi^-$	< 4	705	552
						$K\bar{K}$ indic. seen,	< 2.5	267	388
D(1285)	η'(A)	$0^+(A)+$	1285 ±4	31 ±4	1.65 ±.04	$K\bar{K}\pi$(mainly $\pi_N(1016)\pi$)	seen	154	304
						$K^*\bar{K}+\bar{K}^*K$		-100	
$J^P = 0^-, 1^+, 2^-$ with 1^+ favored						ππρ	not seen	256	356
$A2_L(1270)$	π(N)	$1^-(N)+$	1269 ±5	26 ±7	1.61 ±.03	ρπ (and π+neutrals)	dominant	364	387
see footnote (n)						ηπ indication suggests J^P = N		580	504
						$K\bar{K}$ indication seen			
$A2_H(1315)$	π(2+)	$1^-(2^+)+$	1315 ±4	24 ±12 S=1.6*	1.73 ±.04	ρπ (and π+neutrals)	dominant	410	420
see footnote (n)						$K\bar{K}$	seen	327	434
						ηπ	indication seen	626	532
→ E(1420)	η(A)	$0^+(0^-)+$	1424 ±6	71 ±10 S=1.2*	2.03 ±.10	$K^*\bar{K}+\bar{K}^*K$	50 ±10	38	157
						$\pi_N(1016)\pi$	50 ±10	268	328
						ππη	< 88	596	569
$J^P = 1^+$ not yet excluded						ππρ	not seen	384	455
→ f'(1515)	η(2+)	$0^+(2^+)+$	1514 ±5	73 ±23 S=1.8*	2.29 ±.11	$K\bar{K}$	72 ± 12 (o)	518	570
						$K^*\bar{K}+\bar{K}^*K$	10 ± 10 (o)	128	294
						ππ	< 14	1235	744
						ηππ	18 ± 10	686	624
						ηη	< 40	417	522
$\pi_A(1640)$ →3π	π(A) ?	$1^-(A)+$	1633 ±9 S=1.2*	93 ±24	2.73 ±.18	3π	dominant	1245	797
						† [$\pi^\pm\rho^0$/all $\pi^\pm\pi^+\pi^-$]	< 40	745	637
						† [$\pi^\pm f(\to\pi^+\pi^-)$/all $\pi^\pm\pi^+\pi^-$]	35±20	252	320
						πη	< 9	966	727
						$K\bar{K}$	not seen	654	658
						$\pi^\pm 2\pi^+2\pi^-$	< 10	935	714
Low signal/background; may be partly Deck effect and/or several resonances.									
→ $\rho_N(1650)$ ("g" → 2π)	ρ(N)	$1^+(N)-$	1650 (q) ±20	120 (q) ±30	2.72 ±.20	2π	dominant	1385	820
($J^P = 1^-, 3^-, \ldots$ with 3^- favored)						$K\bar{K}$ indication seen,	< 16	668	667
						(other possible modes see under ρ(1700) below)			
ρ(1700)? → 4π	ρ( )	$1^+(\ )-$	1700 (q) ±20	110 (q) ±25	2.89 ±.19	4π	dominant	1141	792
						† [$\pi^\pm A_2^0(\to\pi^+\pi^-\pi^0)$/all $\pi^\pm\pi^+\pi^-\pi^0$]	40±20	263	333
						† [$\pi^\pm\omega(\to\pi^+\pi^-\pi^0)$/all $\pi^\pm\pi^+\pi^-\pi^0$]	25±10	777	661
						† [$\rho^\pm\rho^0$]	seen	170	371
						$\pi^\pm\phi/\pi^\pm\pi^+\pi^-\pi^0$	< 11	540	532
						$\pi^\pm 2\pi^+2\pi^-\pi^0$	< 15	862	699
						2π (if ‡ $\rho_N(1650)$)	< 10	1420	838

Not yet clear whether this is just an alternative mode of the $\rho_N(1650)$, or a different resonance. The branching ratios are therefore only tentative.

→ There is no well-established Y = 0 meson resonance with M > 1700 MeV. For a list of some possible states see footnote (p).

→ The following bumps, excluded above, are listed among the data cards: σ(410); $\eta_{0+}(720)$; H(990); A1.5(1170); ρρ(1410); $K_SK_S(1440)$; π/ρ(1550), φ(1650), R(1750); η or ρ(1830)→4π; φ or π(1830)→ωππ; S(1930); T(2200); $N\bar{N}_{I=0}(2380)$, U(2380); κ(725); $K_N(1100\text{-}1200)$; $K_{A(I=3/2)}(1175)$; $K_{A(I=3/2)}(1265)$; $K_{A(I=1/2)}(1280)$; $K_{N(I=1/2)}(1660)$; $K^*(2240)\to\bar{Y}N$. (See note (p).)

* Quoted error includes scale factor $S = \sqrt{\chi^2/(N-1)}$. See footnote to Table S.

† Square brackets indicate a subreaction of the previous (unbracketed) decay mode.

§ This is only an educated guess; the error given is larger than the error of the average of the published values (see listings for the latter).

(a) ΓM is the half-width of the resonance when plotted against M^2.

(b) For decay modes into ≥ 3 particles p_{max} is the maximum momentum that any of the particles in the final state can have. The momenta have been calculated using the averaged central mass values, without taking into account the widths of the resonances.

(c) The values given for M(ρ) and Γ(ρ) and their errors are not average values from various experiments, but rather are intended to give the range where we believe the actual values are most likely to fall. Contrast the results tabulated in this note:

	M (MeV)	Γ (MeV)	
ρ^0	760±6	112±12	from $e^+e^-\to\pi^+\pi^-$, fits with energy-independent width
ρ^0	754±9	105±20	
ρ^0		105±15	from πN→ππN, ππ phase shift analysis with Chew-Low extrapolation, and energy-independent width
ρ^-	755±5	110± 9	
ρ^-	767±2	135±10	similar, but energy-dependent width and off-shell corrections
ρ^-	764±2	147±4	from πN→ππN, fits in phys. region, energy-dependent width.

Energy-independent width is a narrow-resonance approximation which tends to give lower mass and width. Thus an analysis of all $e^+e^-\to\pi^+\pi^-$ data with Omnès' formula and energy-dependent width gives M = 770±4 MeV, Γ = 122±6 MeV (M. Roos, priv. comm.).

(d) The quoted value of the rate $\rho^0\to e^+e^-$ is the average from two $e^+e^-\to\pi^+\pi^-$ experiments (which alone give an average of (0.0060±0.0006)%) and one photoproduction experiment of high mass resolution. Interference effects with ω decay are hoped to be small.

(e) Warning: The values given in the literature, and in our table, for the rate $\rho^0\to\mu^+\mu^-$ may be somewhat too high, due to possible interference with ω decay.

(Footnotes continued on p. 28.)

Table 2.1 (continued)

BARYONS January, 1969

Particle or resonance †	I(J^P) ——= estab.	Beam π, K (BeV) (BeV/c)	Mass (MeV)	Γ (MeV)	$M^2 \pm \Gamma M$ (BeV^2)	Partial decay modes: Mode	Fraction (%)	p or $p^{\dagger}_{max}$ (MeV/c)	$4\pi\lambda\!\!\!^-{}^2$ (mb)
p n	$1/2(1/2^+)$		938.3 939.6		0.880 0.883		See Table S		
N'(1470)	$1/2(1/2^+)$ P_{11}	T=0.52πp p=0.64	1460	260	2.13 ±0.38	Nπ Nππ [Nσ][a] [Δπ][a]	55 45 [domin] [seen]	412 360 271 162	28.8
N(1518)	$1/2(3/2^-)$ D_{13}	T=0.60 p=0.73	1515	115	2.30 ±0.17	Nπ Nππ [Δ(1236)π][a] Nη	50 50 [domin] ~ 0.5	452 406 219 137	23.9
N(1550)	$1/2(1/2^-)$ S_{11}	T=0.62 p=0.75	1525	80	2.33 ±0.12	Nπ Nη Nππ	35 65 small	459 161 414	23.1
N(1680)	$1/2(5/2^-)$ D_{15}	T=0.88 p=1.01	1675	145	2.81 ±0.24	Nπ Nππ [Δ(1236)π][a] ΛK Nη	45 55 [?] <1.6 <2.5	564 530 361 209 374	15.4
N(1688)	$1/2(5/2^+)$ F_{15}	T=0.90 p=1.03	1690	125	2.86 ±0.21	Nπ Nππ [Δ(1236)π][a] ΛK Nη	60 40 [?] <.13 <1.5	574 540 374 234 390	14.9
N'(1710)	$1/2(1/2^-)$ S_{11}	T=0.95 p=1.08	1715	280	2.94 ±0.48	Nπ	65	590	14.0
N''(1750)	$1/2(1/2^+)$ P_{11}	T=1.08 p=1.21	1785	405	3.19 ±0.72	Nπ ΛK	34 seen	636	12.1
N(2190)	$1/2(7/2^-)$ G_{17}	T=1.94 p=2.07	2190	300	4.80 ±0.66	Nπ	35	894	6.21
N(2650)	$1/2(\ ?^-)$	T=3.12 p=3.26	2650	360	7.02 ±0.95	Nπ	(J+1/2)x=0.45[b]	1154	3.67
N(3030)	$1/2(\ ?\ )$	T=4.26 p=4.40	3030	400	9.18 ±1.21	Nπ	(J+1/2)x=0.05[b]	1377	2.62
Δ(1236)	$3/2(3/2^+)$ P_{33} $m_0 - m_{++} =$	T=0.195 p=0.304 0.45±0.85	(++) 1236.0 ±0.6 $m_- - m_{++} = 7.9 \pm 6.8$	120 ±2	1.53 ±0.15	Nπ $N\pi^+\pi^-$ Nγ	100 0 ~ 0.6	231 89 262	91.9
Δ(1640)	$3/2(1/2^-)$ S_{31}	T=0.80 p=0.93	1630	160	2.69 ±0.26	Nπ Nππ	25 75	533	17.2
Δ(1690)	$3/2(3/2^-)$ D_{33}	T=0.87 p=1.00	1670	225	2.79 ±0.38	Nπ	15	560	15.6
Ξ	$1/2(1/2^+)$		(0)1314.7 (-)1321.3		1.73 1.75		See Table S		
Ξ(1530)	$1/2(3/2^+)$ p-wave		(0)1528.9±1.1 (-)1533.8±1.9	7.3 ±1.7	2.34 ±0.01	Ξπ	100	145	
Ξ(1820)	$1/2(\ ?\ )$		1820	≈20	3.31 ±0.04	ΛK̄ Ξπ Ξ(1530)π ΣK̄	≈60 small ≈10 ≈30(?)	396 413 234 306	
Ξ(1930)	$1/2(\ ?\ )$		1930	110	3.72 ±0.21	Ξπ ΛK̄	large small	499 502	
Ξ(2030)	$1/2(\ ?\ )$		2030	50	4.12 ±0.11	Ξπ ΛK̄ ΣK̄ Ξ(1530)π	small ≈50 ≈50 small	573 587 524 421	
Ω^-	$0(3/2^+)$		1672.4		2.80		See Table S		

MESONS & BARYONS

MESONS & BARYONS

Δ	Δ(1910)	3/2($5/2^+$) F_{35}	T=1.27 p=1.40	1880	250	3.53 ±0.47	$N\pi$	20	697	10.1
	Δ(1930)	3/2($1/2^+$) P_{31}	T=1.37 p=1.50	1905	300	3.63 ±0.57	$N\pi$	25	713	9.62
	Δ(1950)	3/2($7/2^+$) F_{37}	T=1.39 p=1.52	1940	210	3.76 ±0.41	$N\pi$ ΣK $\Sigma(1385)K$ $\Delta(1236)\pi$ $\Delta(1236)\rho$	40 2.4 1.4 ≈ 50 seen	735 450 215 564	8.90
	Δ(2420)	3/2($11/2^+$)	T=2.50 p=2.64	2420	310	5.86 ±0.75	$N\pi$ $N\pi\pi$	11 > 20	1024 1007	4.67
	Δ(2850)	3/2($?^+$)	T=3.71 p=3.85	2850	400	8.12 ±1.14	$N\pi$	(J+1/2)x=0.25[b]	1266	3.05
	Δ(3230)	3/2(?)	T=4.94 p=5.08	3230	440	10.4 ±1.4	$N\pi$	(J+1/2)x=0.05[b]	1475	2.24
Λ	Λ	0($1/2^+$)		1115.6		1.24	See Table S			
	Λ(1405)	0($1/2^-$) S_{01}	p<0 K^-p	1405 ±5[c]	40 ±10[c]	1.97 ±0.06	$\Sigma\pi$	100	140	
	Λ(1520)	0($3/2^-$) D_{03}	p=0.392	1518.8 ±1.5	16 ±2	2.31 ±0.02	$N\bar{K}$ $\Sigma\pi$ $\Lambda\pi\pi$ $\Lambda\gamma$	45±4 }S=1.8* 45±4 10±1 0.9±0.2	235 258 251 350	83.6
	Λ'(1670)	0($1/2^-$) S_{01}	p=0.74	1670	25	2.79 ±0.04	$N\bar{K}$ $\Lambda\eta$ $\Sigma\pi$	14 33 45	410 66 387	28.5
	Λ'(1700)	0($3/2^-$) D_{03}	p=0.78	1690	40	2.86 ±0.07	$N\bar{K}$ $\Sigma\pi$ $\Lambda\pi\pi$ $\Sigma\pi\pi$	25 35 ≈ 20 ≈ 20	429 403 419 350	26.1
	Λ(1815)	0($5/2^+$) F_{05}	p=1.05	1815 ±5[c]	75 ±10[c]	3.30 ±0.14	$N\bar{K}$ $\Sigma\pi$ $\Sigma(1385)\pi$ $\Lambda\eta$	65 11 9 ~ 1	538 500 359 346	16.7
	Λ(1830)	0($5/2^-$) D_{05}	p=1.08	1830	80	3.35 ±0.15	$N\bar{K}$ $\Sigma\pi$	10 35	550 510	16.0
	Λ(2100)	0($7/2^-$) G_{07}	p=1.68	2100	140	4.41 ±0.29	$N\bar{K}$ $\Sigma\pi$ $\Lambda\eta$ ΞK $\Lambda\omega$	30 4 <3 ~ 1 <10	748 699 617 483 443	8.68
	Λ(2350)	0(?)	p=2.29 Seen in total c. s.	2350	210	5.52 ±0.49	$N\bar{K}$	(J+1/2)x=0.6[b]	913	5.85
Σ	Σ	1($1/2^+$)		(+)1189.4 (0)1192.5 (-)1197.3		1.41 1.42 1.43	See Table S			
	Σ(1385)	1($3/2^+$) P_{13}	p<0 K^-p S=4.8*! ←→(-) 1388±3	(+)1382±1	(+)36±3 S=2.1* (-)38±8, S=3.7*!	1.92 ±0.05	$\Lambda\pi$ $\Sigma\pi$	90±3 10±3 S=1.4*	208 117	
	Σ(1610)	1(?)	p=0.62	1615	65	2.61 ±0.10	$N\bar{K}$ $\Lambda\pi$ $\Sigma(1385)\pi$	small domin. mode seen	355 406 171	37.9
	Σ(1660)	1($3/2^-$) D_{13}	p=0.72 Decay modes of these two states not separated yet.	1660	50	2.76 ±0.08	$\Lambda(1405)\pi$ $N\bar{K}$	large small for both	197 400	29.9
	Σ(1700)	1(? ?)	p=0.80	1700	110	2.89 ±0.19	$\Lambda\pi$ $\Sigma\pi$	large not disentangled	470 411	25.1
	Σ(1765)	1($5/2^-$) D_{15}	p=0.94	1765 ±5[c]	100 ±15[c]	3.13 ±0.18	$N\bar{K}$ $\Lambda\pi$ $\Lambda(1520)\pi$ $\Sigma(1385)\pi$ $\Sigma\eta$ $\Sigma\pi$	46 16 15 15 ~ 1 ~ 1	497 519 190 317 140 463	19.4
	Σ(1915)	1($5/2^+$) F_{15}	p=1.24	1905	60	3.63 ±0.11	$N\bar{K}$ $\Lambda\pi$	10 5	608 615	12.9
	Σ(2030)	1($7/2^+$) F_{17}	p=1.52	2030	120	4.12 ±0.24	$N\bar{K}$ $\Lambda\pi$ $\Sigma\pi$ ΞK	10 35 10 <2	700 700 652 412	9.92
	Σ(2250)	1(?)	p=2.04 Seen in total c. s.	2250	200	5.06 ±0.45	$N\bar{K}$	(J+1/2)x=0.4[b]	849	6.76
	Σ(2455)	1(?)	p=2.57 Seen in total c. s.	2455	120	6.03 ±0.29	$N\bar{K}$	(J+1/2)x=0.3[b]	979	5.08
	Σ(2595)	1(?)	p=2.95 Seen in total c. s.	2595	~ 140	6.73 ±0.36	$N\bar{K}$	(J+1/2)x=0.25[b]	1064	4.30

(Footnotes are on p. 29.)

MESONS & BARYONS

Table 2.1 (continued)

Footnotes for the MESON Table

(f) Reported values range between 1% and 10%, and depend on assumptions on ρ-ω interference.

(g) This $\omega \to e^+e^-$ value is the average from a $\pi^-p \to e^+e^-n$ experiment (giving 0.0040±.0015% [±.0014% from possible ρω interference]) and an $e^+e^- \to \pi^+\pi^-\pi^0$ experiment (giving 0.0085±.0016%).

(h) This 0^- meson was named η' on discovery, when it looked as if it completed the 0^- nonet. With the recent evidence that the E(1420) is probably also 0^-, it is no longer clear whether η' or E or both are mixed in with the π, η, K octet; so the name η' may be misleading.

(i) Empirical limits on fractions for other decay modes of η'(958): $\pi^+\pi^- < 7\%$, $3\pi < 7\%$, $4\pi < 1\%$, $6\pi < 1\%$, $\pi^+\pi^-e^+e^- < 0.6\%$, $\pi^0e^+e^- < 1.3\%$, $\eta e^+e^- < 1.1\%$, $\pi^0\rho^0 < 4\%$, $\pi^0\omega < 8\%$.

(j) Empirical limits on fractions for other decay modes of φ(1019): $\pi^+\pi^- < 20\%$, $\eta\gamma < 8\%$, η + neutrals < 13%, $\pi^+\pi^-\gamma < 4\%$, $\omega\gamma < 5\%$, $\rho\gamma < 2\%$.

(k) Width of $\eta_{0+}(1070) \to K_SK_S$: Average value from two bubble chamber experiments is Γ = (72 ± 13) MeV, whereas two spark chamber experiments give Γ>100 MeV. The latter also allow a scattering length fit. It is not clear whether the reported narrow (Γ ≲ 25 MeV) $\pi^+\pi^-$ enhancements near 1070 MeV have anything to do with the $\eta_{0+}(1070)$.

(ℓ) ρπ fraction of 3π mode difficult to distinguish because ρ bands cover most of the Dalitz plot.

(m) Empirical limits on fractions for decay modes of B(1220): ππ < 30%, $K\bar{K} < 2\%$, 4π < 50%, φπ < 1.5%, ηπ < 25%, $(K\bar{K})^{\pm}\pi^0 < 8\%$, $K_SK_S\pi^{\pm} < 2\%$, $K_SK_L\pi^{\pm} < 6\%$.

(n) Although the splitting of the A2 needs further confirmation, we give the results from the two published experiments that have observed a split A2. Since most experiments have only seen one, rather wide, A2 enhancement, we here list its ("combined") properties: $I^G(J^P)C_n = 1^-(2^+)+$; M = 1297±10 MeV (S=1.8*) (§), Γ = 91±10 MeV (S=1.1*) (§); partial decay modes: ρπ 86±2%, $K\bar{K}$ 2.4 ± 0.5%, ηπ 11±2%, η'π 0.5±0.4% (S=2.1*); $\pi^+\pi^-\pi^0$ (excl. ρπ) < 17%.

(o) There is only a weak indication for a $K^*\bar{K} + \bar{K}^*K$ mode of the f'(1514). If this mode does not exist, the $K\bar{K}$ branching fraction will have to be reported as (80 ± 13)% (rather than (72 ± 12)% as given in the table), and ηππ as (20 ± 13)%.

(p) See the listings for many statistically weak Y = 0 bumps with M ≥1700 MeV, seen in bubble chambers. We tabulate here 9 statistically strong bumps seen with a missing mass spectrometer ($\pi^-p \to p(MM)^-$) or in HBC or counter experiments on $N\bar{N}$ elastic scattering or total cross sections.

	Name	I	M (MeV)		Γ (MeV)	Decay Modes Observed	
	R1(1630)	≥1	1630 ± 15		≤ 21	1/3/>3 charg. part. ≈ .37/.59/.04	(MMS)⁻
	R2(1700)	≥1	1700 ± 15		≤ 30	1/3/>3 charg. part. ≈ .43/.56/.01	
	R3(1750)	≥1	1748 ± 15		< 38	1/3/>3 charg. part. > .14/<.80/.15	
?	$N\bar{N}$(1925)	0, 1	≈ 1925		≈ 10	structure in $p\bar{p}$ backw. el. scatt.	
	S(1930)	≥1	1929 ± 14		< 35	1/3/>3 charg. part. ≈ 0/.92/ 0	
?	$N\bar{N}$(1945)	0, 1	≈ 1945		≈ 22	structure in $p\bar{p}$ backw. el. scatt.	
?	$N\bar{N}$(2190)	1	2190 ± 10	! ⇄	≈ 85	structure in $N\bar{N}$ total cross section	
	T(2200)	≥1	2195 ± 15		≤ 13	(MM)⁻ → 3 charged particl. ≈ 94%	
?	$N\bar{N}$(2345)	1	2345 ± 10	! ⇄	≈ 140	structure in $N\bar{N}$ total cross section	
	U(2380)	≥1	2382 ± 24		≤ 30	(MM)⁻ → 1/3/>3 chrgd part.≈30/45/25	
	$N\bar{N}$(2380)	0	2380 ± 10		≈ 140	structure in NN total cross section	

There is no evidence on the G, J, or P quantum numbers of these bumps (apart from the suggestion of ℓ = odd for $N\bar{N}$(1925), ℓ = even for $N\bar{N}$(1945)), nor is there satisfactory agreement between them and the other bubble chamber claims. Further, the σ_{tot} ($N\bar{N}$) bumps are broader than the (MM)⁻ bumps, and there is no evidence for or against their interpretation as resonances.

(q) Taken from compilation by T. Ferbel, Proc. 1968 Philadelphia Conf. See the data listings for averages of the values given in the literature. Also see B. French's review of Mesons (Proc. 14th International Conf. High Energy Physics, Vienna (1968), p. 91) for possible differences between M and Γ of charged and neutral $\rho_N(1650)$.

(r) See note in listings. Some investigators see a broad enhancement in mass ($K\pi\pi$) from 1200 - 1350 MeV, and others see structure. A further bump at 1280 MeV, Γ = 80 MeV, has been suggested. In light of this confusion, the masses, widths, quantum numbers, and branching ratios are at best tentative. For the mass region 1200 - 1350 MeV, the decay rate into $K^*(890)\,\pi$ is large, and a $K\rho$ decay is seen. The $K\eta$, $K\omega$ and $K\pi$ rates are less than a few percent.

(s) This $\eta' \to \gamma\gamma$ value is from a constrained fit under the assumption that $\eta\pi\pi$, $\pi^+\pi^-\gamma$ (inclusive $\rho^0\gamma$), and $\gamma\gamma$ are the only existing decay modes. Note that direct measurement of the $\eta' \to \gamma\gamma$ branching fraction gave the slightly different result of $(5.5^{+3.6}_{-3.0})\%$.

Mixing angles from Quadratic SU(3) Mass Formula: 0^- nonet (π, K, η, η') $\theta = 10.4° \pm 0.2°$; alternative 0^- nonet (π, K, η, E) $\theta = 6.2° \pm 0.1°$; 1^- nonet ($\rho(m = 765\pm15$ MeV), K^*, ϕ, ω) $\theta = 39.9\pm1.1°$; 2^+ nonet ($A2_H$, $K_N(1420)$, f', f) $\theta = 29.9°\pm2.2°$.

Footnotes for the BARYON Table

* Quoted error includes an S(scale) factor. See footnote to Table S.

‡ For decay modes into ⩾ 3 particles p_{max} is the maximum momentum that any of the particles in the final state can have. The momenta have been calculated using the averaged central mass values, without taking into account the widths of the resonances.

a. Square brackets indicate a sub-reaction of the previous unbracketed decay mode.

b. J is not known; x is Γ_{el}/Γ.

c. This is only an educated guess; the error given is larger than the error of the average of the published values (see listings for the latter).

† For the baryon states, the name [such as N(1470)] contains the mass, which shifts by 5 or 10 MeV with each new analysis. We can't keep up with changing labels in the card-listing section, so we don't try. The name (col. 1) is the same as can be found in large print in the listings. The best current value of the mass (col. 4) is what we use to determine the beam parameters, $M^2\pm\Gamma M$, c.m. decay momenta, etc., that are found in other columns.

→ An arrow at the left of the Table indicates a candidate that has been omitted because the evidence for the existence of the effect and (or) for its interpretation as a resonance is open to considerable question. See listings for information on the following: $\Delta(1690P_{33}$, $N(1730)D_{13}$, $N(1860)P_{13}$, $N(1980)D_{13}$, N(2080), $N_?(3245)$, N(3690), N(3755), $Z_0(1865)$, $Z_1(1900)$, Λ(1327), $\Lambda(1745)P_{01}$, $\Lambda(1750)S_{01}$, $\Lambda(1860)F_{07}$, Σ(1440), $\Sigma(1650)S_{11}$, Σ(1780), Σ(1880), and Ξ(1705).

An essential feature of the baryons is that they all have half-integral spin values. It follows, as a consequence of the connection between spin and statistics, that baryons obey Fermi–Dirac statistics. Coupled with their nucleonic character ($B = 1$), it also follows that baryons cannot be created or destroyed individually, but only in pairs involving a baryon and an antibaryon ($B = -1$)[5]. Examples of permitted reactions (provided there is sufficient energy available) include

$$P + P \to P + \Lambda^0 + \Sigma^+ + \overline{\Xi^0}, \tag{3a}$$

$$P + \overline{P} \to \Sigma^0 + \overline{\Lambda^0}. \tag{3b}$$

Forbidden reactions include

$$P + P \not\to \Sigma^+ + P \qquad (\Delta S = 1), \tag{4a}$$

$$\overline{P} + P \not\to \Lambda^0 + \Lambda^0 \qquad (\Delta B = 2). \tag{4b}$$

2.1.2 Mesons

Having $B = 0$, and integral spin values, mesons obey Bose–Einstein statistics and can be created and annihilated singly, or in any numbers, provided none of the other selection rules is violated. Thus, for example,

$$\gamma + P \to N + \pi^+, \tag{5a}$$

$$\pi^- + P \to \Sigma^0 + K^0, \tag{5b}$$

$$\pi^+ + P \to \Xi^0 + 2K^+, \tag{5c}$$

$$K^- + P \to \Lambda^0 + K^+ + K^- \tag{5d}$$

are all allowed, while

$$\pi^- + P \not\to \Lambda^0 + N, \tag{6a}$$

$$\pi^- + P \not\to \Sigma^+ + K^-, \tag{6b}$$

$$K^+ + P \not\to \Sigma^+ + \pi^+ \tag{6c}$$

are forbidden by strangeness or baryon conservation.

In the above examples, we have used the accepted classifications [see Equation (2)] of the π-mesons as an $S = \mathcal{Y} = 0$ isotopic triplet, and of the K^+, K^0 mesons as an $S = \mathcal{Y} = 1$ isotopic doublet, whose antiparticles K^-, $\overline{K^0}$ form a doublet with $S = \mathcal{Y} = -1$. Adding to these the $S = \mathcal{Y} = 0$ isotopic singlet (e.g., η^0) completes the types of known mesons, although there is generally more than one example (i.e., with different spin, parity, and/or mass values) of each type. Here again, even assuming the exclusion of multiply charged mesons, the Gell-Mann–Nishijima scheme would permit singly charged $S = \mathcal{Y} = \pm 2$, isotopic-singlet mesons; no such particles exist among the mesons thus far established.

---

[5] To every particle there corresponds an antiparticle, all of whose quantum numbers are the same as those of the particle, except that those numbers whose sign is significant (i.e., B, S, t_3, Q, j_3) change sign. Conservation of $B = \Sigma_i B_i$ means that in any interaction the difference between the number of baryons and the number of antibaryons remains a constant.

Owing to its bosonic nature, the antiparticle of a meson is another meson of the same type, but with opposite charge (i.e., $\overline{\pi^+} = \pi^-$, $\overline{K^+} = K^-$). In the case of the K^0, with $S = \mathcal{Y} = 1$, the antiparticle $\overline{K^0}$ ($S = \mathcal{Y} = -1$) is a distinctly different particle which, for example, cannot be produced in association with an $S = -1$ hyperon in reactions involving pions and nucleons [Equation (6b)]. The π^0, on the other hand, is its own antiparticle, a property which it shares with the photon (γ) and with all other neutral mesons of $S = \mathcal{Y} = 0$ (e.g., η^0, ω^0, ρ^0).

In addition to the invariance properties of the strong interactions discussed above, the laws governing these interactions are the same for systems of antiparticles as for systems of particles. This identity (indistinguishability) of the laws of nature for systems of particles and antiparticles is referred to as charge-conjugation invariance.

Formally, the operation of changing particles to their antiparticles may be described in terms of a charge-conjugation operator $\mathcal{C}$. Thus, for example, $\mathcal{C}\pi^+ = C_\pi \pi^-$, $\mathcal{C}P = C_{\mathfrak{N}}\overline{P}$, and so on. Since successive operations with $\mathcal{C}$ must return us to the original state, $\mathcal{C}^2\pi^+ = C_\pi^2\pi^+ = \pm\pi^+$, we have the general restriction on the charge-conjugation quantum number $C^2 = \pm 1$. In the case of self-conjugate particles, e.g., neutral mesons with $S = \mathcal{Y} = 0$, we require $C = \pm 1$, hence $C^2 = 1$.

As is the case for all other invariance principles, the invariance of the strong and electromagnetic interactions under the charge-conjugation operation leads to a conservation law, the conservation of the value of $C = \pm 1$ for neutral systems with $S = \mathcal{Y} = 0$. Thus, assigning a value of C to each neutral system, the charge-conjugation invariance law requires that this value be the same in the final as in the initial state of the system.[6]

The characteristics of the annihilation of a particle-antiparticle state into photons provide a striking example of the effects of charge-conjugation invariance. Consider the annihilation of the various possible states of positronium: the atomic combination of an electron and a positron. These states are characterized by the value of the total spin, $I = 0$ or 1, the orbital angular momentum, L, the parity,[7] $P = -(-1)^L$, and the total angular momentum, $\mathbf{J} = \mathbf{I} + \mathbf{L}$. The process of charge conjugation is equivalent to the combined operations of space inversion or parity, $\mathcal{P}$, and of spin exchange, $\mathcal{I}$:

$$\mathcal{C} = \mathcal{P} \times \mathcal{I}, \tag{7a}$$

$$C = -(-1)^L \times -(-1)^I = (-1)^{I+L}, \tag{7b}$$

since the state of $I = 1(0)$ is symmetric (antisymmetric) with respect to the interchange of the two spin $\frac{1}{2}$ particles.

As for the photon, its charge-conjugation quantum number is -1,

$$\mathcal{C}\gamma = -\gamma, \tag{8a}$$

$$C(n\gamma) = (-1)^n, \tag{8b}$$

---

[6] Unlike the other quantum numbers whose sign is significant (say, B, S) the sign of C is the same for *bosonic* particles and their antiparticles. The same is true of the intrinsic parity P. Indeed, as we shall see in the following discussion, C can be thought of as a sort of "intrinsic parity in charge space."

[7] Since the intrinsic parity of a particle of spin $\frac{1}{2}$, which obeys the Dirac equation, is opposite to that of its antiparticle, the parity of e^+e^- in the S ($L = 0$) state is -1.

since reversing the signs of the charges and momenta of all of the particles in a system (charge-conjugation) reverses the sign of the electric field vector, while preserving the direction of the magnetic field. Accordingly, we immediately arrive at the selection rule for the annihilation of positronium in its ground ($L=0$) states: singlet positronium, $I=0$, decays into an even number of photons, that is, two; triplet positronium, $I=1$, must decay into an odd number of photons, of which the minimum number which permits the conservation of momentum and energy is three.

We list in Table 2.2 the values of the charge-conjugation quantum numbers of the lowest states of positronium, as derived from Equation (7b). These same values of C apply to the corresponding states of any particle-antiparticle system of (Dirac) particles of spin $\frac{1}{2}$. Hence, the same selection rules may be applied to the annihilation of, say, a P–$\overline{P}$ or N–$\overline{N}$ or Λ^0–$\overline{\Lambda^0}$ pair.

However, in the case of baryon-antibaryon annihilation, the strong interactions dominate, so that the observed annihilation products are predominantly mesons. As noted above, neutral mesons (of $S=\mathcal{Y}=0$) may also be assigned definite values of the charge-conjugation quantum number C. We may, for example, do this empirically, using the observation that the π^0-meson decays into two photons; from Equation (8b) we deduce that $C(\pi^0)=+1$, that is,

$$\mathcal{C}\pi^0=\pi^0, \tag{9a}$$

$$C(n\pi^0)=+1. \tag{9b}$$

The same is true of the η^0-meson (which has the same spin and parity, $I=0^-$, as the π^0, but is an isotopic singlet). Among the other neutral mesons, the ω^0 ($I=1^-$, $t=0$) is observed to decay into $\pi^0+\gamma$, from which we conclude $C(\omega^0)=-1$, while the f^0 ($I=2^+$, $t=0$) decays into $2\pi^0$, whence $C(f^0)=+1$.

By this kind of reasoning, we may deduce the values of the charge-conjugation numbers of all the neutral, self-conjugate mesons. These are included in the compilation of particle properties in Table 2.1. It may be noted that the mesonic C-values are in all cases identical with the value of C, given in Table 2.2, for the baryon-antibaryon compound of the same value of J^P. This is but one among many evidences of the utility of the model that describes mesons as baryon-antibaryon compound states. However, it is not theoretically excluded that there might exist mesons that cannot be described in terms of the possible baryon-antibaryon combinations, say, a 0^+ meson with $C=-1$, etc.

Up to this point, we have excluded K-mesons from our discussion, since the K^0 and $\overline{K^0}$ are not self-conjugate. However, it has been observed that the $P+\overline{P}$ system, or specifically the ϕ^0-meson ($I=1^-$, $t=0$, $S=\mathcal{Y}=0$), decays rapidly into a final $K^0+\overline{K^0}$ state which, since the ϕ^0 has a definite value of $C(=-1)$, must also have the same definite C value. It is, in fact, possible and convenient to treat neutral K-mesons in terms of combinations with definite values of C. Such a pair of states is

$$K_1^0=\sqrt{\tfrac{1}{2}}\,(K^0+\overline{K^0}), \tag{10a}$$

$$K_2^0=\sqrt{\tfrac{1}{2}}\,(K^0-\overline{K^0}), \tag{10b}$$

Table 2.2 $\mathfrak{N}-\overline{\mathfrak{N}}$ *Combinations and Their Decay Properties*

$\mathfrak{N}-\overline{\mathfrak{N}}$ state	Spin and parity	t	C	G	POSSIBLE DECAYS: 2π	3π	$\pi+\gamma$'s	$(n\gamma)$ min	$K-\overline{K}$	Associated meson
$^1S_0$	0^-	0	+	+	no (P)	no (G); also no 4π	$\pi^0+2\gamma$ $\pi^++\pi^-+\gamma$	2	no (P)	η, η', (E)
		1	+	−	no (P, G)	yes $\left(\frac{\pi^\pm\pi^+\pi^-}{\pi^\pm 2\pi^0}=4;\ \frac{\pi^+\pi^-\pi^0}{3\pi^0}=\frac{2}{3}\right)$	$\pi+2\gamma$ $2\pi+\gamma$ (no $2\pi^0$)			π
$^3S_1$	1^-	0	−	−	no (G)	yes (no $3\pi^0$)	$\pi^0+\gamma$	3	yes $\frac{K^++K^-}{K^0+\overline{K^0}}=1$ $K^0\overline{K^0}=K_1^0K_2^0$	ω, ϕ
		1	−	+	yes (no $2\pi^0$)	no (G)	$\pi+\gamma$			ρ
$^1P_1$	1^+	0	−	−	no (P, G)	yes (no $3\pi^0$)	$\pi^0+\gamma$	3	no (P)	
		1	−	+	no (P)	no (G)	$\pi+\gamma$			B
$^3P_0$	0^+	0	+	+	yes $\left(\frac{\pi^+\pi^-}{2\pi^0}=2\right)$	no (P, G)	$\pi^0+2\gamma$	2	yes ($K_1^0K_1^0$)	$\eta_N(S^*)$
		1	+	−	no (G)	no (P)	$\pi+2\gamma$ $2\pi+\gamma$		no $K\overline{K}+\pi$ (P)	$\delta(\pi_N)$
$^3P_1$	1^+	0	+	+	no (P)	no (G)	$\pi^0+2\gamma$	4	no (P, G)	D
		1	+	−	no (P, G)	yes (see $^1S_0$)	$\pi+2\gamma$ $\pi^\pm+\gamma$ $2\pi+\gamma$ (no $2\pi^0$)			A_1
$^3P_2$	2^+	0	+	+	yes (see $^3P_0$)	no (G)	$\pi^0+2\gamma$	2	yes ($K_1^0K_1^0$)	f, f'
		1	+	−	no (G)	yes (see $^1S_0$)	$\pi^\pm+\gamma$ $\pi^0+2\gamma$ $\pi^++\pi^-+\gamma$			A_2
$^1D_2$	2^-	0	+	+	no (P)	no (G)	$\pi^0+2\gamma$	2	no (P)	
		1	+	−	no (P, G)	yes (see $^1S_0$)	$\pi^\pm+\gamma$ $\pi^0+2\gamma$ $\pi^++\pi^-+\gamma$			$\pi_A(1640)$

with the values of $C=-1$ and $+1$, respectively.[8] Thus, the $P+\overline{P}$ system in the $^3S_1$ state ($J=1^-$), or the ϕ^0-meson, with $C=-1$, can decay only into the $K_1^0K_2^0$ combination, while the $^3P_0$ state ($J=0^+$) or η_N-meson, with $C=+1$, would decay into the $K_1^0K_1^0$ and $K_2^0K_2^0$ combinations only.

Since it is the K^0 and $\overline{K^0}$ that are produced in the strong interactions, all this would be rather academic were it not for the convenient fact that, owing to the peculiar (parity-nonconserving) nature of the weak decays of the K-mesons into pions, it is precisely the K_1^0 and K_2^0 combinations that are relevant in the neutral K-meson decays, the former being relatively short-lived and decaying into two pions, while the latter is considerably longer lived and decays into three pions. Thus, it has been experimentally verified that the $\phi^0 \to K_1^0K_2^0$, while the $\eta_N \to K_1^0K_1^0$. Conversely, such observations can be used to determine the value of C for any neutral meson that can decay into a $K^0+\overline{K^0}$ pair.

So far we have used the property of charge conjugation to derive selection rules for the decay of neutral $S=\mathcal{Y}=0$ systems into neutral mesons and photons. The selection rules apply equally well, however, to decays into charged mesons, since neutral combinations of charged mesons in states of definite spin and parity have well-defined values of the C quantum number.

For a $\pi^+\pi^-$ or a K^+K^- system, since the members are each other's antiparticles, the operation of charge conjugation is equivalent to the parity operation (reflection about the center of mass), and

$$C=P=(-1)^l=(-1)^J \tag{11}$$

($I_\pi=I_K=0$; $P_\pi=P_K=P_{\overline{K}}=-1$).[9] An interesting consequence of Equation (11) is that the neutral ρ-meson ($I=1^-$, $C=-1$, $t=1$) can decay into $\pi^+\pi^-$, but not into $2\pi^0$. The ϕ^0 or ω^0 ($I=1^-$, $C=-1$, $t=0$) cannot decay into $\pi^+\pi^-$, because a two-pion state of spin 1^- must have $t=1$, but the ϕ^0, having sufficient energy, can decay into K^+K^- or into $K_1^0K_2^0$.

In the case of charged systems with $S=\mathcal{Y}=0$ that *contain strongly interacting particles only,* we may combine the properties of charge conjugation and isospin invariance to derive another conservation principle, that of G-parity. The G-parity operator $\mathcal{G}$ may be thought of as the analogue for isotopic-spin space of the parity operator $\mathcal{P}$ in ordinary space.[10] Thus, thinking of C as determining the "intrinsic" isotopic parity, and $(-1)^t$ as representing the analogue of the "orbital" parity, we have

$$\mathcal{G}=\mathcal{C}e^{i\pi\tau_y}, \tag{12a}$$

[8] Based on the assignment $\mathcal{C}K^0=-\overline{K^0}$, $\mathcal{C}\overline{K^0}=-K^0$.

[9] Note that the value of $P=(-1)^J$ holds for any two-pion or two-kaon system, irrespective of charge, so that any system or particle with $J^P=0^-, 1^+, 2^-, 3^+$, etc., is forbidden by parity conservation from decaying into two pions or two kaons. However, there is an important distinction between the $\pi^+\pi^-$ and the K^+K^- systems. The $\pi^++\pi^-$ being bosons of the same isotopic-spin multiplet, the total wave function must be symmetric, which means that even-parity, two-pion states can have $t=0$ or 2, while odd-parity states must have $t=1$. We note that the $t=1$, $t_3=0$ two-pion wave function $(\pi_1^+\pi_2^- - \pi_1^-\pi_2^+)$, being antisymmetric with respect to interchange of the pions, contains no $\pi_1^0\pi_2^0$ component. The K^+ and K^-, belonging to different isospin multiplets, can be produced in either the $t=0$ or $t=1$ combination, irrespective of the parity.

[10] The isotopic parity operation is defined as a reflection about the x–y plane, $\mathcal{C}$, followed by a rotation of 180° about the y axis.

and, accordingly,

$$G = C(-1)^t. \tag{12b}$$

Correspondingly, for a nucleon-antinucleon combination (Table 2.2), it follows from Equation (7b) that

$$G = (-1)^{I+L+t}. \tag{12c}$$

For pions, $C = 1$, $t = 1$,

$$\begin{aligned} G(\pi) &= -1, \\ G(n\pi) &= (-1)^n. \end{aligned} \tag{12d}$$

For $K\overline{K}$ systems, $C = (-1)^J$ [Equation (11)], and

$$G = (-1)^{J+t}. \tag{12e}$$

The values of the G-parity for the various $\mathfrak{N}$–$\overline{\mathfrak{N}}$ combinations, or the equivalent mesons, as determined from Equation (12b) or (12c), are also given in Table 2.2. These, in turn, determine the decay properties of such systems, *whether charged or neutral,* into strongly interacting particles; thus, pionic decay of systems with $G = +1$ can be into an even number of pions only, while systems with $G = -1$ can only decay into an odd number of pions. It is important to note that the conservation of G-parity, unlike C and P conservation, may be violated by virtue of the electromagnetic interactions (which do not conserve t). Thus, for example, the η^0-meson ($I = 0^-$, $t = 0$, $G = +1$), being forbidden by P conservation from decaying into two pions, takes advantage of the possibility of virtual photon emission and reabsorption to decay into three pions despite the violation of G conservation entailed by this decay.

The decay properties of the most simple $\mathfrak{N}$–$\overline{\mathfrak{N}}$ states and their corresponding mesons, as determined by the considerations developed above, have been summarized in Table 2.2.

PROBLEMS

1. The deuteron has spin 1^+ and isospin 0. Consider the combinations of a deuteron-antideuteron in the states of orbital angular momentum $L = 0$ and $L = 1$. Derive the values of J, P, t, C, G for the various possible combinations, and construct a table, analogous to Table 2.2, of their simplest strong and electromagnetic decay modes.
2. From the observation that the capture reaction

$$\pi^- + D \to N + N$$

proceeds strongly with stopped (zero kinetic energy) pions, and assuming that the capture takes place from an orbital S-state, prove that the intrinsic parity of the π^- is negative. (List any other assumptions required in reaching this conclusion.)

3. Consider a hypothetical neutral meson ζ_0, of $J^P = 0^+$, $G = -1$, $t = 0$, of mass = 3.5 pion masses. Ignoring the weak interactions, what would be its most

prominent decay modes? Which conservation laws prevent each of the following decays?

(a) $\zeta_0 \rightarrow \gamma + \gamma$,
(b) $\zeta_0 \rightarrow \pi^+ + \pi^-$,
(c) $\zeta_0 \rightarrow \pi^+ + \pi^- + \pi^0$,
(d) $\zeta_0 \rightarrow \pi^+ + \pi^- + \pi^+ + \pi^-$,
(e) $\zeta_0 \rightarrow \pi^0 + \gamma$.

2.2 The Weak Interactions

Included in Table 2.1 are a group of particles of spin $\frac{1}{2}$, all lighter than the nucleons, which can be described by the free Dirac equation, except for very small corrections arising out of their interactions with the electromagnetic field. These particles, called *leptons,* are coupled with the strongly interacting particles through the β-decay interactions, which are, however, so weak[11] as to have no observable influence on the static properties of the leptons.

In all, there are four known leptons, e^-, ν_e, μ^-, ν_μ, and, correspondingly, four antileptons, e^+, $\bar{\nu}_e$, μ^+, $\bar{\nu}_\mu$. Their emission and absorption in the weak interactions is governed by the following important features.

2.2.1 Maximum Parity Nonconservation

Maximum parity nonconservation has the consequence that a lepton emitted in the β-decay process is always polarized along its direction of flight (longitudinal polarization), the degree of longitudinal polarization normally being equal to $\pm(v/c)$ of the lepton. The form of the interaction is such that leptons tend to be left-handed (i.e., spin-directed opposite to their momentum), while antileptons tend to be right-handed. In particular, for the neutrinos, which have zero mass (and hence $v/c = 1$), the degree of longitudinal polarization (*helicity*) is always complete, the neutrino and antineutrino *always* having, respectively, the helicities -1 and $+1$. As a consequence, it is possible to distinguish in a unique and absolute fashion between the ν and $\bar{\nu}$, a possibility that would not exist if parity were conserved in the β-decay interactions.

2.2.2 Lepton Conservation

Lepton conservation means the conservation of lepton number. Let l equal $+1$ for leptons and -1 for antileptons. Then, in all known interactions $l = \Sigma_i l_i$ is constant. Of course, owing to their Fermi–Dirac nature, leptons can only be produced or destroyed in pairs. However, the law of lepton conservation requires that such a pair consist of a lepton plus an antilepton.

---

[11] The relative strengths of the strong, electromagnetic, and weak interactions are given by the ratio of their coupling constants:

$$g_s : e : g_w \approx 1 : 10^{-1} : 10^{-5},$$

where the constants are so defined as to make $g^2/\hbar c$ dimensionless.

2.2.3 The Two-Neutrino Hypothesis

According to this hypothesis, the four leptons can be divided into two leptonic doublets, (e^-, ν_e) and (μ^-, ν_μ), and correspondingly so can the antileptons. The conservation of leptons holds separately for the two doublets — i.e., the two types of neutrinos, ν_e and ν_μ, are distinguishable, although only on the basis of their origin and the type of interactions they can produce. Thus, in the inverse β-decay processes,

$$\bar{\nu} + P \rightarrow N + e^+ \text{ or } N + \mu^+ , \tag{13}$$

it turns out that only the latter occurs when the projectiles are antineutrinos produced in the decay

$$\pi^- \rightarrow \mu^- + \bar{\nu} , \tag{14}$$

while the former occurs both with antineutrinos produced in nuclear β decay[12] and those produced in the decay

$$K^- \rightarrow \pi^0 + e^- + \bar{\nu} . \tag{15}$$

This corresponds of course to the assignment of $\bar{\nu}_\mu$ and $\bar{\nu}_e$, respectively, to the antineutrinos produced in reactions (14) and (15), in accordance with the two-neutrino hypothesis.

2.2.4 Universal β-decay Coupling

In the observed β-decay couplings, all the weak decays appear to be connected through a common origin and interaction form. Thus, we may describe all the observed β-decay processes, for example,

$$\mu^- \rightarrow e^- + \bar{\nu}_e + \nu_\mu , \tag{16a}$$

$$\left.\begin{array}{l} N \rightarrow P + e^- + \bar{\nu}_e \\ \Sigma^+ \rightarrow \Lambda^0 + e^+ + \nu_e \end{array}\right\} , \tag{16b}$$

$$\left.\begin{array}{l} P + \bar{\nu}_\mu \rightarrow N + \mu^+ \\ \Sigma^- \rightarrow \Lambda^0 + \mu^- + \bar{\nu}_\mu \end{array}\right\} , \tag{16c}$$

$$\left.\begin{array}{l} \Sigma^- \rightarrow N + e^- + \bar{\nu}_e \\ \Lambda^0 \rightarrow P + \mu^- + \bar{\nu}_\mu \end{array}\right\} , \tag{16d}$$

in terms of four basic Feynman diagrams, each involving four fermions, as illustrated in Figure 2.1(a).

Universality is simply the statement that the form of the interaction, at each of the vertices shown in Figure 2.1(a), is the same. Pictorially, this may be

[12] The "existence" of the neutrino was first demonstrated by the observation of the first variant of reaction (13), using the antineutrinos from the β decays of the neutron-rich fission products from a uranium fission reactor; see F. Reines, C. L. Cowan, Jr., F. B. Harrison, A. D. McGuire, and H. W. Kruse, *Phys. Rev., 117:* 159 (1960).

described [see Figure 2.1(b)] in terms of a universal tetrahedron, each of whose four vertices is connected to all the other three by an interaction of the same form.

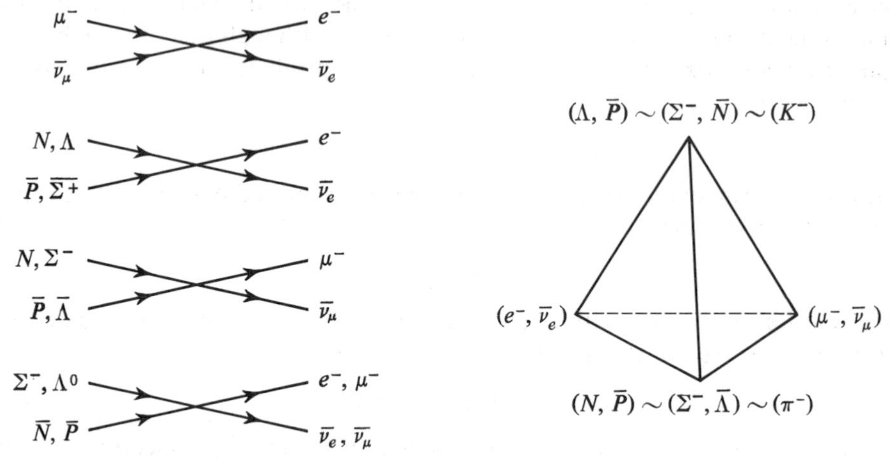

(a) (b)

Figure 2.1 Universal β-decay diagrams. (a) Four-fermion vertices. (b) Puppi, Marshak, Dallaporta, Gell-Mann tetrahedron. *Note:* Any one of the arrows may be reversed by, at the same time, changing the corresponding particle to its antiparticle. Also, all the particles may be simultaneously changed to their antiparticles, keeping the arrows the same, to describe e^+ and μ^+ emission.

In the formal language of β-decay theory,[13] we may define the weak interaction Lagrangian as the square of a current

$$\mathcal{L}_w = \frac{G}{\sqrt{2}} J_\alpha^\dagger \cdot J_\alpha, \tag{17}$$

where G is the universal Fermi coupling constant and J_α is the α component of a 4-vector current that has four terms, each representing one of the vertices of the (anti) tetrahedron of Figure 2.1(b),

$$J_\alpha = j_\alpha^e + j_\alpha^\mu + j_\alpha^0 + j_\alpha^1, \tag{18a}$$

$$j_\alpha^e = e^\dagger \gamma_\alpha (1 + \gamma_5) \nu_e, \tag{18b}$$

$$j_\alpha^\mu = \mu^\dagger \gamma_\alpha (1 + \gamma_5) \nu_\mu . \tag{18c}$$

The two terms in (18b) or (18c) describe a vector (γ_α) and an axial vector $(-\gamma_\alpha \gamma_5)$ interaction. They lead to final states with opposite parity; the equality of their coefficients gives rise to the property of maximum parity violation.

[13] E. Fermi, *Zeits. f. Phys.*, *88:* 161 (1934).

The term j_α^0 represents the strangeness 0 (π-meson-like) vertex and may be written

$$j_\alpha^0 = \sum_i a_i \overline{N}_i \gamma_\alpha (1 + a\gamma_5) P_i , \tag{18d}$$

where by $(\overline{N}_i, P_i)$ we mean any one of the possible (π^+-like) vertices, say, $(\overline{N}, P)$, $(\overline{\Lambda}, \Sigma^+)$, $(\overline{\Sigma^-}, \Sigma^0)$, or $(\overline{\Xi^-}, \Xi^0)$. These are combined with relative strengths a_i, which may be determined empirically from the relative rates of the various β-decay processes or may possibly be derived from some model of the β-decay process. The constant a arises from the "renormalization" of the simple diagrams in Figure 2.1(a) due to virtual meson emission and absorption in the strong interactions;[14] it is found empirically to have the value 1.18.

The strangeness +1 (K^+-meson-like) vertex has for its corresponding current

$$j_\alpha^1 = \sum_i b_i \overline{\Lambda}_i \gamma_\mu (1 + b\gamma_5) P_i , \tag{18e}$$

where, in this case, the pair $(\overline{\Lambda}_i, P_i)$ stands for $(\overline{\Lambda}, P)$, $(\overline{\Sigma^-}, N)$, $(\overline{\Xi^-}, \Lambda)$, $(\overline{\Xi^0}, \Sigma^+)$, etc. — i.e., $S = 1$ with $Q = 1$, or K^+-like combinations.

2.2.5 $\Delta S = \Delta Q$

From the form we have adopted for the universal weak interactions, it may be noted that in strange particle decays where an e^- or μ^- is emitted (e.g., $\Lambda^0 \to P + e^- + \bar{\nu}_e$, $\Sigma^- \to N + \mu^- + \bar{\nu}_\mu$), both the charge of the baryon and its strangeness increase by one unit; for decays with emission of e^+ or μ^+, both charge and strangeness decrease by one unit. Since, for the "metastable" baryons, the masses increase with decreasing strangeness number, we should only observe e^- or μ^- emission in the strangeness-changing decays of the hyperons. This is, in fact, the case: the decays $\Lambda^0 \to P + e^- + \bar{\nu}_e$, $\Sigma^- \to N + e^- + \bar{\nu}_e$ are prominent, while the possible decay $\Sigma^+ \to N + e^+ + \nu_e$ ($\Delta S = -\Delta Q$) has not been observed; its rate is less than that of the Σ^- β decay by at least a factor of 10.

We may note that the β decays of the π- and K-mesons follow directly from the nature of the universal tetrahedron, since the mesons may be thought of as virtual baryon-antibaryon combinations whose direct (weak) annihilation into two leptons is foreseen by the nature of the diagrams of Figure 2.1(a). These mesons may also decay into a π-meson plus two leptons, for example,[15]

$$\begin{aligned} K^+ &\to \pi^0 + e^+ + \nu_e , \\ K^- &\to \pi^0 + e^- + \bar{\nu}_e , \end{aligned} \tag{19a}$$

[14] According to the Conserved Vector Current (CVC) hypothesis of Feynman and Gell-Mann [*Phys. Rev., 109:* 193 (1958); also, S. Gershtein and J. Zel'dovich, *JETP, 2:* 576 (1956)], the vector coupling constant is not altered by the strong interactions. (G_V is the same for nuclear β decay and μ-meson decay to within ~2 percent.)

[15] The CVC theory, mentioned in note 14, predicts for the corresponding pion-decay rate

$$\frac{\pi^+ \to \pi^0 + e^+ + \nu_e}{\pi^+ \to \mu^+ + \nu_\mu} = 1.07 \times 10^{-8} .$$

The experimentally observed value is $(1.02 \pm 0.07) \times 10^{-8}$.

which are in accord with the $\Delta S = \Delta Q$ rule. For the decay of the neutral K-mesons, on the other hand, the rule permits

$$\begin{aligned} K^0 &\to \pi^- + l^+ + \nu_l, \\ \overline{K^0} &\to \pi^+ + l^- + \bar{\nu}_l, \end{aligned} \tag{19b}$$

but forbids

$$\begin{aligned} K^0 &\not\to \pi^+ + l^- + \bar{\nu}_l, \\ \overline{K^0} &\not\to \pi^- + l^+ + \nu_l. \end{aligned} \tag{19c}$$

This prediction is in accord with the observations which, however, owing to the difficulty of disentangling the K^0 and $\overline{K^0}$ decays (for reasons to be discussed below) are still of rather limited accuracy.

2.2.6 Nonleptonic Decays

Those strongly interacting particles that have sufficient mass to decay into other strongly interacting particles or into such particles and photons, without violating any of the relevant selection rules for such decays, will, of course, do so — e.g., $\rho^\pm \to \pi^\pm + \pi^0$, $K^* \to K + \pi$, $\Sigma^0 \to \Lambda^0 + \gamma$. However, a number of the most important hyperons and the K-mesons can only decay into other hadrons by violation of the conservation of strangeness. Owing to the direct link between the $S = 0$ and $S = \pm 1$ baryonic vertices [Figure 2.1(b)], we may have direct weak decays of strange particles into strongly interacting particles only. These are, in fact, the most prominent among the hyperon decays, for example,

$$\Lambda^0 \to P + \pi^-, \tag{20a}$$

$$\Sigma^+ \to N + \pi^+, \tag{20b}$$

$$\Xi^0 \to \Lambda + \pi^0, \tag{20c}$$

since two-body final states are favored by phase-space considerations. Table 2.1 also lists the observed weak decay modes of the hadrons, both leptonic and nonleptonic, with their measured decay rates, branching ratios, and some of the other properties characterizing their decay distributions.

Owing to the relationship

$$Q = t_3 + \frac{B + S}{2}, \tag{21}$$

coupled with baryon conservation ($\Delta B = 0$) and the $\Delta S = \Delta Q$ rule, we have for such decays

$$\Delta t_3 = \Delta Q - \frac{\Delta S}{2} = \pm\frac{1}{2}. \tag{22}$$

However, Equation (22) tells us nothing about the change of total isotopic spin (Δt) in such weak nonleptonic decays.

It has been observed empirically that these decays obey an isotopic-spin selection rule

$$\Delta t = \pm \tfrac{1}{2} \tag{23}$$

to within a few percent in all cases. Thus, for example, the $\Delta t = \pm\frac{1}{2}$ rule predicts for the ratio of the Λ^0-decay rates

$$\frac{\Lambda^0 \to P + \pi^-}{\Lambda^0 \to N + \pi^0} = 2, \tag{24}$$

since the final nucleon-pion state must have $t = \frac{1}{2}$, $t_3 = -\frac{1}{2}$ ($t_\Lambda = Q_\Lambda = 0; S_\Lambda = -1$). This combination is $(\sqrt{2}\, P\pi^- - N\pi^0)$, which leads to Equation (24) for the rates (amplitudes squared).

For the K-mesons ($t = \frac{1}{2}$), the $\Delta t = \pm\frac{1}{2}$ selection rule permits the decays

$$K^0, \overline{K^0} \to \pi^+\pi^- \text{ or } \pi^0\pi^0 \tag{25}$$

(with a predicted and observed ratio of two, since the final state must have $t = 0$), but forbids the decays

$$K^\pm \not\to \pi^\pm + \pi^0, \tag{26}$$

since a final $t = 1$ state of two pions must have an odd value of the total angular momentum, while the spin of the K-mesons is 0 (see Section 2.1.2). Although the decay reaction (26) is observed, its rate is less than that of the K^0's [Equation (25)] by a factor of $\gtrsim 400$, indicating a high degree of forbiddenness.[16]

2.2.7 Further Consequences of Parity Nonconservation (*TCP* and All That)

One of the most important features of the universal weak interaction just described is that while the interaction is not invariant with respect to the parity operation $\mathcal{P}$, neither is it invariant with respect to the charge-conjugation operation $\mathcal{C}$. However, the interaction is invariant with respect to the combined operation $\mathcal{CP}$.[17] In the particular case of neutral systems with $S = \mathcal{Y} = 0$, the quantum number $CP = \pm 1$ is therefore conserved in the weak decays.

This feature has most interesting consequences in the case of the decays of the neutral kaons. We have previously noted that the combinations

$$\begin{aligned} K_1^0 &= \sqrt{\tfrac{1}{2}}\,(K^0 + \overline{K^0}), \\ K_2^0 &= \sqrt{\tfrac{1}{2}}\,(K^0 - \overline{K^0}), \end{aligned} \tag{27a}$$

are eigenstates of $\mathcal{C}$, with $C = \mp 1$ respectively. They are also eigenstates of $\mathcal{P}$,

[16] We do not expect isotopic-spin selection rules to be exact, owing to the possibility of intervention of virtual photon emission and absorption processes, which permit the violation of isotopic-spin conservation and, in the case of the $K^\pm$ decays, allow, for example, weak decays with $\Delta t = \pm\frac{3}{2}$, but with much reduced amplitude owing to the relative smallness of the electromagnetic coupling.

[17] That is, the laws of β decay look different in a right- and left-handed coordinate system, or in an antiuniverse as compared to a universe, but they would be identical to ours in an antiuniverse that is the mirror image of ours.

with $P = -1$ in both cases (the kaons have negative intrinsic parity); they are therefore also eigenstates of $\mathcal{C}\mathcal{P}$, with $CP = \pm 1$.

Consider the decays of the K^0's into pions. A two-pion final state of $J = 0^+$ has $C = (-1)^J = +1$, $P = +1$ and, thus, $CP = +1$. A three-pion final state of spin 0 has $J = 0^-$ ($P = -1$) and $t = 1$, $G = -1$, hence $C = +1$ [$G = C(-1)^t$] and $CP = -1$.[18] Thus, the simplest weak pionic decays of the K^0's are

$$\begin{aligned} K_1^0 &\to 2\pi, \\ K_2^0 &\to 3\pi, \end{aligned} \tag{27b}$$

of which the former has the much shorter mean life due to the larger available phase space.

Now, although it is the $K_{1,2}^0$ which, being eigenstates of the weak interactions, do the decaying, it is the K^0 and $\overline{K^0}$ which are actually produced in the strong interactions. These are, however, combinations of the $K_{1,2}^0$ [invert Equation (27a)]:

$$\begin{aligned} K^0 &= \sqrt{\tfrac{1}{2}}\,(K_1^0 + K_2^0), \\ \overline{K^0} &= \sqrt{\tfrac{1}{2}}\,(K_1^0 - K_2^0). \end{aligned} \tag{27c}$$

The result is that, if we produce a pure K^0 or $\overline{K^0}$ beam, the K_1^0 component will decay much more rapidly than the K_2^0, resulting, after a time which is long, say, compared to the K_1^0 lifetime but not too long compared to the lifetime of K_2^0, in a beam that is essentially pure K_2^0, i.e., an equal mixture of K^0 and $\overline{K^0}$.

This mixing phenomenon may be observed in a number of ways, for example, by observing the pion decays of the $K_{1,2}^0$ or by observing directly the K^0 or $\overline{K^0}$ components by virtue of their different strong interactions.[19] We shall discuss these phenomena in detail in Chapter 8.

We note, further, that since $K_{1,2}^0$ are equal mixtures of $S = 1$ and $S = -1$, the $\Delta S = \Delta Q$ rule does not inhibit their β decays, so that each should decay with equal probability into both of the final states of (19b). Thus, another means of investigating the $K^0 \longleftrightarrow \overline{K^0}$ conversion process is through observation of these leptonic decay processes (generally designated K_{e3} and $K_{\mu 3}$).

Another feature of the $K_{1,2}^0$ phenomenon is worth noting. Since the K_1^0 and K_2^0 are *not* antiparticles of each other, there is no reason for them to have exactly the same mass. In fact, owing to the difference in their weak interactions, it is to be expected that there should be a small difference in their total energies (hence masses). That this difference will be very small is a consequence of the fact that the $K^0 \longleftrightarrow \overline{K^0}$ conversion process, which results from weak interactions (e.g.,

[18] Bose statistics requires a wave function even under interchange of any two pions. The space part is even, whence $t_{2\pi} = 0$ or 2; the third pion has $t_\pi = 1$, hence possible values of $t = 1, 2, 3$. The $\Delta t = \frac{1}{2}$ selection rule then chooses $t = 1$ for the 3π state resulting from K^0 decay. Note that the negative parity of the space-symmetric state comes from the intrinsic parity $P_{\text{int}}(n\pi) = (-1)^n$.

[19] Thus, for example, $\overline{K^0}$'s can produce hyperons in a reaction like $\overline{K^0} + P \to \Lambda^0 + \pi^+$, while strangeness conservation prevents the K^0 from doing so.

$K^0 \longleftrightarrow \pi^+ + \pi^- \longleftrightarrow \overline{K^0}$) is a two-step process; and hence its matrix element is proportional to g_w^2, which is very small indeed.[20] However, effects of this small mass difference can be measured in observations on the $K^0 \longleftrightarrow \overline{K^0}$ conversion phenomenon discussed above, and the mass difference is indeed observed to be of the expected order of magnitude

$$\Delta mc^2 \cong \frac{1}{2}\frac{\hbar}{\tau_{K_1^0}} \cong 5 \times 10^{-6}\,\text{eV}. \tag{27d}$$

This observation confirms that feature of the universal weak interaction that requires the selection rule $\Delta S = \pm 1$ in the weak decays of the strange particles. If there were a direct $\Delta S = \pm 2$ effect of strength comparable to the $\Delta S = \pm 1$ term in the weak-decay Lagrangian, it would generally lead to a much more rapid $K^0 \longleftrightarrow \overline{K^0}$ conversion rate and much larger K_1^0–K_2^0 mass difference, by a factor of $\sim 10^{6-7}$. This selection rule is further confirmed, but with much less precision, by the absence of decays of the type

$$\Xi \not\rightarrow N + \pi. \tag{28}$$

Although the main features of the $K_{1,2}^0$ decays, as discussed above and in greater detail in Chapter 8, have been confirmed experimentally, a further complication has been introduced by the startling observation of Christenson, Cronin, Fitch, and Turlay[21] of a relatively weak, but nevertheless finite, decay mode,

$$K_2^0 \rightarrow 2\pi, \tag{29}$$

a decay in violation of CP conservation as discussed above [Equation (27b)]. Since it is currently believed on quite general theoretical grounds[22] that, for essentially all theories of possible physical interest, the combined operation of time reversal, charge conjugation, and parity (TCP) is an invariant operation, a violation of CP invariance implies a compensating violation of T invariance.

The observed CP violation in K_2^0 decay is, as noted, quite small. Thus, the relative amplitude:

$$\frac{A(K_2^0 \rightarrow \pi^+\pi^-)}{A(K_1^0 \rightarrow \pi^+\pi^-)} = (1.90 \pm 0.05) \times 10^{-3}. \tag{30}$$

In addition, there is, at least at the time of this writing, some question as to whether the $K_2^0 \rightarrow 2\pi$ decay satisfies the $\Delta t = \frac{1}{2}$ selection rule [Equation (25)],

---

[20] For the two-step process envisaged, the mass difference is expected to be $\sim \xi G^2 m_K^5/4\pi^2 \approx 10^{-4}\xi$ eV, where $GM_P^2 = g_w \cong 10^{-5}$, and ξ is a kinematical factor, expected to be $\sim \frac{1}{10}$. For a direct ($\Delta S = 2$) weak conversion process of coupling strength G', on the other hand, one would expect a mass difference of $\sim \xi G' m_K^3 \approx 10^3 (G'/G)\xi$ eV. Note that the same interaction that is responsible for the $K_{1,2}^0$ decays, whose rate is proportional to the interaction matrix element squared, is also responsible for the mass difference, but in this case the energy shift results from a second-order (two-stage) process, which leads again to the square of the matrix element; hence, Equation (27d) provides a reasonable order-of-magnitude estimate for the mass difference.

[21] *Phys. Rev. Letters, 13:* 138 (1964).

[22] G. Lüders, *Ann. Phys., 2,* 1 (1957). It should, of course, be remembered that, in the final analysis, the validity of TCP invariance for all physical processes is an experimental question.

which would require that the ratio of $K_2^0 \to 2\pi^0$ to $K_1^0 \to 2\pi^0$ be the same as that of the charged mode [Equation (30)].[23]

CP nonconservation has also been observed in the $K_2^0 \to \pi^{\pm}l^{\mp}\nu$ decays (the K_{l3} decays). As previously noted, CP conservation predicts equality of the rates of decay into $\pi^- l^+ \nu$ and $\pi^+ l^- \bar{\nu}$. However, small deviations of their ratio from unity (0.81 ± 0.27 percent and 0.45 ± 0.07 percent for the μ and e decays, respectively)[24] have recently been detected.

Little more of a definitive nature can be said at this stage concerning the nature of the CP-violating weak interaction, since the phenomenon has not yet been observed in any weak decays not involving the K_2^0.

2.2.8 Intermediate Bosons?

In his original conception of the meson field theory of nuclear interactions, Yukawa attempted to assign to the mesons still another role — that of acting as the intermediary for the weak interactions. In this case, one could replace a four-fermion β-decay vertex [Figure 2.1(a)] by two, connected three-particle vertices, as indicated in Figure 2.2, each of which would be much easier to treat by conventional field-theoretic means.

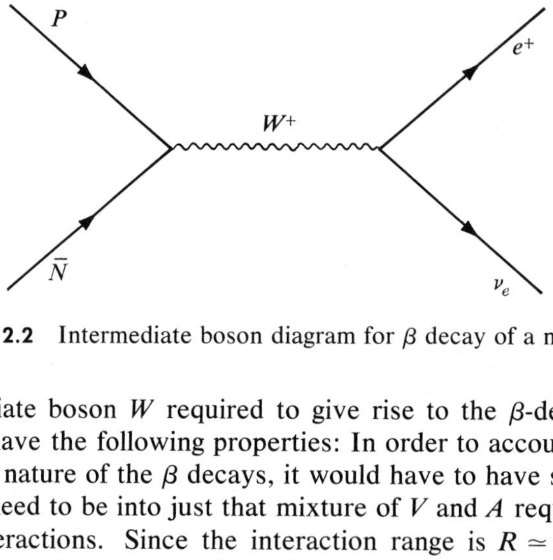

Figure 2.2 Intermediate boson diagram for β decay of a nucleon.

The intermediate boson W required to give rise to the β-decay interactions would need to have the following properties: In order to account for the vector and axial vector nature of the β decays, it would have to have spin 1. Its decay would, in fact, need to be into just that mixture of V and A required to describe the β-decay interactions. Since the interaction range is $R \simeq \hbar/M_W c$, its mass would have to be very large to allow the two-step decay process depicted in Figure 2.2 to be approximated by the essentially point-interaction (i.e., very short range) vertices of Figure 2.1(a). Another indication of the large mass required for the W is obtained from consideration of the form of the Lagrangian describing the W β-decay processes:

---

[23] Gaillard, *et al., Phys. Rev. Letters, 18:* 20 (1967); Cronin, *et al., Phys. Rev. Letters, 18:* 25 (1967).
[24] Dorfan, *et al., Phys. Rev. Letters, 19:* 987 (1967); Bennett, *et al., Phys. Rev. Letters, 19:* 993 (1967).

$$\mathcal{L}_W = g_W(J_\alpha^\dagger W_\alpha + J_\alpha W_\alpha^\dagger). \tag{31}$$

To obtain, via a two-stage process as in Figure 2.2, the same β-decay rates as given by the normal β-decay Lagrangian, Equation (17), requires

$$\frac{g_W^2}{M_W^2} = \frac{G}{\sqrt{2}}. \tag{32}$$

Hence, if we would like the intermediate bosons to be coupled relatively strongly to nucleons, i.e., $g_W^2/\hbar c \approx 0.01 - 1$, and still maintain the weakness of the observed β-decay coupling,

$$\frac{(M_p^2 G)^2}{\hbar c} \approx 10^{-10}, \tag{33}$$

we require $M_W \gg M_p$.

In the intermediate boson theory of the weak interactions, all the weak decays originate as alternative decay modes of the W:

$$W^\pm \rightarrow l^\pm + \begin{Bmatrix} \nu \\ \bar{\nu} \end{Bmatrix} \tag{34a}$$

$$\rightarrow \pi^\pm + \pi^0 \tag{34b}$$

$$\rightarrow K^\pm + \pi^0. \tag{34c}$$

To account both for the neutral nonleptonic decay modes of the K^0's and for the $\Delta t = \frac{1}{2}$ selection rule of the $\Delta S = \pm 1$ decays, the W must be an isotopic doublet (W^+, W^0) with the antiparticles $\overline{W} = (W^-, \overline{W^0})$. However, since there are no neutral leptonic decays observed (i.e., no $e^+ + e^-$ or $\nu + \bar{\nu}$ weak decays), it must be assumed that the neutral W's have only nonleptonic decay modes.

If the W exists, it could be demonstrated by observation of neutrino-induced reactions of the form

$$\nu_\mu + N \rightarrow N + \mu^- + W^+ \tag{35}$$
$$\qquad\qquad\qquad\quad \hookrightarrow e^+ + \nu_e,$$

an interaction that would require a two-stage weak interaction process in the absence of the W, and that would under this circumstance be unobservably weak. So far, interactions with neutrinos of energies up to ~ 10 GeV, at the CERN and the Brookhaven accelerators, have not produced any examples of reaction (35), thereby setting an upper limit of $M_W \gtrsim 2$ GeV/c^2.

The search for the W will be one of the most interesting aspects of future high-energy accelerator experimentation.

PROBLEMS

1. The following reactions may be divided among three categories:

   A. allowed by all known conservation laws;
   B. forbidden by some conservation law(s) *and* never observed experimentally;

C. forbidden by some conservation law(s) *but* observed and can be explained by some known or presumed violation.

Identify each reaction, with respect to categories A, B, and C and, if it falls into category B or C, give the conservation law responsible for its inhibition and the selection rule(s) determining its behavior.

(a) $\pi^+ + \pi^- \to \mu^+ + e^-$,
(b) $\pi^0 \to 3\gamma$,
(c) $\mu^+ \to e^+ + \nu_e + \bar{\nu}_\mu$,
(d) $K_1^0 \to 2\pi^0$,
(e) $\omega^0 \to 2\gamma$,
(f) $K^- + \Sigma^+ \to \pi^- + P$,
(g) $\Lambda^0 \to \pi^0 + N$,
(h) $\rho^0 \to 2\pi^0$,
(i) $\omega^0 \to \pi^+ + \pi^- + \pi^0$,
(j) $\eta^0 \to 3\pi^0$,
(k) $e^+ + e^- \to \gamma$,
(l) $P \to e^+ + \gamma$.

2. Show that for weak interactions that are invariant under *TCP* the decay lifetimes of particles and antiparticles are the same. Assume an interaction Hamiltonian of the form

$$H = H^+ + H^-,$$

where

$$\mathcal{P} H^{\pm} \mathcal{P}^{-1} = \pm H^{\pm}.$$

3. What are the transformation properties under space reflection (parity) of the following elements of possible weak-decay Lagrangians,

(a) $\bar{\psi}\sigma_{\mu\nu}\psi$,
(b) $\bar{\psi}\sigma_{\mu\nu}\gamma_5\psi$,

where

$$2i\sigma_{\mu\nu} = \gamma_\mu\gamma_\nu - \gamma_\nu\gamma_\mu,$$

and the γ's are the Dirac matrices?[25]

[25] See P. A. M. Dirac, *The Principles of Quantum Mechanics*, The Clarendon Press, Oxford (1947).

3

Kinematics of High-Energy Reactions

The serious student of elementary particle phenomena will soon find, in his attempts at understanding the vast variety of observations, that most of the detailed behavior of systems of elementary particles is determined by considerations deriving from the application of the various conservation principles obeyed by such systems. It is only after extracting the consequences of such well-understood "kinematical" requirements as energy-momentum, angular momentum, isotopic-spin conservation, and so on, that he may discover those new and unpredictable dynamical features which may provide new insights into the nature of elementary particles and their interactions.

In Chapters 3–11 we summarize and review briefly, mainly through specific examples, the effects of such kinematical considerations on the behavior of the elementary particles.

Observations concerning the production and decay of elementary particles are, perforce, normally performed in the laboratory coordinate system (*lab*). For their interpretation, however, we frequently require the conversion of such observations into a coordinate system moving with respect to the observer. The transformations between systems moving with uniform velocity with respect to each other are, in the framework of special relativity, the Lorentz transformations. In the limit of small velocities (compared to the speed of light, c) the transformations reduce to the simple Galilean vector addition of velocities. For high speeds, they are more complicated.

In the following, we review the kinematics of special relativity: Consider a particle of rest mass m, velocity $\mathbf{v}$ ($\boldsymbol{\beta} = \mathbf{v}/c$). Let

$$\gamma = (1 - \beta^2)^{-1/2}. \tag{1}$$

Then, the momentum is

$$\mathbf{p} = \gamma m c \boldsymbol{\beta}, \tag{2}$$

and the (total) energy is

$$\epsilon = \gamma m c^2. \tag{3}$$

Note that

$$c\mathbf{p} = \boldsymbol{\beta}\epsilon \tag{4}$$

and

$$\epsilon^2 = \gamma^2 m^2 c^4 = c^2 p^2 + m^2 c^4. \tag{5}$$

From (5), since m^2c^4 is an invariant (constant) of the motion, we conclude that $(cp_x, cp_y, cp_z, i\epsilon)$ represent the four components of an invariant 4-vector, whose transformation properties are simply the Lorentz transformations of special relativity, identical with those of (x, y, z, ict).

Consider a coordinate system moving with the velocity $\boldsymbol{\beta}_c$ $[\gamma_c = (1-\beta_c^2)^{-1/2}]$ with respect to the *lab*. Let our particle have velocity $\boldsymbol{\beta}_0$ in this system, with $\cos\theta_0 = (\boldsymbol{\beta}_0 \cdot \boldsymbol{\beta}_c)/(\beta_0\beta_c)$ (its energy is $\epsilon_0 = \gamma_0 mc^2$, momentum $\mathbf{p}_0 = \gamma_0 mc\boldsymbol{\beta}_0$). Then, in the *lab*,

$$cp\cos\theta = \gamma_c(cp_0\cos\theta_0 + \beta_c\epsilon_0), \tag{6a}$$

$$cp\sin\theta = cp_0\sin\theta_0, \tag{6b}$$

$$\epsilon = \gamma_c(\epsilon_0 + cp_0\,\beta_c\cos\theta_0). \tag{6c}$$

From (6), we obtain ϵ [or $p = (1/c)\sqrt{\epsilon^2 - m^2c^4}$] and θ. These are

$$\epsilon = \gamma_c\epsilon_0(1 + \beta_c\beta_0\cos\theta_0), \tag{7a}$$

$$\operatorname{ctn}\theta = \gamma_c\left(\operatorname{ctn}\theta_0 + \frac{\beta_c}{\beta_0}\csc\theta_0\right). \tag{7b}$$

Relations (6a)–(6c) and (7a)–(7b) contain, within them, all the transformations required. Thus, we have the following possibilities, among others:

1. Suppose we want to invert, and go from the *lab* ($\boldsymbol{\beta}$, θ) to the moving system. We simply invert the direction of $\boldsymbol{\beta}_c$ ($\beta_c \to -\beta_c$) and interchange all subscript with nonsubscript symbols ($\epsilon \longleftrightarrow \epsilon_0$, $\theta_0 \longleftrightarrow \theta$, etc.):

$$\epsilon_0 = \gamma_c\epsilon(1 - \beta_c\beta\cos\theta), \tag{8a}$$

$$\operatorname{ctn}\theta_0 = \gamma_c\left(\operatorname{ctn}\theta - \frac{\beta_c}{\beta}\csc\theta\right), \tag{8b}$$

and so on.

2. Let $\boldsymbol{\beta}_c = \boldsymbol{\beta}$ (i.e., $\boldsymbol{\beta}_0 = 0$): This means that the moving system is sitting on the particle (we refer to this as the rest frame, or *cm*, of the particle). Then $\mathbf{p}_0 = 0$, $\epsilon_0 = mc^2$, $\gamma_c = \gamma$, $\epsilon = \gamma\epsilon_0$, etc.

3. Now, in general, the above considerations apply to any system, even a

complex one with internal energy. We can always find one system in which the total momentum vanishes. We call this the center-of-mass or center-of-momentum or baryocentric system (*cm*), with total energy E_0. Then, since the total *cm* momentum is $P_0 = 0$, we may define an effective rest mass M,

$$M = \frac{E_0}{c^2}, \tag{9}$$

and, provided we can determine the velocity of the *cm* with respect to the *lab*, all the properties in any other coordinate frame follow from the transformations developed above. We consider, in some detail, the following applications.

3.1 Decay Processes

For simplicity, we look at the two-body decay $A \to B + C$. Let M, m_1, m_2 be the three rest masses, respectively. Then the energy release (Q-value) is

$$Q = (M - m_1 - m_2)\,c^2. \tag{10}$$

In the rest frame we have, from conservation of energy,

$$Mc^2 = \epsilon_1 + \epsilon_2 \tag{11a}$$

with

$$\epsilon_{1,2}^2 = m_{1,2}^2 c^4 + p_{1,2}^2 c^2 \tag{11b}$$

and, from conservation of momentum,

$$p_1 = p_2. \tag{12}$$

Combining (11) and (12), we have

$$\epsilon_{1,2} = \frac{(M^2 + m_{1,2}^2 - m_{2,1}^2)\,c^2}{2M}. \tag{13}$$

EXAMPLE

Consider $\pi^\pm \to \mu^\pm + \nu$:

$$M_\pi c^2 = 139.6 \text{ MeV},$$
$$M_\mu c^2 = 105.7 \text{ MeV},$$
$$M_\nu c^2 = 0.$$

$$\epsilon_\nu = cp = \frac{(M_\pi^2 - M_\mu^2)\,c^2}{2M_\pi} = \frac{(M_\pi + M_\mu)(M_\pi - M_\mu)\,c^2}{2M_\pi}$$
$$= \frac{245.3 \times 33.9}{2 \times 139.6} = 29.8 \text{ MeV},$$

$$\epsilon_\mu = 139.6 - 29.8 = 109.8 \text{ MeV},$$
$$\kappa_\mu = \epsilon_\mu - m_\mu c^2 = 109.8 - 105.7 = 4.1 \text{ MeV (kinetic energy)},$$
$$p_\mu = p_\nu = 29.8 \text{ MeV}/c.$$

In addition, the decay process has a mean life τ_0 (in the rest system of A),

$$\frac{dN}{dt_0} = -\frac{1}{\tau_0}, \tag{14a}$$

and the decay products are emitted with some angular distribution $dN/d\Omega_0$ (note that particles 1 and 2 are emitted back to back); for isotropic emission,

$$\frac{dN}{d\Omega_0} = \frac{1}{4\pi}. \tag{14b}$$

Now, suppose the particle A is moving with speed β_0. What does the decay process look like in the *lab*?

3.1.1 The Decay Rate

The *lab* decay rate is

$$\frac{dN}{dt} = \frac{dN}{dt_0}\frac{dt_0}{dt} = -\frac{1}{\tau_0}\frac{dt_0}{dt} = -\frac{1}{\tau}, \tag{14c}$$

$$\tau = \tau_0 \frac{dt}{dt_0}. \tag{15a}$$

But

$$ct = \gamma_0(ct_0 + \beta_0 x_0), \qquad \text{with } x_0 = 0. \tag{15b}$$

(The origin is on the particle.) Hence

$$dt = \gamma_0\, dt_0, \tag{15c}$$

$$\tau = \gamma_0 \tau_0 = \frac{\tau_0}{(1-\beta_0^2)^{1/2}}. \tag{15d}$$

This is the well-known time-dilation effect.

3.1.2 The Energy Distribution

The *lab* energy is

$$\epsilon_1 = \gamma_0(\epsilon_{10} + c\beta_0 p_{10} \cos\theta_{10}), \tag{16a}$$

where ϵ_{10}, p_{10}, θ_{10} refer to particle 1 (B) in the rest frame of the decaying particle (A). We note that ϵ_1 varies between the extremes

$$\begin{aligned} \epsilon_{1\,\min}^{\;\max} &= \gamma_0(\epsilon_{10} \pm c\beta_0 p_{10}) \\ &= \gamma_0\epsilon_{10}(1 \pm \beta_0\beta_{10}). \end{aligned} \tag{16b}$$

The energy spectrum is

$$d\epsilon_1 = \gamma_0\beta_0\beta_{10}\epsilon_{10}\, d(\cos\theta_{10}) = \frac{\gamma_0\beta_0\beta_{10}\epsilon_{10}}{2\pi}\, d\Omega_{10}, \tag{17a}$$

$$\frac{dN_1}{d\epsilon_1} = \frac{dN_1}{d\Omega_{10}} \frac{d\Omega_{10}}{d\epsilon_1} = \frac{2\pi}{\gamma_0\beta_0\beta_{10}\epsilon_{10}} \frac{dN}{d\Omega_0}. \tag{17b}$$

For isotropic emission in the rest frame,

$$\frac{dN_1}{d\epsilon_1} = \frac{1}{2\gamma_0\beta_0\beta_{10}\epsilon_{10}} = \frac{1}{2\gamma_0\beta_0 c p_{10}} = \frac{(1-\beta_0^2)^{1/2}}{2\beta_0\beta_{10}\epsilon_{10}}$$

$$= \frac{1}{2m_1c^2} \frac{(1-\beta_0^2)^{1/2}(1-\beta_{10}^2)^{1/2}}{\beta_0\beta_{10}}. \tag{17c}$$

3.1.3 The Angular Distribution

The angular distribution is

$$\frac{dN_1}{d\Omega_1} = \frac{dN_1}{d\Omega_{10}} \frac{d\Omega_{10}}{d\Omega_1} = J_1 \frac{dN_1}{d\Omega_{10}}, \tag{18}$$

$$J_1 = \frac{d\Omega_{10}}{d\Omega_1} = \frac{1}{J_{10}} = \frac{d(\cos\theta_{10})}{d(\cos\theta_1)}. \tag{19a}$$

Starting with

$$\operatorname{ctn}\theta_1 = \gamma_0\left(\operatorname{ctn}\theta_{10} + \frac{\beta_0}{\beta_{10}}\csc\theta_{10}\right) = \frac{\gamma_0}{\sin\theta_{10}}\left(\cos\theta_{10} + \frac{\beta_0}{\beta_{10}}\right), \tag{20a}$$

we obtain, by differentiation (and some manipulation),

$$J_{10} = \frac{d\Omega_1}{d\Omega_{10}} = \frac{1}{J_1} = \frac{p_{10}^3}{p_1^3}\gamma_0\left(1 + \frac{\beta_0}{\beta_{10}}\cos\theta_{10}\right). \tag{19b}$$

As long as $\beta_0/\beta_{10} < 1$ (i.e., the velocity of the emitted particle is greater than that of the moving system), $J_{10} > 0$ for all θ_{10}, and θ_1 increases monotonically from $0° \to 180°$ as θ_{10} goes through the same range of angles.

However, for $\beta_0/\beta_{10} > 1$, we note from (20a) that $\operatorname{ctn}\theta_1 > 0$ for all θ_{10}, and from (19b) that $J_{10} = 0$ at $\cos\theta_{10}^{(m)} = -\beta_{10}/\beta_0$ corresponding to the maximum possible $\theta_{1\max} \le 90°$:

$$\operatorname{ctn}\theta_{1\max} = \gamma_0\left(\frac{\beta_0}{\beta_{10}} - \frac{\beta_{10}}{\beta_0}\right)\csc\theta_{10}^{(m)}$$

$$= \frac{(\beta_0^2 - \beta_{10}^2)^{1/2}}{\beta_{10}(1-\beta_0^2)^{1/2}}. \tag{20b}$$

That is, θ_1 is a double-valued function of θ_{10}, except at $\theta_{1\max}$, where $dN/d\Omega_1 \to \infty$. One can, of course, distinguish between the two possible θ_{10} values, at a given value of θ_1, on the basis of the energy; ϵ_1 remains single-valued.

PROBLEMS

1. Consider a π^0, moving with speed β in the *lab*, which decays into two photons, $\pi^0 \rightarrow 2\gamma$. In the π^0 *cm*, each photon has energy $\epsilon_0 = m_\pi c^2/2 = 67.5$ MeV $= cp_0$ $(\beta_\gamma = \beta_{0\gamma} = 1)$. The photons are emitted isotropically in the π^0 rest system $(j_\pi = 0)$.

   (a) Show that the resulting *lab* energy distribution of the photons is constant,

   $$\frac{dN}{dE_\gamma} = \frac{1}{\gamma\beta m_\pi c^2},$$

   between the limits

   $$E_{\gamma\,\min}^{\max} = \tfrac{1}{2}\gamma m_\pi c^2(1 \pm \beta).$$

   (b) Since $\beta_{0\gamma}/\beta > 1$ in this case, all angles are possible for the γ in the *lab*. Derive the angular and energy distribution of the photons in the *lab* and show that the *lab* angle between the two γ's $(\theta = \theta_1 + \theta_2)$ has the distribution

   $$\frac{dN}{d\theta} = \frac{m_\pi c}{p_\pi} \cdot \frac{\cos\theta/2}{4\sin^2\frac{\theta}{2}\left\{\left(\frac{\epsilon_\pi}{m_\pi c^2}\right)^2 \sin^2\frac{\theta}{2} - 1\right\}^{1/2}}.$$

   (c) Sketch this angular distribution from $\theta = 180°$ to its minimum angle

   $$\theta_{\min} = 2\sin^{-1}\left(\frac{m_\pi c^2}{\epsilon_\pi}\right).$$

   (d) Apply the results of (a), (b), (c) to the case of the π^0 produced by the capture *at rest* of a π^- in the reaction

   $$\pi^- + P \rightarrow N + \pi^0.$$

2. Consider the decay $\pi^+ \rightarrow \mu^+ + \nu_\mu$ for a beam of π-mesons of momentum $p_\pi = 140$ MeV/c. Assuming isotropic decay in the pion rest frame, find the energy and angular distribution of the μ^+ mesons in the *lab*.
3. The measured momentum of μ-mesons, from decay of pions at rest, is found to be $p_\mu = (29.80 \pm 0.04)$ MeV/c. Using the values of m_π and m_μ from Table 2.1, find the value of the neutrino mass, and its uncertainty, $\epsilon \pm \delta\epsilon$. Which one of the input data has to be improved to give the greatest decrease in $\delta\epsilon$?

3.2 Reactions

As a second application we consider reactions of the general type

$$a + b \rightarrow c + d + \cdots. \tag{21}$$

Let $M_a = m$, $M_b = M$, and assume the target (b) at rest in the *lab*. Then, the total *lab* energy is

$$E = \epsilon + Mc^2,$$
$$\epsilon^2 = p^2c^2 + m^2c^4, \tag{22a}$$

and the total momentum is

$$P = p. \tag{22b}$$

Consider a system moving with speed β_0 in the same direction as $\boldsymbol{\beta}(\mathbf{p})$.

$$E_0 = \gamma_0(E - \beta_0 cP), \tag{23a}$$

$$cP_0 = \gamma_0(cP - \beta_0 E). \tag{23b}$$

The *cm* is defined by

$$P_0 = 0, \tag{24a}$$

$$\beta_0 = \frac{cP}{E} = \frac{cp}{\epsilon + Mc^2}, \tag{24b}$$

$$\gamma_0 = (1 - \beta_0^2)^{-1/2} = E(E^2 - P^2)^{-1/2}, \tag{24c}$$

$$\begin{aligned} E_0 &= (E^2 - P^2)^{1/2} \\ &= (2\epsilon Mc^2 + M^2c^4 + m^2c^4)^{1/2} \\ &= [2\kappa Mc^2 + (M + m)^2c^4]^{1/2}, \end{aligned} \tag{24d}$$

where $\epsilon = \kappa + mc^2$.

3.2.1 Thresholds

Let m_i be the masses of the reaction products. The minimum energy, for the reaction just to go, is given by the condition

$$E_{0t} = \sum m_i c^2 \tag{25a}$$

since only in the *cm* is it possible for all the reaction products to have zero momentum. Let ϵ_t be the threshold bombarding energy of the projectile *a*. Then

$$2\epsilon_t Mc^2 + M^2c^4 + m^2c^4 = \left(\sum m_i c^2\right)^2, \tag{25b}$$

$$\epsilon_t = \frac{\left[\left(\sum m_i\right)^2 - M^2 - m^2\right]c^2}{2M}. \tag{25c}$$

EXAMPLE

Threshold for photopion production,

$$\gamma + P \rightarrow P + \pi^0,$$

$m_\gamma = 0,\ m_P = M,\ m_\pi = \mu.$

$$\begin{aligned} \epsilon_{\gamma t} &= \frac{[(M + \mu)^2 - M^2]\,c^2}{2M} = \mu c^2\left(1 + \frac{\mu}{2M}\right) \\ &= 135.0\ (1.072) = 135.0 + 9.7 = 144.7\ \text{MeV}. \end{aligned}$$

3.2.2 Cross Sections

In general, in observing reactions, one is interested in interpreting observed *lab* cross sections in terms of the equivalent *cm* values, since it is the latter that are characteristic of the dynamics and independent of the frame in which they are observed. All the considerations of the previous section on decay processes may be used for the discussion of this problem, without alteration in any respect. Indeed, for kinematical purposes we may view the reaction as

$$a + b \rightarrow A \rightarrow c + d + \cdots, \tag{21a}$$

where the reaction products behave as though we were observing the decay of a particle A of mass $Mc^2 = E_0$ moving with a velocity $\boldsymbol{\beta}_0$ with respect to the *lab* system.

We will not go here into the complications of three or more body decays, except for one brief comment: Suppose that, in the *lab*, one observes some particle, say, c, produced in the reaction, and one determines its energy as well as angular distribution — i.e., one measures $d^2N/d\epsilon\, d\Omega$. Then, to obtain the *cm* distribution $d^2N/d\epsilon_0\, d\Omega_0$, we may take advantage of the existence of a physical invariant

$$p\, d\epsilon\, d\Omega = p_0\, d\epsilon_0\, d\Omega_0. \tag{26}$$

PROBLEMS

1. Show that, for the colinear collision of two particles of masses m_1 and m_2, the relative velocity in any coordinate system is given by

$$\beta_{\text{rel}} = \frac{c^2\{(\mathbf{p}_1 \cdot \mathbf{p}_2)^2 - m_1^2 m_2^2\, c^4\}^{1/2}}{\epsilon_1 \epsilon_2}.$$

2. A storage-ring experiment consists of counter-rotating beams of electrons and positrons that collide head-on. One such device, operating at Frascati, Italy, attains an energy of 1.5 GeV for both the electrons and the positrons. What energy accelerator would be required for bombarding electrons in a stationary target with accelerated positrons at an equivalent (same *cm*) energy?
3. Consider the reaction

$$a + P \rightarrow \mathfrak{N} + \mathfrak{N} + \overline{\mathfrak{N}}.$$

(a) Find the threshold kinetic energy of the projectile a on a stationary target P for

(i) $a = \gamma$,
(ii) $a = \pi$.

(b) How will the reaction be modified (keeping a minimum number of particles, with only one $\overline{\mathfrak{N}}$, on the right-hand side) for

(iii) $a = P$?

(c) Suppose the target consists of complex nuclei of radius $R = 1.2\, A^{1/3}$ f. Assume that the nucleons in the nucleus have a momentum distribution corresponding to a Fermi gas at 0°K. Find the threshold kinetic energies in this case for $a = \gamma, \pi, P$.

4. Consider the elastic collision of a projectile, of momentum p_1 and energy ϵ_1, with a stationary target of mass m_2. Show that, for the scattering of m_2 through the *cm* angle θ_0, the final *lab* kinetic energy of the target particle is

$$\kappa_2 = \frac{2m_2p_1^2c^4}{E_0^2}\sin^2\frac{\theta_0}{2}.$$

5. Consider the inelastic process $\pi^- + P \rightarrow \eta^0 + N$ at a pion *lab* energy 50 MeV above threshold. Assume isotropic production of the η^0 in the *cm*. Compute the *lab* kinetic energy and angular distributions of the product neutrons.
6. Consider the inelastic reaction $N + P \rightarrow N + P + \pi^0$ with a neutron of *lab* momentum 1.5 GeV/c incident on a target proton at rest. Compute the minimum and maximum values of the π^0 energy in both the *cm* and *lab*. Compare these with the corresponding quantities for the reaction

$$N + P \rightarrow D + \pi^0.$$

Note: The binding energy of the deuteron is 2.2 MeV.
7. In the early experiments of Fermi, *et al.*,[1] on pion-nucleon scattering, the charge-exchange scattering $\pi^- + P \rightarrow \pi^0 + N$ was measured by detecting a *single* γ from the decay $\pi^0 \rightarrow 2\gamma$ and measuring the angular distribution of these photons, $d\sigma_\gamma/d\Omega$. Assume that at some fixed incident energy, corresponding to the *cm* energy ϵ_0 of the π^0, this photon distribution in the *cm* is given by an expansion in Legendre polynomials

$$\frac{d\sigma_\gamma}{d\Omega_0} = \sum_{n=0}^{N} a_n P_n(\cos\theta_{0\gamma}).$$

(Assume that the efficiency of the photon detector is independent of the photon energy and known.)

Show that the *cm* angular distribution of the π^0's produced in the charge-exchange reaction is given by the expression

$$\frac{d\sigma_{\pi^0}}{d\Omega_0} = \sum_{n=0}^{N} b_n P_n(\cos\theta_{0\pi}),$$

where

$$a_n = b_n \xi_n(\gamma_\pi)$$

with

$$\xi_n(\gamma_\pi) = \frac{1}{2\gamma_\pi^2}\int_0^\pi \frac{P_n(\cos\alpha)\sin\alpha\, d\alpha}{(1-\beta_\pi\cos\alpha)^2}.$$

Note that the *cm* energy of the π_0 is $\epsilon_0 = \gamma_\pi m_\pi c^2 = m_\pi c^2/(1-\beta_\pi^2)^{1/2}$. *Hint:* Work backward from the π^0 to the γ angular distribution. The proof requires the use of the addition theorem for the Legendre polynomials.

---

[1] *Phys. Rev. 91:* 155; *92:* 161 (1953).

3.3 Natural Units

In treating elementary particles, it is useful to adopt a system of units appropriate to the dimensions of the phenomena involved. Generally, speeds approach the speed of light, $c = 2.998 \times 10^{10}$ cm/sec; angular momenta are in small half-integral units of $\hbar = 1.05 \times 10^{-27}$ erg-sec or 6.58×10^{-22} MeV-sec; and energies are in the hundreds of MeV. The most convenient system is the one in which we set [2]

$$\hbar = c = 1. \tag{27}$$

In this system, energies, momenta, and masses are given in units of MeV, MeV/c, and MeV/c^2. Thus, we would write (dropping the c's for economy of notation):

$$\epsilon^2 = p^2 + m^2. \tag{27a}$$

In the natural system, the dimensionless fine structure constant is

$$\frac{e^2}{\hbar c} \to e^2 = \frac{1}{137}. \tag{27b}$$

A particle of mass m has the Compton wavelength

$$\frac{\hbar}{mc} \to \frac{1}{m}, \tag{27c}$$

and a resonance of natural width $\Gamma = \Delta mc^2$ has the decay mean life [3]

$$\tau = \frac{\hbar}{\Delta mc^2} \to \frac{1}{\Delta m} = \Gamma^{-1}. \tag{27d}$$

In particular, a convenient unit of mass (momentum, energy) is the rest mass of the pion, which we take as $\mu_0 = 137$ MeV/c^2 (an average of the masses of the $\pi^\pm$ and π^0). Accordingly, the natural unit of length is

$$l_0 = \frac{\hbar}{\mu_0 c} \to \frac{1}{\mu_0} = 1.44 \times 10^{-13} \text{ cm} = 1.44 \text{ f}. \tag{27c$'$}$$

The natural unit of time is

$$\tau_0 = \frac{\hbar}{\mu_0 c^2} \to \frac{1}{\mu_0} = 0.48 \times 10^{-23} \text{ sec}. \tag{27d$'$}$$

In units of the pion mass, those of the proton and electron are

$$M = m_p = 6.85\mu_0 \qquad (938 \text{ MeV}/c^2), \tag{28a}$$

$$m = m_e = 3.73 \times 10^{-3}\mu_0 \qquad (0.511 \text{ MeV}/c^2), \tag{28b}$$

---

[2] The magnitudes are taken as unity, but these quantities retain their proper units, of course.

[3] Since length and time, in the natural system of units, are both expressed as an inverse mass, it is necessary for the reader to keep in mind the missing factors of $\hbar$ and c; with some practice, this becomes habitual.

and a convenient unit of cross section is

$$\sigma_0 = \pi\left(\frac{\hbar}{\mu_0 c}\right)^2 = \pi l_0^2 = 6.5 \times 10^{-26}\ \text{cm}^2 = 65\ \text{mb}. \tag{28c}$$

For the rest of this book, we shall use natural units throughout.

3.4 Some Useful Invariants

Let $\not{q}$ be a 4-vector, with time-like (fourth) component q_0 and space-like components q_x, q_y, q_z (3-vector $\mathbf{q}$). Then the length of this 4-vector,

$$\not{q}^2 = q_0^2 - q^2, \tag{29}$$

is invariant with respect to Lorentz transformations. Some examples of useful 4-vectors are the proper time (or invariant distance) $\tau = (t, \mathbf{r})$,

$$\tau^2 = t^2 - r^2, \tag{29a}$$

energy-momentum $\not{p} = (\epsilon, \mathbf{p})$,

$$\not{p}^2 = \epsilon^2 - p^2 = m^2, \tag{29b}$$

charge 4-current $\not{j} = (\rho, \mathbf{j})$ (ρ is the density of charge), the 4-divergence, or d'Alembertian $\Box = (\partial/\partial t, \boldsymbol{\nabla})$.

The dot product of two 4-vectors,

$$\not{q}_1 \cdot \not{q}_2 = q_{01}q_{02} - \mathbf{q}_1 \cdot \mathbf{q}_2, \tag{30}$$

is a Lorentz-invariant scalar. Thus, the law of charge conservation (continuity equation),

$$\Box \cdot \not{j} = \frac{\partial \rho}{\partial t} - \nabla \cdot \mathbf{j} = 0, \tag{30a}$$

holds in all Lorentz frames.

The sum (difference) of two 4-vectors,

$$\not{q}_1 \pm \not{q}_2 = (q_{01} \pm q_{02}, \mathbf{q}_1 \pm \mathbf{q}_2), \tag{30b}$$

being itself a 4-vector, its square is also Lorentz invariant.

3.4.1 Invariant Masses and Resonances

Consider a reaction with many particles in the final state:

$$a + b \to c + d + e + \cdots. \tag{31}$$

It frequently happens that a group of the reaction products are, in fact, the decay products of an unstable particle, for example,

$$\begin{array}{l} a + b \to c + d' \\ \qquad\qquad\ \ \hookrightarrow d + e + f. \end{array} \tag{31a}$$

In this case, the invariant total 4-momentum squared of the decay products of d',

$$\left(\sum p_i\right)^2 = (p_d + p_e + p_f)^2 = \left(\sum \epsilon_i\right)^2 - \left(\sum \mathbf{p}_i\right)^2 = M^2, \tag{31b}$$

yields the mass of the unstable particle. This follows from the fact that in the rest frame of the unstable particle

$$P_0^2 = E_0^2 = M^2 = \left(\sum p_{0i}\right)^2 = \left(\sum \epsilon_{0i}\right)^2, \tag{31c}$$

since

$$\left(\sum \mathbf{p}_{0i}\right)^2 = 0. \tag{31d}$$

Thus, in any reaction in which an unstable particle is produced, the spectrum of invariant masses of the corresponding products will exhibit a line corresponding to the mass of that unstable particle.[4]

3.4.2 Two-Body Reactions

Consider the reaction (Figure 3.1)

$$1 + 2 \rightarrow 3 + 4 \tag{32}$$

with the particle 4-momenta, respectively, $p_1, p_2, -p_3, -p_4$ ($m_i^2 = p_i^2$). Conservation of energy-momentum requires

$$p_1 + p_2 + p_3 + p_4 = 0. \tag{32a}$$

It is convenient to define three invariant quantities

$$s = (p_1 + p_2)^2 = (p_3 + p_4)^2, \tag{33a}$$

$$t = (p_1 + p_3)^2 = (p_2 + p_4)^2, \tag{33b}$$

$$u = (p_1 + p_4)^2 = (p_2 + p_3)^2. \tag{33c}$$

Only two of these invariants are independent, since they are connected by the relationship

$$s + t + u = \sum_{i=1}^{4} m_i^2. \tag{33d}$$

These invariants have a simple meaning with respect to reaction (32): s is the *cm* energy squared [Equations (24a)–(24d)]

$$s = E_0^2, \tag{33a'}$$

[4] This line will, of course, have a natural width ΔM arising from the finite lifetime, τ, of the unstable particle, according to the uncertainty principle $\Delta M c^2 = \hbar/\tau$.

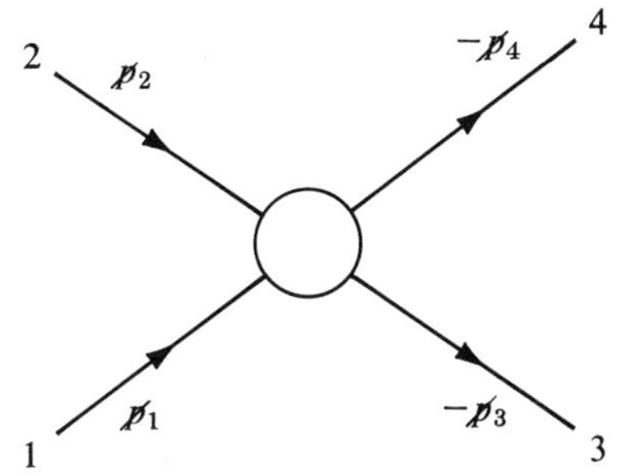

Figure 3.1 General diagram for two-body reactions.

while t and u represent, respectively, the invariant 4-momentum transfer between particles 1 and 3 or 4.

The expressions become simpler when we consider the *cm* system, for which (see Figure 3.2)

$$\mathbf{p}_{01} = -\mathbf{p}_{02} = \mathbf{p}_0, \qquad -\mathbf{p}_{03} = \mathbf{p}_{04} = \mathbf{p}_0'. \tag{34}$$

Then

$$p_0^2 = \epsilon_{01}^2 - m_1^2 = \epsilon_{02}^2 - m_2^2, \qquad p_0'^2 = \epsilon_{03}^2 - m_3^2 = \epsilon_{04}^2 - m_4^2, \tag{34'}$$

and

$$s = (\epsilon_{01} + \epsilon_{02})^2 = m_1^2 + m_2^2 + 2(p_0^2 + \epsilon_{01}\epsilon_{02}), \tag{34a}$$

$$t = m_1^2 + m_3^2 - 2\epsilon_{01}\epsilon_{03} + 2p_0p_0' \cos\theta, \tag{34b}$$

$$u = m_1^2 + m_4^2 - 2\epsilon_{01}\epsilon_{04} - 2p_0p_0' \cos\theta. \tag{34c}$$

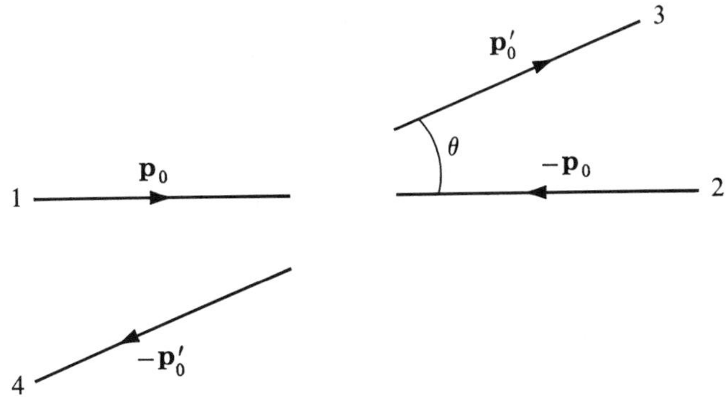

Figure 3.2 Two-body reaction in the *cm*.

EXAMPLES

1. Elastic scattering, i.e., $m_1 = m_3 = \mu$; $m_2 = m_4 = m$; $p_0 = p_0'$; $\epsilon_{01} = \epsilon_{03}$; $\epsilon_{02} = \epsilon_{04}$. Then

$$s = \mu^2 + m^2 + 2(p_0^2 + \epsilon_{01}\epsilon_{02}), \tag{35a}$$

$$t = -2p_0^2(1 - \cos\theta), \tag{35b}$$

$$u = \mu^2 + m^2 - 2(\epsilon_{01}\epsilon_{04} + p_0^2 \cos\theta). \tag{35c}$$

2. High-energy limit, for which we apply the approximation

$$\epsilon_i = (p_i^2 + m_i^2)^{1/2} \cong p_i + \frac{m_i^2}{2p_i}. \tag{36}$$

Then

$$s \cong 2m_1^2 + 2m_2^2 + 4p_0^2, \tag{36a}$$

$$t' \equiv t + (p_0 - p_0')\left(\frac{m_3^2}{p_0'} - \frac{m_1^2}{p_0}\right) \cong -2p_0 p_0'(1 - \cos\theta), \tag{36b}$$

$$u' \equiv u + (p_0 - p_0')\left(\frac{m_4^2}{p_0'} - \frac{m_1^2}{p_0}\right) \cong -2p_0 p_0'(1 + \cos\theta). \tag{36c}$$

For the case of elastic scattering ($p_0 = p_0'$), we obtain, in the high-energy limit,

$$t' = t \cong -2p_0^2(1 - \cos\theta), \tag{36b$'$}$$

$$u' = u \cong -2p_0^2(1 + \cos\theta). \tag{36c$'$}$$

The invariants s, t, u have the further utility that they may be used to describe, in addition to the reaction (32) and its inverse ($3 + 4 \to 1 + 2$), the entire set of possible reactions among the particles 1, 2, 3, 4 and their antiparticles, $\overline{1}$, $\overline{2}$, $\overline{3}$, $\overline{4}$. Thus, in the case of the reaction

$$1 + \overline{3} \rightleftharpoons \overline{2} + 4, \tag{32$'$}$$

t represents the *cm* energy, u the 4-momentum transfer between 1 and 4, and s the 4-momentum transfer between 1 and $\overline{2}$; for the reaction

$$1 + \overline{4} \rightleftharpoons 3 + \overline{2}, \tag{32$''$}$$

u is the *cm* energy, s the 4-momentum transfer between 1 and $\overline{2}$, t between 1 and 3. An example of a set of possible reactions of this type is

$$\pi^+ + P \rightleftharpoons \pi^+ + P, \qquad \pi^- + \overline{P} \rightleftharpoons \pi^- + \overline{P}, \tag{37a}$$

$$\pi^+ + \pi^- \rightleftharpoons \overline{P} + P, \qquad \pi^- + \pi^+ \rightleftharpoons P + \overline{P}, \tag{37b}$$

$$\pi^+ + \overline{P} \rightleftharpoons \pi^+ + \overline{P}, \qquad \pi^- + P \rightleftharpoons \pi^- + P. \tag{37c}$$

(In each pair of reactions, the second is obtained from the first by charge conjugation.) Considering this set of reactions, the first is said to proceed through the "s-channel," the second through the "t-channel," and the third through the "u-channel."

Perhaps the greatest advantage of the use of these invariants in the description of high-energy two-body interactions is that it enables the derivation of some important analytical relations among the cross sections corresponding to the set of reactions (32), (32′), (32″). Thus, considering the conventional description of reaction (32), in which the incident plane wave $\psi_{\text{in}} = e^{ip_0 z}$ gives rise to a scattered outgoing wave of the asymptotic form

$$\psi_{\text{out}} = f(E_0, \theta)\frac{e^{ip_0' r}}{r},$$

the differential cross section

$$\frac{d\sigma}{d\Omega}(1 + 2 \to 3 + 4) = \frac{p_0'}{p_0}|f(E_0, \theta)|^2 \tag{38a}$$

may be put into Lorentz-invariant form as follows: We define the invariant (and dimensionless) reaction amplitude

$$A(s, t, u) = s^{1/2} f(E_0, \theta), \tag{38b}$$

and, taking advantage of Equation (34b), we rewrite (38a) in terms of the three kinematical invariants:

$$\frac{d\sigma}{dt} = \frac{\pi}{p_0^2 s}|A(s, t, u)|^2. \tag{38c}$$

$A(s, t, u)$ should, then, apply to all the reactions in all three channels, (32), (32′), and (32″), provided the analytical behavior of $A(s, t, u)$ is known over the entire applicable range of the variables.[5]

As an example, consider the process of elastic scattering

$$1 + 2 \to 1 + 2 \tag{39}$$

with the amplitude $A_0(s, t, u)$. The optical theorem enables us to obtain the *total* cross section for $1 + 2$, in terms of the imaginary part of the forward elastic scattering amplitude:

$$\begin{aligned}\sigma_{\text{tot}}(1 + 2) &= \frac{4\pi}{p_0}\operatorname{Im} f(E_0, 0)\\ &= \frac{4\pi}{p_0 s^{1/2}}\operatorname{Im} A(s, t = 0).\end{aligned} \tag{39a}$$

---

[5] The problem is that the range of the variables differs for the different channels. Thus, in the s-channel $s = E_0^2$ is positive, while t and u are negative (over most of the range of interest). Thus, for example, use of the same $A(s, t, u)$ to describe the t-channel reaction requires the analytic continuation of the amplitude into the region of $t > 0$, $s < 0$. [S. Mandelstam, *Phys. Rev.*, *112:* 1344 (1958). See also G. F. Chew, *S-Matrix Theory of Strong Interactions*, W. A. Benjamin, New York (1961).]

Correspondingly, in the u-channel $(1+\bar{2}\to 1+\bar{2})$ the same amplitude will give the total cross section through $(s\to u,\ t\to s,\ u\to t)$:

$$\sigma_{\text{tot}}(1+\bar{2})=\frac{4\pi}{p_0 u^{1/2}}\,\text{Im}\,A(u,s=0). \tag{39b}$$

PROBLEM

Consider the decay $M\to m_1+m_2+m_3$. Prove that

$$m_{12}^2+m_{13}^2+m_{23}^2=C,$$

and find the value of the constant C in terms of the masses. (Note that m_{ij} is the invariant mass of the pair m_i+m_j.)

Phase-Space Considerations

In many instances, the distribution of reaction or decay products is determined primarily by statistical considerations. Thus, in applying Fermi's "golden rule,"

$$\lambda_{fi} = \tau_{fi}^{-1} = \frac{2\pi}{\hbar} |M_{fi}|^2 \frac{dN_f}{dE}, \tag{1}$$

to the computation of the rate of transition[1] from a given initial state i to final state f, there are many processes for which the transition matrix element M_{fi} is essentially independent of the distribution of particles in the final state. In this case, the phase-space density dN_f/dE is the most important factor in determining this distribution.

Consider a system of n independent particles of total energy E and momentum $\mathbf{P}$. The phase-space volume available to this system is

$$N_n = \left(\frac{V}{8\pi^3\hbar^3}\right)^n \int_1 \cdots \int_i \cdots \int_n \prod_{i=1}^{n} d^3\mathbf{p}_i \, \delta\left(\sum \mathbf{p}_i - \mathbf{P}\right) \delta\left(\sum \epsilon_i - E\right), \tag{2}$$

where V is a normalization volume and the last two functions in the multiple integral are introduced to insure momentum and energy conservation.[2] In

---

[1] By considerations of detailed balancing, for a given flux φ_f of incoming particles, the cross section for the formation of the compound state i is

$$\phi_f \sigma_i = \lambda_{fi}. \tag{1a}$$

[2] The expression (2) for the phase-space volume is not Lorentz invariant, and is generally used only for the special baryocentric reference frame, in which the total momentum $\mathbf{P} = 0$ and the total energy E is fixed. In this case, the momentum of one of the particles may be taken as fixed, say, $\mathbf{p}_n = -\mathbf{p}$, and the problem reduced to the computation of $N_{n'}$ $(n' = n - 1)$, where n is the actual number of particles. Equation (2) may easily be written in a Lorentz-invariant form by substituting $\Pi_i \, d^4\not{p}_i$ for $\Pi_i \, d^3\mathbf{p}_i$. It can be shown that this is equivalent to the substitution of $d^3\mathbf{p}_i/\epsilon_i$ for $d^3\mathbf{p}_i$ in Equation (2).

general, the computation of (2) for $n \geq 3$ is complex; it has been widely discussed in the literature.[3]

We indicate in the following the results of the calculation, always in the baryocentric system (*cm*), of the phase-space density dN/dE for $n=2$ and 3 ($n'=1$ and 2).

4.1 $n=2$

In this case there is only one momentum, $\mathbf{p}_1 = -\mathbf{p}_2 = \mathbf{p}$, $E = \epsilon_1 + \epsilon_2$, and equation (2) reduces to[4]

$$N_1 = \frac{V}{(2\pi)^3}\left(\frac{4\pi}{3}p^3\right). \tag{3}$$

Then

$$\frac{dN_1}{dE} = \frac{V}{(2\pi)^3} 4\pi p^2 \frac{dp}{dE}. \tag{4a}$$

Now,

$$dE = d\epsilon_1 + d\epsilon_2 = pdp\left(\frac{1}{\epsilon_1} + \frac{1}{\epsilon_2}\right), \tag{4b}$$

since

$$\epsilon_i^2 = p_i^2 + m_i^2. \tag{4c}$$

Hence

$$\frac{dN_1}{dE} = \frac{V}{2\pi^2}\frac{p\epsilon_1\epsilon_2}{E} = \frac{V}{2\pi^2}\frac{p^2}{(v_1 + v_2)}. \tag{4d}$$

Note that Equation (4d) applies for all values of the particle velocities, both in the nonrelativistic and in the relativistic limits.

4.2 $n=3$

In the *cm*, $E = M = \epsilon_1 + \epsilon_2 + \epsilon_3$, $\mathbf{p}_1 + \mathbf{p}_2 + \mathbf{p}_3 = 0$. We fix the momentum of one (say, the third) of the products,

$$-\mathbf{p} = \mathbf{p}_1 + \mathbf{p}_2, \tag{5a}$$

and compute the volume of phase space available to the other two, $N_1(p, M - \epsilon_3)$. This is the volume enclosed by the locus of all possible endpoints of the vector $\mathbf{p}_1$, subject to (5a), as depicted in Figure 4.1. This volume is given by

$$N_1 = \frac{4\pi}{3}(OC)^2\left(\frac{AB}{2}\right)\cdot\left(\frac{V}{8\pi^3}\right). \tag{5b}$$

---

[3] R. Hagedorn, *Relativistic Kinematics,* W. A. Benjamin, New York (1963).
[4] Recall that we have adopted the natural system of units, $\hbar = c = 1$.

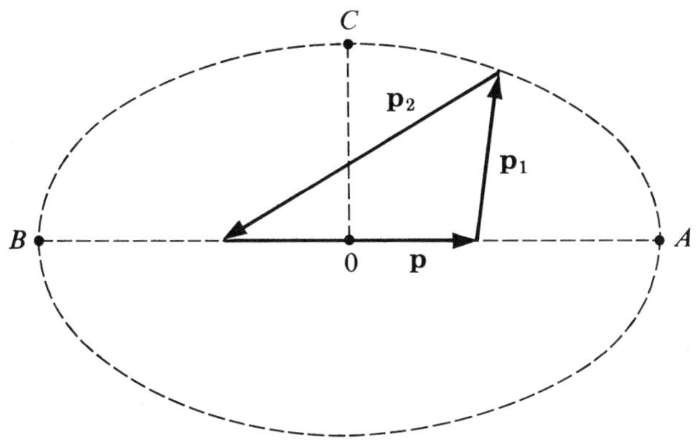

Figure 4.1 Volume in phase space defined by $\mathbf{p}_1+\mathbf{p}_2=-\mathbf{p}$.

The direction and the magnitude of $p_3=p$ being arbitrary, the contribution to the phase-space density for values of p_3 between p and $p+dp$ is

$$d\left(\frac{dN_2}{dE}\right)=\left(\frac{V}{8\pi^3}\right)\cdot 4\pi p^2\,dp\,\frac{dN_1}{dE}. \tag{5c}$$

Generally, the dimensions of the phase-space spheroid, Figure 4.1, are determined by the energy condition

$$M=\epsilon_1+\epsilon_2+\epsilon_3. \tag{5d}$$

The computation, however, is analytically manageable only in the two extremes, the nonrelativistic case (v_1, v_2, $v_3 \ll c$) and the extreme relativistic case ($\epsilon_i \gg m_i$ for all three products).

4.2.1 Nonrelativistic Case

We may write

$$\epsilon_i=\frac{p_i^2}{2m_i}+m_i, \tag{6a}$$

$$\sum_{i=1}^{3}\frac{p_i^2}{2m_i}=(M-m_1-m_2-m_3)=(M-m)=Q. \tag{6b}$$

Equations (5a) and (6b) then yield, by straightforward manipulation, that the spheroid is a sphere of radius R,

$$OC^2=\left(\frac{AB}{2}\right)^2=R^2=\frac{2m_1m_2}{(m_1+m_2)}Q\left(1-\frac{p^2}{p_m^2}\right), \tag{6c}$$

whose size depends on the available reaction energy Q and the maximum possible momentum of the third particle

$$p_m^2 = \frac{2Qm_3(m_1+m_2)}{m_1+m_2+m_3} = \frac{2Qm_3(m_1+m_2)}{m}. \tag{6d}$$

Substitution into Equation (5c) yields

$$d\left(\frac{dN_2}{dE}\right) = \frac{64\pi^2V^2}{(2\pi)^6}\left(\frac{m_1m_2m_3}{m}\right)^{3/2} Q^2(1-x^2)^{1/2}x^2\,dx$$
$$= \frac{32\pi^2V^2}{(2\pi)^6}\left(\frac{m_1m_2m_3}{m}\right)^{3/2} Q^2(1-\bar{\kappa})^{1/2}\bar{\kappa}^{1/2}\,d\bar{\kappa}, \tag{6e}$$

where

$$\bar{\kappa} = x^2 = \left(\frac{p}{p_m}\right)^2 \tag{6f}$$

is the kinetic energy of particle 3 relative to its maximum possible value

$$\kappa_m = \frac{p_m^2}{2m_3} = \left(\frac{m_1+m_2}{m}\right)Q. \tag{6g}$$

From Equation (6e) we note that the phase-space kinetic energy distribution of any one of the decay products is described by the function $(1-\bar{\kappa})^{1/2}\bar{\kappa}^{1/2}$, which is a half circle with the center at $\bar{\kappa} = \frac{1}{2}$, as depicted in Figure 4.2.

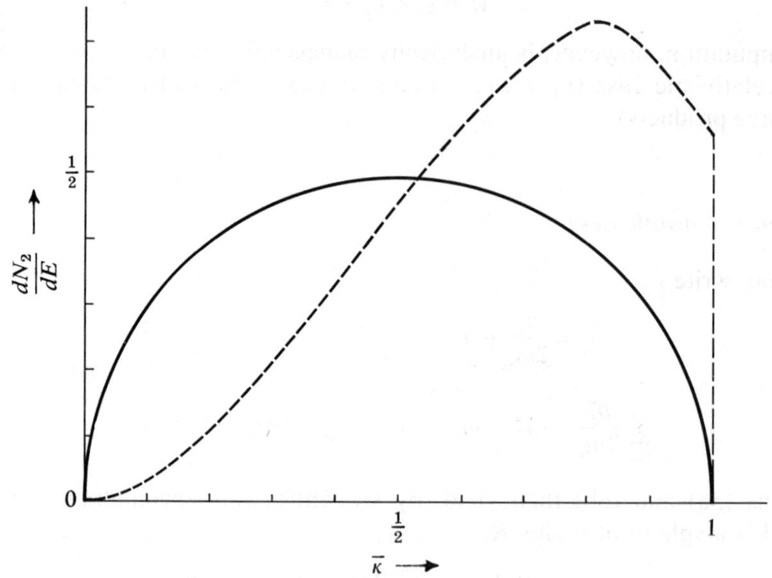

Figure 4.2 Phase-space functions for three-body decay. The solid curve is for the nonrelativistic approximation, with arbitrary normalization. The broken curve is for the extreme relativistic case, normalized to the same area as for the nonrelativistic case.

From Equation (6e) we may obtain the total phase-space density for three-body decay in the nonrelativistic case

$$\frac{dN_2}{dE} = \int_{\bar{\kappa}=0}^{1} d\left(\frac{dN_2}{dE}\right) = \frac{4\pi^3 V^2}{(2\pi)^6}\left(\frac{m_1 m_2 m_3}{m_1 + m_2 + m_3}\right)^{3/2} Q^2. \tag{6h}$$

4.2.2 Extreme Relativistic Case

We use the approximation

$$\epsilon_i = p_i \tag{7a}$$

which, according to Equations (5a) and (5d), gives

$$M = (p_1 + p_2 + p). \tag{7b}$$

Our phase-space spheroid of revolution (Figure 4.1) now has

$$AB = (M - p), \tag{7c}$$

$$4(OC)^2 = M(M - 2p), \tag{7d}$$

$$N_1 = \frac{\pi}{6}\left(\frac{V}{8\pi^3}\right)(M^3 - 3M^2 p + 2Mp^2), \tag{7e}$$

and

$$d\left(\frac{dN_2}{dE}\right) = \frac{\pi^2}{4}\frac{V^2}{(2\pi)^6} M^5\left(1 - x + \frac{1}{6}x^2\right) x^2\, dx \tag{7f}$$

with $x = p/p_m$ and

$$p_m = \frac{M}{2} \tag{7g}$$

(corresponding to $p_1 = p_2 = p_m/2$). (See Figure 4.2 for the distribution in x.)

Integrating over $x = 0 \rightarrow 1$, we obtain for the total phase-space density in the extreme relativistic case:

$$\frac{dN_2}{dE} = \frac{7\pi^2}{240}\frac{V^2}{(2\pi)^6} M^5. \tag{7h}$$

Each of the two cases of three-body final states derived above is directly applicable to a situation observed in nature. Thus, for example, in the three-pion decay of the K-meson, the mass of the K being ≈ 498 MeV/c^2, and the mass of the three pions being ≈ 414 MeV/c^2, we have $Q \simeq 84$ MeV [Equation (6b)] to be shared among the three pions. In this case, the nonrelativistic approximation ($\kappa_i \ll m_i \simeq$ 137 MeV) is a good one, and we expect Equation (6e) to provide a reasonable approximation to the distribution of kinetic energy between the permitted limits $0 \rightarrow \frac{2}{3}Q \cong 56$ MeV [Equation (6g)], provided the decay matrix element for $K \rightarrow 3\pi$ is relatively energy independent. This turns out to be a good first approximation.

For the extreme relativistic case, we may consider the decay $\mu^{\pm} \rightarrow e^{\pm} + \nu + \bar{\nu}$, since $M_{\mu} \cong 106 \text{ MeV}/c^2$, $m_e \cong 0.5 \text{ MeV}/c^2$, $m_2 = m_3 = 0$. In this case, Equation (7f) provides a good approximation to the energy distribution of the decay electron.

One additional point deserves comment: For final states that include hadrons only, it is frequently a good approximation to consider the interaction to be so strong as to result in a statistical distribution of the product particles within an interaction volume $\mathcal{V}$, characteristically of the dimensions of the pion Compton wavelength

$$\mathcal{V} \simeq \mu_0^{-3}. \tag{8}$$

Under these conditions, we may assume the particle wave functions to be essentially constant over the interaction volume, and to vanish outside it, so that we may approximate the interaction matrix element by an expression of the form

$$|M_{ba}|^2 \simeq M_0^2 \left(\frac{\mathcal{V}}{V}\right)^n. \tag{9}$$

As a consequence, the decay rate [Equation (1)] is essentially given by the phase-space density for the emission of n particles with, however, the normalization volume V in Equation (2) replaced by the interaction volume $\mathcal{V}$. This *ansatz* enables us, for many processes involving multiple hadron production, to predict the relative rates of production of different numbers or type distributions of hadrons resulting from the same initial interaction, i.e.,

$$\frac{\lambda_j}{\lambda_k} \cong \left(\frac{dN_j}{dN_k}\right)\left(\frac{\mathcal{V}}{V}\right)^{(j-k)}, \tag{10}$$

a form that is independent of the normalization volume V. Such considerations appear,[5] for example, to be applicable to problems of multiple pion production at very high energies and, to a first approximation, to the problem of multiple hadron production in P–$\bar{P}$ annihilation.

4.2.3 Dalitz Plots

In the three-body decays discussed above, Dalitz[6] has indicated a very useful geometrical approach for comparing the observations with the phase-space predictions, as a means of extracting from the observations the properties of the decay matrix elements, $|M_{fi}|^2$ in Equation (1). For simplicity, we consider a decay into three particles of equal mass:

$$M \rightarrow 3m, \tag{11a}$$

$$Q = (M - 3m). \tag{11b}$$

---

[5] E. Fermi, *Elementary Particles,* Yale University Press, New Haven (1951), p. 79.

[6] R. H. Dalitz, *Phil. Mag., 44:* 1068 (1953); E. Fabri, *Nuovo Cimento, 11:* 479 (1954).

Consider the equilateral triangle (1, 2, 3) of Figure 4.3, with unit altitude (side = $2/\sqrt{3}$). Let $y_i = \kappa_i/Q$ represent the kinetic energies of the decay products; since

$$\sum \kappa_i = Q, \qquad \sum y_i = 1, \tag{11c}$$

it follows from geometrical considerations that each possible distribution of decay energies may be represented by a point inside the triangle, with the distance from the three sides equal to the respective values of the y_i's. Thus, the point P represents one possible decay.

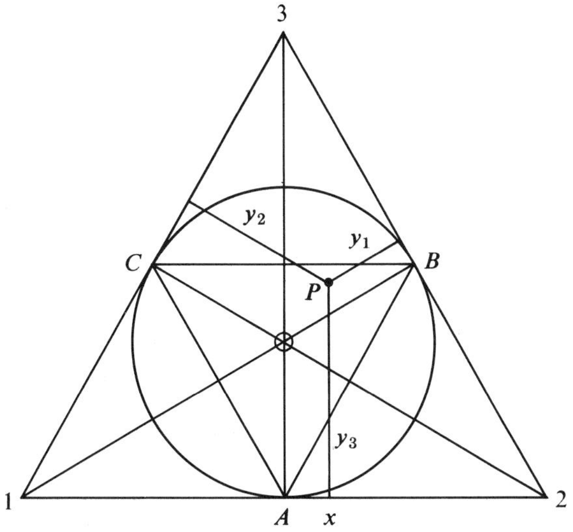

Figure 4.3 Dalitz triangle for the decay $M \rightarrow 3m$.

However, not all points in the triangle are accessible to the three-body decay. In the nonrelativistic limit, $y_{i_{max}} = \frac{2}{3}$ [see Equation (6g)], so that the available points all lie within the inscribed circle ABC. In the extreme relativistic case, $y_{i_{max}} = \frac{1}{2}$ [Equation (7g)] and the available points are confined to within the inscribed triangle ABC. In the intermediate case, the boundaries of the permitted region are intermediate between the inscribed triangle and circle.

It is useful to note that the triangular Dalitz plot can also be taken as an ordinary two-dimensional representation of the decay distribution; if we consider as the y axis in Figure 4.3 the vertical altitude of the triangle, and as the x axis its horizontal base, then it is readily demonstrated that, for a given point P, $x = (y_2 - y_1)/\sqrt{3}$, $y = y_3$ ($y_i = 3p_i^2/4mQ$). The circular form of the boundary follows, in the nonrelativistic case, from the relationship

$$\frac{y_2 - y_1}{\sqrt{3}} = y^{1/2}(1 - y)^{1/2} \cos \theta, \tag{11d}$$

$$\cos\theta = \frac{(\mathbf{p}_1 + \mathbf{p}_2)\cdot(\mathbf{p}_1 - \mathbf{p}_2)}{|\mathbf{p}_1 + \mathbf{p}_2||\mathbf{p}_1 - \mathbf{p}_2|}. \tag{11e}$$

As to the distribution of decay points within the permitted regions, these may be shown, from the relativistically invariant form of Equation (2), to be uniform for the case of pure phase space, i.e.,

$$d^2N_2 = \text{const. } d\epsilon_1\, d\epsilon_2. \tag{11f}$$

Hence, any systematic deviation of the observed distribution from uniformity indicates an effect of the matrix element for the three-body decay. Thus, for example, if angular momentum conservation requires one or more of the decay products to be emitted with finite angular momentum relative to the others, the angular momentum barrier penetration factors will tend to decrease the density of points in the regions of the corresponding vertices of the inscribed triangle in Figure 4.3, and to increase the density of points in the region of the center O.

In terms of Figure 4.3, the distribution in energy of the third particle, obtained by integration over the energies of the others, is equivalent to the projection of the density distribution on an axis perpendicular to the corresponding side (for example, on a vertical axis for the distribution of the kinetic energies of particle 3). For pure phase space, these distributions are given by Equations (6e) and (7f) for the nonrelativistic and extreme relativistic cases, respectively.

A circumstance of special interest in the three-body decay discussed above is the case where two of the observed particles result from the decay of an unstable intermediary, for example, if particles 2 and 3 are the decay products of an intermediary of mass M_{23}. In this case, we are really dealing with the two-body decay

$$M \to 1 + (23) \tag{12}$$

for which the momentum p, and energy ϵ, of particle 1 will be constant. This will be immediately observed in the Dalitz plot, Figure 4.3, since all of the points will lie in a slanting band at a fixed value of y_1, whose width will correspond to the decay width of the particle (23).

Since the invariant mass of 2 plus 3 is

$$\begin{aligned} M_{23}^2 &= (\not{p}_2 + \not{p}_3)^2 \\ &= (M - \not{p}_1)^2 \\ &= M^2 + m_1^2 - 2M\epsilon_1, \end{aligned} \tag{12a}$$

the observed (fixed) value of ϵ_1 immediately yields the invariant mass M_{23}. Furthermore, Equation (12a), and its equivalent for M_{31}^2 and M_{12}^2, indicates that the variables M_{ij}^2 are equivalent to the variables ϵ_k for describing the decay distribution.

This suggests another useful way of depicting the three-particle decay under consideration. Consider a plot, as in Figure 4.4, in which we adopt as the two rectangular axes M_{23}^2 and M_{31}^2. Each point corresponds to a possible decay, since fixing $M_{31}(\epsilon_2)$ and $M_{23}(\epsilon_1)$ fixes $\epsilon_3 = M - \epsilon_1 - \epsilon_2$, with the limits of the distribution determined by the range of possible values of $\epsilon_i = m_i \to \epsilon_{i\max}$ as determined by

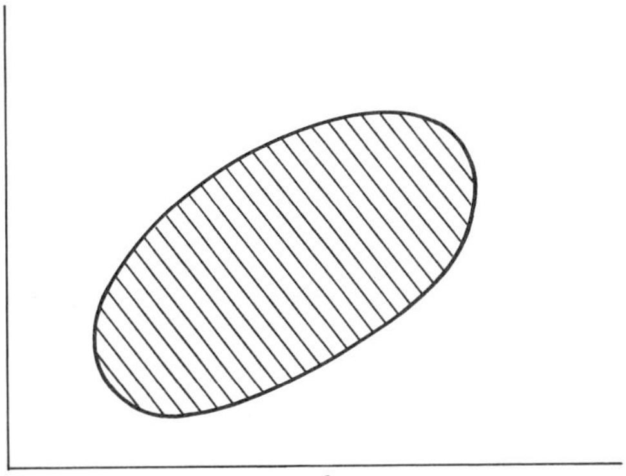

Figure 4.4 Dalitz plot of the invariant mass distribution in three-body decays.

Equation (12a). Furthermore, since

$$dM_{23}^2\, dM_{31}^2 = 4M^2\, d\epsilon_1\, d\epsilon_2\,, \tag{12b}$$

the uniformity of the phase-space distribution in Figure 4.3 implies a uniform distribution of the decay points in Figure 4.4, provided of course that the distribution corresponds to pure phase space. For an intermediate particle of unique mass M_{23}, on the other hand, the observed points will all lie in a vertical band at the value M_{23}^2, whose width is proportional to the resonance's decay width. The Dalitz plots in the form of Figure 4.4 contain essentially all the information contained in the triangular plot, Figure 4.3, and are convenient for detecting short-lived intermediate states.

The considerations, developed above for three-body decays, can be readily extended to decays involving $n > 3$. In this case, it is more difficult in general to obtain simple geometrical representations of the phase-space distributions. However, in the general case, one can always derive the invariant phase-space distribution of the invariant mass of, say, k of the n particles, by using the relationship

$$d^4\Big(\sum \not{p}_j - \not{P}\Big) = \int d^4\not{p}_k\, \delta^4\Big(\not{P} - \not{p}_k - \sum_{j=k+1}^{n} \not{p}_j\Big) \times \delta^4\Big(\not{p}_k - \sum_{j=1}^{k} \not{p}_j\Big) \tag{13}$$

in the Lorentz-invariant form of Equation (2) and integrating over the remaining $(n-k)$ 4-momenta.[7]

PROBLEMS

1. Using the masses from Table 2.1, compare the phase-space factors for the decays

$$K_1^0 \to 2\pi,$$

---

[7] R. Hagedorn, *Relativistic Kinematics*, W. A. Benjamin, New York (1963).

$$K^+ \to 2\pi,$$
$$K^+ \to \mu^+ + \nu_\mu,$$
$$K^+ \to e^+ + \nu_e.$$

Use this comparison, together with Equation (1) and the decay rates from Table 2.1, to obtain the relative values of the decay matrix elements. What conclusions do you draw from this comparison?

2. The observed energy distribution of the electrons in the decay

$$\mu \to e + \nu + \bar{\nu}$$

is

$$\frac{dN}{dx} \cong 2x^2(3 - 2x),$$

where $x = \epsilon/\epsilon_{max}$. Compare this with the pure phase-space distribution (normalized to the same total decay rate).

3. There is evidence, from observations in hydrogen bubble chambers on the reaction

$$\pi^- + P \to P + \pi^+ + \pi^- + \pi^-,$$

that this reaction proceeds in part through the following sequence of resonances:

$$\pi^- + P \to A_1^- \text{ (1070 MeV)} + P$$
$$\hookrightarrow \rho^0 \text{ (765 MeV)} + \pi^-$$
$$\hookrightarrow \pi^+ + \pi^-.$$

(a) Assuming that the bubble chamber is immersed in a magnetic field, so that the momenta of all charged particles can be accurately measured, how can these measurements be used to establish the existence of the A_1?

(b) Assuming that you can extract, from the observed four-pronged events, a relatively pure sample of events in which the A_1 is produced, what sort of distribution would you predict in a Dalitz plot of M_{12} *versus* M_{13} involving the three-product pions? (Note that there are two combinations of $\pi^+ + \pi^-$ possible, only one of which should correspond to the ρ^0-decay product of the A_1.)

(c) How are the previous considerations influenced by the widths of the A_1 ($\Gamma_{A_1} \approx 100$ MeV) and of the ρ^0 ($\Gamma_{\rho^0} \approx 120$ MeV)?

(d) What is the effect of a background of 3π's produced in the original reaction with a pure four-body phase-space distribution?

S-Matrix Theory

We now consider a number of general properties of the matrix elements or reaction amplitudes (including those which describe decays) that follow from the "S-matrix" formulation of reaction theory. These results are based on an approach due to Heisenberg;[1] some applications to reactions and to decays are discussed in detail by a number of authors.[2] Our approach follows that of Fermi.[3]

5.1 The Fermi–Watson Theorem

The S-matrix is a formal device for describing the connections between all possible reactions, consistent with known conservation laws, which can be associated with a given group of particles. A given set of possible reactions, for example,

$$A + B \to A + B \quad \text{(elastic scattering),} \tag{1a}$$

$$\to A' + B' \quad \text{(inelastic scattering),} \tag{1b}$$

$$\to C + D \quad \text{(transmutations),} \tag{1c}$$

$$\to A + B + E \quad \text{(particle production),} \tag{1d}$$

$$\to Y \quad \text{(inverse decay),} \tag{1e}$$

and so on, is represented by the matrix

$$S = (S_{ij}) \tag{2}$$

[1] W. Heisenberg, *Z. Physik, 120:* 513 and 673 (1943).
[2] J. M. Blatt and V. F. Weisskopf, *Theoretical Nuclear Physics,* John Wiley and Sons, New York (1952); K. Aizu, *Proc. Int. Conf. Theoret. Phys.*, Kyoto and Tokyo (1953); K. M. Watson, *Phys. Rev., 95:* 228 (1954); and G. Takeda, *Phys. Rev., 101:* 1547 (1956).
[3] E. Fermi, *Suppl. Nuovo Cimento, 2:* 17 (1955).

in terms of which a given incident wave,

$$\psi_i^{\text{in}} = (4\pi v_i)^{-1/2} \frac{e^{-ik_i r}}{r}, \tag{3a}$$

is converted into the various possible outgoing waves,

$$S\psi_i^{\text{in}} = \sum_j S_{ij}\psi_j^{\text{out}}, \tag{2a}$$

where

$$\psi_j^{\text{out}} = (4\pi v_j)^{-1/2} \frac{e^{ik_j r}}{r}. \tag{3b}$$

[The normalizations in Equations (3a) and (3b) are chosen to correspond to unit flux.]

Pictorially, as indicated in Figure 5.1, we may think of the S-matrix as sum-

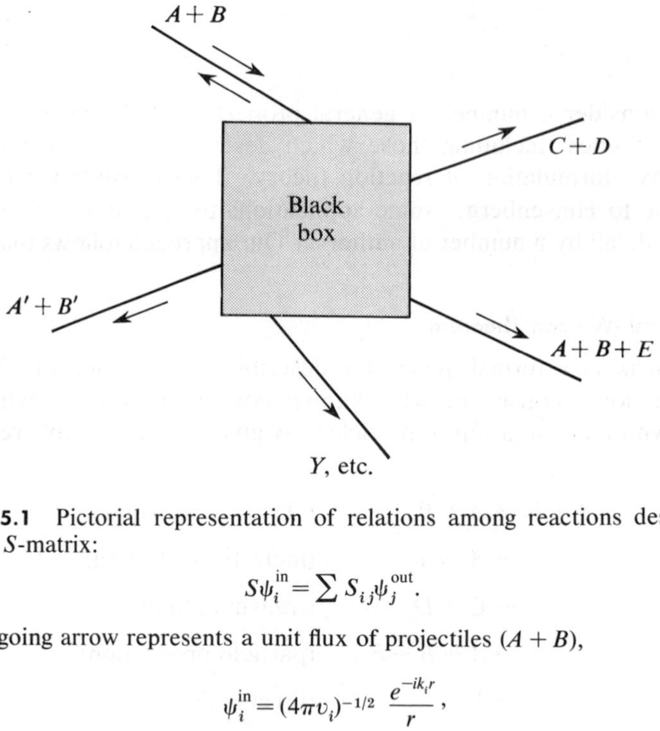

Figure 5.1 Pictorial representation of relations among reactions described by the S-matrix:

$$S\psi_i^{\text{in}} = \sum S_{ij}\psi_j^{\text{out}}.$$

The ingoing arrow represents a unit flux of projectiles ($A + B$),

$$\psi_i^{\text{in}} = (4\pi v_i)^{-1/2} \frac{e^{-ik_i r}}{r},$$

and the outgoing arrows represent appropriate fluxes in the exit channels of form

$$\psi_j^{\text{out}} = (4\pi v_j)^{-1/2} \frac{e^{ik_j r}}{r}.$$

The S-matrix elements are the appropriate reaction amplitudes:

$$\sigma(i \to f) = \frac{1}{4k_i^2} |S_{if}|^2.$$

marizing the effects of a "black box" which distributes the outgoing states among the various exit channels according to the requirements of the conservation laws and the strengths of the interactions concerned.

The form of the S-matrix is primarily determined by the following two physical requirements.

5.1.1 Conservation of Flux

In the steady state, for unit incident flux, the total reaction rate must be unity. The mathematical expression of this condition is that the S-matrix be unitary:[4]

$$S\tilde{S}^* = 1, \tag{4a}$$

where

$$(\tilde{S}^*)_{ij} = S^*_{ji}\,. \tag{4b}$$

5.1.2 Time-Reversal Invariance

The assumption that the interactions are invariant with respect to inversion of the time axis ($\psi \rightarrow \psi^*$) gives rise to the requirement that the S-matrix must be symmetrical:

---

[4] This requirement on the S-matrix is usually referred to as "unitarity." Its consequence is generally to place upper bounds on the possible values of the S-matrix elements. In particular, the unitarity condition, when applied to the submatrices (projections) of the S-matrix representing specific angular momentum states, leads to upper bounds on the amplitudes corresponding to the absorption of the specific angular momentum components contained in an incident plane wave. (See Blatt and Weisskopf, *Theoretical Nuclear Physics*, John Wiley and Sons, New York (1952). The common expression of the unitary condition is the optical theorem

$$\sigma^{AB}_{\text{tot}} = \frac{4\pi}{k_A}\,\text{Im}\, f(\theta = 0), \tag{4c}$$

which relates the total cross section to the imaginary part of the amplitude for elastic scattering, $f(\theta)$, evaluated in the forward direction, $\theta = 0$. Since $f(\theta)$ is defined such that

$$\frac{d\sigma_{\text{el}}}{d\Omega} = |f(\theta)|^2, \tag{4d}$$

$f(\theta)$ may be expressed in terms of the diagonal elements of the S-matrix:

$$\begin{aligned} f(\theta) &= \sum_l (2l+1)\,\frac{(-1 + S^l_{ii})}{2ik}\,P_l(\cos\theta) \\ &= \frac{1}{k}\sum_l (2l+1)\, a_l P_l(\cos\theta). \end{aligned} \tag{4e}$$

For the case of elastic scattering, the unitary condition applies to the separate components in the form

$$a_l^* a_l = \text{Im}\, a_l\,. \tag{4f}$$

Such restrictions lead to the oft-referred-to "unitary bounds" on the magnitudes of scattering and reaction amplitudes.

$$S_{ij} = S_{ji}. \tag{5}$$

Combining Equations (4) and (5), we have

$$(\tilde{S}^*)_{ij} = S^*_{ji} = S^*_{ij}, \tag{6a}$$

$$SS^* = 1. \tag{6b}$$

Now, as noted, the elements S_{ij} are nonzero only when the transitions between channels are permitted by the conservation laws. Accordingly, it is usually more convenient, rather than dealing with the S-matrix in its entirety, to project out the various submatrices corresponding to a given set of conserved quantum numbers — in particular, to states of a specified value of the total angular momentum. Unless otherwise noted, in the remainder of this section we shall be concerned with the properties of such self-contained units of the complete S-matrix.

In many cases of physical interest, the portion of the S-matrix corresponding to a given incident channel may be nearly diagonal — i.e., the off-diagonal elements small as compared to the diagonal elements — at least for reactions at relatively low energy as compared to the thresholds for the most important possible inelastic reactions. As an example, if we consider the projections of the S-matrix corresponding to the possible reactions of $\pi + \mathfrak{N}$ at relatively low energies, and choose as our initial $(A + B)$ state a $\pi + \mathfrak{N}$ state of definite angular momentum, parity, and definite isotopic spin, then the possible exit channels will include, in addition to elastic scattering, $\mathfrak{N} + \gamma$, $\mathfrak{N}' + \pi$ (with a different isotopic spin, to the extent that charge independence is violated), $\mathfrak{N}' + \pi + \gamma$, Λ or Σ plus K (for initial states of appropriately high energy), and so on. All of these are only relatively weakly connected to the initial state; accordingly, in such situations, to a good approximation the S-matrix may be written

$$S = S_0 + i\epsilon, \tag{7a}$$

where S_0 is diagonal, and the elements of ϵ are all small.

We consider, first, some properties of S_0 in the lowest order. From Equation (6b) we have

$$|S_{0jj}|^2 = 1, \tag{7b}$$

$$S_{0jj} = e^{2i\alpha_j}. \tag{7c}$$

The factor 2 in the exponent of (7c) has been chosen so that α_j is the conventional scattering phase shift; this follows from the form of the elastic scattering cross section corresponding to an incident plane wave

$$\psi^{\text{in}} = v_i^{-1/2}\, e^{ikz}, \tag{8}$$

from which we must first extract the portion corresponding to the incident spherical wave of the required angular momentum [Equation (3a)] and then subtract that portion corresponding to an outgoing spherical wave; the net result of these manipulations is

$$\sigma_{jj}^{(l)} = \frac{(2l+1)}{4k_j^2}\,|S_{0jj}^{l} - 1|^2, \tag{9}$$

which defines S_{0jj} in terms of the conventional phase shifts, Equation (7c).

Now applying Equation (6b) to the S-matrix described by Equation (7a) and keeping terms to first order in ϵ,

$$(S_0 + i\epsilon)(S_0^* - i\epsilon^*) = 1, \tag{10a}$$

$$S_0 S_0^* + i(\epsilon S_0^* - S_0\epsilon^*) + \epsilon\epsilon^* = 1, \tag{10b}$$

$$1 + i(\epsilon S_0^* - S_0\epsilon^*) \cong 1, \tag{10c}$$

we obtain the condition

$$\epsilon S_0^* = S_0 \epsilon^* . \tag{10d}$$

We may write for the elements of ϵ

$$\epsilon_{ij} = \rho_{ij}\, e^{i\alpha_{ij}}(1 - \delta_{ij}), \tag{11a}$$

with ρ_{ij} real and $|\rho_{ij}| \ll 1$. Combining Equations (7), (10), and (11a), we obtain, by straightforward matrix algebra,

$$\epsilon_{ij} = \rho_{ij}\, e^{i(\alpha_i + \alpha_j)} . \tag{11b}$$

Equation (11b) contains the essence of the *Fermi–Watson theorem.* Thus, for example, if we are interested in the weak decays of the hyperons, we may think of these as though they come about through the absorption by the hyperon Y of a "spurion" x (see Section 7.4.3),

$$x + Y \to N + \pi, \tag{12a}$$

which is the inverse of reaction (1e). Now, the strength of reaction (12a) is determined by that of the weak interactions for which, as we have noted in Section 2.2, the coupling strength is very small compared to both the strong and the electromagnetic interactions. Accordingly, in the "elastic scattering" reaction

$$x + Y \to x + Y, \tag{12b}$$

the spurion scattering phase shift, which in any field theoretic estimate will be proportional to g_w^2, is expected to be very much smaller than any corresponding scattering phase shift related to a strong interaction. Thus, in Equation (11b) we have $\alpha_j \cong 0$; α_i is the $\pi + \mathfrak{N}$ scattering phase shift in the state of appropriate angular momentum and isotopic spin. Hence the amplitude for decay from the state j $(x + Y)$ into i $(\pi + \mathfrak{N})$ may be written

$$A_j = \epsilon_{ij} = a_j\, e^{i\alpha_i}, \tag{12c}$$

so that the *absolute* phase of the *weak* decay amplitude is given by the *strong* scattering phase shift in the final state.

Another application is to photoproduction reactions, say,

$$\gamma + N \to N + \pi. \tag{13}$$

Here, the amplitude corresponding to a definite final state is again given by an equation of the form of (12c), since the phase shift (α_j) for elastic (Compton) photon scattering is very much smaller than for elastic pion scattering, $\alpha_j \ll \alpha_i$.

It is of interest to derive the lowest-order correction to the elastic scattering phase shifts (diagonal terms) arising from the small nondiagonal contribution, ϵ, to the S-matrix. Thus, from Equations (10a)–(10d),

$$S_0 S_0^* \cong 1 - \epsilon\epsilon^* , \tag{14a}$$

and

$$(S_0 S_0^*)_{ii} = 1 - \sum_j \rho_{ij}^2 = \xi_i^2 \lesssim 1. \tag{14b}$$

Thus, we may write

$$S_{0ii} = \xi_i e^{2i\alpha_i} = e^{2i(\alpha_i + i\eta_i)} \tag{14c}$$

with

$$e^{-2\eta_i} = \left(1 - \sum_j \rho_{ij}^2\right)^{1/2} \cong 1 - \frac{1}{2}\sum_j \rho_{ij}^2 , \tag{14d}$$

$$\eta_i \cong \frac{1}{4}\sum_j \rho_{ij}^2 . \tag{14e}$$

The effect of the weak reaction channels is thus to introduce a small imaginary component into the scattering phase shift.

Returning to the general form of the S-matrix, Equations (1) through (6), we may note another important general consequence. Consider the reaction $i \to j$: from the preceding discussion we have, for given incident and outgoing channels,[5]

$$\frac{d\sigma}{d\Omega}(i \to j) = \frac{1}{4k_i^2}|S'_{ij}|^2 . \tag{15a}$$

If the incident particles, say, $(A + B) = i$, have spins s_A and s_B and the outgoing particles, $(C + D) = j$, have spins s_C and s_D, the cross section for an incident unpolarized plane wave is obtained by averaging over initial and summing over final spin states:

$$\frac{d\sigma}{d\Omega}(A + B \to C + D) = \frac{(2k_i)^{-2}}{(2s_A + 1)(2s_B + 1)} \sum_{m_i}\sum_{m_j} |S'_{ij}|^2 . \tag{15b}$$

The cross section for the inverse reaction is

$$\frac{d\sigma}{d\Omega}(C + D \to A + B) = \frac{(2k_j)^{-2}}{(2s_C + 1)(2s_D + 1)} \sum_{m_j}\sum_{m_i} |S'_{ji}|^2 . \tag{15c}$$

But time-reversal invariance requires

[5] S'_{ij} is an abbreviation for the sum over all available intermediate states. Furthermore, each amplitude, S_{ij}, which characterizes the S-matrix element connecting an incoming spherical wave to an outgoing spherical wave, must be multiplied by the appropriate spherical harmonic to describe the angular distribution of the component of the outgoing wave associated with the corresponding component of an incident plane wave.

$$S'_{ij} = S'_{ji}, \tag{16}$$

which results in the *principle of detailed balancing:*

$$k_i^2(2s_A + 1)(2s_B + 1)\frac{d\sigma}{d\Omega}(A + B \to C + D)$$
$$= k_j^2(2s_C + 1)(2s_D + 1)\frac{d\sigma}{d\Omega}(C + D \to A + B). \tag{17}$$

PROBLEM

Consider the elements of the S-matrix for the two-channel system:

1. $\pi + P \to \pi + P$, $S_{\pi\pi}$,
2. $\gamma + P \to \pi + P$, $S_{\gamma\pi}$,
3. $\pi + P \to \gamma + P$, $S_{\pi\gamma}$,
4. $\gamma + P \to \gamma + P$, $S_{\gamma\gamma}$,

at energies below the 2π threshold. It is observed that the angular distribution of (1) is asymmetric below and above an incident pion-kinetic energy of 200 MeV, but symmetric at this energy.[6]

(a) Assuming for the $\gamma\gamma$ scattering phase shift [reaction (4)] $\alpha_{\gamma\gamma} \ll \alpha_{\pi\pi}$ [reaction (1)], at what energies would you expect the angular distributions of reactions (2) and (3) to be symmetric? Why?

(b) Suppose time-reversal invariance were to break down in the interactions of photons with hadrons.[7] This would lead to the general relation

$$S^{(j)}_{\gamma\pi} = e^{i\delta_j} S^{(j)}_{\pi\gamma},$$

where δ_j is characteristic of the state of given j and parity. What will be the effect of such a breakdown on the detailed balancing between $d\sigma_{\gamma\pi}$ and $d\sigma_{\pi\gamma}$?

5.2 "Cusps" and Associated Phenomena

A number of useful connections between the reaction amplitudes for inelastic, elastic, and production processes follow, as shown in the preceding section, directly from the general properties of the S-matrix.

Other interesting effects of this nature may occur in the behavior of reaction cross sections at energies corresponding to the inception (threshold) of new, competing reactions. Such effects, manifested as discontinuities in the curves of cross section versus energy, were first discussed by Wigner. More recently, their possible importance with respect to reactions involving strange particles has been pointed out by Adair and by Baz' and Okun'.[8]

[6] For plots of the angular distributions, see J. D. Jackson, *The Physics of Elementary Particles*, Princeton University Press, Princeton, N.J. (1958), p. 15.

[7] See N. Christ and T. D. Lee, *Phys. Rev.*, *148:* 1520 (1966).

[8] E. P. Wigner, *Phys. Rev.*, *73:* 1002 (1948); R. K. Adair, *Phys. Rev.*, *111:* 632 (1958); A. N. Baz' and L. B. Okun', *JETP* (USSR), *35:* 757 (1958).

To illustrate the form and to understand better the origin of such effects, we consider a simple system $(a+A)$ having only two possible reaction channels (say, $a+A$ and $b+B$). The scattering matrix

$$S=\begin{pmatrix}\xi_a e^{2i\alpha_a} & i\rho e^{i\alpha_{ab}}\\ i\rho e^{i\alpha_{ab}} & \xi_b e^{2i\alpha_b}\end{pmatrix} \tag{18a}$$

describes both elastic scattering processes,

$$a+A\rightarrow a+A, \tag{18b}$$

$$b+B\rightarrow b+B, \tag{18c}$$

through the diagonal elements, as well as the inelastic reactions,

$$a+A\rightleftharpoons b+B, \tag{18d}$$

through the off-diagonal elements, as previously discussed. Equation (18a) already embodies the symmetry requirement on the S-matrix; then, to satisfy the unitarity requirement $S\tilde{S}=1$,

$$\xi_a^2=\xi_b^2=1-\rho^2 \tag{19a}$$

and

$$\alpha_{ab}=\alpha_a+\alpha_b. \tag{19b}$$

We now consider the effect of the onset of reaction (18d) on the cross section for elastic scattering (18b). Near threshold, the dominant term in the amplitude for reaction (18d) is that corresponding to S-wave production of the products, $b+B$, for which we may write [9]

$$\rho^2\cong 2ak, \tag{20}$$

where a is a constant (length) and k is the *cm* wave number of the reaction product b. For incident wave number K the cross sections are

$$\sigma_{ab}=\frac{\pi\rho^2}{K^2}=\frac{2\pi ak}{K^2}, \tag{21a}$$

$$\sigma_{aa}(E_a>E_t)=\frac{4\pi}{K^2}\left|\frac{(1-ak)\,e^{2i\alpha_a}-1}{2i}\right|^2\approx\frac{4\pi}{K^2}(1-ak)\sin^2\alpha_a, \tag{21b}$$

with, in terms of the incident *cm* energy, E_a, and the threshold energy, E_t,

$$K^2=2\mu_a E_a, \tag{22a}$$

$$k^2=2\mu_b(E_a-E_t), \tag{22b}$$

the μ's being appropriate reduced masses.

---

[9] The form of ρ^2 [Equation (20)] assumes that the matrix element for S-wave production of the products, $b+B$, is essentially energy independent over the energy range $(E_a-E_t)\ll E_a$; the k dependence then arises from the phase-space density available to the reaction products (see Section 1.2 and Chapter 4).

Note that as the threshold energy is approached *from above* ($k \to 0$), $\sigma_{ab} \to 0$, $\sigma_{aa} \to \sigma_0 = (4\pi/K^2)\sin^2\alpha_{ao}$; but the derivative $d\sigma_{aa}/dE_a \to -\infty$, indicating that there is a discontinuity in the scattering cross section at $E_a = E_t$. To specify fully the nature of this discontinuity, it is necessary to consider the behavior of σ_{aa} as $E_a \to E_t$ from below. Of course, for $E_a < E_t$, we require $\rho = 0$, but in the immediate vicinity of the threshold, albeit below, effects of reaction (18d) are still present; these may be derived by observing, from (22b), that k becomes imaginary for $E_a < E_t$,

$$k \to i\kappa = i(2\mu_b)^{1/2}(E_t - E_a)^{1/2}, \tag{23a}$$

while the phase shift for elastic (S-wave) $b + B$ scattering also becomes imaginary:

$$\alpha_b \to ia_b = i\xi_b\kappa \tag{23b}$$

and

$$\rho^2 \approx 2ia\kappa\, e^{-2a_b}. \tag{23c}$$

Substitution into (21b) yields

$$\sigma_{aa}(E_a < E_t) \simeq \frac{4\pi}{K^2}\{\sin^2\alpha_a - a\kappa\, e^{-2\xi_b\kappa}\sin\alpha_a\cos\alpha_a\}. \tag{21b$'$}$$

Equation (21b′) joins onto Equation (21b) at $E_a = E_t$, but not smoothly; rather, approaching the threshold from below, $d\sigma_{aa}/dE_a \to \infty$ for α_a lying in the first or third quadrant, while $d\sigma_{aa}/dE_a \to -\infty$ for α_a in the second or fourth quadrant. The possible forms of this scattering cross section anomaly are illustrated in Figure 5.2.

In the more general case, where the reaction of interest (scattering, in the cases considered above) is coupled to more than one channel, the threshold anomaly can have other shapes, in addition to those illustrated in Figure 5.2. Below the threshold for a new inelastic channel, the differential scattering cross

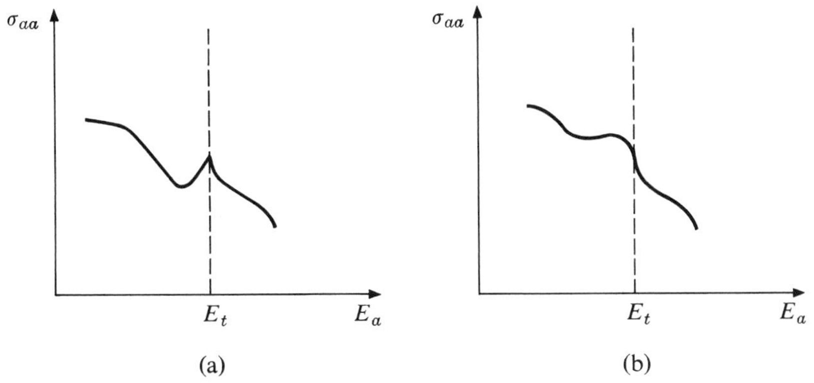

Figure 5.2 Cusp anomalies exhibited by elastic scattering at the threshold of an inelastic channel.

section has the following form:[10]

$$\frac{d\sigma_0}{d\Omega} = \frac{1}{4K^2} \sum_l |s_l P_l(\theta)|^2 = |F(\theta)|^2 = |f(\theta)\, e^{i\delta}|^2 . \tag{24a}$$

(The subscript l symbolizes all the quantum numbers characterizing a given combination of initial and final channels.) Near the threshold for a new reaction, say, $a + A \to b + B$, the only amplitude whose alteration we need to consider is that corresponding to the set of channels L which leads to S-wave production of the products $b + B$. For this amplitude we may write

$$s_L = s_{0L} - ak\, e^{i\alpha} , \tag{24b}$$

in which the symbols have the same meaning as in the preceding discussion and, in particular, $k \to i\kappa$ below the threshold. Accordingly, near the threshold Equation (24a) becomes

$$\frac{d\sigma}{d\Omega} = \left| f(\theta)\, e^{i\delta} - \frac{ak\, e^{i\alpha} P_L(\theta)}{2iK} \right|^2 \tag{24c}$$

$$\simeq \frac{d\sigma_0}{d\Omega} - \frac{ak}{K} f(\theta)\, P_L(\theta) \sin(\alpha - \delta) \qquad (\text{for } E_a > E_t) \tag{24d}$$

$$\simeq \frac{d\sigma_0}{d\Omega} - \frac{a\kappa}{K} f(\theta)\, P_L(\theta) \cos(\alpha - \delta) \qquad (\text{for } E_a < E_t) . \tag{24e}$$

The threshold anomalies have the forms of (a) and (b) of Figure 5.2 if $0 < (\alpha - \delta) < \pi/2$ or $\pi/2 < (\alpha - \delta) < \pi$, respectively. For $(\alpha - \delta)$ in the third and fourth quadrants, the shapes of the anomalies are reversed, as illustrated in Figure 5.3.

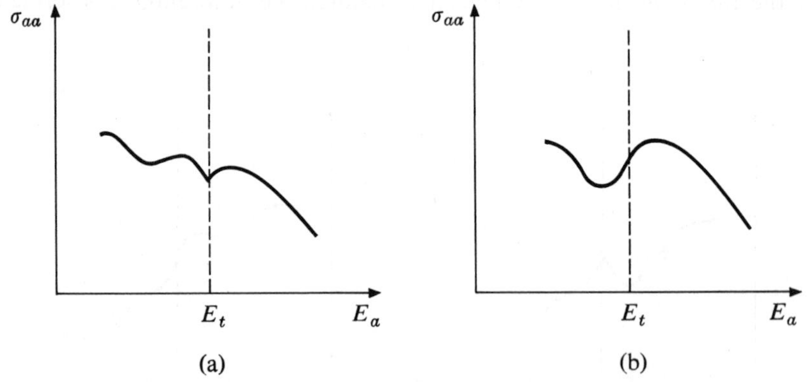

Figure 5.3 Other possible threshold anomalies in the general case.

[10] We assume, for simplicity, no spin dependence. The generalization to include spin dependence does not introduce any new physics.

A few additional comments concerning formal S-matrix theory are of interest: Consider a reacting system with $n-1$ channels, below the threshold for an nth channel. Let the S-matrix elements be $s_{ij}=s_{ji}$:

$$\sum_{l=1}^{n-1} s_{il}s_{lj}^* = \delta_{ij}. \tag{25a}$$

Now, above the threshold, we have a new row and a new column added to the S-matrix,

$$s'_{in}=s'_{ni}=m_i k^{1/2}, \tag{25b}$$

while the old elements become

$$s'_{ij}=s_{ij}+a_{ij}k. \tag{25c}$$

Application of $SS^*=1$ both above and below the threshold yields

$$\sum_{l=1}^{n-1} s_{jl}m_l^* = -m_j e^{-2i\alpha_n}, \tag{25d}$$

which is a set of $n-1$ simultaneous equations for determining, essentially, the phases of the m_j's and

$$a_{ij}=\tfrac{1}{2}m_i m_j e^{-2i\alpha_n}. \tag{25e}$$

It is the form of this last expression which permits us to write Equation (24b) and to derive the forms of the anomaly shown in Figure 5.3.

There are a number of additional features of these "cusp" anomalies that are more or less directly derivable from the S-matrix formalism as outlined above. Thus, while a given channel (say, $a+A \to c+C$) may exhibit any one of the four forms of the anomaly at the threshold for a new reaction, only those anomalies shown in Figures 5.2(a) and 5.3(b) (in which the cross section below threshold is less than it would have been in the absence of the new channel) appear if we consider the sum of all processes but the new one

$$\sigma=\sum_{l=1}^{n-1}\sigma_{al}.$$

Finally, a possible use of these phenomena is to determine the intrinsic parities of the products in the new channel $(b+B)$ relative to those in the reaction in which the anomaly is observed. This possibility arises from the determination of the orbital angular momentum of the channel that exhibits the anomaly [P_L in Equation (24c)] through the condition that it proceed through the same initial channel as gives rise to S-state production of the new products.

6

Angular Momentum Conservation

A great deal of useful information about elementary particles is obtained from observations on the angular distributions of the products of their decays and their interactions. In this chapter, we summarize the main results of the application of angular momentum conservation to such processes.

6.1 Decays

The simplest applications of angular momentum conservation to elementary particle phenomena are encountered in processes where the initial state is characterized by a unique set of quantum numbers — namely, in particle decays.

6.1.1 General

Consider the two-body decay

$$A \to B + C \tag{1}$$

in the rest frame of the parent particle A. Let S, s_1, s_2 be the spins, respectively, of A, B, and C. Since the decay products may have relative (orbital) angular momentum l, the conservation of total angular momentum requires

$$\mathbf{S} = \mathbf{s}_1 + \mathbf{s}_2 + \mathbf{l}, \tag{2a}$$

and, for the projections along an arbitrary z axis,

$$M = m_1 + m_2 + m_l . \tag{2b}$$

In addition, if the intrinsic parities of the particles are, respectively, π_A, π_B, π_C, parity conservation requires

$$\pi_A = \pi_B \pi_C (-1)^l . \tag{2c}$$

Generally, in combining three angular momenta, as in Equation (2a), we first combine two, and then add the third, the choice of the order of combination being dictated either by convenience or by the form (dynamics) of the interactions among the particles. We shall, in the following, assume that the system is characterized by the total (channel) spin of $B + C$:

$$\mathbf{s} = \mathbf{s}_1 + \mathbf{s}_2 , \tag{3a}$$

$$s_1 + s_2 \geq s \geq |s_1 - s_2| . \tag{3b}$$

Subject to angular momentum conservation [Equations (2a) and (3a)] and parity conservation [Equation (2c)], the parent particle A can generally decay through a number of channels, characterized by the values of s and l, to which we assign the decay amplitudes $a_{s,l}$. These amplitudes are, in general, complex, but their phases are determined, through the Fermi–Watson theorem, by the scattering phase shifts of $B + C$ at the appropriate energy and in the appropriate states $\mathbf{s} + \mathbf{l} = \mathbf{S}$.

Let $\chi_s^{m=m_1+m_2}$ be the spin wave functions for the combinations (3a). Then, the decay amplitude for a given initial state (S, M) is

$$A_{S,M} = \sum_{s,l,m_l=M-m} a_{s,l} \, C^{S,M}_{s,m;\, l,m_l} \, \chi_s^m \, Y_l^{m_l}(\theta, \varphi). \tag{4}$$

where the $C^{S,M}_{s,m;\, l,m_l}$ are the Clebsch–Gordan coefficients corresponding to the possible angular momentum combinations and the $Y_l^{m_l}(\theta, \varphi)$ are the associated Legendre polynomials.[1] The decay angular distribution is then given by

$$W_{S,M}(\theta, \varphi) = \sum_{s,m_l} \left| \sum_l a_{s,l} \, C^{S,M}_{s,m;\, l,m_l} \, Y_l^{m_l}(\theta, \varphi) \right|^2 , \tag{4a}$$

where we have taken advantage of the orthogonality of the spin states

$$\chi_s^m (\chi_{s'}^{m'})^* = \delta_{s,s'} \, \delta_{m,m'} . \tag{5}$$

Using the property of the Legendre polynomials,

$$\int Y_l^{m_l} \, Y_{l'}^{m_{l'}} \, d\Omega = \delta_{l,l'} \, \delta_{m_l,m_{l'}} , \tag{5a}$$

we obtain the total decay rate

$$\lambda_{S,M} = \sum_{s,l,m_l} |a_{s,l} \, C^{S,M}_{s,m;\, l,m_l}|^2 . \tag{4b}$$

Given an initial state distribution (polarization) characterized by the probabilities $P_{S,M}$,

[1] Tables of Clebsch–Gordan coefficients and expressions for the associated Legendre polynomials are given in Appendixes 1 and 2.

$$\sum_M P_{S,M} = 1, \tag{6}$$

we have

$$\lambda_S = \sum_M P_{S,M} \lambda_{S,M}. \tag{6a}$$

In particular, for an initially unpolarized parent

$$P_{S,M} = (2S+1)^{-1}, \tag{7a}$$

we obtain

$$\bar{\lambda}_S = (2S+1)^{-1} \sum_M \lambda_{S,M}. \tag{7b}$$

Even without resort to detail, a number of general theorems follow from the properties of the $Y_l^{m_l}(\theta, \varphi)$. Thus:

1. For an initially unpolarized parent,

$$W_S(\theta, \varphi) = \sum_M P_{S,M} W_{S,M} = (2S+1)^{-1} \sum_M W_{S,M}(\theta, \varphi) = \text{const.} \tag{4a$'$}$$

2. For parity-conserving decays, in general and irrespective of the initial polarization,

$$W_S(\theta, \varphi) = \sum_{j=0}^{l\,\max} \alpha_j \cos^{2j} \theta. \tag{4a$''$}$$

This follows from Equation (2c), which requires that the possible l-values must differ by two units. Thus, parity-conserving decays are always symmetric about 90°.

EXAMPLES

1. Decay of a heavy meson into two pseudoscalar mesons, e.g., $\rho(S = 1^-) \to 2\pi$; $\phi(S = 1^-) \to 2K$; $K^*(S = 1^-) \to K\pi$; $f_0(S = 2^+) \to 2\pi$. In general, since $s_1 = s_2 = 0^-$, $s = 0^+$, we have simply $S = l$, and $\pi_A = (-1)^l$ (if the decay conserves parity). For $S = 0$, $W_{S=0} = \text{const.}$ For $S \geq 1$, the decay angular distributions are isotropic only for an unpolarized parent; otherwise, the decay distribution depends on the state of initial polarization. Thus:

$$W_{1,\pm 1} = |Y_1^{\pm 1}|^2 = \frac{3}{8\pi} \sin^2 \theta, \tag{8a}$$

$$W_{1,0} = \frac{3}{4\pi} \cos^2 \theta, \tag{8b}$$

while

$$W_{2,\pm 2} = \frac{15}{32\pi} \sin^4 \theta, \tag{8c}$$

$$W_{2,\pm 1} = \frac{15}{8\pi} \sin^2 \theta \cos^2 \theta, \tag{8d}$$

$$W_{2,0} = \frac{5}{16\pi}(3\cos^2\theta - 1)^2. \tag{8e}$$

Note that, in each case, for an initially unpolarized parent [Equation (4a′)]

$$W_S = \frac{1}{4\pi}.$$

2. Decay of $\mathfrak{N}^*(\frac{3}{2}^+) \to \mathfrak{N} + \pi$. In this case, $s_1 = \frac{1}{2}^+$, $s_2 = 0^-$, $s = \frac{1}{2}^-$, $l = 1$, and

$$W_{3/2,\pm 3/2} = |Y_1^{\pm 1}|^2 = \frac{3}{8\pi}\sin^2\theta, \tag{9a}$$

$$W_{3/2,\pm 1/2} = \left|\sqrt{\frac{2}{3}}\,Y_1^0\right|^2 + \left|\sqrt{\frac{1}{3}}\,Y_1^{\pm 1}\right|^2 = \frac{1}{8\pi}(3\cos^2\theta + 1), \tag{9b}$$

and again, for $P_{S,M} = \frac{1}{4}$,

$$W_S = \frac{1}{4\pi}. \tag{9c}$$

3. Decay of a heavy meson into three pions, e.g., $\omega^0 \to \pi^+\pi^-\pi^0$. Here we have $s = 0^-$, but a three-body final state, to which we can assign two independent orbital angular momenta, as follows: Let the momenta of the three product pions be $\mathbf{p}_1$, $\mathbf{p}_2$, and $\mathbf{p}_3 = \mathbf{p} = -(\mathbf{p}_1 + \mathbf{p}_2)$. Referring to Figure 6.1(a), we may consider the first two particles to represent a "di-pion" of total energy $M_{12}^2 = (E_1 + E_2)^2 - p^2$, with internal momentum (equal and opposite for π_1 and π_2) $\mathbf{q}$ and internal angular momentum $\mathbf{L}$; to this must be added the orbital angular momentum $\mathbf{l}$ of the third or odd pion to obtain the total angular momentum (spin) of the system

$$\mathbf{S} = \mathbf{L} + \mathbf{l}. \tag{10a}$$

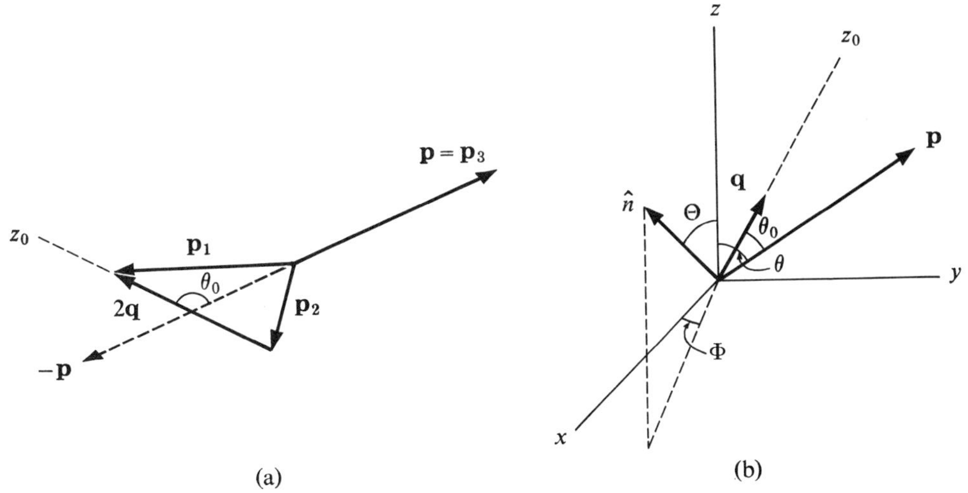

Figure 6.1 Momenta and angles characterizing a three-body decay.

The parity of the parent is ($\pi_\pi = -1$)

$$\pi_A = (-1)^{L+l+1}. \tag{10b}$$

This way of describing the three-body final state reduces the problem to that of the two-body decay treated above, with one of the bodies being a di-pion of spin $s_1 = L$ and the second being a pion of spin $s_2 = 0$. The angular distribution of the odd pion is, for a parent state of initial polarization (S,M), given by Equation (4a) with $s,m \to L,m_L$. Considering the special case of $\omega^0 \to 3\pi$, for example, since $S = 1^-$, the simplest decay combination[2] is $L = l = 1$. Then, from (4a),

$$W_{1,\pm 1}(\theta) = \frac{3}{8\pi}(1 + \cos^2\theta), \tag{11a}$$

$$W_{1,0}(\theta) = \frac{3}{8\pi}\sin^2\theta. \tag{11b}$$

As expected, for an initially unpolarized state,

$$(2S+1)^{-1}\sum W_{S,M} = \frac{1}{4\pi}. \tag{11c}$$

If, however, instead of considering the direction of emission of the odd particle with respect to an arbitrary z axis, we look at the normal to the decay plane, $\hat{n}$ [see Figure 6.1(b)], this corresponds to the direction of the total angular momentum vector of the system, and its distribution is characterized by the spherical harmonics $Y_S^M(\Theta, \Phi)$.

The same considerations can be applied to the permitted three-pion decays of any heavy meson of given spin and parity S^π. Table 6.1 shows the l–L

Table 6.1 Angular Momentum States for 3π Decays

l	L	S^π	t
0	0	$\underline{0}^-$	1, 3
1	0	$\underline{1}^+$	1, 3
0	1	1^+	0, 2
1	1	$0^-, 1^-, 2^-$	0, 2
0 2	2 0	$\underline{2}^-$	1, 3
1	2	$1^+, \underline{2}^+, \underline{3}^+$	1, 3
2	1	$1^+, 2^+, 3^+$	0, 2
3	0	$\underline{3}^+$	1, 3
0	3	3^+	0, 2
2	2	$0^-, \underline{1}^-, 2^-, \underline{3}^-$	1, 3

[2] $L = l \pm 1$ is excluded by parity conservation and $L = l$ even are all excluded by isotopic-spin conservation (to be shown in a subsequent section), leaving only $L = l$ odd. It can be shown that the other possibilities lead to the same angular distribution of the odd pion.

combinations corresponding to initial states of $S \leq 3$. Also shown (column 4) are the permitted isotopic spin values of the final 3π states, the division between even and odd values arising out of the requirement, from Bose statistics, that the final wave function be symmetric under interchange of any two pions. Table 6.1 permits us to calculate the odd-pion decay distribution in the 3π decay of any polarized heavy meson. A number of interesting features may be noted:

(a) There is no possible 3π final state for a 0^+ meson (provided parity is conserved in the decay). This, coupled with the fact that there is no possible 2π final state for the decay of a 0^- meson, leads to the conclusion that parity cannot be conserved in the decay of the K-meson (0^-) for which both the $2\pi(\theta)$ and the $3\pi(\tau)$ decays are observed. It was in order to explain this "θ–τ paradox" that Lee and Yang were led to postulate the nonconservation of parity in the weak interactions.

(b) In the case of charged meson decay ($A^\pm \rightarrow \pi^\pm + \pi^\pm + \pi^\mp$ or $\pi^\pm + 2\pi^0$) or of neutral meson decay into $3\pi^0$'s, two of the pions being identical, if we consider the identical pions to make up the di-π, Bose statistics permits even L-values only. This narrows down considerably the number of decay possibilities for charged mesons. If, further, we assume that, due to angular momentum barrier effects, the final state with the lowest possible value of $l+L$ will dominate in the decay, the combinations that, under this circumstance, will be most important in the decay of charged mesons are underlined in column 3 of Table 6.1.

(c) Even in the case of an unpolarized parent (for which the distribution of **p** or **q** with respect to an arbitrary space axis is always isotropic) it is possible to obtain useful information relating to the parent meson spin value by considering the distribution of the odd pion with respect to an axis fixed by the internal coordinates of the system. Specifically, referring to Figure 6.1, let us choose the reference axis (z_0) to lie along the direction of **q**, the internal momentum of the di-π. In this coordinate system, the value of $m_L = 0$, so that Equation (4a) becomes

$$W_{S,M}(\theta_0, \varphi_0) = \left| \sum a_{l,L}\, C^{S,M}_{L,0;\, l,M} Y^M_l(\theta_0, \varphi_0) \right|^2, \tag{12a}$$

$$W_S(\theta_0, \varphi_0) = \sum_M W_{S,M}(\theta_0, \varphi_0), \tag{12b}$$

which, except for the case when either l or $L = 0$, generally yields a distribution that is not isotropic. The distributions of the odd pion, relative to the internal momentum of the di-pion, are given in Tables 6.2 and 6.3 for the most likely decay modes of heavier mesons with various S^π and t values.

(d) We may obtain additional information by considering the distribution of the momenta or energies of the decay pions. In Section 4.2, we have noted that a pure phase-space distribution would give rise to a uniform distribution of decay points when plotted in a Dalitz diagram or, alternatively, in the nonrelativistic approximation, to a distribution for the odd pion

Table 6.2 Decay Properties of $t=1$ Mesons into $2\pi^{(\text{iden.})}+\pi^{(\text{odd})}$

S^π	l	L	$W(\theta_0)$
0^+	—	—	—
0^-	0	0	$(4\pi)^{-1}$
1^+	1	0	$(4\pi)^{-1}$
1^-	2	2	$\frac{15}{32\pi}\sin^2 2\theta_0$
2^+	1	2	$\frac{3}{8\pi}\sin^2\theta_0$
2^-	$\begin{Bmatrix}0\\2\end{Bmatrix}$	$\begin{Bmatrix}2\\0\end{Bmatrix}$	$\frac{1}{8\pi}[\lvert a_{02}\rvert^2+\lvert a_{20}\rvert^2+\text{Re }a_{02}a_{20}^*(3\cos^2\theta_0-1)]$
3^+	$\begin{Bmatrix}1\\3\end{Bmatrix}$	$\begin{Bmatrix}2\\0\end{Bmatrix}$	$\frac{1}{8\pi}[\lvert a_{30}\rvert^2+\frac{3}{7}\lvert a_{12}\rvert^2(2+\cos^2\theta_0)+3\text{ Re }a_{30}a_{12}^*(3\cos^2\theta_0-1)]$
3^-	2	2	$\frac{15}{224\pi}(5+3\cos^2\theta_0)\sin^2\theta_0$

$$dN=\frac{8}{\pi}\bar{\kappa}^{1/2}(1-\bar{\kappa})^{1/2}\,d\bar{\kappa}, \tag{13a}$$

where

$$\bar{\kappa}=\frac{p^2}{p_m^2}=\frac{3}{4}\frac{p^2}{mQ}. \tag{13b}$$

Even assuming no other (dynamical) dependence of the matrix element on $\bar{\kappa}$, we see that the effect of the internal angular momenta will be to introduce angular momentum barrier penetration factors, $v_l(pR)\,v_L(qR)$, as multiplicative factors into Equation (13a). These have the property [3]

$$v_l(x)\simeq\frac{x^{2l}}{[(2l-1)!!]^2}\qquad(\text{for } x\to 0), \tag{14a}$$

$$v_l(x)\gtrapprox 1\qquad(\text{for } x\gg l). \tag{14b}$$

In the nonrelativistic approximation, assuming $pR,\ qR\ll 1$ (short-range approximation) and recalling as well

$$q^2=mQ(1-\bar{\kappa}), \tag{15}$$

a given decay, characterized by a given l–L combination, will exhibit the pion energy distribution

$$\frac{dN}{d\bar{\kappa}}\cong M^2(\kappa)\,\bar{\kappa}^{l+1/2}(1-\bar{\kappa})^{L+1/2} \tag{13c}$$

in which the $M^2(\kappa)$ contains any additional energy dependence introduced by the matrix element. Thus, the net effect of finite l–L values is to cause a concentration of the density of points on the Dalitz plot away from small values

[3] See J. M. Blatt and V. F. Weisskopf, *Theoretical Nuclear Physics,* John Wiley and Sons, New York (1952), p. 361.

Table 6.3 Decay Properties of $t=0$ into $\pi^+\pi^-\pi^0$

S^π	l	L	$W(\theta_0)$
0^+	—	—	—
0^-	1	1	$(4\pi)^{-1}$
1^+	0	1	$(4\pi)^{-1}$
1^-	1	1	$\frac{3}{8\pi}\sin^2\theta_0$
2^+	2	1	$\frac{3}{8\pi}\sin^2\theta_0$
2^-	1	1	$\frac{3}{40\pi}(3+\cos^2\theta_0)$
3^+	$\begin{cases}2\\0\end{cases}$	$\begin{matrix}1\\3\end{matrix}\Big\}$	$\frac{1}{4\pi}[\lvert a_{03}\rvert^2+\lvert a_{21}\rvert^2(2+\cos^2\theta_0)+\sqrt{3}\,\mathrm{Re}\,a_{03}a_{21}^*(3\cos^2\theta_0-1)]$
3^-	$\begin{cases}3\\1\end{cases}$	$\begin{matrix}1\\3\end{matrix}\Big\}$	$\frac{3}{16\pi}[\lvert a_{31}\rvert^2+\lvert a_{13}\rvert^2-\frac{1}{2}\mathrm{Re}\,a_{31}a_{13}^*(5\cos^2\theta_0-1)]\sin^2\theta_0$

of the kinetic energies, the form of the deviations from a uniform distribution being a characteristic feature of the spin and parity of the parent meson (Tables 6.1–6.3).

(e) From the point of view of Dalitz plots, as opposed to angular distributions, it is frequently more useful to describe the decay amplitudes in terms of the various possible invariant combinations of the particle momenta, **p**, or energies, ϵ, with the appropriate spins.[4] Thus, the decay of a 0^- meson requires a scalar combination, e.g., $\epsilon_1\epsilon_2\epsilon_3$. In general, we may assign to each S^π value certain invariant forms which describe the main (i.e., kinematical) features of the momentum dependence of the decay matrix element. Such forms are shown in Table 6.4.

Table 6.4 Invariant Forms for Heavy-Meson Decay into 3π

S^π	Form	l	L
0^-	$a(\epsilon_1^2+\epsilon_2^2+\epsilon_3^2)+b\epsilon_1\epsilon_2\epsilon_3$	0	0
	$(\epsilon_1-\epsilon_2)(\epsilon_2-\epsilon_3)(\epsilon_3-\epsilon_1)$	1	1
1^+	$\mathbf{p}_1\epsilon_2\epsilon_3+\mathbf{p}_2\epsilon_3\epsilon_1+\mathbf{p}_3\epsilon_1\epsilon_2$	1	0
	$a[\epsilon_1(\mathbf{p}_2-\mathbf{p}_3)+\epsilon_2(\mathbf{p}_3-\mathbf{p}_1)+\epsilon_3(\mathbf{p}_1-\mathbf{p}_2)]+$ $b[\mathbf{p}_1\epsilon_1(\epsilon_2-\epsilon_3)+\mathbf{p}_2\epsilon_2(\epsilon_3-\epsilon_1)+\mathbf{p}_3\epsilon_3(\epsilon_1-\epsilon_2)]$	0	1
1^-	$(\epsilon_1-\epsilon_2)(\epsilon_2-\epsilon_3)(\epsilon_3-\epsilon_1)(\mathbf{p}_1\times\mathbf{p}_2+\mathbf{p}_2\times\mathbf{p}_3+\mathbf{p}_3\times\mathbf{p}_1)$	2	2
	$\epsilon_1(\mathbf{p}_2\times\mathbf{p}_3)+\epsilon_2(\mathbf{p}_3\times\mathbf{p}_1)+\epsilon_3(\mathbf{p}_1\times\mathbf{p}_2)$	1	1

PROBLEMS

1. Consider the decay of a heavy meson of spin parity S^π into a vector meson ($s_1=1^-$) and a pseudoscalar ($s_2=0^-$), followed by the decay of the vector meson into two pseudoscalars. Assume initially unpolarized heavy mesons.

[4] For example, see C. Zemach, *Phys. Rev., 133:* B1201 (1964).

Prepare a table showing the possible orbital angular momenta, l, and the angular distributions of the pseudoscalar meson with respect to (a) the direction of emission of the vector meson decay products in the *cm* of the vector meson, and to (b) the normal to the decay plane, for all possible values of $S \leq 3$. (See Figure 6.1 for the definitions of the angles.)

2. Let $\mathbf{e}$ represent the polarization vector of a ρ- or ω-meson (spin 1^-). Show that

(a) the decay matrix element for $\rho \to 2\pi$ is proportional to the invariant form

$$\mathbf{e} \cdot \mathbf{q},$$

where $\mathbf{q}$ is the relative momentum of the two decay pions.

(b) The simplest invariant form for the decay $\omega \to \pi^+ + \pi^- + \pi^0$ is

$$\mathbf{e} \cdot \mathbf{p} \times \mathbf{q},$$

where $\mathbf{q}$ is the relative decay momentum of the charged pions and $\mathbf{p}$ is the momentum of the π^0 in the *cm* of the ω.

6.1.2 Decays Involving Photons

Photons (and neutrinos) differ from particles of finite rest mass in that the normal state of photon polarization is along the direction of its motion. Thus, the photon may be considered as a particle of spin 1 with but two states[5] $\psi_\pm$ with $m_\gamma = \pm 1$. Correspondingly the statistical weight of an unpolarized photon beam is 2.

Photons can also carry orbital angular momentum, $l > 0$. However, unlike particles of finite rest mass, a given l-value can give rise to either parity, depending on whether the radiation is electric (E) or magnetic (M). Thus, for a given multipole (value of 2^l), we have

$$\pi_\gamma^E = (-1)^l, \tag{17a}$$

$$\pi_\gamma^M = -(-1)^l. \tag{17b}$$

The angular distribution of a given multipole is described by the vector spherical harmonics,

$$\sqrt{l(l+1)}\, \mathbf{X}_{l,m}(\theta, \varphi) = -i(\mathbf{r} \times \nabla)\, Y_{l,m}(\theta, \varphi), \tag{18a}$$

where

$$\nabla = \mathbf{r}_0 \frac{\partial}{\partial r} + \boldsymbol{\theta}_0 \frac{1}{r}\frac{\partial}{\partial \theta} + \boldsymbol{\varphi}_0 \frac{1}{r \sin\theta}\frac{\partial}{\partial \varphi} \tag{18b}$$

($\mathbf{r}_0$, $\boldsymbol{\theta}_0$, $\boldsymbol{\varphi}_0$ are unit vectors), in terms of which the asymptotic electric and magnetic fields are

[5] These states correspond to right- and left-handed circularly polarized photons. Linearly polarized photon beams are a coherent superposition of the two circularly polarized eigenstates

$$\psi^\gamma_{x,y} = \psi^\gamma_+ \pm \psi^\gamma_- . \tag{16}$$

$$\mathbf{E}^M_{l,m} = \frac{e^{i(kr-\omega t - l\pi/2)}}{kr} \mathbf{X}_{l,m}, \tag{19a}$$

$$\mathbf{H}^M_{l,m} = -\frac{i}{k} \nabla \times \mathbf{E}^M_{l,m}, \tag{19b}$$

and

$$\mathbf{E}^E_{l,m} = -\frac{i}{k} \nabla \times \mathbf{H}^E_{l,m}, \tag{20a}$$

$$\mathbf{H}^E_{l,m} = \frac{e^{i(kr-\omega t - l\pi/2)}}{kr} \mathbf{X}_{l,m}. \tag{20b}$$

By convention, the angular part of the photon amplitude is associated with its electric field vector:

$$\psi^M_{l,m} = \mathbf{X}_{l,m}, \tag{21a}$$

$$\psi^E_{l,m} = -\mathbf{r}_0 \times \mathbf{X}_{l,m}. \tag{21b}$$

In either case, the angular distribution of photons with a given value of (l, m) is given by the Poynting vector

$$Z_{l,m}(\theta) = \mathbf{X}_{l,m} \cdot \mathbf{X}^*_{l,m} \tag{22}$$

Expressions for $\mathbf{X}_{l,m}$ and $Z_{l,m}$ are given in Appendix 3 for $l \leq 3$.

EXAMPLES

1. The decay $\Sigma^0 \to \Lambda^0 + \gamma$ requires $M1$ (magnetic dipole) photon emission, since $S(\Sigma^0) = S(\Lambda^0) = \frac{1}{2}^+$. Consider the initial state $M_{\Sigma^0} = \frac{1}{2}$. The final state $(S = M = \frac{1}{2})$ is then

$$\boldsymbol{\psi} = \sqrt{\tfrac{1}{3}}\, \chi^{1/2}_{1/2}(\Lambda^0)\, \boldsymbol{\psi}^M_{1,0} - \sqrt{\tfrac{2}{3}}\, \chi^{-1/2}_{1/2}(\Lambda^0)\, \boldsymbol{\psi}^M_{1,1}, \tag{23a}$$

and

$$W_\gamma(\theta) = \boldsymbol{\psi} \cdot \boldsymbol{\psi}^* = \frac{1}{3} Z_{1,0} + \frac{2}{3} Z_{1,1} = \frac{1}{8\pi}(\sin^2\theta + 1 + \cos^2\theta) = \frac{1}{4\pi}. \tag{23b}$$

However, the product Λ^0 is polarized:

$$P_\Lambda = \frac{|\langle \chi^{1/2}_{1/2} | \boldsymbol{\psi} \rangle|^2 - |\langle \chi^{-1/2}_{1/2} | \boldsymbol{\psi} \rangle|^2}{|\boldsymbol{\psi}|^2} = \frac{\frac{1}{3} Z_{1,0} - \frac{2}{3} Z_{1,1}}{\frac{1}{3} Z_{1,0} + \frac{2}{3} Z_{1,1}} = -\cos^2\theta, \tag{23c}$$

$$\overline{P}_\Lambda = \int P_\Lambda |\boldsymbol{\psi}|^2 \, d\Omega = -\frac{1}{3}. \tag{23d}$$

2. Decay of a vector meson $(1^-) \to \pi^0(0^-) + \gamma$. Here, again, the photon is $M1$, and for a given initial polarization state m,

$$\boldsymbol{\psi}_{1,m} = \boldsymbol{\psi}^M_{1,m}, \tag{24a}$$

giving

$$W^{\gamma}_{1,\pm1} = Z_{1,\pm1} = \frac{3}{16\pi}(1 + \cos^2\theta),$$
$$W^{\gamma}_{1,0} = Z_{1,0} = \frac{3}{8\pi}\sin^2\theta. \tag{24b}$$

For an initially unpolarized parent,

$$W^{\gamma} = \frac{1}{3}\sum_{m} W^{\gamma}_{1,m} = \frac{1}{4\pi}, \tag{24c}$$

as expected.

PROBLEM

Consider the decay $\pi^0 \to 2\gamma$. Let $\mathbf{e}_1$ and $\mathbf{e}_2$ represent the polarization vectors of the two photons, and $\mathbf{q} = \mathbf{p}_1 - \mathbf{p}_2$ represent the relative momentum of the two photons. Since photons are bosons, the invariant form of the decay matrix elements must be even with respect to interchange of the indices 1 and 2. Using only forms that are linear in e_1, e_2, and q:

(a) What is the invariant form corresponding to the π^0 decay (spin 0^-)?
(b) What form would you use for the 2γ decay of a spin 0^+ neutral meson?
(c) What about spin 1?

6.1.3 Parity-Nonconserving Decays

We have previously noted that the weak decays of the K-mesons violate parity conservation, since the 2π and 3π final states cannot both be accessible to a particle of spin 0 if parity were conserved. However, as far as these K-meson decay modes are concerned, this statement exhausts the observable consequences of the assumption of parity nonconservation.

If, on the other hand, parity nonconservation is a universal feature of the weak interactions, there are many other observable consequences.[6] We consider, in the following, the effects of parity nonconservation, when combined with the requirements of angular momentum conservation, on the two categories of weak interactions — the weak decays of hadrons in which the products are only hadrons (baryons and mesons), and the weak decays involving leptons (muons, electrons, and neutrinos).

Nonleptonic Decays • In addition to the K-meson decays into two or three pions, the nonleptonic decays include the most probable two-body decays of the hyperons, which obey the strangeness selection rule $\Delta S = \pm 1$.

$$\Lambda^0 \to \mathfrak{N} + \pi, \tag{25a}$$

[6] T. D. Lee and C. N. Yang, *Phys. Rev., 104:* 254 (1956).

$$\Sigma \rightarrow \mathfrak{N} + \pi, \tag{25b}$$

$$\Xi \rightarrow \Lambda^0 + \pi, \tag{25c}$$

$$\Omega^- \rightarrow \Xi + \pi \tag{25d}$$

$$\rightarrow \Lambda^0 + K^- . \tag{25e}$$

The first three of these, (25a)–(25c), are characterized by $S(\text{parent}) = \frac{1}{2}^+$, $s_1 = \frac{1}{2}^+$, $s_2 = 0^-$. Parity conservation requires $l = 1$ (P-wave pion emission) but, if parity is not conserved, $l = 0$ (S-wave pion emission) is also possible. Referring to Figure 6.2, we consider an initial hyperon (Λ, Σ, Ξ) state of $m = \pm\frac{1}{2}$ with respect to

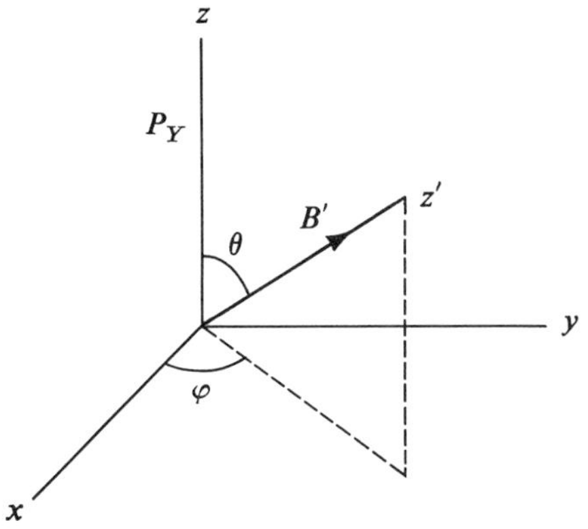

Figure 6.2 Angles (θ, φ) characterizing the decay of a hyperon, polarized along the z axis, into a product baryon, B', emitted along the z' axis, and a meson emitted along $-z'$.

the z axis. Let S represent the amplitude for emission of an S-wave pion (violating parity conservation), and P the amplitude for the (parity-conserving) emission of a P-wave pion. The final-state wave function is then [7]

$$\psi_{1/2,\pm 1/2} = S\,\chi_\pm(s_1 = \tfrac{1}{2},\ s_2 = 0,\ l = 0) + P\,\chi_\pm(s_1 = \tfrac{1}{2},\ s_2 = 0,\ l = 1), \tag{26a}$$

with

$$\chi_\pm\left(s_1 = \frac{1}{2},\ s_2 = 0,\ l = 0\right) = \begin{Bmatrix}\alpha\\ \beta\end{Bmatrix} Y_0^0(\theta, \phi), \tag{26b}$$

$$\chi_\pm\left(s_1 = \frac{1}{2},\ s_2 = 0,\ l = 1\right) = \pm\sqrt{\frac{1}{3}} \begin{Bmatrix}\alpha\\ \beta\end{Bmatrix} Y_1^0(\theta, \phi) \mp \sqrt{\frac{2}{3}} \begin{Bmatrix}\beta\\ \alpha\end{Bmatrix} Y_1^{\pm 1}(\theta, \phi), \tag{26c}$$

yielding

$$\psi_{1/2,\pm 1/2} = \left(SY_0^0 \pm \sqrt{\frac{1}{3}}\,PY_1^0\right) \begin{Bmatrix}\alpha\\ \beta\end{Bmatrix} \mp \sqrt{\frac{2}{3}}\,PY_1^{\pm 1} \begin{Bmatrix}\beta\\ \alpha\end{Bmatrix}. \tag{26d}$$

[7] Recall that α and β are, respectively, the spin eigenfunctions of the product baryon with $m_1 = +\frac{1}{2}$ and $m_1 = -\frac{1}{2}$.

The decay angular distribution is given by

$$W_{\pm 1/2} = |\psi_{1/2,\pm 1/2}|^2 = \frac{(|S|^2 + |P|^2)}{4\pi}(1 \mp a \cos\theta), \tag{27a}$$

with

$$a = \frac{2 \text{ Re } S^*P}{|S|^2 + |P|^2}. \tag{27b}$$

In particular, for a given initial polarization, P_Y, characterized by the probabilities f and $(1-f)$, for the initial states $m = +\frac{1}{2}$ and $-\frac{1}{2}$, respectively, and defining the polarization of the initial hyperon by

$$P_Y = f - (1-f) = 2f - 1, \tag{28a}$$

we obtain for the resulting angular distribution

$$\begin{aligned} W &= fW_{1/2} + (1-f)\,W_{-1/2} \\ &= (4\pi)^{-1}(|S|^2 + |P|^2)(1 - P_Y a \cos\theta). \end{aligned} \tag{28b}$$

Equation (28b) contains some of the most important features of parity nonconservation in the spin $\frac{1}{2}$ hyperon decays. Thus, we note immediately that the characteristic feature of the nonconservation of parity is the appearance of an asymmetry ($\cos\theta$ term) in the decay distribution, whose magnitude is determined by the asymmetry parameter a, as well as by the degree of initial polarization P_Y of the decaying hyperon. The nonvanishing of both a and P_Y is required for the observation of this characteristic asymmetry.

There is, however, another feature of such parity-nonconserving decays that is not dependent on the degree of initial polarization P_Y. Consider the longitudinal (along its direction of motion) polarization of the product baryon ($B' = \mathfrak{N}$ or Λ) emitted along z' in Figure 6.2. It may be shown by a straightforward computation that

$$P^l_{B'} = \frac{P_Y \cos\theta - a}{1 - P_Y a \cos\theta}. \tag{29a}$$

Averaging over all directions of the decay,

$$\bar{P}^l_{B'} = \frac{\int P^l_{B'}\, W(\theta)\, d(\cos\theta)}{\int W(\theta)\, d(\cos\theta)} = -a, \tag{29b}$$

we obtain the result that the *average longitudinal polarization* of the product hyperon is determined entirely by the asymmetry parameter of the decay a, irrespective of the degree of initial polarization of the parent hyperon.

Thus, we note that measurement of the decay angular distribution $W(\theta)$ and the longitudinal polarization of the product baryon $P^l_{B'}$ serve to determine both the initial hyperon polarization P_Y and the asymmetry parameter a as well as the total decay probability

$$\lambda = \int W(\theta)\, d\Omega = |S|^2 + |P|^2. \tag{28c}$$

However, at least one additional measurement is required to obtain both S and P, since these are in general complex, i.e.,

$$S = |S|\, e^{i\xi_s}, \tag{30a}$$

$$P = |P|\, e^{i\xi_p}, \tag{30b}$$

$$\frac{P}{S} = \frac{|P|}{|S|}\, e^{i(\xi_p - \xi_s)} = x e^{i\xi}, \tag{30c}$$

$$\lambda = |S|^2 (1 + x^2), \tag{30d}$$

$$a = \frac{2x \cos \xi}{1 + x^2}. \tag{30e}$$

Such a measurement can be, for example, the value of the transverse polarization of the product baryon. Referring to Figure 6.2, we define the x axis as being normal to the z–z' plane ($\varphi = \pi/2$). Then

$$P^x_{B'} = \frac{P_Y b \sin \theta}{1 - P_Y a \cos \theta}, \tag{31a}$$

where

$$b = \frac{2 \text{ Im } S^* P}{|S|^2 + |P|^2} = \frac{2x \sin \xi}{1 + x^2}. \tag{31b}$$

Measurement of both a and b determines both

$$\xi = \tan^{-1} \frac{b}{a} \tag{31c}$$

and x. Another possibility is to measure the component of the polarization of the product baryon along the z axis (axis of the parent hyperon polarization). This is given by

$$P^z_{B'} = \frac{P_Y \left(c + \dfrac{2x^2}{1 + x^2} \cos^2 \theta\right) - a \cos \theta}{1 - P_Y a \cos \theta}, \tag{32a}$$

where

$$c = \frac{|S|^2 - |P|^2}{|S|^2 + |P|^2} = \frac{1 - x^2}{1 + x^2}. \tag{32b}$$

[Note that Equation (32a) reduces to Equation (29a) for the case $\theta = 0$, and to $P^z_{B'}(\theta = \pi/2) = P_Y c$.]

Another parameter which is sometimes used to characterize the decay is

$$\Phi = \tan^{-1} \frac{b}{c}. \tag{33}$$

Among the parameters used to describe the parity-nonconserving decays, the phase angle $\xi = \xi_p - \xi_s$ is, in general, predetermined as a consequence of the Fermi–Watson theorem, *provided that the weak decays are time-reversal invariant.* In this case, ξ_p and ξ_s are, respectively, the phase shifts for the product π–B' scattering in the $P_{1/2}$ and $S_{1/2}$ states at the *cm* energy corresponding to the decay. In the case of reactions (25a) and (25b), these phase shifts are experimentally determined and generally quite small [see Table 6.5(b)]. Within the accuracy of measurement for all the decays studied so far,[8] $b \approx 0$.

The measured decay parameters for the decays (25a)–(25e) are summarized in Table 6.5(a). Column 3 gives the total decay rate for the hyperon in question, while column 4 gives the branching ratio for the decay mode indicated. Columns 5 and 6 show, respectively, the values of the asymmetry parameter a and the sign parameter Φ, as determined from observations on the decay angular distributions and polarizations.

The measured pion-nucleon scattering phase shifts, at the energies and in the states appropriate to the Λ^0_- and Σ^+_0 decays, are given in Table 6.5(b). The only value of ξ so far determined from weak decay observations is that of the Λ^0 decay (see footnote 8) for which the value obtained is in excellent agreement with the value of $\xi_p - \xi_s$ from the scattering phase shifts [Table 6.5(b), row 1], which is the value expected, provided the decay is time-reversal invariant and the final π–$\mathfrak{N}$ state has $j = t = \frac{1}{2}$.

The last three decays included in Table 6.5(a), those of the Ω^-, differ from the others in that the parent hyperon, the Ω^-, has spin $\frac{3}{2}^+$. Hence the possible final states are $P_{3/2}$ ($s_1 = \frac{1}{2}^+$, $s_2 = 0^-$, $l = 1$), which is parity conserving, and $D_{3/2}$ ($s_1 = \frac{1}{2}^+$, $s_2 = 0^-$, $l = 2$), which violates parity conservation. For the states of initial Ω^- polarization characterized by $M = \pm\frac{3}{2}, \pm\frac{1}{2}$, the decay angular distributions are

$$8\pi W_{\pm 3/2} = [|P|^2 + |D|^2]\, 3 \sin^2\theta\, (1 \mp a' \cos\theta), \tag{34a}$$

$$8\pi W_{\pm 1/2} = [|P|^2 + |D|^2]\, (1 + 3\cos^2\theta) \left\{1 \pm a' \cos\theta \frac{(5 - 9\cos^2\theta)}{(1 + 3\cos^2\theta)}\right\}, \tag{34b}$$

with

$$a' = \frac{2 \operatorname{Re} P^*D}{|P|^2 + |D|^2}, \tag{34c}$$

from which the decay angular correlations follow for any state of given initial polarization.

We may also compute the polarization of the product hyperon with respect to any predetermined axis. Thus, for example, with respect to the initial (fixed) axis of Ω^- polarization,

$$P^z_{B'}\left(M = \pm\frac{3}{2}\right) = \pm \frac{|P|^2 + |D|^2 (\cos^2\theta - \sin^2\theta) \mp 2 \operatorname{Re} P^*D \cos\theta}{|P|^2 + |D|^2 \mp 2 \operatorname{Re} P^*D \cos\theta}, \tag{35a}$$

[8] Accurate measurements of the $\Lambda^0 \rightarrow P + \pi^-$ decay parameters do detect a value of b different from zero, i.e., $b = -0.10 \pm 0.07$, leading to a finite value of $\xi = -9.0° \pm 5.5°$. [O. E. Overseth and R. F. Roth, *Phys. Rev. Letters, 19:* 391 (1967).]

Table 6.5 (a) Nonleptonic Weak Decay Properties of the Hyperons [a]

Decay	Symbol	Decay rate (10^{10} sec^{-1})	Branching ratio	a	Φ	c (derived)
$\Lambda \to P\pi^-$	Λ^0_-	0.400 ± 0.007	0.664 ± 0.017	0.663 ± 0.023	$(-7 \pm 7)°$	0.74
$\to N\pi^0$	Λ^0_0		0.336 ± 0.011	0.73 ± 0.18	—	—
$\Sigma^+ \to N\pi^+$	Σ^+_+	1.234 ± 0.020	0.472 ± 0.015	0.01 ± 0.04	$(180 \pm 30)°$	-1.0
$\to P\pi^0$	Σ^+_0		0.528 ± 0.015	-0.96 ± 0.07	—	—
$\Sigma^- \to N\pi^-$	Σ^-_-	0.604 ± 0.011	1.0	-0.02 ± 0.04	—	—
				(-0.10 ± 0.04)	$(-22 \pm 30)°$	(0.90)[b]
$\Xi^0 \to \Lambda\pi^0$	Ξ^0_0	0.33 ± 0.06	1.0	-0.33 ± 0.10	—	—
$\Xi^- \to \Lambda\pi^-$	Ξ^-_-	0.572 ± 0.016	1.0	-0.391 ± 0.032	$(1.2 \pm 7.5)°$	0.92
$\Omega^- \to \Xi^0\pi^-$	Ω^-_-	0.67 ± 0.22	~ 0.5	—	—	—
$\to \Xi^-\pi^0$	Ω^-_0			—	—	—
$\to \Lambda K^-$	$\Omega^-_{K^-}$		~ 0.5	—	—	—

[a] J. P. Berge, *Proceedings of the XIII International Conference on High-Energy Physics,* University of California Press, Berkeley (1966), p. 46.
[b] Hertzbach, *et al., Phys. Rev. Letters, 19:* 979 (1967).

Table 6.5 (b) π–$\mathfrak{N}$ Scattering Phase Shifts Appropriate to Λ and Σ Decays

Decay	$p_{\pi,cm}$ (MeV/c)	j	t	ξ_s (rad)	ξ_p (rad)
Λ^0_-	100	$\frac{1}{2}$	$\frac{1}{2}$	0.107 (6.10°)	−0.020 (−1.14°)
	100	$\frac{1}{2}$	$\frac{3}{2}$	−0.0678 (−3.88°)	−0.0128 (−0.74°)
Σ^+_0	189	$\frac{1}{2}$	$\frac{1}{2}$	0.164 (9.40°)	−0.0317 (−1.82°)
	189	$\frac{1}{2}$	$\frac{3}{2}$	−0.176 (−10.06°)	−0.0608 (−3.49°)

$$P^z_{B'}\left(M = \pm\frac{1}{2}\right) = \pm\frac{|P|^2(5\cos^2\theta - 1) + |D|^2(18\cos^4\theta - 15\cos^2\theta + 1) \mp \text{Re}\, P^*D\cos\theta(3\cos^2\theta + 1)}{(|P|^2 + |D|^2)(3\cos^2\theta + 1) \mp 2\,\text{Re}\, P^*D\cos\theta(9\cos^2\theta - 5)}. \tag{35b}$$

In the particular case of no initial polarization (equal initial population of all four M states), and taking $\theta = 0$, we obtain for the average longitudinal polarization of the product hyperon

$$\overline{P}^l_{B'} = -a', \tag{36}$$

the same result as in the case of $\frac{1}{2}^+$ decay [Equation (29b)].

In comparing different processes, it is usually convenient to extract from the observed decay amplitudes the trivial kinematical factors, e.g., phase space.

In the case of the decays of spin $\frac{1}{2}$ hyperons, this is generally done by assuming for the form for the nonleptonic decay Hamiltonian

$$H_{\text{int}} = \bar{u}_{B'}(A + B\gamma_5)u_Y, \tag{37}$$

where the u's are Dirac spinors and the A and B terms lead, respectively, to S and P; thus

$$\lambda_{Y \to B'} = \frac{q}{8\pi M^2 \mu} \{[(M+m)^2 - \mu^2]|A|^2 + [(M-m)^2 - \mu^2]|B|^2\} = |S|^2 + |P|^2, \tag{37a}$$

where M, m, μ are the masses of the parent hyperon Y, product baryon B', and the pion, while q is the product pion momentum.[9] The values of A and B, derived from the most accurate available measurements of the hyperon decay parameters [Table 6.5(a) and (b)] are given in Table 6.6. These will be compared with available theories in Chapter 18.

Table 6.6 Values of the S- and P-Wave Decay Amplitudes for Hyperon Nonleptonic Decays [a]

Decay	$A \times 10^5$ sec$^{-1/2}$	$B \times 10^5$ sec$^{-1/2}$
Λ^0_-	1.551 ± 0.024	11.045 ± 0.48
Σ^-_-	1.861 ± 0.017	-0.15 ± 0.39
Σ^+_+	0.008 ± 0.034	19.08 ± 0.35
Σ^+_0 $(c > 0)$ [b]	1.56 ± 0.14	-11.7 ± 1.9
$(c < 0)$	1.17 ± 0.19	-15.6 ± 1.4
Ξ^-_-	2.022 ± 0.029	-6.63 ± 0.57

[a] J. P. Berge, *Proceedings of the XIII International Conference on High-Energy Physics*, University of California Press, Berkeley (1966), p. 46.
[b] For the other cases the sign of c is known through $\Phi = \tan^{-1} b/c$ (see Table 6.5).

Leptonic Decays • We have already discussed, in Section 2.2, the main properties of the leptonic decay processes (β decay) and some of the consequences of parity nonconservation on these decays. In the following, we give a simple kinematical description of the β-decay process and indicate how most of its important features follow from the application of angular momentum conservation within this framework: [10]

Leptons are described by the Dirac equation

$$(c\boldsymbol{\alpha} \cdot \mathbf{p} + \beta mc^2)\,\psi = E\psi, \tag{38}$$

[9] Equation (37) holds, of course, only for spin $\frac{1}{2}$ hyperon decays. For the Ω^- decay one might attempt to use the same kinematical factors (37a) or, alternatively, approximate them by $S \simeq (q'/M)$, $P \simeq (q'/M)\, v_1(qR)$, $D \simeq (q'/M)\, v_2(qR)$, where the $v_l(qR)$ are the angular momentum barrier penetration factors, with $R \approx 1/2\mu$ and $q' = qE_1E_2 = qE_\pi E_{B'}$

[10] B. T. Feld, *Phys. Rev.*, *107:* 797 (1957). For a comprehensive review of the current situation with regard to the invariance properties of the β-decay interactions, see T. D. Lee and C. S. Wu, *Ann. Rev. Nucl. Sci.*, *15:* 387 (1965).

where α_i and β are 4×4 matrices,

$$\alpha_i = \begin{pmatrix} 0 & \sigma_i \\ \sigma_i & 0 \end{pmatrix}, \qquad \beta = \begin{pmatrix} 1 & 0 \\ 0 & -1 \end{pmatrix},$$

with the σ_i being the three Pauli spin matrices and the 1 the 2×2 unit matrix. The solution of Equation (38) may be written

$$\psi = \begin{pmatrix} u \\ v \end{pmatrix}, \tag{38a}$$

where u and v are two-component spinors connected by the relation

$$v = \frac{\boldsymbol{\sigma} \cdot \mathbf{p}}{E + m} u. \tag{38b}$$

Note that u and v have opposite parity. Thus, if $u_{1/2}$ represents an $S_{1/2}$ state with $m = \frac{1}{2}$,

$$u_{1/2} = \begin{pmatrix} 1 \\ 0 \end{pmatrix} e^{ipr}, \tag{39a}$$

then

$$\begin{aligned} v_{1/2} &= \left(\frac{p}{E + m}\right) \sqrt{\frac{4\pi}{3}} \begin{pmatrix} Y_1^0 \\ -\sqrt{2}\, Y_1^1 \end{pmatrix} e^{ipr} \\ &= \left(\frac{p}{E + m}\right) \begin{pmatrix} \cos\theta \\ \sin\theta\, e^{i\varphi} \end{pmatrix} e^{ipr}, \end{aligned} \tag{39b}$$

which represents a $P_{1/2}$ state still, of course, with $m = \frac{1}{2}$.

We may generalize these considerations as follows: Let

$$\varphi^S_{\pm 1/2} = a \begin{Bmatrix} \alpha \\ \beta \end{Bmatrix} \tag{40a}$$

represent a lepton emitted in the $S_{1/2}$ state with $m = \pm\frac{1}{2}$, and

$$\varphi^P_{\pm 1/2} = b \begin{Bmatrix} -\alpha \cos\theta - \beta \sin\theta\, e^{i\varphi} \\ \beta \cos\theta - \alpha \sin\theta\, e^{-i\varphi} \end{Bmatrix} \tag{40b}$$

represent emission of the lepton in the $P_{1/2}$ state. From Equations (39a) and (39b), we have

$$\left|\frac{b}{a}\right| = \frac{p}{E + m}, \tag{40c}$$

$$\frac{2 \operatorname{Re} ab^*}{|a|^2 + |b|^2} = \zeta = \pm\frac{v}{c}, \tag{40d}$$

where ζ is known as the "chirality" of the lepton.[11]

---

[11] For leptons, which are weakly interacting, the Fermi–Watson theorem implies that a and b are both real.

1. *Parity nonconservation* implies

$$\varphi_{\pm 1/2} = \varphi^S_{\pm 1/2} + \varphi^P_{\pm 1/2}$$
$$= \left[(a \mp b \cos\theta) \begin{Bmatrix}\alpha\\ \beta\end{Bmatrix} - b \sin\theta\, e^{\pm i\varphi} \begin{Bmatrix}\beta\\ \alpha\end{Bmatrix}\right]. \tag{40e}$$

Now, let the z axis lie along the direction of emission of the lepton ($\theta = 0$). Then

$$\varphi^l_{\pm 1/2} = (a \mp b) \begin{Bmatrix}\alpha\\ \beta\end{Bmatrix}. \tag{40f}$$

2. The *longitudinal polarization* of the emitted lepton, for the case of zero initial polarization, is

$$P^l = \frac{|\varphi^l_{1/2}|^2 - |\varphi^l_{-1/2}|^2}{|\varphi^l_{1/2}|^2 + |\varphi^l_{-1/2}|^2} = -\zeta. \tag{41}$$

That is, the longitudinal polarization (helicity) is the negative of the chirality.

3. When Equation (40d) holds,

$$P^l = \mp \frac{v}{c}. \tag{41a}$$

This is known as *maximum parity violation*. In particular, for particles of zero rest mass (neutrinos), $v/c = 1$, and the helicity is maximum. In this case, $b = \pm a$. We define the neutrino as the lepton with $b = a = \sqrt{\tfrac{1}{2}}$ (positive chirality), so that

$$\psi^l_\nu = \beta, \qquad P^l_\nu = -1; \tag{42a}$$

that is, the neutrino is always "left-handed." For the antineutrino, on the other hand, $b = -a = \sqrt{\tfrac{1}{2}}$,

$$\psi^l_{\bar\nu} = \alpha, \qquad P^l_{\bar\nu} = 1, \tag{42b}$$

and the $\bar\nu$ always has its spin pointing in the direction of its motion. For a particle of finite rest mass, however, both positive and negative helicities are possible.

4. The *universal β-decay interaction* implies $\zeta = +v/c$ for all leptons (e^-, μ^-, ν_e, ν_μ) and $\zeta = -v/c$ for all antileptons (e^+, μ^+, $\bar\nu_e$, $\bar\nu_\mu$).

5. Finally, the *conservation of leptons* requires that the number of leptons minus the number of antileptons remains constant in all weak interactions.

EXAMPLE

The decays

$$K^\pm \text{ or } \pi^\pm \rightarrow \mu^\pm + \begin{Bmatrix}\nu_\mu\\ \bar\nu_\mu\end{Bmatrix}$$
$$\hookrightarrow e^\pm + \begin{Bmatrix}\nu_e\\ \bar\nu_e\end{Bmatrix} + \begin{Bmatrix}\bar\nu_\mu\\ \nu_\mu\end{Bmatrix} \tag{43}$$

demonstrate in a most striking fashion the principles outlined above. The following experimental observations are relevant:

(a) The electron energy spectrum for the μ-meson decays has a finite intercept at the maximum electron energy (see Figure 6.3).

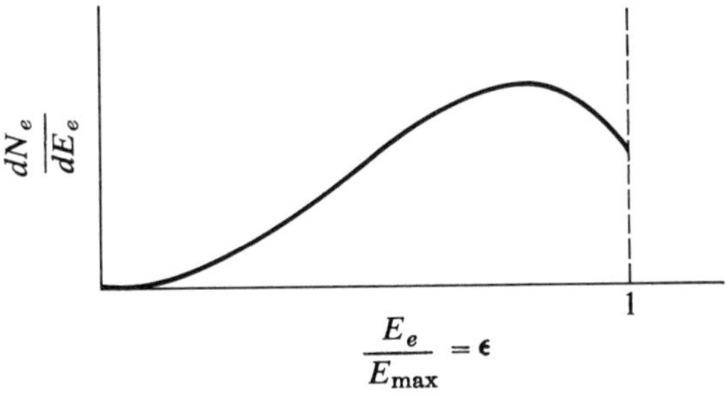

Figure 6.3 Electron spectrum in μ-meson decay.

(b) Let θ be the direction of the electron emission (in the *cm* of the μ) with respect to the direction of motion of the μ-meson (see Figure 6.4).

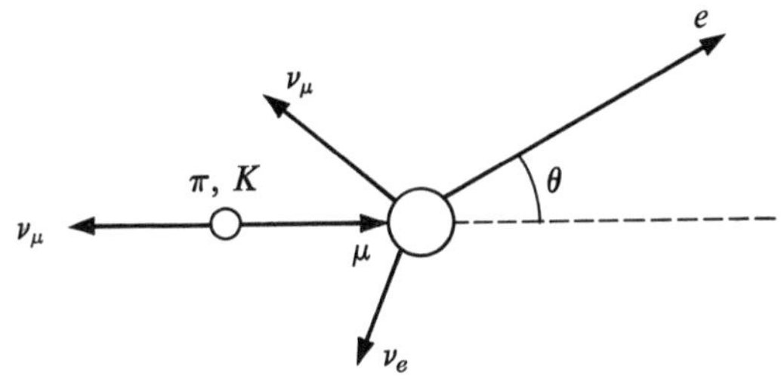

Figure 6.4 Angular correlations in μ-meson decay.

The observed distribution in ϵ and θ is

$$4\pi W(\epsilon, \theta)\, d\epsilon = 2\epsilon^2\, d\epsilon \left[(3 - 2\epsilon) + (1 - 2\epsilon)\frac{v_e}{c}\cos\theta\right]. \tag{43a}$$

In particular,

$$4\pi W(\epsilon \to 1, \theta) = 1 - \frac{v}{c}\cos\theta, \tag{43b}$$

$$4\pi W(\epsilon \to 0, \theta) = 1 + \frac{1}{3}\frac{v}{c}\cos\theta, \tag{43c}$$

$$P^l_{e^\pm} = \pm\frac{v}{c}, \qquad \text{for } \epsilon \to 1,\ \theta \cong \pi. \tag{43d}$$

In the π decay,

$$\frac{\lambda(\pi \to e\nu)}{\lambda(\pi \to \mu\nu)} = (1.24 \pm 0.03) \times 10^{-4}, \tag{43e}$$

while

$$\frac{\lambda(K \to e\nu)}{\lambda(K \to \mu\nu)} = (1.95 \pm 0.65) \times 10^{-5}. \tag{43f}$$

(c) We may draw the following conclusions from these facts:

(i) The finite intercept of the electron spectrum at $\epsilon = 1$ (Figure 6.3) demonstrates that the two neutrinos from the μ decay cannot be identical, since the maximum electron energy corresponds to the two neutrinos being emitted in the same direction (opposite to the electron) and with the same momentum (Figure 6.4). Since neutrinos obey the Pauli principle, the wave function would necessarily vanish at this extreme if the neutrinos were identical; it clearly does not. However, all this proves is that the two neutrinos are different.

(ii) The proof that the two neutrinos in question have opposite helicity is derived from the observed angular distribution of the electrons. Since the $\pi^\pm$ and $K^\pm$ have spin 0, the decay muon and ν must have the same helicities (they are emitted back to back). Lepton conservation and universality then require

$$P^l_{\mu^\pm} = \mp 1, \qquad \psi_{\mu^\pm} = \begin{Bmatrix} \beta \\ \alpha \end{Bmatrix}. \tag{44a}$$

Since, for the $\mu^\pm$ decay with $\epsilon \to 1$, as noted above, the total neutrino spin $S(\nu) + S(\bar{\nu}) = 0$, the electron must be emitted in the same spin state as the parent muon, i.e., from Equation (40e),

$$\psi_{e^\pm} = \varphi_{\mp 1/2} = \left[(a_\pm \pm b_\pm \cos\theta) \begin{Bmatrix} \beta \\ \alpha \end{Bmatrix} - b_\pm \sin\theta\, e^{\mp i\varphi} \begin{Bmatrix} \alpha \\ \beta \end{Bmatrix} \right], \tag{44b}$$

from which it follows that

$$4\pi W_{e^\pm}(\theta) = 1 \pm \zeta_\pm \cos\theta. \tag{44c}$$

The universality principle gives

$$\zeta_\pm = \mp \frac{v}{c}, \tag{44d}$$

so that, as required by the observation, Equation (43b),

$$4\pi W_e(\theta) = 1 - \frac{v}{c} \cos\theta. \tag{44e}$$

We note that in this case the electron is emitted at $\theta \cong \pi$ with helicity

$$P^l_{e^\pm} = \pm \frac{v}{c}, \tag{44f}$$

as required by the universality principle, (4) above, and as is also observed in Equation (43d).

At the low-energy extreme ($\epsilon \to 0$), on the other hand, the ν and $\bar{\nu}$ in the μ decay are emitted back to back, and hence $S(\nu) + S(\bar{\nu}) = 1$. Let $\varphi_{\nu\bar{\nu}}^{1,0,-1}$ represent the spin wave functions of the $(\nu + \bar{\nu})$ system in the states $m = 1, 0, -1$. Angular momentum conservation then requires for the $\mu^{\pm}$ decays,

$$\begin{aligned} \psi_{\mu^+} &= \varphi_{-1/2}^{1/2} = \sqrt{\tfrac{1}{3}}\, \phi_{\nu\bar{\nu}}^{0} \psi_{e^+}^{-1/2} - \sqrt{\tfrac{2}{3}}\, \phi_{\nu\bar{\nu}}^{-1} \psi_{e^+}^{1/2}, \\ \psi_{\mu^-} &= \varphi_{1/2}^{1/2} = -\sqrt{\tfrac{1}{3}}\, \phi_{\nu\bar{\nu}}^{0} \psi_{e^-}^{1/2} + \sqrt{\tfrac{2}{3}}\, \phi_{\nu\bar{\nu}}^{1} \phi_{e^-}^{-1/2}, \end{aligned} \tag{45a}$$

with the $\phi_{e^{\pm}}^{\pm 1/2}$ given by Equation (40e).

Integrating over all $\nu\nu'$ directions, we obtain

$$4\pi W_{e^{\pm}}(\theta) = 1 \mp \tfrac{1}{3}\zeta_{e^{\pm}} \cos\theta, \tag{45b}$$

which, when we again apply the universality principle [Equation (44d)], gives

$$4\pi W_{e^{\pm}}(\theta) = 1 + \frac{1}{3}\frac{v}{c} \cos\theta, \tag{45c}$$

as is observed [Equation (43c)].

(iii) Finally, we consider the decay rates of K or $\pi \to e\nu$ relative to K or $\pi \to \mu\nu$. From the conservation of leptons, $K^{\pm}$ or $\pi^{\pm} \to l^{\pm} + \begin{Bmatrix} \nu \\ \bar{\nu} \end{Bmatrix}$ while the conservation of angular momentum and the zero spin of the K and π require the helicity of the $l^{\pm}$ to be the same as that of the $\begin{Bmatrix} \nu \\ \bar{\nu} \end{Bmatrix}$. We note that, in each case, this requirement of angular momentum conservation is opposite to the "natural" helicity of the charged lepton. Choosing the z axis along the direction of emission of the charged lepton, we see that Equation (40f) gives for the wave function of the lepton resulting from the K or π decay:

$$\psi_{l^{\pm}} = (a_{\pm} \mp b_{\pm}) \begin{Bmatrix} \alpha \\ \beta \end{Bmatrix}. \tag{46a}$$

The relative decay rates are

$$\begin{aligned} \frac{\lambda_{e^{\pm}}}{\lambda_{\mu^{\pm}}} &= \frac{|a_{\pm}^{e} \mp b_{\pm}^{e}|^2\, (dN/dE)_{e\nu}}{|a_{\pm}^{\mu} \mp b_{\pm}^{\mu}|^2\, (dN/dE)_{\mu\nu}} \\ &= \frac{(1 \pm \zeta_{e^{\pm}})\, (dN/dE)_{e\nu}}{(1 \pm \zeta_{\mu^{\pm}})\, (dN/dE)_{\mu\nu}} \\ &= \frac{[1 - (v_e/c)]\, (dN/dE)_{e\nu}}{[1 - (v_\mu/c)]\, (dN/dE)_{\mu\nu}} \\ &= \frac{(M^2 - m_e^2)^2\, m_e^2}{(M^2 - m_\mu^2)^2\, m_\mu^2}, \end{aligned} \tag{46b}$$

where M is the mass of the parent (K or π) particle. Substituting into Equation (46b) (and applying a radiative correction factor of 0.965 for the π and 0.815 for the K decay), we obtain the predicted values

$$\frac{\lambda_\pi \to e\nu}{\lambda_\pi \to \mu\nu} = 1.23 \times 10^{-4}, \tag{46c}$$

$$\frac{\lambda_K \to e\nu}{\lambda_K \to \mu\nu} = 2.10 \times 10^{-5}, \tag{46d}$$

in excellent accord with Equations (43e) and (43f).

The same principles may be applied to nuclear β decay, e.g.,

$$N \to P + e^- + \bar{\nu}_e. \tag{47}$$

In this case the two leptons can combine into the state $S(e^- + \bar{\nu}_e) = 0$ (Fermi decay) or $S(e^- + \bar{\nu}_e) = 1$ (Gamow–Teller), leading, respectively, to the selection rules $\Delta J = 0$ and $\Delta J = 0, \pm 1$. However, since there are three particles of spin $\frac{1}{2}$ in the final state, the spin and angular correlations are considerably more complicated. The interested reader is referred to the literature.[12]

PROBLEMS

1. A system of spin $\frac{1}{2}$ has, with respect to an arbitrary coordinate system, the eigenstates α and β corresponding, respectively, to the eigenvalues $s_z = m = +\frac{1}{2}$ and $-\frac{1}{2}$. Let z' be an arbitrary direction, characterized by the polar angle Θ and azimuthal angle Φ.

   (a) Expressing the transformation between the eigenvectors of s_z and those of $s_{z'}$ by the relations

   $$\alpha = \xi\alpha' + \eta\beta',$$
   $$\beta = -\eta^*\alpha' + \xi^*\beta',$$

   show that

   $$\xi = -\sqrt{\tfrac{1}{2}}\,(1 + \cos\Theta)^{1/2} e^{i\Phi},$$
   $$\eta = \sqrt{\tfrac{1}{2}}\,(1 - \cos\Theta)^{1/2}.$$

   (b) Consider the parity-nonconserving decay $Y(s = \frac{1}{2}) \to B(s = \frac{1}{2}) + \pi$, characterized by the asymmetry parameter

   $$a = \frac{2\,\mathrm{Re}\,S^*P}{|S|^2 + |P|^2}.$$

   Starting with hyperons polarized along the z axis, with

   $$P_Y^z = 2f - 1 \le 1,$$

   derive an expression for the polarization, $P_B^{z'}$, of the product baryon with respect to the z' axis.

[12] B. T. Feld, *Phys. Rev., 107:* 797 (1957); T. D. Lee and C. S. Wu, *Ann. Rev. Nucl. Sci., 15:* 38 (1965).

(c) Show that this expression reduces to Equations (29a) and (31a) for the proper choices of Θ and Φ.

2. Consider the decay $N \rightarrow P + e^- + \bar{\nu}_e$ with maximum parity nonconservation (i.e., $V - A$ theory) for the electron-neutrino current. Assume, however, that the relative strength of the nucleonic Fermi (V) and Gamow–Teller (A) decay matrix elements is $-a_n$ ($a_n \approx 1.2$).

   (a) Starting with polarized neutrons, derive an expression for the angular distribution of the decay electrons with respect to the neutron polarization axis. Show that the decay asymmetry vanishes for $a_n = 1$.
   (b) Derive an expression for the electron-neutrino angular correlation function, $W(\theta_{e\bar{\nu}})$.
   (c) Derive expressions for the longitudinal and transverse polarizations of the decay proton, and for the proton polarization with respect to the neutron polarization axis.
   (d) What would be the experimentally observable consequences of a violation of time-reversal invariance?

3. A Majorana particle is a spin $\frac{1}{2}$ particle satisfying the Dirac equation, with the additional condition that under the operation of charge conjugation

$$\mathcal{C}\Psi = \Psi.$$

Show that, under the parity operation,

$$\mathcal{P}\Psi(x)\mathcal{P}^{-1} = \pm i\gamma_4 \Psi(-x).$$

4. Consider the decay $\pi^+ \rightarrow \mu^+ + \nu_\mu$. Let the z axis be along the direction of the emitted μ^+. Show that, if the μ^+ is longitudinally polarized, i.e., $\langle \sigma_z \Psi(\mu^+) \rangle \neq 0$, then the assumption of TCP invariance for the π–μ decay leads to the conclusion that C is violated, without necessity of consideration of the properties of the $\pi^- \rightarrow \mu^- + \bar{\nu}_\mu$ decay.

6.2 Reactions

The most useful information concerning the interactions of elementary particles is derived from the two-body reactions [13]

$$a + A \rightarrow B + C. \tag{48}$$

6.2.1 General

Let

$$\mathbf{S} = \mathbf{s}_a + \mathbf{s}_A \tag{48a}$$

[13] Frequently, one or more of the products is unstable, so that > 2 particles are observed in the final state. However the properties of reaction (48) may generally be reconstructed by use of the kinematical relations discussed in Chapter 3.

be the channel spin of the projectile (a) plus target (A) in the initial state, and

$$\mathbf{s} = \mathbf{s}_B + \mathbf{s}_C \tag{48b}$$

be the channel spin in the final state. The reaction may be viewed as though it took place in two stages: first, combination of S with the incident orbital angular momenta L into one of the possible intermediate states, J, and subsequently, decay of the intermediate state into a final state of spin s and orbital angular momentum l, with

$$\mathbf{S} + \mathbf{L} = \mathbf{J} = \mathbf{s} + \mathbf{l}, \tag{48c}$$

where

$$S + L \geq J \geq |S - L|, \tag{48d}$$

$$s + l \geq J \geq |s - l|, \tag{48e}$$

and with a further restriction due to parity conservation

$$\pi_a \pi_A (-1)^L = \pi_B \pi_C (-1)^l. \tag{48f}$$

For a given initial channel spin state (S, M), and choosing our z axis in the direction of the projectile momentum,[14] $\mathbf{k}_a$, we see that the various possible combinations that contribute to the cross section for (48) may be constructed with the aid of diagrams like Figure 6.5. In essence, we require the consecutive appli-

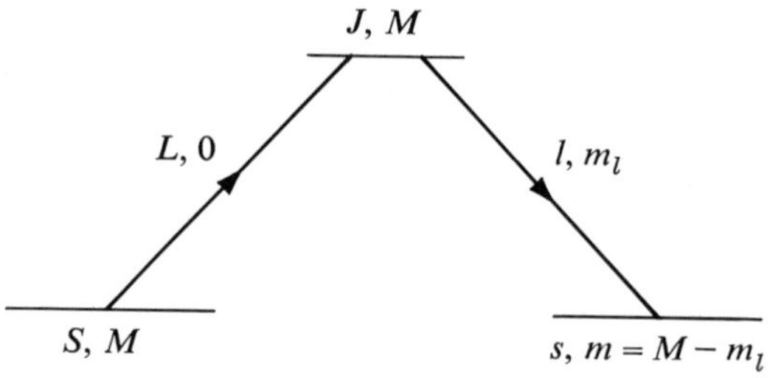

Figure 6.5 Diagram illustrating the typical absorption and decay sequence in the general two-body reaction.

cation of Equation (4) (Section 6.1) to the inverse decay ($\mathbf{S} + \mathbf{L} \rightarrow \mathbf{J}$) followed by the actual decay ($\mathbf{J} \rightarrow \mathbf{s} + \mathbf{l}$), with the simplification that only the state $m_L = 0$ contributes to the first step. Finally, averaging over initial states and summing over final, with the insertion of the appropriate weight factor for the fraction of the incident plane wave that contributes to the different incident L-values, yields the conventional form [15] of the differential cross section in the cm for an unpolarized target

[14] This choice assures the value $m_L = 0$.

[15] Blatt and Weisskopf, *Theoretical Nuclear Physics*, John Wiley and Sons, New York (1952).

$$\frac{d\sigma}{d\Omega}=\frac{(2k_a)^{-2}}{(2s_a+1)(2s_A+1)}\sum_{S,M}\sum_{s,m}|A^{S,M}_{s,m}|^2, \tag{49}$$

where

$$A^{S,M}_{s,m}=\sum_{L,J,l}[4\pi(2L+1)]^{1/2}a^{L,J,l}_{S,s}\,C^{J,M}_{S,M;\,L,0}\,C^{J,M}_{s,m;\,l,M-m}\,Y^{m_l}_l(\theta,\varphi). \tag{49a}$$

Some general properties of the reaction amplitudes $a^{L,J,l}_{S,s}$ have been discussed in Chapter 5.

EXAMPLE

Meson (0^-) + nucleon ($\frac{1}{2}^+$) $\to$ meson (0^-) + baryon ($\frac{1}{2}^+$).

For example,

$$\begin{aligned}\pi+\mathfrak{N}&\to\pi+\mathfrak{N}\\&\to K+\Lambda,\\K^-+P&\to\pi^0+\Sigma^0.\end{aligned} \tag{50}$$

In this case $S=s=\frac{1}{2}$, while parity conservation permits $L=l$ only. There are then two types of diagram, as seen in Figure 6.6, giving

$$A^{1/2,\pm1/2}_{1/2,\pm1/2}=2k_af_{\pm1/2}=\sum_l\left(\frac{4\pi}{2l+1}\right)^{1/2}[(l+1)\,a^+_l+la^-_l]\,Y^0_l(\theta,\varphi)=2k_af, \tag{50a}$$

$$A^{1/2,\pm1/2}_{1/2,\mp1/2}=2k_ag_{\pm1/2}=\sum_l\left[\frac{4\pi l(l+1)}{2l+1}\right]^{1/2}[a^+_l-a^-_l]\,Y^{\pm1}_l(\theta,\varphi)=\pm2k_age^{\pm i\varphi}, \tag{50b}$$

where

$$a^{\pm}_l=a^{l,J=l\pm1/2,l}_{1/2,1/2}. \tag{50c}$$

Then, from Equation (49),

$$\frac{d\sigma}{d\Omega}=|f|^2+|g|^2. \tag{49'}$$

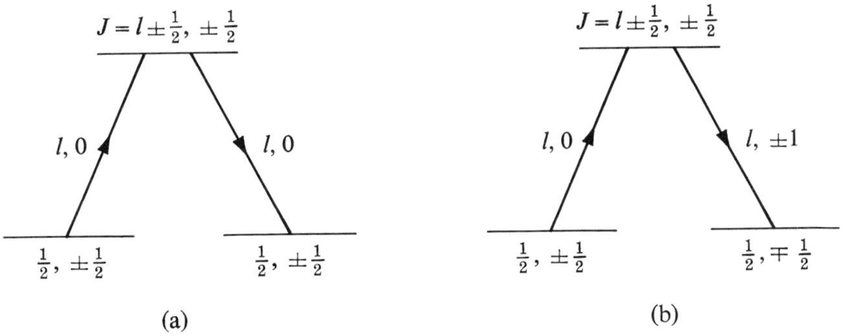

Figure 6.6 Typical reaction diagrams for $0+\frac{1}{2}\to\frac{1}{2}'+0'$. (a) Spin-nonflip. (b) Spin-flip.

Note that for $a^+ = a^-$ (i.e., no spin-orbit interaction) $g = 0$, and Equation (50a) reduces to the case of the scattering of spinless particles.

The nonvanishing of g gives rise to the possibility of transverse polarization of the product baryon, with

$$P_x = \frac{2 \operatorname{Im} fg^*}{|f| + |g|^2} \sin \varphi. \tag{49''}$$

In the absence of a polarized target, $d\sigma/d\Omega$ and P_x are the only observable properties of the scattering; these two measurements alone are insufficient to determine completely the complex amplitudes f and g. However, if a target of polarized protons is available, other combinations of f and g may be obtained. In this case, for scattering in the plane normal to the initial polarization, one may compare the cross section for scattering to the left and the right of the direction of the incident momentum. The average value yields $|f|^2 + |g|^2$, while the difference yields $\operatorname{Im} fg^*$. From scattering in the plane defined by the target polarization and the projectile momentum, on the other hand, one may obtain the combinations $|f|^2 - |g|^2$ and $\operatorname{Re} fg^*$.

Consider the set of unit vectors defined in Figure 6.7 (projectile along the z axis; scattering in the $y - z$ plane). The scattering amplitude may be written

$$(2k_a)^{-1}A = f + ig\, \boldsymbol{\sigma} \cdot \mathbf{n}. \tag{49a'}$$

For a given initial polarization vector $\mathbf{P}_i$, the polarization vector of the product baryon $\mathbf{P}_f$ is given by the expression

$$\begin{aligned} \frac{d\sigma}{d\Omega}\mathbf{P}_f = \overline{\frac{d\sigma}{d\Omega}} \{&(P + \mathbf{P}_i \cdot \mathbf{n})\,\mathbf{n} \\ &+ (A\mathbf{P}_i \cdot \mathbf{k}_i + R\mathbf{P}_i \cdot \mathbf{s}_i)\,\mathbf{s}_f \\ &+ (A'\mathbf{P}_i \cdot \mathbf{k}_i + R'\mathbf{P}_i \cdot \mathbf{s}_i)\,\mathbf{k}_f\}, \end{aligned} \tag{51}$$

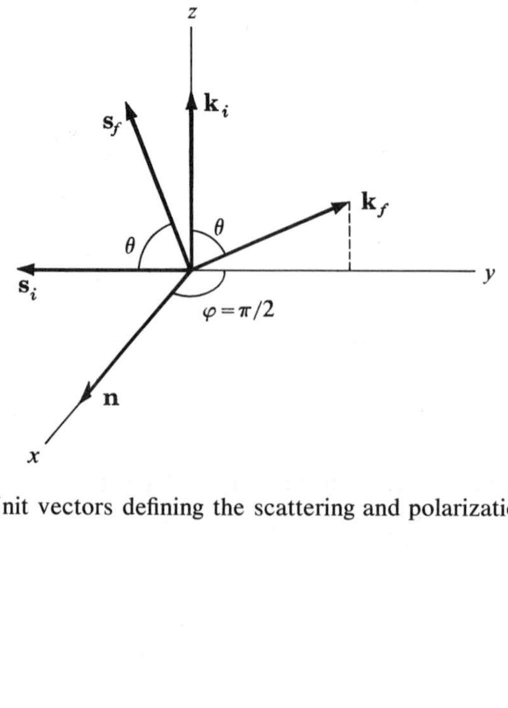

Figure 6.7 Unit vectors defining the scattering and polarization parameters.

where $\overline{d\sigma/d\Omega}$ is given by Equation (49′), $P = P_x/\sin\varphi$ of Equation (49″), while

$$\frac{2|f|^2}{|f|^2+|g|^2} = 1 - A\sin\theta + R\cos\theta, \tag{51a}$$

$$\frac{2|g|^2}{|f|^2+|g|^2} = 1 + A'\sin\theta - R'\cos\theta, \tag{51b}$$

$$\frac{2\,\mathrm{Re}\,fg^*}{|f|^2+|g|^2} = A\sin\theta + R\cos\theta. \tag{51c}$$

PROBLEMS

1. Consider the inelastic scattering process $a + A \to b + B$, with $s_a = 0^-$, $s_A = \frac{1}{2}^+$, $s_b = 0^+$, $s_B = \frac{1}{2}^+$.
   (a) Draw the typical reaction diagrams describing the permitted sequences of absorptions and decays corresponding to this reaction.
   (b) Derive expressions for the amplitudes $A^{S,M}_{s,m}$ [see Equation (49a)].
   (c) Show how, by appropriate definition of the amplitudes f and g, these may be cast into forms that are formally identical with Equations (50a) and (50b).

   From (c), one concludes that, for a given set of spins, a measurement of the angular distribution of the reaction cannot distinguish between the possible values of the relative parities of the products.

   (d) Can you devise a measurement that is capable of resolving this ambiguity?

   Note: you may assume the availability of polarized targets and analyzers for measuring the polarization of B.
2. Show that, for the scattering process $0^- + \frac{1}{2}^+ \to 0^- + \frac{1}{2}^+$, Equation (49a′) represents the most general form of the scattering matrix that satisfies both rotation and reflection invariance.
3. Consider the elastic scattering

$$\pi + \mathfrak{N} \to \pi + \mathfrak{N}$$

   under the assumption that parity is *not* conserved.

   (a) Show that, in general, the effects of parity nonconservation are not observable in an experiment in which only the angular distribution of scattering by an unpolarized nucleon target is measured.
   (b) Referring to Problem 1 of Section 6.1.3, derive the polarization of the scattered nucleon
      (i) with respect to an arbitrary z' axis, making the angles Θ and Φ with respect to the original coordinate system;
      (ii) along a direction normal (transverse) to the plane of the scattering. *Hint:* let $z' = x$, i.e., $\Theta = \pi/2$, $\Phi = 0$;
      (iii) along an arbitrary direction in the plane of the scattering (longitudinal polarization). *Hint:* in this case, it is convenient to take $\Phi = \varphi = 0$.
   (c) How can you tell if parity is or is not conserved?

Note: if f_1, g_1 and f_2, g_2 are the spin-flip and spin-nonflip amplitudes corresponding, respectively, to the parity-conserving and parity-violating processes, then you should find

(a) $\frac{d\sigma}{d\Omega}=\frac{d\sigma_1}{d\Omega}+\frac{d\sigma_2}{d\Omega}$;

(b) $\frac{d\sigma}{d\Omega}P_x=2\ \mathrm{Im}\ (f_1g_1^*+f_2g_2^*)\sin\varphi-2\ \mathrm{Re}\ (f_1g_2^*+f_2g_1^*)\cos\varphi,$

$$\frac{d\sigma}{d\Omega}P_l=-2\ \mathrm{Re}\ [(f_1f_2^*-g_1g_2^*)\cos\Theta+(f_1g_2^*+f_2g_1^*)\sin\Theta].$$

4. Derive the amplitudes characterizing the reaction

$$\pi(0^-)+\mathrm{He}(0^+)\rightarrow\rho(1^-)+\mathrm{He}(0^+)$$

and use these to derive expressions for the angular distribution and polarization of the product ρ-meson.

5. At a certain pion energy, the π–P elastic-scattering cross section (in the *cm*) is observed to have the form

$$k^2\frac{d\sigma}{d\Omega}\cong 1.0+0.1\cos\theta+3.2\cos^2\theta.$$

Neglect all amplitudes corresponding to $l>2$, and write the scattering amplitudes in the form

$$a_l^\pm=2e^{i\alpha_l^\pm}\sin\alpha_l^\pm.$$

(a) Show that there is a solution corresponding to $\alpha_1^+=(\pi/2)+\delta_1^+$ with the remaining $\alpha_l^\pm=\delta_l^\pm$, where the $\delta_l^\pm$ are all small.
(b) Show that there is an equally good solution with $\alpha_2^-=(\pi/2)+\delta_2^-$, and the rest of the phase shifts small. This is an example of the *Minami ambiguity*.
(c) Assuming that there is a physical reason why the $\alpha_2^\pm\approx 0$, show that there is still a third possible solution with both α_1^+ and α_1^- having appreciable values. This is known as the *Yang ambiguity*.
(d) What experiments could be performed to resolve these ambiguities?

6.2.2 Reactions with a Photon Beam

The general expressions for two-body reactions, derived in the preceding section, must be modified when the projectile [particle a in Equation (48)] is a photon. In the first place, as noted in Section 6.1.2, the spin 1 of the photon and its orbital angular momentum are inextricably connected, so that we can only refer to the multipolarity l_γ. Hence, referring to reaction (48) with $a=\gamma$, we take $S=s_A$ in Equation (48a) and $L=l_\gamma$ in Equations (48c) and (48d). Second, the parity relation is different for electric and magnetic multipoles:

$$\pi_A(-1)^{l_\gamma^E}=\pi_B\pi_C(-1)^l=-\pi_A(-1)^{l_\gamma^M}. \tag{52a}$$

Third, the photon always carries the helicity ± 1 (and a statistical weight of $2 \neq 2S_\gamma + 1$), so that the diagram in Figure 6.5 is replaced by that in Figure 6.8.

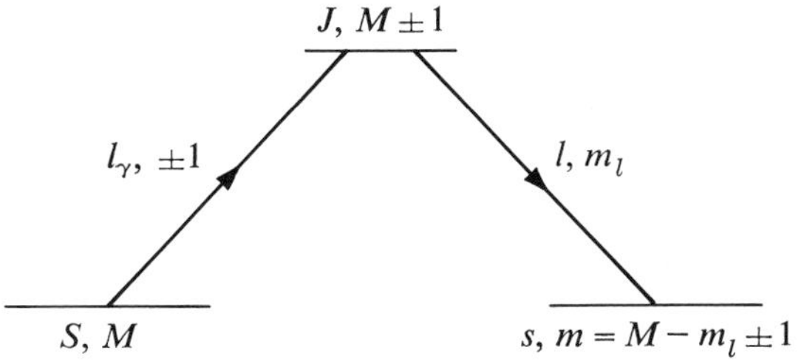

Figure 6.8 Diagram illustrating absorption and decay sequence in a reaction with a photon beam.

The differential cross section becomes, in this case,

$$\frac{d\sigma}{d\Omega} = \frac{(2k_\gamma)^{-2}}{2(2S+1)} \sum_{M} \sum_{m_\gamma = \pm 1} \sum_{s,m} |A_{s,m}^{S,M\pm 1}|^2, \tag{52b}$$

with

$$A_{s,m}^{S,M\pm 1} = \sum_{l_\gamma, J, l} [2\pi(2l_\gamma + 1)]^{1/2} \epsilon_\gamma a_{ME,s}^{l_\gamma, J, l} C_{S,M;\, l_\gamma, \pm 1}^{J,M\pm 1} C_{s,m;\, l, M\pm 1 - m}^{J,M\pm 1} Y_l^{m_l}(\theta, \varphi). \tag{52c}$$

The factor ϵ_γ arises from the properties of the vector spherical harmonics for $\theta = 0$ (see Appendix 3):

$$\epsilon_\gamma^M = +1, \; \epsilon_\gamma^E = -m_\gamma. \tag{52d}$$

EXAMPLE

$\gamma + P \rightarrow B(\frac{1}{2}^+) + \text{meson } (0^-)$. Here, $\pi_A = -\pi_B \pi_C$, so that Equation (52a) requires

$$l = l_\gamma^M = l_\gamma^E \pm 1. \tag{52e}$$

There are now four basic reaction diagrams, as illustrated in Figure 6.9, while the permitted photon multipoles associated with small J- and l-values are given in Table 6.7.

Table 6.7 Permitted Combinations of l_γ^{ME}, J, l for the Reaction $\gamma + P \rightarrow B(\frac{1}{2}^+) + \text{Meson } (0^-)$

J^π	l	γ-multipole
$\frac{1}{2}^-$	0	$E1$
$\frac{1}{2}^+$	1	$M1$
$\frac{3}{2}^+$	1	$M1$, $E2$
$\frac{3}{2}^-$	2	$E1$, $M2$
$\frac{5}{2}^-$	2	$M2$, $E3$
$\frac{5}{2}^+$	3	$E2$, $M3$

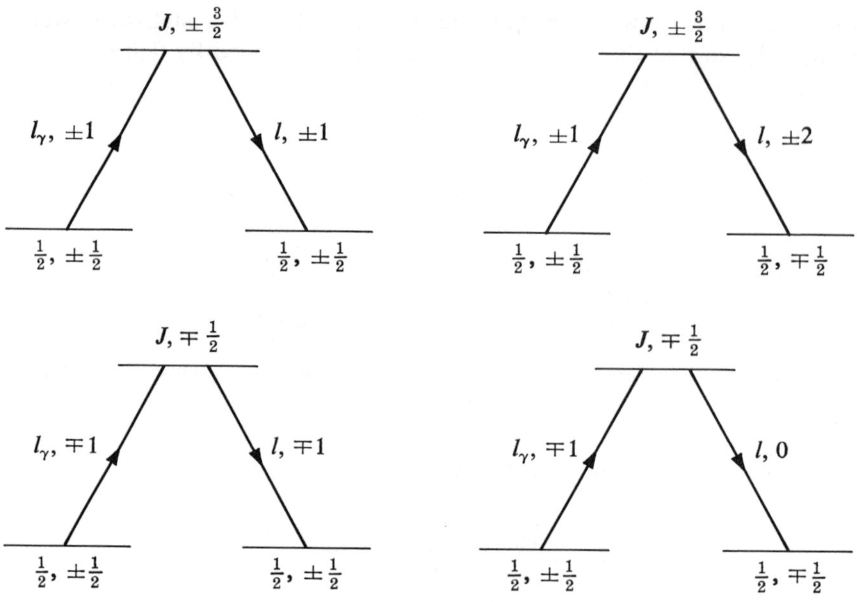

Figure 6.9 Typical reaction diagrams for $\gamma + \frac{1}{2} \rightarrow \frac{1}{2}' + 0^-$.

Expressions for the reaction amplitudes [Equation (52c)] associated with the diagrams of Figure 6.9 are: [16]

$$A^{1/2,\pm3/2}_{1/2,\pm1/2} = \mp\sum_{l\geq1}\sqrt{\frac{2\pi}{2l+1}}\,\{(l+2)\,a^{2l+1}_{Ml} + (l-1)\,a^{2l-1}_{Ml} + \sqrt{l(l+2)}\,a^{2l+1}_{E(l+1)} + \sqrt{l^2-1}\;a^{2l-1}_{E(l-1)}\}\,Y^{\pm1}_{l}(\theta,\varphi)$$

$$\equiv X\sin\theta\, e^{\pm i\varphi}. \tag{53a}$$

$$A^{1/2,\pm3/2}_{1/2,\mp1/2} = \sum_{l\geq2}\sqrt{\frac{2\pi}{2l+1}}\,\{\sqrt{(l+2)(l-1)}\,(a^{2l+1}_{Ml} - a^{2l-1}_{Ml}) + \sqrt{l(l-1)}\,a^{2l+1}_{E(l+1)} - \sqrt{(l+1)(l+2)}\,a^{2l-1}_{E(l-1)}\}\,Y^{\pm2}_{l}(\theta,\varphi)$$

$$\equiv Z\sin^2\theta\, e^{\pm 2i\varphi}. \tag{53b}$$

$$A^{1/2,\mp1/2}_{1/2,\pm1/2} = \pm\sum_{l\geq1}\sqrt{\frac{2\pi}{2l+1}}\,\{l\,a^{2l+1}_{Ml} + (l+1)\,a^{2l-1}_{Ml} - \sqrt{l(l+2)}\,a^{2l+1}_{E(l+1)} + \sqrt{l^2-1}\;a^{2l-1}_{E(l-1)}\}\,Y^{\mp1}_{l}(\theta,\varphi)$$

$$\equiv Y\sin\theta\, e^{\mp i\varphi}. \tag{53c}$$

---

[16] Owing to the redundancy of information, we abbreviate $a^{l_\gamma,J,l}_{ME,s}$ as $a^{2J}_{MEl_\gamma}$.

$$A^{1/2,\mp 1/2}_{1/2,\mp 1/2} = \pm \sum_{l \geq 0} \sqrt{\frac{2\pi}{2l+1}} \{\sqrt{l(l+1)}\,(a^{2l+1}_{Ml} - a^{2l-1}_{Ml}) - \sqrt{(l+1)(l+2)}\,a^{2l+1}_{E(l+1)} + \sqrt{l(l-1)}\,a^{2l-1}_{E(l-1)}\}\, Y^0_l(\theta, \varphi)$$
$$\equiv \mp K. \tag{53d}$$

As long as the incident photon energy is not too large, relative to the threshold of the reaction in question, the number of available intermediate states will be limited by the angular momentum barriers inhibiting the emission of the product meson. In this case, it is convenient, albeit rather arbitrary, to expand the reaction parameters (K, X, Y, Z) in ascending powers of the Legendre polynomials, $P_l(\theta)$, keeping only those terms corresponding to $l \leq l_{\max}$, e.g.,

$$K = K_0 + K_1 \cos\theta + K_2 \tfrac{1}{2}(3\cos^2\theta - 1) + \cdots. \tag{54}$$

We list below the terms in such an expansion[17] corresponding to $l_{\max} = 2$ ($J_{\max} = \frac{5}{2}$; see Table 6.7).

$$\begin{aligned} K_0 &= a^1_{E1}, \\ K_1 &= a^1_{M1} - a^3_{M1} + \sqrt{3}\, a^3_{E2}, \\ K_2 &= -a^3_{E1} + \sqrt{3}\, a^3_{M2} - \sqrt{3}\, a^5_{M2} + \sqrt{6}\, a^5_{E3}. \end{aligned} \tag{54a}$$

[17] It is, however, useful to sum over all the electric multipole terms that arise from straightforward electric photon absorption (Born term), since these exhibit "retardation" effects, which are of importance in photoproduction processes of a nonresonant character, even for relatively low photon energies. This may be accomplished by replacing the a_{El_γ} terms in Equations (53a)–(53d) as follows:

$$\text{in } K_0: \quad a^1_{E1} \to a_E \left[1 - \frac{q^2 \sin^2\theta}{(\kappa^2 + |\mathbf{k} - \mathbf{q}|^2)}\right], \tag{54a'}$$

$$\text{in } X_1 \text{ and } Y_1: \quad a^3_{E1} \cos\theta \to \frac{2}{3} a_E q \frac{(k - q\cos\theta)}{(\kappa^2 + |\mathbf{k} - \mathbf{q}|^2)}, \tag{54b'}$$

$$\text{in } Z_0: \quad a^3_{E1} \to \frac{2}{3} \frac{a_E q^2}{(\kappa^2 + |\mathbf{k} - \mathbf{q}|^2)}, \tag{54c'}$$

where

κ is the pion Compton wavelength ($\kappa = \mu^{-1}$),
$\mathbf{k}$ is the photon *cm* momentum,
$\mathbf{q}$ is the pion *cm* momentum.

These substitutions should normally replace all the electric multipole terms; however, in the special case of electric excitation of a resonance process (e.g., a^3_{E2} for the $J = \frac{3}{2}^+$ nucleon resonance excitation, a^1_{E1} for the $J = \frac{3}{2}^-$ nucleon isobar), the resonant amplitude must be included *in addition* to the Born terms given above.

In the approximation of large baryon mass $M_B \gg \mu$, Equations (54a')–(54c') become

$$a^1_{E1} \gtrsim a_E \left\{1 - \frac{\beta^2_\pi \sin^2\theta}{2(1 - \beta_\pi \cos\theta)}\right\}, \tag{54a''}$$

$$a^3_{E1} \cos\theta \gtrsim \tfrac{1}{3} a_E \beta_\pi, \tag{54b''}$$

$$a^3_{E1} \gtrsim \frac{1}{3} a_E \frac{\beta^2_\pi}{(1 - \beta_\pi \cos\theta)}. \tag{54c''}$$

See B. T. Feld, *Ann. Phys.* (New York), *4:* 189 (1958).

$$X_0 = \frac{1}{2}(3a^3_{M1} + \sqrt{3}\, a^3_{E2}),$$
$$X_1 = \frac{\sqrt{3}}{2}(\sqrt{3}\, a^3_{E1} + a^3_{M2} + 4a^5_{M2} + 2\sqrt{2}\, a^5_{E3}). \tag{54b}$$

$$Y_0 = \frac{1}{2}(2a^1_{M1} + a^3_{M1} - \sqrt{3}\, a^3_{E2}),$$
$$Y_1 = \frac{\sqrt{3}}{2}(-\sqrt{3}\, a^3_{E1} + 3a^3_{M2} + 2a^5_{M2} - 2\sqrt{2}\, a^5_{E3}). \tag{54c}$$

$$Z_0 = \frac{\sqrt{3}}{2}\left(\sqrt{3}\, a^3_{E1} + a^3_{M2} - a^5_{M2} - \sqrt{\frac{1}{2}}\, a^5_{E3}\right). \tag{54d}$$

Substituting Equations (53a)–(53d) into the expression for $d\sigma/d\Omega$ [Equation (52b)], we obtain for an unpolarized target:

$$8\pi k_\gamma^2 \frac{d\sigma}{d\Omega} = |K|^2 + (|X|^2 + |Y|^2 + |Z|^2 \sin^2\theta)\sin^2\theta. \tag{55a}$$

Correspondingly, for the transverse polarization of the product baryon, we have

$$8\pi k_\gamma^2 \frac{d\sigma}{d\Omega} P_x = 2\,\mathrm{Im}\,(KY^* + XZ^* \sin^2\theta)\sin\theta\sin\varphi. \tag{55b}$$

PROBLEMS

1. Assume that the reaction for photoproduction of pions proceeds through a resonant intermediate state

$$\gamma + P \to \mathfrak{N}^*(J^\pi) \to \mathfrak{N}(\tfrac{1}{2}^+) + \pi(0^-).$$

Derive the angular distribution and transverse polarization of the product nucleon for each of the J^π values listed in Table 6.7. Neglect the contribution of all multipoles except those leading to the resonant intermediate state $\mathfrak{N}^*(J^\pi)$.

2. Consider the reaction

$$\gamma + \mathfrak{N} \to \mathfrak{N}^*(\tfrac{3}{2}^+) + \pi.$$

(a) Draw the reaction diagrams (Figure 6.9) corresponding to this reaction.
(b) Derive general expressions for the reaction amplitudes in terms of the various possible $a^{l_\gamma, J, l}_{ME\, l_\gamma}$ and the spherical harmonics, Y_l^m.
(c) Using the reaction amplitudes of (b), obtain expressions for $d\sigma/d\Omega$ and P_x.
(d) Assuming that the reaction proceeds through a definite intermediate (resonant) state

$$\gamma + P \to \mathfrak{N}^*(J^\pi) \to \mathfrak{N}^*(\tfrac{3}{2}^+) + \pi,$$

derive expressions for $d\sigma/d\Omega$ and P_x, when $J^\pi = \frac{1}{2}^+[\mathfrak{N}^*(1470)]$, $\frac{3}{2}^-[\mathfrak{N}^*(1518)]$, and $\frac{5}{2}^+[\mathfrak{N}^*(1688)]$.

3. Consider the reaction

$$\gamma + P \to \mathfrak{N}^*(\tfrac{3}{2}^+) \to \mathfrak{N}(\tfrac{1}{2}^+) + \pi,$$

using a plane-polarized photon beam, with its electric vector in the x direction and its momentum in the z direction. Derive expressions for $d\sigma/d\Omega$ and P_x in this case.

6.2.3 Helicity Representation; The Spin-Density Matrix

In considering reactions among particles with spin, especially in the relativistic, high-energy domain, it is frequently more convenient to describe the spin states in terms of the components of the particle spins along their directions of motion, rather than with respect to some arbitrary z axis fixed in space (as we have done in the preceding sections). This description of the angular momentum states involved in the reaction is known as the helicity representation.[18] We summarize in this section the main features of this description for reactions of the form

$$a + b \to c + d \tag{56}$$

and give expressions relating the description of reaction (56) in the helicity representation to that of the "conventional" representation discussed in the preceding sections.

Consider the elements of the reaction or T-matrix [19] between an initial and a final state, $\langle f|T(s, t)|i\rangle$. For given initial and final states, characterized by the helicities λ_a, λ_b and λ_c, λ_d and by the cm incident momentum p, energy $s^{1/2}$, and 4-momentum transfer t, the differential cross section is

$$\frac{d\sigma}{d\Omega}(s, t; \lambda_i) = \left(\frac{2\pi}{p}\right)^2 |\langle\lambda_d\lambda_c|T(s, t)|\lambda_b\lambda_a\rangle|^2. \tag{57}$$

For an unpolarized target, the average-over-initial helicities and sum-over-final helicities give [20]

$$\frac{d\sigma}{d\Omega}(s, t) = (2s_a + 1)^{-1}(2s_b + 1)^{-1}\left(\frac{2\pi}{p}\right)^2 \sum_{\lambda_i} |\langle\lambda_d\lambda_c|T|\lambda_b\lambda_a\rangle|^2. \tag{57a}$$

Equations (57) and (57a) may be regarded as defining the helicity amplitudes $\langle\lambda_d\lambda_c|T|\lambda_b\lambda_a\rangle$ through the expression for the differential cross section for reaction (56). Note that the helicity representation has the property that it does not

---

[18] M. Jacob and G. C. Wick, *Ann. Phys.* (New York), *7:* 404 (1959).

[19] The T-matrix is conventionally defined in terms of the S-matrix and the unit matrix 1, $iT = S - 1$, with the required kinematical factors, etc. [Equation (49) and Chapter 5, Equation (9)], being incorporated into the definition of T [Equation (57)].

[20] For massless particles, only two helicities, $\lambda_i = \pm s_i$, are possible (e.g., $\lambda_\nu = \pm\frac{1}{2}$, $\lambda_\gamma = \pm 1$), and the statistical weight is always 2.

introduce the intermediate channel states into the formalism, at least not at an early stage. This feature has the advantage of avoiding a premature decision concerning the physical (dynamical) relevance of these states, but it also has the disadvantage that it may obscure the physics in those cases where a limited number of channel states are decisive in determining the nature of the reaction in question. In addition, the helicity representation, by avoiding reference to an arbitrary space axis (spins are always referred to the physically meaningful directions of motion of the particles concerned), is both suitable to a relativistic treatment and more economical in its formalism than the conventional representation. Nevertheless, as far as the formal results are concerned, the two representations are generally equivalent, and the choice between them is a matter of computational convenience.[21]

Instead of using the reaction matrix element T [Equation (57)] it is more convenient to use the relativistically invariant amplitude $A(s, t)$, defined by

$$A(s, t) = \left(\frac{\pi s}{pp'}\right)^{1/2} T(s, t), \tag{58}$$

where p and p' are, respectively, the incident and product *cm* 3-momenta. Converting $d\sigma/d\Omega$ to $d\sigma/dt$ (see Section 3.2.2), we obtain

$$\frac{d\sigma}{dt}(s, t; \lambda_i) = \frac{(2\pi)^2}{sp^2} |\langle\lambda_d\lambda_c|A(s, t)|\lambda_b\lambda_a\rangle|^2 . \tag{57b}$$

The amplitudes $T(s, t)$ or $A(s, t)$ contain contributions from all possible intermediate states of spin j. Taking the z axis along the direction of the incident particle a, and defining the angles θ, φ by the direction of c, we may write

$$\langle\lambda_d\lambda_c|A|\lambda_b\lambda_a\rangle = \frac{1}{4\pi}\sum_j (2j+1)\langle\lambda_d\lambda_c|A_j|\lambda_b\lambda_a\rangle\, e^{i(\lambda-\mu)\varphi} d^j_{\lambda\mu}(\theta), \tag{59}$$

where

$$\begin{aligned} \lambda &= \lambda_a - \lambda_b, \\ \mu &= \lambda_c - \lambda_d, \end{aligned} \tag{59a}$$

and the $d^j_{\lambda\mu}(\theta)$ are the rotation matrices, defined in Appendix 4. Substituting (59) into (57b), we obtain, after some manipulation and using the correspondence $d^l_{00}(\theta) = P_l(\cos\theta)$ (see Appendix 4),

$$sp^2\frac{d\sigma}{dt}(s, t; \lambda_i) = \sum_{j,j'}\left(j+\frac{1}{2}\right)\left(j'+\frac{1}{2}\right)(-1)^{\lambda-\mu}\cdot\langle\lambda_d\lambda_c|A_j|\lambda_b\lambda_a\rangle^*\langle\lambda_d\lambda_c|A_{j'}|\lambda_b\lambda_a\rangle$$
$$\cdot\sum_l C^{l,0}_{j,\lambda;\,j',-\lambda}\,C^{l,0}_{j,\mu;\,j',-\mu}\,P_l(\cos\theta). \tag{57c}$$

Finally, the cross section is obtained by summing over the final helicities and averaging over the initial [(see Equation (57a)]. The final result may, of course,

---

[21] For the use of the conventional representation in relativistic situations see: H. P. Stapp, *Phys. Rev., 103:* 425 (1956); Chou Kuang-Chao and M. I. Shirokov, Sov. Phys. *JETP, 7:* 851 (1958).

be compared with that obtained in the conventional representation (Section 6.2.1) for connections between the helicity amplitudes, $A_j(s, t)$, and those corresponding to a given combination of channel spins and total angular momentum. On the other hand, while the computation of polarization state distributions of the products (or decay angular correlations in the case of unstable products) is generally complicated in the conventional representation — since it involves going from initial particle polarization states to channel spins and back again to the individual product polarization states — the use of the helicity representation leads to a description of the product polarizations in a much more direct fashion.

The distribution of the product polarization states in reaction (56) is most conveniently given in terms of the elements of the spin-density matrix, $\rho^{(n)}$ (n = particle c or d). Let the product wave function, corresponding to a given initial configuration i, be $\psi_i^{(n)}$; in terms of the $(2s_n + 1)$ fundamental substates, $\psi_m^{(n)}$, we have

$$|\psi_i^{(n)}\rangle = \sum_{m=-s_n}^{s_n} a_m^{(i)} |\psi_m^{(n)}\rangle, \tag{60}$$

and the spin-density matrix elements become

$$\rho_{m,m'}^{(n)} = \sum_i w_i\, a_m^{(i)*}\, a_{m'}^{(i)}, \tag{60a}$$

where the w_i are the weights of the various possible independent (incoherent) initial configurations.[22] For a given observable, represented by the operator Q,

$$Q_{m,m'}^{(n)} = \langle \psi_m^{(n)*} | Q | \psi_{m'}^{(n)} \rangle, \tag{60b}$$

the average value is

$$\langle Q^{(n)} \rangle = \sum_{m,m'} Q_{m,m'}^{(n)} \rho_{m',m}^{(n)} = \sum_m [Q\rho]_{m,m} = \text{tr}\,(Q\rho). \tag{60c}$$

In particular, the polarization vector is the average value of the particle's spin

$$\mathbf{P}^{(n)} = \text{tr}\,(\mathbf{S}_n \rho^{(n)}), \tag{60c$'$}$$

while normalization requires

$$1 = \text{tr}\,(\rho), \tag{60d}$$

and the reality of observable quantities [Equation (60c)] requires that $\rho^{(n)}$ be a Hermitian matrix

$$\rho_{m,m'} = \rho_{m',m}^* . \tag{60e}$$

In any given physical situation, the values of the matrix elements of $\rho^{(n)}$ will depend on the choice of the set of basis functions, $\psi_m^{(n)}$ — i.e., on the choice of coordinate axes. In the conventional representation, the z axis is taken as the

[22] For initially unpolarized projectile and target, the $w_i = [(2s_a + 1)(2s_b + 1)]^{-1}$. Generally, the sum over i includes a summation over the possible substates, m_d or m_c, of the second product particle.

incident direction, while the x axis is generally taken as the normal to the production plane (direction of $\mathbf{p}_a \times \mathbf{p}_c$). The decay angles with respect to this coordinate system are frequently referred to as the "Adair angles," although the analysis in terms of these angles is generally most useful for events in which the decaying particle (c or d) is produced in the forward direction since, in this case, the orbital angular momentum cannot contribute any z component, and the initial and final m-values are therefore the same [that is, $\lambda = \mu$, Equation (59a)].

In terms of the helicity amplitudes, and specifying $n = d$, with the z axis in the direction of the incident particle b in the rest frame of d, we have [23]

$$\rho^d_{m,m'} = N \sum_{\lambda_c \lambda_b \lambda_a} \langle m'\lambda_c|A|\lambda_b\lambda_a\rangle^* \langle m\lambda_c|A|\lambda_b\lambda_a\rangle \tag{61}$$

with

$$N^{-1} = \sum_{m\lambda_c\lambda_b\lambda_a} |\langle m\lambda_c|A|\lambda_b\lambda_a\rangle|^2, \tag{61a}$$

assuring the unit value of the trace of ρ. Equations (61) and (61a) can, in turn, be expressed in terms of the components $A_j(s, t)$ by use of Equation (59).

If, finally, the particle d is unstable,

$$d \to \alpha + \beta, \tag{62}$$

the decay angular distribution of the products, in the rest frame of d, is given in terms of the decay amplitudes

$$A'_m(\lambda_\alpha\lambda_\beta) = \left(\frac{4\pi}{2s_d + 1}\right)^{1/2} d^{s_d}_{m\Lambda}(\theta)\, e^{i(m-\Lambda)\varphi}\, a_d(\lambda_\alpha\lambda_\beta) \qquad (\Lambda = \lambda_\alpha - \lambda_\beta) \tag{62a}$$

by the expression

$$W(\theta, \varphi) = N' \sum_{mm'\lambda_\alpha\lambda_\beta} |a_d(\lambda_\alpha\lambda_\beta)|^2\, e^{i(m-m')\varphi}\, d^{s_d}_{m\Lambda}(\theta)\, d^{s_d}_{m'\Lambda}(\theta)\, \rho^d_{m,m'} \tag{62b}$$

Generally, by appropriate choice of the reference frame it is possible to simplify the form of the density matrix — e.g., to render it diagonal, in which case there is no polarization if $\rho_{m,m} = \rho_{-m,-m}$, although there will usually be a spin "alignment" unless the diagonal elements of ρ are all equal. Frequently, the choice of reference frame is dictated by the desire to determine the unknown spin of an unstable product, as is done in the Adair analysis referred to in the preceding discussion. Conversely, the determination of the polarization state of an unstable product of known spin, by using its decay angular distribution to determine the elements of its spin-density matrix, is important for an understanding of the reaction in which it is produced; in this case, also, the nature of the reaction

[23] To obtain $\rho^c_{m,m'}$, we simply interchange $c \leftrightarrow d$ and $a \leftrightarrow b$ in Equations (61) and (62).

mechanism responsible (or under investigation) determines the choice of reference frame.[24]

There are two situations of special physical interest:

s-Channel or Resonant Reactions • In such reactions the dominant mechanism is that illustrated by Figure 6.10, especially when only a few intermediate states

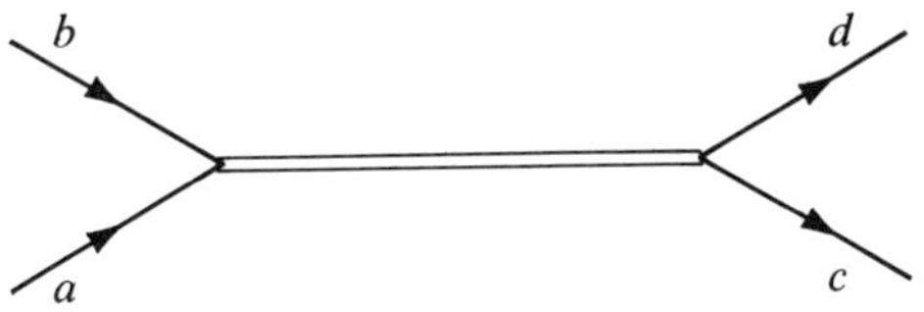

Figure 6.10 s-channel reactions.

are important. In considering such reactions, it is desirable to express the matrix elements A_j or T_j in the representation in which j, l, s, $m = m_l + m_s$ are the good quantum numbers. This may be done by the use of the transformation matrix

$$\langle jmls | jm\lambda_b\lambda_a\rangle = \sqrt{\frac{2l+1}{2j+1}}\, C^{j,\lambda=\lambda_a-\lambda_b}_{l,0;\, s,\lambda}\, C^{s,\lambda}_{s_a,\lambda_a;\, s_b,-\lambda_b} \tag{63}$$

which yields[25]

$$\langle jm\lambda_d\lambda_c | A_j | jm\lambda_b\lambda_a\rangle = \sum_{lsl's'} \sqrt{\frac{(2l+1)(2l'+1)}{(2j+1)^2}} \cdot C^{j,\lambda}_{l,0;s,\lambda}\, C^{s,\lambda}_{s_a,\lambda_a;s_b,-\lambda_b}\, C^{j,\mu}_{l',0;s',\mu}\, C^{s',\mu}_{s_c,\lambda_c;s_d,-\lambda_d} \cdot \langle jml's' | A_j | jmls\rangle. \tag{63a}$$

Thus, for example, the reaction $\pi^- + P \rightarrow N + \eta^0$ seems to be dominated near threshold by an s-channel resonance with $j = \frac{1}{2}^-$, for which the resonant (Breit–Wigner) amplitude $A_{1/2}$ corresponding to $l = l' = 0$, $s = s' = \frac{1}{2}$, $j = \frac{1}{2}^-$ gives the major contribution. Another example of the usefulness of the s-channel representation is in the description of elastic scattering in the "optical approximation," for which we may write

$$\langle jmls | A_j | jmls\rangle = 1 - \eta_l,$$

with η_l a smoothly varying function of the impact parameter $r = l/p$.

---

[24] A number of examples are given in the papers of Jacob and Wick, *Ann. Phys.* (New York), *7:* 404 (1959) and G. C. Wick, *Ann. Phys., 18:* 65 (1962). See also L. Montanet, *CERN Report,* 67–23; N. Byers, *CERN Report,* 67–20; S. M. Berman and M. Jacob, *Stanford Linear Accelerator Report,* SLAC–43 (1967). Additional examples and references are given in the remainder of this section.

[25] Photons require somewhat special treatment since their spin cannot be separated from their orbital angular momentum or multipolarity l_γ. Thus, if $a = \gamma$, then $\lambda = \pm 1$ only, and the first two Clebsch–Gordan coefficients in Equation (63a) are replaced by $\epsilon_\gamma C^{j,\lambda}_{l_\gamma,\pm 1;\, s_b,-\lambda_b}$, with $\epsilon_\gamma = 1$ for all Ml_γ, and $\epsilon_\gamma = -\lambda_\gamma$ for all El_γ.

t-Channel or Exchange Reactions • Such reactions are dominated by the exchange of a virtual particle or particles, as illustrated in Figure 6.11. In this case,

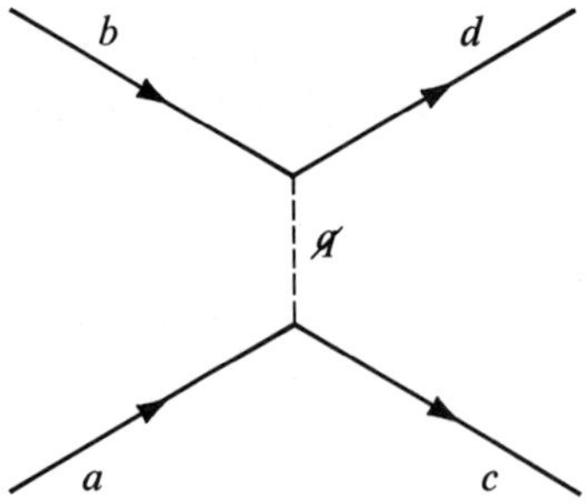

Figure 6.11 t-channel reactions.

it is useful to consider the amplitudes $B(s, t)$ corresponding to the direct-channel (resonance) reaction

$$a + \bar{c} \to \bar{b} + d \tag{56a}$$

which are connected to the $A(s, t)$ through

$$\langle \lambda_d \lambda_c | A | \lambda_b \lambda_a \rangle = \sum_{\lambda_i'} d^{s_d}_{\lambda_d' \lambda_d}(\psi_d)\, d^{s_c}_{\lambda_{\bar{c}}' \lambda_c}(\psi_c)\, d^{s_b}_{\lambda_{\bar{b}}' \lambda_b}(\psi_b)\, d^{s_a}_{\lambda_a' \lambda_a}(\psi_a)$$

$$\cdot (-1)^{\lambda_a' - \lambda_a + \lambda_{\bar{c}}' - \lambda_c} \langle \lambda_d' \lambda_{\bar{b}}' | B | \lambda_{\bar{c}}' \lambda_a' \rangle, \tag{64}$$

where ψ_i is the angle between the directions of the *cm* of the s-channel and of the t-channel in the rest frame of the ith particle.[26]

$$\tan \psi_i = \pm \frac{m_i}{E_i} \left\{ \frac{\sin \theta}{(p_i E_j / p_j E_i) - \cos \theta} \right\}, \tag{64a}$$

where p_i and E_i are the *cm* momentum and energy of the particle in question, while p_j and E_j apply to the "companion" particle — i.e., for $i = a$, $j = c$; $i = b$, $j = d$, and vice versa. The +(−) sign goes with $i = a$ or b (c or d). Theta (θ) is the *cm* angle between a and c, so that $(0 < \psi_{a,c} < \pi)$ and $(\pi < \psi_{b,d} < 2\pi)$.

Since all of the expressions derived above for the s-channel, in terms of $A(s, t)$, hold equally well for the t-channel in terms of $B(s, t)$, there is no need to repeat them. This approach has the advantage that, in the case of exchange of a particle with relatively simple properties,[27] the expressions for the cross section and density matrix are generally much simpler when derived in terms of the B. Thus, for example, for exchange of a particle q of spin j, we may write in general

$$\langle \lambda_d \lambda_{\bar{b}} | B(s, t) | \lambda_{\bar{c}} \lambda_a \rangle = f_{\lambda_i}(t)\, d^j_{\lambda_{\bar{b}} - \lambda_d, \lambda_a - \lambda_{\bar{c}}}(\cos \theta_t). \tag{65}$$

---

[26] T. L. Trueman and G. C. Wick, *Ann. Phys.* (New York), *26:* 322 (1964).
[27] K. Gottfried and J. D. Jackson, *Nuovo Cimento, 33:* 309 (1964).

In the asymptotic region[28] of large s and small t ($\cos\theta_t \gg 1$), the cross section behavior is determined by the analytical form of the $d^j_{\lambda\mu}$ in Equation (65), which results in

$$\langle \lambda_a \lambda_{\bar{b}} | B | \lambda_{\bar{c}} \lambda_a \rangle \propto s^j, \tag{65a}$$

$$\frac{d\sigma}{dt} \propto s^{(2j-2)}. \tag{65b}$$

The case of $j=0$ is of special interest (one-pion or one-kaon exchange); in this case, for all s and t,

$$\frac{d\sigma}{dt} = \frac{f^2(t)}{sp^2}. \tag{65c}$$

In addition, the density matrix generally assumes a much simpler form when considered in the t-channel representation. Physically, this may be readily understood if we recall (see Figure 6.11) that the elements of, say, $\rho^c_{m,m'}$ describe the state of polarization of c in its own rest frame, in which the incident particle a and the exchanged particle q have equal and opposite momentum. Since particles cannot carry orbital angular momentum along their direction of motion, the z component of the angular momentum is $m_c = \lambda_a - \lambda_q$ (z axis along $\mathbf{p}_a$). In particular, if $j_q = 0$ (e.g., the case of pseudoscalar meson exchange[29]), we have $m_c = \lambda_a$.

EXAMPLES

1. Consider the reaction

$$psc + b \rightarrow v + d, \tag{56b}$$

where psc stands for a meson of $s_a = 0^-$ (π, K) and v for a meson of $s_c = 1^-$ (ρ, ω, ϕ, K^*). Let the vector meson decay into two pseudoscalars ($\rho \rightarrow 2\pi$, $K^* \rightarrow K\pi$, etc.). For an arbitrary choice of coordinate axes, the decay angular distribution is given in terms of the corresponding spin-density matrix elements of v:

$$\begin{aligned} W_{1^-}(\theta, \varphi) = \frac{3}{8\pi} \{ &(\rho_{11} + \rho_{-1-1}) \sin^2\theta + 2\rho_{00}\cos^2\theta \\ &+ 2\sin^2\theta\,(\sin 2\varphi \,\mathrm{Im}\,\rho_{1-1} - \cos 2\varphi\,\mathrm{Re}\,\rho_{1-1}) \\ &+ \sqrt{2}\sin 2\theta\,(\sin\varphi\,\mathrm{Im}\,\rho_{10} - \cos\varphi\,\mathrm{Re}\,\rho_{10}) \\ &+ \sqrt{2}\sin 2\theta\,(\sin\varphi\,\mathrm{Im}\,\rho_{-10} + \cos\varphi\,\mathrm{Re}\,\rho_{-10})\}. \end{aligned} \tag{66}$$

However, specifying to the rest frame of v, with the z axis in the direction of the incident psc, Equation (66) reduces to

---

[28] This corresponds to a physically realizable situation in the s-channel, but not in the t-channel.

[29] L. Stodolsky and J. J. Sakurai [*Phys. Rev. Letters, 11:* 90 (1963)] have proposed a model for ρ exchange, where the exchanged ρ ($s_\rho = 1^-$) behaves like a photon, i.e., it carries $\lambda_\rho = \pm 1$ only. In this case $m_c = \lambda_a \pm 1$.

$$W_{1^-}(\theta, \varphi) = \frac{3}{4\pi} \{\rho_{11} \sin^2 \theta + \rho_{00} \cos^2 \theta - \rho_{1-1} \sin^2 \theta \cos 2\varphi$$
$$- \sqrt{2}\, \text{Re}\, \rho_{10} \sin 2\theta \cos \varphi\}, \quad (66a)$$

by taking advantage of the properties of the density matrix

$$\rho_{m,m'} = (-1)^{m-m'} \rho_{-m,-m'}, \quad (66b)$$

$$e^{i(m-m')\varphi} \rho_{m,m'} = \cos(m - m')\varphi \cdot \text{Re}\, \rho_{m,m'}. \quad (66c)$$

Note: $\rho_{11} = \frac{1}{2}(1 - \rho_{00})$, from the normalization condition tr $\rho = 1$.

The assumption of spin 0 meson exchange in the t-channel implies that $m_v = \lambda_\pi = 0$; i.e., $\rho_{11} = \rho_{1-1} = \text{Re}\, \rho_{10} = 0$; $\rho_{00} = 1$.

$$W^{\pi}_{1^-}(\theta, \varphi) = \frac{3}{4\pi} \cos^2 \theta. \quad (66d)$$

The photoproduction of vector mesons can also be treated in a simple fashion. Consider, instead of reaction (56b), the reaction

$$\gamma + b \rightarrow v + d. \quad (56c)$$

In this case, for spin 0 meson exchange and assuming an unpolarized incident photon beam, we have $m_v = \lambda_\gamma = \pm 1$; i.e., $\rho_{00} = \rho_{1-1} = \text{Re}\, \rho_{10} = 0$, giving

$$W^{\gamma}_{1^-}(\theta, \varphi) = \frac{3}{8\pi} \sin^2 \theta. \quad (66e)$$

2. Consider the reaction

$$a + P \rightarrow c + \Delta(s_\Delta = \tfrac{3}{2}^+). \quad (56d)$$

In this case, the distribution of decay of the Δ baryon,

$$\Delta(\tfrac{3}{2}^+) \rightarrow B(\tfrac{1}{2}^+) + psc(0^-), \quad (67)$$

observed in the Δ rest frame, with the z axis taken along the direction of the parent P in this coordinate system, is given by

$$W_\Delta(\theta, \varphi) = \frac{3}{4\pi} \left\{\rho_{33} \sin^2 \theta + \rho_{11} \left(\frac{1}{3} + \cos^2 \theta\right) - \frac{2}{\sqrt{3}} \text{Re}\, \rho_{3-1} \sin^2 \theta \cos 2\varphi\right.$$
$$\left. - \frac{2}{\sqrt{3}} \text{Re}\, \rho_{31} \sin 2\theta \cos \varphi\right\}. \quad (67a)$$

For reaction (56d), spin 0 meson exchange in the t-channel requires $m_\Delta = \lambda_p = \pm\frac{1}{2}$, with $\rho_{33} = \rho_{3-1} = \rho_{31} = 0$, giving

$$W_\Delta(\theta, \varphi) = \frac{1}{8\pi} (1 + 3 \cos^2 \theta). \quad (67b)$$

Note that this result holds irrespective of the projectile particle (a) and other product (c), provided spin 0 meson exchange dominates.

3. Finally, consider the production of a spin 2 meson [say $f^0(1260)$, $f'(1515)$, $A_2(1300)$, $K^*(1420)$]. The distribution of its decay into two spin 0 mesons ($f^0 \rightarrow 2\pi$, etc.) is given by the expression

$$W_2(\theta, \varphi) = \frac{15}{16\pi}\left\{3\rho_{00}\left(\cos^2\theta - \frac{1}{3}\right)^2 + 4\rho_{11}\sin^2\theta\cos^2\theta + \rho_{22}\sin^4\theta \right.$$
$$- \left[4\,\mathrm{Re}\,\rho_{21}\sin^2\theta + 4\sqrt{6}\,\mathrm{Re}\,\rho_{10}\left(\cos^2\theta - \frac{1}{3}\right)\right]\sin\theta\cos\theta\cos\varphi$$
$$- \left[4\rho_{1-1}\cos^2\theta - 2\sqrt{6}\,\mathrm{Re}\,\rho_{20}\left(\cos^2\theta - \frac{1}{3}\right)\right]\sin^2\theta\cos 2\varphi$$
$$\left. + 4\,\mathrm{Re}\,\rho_{2-1}\sin^3\theta\cos 3\varphi + \rho_{2-2}\sin^4\theta\cos 4\varphi\right\} \tag{68}$$

with the normalization condition

$$\rho_{00} = 1 - 2\rho_{11} - 2\rho_{22}\,. \tag{68a}$$

For production by a spin 0 meson exchange process, all the density matrix elements except ρ_{00} vanish, leaving only the first term in Equation (68). In the case of production through the exchange of a meson of some other spin and parity, other conditions may be shown to hold among the density matrix elements.[30]

PROBLEM

Consider the reactions

$$\pi + P \rightarrow c + \Delta,$$

in which c is either a pion or a rho. If, in the latter case the dominant production mechanism is one-pion exchange (OPE) in the t-channel, then we would expect one-rho exchange to dominate for the case $c = \pi$. Why? Assuming that this is the case, and that the exchanged rho is of the Stodolsky–Sakurai type, i.e., $\lambda_\rho = \pm 1$ only, show that the resulting distribution of the Δ decay [Equation (67)] is

$$W(\theta, \phi) = \frac{1}{16\pi}(5 - 3\cos^2\theta).$$

---

[30] R. H. Dalitz, *Proceedings of the International School of Physics Enrico Fermi,* Course XXXIII, Academic Press, New York (1966), p. 141. Thus, for example, for production of a 2^+ meson by a vector meson exchange process, Dalitz has shown that only ρ_{11} and ρ_{1-1} can be nonvanishing.

7

Isotopic-Spin Conservation

The concept of isotopic spin was first introduced by Heisenberg [1] as a formal device for describing the effects of "charge independence" of the nuclear forces. Starting from the description of the nucleon $\mathfrak{N}$ as a dichotomic system (i.e., one having two eigenstates),

$$\text{Proton} = P = \begin{pmatrix} 1 \\ 0 \end{pmatrix}, \tag{1a}$$

$$\text{Neutron} = N = \begin{pmatrix} 0 \\ 1 \end{pmatrix}, \tag{1b}$$

the isotopic-spin properties follow from the most elementary consideration of the types of operations that can be performed on such a system. These operations are:

1. *Identification,* for which we define the identification operator $\mathcal{I}_3$:

$$\mathcal{I}_3 P = (+1)P, \tag{2a}$$

$$\mathcal{I}_3 N = (-1)N, \tag{2b}$$

$$\mathcal{I}_3 = \begin{pmatrix} 1 & 0 \\ 0 & -1 \end{pmatrix}. \tag{2}$$

Operation with $\mathcal{I}_3$ on a nucleon wave function tells us whether it corresponds to a proton (eigenvalue +1) or neutron (−1).

[1] W. Heisenberg, *Z. Physik, 77:* 1 (1932); see also B. Cassen and E. U. Condon, *Phys. Rev., 50:* 846 (1936); E. Wigner, *Phys. Rev., 51:* 106 (1937).

2. *Charge-exchange,* for which we define the exchange operators $\mathcal{I}_+$ and $\mathcal{I}_-$:

$$\mathcal{I}_+ P = 0, \qquad \mathcal{I}_- P = N, \tag{3a}$$

$$\mathcal{I}_+ N = P, \qquad \mathcal{I}_- N = 0, \tag{3b}$$

$$\mathcal{I}_+ = \begin{pmatrix} 0 & 1 \\ 0 & 0 \end{pmatrix}, \qquad \mathcal{I}_- = \begin{pmatrix} 0 & 0 \\ 1 & 0 \end{pmatrix}. \tag{3}$$

These are not Hermitian matrices, since they do not correspond to an observable of the system. They merely permit the description of interactions in which the nucleons change from one to the other — operations that must be readily accessible if the interactions are independent of the nucleon charge.

However, we may form two linearly independent Hermitian operators from $\mathcal{I}_+$ and $\mathcal{I}_-$, namely,

$$\mathcal{I}_1 = \mathcal{I}_+ + \mathcal{I}_- = \begin{pmatrix} 0 & 1 \\ 1 & 0 \end{pmatrix}, \tag{3c}$$

$$\mathcal{I}_2 = \frac{1}{i}(\mathcal{I}_+ - \mathcal{I}_-) = \begin{pmatrix} 0 & -i \\ i & 0 \end{pmatrix}. \tag{3d}$$

3. *Class identification,* for which we define the class operator $\mathcal{C}$: This operator simply tells us that we have a nucleon:

$$\mathcal{C}P = cP, \tag{4a}$$

$$\mathcal{C}N = cN, \tag{4b}$$

$$\mathcal{C} = c\begin{pmatrix} 1 & 0 \\ 0 & 1 \end{pmatrix} = cI. \tag{4}$$

It is a multiple of the identity operator and can, in fact, be formed from the three operators $\mathcal{I}_1$, $\mathcal{I}_2$, $\mathcal{I}_3$:

$$\mathcal{C} = \mathcal{I}^2 = \mathcal{I}_1^2 + \mathcal{I}_2^2 + \mathcal{I}_3^2 = 3 \cdot I. \tag{4c}$$

Now, Equations (2)–(4) are just the Pauli spin operators, invented by Pauli to describe a system of intrinsic angular momentum $\hbar/2$. Indeed, the set of operators

$$\tau_j = \tfrac{1}{2}\mathcal{I}_j$$

is a set of angular momentum operators, obeying the ordinary commutation rules for angular momentum operators:

$$[\tau_i, \tau_j] = i\tau_k \qquad (i, j, k \text{ cyclic}), \\ [\tau_i, \tau^2] = 0. \tag{5}$$

It is the formal identity of these operators and the rotation operators that leads to the name "isotopic spin." We may think of these operators as describing rotations in a fictitious space — charge space — just as the angular momentum operators describe rotations in ordinary space. The operators τ_1, τ_2, τ_3 represent the three (x, y, z) components of a vector in charge space; $\tau^2 = \tau_1^2 + \tau_2^2 + \tau_3^2$ is the square of the vector's length. The concept of isotopic invariance (charge independence) may be expressed by the statement that the length of a vector in charge space is independent of the choice of coordinate axes. We investigate some consequences of this description in the following sections.

7.1 The Strong Interactions

The usefulness of the isotopic-spin concept becomes evident when we consider systems containing more than one nucleon.

7.1.1 Systems of Two Nucleons

Let us consider two nucleons. There are four possible states (as far as charge is concerned; we consider, for the moment, the nucleons as though they were always distinguishable); these states are shown in Table 7.1.

We may define the total isotopic spin,

$$\mathbf{t} = \boldsymbol{\tau}_1 + \boldsymbol{\tau}_2, \tag{6}$$

which is merely an abbreviation for the three operations

$$t_i = \tau_{i1} + \tau_{i2}. \tag{6a}$$

Since, formally, the τ operators are identical with spin $\frac{1}{2}$ operators, the t's are just the same as the angular momentum operators corresponding to the combination of two spin $\frac{1}{2}$'s. Thus, there are two sets of eigenstates, one set corresponding to $t = 1$ and the other to $t = 0$; these are given in Table 7.2. The first three ($t = 1$) are symmetric with respect to interchange of the two nucleons; the last ($t = 0$) is antisymmetric.

Table 7.1 States of Two Nucleons

Combination	Charge (Q)	$\sum \tau_3$
PP	2	1
PN	1	0
NP	1	0
NN	0	−1

Table 7.2 Combinations of Two Nucleons Corresponding to $t = 1$ and 0

Isospin state	t_3	t^2
$\chi_1^1 = PP$	1	2
$\chi_1^0 = \sqrt{\frac{1}{2}}\,(PN + NP)$	0	2
$\chi_1^{-1} = NN$	−1	2
$\chi_0^0 = \sqrt{\frac{1}{2}}\,(PN - NP)$	0	0

If we now introduce the *Pauli principle* — that the wave function for two identical fermions (nucleons) must be *antisymmetric* with respect to interchange of the two particles — a two-nucleon system may have two types of wave function:

$$\psi_a = \chi_1^{t_3} \varphi_a(\mathbf{r}, s), \tag{7a}$$

$$\psi_s = \chi_0^0 \varphi_s(\mathbf{r}, s), \tag{7b}$$

in which the φ's describe the space and spin state of the two-nucleon system. Generally, the nucleons having spin $\frac{1}{2}$, the total spin, s, of the two-nucleon system can be 0 or 1, the former being antisymmetric with respect to exchange of the constituents, and the latter being symmetric. As for the space dependence of φ, it is symmetric (even-parity) for states of even orbital angular momentum l, and antisymmetric for odd. Hence, the behavior of the φ's under interchange of the two nucleons is as $-(-1)^{s+l}$, so that $(s+l)$-odd goes with φ_s and $(s+l)$-even with φ_a.

Pauli tells us that an antisymmetrical $\varphi(\varphi_a)$ goes with a symmetrical $\chi(\chi_1)$, and vice versa. Heisenberg (charge independence) says that the interaction depends only on the symmetry or antisymmetry of φ. Thus, there are two interactions (Hamiltonians), one, H_a, going with φ_a and the other, H_s, going with φ_s. We want to write a general two-nucleon Hamiltonian that contains this principle:

$$H\psi_a = H_a\psi_a, \tag{8a}$$

$$H\psi_s = H_s\psi_s. \tag{8b}$$

Let

$$H = H_a O_a + H_s O_s, \tag{8}$$

where O_a and O_s are "projection" operators, which pick out the appropriate eigenfunctions, i.e.,

$$O_a\chi_1 = \chi_1, \qquad O_s\chi_1 = 0, \tag{8c}$$

$$O_a\chi_0 = 0, \qquad O_s\chi_0 = \chi_0. \tag{8d}$$

It is easy to see that the O's may be expressed in terms of the τ's, as follows,

$$O_a = \tfrac{3}{4} + \boldsymbol{\tau}_1 \cdot \boldsymbol{\tau}_2, \tag{8e}$$

$$O_s = \tfrac{1}{4} - \boldsymbol{\tau}_1 \cdot \boldsymbol{\tau}_2, \tag{8f}$$

$$\boldsymbol{\tau}_1 \cdot \boldsymbol{\tau}_2 = \tau_{11}\tau_{12} + \tau_{21}\tau_{22} + \tau_{31}\tau_{32}, \tag{9}$$

and, therefore, that the most general charge-independent Hamiltonian for the two-nucleon system may be written

$$H = \left(\frac{3H_a + H_s}{4}\right) + (H_a - H_s)\boldsymbol{\tau}_1 \cdot \boldsymbol{\tau}_2$$

$$= H_1 + H_2\boldsymbol{\tau}_1 \cdot \boldsymbol{\tau}_2. \tag{8$'$}$$

At low energies, such that the two nucleons are in a relative S state, it is observed that the triplet spin state ($s=1$) is bound (the deuteron) while the singlet ($s=0$) is not. Thus the $t=0$ interaction (H_s) is stronger than the $t=1$ (H_a).

We may apply this formalism to multinucleon systems, following Wigner. Assume A nucleons (Z protons, $N=A-Z$ neutrons) and only two-body interactions:

$$H_{ij}=H_{ij}^{(1)}+H_{ij}^{(2)}\boldsymbol{\tau}_i\cdot\boldsymbol{\tau}_j, \tag{10}$$

$$2H=\sum\sum_{j\neq i} H_{ij}^{(1)}+\sum\sum_{j\neq i} H_{ij}^{(2)}\boldsymbol{\tau}_i\cdot\boldsymbol{\tau}_j. \tag{10a}$$

For such a Hamiltonian (recall atomic physics [2]) the good quantum numbers are τ_i^2; $t^2=(\Sigma_i\boldsymbol{\tau}_i)^2=\Sigma_i\tau_i^2+\Sigma\Sigma_{j\neq i}\boldsymbol{\tau}_i\cdot\boldsymbol{\tau}_j$; $t_3=\Sigma\tau_{3i}=(Z-N)/2$. The problem of the building up of nuclei is in many ways similar to that of the building up of the elements. The Pauli principle, of course, plays a major role and leads to the nuclear analogue of electronic shells (periodic structure). It can be shown that, for the nuclear forces known from low-energy two-body interactions, the lowest state is generally the one with minimum t, which is $t=|Z-N|/2$. Charge independence says that there should be a one-to-one correspondence between levels belonging to the same isotopic-spin multiplet for nuclei of the same A but different Z (isobars). This is in general observed. Thus, for example, the nuclei ${}_3\text{Li}^7$ and ${}_4\text{Be}^7$ show an almost identical level structure (see Figure 7.1). Another striking example is the ${}_6\text{C}^{14}$, ${}_7\text{N}^{14}$, ${}_8\text{O}^{14}$ triplet, whose known energy levels are shown in Figure 7.2. In this case, the corresponding levels must all have $t\geq 1$. (The extra levels in N^{14} should all correspond to $t=0$, which is not available in C^{14} and O^{14} since these have $t_3=-1$ and $+1$, respectively. However, not all the levels have been identified, and many are not yet known, especially in O^{14}. Nevertheless, the correspondence is quite striking.)

The conservation of isotopic spin also leads to selection rules in nuclear reactions, which may be used to check the isotopic-spin assignments of levels. For example, consider the reaction

$$\text{C}^{12}+\alpha\rightarrow\text{N}^{14}+d. \tag{11}$$

Since the ground states of C^{12}, α, and d all have $t=0$, the reaction can only lead to those levels of N^{14} for which $t=0$. Indeed, it is observed that the levels of N^{14} labeled $t=1$ in Figure 7.2 are not appreciably excited in this reaction.

Of course, isotopic-spin conservation is not absolute since the electromagnetic interactions, present in all nuclei, are manifestly charge dependent. Thus, the coulomb forces lead to shifts in the energies of levels with the same configuration, since the coulomb energy depends on Z. Also, electromagnetic interactions lead to violations of the isotopic-spin conservation rules in nuclear reactions, but these violations are weak in proportion to the weakness of the electromagnetic forces as compared to the nuclear forces.

---

[2] E. U. Condon and G. H. Shortley, *The Theory of Atomic Spectra,* Cambridge University Press, Cambridge, England (1935).

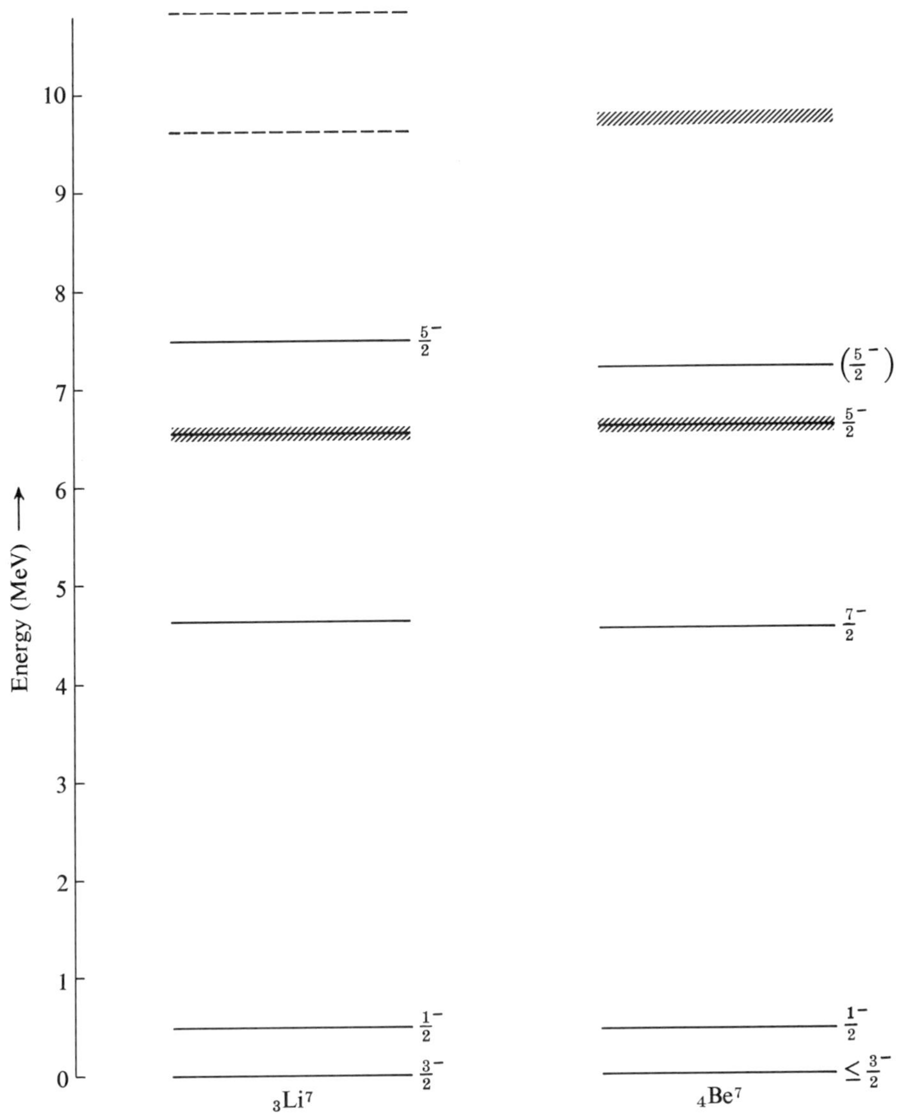

Figure 7.1 Comparison of the nuclear level structures of the $_3Li^7$–$_4Be^7$ doublet.

7.1.2 The Pion-Nucleon System

The pions, having $t = 1$, can combine with nucleons ($t = \frac{1}{2}$) into two states, of total isotopic spin $t = \frac{1}{2}$ and $t = \frac{3}{2}$. The properties of these combinations are summarized in Table 7.3. Note the relationship

$$Q = t_3 + \tfrac{1}{2}, \tag{12}$$

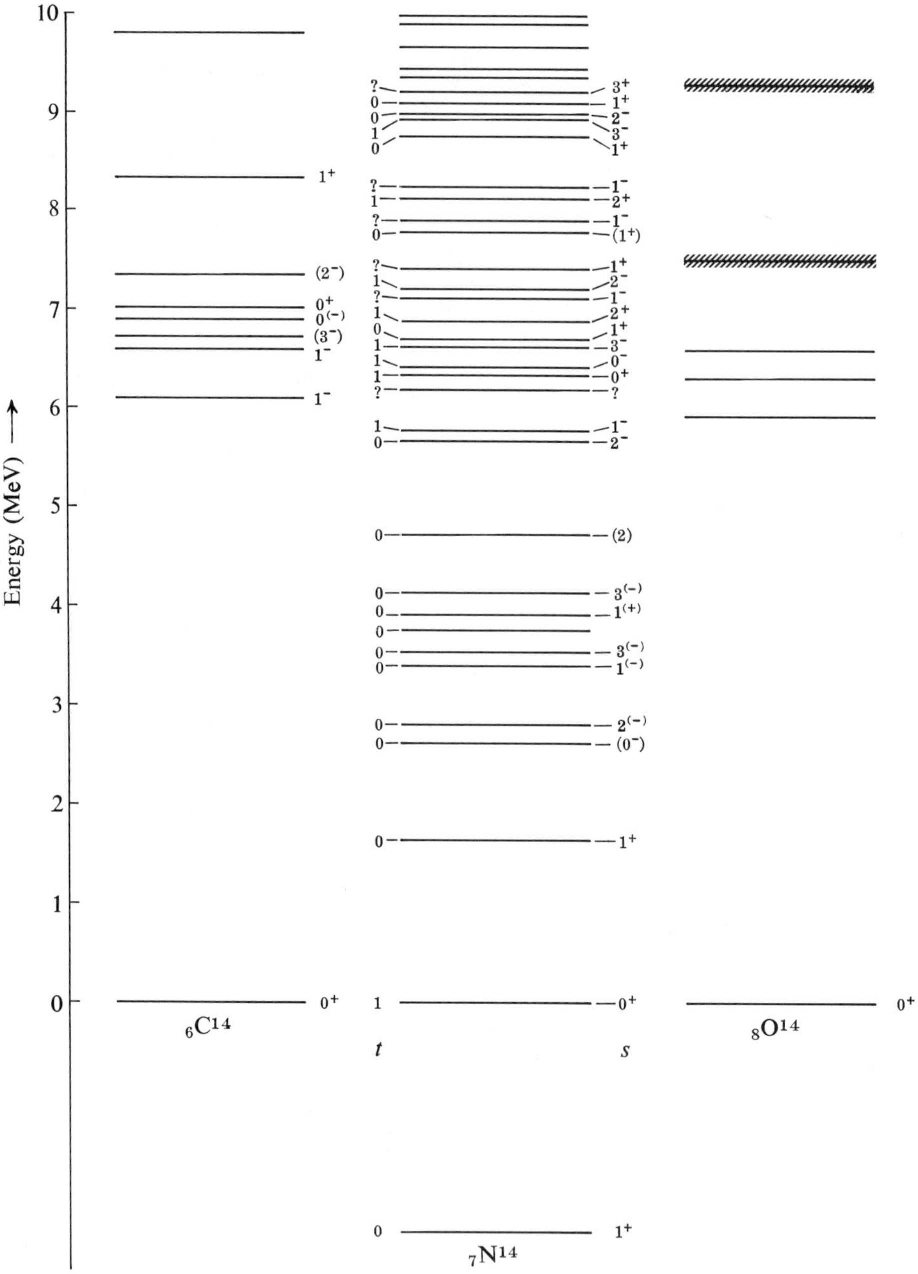

Figure 7.2 Comparison of the nuclear level structures of the $A = 14$ triplet. (Note that the lowest $t = 1$ level of ${}_7N^{14}$ is made to coincide with the ground states of the other members of the isotriplet, so as to facilitate comparison of the spectra.)

which is a special case of the general connection between charge, isospin, and hypercharge [$\mathcal{Y} = (B + S)/2$]:

$$Q = t_3 + \frac{\mathcal{Y}}{2}. \tag{12a}$$

As a consequence of the charge independence of the pion-nucleon interaction, the pion-nucleon scattering processes[3] can be completely described in terms of two amplitudes: A_3, for scattering in the $t = \frac{3}{2}$ state, and A_1, for $t = \frac{1}{2}$. Making use of the combinations given in Table 7.3, we may derive the corresponding scattering amplitudes shown in Table 7.4. For an elastic scattering process, we have

Table 7.3 Nucleon-Pion Combinations

(a) Individual Charge States

State	t_3	Charge (Q)	Isospin state
$P\pi^+$	$\frac{3}{2}$	2	$\chi_{3/2}^{3/2}$
$P\pi^0$	$\frac{1}{2}$	1	$\sqrt{\frac{2}{3}}\,\chi_{3/2}^{1/2} + \sqrt{\frac{1}{3}}\,\chi_{1/2}^{1/2}$
$N\pi^+$	$\frac{1}{2}$	1	$\sqrt{\frac{1}{3}}\,\chi_{3/2}^{1/2} - \sqrt{\frac{2}{3}}\,\chi_{1/2}^{1/2}$
$N\pi^0$	$-\frac{1}{2}$	0	$\sqrt{\frac{2}{3}}\,\chi_{3/2}^{-1/2} - \sqrt{\frac{1}{3}}\,\chi_{1/2}^{-1/2}$
$P\pi^-$	$-\frac{1}{2}$	0	$\sqrt{\frac{1}{3}}\,\chi_{3/2}^{-1/2} + \sqrt{\frac{2}{3}}\,\chi_{1/2}^{-1/2}$
$N\pi^-$	$-\frac{3}{2}$	-1	$\chi_{3/2}^{-3/2}$

(b) Isospin States

t	t_3	Combination
$\frac{3}{2}$	$\frac{3}{2}$	$N\pi^+$
$\frac{3}{2}$	$\frac{1}{2}$	$\sqrt{\frac{2}{3}}\,P\pi^0 + \sqrt{\frac{1}{3}}\,N\pi^+$
$\frac{3}{2}$	$-\frac{1}{2}$	$\sqrt{\frac{2}{3}}\,N\pi^0 + \sqrt{\frac{1}{3}}\,P\pi^-$
$\frac{3}{2}$	$-\frac{3}{2}$	$N\pi^-$
$\frac{1}{2}$	$\frac{1}{2}$	$\sqrt{\frac{1}{3}}\,P\pi^0 - \sqrt{\frac{2}{3}}\,N\pi^+$
$\frac{1}{2}$	$-\frac{1}{2}$	$-\sqrt{\frac{1}{3}}\,N\pi^0 + \sqrt{\frac{2}{3}}\,P\pi^-$

$$2iA_{t,j} = e^{2i\alpha_{t,j}} - 1, \tag{13}$$

where α is in general complex (see Chapter 5). For a resonant elastic scattering in the state (t, j)

$$\alpha_{t,j} = \tan^{-1}\frac{\Gamma}{2(E_r - E)}. \tag{13a}$$

[3] These same considerations hold for any reaction of the form

$$a(t = 1) + b(t = \tfrac{1}{2}) \rightarrow a'(t = 1) + b'(t = \tfrac{1}{2}). \tag{12b}$$

Table 7.4 Amplitudes for Pion-Nucleon Scattering

Scattering process	A_j
$\pi^+P \to \pi^+P$ $\pi^-N \to \pi^-N$	$A_{3,j}$
$\pi^-P \to \pi^-P$ $\pi^+N \to \pi^+N$	$\frac{1}{3}(A_{3,j}+2A_{1,j})$
$\pi^-P \to \pi^0N$ $\pi^+N \to \pi^0P$	$\frac{\sqrt{2}}{3}(A_{3,j}-A_{1,j})$
$\pi^0P \to \pi^0P$ $\pi^0N \to \pi^0N$	$\frac{1}{3}(2A_{3,j}+A_{1,j})$

In the case of pion-nucleon scattering, at least in the energy range $E_\pi \lesssim 1.5$ GeV, the scattering is dominated by the excitation of nucleonic resonances (isobars) of which the most important is the $\mathfrak{N}^*(3, 3)$ $[t=\frac{3}{2}, j=\frac{3}{2}^+]$ of mass 1238 MeV/c^2. We shall consider some effects of this resonance on scattering and related processes in a later section.

However, in addition to the resonant behavior of $\alpha_{3,3}$, systematic analysis of the pion-nucleon scattering data over the energy range $0 < E_\pi \lesssim 1.5$ GeV has, as noted, exhibited the presence of a number of other scattering resonances.[4] Analysis of these data, which include total cross sections, differential cross sections from unpolarized targets and, at some energies, from polarized targets, some scattered polarization measurements, and inelasticity observations (on the three connected reactions $\pi^+P \to \pi^+P$, $\pi^-P \to \pi^-P$, and $\pi^-P \to \pi^0N$) is complicated by a number of factors. The measurements, made at a variety of energies and by a variety of techniques at different laboratories, are sometimes not internally consistent; as the energy increases, a greater number of phase shifts, corresponding to $l \leq l_{\text{max}}(E) \approx kR$, must be taken into account; once a given l-value comes into play, the corresponding phase shift cannot be neglected, even when it does not exhibit a resonant behavior. This leads to the problem of ambiguities, already present even at low pion energies, as illustrated in Problem 5 of Section 6.2.1; this problem becomes even more serious at higher energies as more phase shifts come into prominence. Furthermore, almost all the higher resonances are strongly inelastic, so that their scattering phase shifts are complex, i.e.,

$$\begin{aligned} 2iA_{t,j} &= e^{2i(\alpha_r+i\alpha_i)_{t,j}} - 1 \\ &= \eta_{t,j}e^{2i\delta_{t,j}} - 1, \end{aligned} \tag{13'}$$

with

[4] See L. D. Roper, R. M. Wright, and B. T. Feld, *Phys. Rev., 138:* B 190 (1965); B. H. Bransden, P. J. O'Donnell, and R. G. Moorhouse, *Phys. Letters, 19:* 420 (1965); P. Auvil, A. Donnachie, A. T. Lea, and C. Lovelace, *Phys. Letters, 12:* 76 (1964); P. Bareyere, C. Bricman, A. V. Stirling, and G. Villet, *Phys. Letters, 18:* 342 (1965).

$$0 \leq \eta_{t,j} \leq 1. \tag{13''}$$

As a consequence, the phase-shift analyses at energies $E_\pi \gtrsim 500$ MeV are subject to considerable uncertainties and ambiguities.

In carrying out such analyses, it is convenient to represent the scattering amplitudes, A_i, by use of the *Argand diagram*, which is a plot of Im A_i versus Re A_i. Since

$$\text{Re}\, A_i = \tfrac{1}{2}\eta_i \sin 2\delta_i, \tag{13b}$$

$$\text{Im}\, A_i = \tfrac{1}{2}(1 - \eta_i \cos 2\delta_i), \tag{13c}$$

the complex phase shift at a given pion energy is represented by a point that lies inside a circle of unit diameter, as shown in Figure 7.3, with the center at

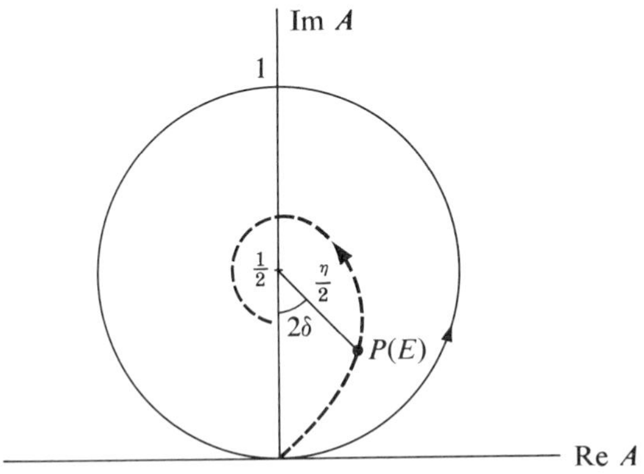

Figure 7.3 Argand diagram for describing elastic scattering amplitudes.

($\text{Re}\, A_i = 0$, $\text{Im}\, A_i = \frac{1}{2}$). Pure elastic scattering ($\eta = 1$) is represented by this limiting circle, the points for increasing E_π starting at the origin and moving around the circumference in a counterclockwise direction; the energy of crossing of the imaginary axis corresponds to the resonance energy E_r, while the half-width $\Gamma/2$ is given by $E(\delta = \pi/2) - E(\delta = \pi/4)$. For the case of finite, but constant inelasticity ($\eta < 1$), the phase shift describes a circle of radius $\eta/2$ centered at ($\text{Re}\, A = 0, \text{Im}\, A = \frac{1}{2}$).

However, in any actual case the inelasticity also varies with E, starting from $\eta = 1$ at $E = 0$. Hence, the Argand diagrams corresponding to the various pion-nucleon scattering phase shifts, $\alpha_{t,j}$, exhibit much more complicated behavior patterns than the simple cases described above. Figure 7.4, taken from a summary by Lovelace,[5] compares the results of two independent phase shift analyses for the π–$\mathfrak{N}$ scattering amplitudes corresponding to $l \leq 4$. The parameters

[5] C. Lovelace, *Proceedings of the Heidelberg International Conference on Elementary Particles* (North Holland, 1968), p. 79; see also P. Bareyere, C. Bricman, and G. Villet, *Phys. Rev., 165:* 1730 (1968).

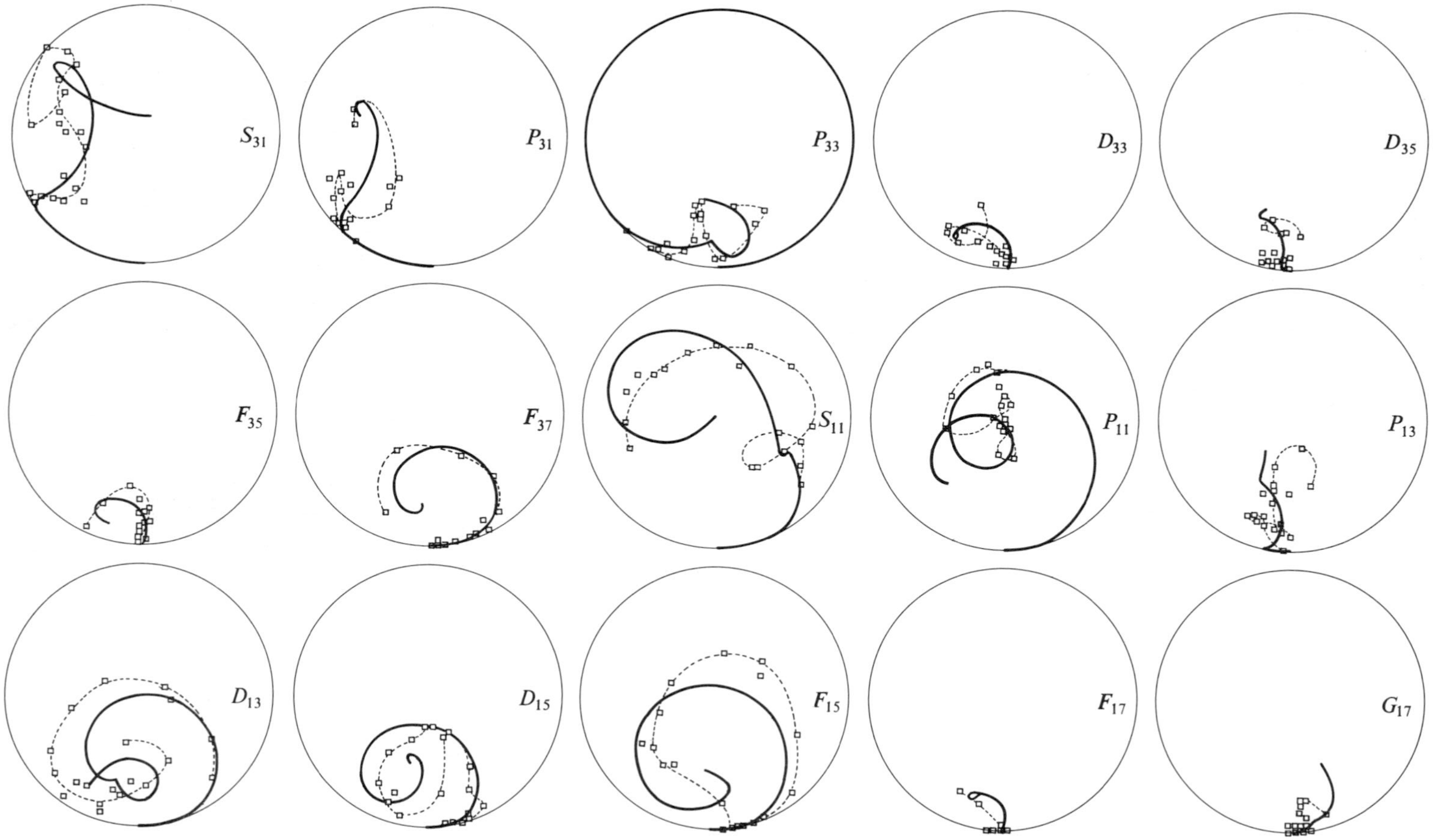

Figure 7.4 Argand diagrams for π–$\mathfrak{N}$ scattering phase shifts.

deduced for the most probable pion-nucleon scattering resonances of mass $\lesssim 2400$ MeV/c^2 are summarized in Table 7.5.

One further point should be noted: One way of defining a resonance is through the condition that the real part of the phase shift, δ, must pass through 90° from below. For $\delta = \pi/2$, Im $A_r \geq \frac{1}{2}$ [see Equation (13c)]. However, some of the Argand diagrams that appear to exhibit resonant behavior — i.e., describe, more or less, a counterclockwise circle — cross the Im A axis at a value $< \frac{1}{2}$. For such "resonances," the real part of the phase shift never reaches 90° but, rather, attains a maximum, $\delta_{max} < \pi/2$, and then decreases again, passing through $\delta_r = 0°$ at $E = E_r$. Clearly, there is some ambiguity in the definition of a "resonance" for the case of highly inelastic reactions.

Table 7.5 Relatively Well-established π–$\mathfrak{N}$ Scattering Resonances

Partial wave	Isobar mass (MeV/c^2)	Γ (MeV)	$\eta_r = \Gamma_{el}/\Gamma_{tot}$
$P_{3,3}$	1236	125	1
$P_{1,1}$	1466	211	0.66
$D_{1,3}$	1526	114	0.57
$S_{3,1}$	1635	177	0.28
$D_{1,5}$	1678	173	0.39
$F_{1,5}$	1692	132	0.68
$S_{1,1}$	1709	300	0.79
$F_{3,7}$	1946	221	0.39
$G_{1,7}$	2265	298	0.35
$H_{3,11}$	~ 2400	~ 340	~ 0.18

PROBLEMS

1. Charge symmetry, which is a weaker condition than charge independence (isotopic invariance), requires that the interaction Hamiltonian shall be invariant with respect to reflection about the 1–2 plane in charge space ($t_3 \to -t_3$). Show that the most general form of a charge-symmetric interaction between two nucleons is

$$H = H_0 + H_1\, \boldsymbol{\tau}_1 \cdot \boldsymbol{\tau}_2 + H_2\, \tau_{31}\tau_{32},$$

where $H_i = H_i(\boldsymbol{\sigma}, \mathbf{r})$.

Discuss the problem of isotopic-spin conservation for a two-nucleon system subject to this interaction Hamiltonian.

2. The nucleon charge operator is

$$Q = (\tau_3 + \tfrac{1}{2})\, e.$$

(a) How must the two-nucleon interaction Hamiltonian [Equation (8′)] be modified to take into account the Coulomb interaction between two protons?

(b) Show that the Coulomb interaction is not invariant with respect to rotations in isotopic-spin (charge) space.
(c) Discuss the problem of mixing of states of different isotopic spin through the Coulomb interaction
 (i) in the two-nucleon system;
 (ii) in complex nuclei.
(d) Another source of breakdown of isotopic invariance is the neutron-proton mass difference, $M_N - M_P \cong 1.3\ \text{MeV}/c^2$. Assuming a term in the two-nucleon interaction Hamiltonian proportional to the sum of the masses of the constituents, derive an expression for the dependence of this term on the isotopic-spin operators. Give a rough comparison of the relative effects of this term and of the Coulomb interaction term in splitting the energies of substates of an isotopic triplet ($t = 1$) having the same spin and space configurations.

3. The proton and neutron have different magnetic moments:

$$\boldsymbol{\mu}_P \cong 2.793\ \mu_0 \times 2\mathbf{s}_P,$$
$$\boldsymbol{\mu}_N \cong -1.913\ \mu_0 \times 2\mathbf{s}_N.$$

(a) Give an expression for the nucleon magnetic moment operator (in terms of τ_3).
(b) Assume that the deuteron is in the $^3S_1$ spin state with $t = 0$. Compute the corresponding value of the deuteron magnetic moment (i.e., the expectation value of $\boldsymbol{\mu} = \boldsymbol{\mu}_P + \boldsymbol{\mu}_N$ in the state $m_s = 1$) and compare with the experimental value. What is the source of the discrepancy, if any?

4. The relationships among the π–$\mathfrak{N}$ scattering amplitudes (Table 7.3) lead to a "triangle inequality" among the scattering cross sections:

$$\sigma(\pi^+P \to \pi^+P) \leq \{\sqrt{\sigma(\pi^-P \to \pi^-P)} + \sqrt{2\sigma(\pi^-P \to \pi^0N)}\}^2.$$

(a) Check the experimental validity of this inequality against the total cross section data.[6]
(b) Derive and check a second independent triangle inequality among the same cross sections.

5. The total $\pi\mathfrak{N}$ cross section in the $t = \frac{3}{2}$ state is

$$\sigma_{\text{tot}}(t = \tfrac{3}{2}) = \sigma_{\text{tot}}(\pi^+P).$$

Why? Show that

$$\sigma_{\text{tot}}(t = \tfrac{1}{2}) = \tfrac{3}{2}\sigma_{\text{tot}}(\pi^-P) - \tfrac{1}{2}\sigma_{\text{tot}}(\pi^+P).$$

6. Consider the set of $K\mathfrak{N}$ scattering reactions

$$K^+P \to K^+P, \tag{1}$$

$$K^0P \to K^0P, \tag{2}$$

[6] See G. Källen, *Elementary Particle Physics*, Addison-Wesley, Reading, Mass. (1964), pp. 72–74.

$$K^+N \to K^+N, \tag{3}$$

$$K^0N \to K^0N, \tag{4}$$

$$K^+N \to K^0P, \tag{5}$$

$$K^0P \to K^+N. \tag{6}$$

(a) Assuming isotopic invariance, there are two independent amplitudes, A_1 and A_0, corresponding, respectively, to scattering in the $t=1$ and $t=0$ states. Give expressions for the cross sections for reactions (1) to (6) in terms of these amplitudes. What relationships are there among these cross sections?

(b) Assuming an interaction Hamiltonian of the form

$$H_{K\mathfrak{N}} = H_1 + H_2\,\boldsymbol{\tau}_K \cdot \boldsymbol{\tau}_{\mathfrak{N}}$$

and a scattering amplitude of the form

$$A_{fi} = A\langle \psi_f^* | H_{K\mathfrak{N}} | \psi_i \rangle$$

with f and i representing the final and initial $K\mathfrak{N}$ state wave functions, derive expressions for the cross sections in terms of $\langle H_1\rangle$ and $\langle H_2\rangle$. Compare with (a) above.

(c) What are the relations among the cross sections in the limits $H_1 \gg H_2$ and $H_1 \ll H_2$?

7. The cross section for $K^- + P$ shows a resonance at $p_K \cong 400$ MeV/c.[7] This resonance appears in the reactions

$$K^-P \to \Sigma\pi,$$
$$\to \Lambda\pi\pi,$$

but not in the reaction

$$K^-P \to \Lambda^0\pi^0.$$

(a) What conclusions can you draw on the isotopic-spin value of the resonance?

(b) Derive the relations to be expected for the relative probabilities of the various possible charge states among the products of this resonant interaction.

8. The first two of the reactions

$$\pi^-P \to P\pi^-\pi^0 \tag{1}$$

$$\to N\pi^+\pi^- \tag{2}$$

$$\to N\pi^0\pi^0 \tag{3}$$

have been extensively studied in hydrogen bubble chambers. Assume that all

[7] See Ferro-Luzzi, *et al.*, *Phys. Rev. Letters*, *8*: 28 (1962).

charged particles can be identified and their momenta accurately measured, and that neutral particles escape detection.

(a) How would you determine that an observed event with two charged products (two-prong event) corresponds to either reaction (1) or (2), and not to either an elastic scattering or to an inelastic reaction with more than one neutral product?
(b) How would you determine whether two of the products were produced in a resonance? *Hint:* sketch the appropriate Dalitz plots.
(c) Assume the two pions are produced in a resonant state. What are the relative probabilities of the three reactions for
  (i) $t_{2\pi} = 0$,
  (ii) $t_{2\pi} = 1$,
  (iii) $t_{2\pi} = 2$.
(d) Assume that one $\mathfrak{N}\pi$ combination is formed in a resonant state, i.e.,

$$\pi^- P \to \mathfrak{N}^* + \pi' \quad \mathfrak{N}^* \to \mathfrak{N} + \pi,$$

and that the nonresonant pion (π') is kinematically distinguishable in each case.
  (i) Choosing $\pi' = \pi^0$, what are the relative probabilities of reactions (1) and (3) for $t(\mathfrak{N}^*) = \frac{3}{2}$, and for $t(\mathfrak{N}^*) = \frac{1}{2}$?
  (ii) Choosing $\pi' = \pi^-$, what are the relative probabilities of reactions (1) and (2) for $t(\mathfrak{N}^*) = \frac{3}{2}$ and $\frac{1}{2}$?
(e) Suppose the reaction goes through an intermediate resonance

$$\pi^- + P \to \mathfrak{N}^{**} \to \mathfrak{N}^* + \pi'.$$

Derive the relative probabilities for reactions (1) to (3) for the four possible combinations of $t(\mathfrak{N}^{**}) = \frac{3}{2}$ or $\frac{1}{2}$, and $t(\mathfrak{N}^*) = \frac{3}{2}$ or $\frac{1}{2}$.

9. Consider the reaction

$$\pi^- + D \to N + N + \pi^0$$

for π^- at rest. (Check that the reaction is possible — i.e., exoergic — and compute the energy release.) Using the Pauli principle to determine the possible states of the final di-neutron, and assuming a decay probability $\propto (k_N R)^{2L+1} (k_\pi R)^{2l+1}$ with $R \approx 1$ f, with k_N and k_π, respectively, the momenta of one of the neutrons (assume the other remains at rest) and the pion, and with L and l, respectively, the internal orbital angular momentum of the $2N$ system and the relative orbital angular momentum of the pion, compare the relative probabilities for the most probable final states under the assumption that

(a) π^- and π^0 have the same parity,
(b) π^- and π^0 have opposite parity.

7.2 Photoproduction Reactions

Although the electromagnetic interactions are manifestly charge dependent, the isotopic-spin formalism has, nevertheless, some important consequences for the relationships among photo-nucleon reactions when the products are hadrons. These relationships derive from two sources: first, for final states consisting entirely of hadrons, the isotopic spin is a good quantum number; second, the electromagnetic interaction has, at least in first order, a definite dependence on the isotopic-spin operators, behaving essentially as a combination of a "scalar" and a "vector" in isotopic-spin space, and consequently giving rise to the simple isotopic-spin selection rule

$$\Delta t = 0, \pm 1. \tag{14}$$

As an illustrative example, we consider the set of reactions $\gamma\mathfrak{N} \to \mathfrak{N}'\pi$ — i.e.,

$$\gamma P \to P\pi^0, \tag{15a}$$

$$\gamma P \to N\pi^+, \tag{15b}$$

$$\gamma N \to N\pi^0, \tag{15c}$$

$$\gamma N \to P\pi^-, \tag{15d}$$

To determine the relationships among the four amplitudes corresponding to reactions (15a)–(15d), we consider a special model,[8] in which the target nucleon $\mathfrak{N}$ first dissociates into a (virtual) $\mathfrak{N}'\pi$ state, which is then acted upon by the electromagnetic field. This virtual state has the properties $t_3 = t_{3\mathfrak{N}}$, $t = \frac{1}{2}$ [see Table 7.3(b)], and the interaction Hamiltonian has the general form

$$\begin{aligned} H &= H_0 + H_0' \boldsymbol{\tau}_{\mathfrak{N}'} \cdot \boldsymbol{\tau}_\pi + H_{\mathfrak{N}}\, \tau_{3\mathfrak{N}'} + H_\pi\, \tau_{3\pi} \\ &= H_0 + H_0'\, \boldsymbol{\tau}_{\mathfrak{N}'} \cdot \boldsymbol{\tau}_\pi + \overline{H}(\tau_{3\mathfrak{N}'} + \tau_{3\pi}) + \delta H(\tau_{3\mathfrak{N}'} - \tau_{3\pi}), \end{aligned} \tag{16}$$

in which the first two terms represent the charge-independent final-state interactions. The resulting matrix elements between the initial $\mathfrak{N}$ state, $\chi_{1/2}^{t_3}$, and final $\pi\mathfrak{N}'$ combinations in states of definite isotopic spin (see Table 7.3) are easily obtained.

$$\langle \chi_{1/2}^{1/2} | H | \chi_{1/2}^{1/2} \rangle = H_0 + H_0' + \tfrac{1}{3}\overline{H} - \tfrac{5}{6}\delta H \equiv H^{(0)} + H^{(1)}, \tag{16a}$$

$$\langle \chi_{1/2}^{1/2} | H | \chi_{3/2}^{1/2} \rangle = -\frac{2\sqrt{2}}{3}\,\delta H \equiv H^{(2)}, \tag{16b}$$

$$\langle \chi_{1/2}^{-1/2} | H | \chi_{1/2}^{-1/2} \rangle = H_0 + H_0' - \tfrac{1}{3}\overline{H} + \tfrac{5}{6}\delta H = H^{(0)} - H^{(1)}, \tag{16c}$$

$$\langle \chi_{1/2}^{-1/2} | H | \chi_{3/2}^{-1/2} \rangle = -\frac{2\sqrt{2}}{3}\,\delta H = H^{(2)}. \tag{16d}$$

[8] Although this model is useful for deriving the desired results, these can be shown to be model independent, at least to first order in the electromagnetic coupling.

Combining these with the help of Table 7.3, we obtain the amplitudes corresponding to specific final $\pi\mathfrak{N}'$ states. These are summarized in Table 7.6. We note that in Equations (16)–(16d) and Table 7.6 the term $H^{(0)}$, or $A_{1,j}$, arises out of an interaction that is scalar in isotopic-spin space, while the terms $H^{(1)}$ and $H^{(2)}$, or $A'_{1,j}$ and $A_{3,j}$, are the result of an interaction that has the properties of a vector in isospin space.

Table 7.6 Amplitudes for $\gamma\mathfrak{N} \rightarrow \mathfrak{N}'\pi$

Reaction	A_j
$\gamma P \rightarrow P\pi^0$	$-\sqrt{\tfrac{1}{3}}(A_{1,j}+A'_{1,j})+\sqrt{\tfrac{2}{3}}\,A_{3,j}$
$\gamma P \rightarrow N\pi^+$	$\sqrt{\tfrac{2}{3}}(A_{1,j}+A'_{1,j})+\sqrt{\tfrac{1}{3}}\,A_{3,j}$
$\gamma N \rightarrow N\pi^0$	$\sqrt{\tfrac{1}{3}}(A_{1,j}-A'_{1,j})+\sqrt{\tfrac{2}{3}}\,A_{3,j}$
$\gamma N \rightarrow P\pi^-$	$-\sqrt{\tfrac{2}{3}}(A_{1,j}-A'_{1,j})+\sqrt{\tfrac{1}{3}}\,A_{3,j}$

The amplitudes of Table 7.6 are subject to some additional physical restrictions. Thus, as a result of the Fermi–Watson theorem (Chapter 5) the phases of the complex amplitudes are determined by the pion-nucleon scattering phase shifts $\alpha_{t,j}$ at the *cm* energies and in the states (t, j) under consideration (provided other inelastic processes are unimportant):

$$A_{t,j}=\rho_{t,j}\,e^{i\alpha_{t,j}}. \tag{17}$$

For the special case of resonant interactions, the amplitude may be approximated by a Breit–Wigner formula

$$A_{t,j}\cong\frac{(\Gamma_\gamma\Gamma)^{1/2}_{t,j}}{(E_r-E)-i\Gamma/2}=\left(\frac{\Gamma_\gamma}{\Gamma}\right)^{1/2}\sin\alpha_{t,j}\,e^{i\alpha_{t,j}}. \tag{17a}$$

In addition, it is important to remember that, as a result of the special properties of the electromagnetic field (Section 6.2.2), a state of given angular momentum and parity, j^π, can in general be excited by both electric and magnetic radiation, with multipolarities differing by one. Thus, for example, the excited nucleonic state of $j=\tfrac{3}{2}^+$ can be formed by absorption of both $M1$ and $E2$ radiation. The amplitudes $A_{t,j}$ must, accordingly, be further categorized by the photon multipolarity, $\mathit{ME}l_\gamma$. For a resonant process, Equation (17a), for example, the two possible amplitudes will differ only through the different values of the magnitude of the photon width, Γ_γ.

Another interesting physical situation arises in the consideration of the photoproduction reactions [Equations (15a)–(15d)] very close to threshold ($E_{\gamma\ lab} \approx$ 140 MeV). In this case, the angular momentum barriers, which inhibit low-energy pion emission for $l_\pi > 0$, suppress those photon absorption processes leading to $l_\pi > 0$. This results in the dominance of $E1$ absorption, the only possibility that can give rise to S-wave pion emission. In the absence of any resonant $(j=\tfrac{1}{2}^-)$ process, the amplitudes for $E1$ absorption in reactions (15a)–(15d) will be proportional to the electric dipole moments in the intermediate $\mathfrak{N}'\pi$ states. The electric dipole moments in the intermediate states may be computed using a classical approach, i.e.,

$$\boldsymbol{\mu}_E = Q_\pi \mathbf{r}_\pi + Q_{\mathfrak{N}'} \mathbf{r}_{\mathfrak{N}'}, \tag{18}$$

where the displacement vectors are measured from the *cm* of the target nucleon

$$\mu \mathbf{r}_\pi + M \mathbf{r}_{\mathfrak{N}'} = 0 \tag{18'}$$

(μ and M are, respectively, the pion and nucleon masses), and the charges are expressed in terms of the third components of the isospin vectors

$$\begin{aligned} Q_\pi &= \tau_{3\pi}\, e, \\ Q_{\mathfrak{N}'} &= (\tau_{3\mathfrak{N}'} + \tfrac{1}{2})\, e. \end{aligned} \tag{18''}$$

Accordingly, assuming that the interaction Hamiltonian for S-wave pion photoproduction is proportional to the magnitude of the electric dipole moment in the intermediate state [Equation (18)], the corresponding Hamiltonian has the form

$$H_{E1} = C\left\{\frac{M}{M+\mu}\tau_{3\pi} - \frac{\mu}{M+\mu}\left(\tau_{3\mathfrak{N}'} + \frac{1}{2}\right)\right\}. \tag{16'}$$

Straightforward computation of the matrix elements of (16′) corresponding, for this special case, to Equations (16a)–(16d), leads to the results for the $E1$ ($j = \frac{1}{2}^-$)

Table 7.7 $E1$ Amplitudes near Threshold for $\gamma\mathfrak{N} \to \mathfrak{N}'\pi$

Process	$E_{1,1}/E_0$	$E_{3,1}/E_0$	Sum
$\gamma P \to P\pi^0$	$-\frac{2}{3}\sqrt{\frac{1}{3}}\left(\frac{M-\mu/2}{M+\mu}\right)$	$\frac{2}{3}\sqrt{\frac{1}{3}}$	$\sqrt{\frac{1}{3}}\frac{\mu}{M+\mu}$
$\gamma P \to N\pi^+$	$\frac{2}{3}\sqrt{\frac{2}{3}}\left(\frac{M-\mu/2}{M+\mu}\right)$	$\frac{1}{3}\sqrt{\frac{2}{3}}$	$\sqrt{\frac{2}{3}}\frac{M}{M+\mu}$
$\gamma N \to N\pi^0$	$-\frac{2}{3}\sqrt{\frac{1}{3}}$	$\frac{2}{3}\sqrt{\frac{1}{3}}$	0
$\gamma N \to P\pi^-$	$\frac{2}{3}\sqrt{\frac{2}{3}}$	$\frac{1}{3}\sqrt{\frac{2}{3}}$	$\sqrt{\frac{2}{3}}$

amplitudes shown in Table 7.7. In particular, using the Born approximation to compute the matrix elements, we note that the common factor E_0 has the form [9]

$$E_0 \cong \frac{1}{2} ef \left(\frac{q}{k}\right)^{1/2} \mu^{-1}, \tag{18a}$$

where e and f are the electromagnetic and pion coupling constants, respectively; q and k are the pion and photon *cm* momenta; and μ^{-1} is the pion Compton wave-

[9] This should be multiplied by a retardation factor (see Section 6.2.2), which is relatively unimportant near threshold.

length. Taking advantage of the Fermi–Watson theorem, we may write for the $E1$ amplitude, including the phases,

$$E1 = E_{1,1}e^{i\alpha_1} + E_{1,3}e^{i\alpha_3}, \tag{18b}$$

where α_1 and α_3 are the pion S-wave scattering phase shifts in the states $t=\frac{1}{2}$ and $t=\frac{3}{2}$, respectively.

$$\alpha_1 \simeq 0.16\frac{q}{\mu}, \tag{18c}$$

$$\alpha_3 \simeq -0.11\frac{q}{\mu}, \tag{18d}$$

for $q/\mu < 1$. However, very close to threshold, $\alpha_1 \approx \alpha_3 \approx 0$, so that $E1$ is, to a good approximation, given by the sum of the magnitudes (column 4 of Table 7.7). In this case, we have for the cross sections

$$\sigma(P\pi^0):\sigma(N\pi^+):\sigma(N\pi^0):\sigma(P\pi^-) \cong \frac{1}{2}\left(\frac{\mu}{M}\right)^2 : 1 : 0 : \left(1+\frac{\mu}{M}\right)^2 = 0.011 : 1 : 0 : 1.32, \tag{18e}$$

a result that is in rather good agreement with the observations.[10]

Finally, we note the interesting effect that even those $E1$ amplitudes that are negligibly small near threshold [i.e., $E1(P\pi^0)$ and $E1(N\pi^0)$] can become quite appreciable at higher energies, owing to the difference in the phase shifts α_1 and α_3 (see Figure 7.5).

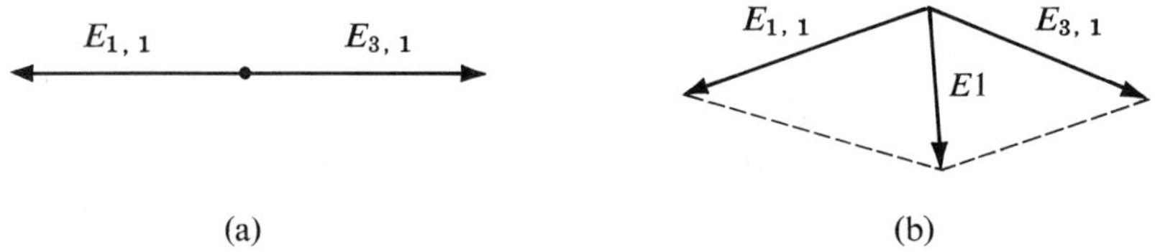

Figure 7.5 Behavior of small $E1$ amplitudes near threshold. (a) At threshold. (b) $q/\mu \sim 1$.

PROBLEMS

1. Consider the reactions

$$\gamma + \mathfrak{N} \rightarrow \mathfrak{N}^*(t=\tfrac{3}{2}) + \pi.$$

(a) Assuming an interaction Hamiltonian of the form of Equation (16), derive relationships among the amplitudes corresponding to the various charge combinations, i.e.,

---

[10] B. T. Feld, *Ann. Phys.* (New York), *4:* 189 (1958).

$$\begin{aligned}\gamma P &\to \mathfrak{N}^{*++}\pi^- \\ &\to \mathfrak{N}^{*+}\pi^0 \\ &\to \mathfrak{N}^{*0}\pi^+ , \\ \gamma N &\to \mathfrak{N}^{*+}\pi^- \\ &\to \mathfrak{N}^{*0}\pi^0 \\ &\to \mathfrak{N}^{*-}\pi^+ .\end{aligned}$$

(b) Let $\mathfrak{N}^* \to \mathfrak{N} + \pi$. Derive expressions for the cross sections corresponding to the various possible $\mathfrak{N}\pi\pi$ charge combinations in the final state.

(c) Assuming $j(\mathfrak{N}^*) = \frac{3}{2}^+$, the reaction near threshold will be dominated by $E1$ photon absorption, leading to S-wave pion emission. Assuming that the matrix element for $E1$ absorption is proportional to the (static) electric dipole moment in a virtual $(\mathfrak{N} \to \mathfrak{N}^*\pi)$ state of the parent nucleon, predict the relative values of the cross section for S-wave pion production near threshold for the reactions listed in (a). [Take $M(\mathfrak{N}^*) = 1236$ MeV/c^2.]

2. Let $\mathbf{p}_i$, $\mathbf{s}_i$, $\mathbf{r}_i$, $\mathbf{t}_i$ represent the momentum, spin, coordinate, and isospin of a particle, and Q_i, $\boldsymbol{\mu}_i$ represent its charge and magnetic moment operators. Consider an interaction Hamiltonian for two particles in Schroedinger (nonrelativistic) theory, including the interaction with an external electromagnetic field, represented by the vector potential $\mathbf{A}(\mathbf{r})$,

$$\begin{aligned}H_{12} = \frac{p_1^2}{2m_1} + \frac{p_2^2}{2m_2} &+ A(\mathbf{s}_1 \cdot \mathbf{p}_2)(\mathbf{s}_2 \cdot \mathbf{p}_1) + B(\boldsymbol{\mu}_1 + \boldsymbol{\mu}_2) \cdot \boldsymbol{\nabla} \times \mathbf{A}(\mathbf{r}) \\ &+ C(Q_1 + Q_2)\frac{\partial \mathbf{A}}{\partial t}(\mathbf{r}) + D[Q_1\mathbf{p}_1 \cdot \mathbf{A}(\mathbf{r}) + Q_2\mathbf{p}_2 \cdot \mathbf{A}(\mathbf{r})] \\ &+ E(\mathbf{t}_1 \times \mathbf{t}_2) \cdot (\mathbf{r}_1 \times \mathbf{p}_1 + \mathbf{r}_2 \times \mathbf{p}_2) + F(\mathbf{t}_1 \cdot \mathbf{t}_2)[(\mathbf{r}_1 - \mathbf{r}_2) \times (\mathbf{p}_1 - \mathbf{p}_2)] \cdot (\mathbf{s}_1 + \mathbf{s}_2) \\ &+ G(\mathbf{s}_1 \cdot \mathbf{p}_1 + \mathbf{s}_2 \cdot \mathbf{p}_2) + H(Q_1 - Q_2)(\mathbf{p}_1 \times \mathbf{p}_2) \cdot (\mathbf{s}_1 \times \mathbf{s}_2) \\ &+ I(Q_1 + Q_2)\,\mathbf{p}_1 \cdot \mathbf{p}_2 + J\frac{Q_1Q_2}{|\mathbf{r}_1 - \mathbf{r}_2|} .\end{aligned}$$

Which of the real coefficients $A, B, C, \cdots, J$ must be zero if H_{12} is invariant under the following operations?

(a) Parity, $\mathcal{P}$.
(b) Charge conjugation, $\mathcal{C}$.
(c) $\mathcal{CP}$.
(d) Time reversal, T.
(e) Rotation in isotopic-spin (charge) space.
(f) Inversion of the t_3 axis.

7.3 Some Effects of the (3, 3) Isobar Resonance

It is observed that the pion-nucleon interaction at low energies is dominated by the nucleon isobar $\mathfrak{N}^*(3, 3)$, of mass 1236 MeV, spin $j = \frac{3}{2}^+$, and isospin $t = \frac{3}{2}$. The effects of this isobar are strikingly evident in almost all interactions at energies permitting its resonant excitation.[11]

[11] B. T. Feld, *Ann. Phys.* (New York), *4:* 189 (1958); E. Fermi, *Suppl. Nuovo Cimento*, *2:* 17 (1955).

7.3.1 Pion-Nucleon Scattering

Pion-nucleon scattering for pion *lab* energies up to ~ 400 MeV is completely dominated by the (3, 3) resonance. Consider the expressions for the pion-nucleon scattering cross section (Section 6.2.1) at energies such that $l_\pi \leq 1$,

$$\frac{d\sigma}{d\Omega} = |f|^2 + |g|^2, \tag{19a}$$

$$qf_{\pm 1/2} = A_0 + (2A_3 + A_1)\cos\theta, \tag{19b}$$

$$qg_{\pm 1/2} = \mp(A_3 - A_1)\sin\theta\, e^{\pm i\varphi}, \tag{19c}$$

$$\begin{aligned} q^2\frac{d\sigma}{d\Omega} = {} & |A_0|^2 + |A_1|^2 + |A_3|^2(3\cos^2\theta + 1) \\ & + 2\,\mathrm{Re}\, A_0(2A_3 + A_1)^*\cos\theta \\ & + 2\,\mathrm{Re}\, A_3A_1^*(3\cos^2\theta - 1), \end{aligned} \tag{19d}$$

$$q^2\sigma = 4\pi(|A_0|^2 + |A_1|^2 + 2|A_3|^2), \tag{19e}$$

where q is the *cm* momentum of the pion and A_0, A_1, and A_3 are, respectively, the amplitudes for pion-nucleon scattering in the $S_{1/2}$, $P_{1/2}$, $P_{3/2}$ states. Dominance by the (3, 3) resonance implies $|A_3| \gg |A_0|, |A_1|$ and, consequently,

$$q^2\frac{d\sigma}{d\Omega} \simeq |A_3|^2(3\cos^2\theta + 1). \tag{19f}$$

For negligible inelastic scattering, we have

$$2iA_j = e^{2i\alpha_j} - 1 = 2i\,e^{i\alpha_j}\sin\alpha_j, \tag{19g}$$

with $\alpha_j = \pi/2$ at resonance. However, for a given combination of pion-nucleon charge states, the amplitudes A_j are combinations of the $t = \frac{3}{2}$ and $t = \frac{1}{2}$ scattering amplitudes, as shown in Table 7.4. Thus, in the case of a $t = \frac{3}{2}$ resonance, we would expect

$$\sigma(\pi^+P \to \pi^+P):\sigma(\pi^-P \to \pi^-P):\sigma(\pi^-P \to \pi^0N) = 9:1:2. \tag{19h}$$

Both the expected $(3\cos^3\theta + 1)$ angular distribution and the 9:1:2 cross-section ratio are observed for pion-nucleon elastic scattering and charge exchange in the low-energy range.

7.3.2 Photoproduction of Pions

Photoproduction of pions is also dominated by the (3, 3) resonance over the range of incident photon energies $E_\gamma \simeq 140 - 550$ MeV (which corresponds in total *cm* energy to the range of incident pion kinetic energies discussed above). Assuming $l_\pi \leq 1$, we note that the differential cross section for photopion production is [12]

---

[12] Our notation for the amplitudes A_j is $\mathcal{M}\!\mathcal{E}\; l_{\gamma,2j}$.

$$8k^2 \frac{d\sigma}{d\Omega} = |E1_1|^2 + |M1_1|^2 + \frac{1}{2}|M1_3|^2(5 - 3\cos^2\theta) + \frac{3}{2}|E2_3|^2(1 + \cos^2\theta)$$
$$+ 2\,\mathrm{Re}\, E1_1(M1_1 - M1_3 + \sqrt{3}\,E2_3)^* \cos\theta$$
$$- \mathrm{Re}\,(M1_1 M1_3^* - \sqrt{3}\,M1_1 E2_3^* + \sqrt{3}\,M1_3 E2_3^*)(3\cos^2\theta - 1), \quad (20a)$$

where k is the photon *cm* momentum. Dominance of the (3, 3) resonance implies the dominance of either $M1_3$ or $E2_3$; experimentally, it is observed that $|M1_3| \gg |E2_3|$, which results in an $\sim (5 - 3\cos^2\theta)$ angular distribution. In fact, this angular distribution is observed, to a good approximation, in the reaction $\gamma P \to P\pi^0$, over the entire energy range; however, as has been anticipated in Section 7.2 (Table 7.7), $E1$ absorption is important at photon energies near threshold for the reaction $\gamma P \to N\pi^+$, giving rise to a significant $\cos\theta$ term in the angular distribution. The total cross section,

$$2k^2\sigma = \pi\{|E1_1|^2 + |M1_1|^2 + 2|M1_3|^2 + 2|E2_3|^2\} \cong \pi|M1_3|^2, \quad (20b)$$

being dominated in the resonance region by a final state with $t = \frac{3}{2}$, exhibits the property

$$\sigma(\gamma P \to P\pi^0) : \sigma(\gamma P \to N\pi^+) \cong 2:1, \quad (20c)$$

as expected from Table 7.6 for the situation in which $A_{3,3} \gg A_{1,3}, A'_{1,3}$.

7.3.3 Elastic (Compton) Scattering of Photons by Nucleons

This reaction also shows significant effects of the (3, 3) resonance for photons in the appropriate energy range. The simplest approach for deriving expressions for the resonant photon-scattering cross section is to note that the amplitudes for both resonant photoproduction and resonant pion scattering are well approximated by the conventional Breit–Wigner formula

$$A_{\mathrm{res}} = \frac{(\Gamma_{\mathrm{in}}\Gamma_{\mathrm{out}})^{1/2}}{(E_r - E) - i\Gamma/2}. \quad (21)$$

Hence, assuming only resonant processes, we expect

$$\frac{\sigma_{\gamma P \to \gamma P}}{\sigma_{\gamma P \to \pi P}} = \frac{\sigma_{\pi P \to \gamma P}}{\sigma_{\pi P \to \pi P}} = \frac{\Gamma_\gamma}{\Gamma_\pi}. \quad (21a)$$

Using the principle of detailed balancing (Section 5.1.2), we see that

$$2k^2\sigma_{\gamma P \to \pi P} = q^2\sigma_{\pi P \to \gamma P}. \quad (21b)$$

Equation (21a) then gives

$$\sigma_{\gamma P \to \gamma P} = \frac{q^2}{2k^2}\left(\frac{\Gamma_\gamma}{\Gamma_\pi}\right)^2 \sigma_{\pi P \to \pi P}. \quad (21c)$$

In the region of the resonance ($E_\gamma \approx 300$ MeV), Equation (21c) predicts a photon-scattering cross section of $\approx 2.2\ \mu$b (microbarns) while even in the region of the photopion threshold [13] ($E_\gamma \approx 150$ MeV), the resonant cross section is $\approx 0.05\ \mu$b.

The significance of these cross-section values may be seen when they are compared with the normal Thompson scattering cross section

$$\sigma_{\mathrm{Th}} = \frac{8\pi}{3}\left(\frac{e^2}{Mc^2}\right)^2 = 0.20\ \mu\mathrm{b}. \tag{21d}$$

Thus, in the resonance region, both the resonant amplitude [Equation (21) with $\Gamma_{\mathrm{in}} = \Gamma_{\mathrm{out}} = \Gamma_\gamma$] and the Thompson amplitude ($A_{\mathrm{Th}} \cong -e^2/M$) must be taken into account. The result, for the differential cross section, is

$$2\frac{d\sigma}{d\Omega}(\gamma\gamma) = |A_{\mathrm{Th}}|^2(1+\cos^2\theta) + (4k)^{-2}|A_{\mathrm{res}}|^2(7+3\cos^2\theta)$$

$$+ k^{-1}\,\mathrm{Re}\,A_{\mathrm{Th}}A^*_{\mathrm{res}}\cos\theta. \tag{21e}$$

The simple approach outlined above accounts for the main observed features of the elastic scattering of photons on protons in the (3, 3) resonance region.

7.3.4 Resonance Effects in Reactions Involving Two Nucleons

Effects of the isobar resonance are also observed in reactions involving two nucleons. In particular, the reactions

$$\pi + D \rightleftharpoons \mathfrak{N} + \mathfrak{N} \tag{22}$$

and

$$\gamma + D \rightleftharpoons P + N \tag{23}$$

tend to proceed through an $\mathfrak{N}^*(3, 3) + \mathfrak{N}$ intermediate state, provided that the projectile energy is in the range appropriate to $\mathfrak{N}^*(3, 3)$ excitation. Assuming the dominance of this intermediate state and assuming, further, that the relative $\mathfrak{N}^* + \mathfrak{N}$ energy in the intermediate state is low enough so that only the S state $[l(\mathfrak{N}^* + \mathfrak{N}) = 0]$ is appreciable, we may immediately conclude that the total angular momentum involved in the interaction is $j^* = \frac{3}{2}^+ \pm \frac{1}{2}^+ = 2^+$ or 1^+. Furthermore, the total isospin is $t^* = \frac{3}{2} \pm \frac{1}{2} = 2$ or 1, of which only the latter is possible for two nucleons or for a pion plus a deuteron ($t = 0$). Since the Pauli principle limits the $t = 1$ two-nucleon states to ${}^1S_0(0^+)$, ${}^3P_1(0^-, 1^-, 2^-)$, ${}^1D_2(2^+)$, etc., we conclude that reactions (22) and (23) must, if they are resonant in the sense described above, proceed through the unique intermediate state $j = 2^+$, $t = 1$.

A number of important consequences follow from this conclusion:

1. The ratio of the cross sections

$$\frac{\sigma(\pi^+ D \rightleftharpoons PP)}{\sigma(\pi^0 D \rightleftharpoons PN)} = 2 \tag{22a}$$

is a simple consequence of isospin conservation.

---

[13] Even though $q \to 0$ at threshold, the factors in Equation (21c) combine so as to insure that the photon-scattering amplitude passes smoothly through the photopion threshold.

2. The differential cross sections are

$$q^2 \frac{d\sigma}{d\Omega}(\pi^0 D \to PN) = \frac{5}{6} |A^{\pi}_{\text{res}}|^2 (1 + 3 \cos^2 \theta), \tag{22b}$$

$$k^2 \frac{d\sigma}{d\Omega}(\gamma D \to PN) = \frac{5}{24} |A^{\gamma}_{\text{res}}|^2 (5 - 3 \cos^2 \theta). \tag{23a}$$

3. The ratio of the cross sections is [14]

$$\frac{k^2\sigma(\gamma D \to PN)}{q^2\sigma(\pi^0 D \to PN)} = \frac{1}{2}\frac{\Gamma_\gamma}{\Gamma_\pi}. \tag{24}$$

We would also expect resonant effects in nucleon-nucleon elastic scattering, but these turn out to be small in relation to the other elastic scattering processes. For reactions (22) and (23), on the other hand, the resonant process competes quite favorably with other processes over a relatively large range of energies.

PROBLEMS

1. Assume that in the region of $E_\pi \approx 670$ MeV (total energy of the incident pion), the $\pi\mathfrak{N}$ reaction is dominated by resonant capture into the $\mathfrak{N}^*(1470\ \text{MeV}/c^2)$ state with $j = \frac{1}{2}^+$, $t = \frac{1}{2}$. Repeat the considerations of Sections 7.3.1 through 7.3.4 for this case.
2. In the case of $\mathfrak{N}^*(1470)$, in addition to the $(\mathfrak{N}\pi)$ decay mode, there is also a prominent decay

$$\mathfrak{N}^*(1470) \to \mathfrak{N}^*(1236) + \pi.$$

   How does this affect the considerations of the previous problem?
3. At an incident pion kinetic energy of 310 MeV, the phase shifts (Fermi solution) for π^+P scattering are found to be

$$\alpha(t = \tfrac{3}{2}, j = \tfrac{1}{2}^-) = \alpha_3 = -(17.2 \pm 2.5)^\circ,$$
$$\alpha(t = \tfrac{3}{2}, j = \tfrac{1}{2}^+) = \alpha_{3,1} = -(2.9 \pm 4.0)^\circ,$$
$$\alpha(t = \tfrac{3}{2}, j = \tfrac{3}{2}^+) = \alpha_{3,3} = +(135.0 \pm 0.6)^\circ.$$

   Calculate the polarization of the recoil proton as a function of the scattering angle θ.

7.4 Decay Processes

With the exception of the proton, all hadrons eventually decay. If the decay into lighter hadrons is energetically possible, without violating *any* of the conservation principles [B = baryon number, l = lepton number, Q = charge,

---

[14] By detailed balancing,

$$\frac{d\sigma(\pi^0 D \to PN)}{d\sigma(PN \to \pi^0 D)} = \frac{4p^2}{3q^2}, \tag{24a}$$

where p and q are, respectively, the *cm* nucleon and pion momenta.

j = angular momentum, t = isospin, G = isotopic parity, $S(\mathcal{Y})$ = strangeness (hypercharge), T = time reversal, C = charge conjugation, P = parity], the decay will be rapid,[15] $\lambda_s \sim \mu = 2 \times 10^{23}$ sec^{-1}, and we refer to it as a "strong" decay. Some examples are $\mathfrak{N}^*(3, 3) \rightarrow \mathfrak{N}\pi$, $\rho \rightarrow 2\pi$, $\omega \rightarrow 3\pi$, $\phi \rightarrow K\bar{K}$. As far as is known, conservation of B, l, Q, and j is never violated in any possible decay. But if strong decay is not permitted, and if the only obstacle to a given decay is isospin t or G conservation, the decay can take place through the intervention of the electromagnetic field; such decays may involve the emission of a photon, or they may not, the possibility existing for changing the isotopic spin through the emission and reabsorption of a virtual photon. For such decays, the normal decay rate will be $\lambda_e \sim \alpha^n \lambda_s = (137)^{-n}\lambda_s$, the value of n being equal to the number of photon emissions plus absorptions involved in the decay. Some examples of electromagnetic decays are $\Sigma^0 \rightarrow \Lambda^0\gamma$, $\omega^0 \rightarrow \pi^0\gamma$, $\pi^0 \rightarrow 2\gamma$, $\omega^0 \rightarrow 2\pi$, and $\eta^0 \rightarrow 3\pi$. If no other decay is energetically permitted (for example, $N \rightarrow P + e^- + \bar{\nu}_e$) or if the decay requires violation of S and/or P and C (but not CP), it may take place through the weak interactions, either with or without the emission of leptons; some examples are $\Lambda \rightarrow \mathfrak{N}\pi$, $K \rightarrow 2\pi$ or 3π, $\pi \rightarrow \mu\nu$, $K \rightarrow \pi\mu\nu$, etc. The rates of such decays are determined by the weak coupling strength, $\lambda_w \sim 10^{-10}\lambda_s$. Finally, the decays $K_2^0 \rightarrow 2\pi$ (also $K_2^0 \rightarrow \pi^\pm + l^\mp + \nu$) violate CP (and presumably also T if TCP is, as generally assumed, inviolate); these decay rates are $\sim 10^{-5}\lambda_w$.

7.4.1 The Strong Decays

All of the baryon isobars, $\mathfrak{N}^*$, Y^*, Ξ^*, and most of the heavy mesons decay rapidly by virtue of the strong interactions. For such decays, isotopic spin is conserved. Given a parent of definite charge, the laws of combination of isotopic spin determine the distribution of product-charge states. Thus, in the two-body decay

$$a \rightarrow b + c, \tag{25}$$

we have, in general,

$$\chi_{t_a}^{t_{a_3}} \rightarrow \sum_{t_{b_3}+t_{c_3}=t_{a_3}} C_{t_b,t_{b_3};\; t_c,t_{c_3}}^{t_a,t_{a_3}} \chi_{t_b}^{t_{b_3}} \chi_{t_c}^{t_{c_3}}. \tag{25a}$$

EXAMPLE

Consider the decay of a heavy meson into two pions: the possible isotopic-spin values are $t_a = 2, 1, 0$, with the following corresponding 2π charge states:

$$\begin{aligned} \chi_2^{\pm 2} &= \pi_1^\pm \pi_2^\pm, \\ \chi_2^{\pm 1} &= \sqrt{\tfrac{1}{2}}(\pi_1^\pm \pi_2^0 + \pi_1^0 \pi_2^\pm), \\ \chi_2^0 &= \sqrt{\tfrac{1}{6}}(\pi_1^+ \pi_2^- + \pi_1^- \pi_2^+ + 2\pi_1^0 \pi_2^0). \end{aligned} \tag{26a}$$

[15] It must be borne in mind that, for low available decay energy or > 2 particles in the final state, the natural decay rate may be reduced by factors of 10–100, or even greater, because of phase-space considerations.

$$\chi_1^{\pm 1} = \pm\sqrt{\tfrac{1}{2}}(\pi_1^{\pm}\pi_2^0 - \pi_1^0\pi_2^{\pm}),$$
$$\chi_1^0 = \sqrt{\tfrac{1}{2}}(\pi_1^+\pi_2^- - \pi_1^-\pi_2^+). \tag{26b}$$

$$\chi_0^0 = \sqrt{\tfrac{1}{3}}(\pi_1^+\pi_2^- + \pi_1^-\pi_2^+ - \pi_1^0\pi_2^0). \tag{26c}$$

Note that the $t = 2$ and $t = 0$ charge combinations are symmetric with respect to interchange of the two pions; the $t = 1$ states are antisymmetric and *contain no $2\pi^0$ combination.* Bose statistics, obeyed by the spin 0 pions, requires even space symmetry, or $j = l$ even for $t = 0$, 2, and odd $j = l$ for $t = 1$. Note, further, that the wave functions corresponding to the same charge state (same t_3) are mutually orthogonal.

The treatment of three-body decays is more complicated. Generally, there are three ways of forming the possible isotopic-spin combinations, depending on which pair one combines as a first step, i.e.,

$$\mathbf{t} = \mathbf{t}_1 + \mathbf{t}_2 + \mathbf{t}_3 = (\mathbf{t}_1 + \mathbf{t}_2) + \mathbf{t}_3 = (\mathbf{t}_2 + \mathbf{t}_3) + \mathbf{t}_1 = (\mathbf{t}_3 + \mathbf{t}_1) + \mathbf{t}_2 = \mathbf{t}_{i,j} + \mathbf{t}_k. \tag{27}$$

Unless nature steps in to provide some physical feature of the decays, capable of distinguishing between the three possibilities, we are free to choose any one, or any combination. However, in a large number of three-body decays observed, one combination scheme is most appropriate owing to the fact that the decays may occur in two stages.

EXAMPLE

Some of the higher nucleon isobars $\mathfrak{N}^{**}$ have an appreciable $\mathfrak{N}\pi\pi$ decay mode, much of which is the result of the sequential decays

$$\begin{aligned}\mathfrak{N}^{**} &\rightarrow \mathfrak{N}^* + \pi \\ &\qquad \hookrightarrow \mathfrak{N} + \pi.\end{aligned} \tag{28}$$

Consider the decay of a $t = \frac{1}{2}$ isobar [say, $\mathfrak{N}^*_{1/2}(1525)$] into the (3, 3) isobar $\mathfrak{N}^*_{3/2}(1236)$ plus a pion; isotopic-spin conservation requires the following sequence:[16]

$$\mathfrak{N}^{*+}_{1/2} \rightarrow \sqrt{\tfrac{1}{2}}\,\mathfrak{N}^{*++}_{3/2}\pi^- - \sqrt{\tfrac{1}{3}}\,\mathfrak{N}^{*+}_{3/2}\pi^0 + \sqrt{\tfrac{1}{6}}\,\mathfrak{N}^{*0}_{3/2}\pi^+, \tag{28a}$$

$$\mathfrak{N}^{*++}_{3/2} \rightarrow P\pi^+, \tag{28b}$$

$$\mathfrak{N}^{*+}_{3/2} \rightarrow \sqrt{\tfrac{2}{3}}\,P\pi^0 + \sqrt{\tfrac{1}{3}}\,N\pi^+, \tag{28c}$$

$$\mathfrak{N}^{*0}_{3/2} \rightarrow \sqrt{\tfrac{2}{3}}\,N\pi^0 + \sqrt{\tfrac{1}{3}}\,P\pi^-. \tag{28d}$$

Hence,

$$\mathfrak{N}^{*+}_{1/2} \rightarrow \sqrt{\frac{1}{2}}\,(P\pi^+)\pi^- + \frac{1}{3}\sqrt{\frac{1}{2}}\,(P\pi^-)\pi^+ - \frac{1}{3}\,(N\pi^+)\pi^0 + \frac{1}{3}\,(N\pi^0)\pi^+ - \frac{\sqrt{2}}{3}\,(P\pi^0)\pi^0. \tag{28e}$$

[16] The wave function for the decay of $\mathfrak{N}^{*0}_{1/2}$ is, by charge symmetry, obtained from that of $\mathfrak{N}^{*+}_{1/2}$ by the substitutions $P \longleftrightarrow N$, $\pi^{\pm} \longleftrightarrow \pi^{\mp}$.

In principle, decays arising from the first and second terms, or from the third and fourth, are distinguishable by virtue of the fact that only the nucleon-pion pair in parentheses will have an invariant mass $\cong$ 1236 MeV/c^2 [i.e., the second pion will have a unique *cm* energy corresponding to the first stage of the decay (28)]. In practice, owing to the relatively large width of the 1236 resonance, there may be considerable overlap of the momentum distributions of the two pions, leading to appreciable interference between terms in (28e) with the same charge states.[17] For cases in which the $(\mathfrak{N}\pi)_{3/2}$ combination can be distinguished, the five charge states in Equation (28e) will be produced in the ratio 9:1:2:2:4.

A case of great interest is the decay of some heavy mesons into three pions. In this instance, Bose statistics permits the separation of the possible isotopic-spin combinations into those that are even (odd) under interchange of any two pions, and therefore go together with states even (odd) under space exchange. Clearly, the states of total isotopic spin $t = 3$ are even since, for example,

$$^{(+)}\chi_3^3 = \pi_1^+\pi_2^+\pi_3^+ . \tag{29a}$$

Both possibilities are available for $t = 2$; thus, a symmetric combination may be obtained by combining two of the mesons into $t_{i,j} = 2$, and then combining these with the third into $t = 2$, for example,

$$^{(+)}\chi_2^2(1, 2; 3) = \sqrt{\tfrac{2}{3}}\,\chi_2^2(1, 2)\pi_3^0 - \sqrt{\tfrac{1}{3}}\,\chi_2^1(1, 2)\pi_3^+ , \tag{29b}$$

where the even two-pion combinations $\chi_2^{t_3}(i, j)$ are given by Equation (26a). Finally, in forming the combined three-pion wave function with $t = 2$, appropriate to a given symmetric space wave function $^{(+)}\phi(i, j; k)$, we have only to take the products and then symmetrize

$$\psi(1, 2, 3) = \sum_{\text{permutations}} {}^{(+)}\phi(i, j; k)\,{}^{(+)}\chi_2(i, j; k). \tag{29b$'$}$$

In a similar fashion, since the $\chi_1(i, j)$ are odd [Equation (26b)], we may form the antisymmetric $t = 2$ combinations from $(t_{i,j} = 1) + (t_k = 1)$, for example,

$$^{(-)}\chi_2^2(i, j; k) = \chi_1^1(i, j)\,\pi_k^+ . \tag{29c}$$

These must be combined with the appropriate odd space wave functions to obtain the three-pion combinations that have the required (even) symmetry with respect to interchange of any two pions.

The case of $t = 1$ is similar to that of $t = 2$, in that we may obtain charge combinations with both even and odd symmetry. The even combination may be obtained in a straightforward fashion, as follows: We note there are two ways of obtaining a $t = 1$ combination which is even under the interchange of two of the

---

[17] A further complication results from the possibility of confusion with the decay sequence

$$\mathfrak{N}^{**} \to \mathfrak{N} + \rho \qquad \rho \to 2\pi \tag{28$'$}$$

owing to the large width of the ρ-meson.

mesons, namely, $(t_{i,j}=2)+(t_k=1)$ and $(t_{i,j}=0)+(t_k=1)$. Consider first the case $t_3=\pm 1$:

$$^{(1)}\chi_1^{\pm 1}(i,j;k)=\sqrt{\tfrac{3}{5}}\,\chi_2^{\pm 2}(i,j)\,\pi_k^{\mp}-\sqrt{\tfrac{3}{10}}\,\chi_2^{\pm 1}(i,j)\,\pi_k^{0}+\sqrt{\tfrac{1}{10}}\,\chi_2^{0}(i,j)\,\pi_k^{\pm}, \tag{29d}$$

$$^{(2)}\chi_1^{\pm 1}(i,j;k)=\chi_0^{0}(i,j)\,\pi_k^{\pm}. \tag{29e}$$

There turns out to be only one linear combination of these two possibilities that is *completely* symmetric with respect to interchange of any two of the pions:

$$^{(+)}\chi_1^{\pm 1}(i,j,k)=\frac{2}{3}\,{}^{(1)}\chi_1^{\pm 1}(i,j;k)+\frac{\sqrt{5}}{3}\,{}^{(2)}\chi_1^{\pm 1}(i,j;k). \tag{29f}$$

A characteristic feature of 3π decays into the even $t=1$, $t_3=\pm 1$ state is the ratio of final $\pi^{\pm}\pi^{+}\pi^{-}$ to $\pi^{\pm}\pi^{0}\pi^{0}$ states. Summing the amplitudes squared for all such combinations in Equation (29f), we obtain

$$\frac{\lambda(\pi^{\pm}\pi^{+}\pi^{-})^{(+)}}{\lambda(\pi^{\pm}\pi^{0}\pi^{0})}=4. \tag{29f$'$}$$

Exactly the same approach may be used to obtain the even $t=1$, $t_3=0$ combination:

$$^{(1)}\chi_1^{0}(i,j;k)=\sqrt{\tfrac{3}{10}}\,\chi_2^{1}(i,j)\,\pi_k^{-}-\sqrt{\tfrac{2}{5}}\,\chi_2^{0}(i,j)\,\pi_k^{0}+\sqrt{\tfrac{3}{10}}\,\chi_2^{-1}(i,j)\,\pi_k^{+}, \tag{29g}$$

$$^{(2)}\chi_1^{0}(i,j;k)=\chi_0^{0}(i,j)\,\pi_k^{0}, \tag{29h}$$

with the same completely symmetric combination,

$$^{(+)}\chi_1^{0}(i,j,k)=\frac{2}{3}\,{}^{(1)}\chi_1^{0}(i,j;k)+\frac{\sqrt{5}}{3}\,{}^{(2)}\chi_1^{0}(i,j;k). \tag{29i}$$

For the case of (29i), we have

$$\frac{\lambda(\pi^{+}\pi^{-}\pi^{0})^{(+)}}{\lambda(\pi^{0}\pi^{0}\pi^{0})}=\frac{2}{3}. \tag{29i$'$}$$

For the antisymmetric $t=1$ combination, on the other hand, there is only one mode of formation, i.e., $(t_{i,j}=1)+(t_k=1)$:

$$^{(-)}\chi_1^{\pm 1}(i,j;k)=\sqrt{\tfrac{1}{2}}\,\{\chi_1^{\pm 1}(i,j)\,\pi_k^{0}-\chi_1^{0}(i,j)\,\pi_k^{\pm}\}, \tag{29j}$$

$$^{(-)}\chi_1^{0}(i,j;k)=\sqrt{\tfrac{1}{2}}\,\{\chi_1^{1}(i,j)\,\pi_k^{-}-\chi_1^{-1}(i,j)\,\pi_k^{+}\}. \tag{29k}$$

For charged decays into an odd $t=1$ state, we have

$$\frac{\lambda(\pi^{\pm}\pi^{+}\pi^{-})^{(-)}}{\lambda(\pi^{\pm}\pi^{0}\pi^{0})}=1, \tag{29j$'$}$$

while the neutral state is characterized by the complete forbiddenness of the $3\pi^0$ combination:

$$\lambda(\pi^{0}\pi^{0}\pi^{0})^{(-)}=0. \tag{29k$'$}$$

Finally, we consider the case $t=0$, for which there is again only one possible combination, obviously odd (i.e., since $t_k = 1$, we require $t_{i,j} = 1$):

$$^{(-)}\chi_0^0(i, j, k) = \sqrt{\tfrac{1}{3}}\,\{\chi_1^1(i, j)\,\pi_k^- + \chi_1^{-1}(i, j)\,\pi_k^+ - \chi_1^0(i, j)\,\pi_k^0\}. \tag{29l}$$

Also in this case, the final $3\pi^0$ combination is forbidden.

The considerations developed above, when combined with the requirements of angular momentum conservation (Section 6.1.1) and those of phase space (Chapter 4), determine the distribution in space, energy, and charge for the observed 3π decays of heavy mesons, summarized in Table 2.2. It is worth observing,[18] however, that the results obtained above, by explicit use of the combinatorial properties of isospin, can be obtained in a direct and elegant fashion by consideration of the vector nature of isospin 1 in charge space. Thus, if the isovector **a** has the components $a_1, a_2, a_3 = a_0$, we may associate a_3 with the π^0 and $\sqrt{\tfrac{1}{2}}\,(a_1 \pm a_2) = a_\pm$ with the $\pi^\pm$. The dot product of two vectors is a scalar ($t = 0$, even),

$$\mathbf{a} \cdot \mathbf{b} = a_0 b_0 + a_+ b_- + a_- b_+ . \tag{30a}$$

From three vectors, we may form a pseudoscalar ($t = 0$, odd):

$$\mathbf{a} \times \mathbf{b} \cdot \mathbf{c} = \begin{vmatrix} a_+ & b_+ & c_+ \\ a_- & b_- & c_- \\ a_0 & b_0 & c_0 \end{vmatrix}, \tag{30b}$$

which is completely equivalent to the combination (29l); or we may form a vector ($t = 1$, even),

$$\mathbf{v} = \mathbf{a}(\mathbf{b} \cdot \mathbf{c}) + \mathbf{b}(\mathbf{c} \cdot \mathbf{a}) + \mathbf{c}(\mathbf{a} \cdot \mathbf{b}), \tag{30c}$$

equivalent to the combinations (29f) and (29i), or a symmetric or antisymmetric tensor ($t = 2$), etc. We have already considered, in Section 6.1.1, how the space wave functions for the 3π decays may be expressed using similar invariant forms composed of the momenta and energies of the decay products (Table 6.4). The requirements from Bose statistics, of the symmetry of the total (product) wave function, limit the possible combinations of such space forms with the isospin forms illustrated above. Some examples of the resulting matrix elements for 3π decays, obtained by combining isospin and space functions with the appropriate symmetry properties, are given in Table 7.8.

PROBLEM

If a nucleon isobar of $t = \tfrac{5}{2}$ existed, it might be produced in the strong (isospin-conserving) reactions

$$\pi^\pm + P \rightarrow \mathfrak{N}_{5/2}^* + \pi' ,$$

and it would probably decay via the cascade process

$$\begin{aligned} \mathfrak{N}_{5/2}^* &\rightarrow \mathfrak{N}_{3/2}^* + \pi_1 \\ &\qquad \hookrightarrow \mathfrak{N} + \pi_2 . \end{aligned}$$

Assuming that the three pions in the final $(\mathfrak{N}\pi_2\pi_1\pi')$ state can be distinguished kinematically (i.e., through the unique invariant masses of the appropriate

[18] See M. Gell-Mann and A. H. Rosenfeld, *Ann. Rev. Nucl. Sci., 7:* 407 (1957); C. Zemach, *Phys. Rev., 133:* B1201 (1964); L. Montanet, *CERN Report,* 67–23 (1967).

combinations), derive the relative probabilities of the various possible charge combinations in the final state for incident π^+ and π^- projectiles.

Table 7.8 Matrix Elements for Decay of a Heavy Meson into 3π

j^π	l	L	t	$M(j, t)$
0^-	1	1	0	$(\mathbf{a}\times\mathbf{b}\cdot\mathbf{c})(E_- - E_0)(E_0 - E_+)(E_+ - E_-)f(E_i^2, E_iE_jE_k)$
0^-	0	0	1	$\mathbf{a}(\mathbf{b}\cdot\mathbf{c})f^{(+)}(2, 3) + \mathbf{b}(\mathbf{c}\cdot\mathbf{a})f^{(+)}(3, 1) + \mathbf{c}(\mathbf{a}\cdot\mathbf{b})f^{(+)}(1, 2)$
1^-	1	1	0	$(\mathbf{a}\times\mathbf{b}\cdot\mathbf{c})f(E_i^2, E_iE_jE_k)\mathbf{p}_i\times\mathbf{p}_j$
1^-	2	2	1	$\mathbf{a}(\mathbf{b}\cdot\mathbf{c})(E_2 - E_3)f^{(+)}(2, 3) + \mathbf{b}(\mathbf{c}\cdot\mathbf{a})(E_3 - E_1)f^{(+)}(3, 1)$ $+ \mathbf{c}(\mathbf{a}\cdot\mathbf{b})(E_1 - E_2)f^{(+)}(1, 2)$
1^+	0	1	0	$(\mathbf{a}\times\mathbf{b}\cdot\mathbf{c})[E_-(\mathbf{p}_0 - \mathbf{p}_+) + E_0(\mathbf{p}_+ - \mathbf{p}_-) + E_+(\mathbf{p}_- - \mathbf{p}_0)]$
1^+	1	0	1	$\mathbf{a}(\mathbf{b}\cdot\mathbf{c})\mathbf{p}_1 + \mathbf{b}(\mathbf{c}\cdot\mathbf{a})\mathbf{p}_2 + \mathbf{c}(\mathbf{a}\cdot\mathbf{b})\mathbf{p}_3$

7.4.2 Electromagnetic Effects; The A Quantum Number

As previously noted, decays that would be strong, were they not prevented by isospin or by G-parity conservation, can usually take place by virtue of the intervention of the electromagnetic field, but at a rate reduced by $\sim \alpha^n$ from the normal strong decay rates. A number of examples of such decays have already been cited, but there is one case of special interest that merits consideration in some detail. This is the decay of the η^0-meson ($j = 0^-$, $t = 0$, $C = +$, $G = +$).

Referring to Table 2.2, we see that the strong decays into 2, 3, and 4 pions (only) are forbidden, the first and last by parity conservation, which holds also for such decays via intervention of virtual photons, but the 3π decay by G-parity only. We may accordingly expect this (3π) decay to occur through the emission and reabsorption of a virtual photon, but with a decay rate reduced by $\sim \alpha^2 \approx 5 \times 10^{-5}$ from the normal strong decay rate. Taking the ω decay as representing a normal strong 3π decay, we have for the width $\Gamma_s(3\pi) \approx 10$ MeV; we therefore expect $\Gamma_\eta(3\pi) \sim \frac{1}{2}$ keV. The η-decay modes and their branching ratios, as listed in Table 2.1 and summarized in Table 15.16, contain both the $\pi^+\pi^-\pi^0$ and the $3\pi^0$ decays as prominent contributors to the η decay. Furthermore, the observed ratio of these decays, $\pi^+\pi^-\pi^0/\pi^0\pi^0\pi^0 \approx \frac{2}{3}$, is essentially what one would expect for a final $t = 1$ state (the space wave function should be predominantly symmetric with $l = L = 0$, which would exclude the antisymmetric $t = 0$ final state).

The other observed decay modes of the η-meson all involve photon emission. Among these, the $\gamma\gamma$ mode is most prominent, being of roughly the same strength as the 3π mode. The $\pi^+\pi^-\gamma$ decay mode is only $\sim \frac{1}{6}$ as strong as the $\gamma\gamma$ decay, while the $\pi^0\gamma\gamma$ mode is $< \frac{1}{4}$ as strong and may, in fact, be very much weaker.

These observations contain a number of surprises: One would expect the $\pi^0\gamma\gamma$ decay mode to be roughly of the same strength as the 3π modes, i.e., $\Gamma(\pi^0\gamma\gamma) \sim \Gamma(3\pi) \sim \alpha^2\Gamma_s(3\pi)$, since both involve two photon vertices and a comparable three-body phase-space factor. However, the $\gamma\gamma$ decay mode might normally be expected to be ~ 10 times as strong purely on the basis of the larger two-body phase-space factor [the ρ-decay rate indicates $\Gamma_s(2\pi) \sim 100$ MeV $\sim 10\ \Gamma_s(3\pi)$]. The $\pi^+\pi^-\gamma$ mode would also be expected to be more important, since its decay rate should contain α rather than α^2, although its width should be somewhat reduced by the $l=1$ angular momentum barrier involved for the $\pi^+\pi^-$ system ($l=1$ is required for the $\pi^+\pi^-$ system by C conservation); instead, this mode is less prominent than either the 3π or the two-photon decay modes of the η.

A qualitative explanation of these observations has been offered by Bronzan and Low.[19] As a result of general considerations relating to the properties of bosonic systems, they have suggested another partially conserved bosonic quantum number, which they call the A quantum number. In their analysis, all bosons are assigned a value of $A=\pm1$, and the total value of A is (partially) conserved in bosonic decays. Violation of A conservation reduces the corresponding decay rate by a factor of $\sim$ 10–100. The assignments of A to the best-known bosons are summarized in Table 7.9. According to these assignments, the $\gamma\gamma$ and $\pi^+\pi^-\gamma$ decay modes of the η are forbidden by A conservation while the other decay modes are allowed.

Table 7.9 A Quantum Numbers (suggested by observed decays)

Boson	γ	π	η	ρ	ω	φ	f
A	+1	−1	−1	+1	−1	+1	+1

Boson	$X^0(\eta')$	$\eta_N(1070)$	$E(1420)$	$f'(1500)$	$\pi_N(1016)$
A	−1	+1	−1	+1	+1

Boson	A_1	B	A_2	K	$K^*(890)$	$K_A(1320)$	$K_N(1420)$
A	−1	+1	−1	−1	+1	−1	+1(?)

It is interesting to observe that A conservation also inhibits the decay $\pi^0 \to 2\gamma$ by the same factor of $\sim$ 10–100, which is in accord with the observation that the width, $\Gamma(\pi^0 \to 2\gamma) \sim 10$ eV, is smaller than what one would predict on the basis of $\Gamma(\pi^0 \to 2\gamma) \sim \alpha^2\Gamma_s$ (taking into account phase space) by roughly this factor. However, as we shall eventually observe (see Section 15.3.3), there are other possible explanations of the observed π^0 and $\eta^0 \to \gamma\gamma$ decay rates that do not require the invoking of the A quantum number. Furthermore, the fact that the $K_N(1420)$ meson decays both into $K\pi$ and $K^*\pi$, with comparable decay rates, casts further doubt on the usefulness of the concept of A conservation, at least as far as the heavier bosons are concerned.

PROBLEM

Referring to the Rosenfeld tables (Table 2.1), can you find any other violations (or confirmations) of A conservation?

---

[19] J. B. Bronzan and F. E. Low, *Phys. Rev. Letters, 12:* 522 (1964).

7.4.3 Weak Decays; Spurion Theory

The characteristics of the weak decays have been discussed in Sections 2.2 and 6.1.3. The main features are:

1. Conservation of charge, baryon, and lepton numbers.
2. Conservation of energy-momentum and angular momentum, but "maximum" violation of parity conservation and, in a much more limited and incompletely understood fashion, violation of CP conservation in the K_2^0 decays.
3. The selection rule $\Delta Q = \Delta S = \pm 1$ for the hadrons.
4. The isotopic-spin selection rule, $\Delta t = \pm \frac{1}{2}$, but with a small (few percent) $\Delta t \geq \frac{3}{2}$ component.

Nonleptonic K Decays • The $\Delta t = \pm\frac{1}{2}$ isotopic-spin selection rule is illustrated in the $K \to 2\pi$ decays. For these decays, the final 2π state must have $t = 0$ or 2, since the space wave function is even (spin 0); since $t_K = \frac{1}{2}$, $\Delta t = \frac{1}{2}$ requires $t = 0$, predicting the ratio [20]

$$\left.\frac{\lambda(K_1^0 \to \pi^+\pi^-)}{\lambda(K_1^0 \to 2\pi^0)}\right]_{\text{th}} = 1.97 \tag{31a}$$

for the decay of the neutral K-meson, and forbidding the $K^\pm \to \pi^\pm\pi^0$ decay. Experimentally,

$$\left.\frac{\lambda(K_1^0 \to \pi^+\pi^-)}{\lambda(K_1^0 \to 2\pi^0)}\right]_{\text{exp}} = 2.26 \pm 0.05 \tag{31b}$$

and

$$\left.\frac{\lambda(K^\pm \to \pi^\pm\pi^0)}{\lambda(K_1^0 \to 2\pi)}\right]_{\text{exp}} = (1.50 \pm 0.07) \times 10^{-3}. \tag{31c}$$

Thus, while these results indicate general agreement with the requirements of the $\Delta t = \frac{1}{2}$ selection rule, the deviations are not insignificant. These deviations can be readily accounted for by assuming a small $\Delta t = \frac{3}{2}$ contribution to the decay matrix elements, the relative magnitude [21] of which is determined by (31c).

The most convenient way of deriving the consequences of the $\Delta t = \frac{1}{2}$ (or $\frac{3}{2}$ or $\frac{5}{2}$) selection rule is by the introduction of the "spurion" concept.[22] The spurion is a fictitious particle carrying strangeness 1, isotopic spin (usually) $t = \frac{1}{2}$, and $t_3 = -\frac{1}{2}$, but with no other physical attributes (i.e., charge, mass, momentum, angular momentum, baryon and lepton number all equal to zero) except parity, which can be ± 1; the antispurion, $\bar{s}$, has $t_3 = +\frac{1}{2}$, $S = -1$, and also has two varieties: the parity changing and parity conserving. The strangeness-violating weak decays can be

[20] The predicted value 2.00 is somewhat reduced by the relative two-body phase space, $\propto q_\pi m_K$.

[21] Virtual emission and absorption of a photon could lead to a $\Delta t = \frac{3}{2}$ matrix element, of order α times the $\Delta t = \frac{1}{2}$ element (relative rates $\sim \alpha^2$). In this regard, the observed result (31c) seems rather larger than what one might expect, by a factor ~ 10. It should be further noted that a $\Delta t = \frac{5}{2}$ process could also lead to a $t = 2$ final state, but for the moment we neglect it as being unnecessary to account for the observations.

[22] G. Wentzel, *Phys. Rev.*, *101:* 1214 (1956).

thought of as arising from the absorption of the appropriate spurion, as depicted for a number of examples in Figure 7.6. The $K \to 2\pi$ decay amplitudes are obtained by summing the contributions of diagrams (a) and (b), with amplitudes A and A', respectively. Thus, for the $K^+ \to \pi^+\pi^0$ decay, we have [23]

$$K^+(\tfrac{1}{2}, \tfrac{1}{2}) + {}^{(-)}\bar{s}'(\tfrac{3}{2}, \tfrac{1}{2}) \to \sqrt{\tfrac{3}{4}}\, A'\chi_2^1(2\pi)$$

$$= \sqrt{\tfrac{3}{8}}\, A'(\pi_1^+\pi_2^0 + \pi_1^0\pi_2^+), \tag{32a}$$

$$\lambda(K^+ \to \pi^+\pi^0) = \tfrac{3}{4}|A'|^2, \tag{32b}$$

while for $K^0 \to 2\pi$, we have

$$K^0(\tfrac{1}{2}, -\tfrac{1}{2}) + {}^{(-)}\bar{s}(\tfrac{1}{2}, \tfrac{1}{2}) \to \sqrt{\tfrac{1}{2}}\, A\chi_0^0(2\pi)$$

$$= \sqrt{\tfrac{1}{6}}\, A(\pi_1^+\pi_2^- + \pi_1^-\pi_2^+ - \pi_1^0\pi_2^0), \tag{33a}$$

$$K^0(\tfrac{1}{2}, -\tfrac{1}{2}) + {}^{(-)}\bar{s}'(\tfrac{3}{2}, \tfrac{1}{2}) \to \sqrt{\tfrac{1}{2}}\, A'\chi_2^0(2\pi)$$

$$= \sqrt{\tfrac{1}{12}}\, A'(\pi_1^+\pi_2^- + \pi_1^-\pi_2^+ + 2\pi_1^0\pi_2^0), \tag{33b}$$

from which, by addition,

$$A(K^0 \to \pi_1^\pm\pi_2^\mp) = \sqrt{\tfrac{1}{6}}\,(A + \sqrt{\tfrac{1}{2}}\, A'), \tag{33c}$$

$$A(K^0 \to \pi_1^0\pi_2^0) = -\sqrt{\tfrac{1}{6}}\,(A - \sqrt{2}\, A'), \tag{33d}$$

$$\frac{\lambda(K^0 \to \pi^\pm\pi^\mp)}{\lambda(K^0 \to \pi^0\pi^0)} = 2\,\frac{|A + \sqrt{\tfrac{1}{2}}\, A'|^2}{|A - \sqrt{2}A'|^2}, \tag{33e}$$

$$\lambda(K_1^0 \to 2\pi) = 2\lambda(K^0 \to 2\pi) = (|A|^2 + |A'|^2). \tag{33f}$$

Use of the experimental values [(31b) and (31c), corrected for phase space] permits the determination of $|A'/A| = 4.5 \times 10^{-2}$ and the relative phase $\delta' - \delta = \pm(66 \pm 13)°$.[24]

That the $K \to 3\pi$ decays are "normal" is easily seen by comparing the ratio of the $K^\pm$ or $K^0 \to 3\pi$ decay rates (approximately equal, Table 2.1) to the $K_1^0 \to 2\pi$ rate

$$\frac{\lambda(K_2^0 \to 3\pi)}{\lambda(K_1^0 \to 2\pi)} \cong 6 \times 10^{-4}, \tag{34a}$$

with the relative phase space (assuming an interaction range $R = m^{-1}$)

$$\frac{dN(3\pi)}{dN(2\pi)} = 87 \left(\frac{m_\pi}{m}\right)^3 \times 10^{-4}. \tag{34b}$$

---

[23] If there were, in addition, $t = \frac{5}{2}$ spurion absorption, with amplitude A'', Equation (32b) would become

$$\lambda(K^+ \to \pi^+\pi^0) = \tfrac{3}{4}|A' - \tfrac{2}{3}A''|^2. \tag{32b'}$$

[24] In principle, assuming time-reversal invariance, $\delta' - \delta$ is fixed by the difference between the S-wave π–π scattering phase shifts in the $t = 2$ and $t = 0$ states so that, if these were known and if the experiments were accurate enough, it would be possible to determine whether a $t = \frac{5}{2}$ spurion is also required.

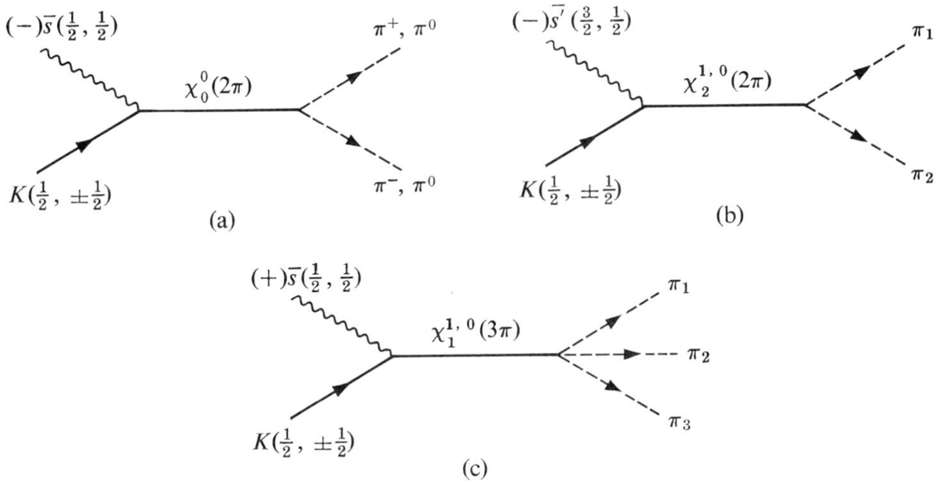

Figure 7.6 Diagrams illustrating spurion absorption processes for $K \to 2\pi$ and $K \to 3\pi$ decays.

Thus, for equal matrix elements, the equality of (34a) and (34b) requires $m \simeq 335$ MeV or $R \simeq 0.58$ f, not an unreasonable value.

Application of spurion theory to the $K \to 3\pi$ decays, Figure 7.6(c), is quite straightforward. Both $K^{\pm}$ and K^0 decays are permitted by absorption of the appropriate parity-conserving $t = \frac{1}{2}$ spurion ${}^{(+)}s$, since the most probable 3π state has even space symmetry ($l = L = 0$) and may therefore be associated with the even $t = 1$ state. Assuming a pure $t = 1$ final state, we note that the charge distributions in 3π decay have previously been derived [Equations (29f′) and (29i′)]:

$$\frac{\lambda(\pi^{\pm}\pi^{+}\pi^{-})}{\lambda(\pi^{\pm}\pi^{0}\pi^{0})} = 4, \qquad \frac{\lambda(\pi^{+}\pi^{-}\pi^{0})}{\lambda(\pi^{0}\pi^{0}\pi^{0})} = \frac{2}{3}. \tag{35a}$$

Experimentally, after we have corrected for phase space, the values are, respectively, 4.17 ± 0.19 and 0.62 ± 0.08. Finally, the spurion absorption depicted in Figure 7.6(c) leads to the prediction

$$\frac{\lambda(K^{\pm} \to 3\pi)}{\lambda(K_2^0 \to 3\pi)} = 1, \tag{35b}$$

which may be compared with the (phase space corrected) observed value of 1.12 ± 0.11. Thus, the agreement between experiment and the $\Delta t = \frac{1}{2}$ rule is excellent.

Nonleptonic Hyperon Decays • The nonleptonic decays of the hyperons have already been discussed in Section 6.1.3, where the effects of the nonconservation of parity have been described in terms of two amplitudes, S and P; we may think of these as representing, respectively, the amplitudes for absorption of the negative and positive parity spurions ${}^{(-)}s$ and ${}^{(+)}s$. Assuming $t = \frac{1}{2}$ spurions only, the diagrams corresponding to the various observed hyperon decays are shown in Figure 7.7. With the aid of these diagrams, we may derive the following general consequences of the $\Delta t = \frac{1}{2}$ selection rule.

1. Λ decays:

$$\Lambda^0 \to A_\Lambda^{\pm}\chi_{1/2}^{-1/2}(\mathfrak{N}\pi) = A_\Lambda^{\pm}(\sqrt{\tfrac{2}{3}}\,P\pi^- - \sqrt{\tfrac{1}{3}}\,N\pi^0), \tag{36a}$$

$$\Lambda_-^0 = \sqrt{\tfrac{2}{3}}\,A_\Lambda^{\pm}, \qquad \Lambda_0^0 = -\sqrt{\tfrac{1}{3}}\,A_\Lambda^{\pm}. \tag{36b}$$

[Note that $A_\Lambda^- = S_\Lambda$, $A_\Lambda^+ = P_\Lambda$, and that the angular distributions in the decay are given by $A_\Lambda(m = \pm\frac{1}{2}) = (4\pi)^{-1/2}\left[(S_\Lambda \mp P_\Lambda \cos\theta)\begin{Bmatrix}\alpha\\ \beta\end{Bmatrix} - P_\Lambda \sin\theta\, e^{\pm i\varphi}\begin{Bmatrix}\beta\\ \alpha\end{Bmatrix}\right]$; see Section 6.1.3]. Thus,

$$S(\Lambda_-^0) + \sqrt{2}\,S(\Lambda_0^0) = 0, \tag{36c}$$

$$P(\Lambda_-^0) + \sqrt{2}\,P(\Lambda_0^0) = 0, \tag{36d}$$

and we have in general

$$\frac{\lambda(\Lambda_-^0)}{\lambda(\Lambda_0^0)} = 2; \qquad a(\Lambda_-^0) = a(\Lambda_0^0); \qquad b(\Lambda_-^0) = b(\Lambda_0^0), \text{ etc.} \tag{36e}$$

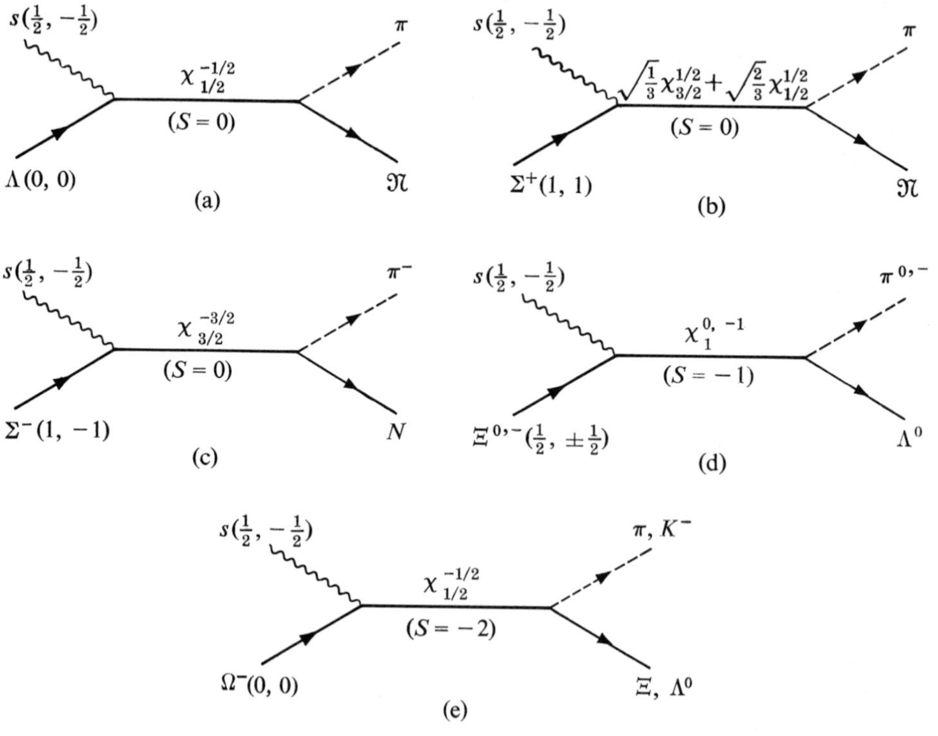

Figure 7.7 Spurion absorption diagrams for nonleptonic hyperon decays.

2. Σ^+ decays: These are given in terms of two general amplitudes, corresponding to spurion absorption into the $t=\frac{1}{2}$ (A_1) and the $t=\frac{3}{2}$ (A_3) states [Figure 7.7(b)]. Each of these is, in turn, a combination of two independent amplitudes, (S_3, P_3) and (S_1, P_1), corresponding to absorption of ${}^{(-)}s$ and ${}^{(+)}s$ spurions. We have seen that we may treat such combinations as vectors in S–P space:

$$\mathbf{A}_i = S_i \mathbf{x}_0 + P_i \mathbf{y}_0 . \tag{37}$$

Figure 7.7(b) then implies

$$\Sigma^+ \rightarrow \sqrt{\tfrac{1}{3}}\, \mathbf{A}_3 \chi_{1/2}^{1/2} + \sqrt{\tfrac{2}{3}}\, \mathbf{A}_1 \chi_{1/2}^{1/2}, \tag{37a}$$

from which follows

$$\mathbf{A}_+^+ = \tfrac{1}{3}(\mathbf{A}_3 + 2\mathbf{A}_1), \tag{37b}$$

$$\mathbf{A}_0^+ = \frac{\sqrt{2}}{3}(\mathbf{A}_3 - \mathbf{A}_1). \tag{37c}$$

These are useful only when combined with a further condition, which comes from the Σ^- decay.

3. Σ^- decay: This is into a pure $t=\frac{3}{2}$ state [Figure 7.7(c)]:

$$\mathbf{A}_-^- = \mathbf{A}_3. \tag{37d}$$

Equations (37b)–(37d) enable us to obtain a general relationship among the three observable amplitudes

$$\sqrt{2}\, \mathbf{A}_0^+ = \mathbf{A}_-^- - \mathbf{A}_+^+. \tag{37e}$$

Since a vector equation holds for each of its components, Equation (37e) must hold separately for the S's and the P's.

This $\Delta t = \frac{1}{2}$ sum rule for the Σ decays (37e) takes an especially interesting form if one imposes some additional conditions arising from the experiments. Thus, using the observation of approximately equal decay rates for the three modes

$$|A_0^+| \cong |A_+^+| \cong |A_-^-|, \tag{37f}$$

we note that the vector relationship assumes the simple geometrical arrangement depicted in Figure 7.8. In fact (see Table 6.6) it turns out that $\mathbf{A}_+^+$ corresponds to pure P-wave emission $(S_+^+ = 0)$, from which we conclude that $\mathbf{A}_-^-$ should be all S-wave and that $\mathbf{A}_0^+$ should be an equal mixture of S- and P-wave decays. These conclusions are strikingly confirmed by the observations, thus providing perhaps the strongest available evidence for the $\Delta t = \frac{1}{2}$ rule.

The simple geometrical relationship among the amplitudes, depicted in Figure 7.8, is only approximately valid, owing to the small phase factors multiplying the S and P amplitudes [see Section 6.1.3, Equations (30) and Table 6.5(b)]. Accepting the Fermi–Watson theorem (or time-reversal invariance), we may derive the phase factors from the corresponding π–$\mathfrak{N}$ scattering phase shifts. However, the phase relationships are simple only for the Σ_-^- decay, since in this case the amplitude is pure $t=\frac{3}{2}$ [Equation (37d)], and $\xi_- = \alpha_{31} - \alpha_3 \cong 6.6°$. For the other two

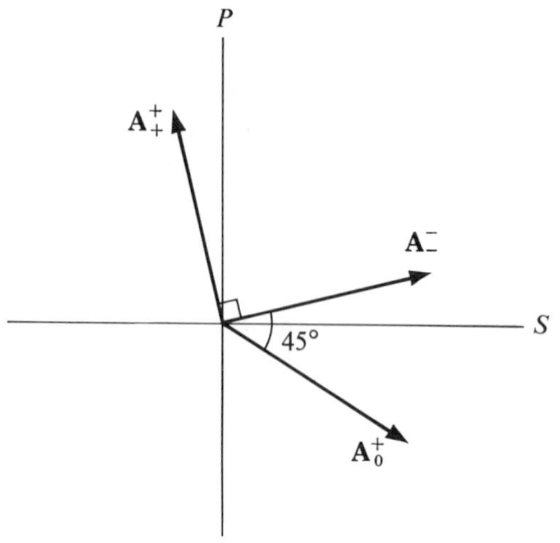

Figure 7.8 Properties of the Σ-decay amplitudes.

decays, making the assumptions (on the magnitudes only) $P_- = P_3 = 0$, $S_- = S_3 = -2S_1$, we obtain,[25] using Equations (37b) and (37c),

$$\begin{aligned} S_+ &\cong 0.11 S_-, \qquad \xi_+ \cong \alpha_{11} + \frac{\pi}{2} \cong 88°, \\ S_0 &\cong \sqrt{\frac{1}{2}}\, S_-, \qquad \xi_0 \cong \frac{3\alpha_{11} - 2\alpha_3 - \alpha_1}{3} \cong 5.3°. \end{aligned} \tag{37g}$$

4. The others: The application of spurion theory to the rest of the hyperon decays [Figure 7.7(d)(e)] proceeds in completely similar fashion. We summarize in Table 7.10 the consequences of the $\Delta t = \frac{1}{2}$ assumption in the form of sum rules for the hyperon nonleptonic decay amplitudes. All of these are in excellent accord with the available experimental information (Table 6.6).

Furthermore, there appear to be some simple relationships among the amplitudes for the different hyperon decays (after kinematical correction as outlined in Section 6.1.3). The most useful among these is the Lee–Sugawara rule[26]

$$2\Xi^-_- - \Lambda^0_- = \sqrt{3}\, \Sigma^+_0 . \tag{38}$$

The derivation of such relationships obviously requires considerations going beyond simple isospin conservation.

Leptonic Decays • The universality of the $\Delta t = \pm\frac{1}{2}$ selection rule for the hadronic components in the β-decay processes implies the $\Delta S = \Delta Q$ rule. This

[25] The arithmetic manipulations involve the combination of vectors, each of whose components is represented by a complex number; we leave the details as an exercise for the reader.

[26] B. W. Lee, *Phys. Rev. Letters, 12:* 83 (1964); H. Sugawara, *Phys. Rev. Letters, 15:* 870 (1965).

Table 7.10 $\Delta t = \frac{1}{2}$ *Sum Rules for Hyperon Nonleptonic Decay Amplitudes*

Decays	Designation	Vector sum rule
$\Lambda^0 \to P\pi^-$	Λ^0_-	$\Lambda^0_- + \sqrt{2}\,\Lambda^0_0 = 0$
$\Lambda^0 \to N\pi^0$	Λ^0_0	
$\Sigma^+ \to P\pi^0$	Σ^+_0	$\sqrt{2}\,\Sigma^+_0 + \Sigma^+_+ - \Sigma^-_- = 0$
$\Sigma^+ \to N\pi^+$	Σ^+_+	
$\Sigma^- \to N\pi^-$	Σ^-_-	
$\Xi^0 \to \Lambda^0\pi^0$	Ξ^0_0	$\sqrt{2}\,\Xi^0_0 - \Xi^-_- = 0$
$\Xi^- \to \Lambda^0\pi^-$	Ξ^-_-	
$\Omega^- \to \Xi^0\pi^-$	Ω^-_-	$\Omega^-_- + \sqrt{2}\,\Omega^-_0 = 0$
$\Omega^- \to \Xi^-\pi^0$	Ω^-_0	

is clear from the Gell-Mann–Nishijima relationship

$$Q = t_3 + \left(\frac{S+B}{2}\right), \tag{39a}$$

$$\Delta Q - \frac{\Delta S}{2} = \Delta t_3. \tag{39b}$$

Since lepton emission always carries away the charge $\Delta Q = \pm 1$, it follows from (39b) that $\Delta S = -\Delta Q$ would give $\Delta t_3 = \pm\frac{3}{2}$, which would require $\Delta t \geq \frac{3}{2}$. However, the important aspect of the decay selection rules (both $\Delta S = \Delta Q$ and spurion theory) is that they primarily imply $\Delta t_3 = \pm\frac{1}{2}$, which is a necessary but not sufficient condition for the $\Delta t = \frac{1}{2}$ rule. Just how fundamental this rule is (neglecting electromagnetic effects) remains an open question.

PROBLEMS

1. Referring to Table 6.5 for the observed hyperon (nonleptonic) decay parameters, compare the experimental results with the predictions of spurion theory (with $t = \frac{1}{2}$ spurions only). Assume a universal spurion-baryon coupling of the form

$$H_1 + H_2\,\boldsymbol{\tau}_s \cdot \boldsymbol{\tau}_B$$

(B refers to the baryons of $t = \frac{1}{2}$ and hypercharge $\mathcal{Y} = \pm 1$). Assume, further, that the *only* energy dependence of the decay rates (amplitudes squared) arises out of the phase-space and barrier penetration factors

$$|S_i|^2 = (C_s^i)^2 \left(\frac{dN}{dE}\right)_i,$$

$$|P_i|^2 = (C_p^i)^2 \, v_1(k_i R) \left(\frac{dN}{dE}\right)_i,$$

with $R \cong 0.8$ f. Use the Σ-decay parameters to determine the expectation values of $\langle H_1 \rangle$ and $\langle H_2 \rangle$. *Note:* the coupling of the spurion to the $t = \frac{3}{2}$ (π–$\mathfrak{N}$) baryonic state is completely determined by the Σ_-^- decay and is, in any event, not involved in the prediction of any of the other hyperonic decays, except, of course, the Σ^+.

2. (a) Can you recast the spurion absorption diagrams of Figure 7.7 so that they reflect more obviously the universal spurion coupling? (b) In terms of this universal coupling, what are the processes responsible for the $K \to 2\pi$ and $K \to 3\pi$ decays? Try to estimate the $K_1^0 \to 2\pi$ decay rate on this basis.
3. Compare the predicted relationships between the Λ, Σ, and Ξ decay matrix elements (before kinematical corrections) with the Lee–Sugawara rule.
4. Assuming the same (universal) spurion coupling with baryons of spin $\frac{3}{2}^+$, predict the Ω^- decay constants.

8

K_1^0–K_2^0 Phenomena

We have previously noted, in Section 2.1.2, that the decays of the neutral K-mesons can be described, to a very good approximation,[1] in terms of the combinations

$$K_{1,2}^0 = \sqrt{\tfrac{1}{2}}\,(K^0 \pm \overline{K^0}), \tag{1}$$

which are eigenstates of the combined operations of charge conjugation, C, and parity, P, with the eigenvalues $CP = \pm 1$. Although their leptonic decay modes are accessible to both values of CP, the pionic decays are into states with specific values of CP, since the final 2π and 3π states have the CP values $+1$ and -1, respectively. Thus, CP conservation requires

$$K_1^0 \rightarrow 2\pi,\ \pi^\pm + \text{leptons, etc.,} \tag{2a}$$

$$K_2^0 \rightarrow 3\pi,\ \pi^\pm + \text{leptons, etc.} \tag{2b}$$

If the leptonic decay modes were dominant, and if, correspondingly, the mean lives of the K_1^0 and K_2^0 were close to each other, there would be little more than pedagogical interest in the distinction between the K_1^0–K_2^0 and the K^0–$\overline{K^0}$ representations. However, owing to the very strong preference of phase space for two-body over three-body decays, the K_1^0 decay goes essentially 100 percent into 2π, with $\tau_1(K_1^0) = 0.86 \times 10^{-10}$ sec, while the K_2^0 decay is shared among many

Note: For an extensive survey of K_1^0–K_2^0 phenomena, see T. D. Lee and C. S. Wu, *Ann. Rev. Nucl. Sci., 16:* 511 (1966).

[1] For the time being, we assume the validity of time reversal invariance for the K decays, which assures CP invariance. We will return at the end of this chapter to the problems raised by the small CP-invariance violation observed in the K_2^0 decays.

three-body decay modes, 3π among them, with a much longer lifetime, $\tau_2(K_2^0) = 0.53 \times 10^{-7}$ sec (see Table 2.1). Only the K_1^0 and K_2^0 exhibit pure exponential decays, with mean lives τ_1 and τ_2, respectively, while the K^0 and $\overline{K^0}$, being mixtures of the decay eigenstates

$$K^0 = \sqrt{\tfrac{1}{2}}\,(K_1^0 + K_2^0), \tag{1a}$$

$$\overline{K^0} = \sqrt{\tfrac{1}{2}}\,(K_1^0 - K_2^0), \tag{1b}$$

exhibit mixed decay distributions, half of them decaying rapidly, with mean life τ_1, and the remainder decaying ~ 650 times more slowly. Since it is the K^0 and/or $\overline{K^0}$ that are produced in the strong interactions, we would generally expect to observe this mixed decay process — rapid decay of half the $K^0(\overline{K^0})$ through $K_1^0 \to 2\pi$, followed by a much slower decay of the remaining half in the mixed mode $K_2^0 \to 3\pi$, $\pi^\pm$ + leptons, etc. Correspondingly, a beam of pure $K^0(\overline{K^0})$ will very rapidly decay into a fifty-fifty K^0–$\overline{K^0}$ mixture. Thus, as a result of the weak decay process, the strangeness of an initial $K^0(\overline{K^0})$ beam is not conserved, but, rather, there takes place, in vacuum and without the intervention of any external forces, a rapid $K^0 \rightleftharpoons \overline{K^0}$ conversion process.

8.1 Effects of Mass Difference

However, the situation is even more complex, and interesting, as a result of the fact that the K_1^0 and K_2^0, being essentially different particles (i.e., not each other's charge conjugate), need not and do not have the same mass. The (small) mass difference $\Delta = M(K_2^0) - M(K_1^0)$ arises out of the difference in their weak decay interactions, and is thus expected to be of the order [2]

$$\Delta = \frac{\kappa\hbar}{\tau_1} = 0.76\kappa \times 10^{-5}\ \text{eV}, \tag{3}$$

with $|\kappa| \sim 1$. Taking into account the possibility of such a mass difference, we can write for the wave functions of the K_1^0 and K_2^0 (in their own *cm*)

$$|K_1^0\rangle = A_1(\mathbf{r})\, e^{-t/2\tau_1}\, e^{iMt}, \tag{3a}$$

$$|K_2^0\rangle = A_2(\mathbf{r})\, e^{-t/2\tau_2}\, e^{i(M+\Delta)t}. \tag{3b}$$

Now, let us consider what happens if we produce a pure K^0 beam, i.e., $A_1(0) = A_2(0) = \sqrt{\tfrac{1}{2}}$, so that $|K^0(0)\rangle = 1$, $|\overline{K^0}(0)\rangle = 0$. We may consider two experimental situations:

1. The amounts of K_1^0 and K_2^0 are measured by observing the rates of 2π and 3π decay in the K^0 beam as a function of the distance from the source, $x = vt$, where

---

[2] The $K^0 \to B\overline{B}$ matrix element, which leads directly to the weak decay, and by two successive applications to the $K^0 \leftrightarrow \overline{K^0}$ conversion, is expected to be $\gamma \sim g_w(M_K/2M_p)^2$, with $g_w \approx GM_P^2 \approx 10^{-5}$. We then expect

$$\Delta \sim \tau_1^{-1} \sim \frac{\gamma^2}{4\pi} M_K \approx 2 \times 10^{-5}\ \text{eV}.$$

v is the velocity of the K^0's produced.[3] Then, as a consequence of the exponential decay rates,

$$P(2\pi) = \langle K_1^{0*} | K_1^0 \rangle = \tfrac{1}{2}\, e^{-t/\tau_1}, \tag{2a$'$}$$

$$P(3\pi) = \frac{\Gamma_{3\pi}}{\Gamma_2} \langle K_2^{0*} | K_2^0 \rangle = \frac{1}{2}\, e^{-t/\tau_2} \frac{\Gamma_{3\pi}}{\Gamma_2}, \tag{2b$'$}$$

where $\Gamma_2 = \hbar/\tau_2$.

2. Alternatively, we may measure the amounts of the K^0 and $\overline{K^0}$ components in the beam; their amplitudes are [see Equations (1a) and (1b)]

$$|K^0\rangle = \tfrac{1}{2}\, e^{iMt} \{e^{-t/2\tau_1} + e^{-t/2\tau_2}\, e^{i\kappa t/\tau_1}\}, \tag{1a$'$}$$

$$|\overline{K^0}\rangle = \tfrac{1}{2}\, e^{iMt} \{e^{-t/2\tau_1} - e^{-t/2\tau_2}\, e^{i\kappa t/\tau_1}\}, \tag{1b$'$}$$

with the corresponding intensities (probabilities)

$$P(K^0) = \langle K^{0*} | K^0 \rangle = \frac{1}{4}\left\{e^{-t/\tau_1} + e^{-t/\tau_2} + 2 \exp\left[-\frac{t}{2}\left(\frac{1}{\tau_1} + \frac{1}{\tau_2}\right)\right] \cos \frac{\kappa t}{\tau_1}\right\}, \tag{1a$''$}$$

$$P(\overline{K^0}) = \langle \overline{K^{0*}} | \overline{K^0} \rangle = \frac{1}{4}\left\{e^{-t/\tau_1} + e^{-t/\tau_2} - 2 \exp\left[-\frac{t}{2}\left(\frac{1}{\tau_1} + \frac{1}{\tau_2}\right)\right] \cos \frac{\kappa t}{\tau_1}\right\}. \tag{1b$''$}$$

Owing to the magnitudes of τ_1 and τ_2, most observations are made over the time range $\tau_1 \lesssim t \ll \tau_2$, for which we may make the convenient approximation

$$P(K^0) \cong \frac{1}{4}\left\{1 + e^{-t/\tau_1} + 2e^{-t/2\tau_1} \cos \frac{\kappa t}{\tau_1}\right\}, \tag{1a$'''$}$$

$$P(\overline{K^0}) \cong \frac{1}{4}\left\{1 + e^{-t/\tau_1} - 2e^{-t/2\tau_1} \cos \frac{\kappa t}{\tau_1}\right\}. \tag{1b$'''$}$$

The variations of the K^0 and $\overline{K^0}$ probabilities over the range $0 < t/\tau_1 \lesssim 3$ are illustrated in Figure 8.1 for values of $\kappa = 0, \frac{1}{2}, 1$, and 2. These curves demonstrate in striking fashion the interference effects in the $K^0 \rightleftharpoons \overline{K^0}$ conversion, which result from a small mass difference between the K_1^0 and K_2^0, and the sensitivity of the conversion rate in the $t \sim \tau_1$ time range to the value of this mass difference.

8.2 Regeneration

There are a number of possibilities for observing the $K^0 \rightleftharpoons \overline{K^0}$ conversion phenomenon and for measuring the K_2^0–K_1^0 mass difference, κ/τ_1. One direct way of measuring the intensity of the K^0 and $\overline{K^0}$ components is by observing the decays, as a function of distance from the source, into $\pi^{\mp} + e^{\pm} + \nu_e(\overline{\nu}_e)$ and taking advantage of the $\Delta S = \Delta Q$ selection rule, which permits $K^0 \to \pi^- + e^+ + \nu_e$ and $\overline{K^0} \to \pi^+ + e^- + \overline{\nu}_e$ only. Another way is to take advantage of the characteristic

[3] Note that, as observed in the *lab*, the time dilatation of the decay rates requires

$$\frac{t}{\tau_i} \to \frac{x(1 - v^2/c^2)^{1/2}}{v\tau_i}.$$

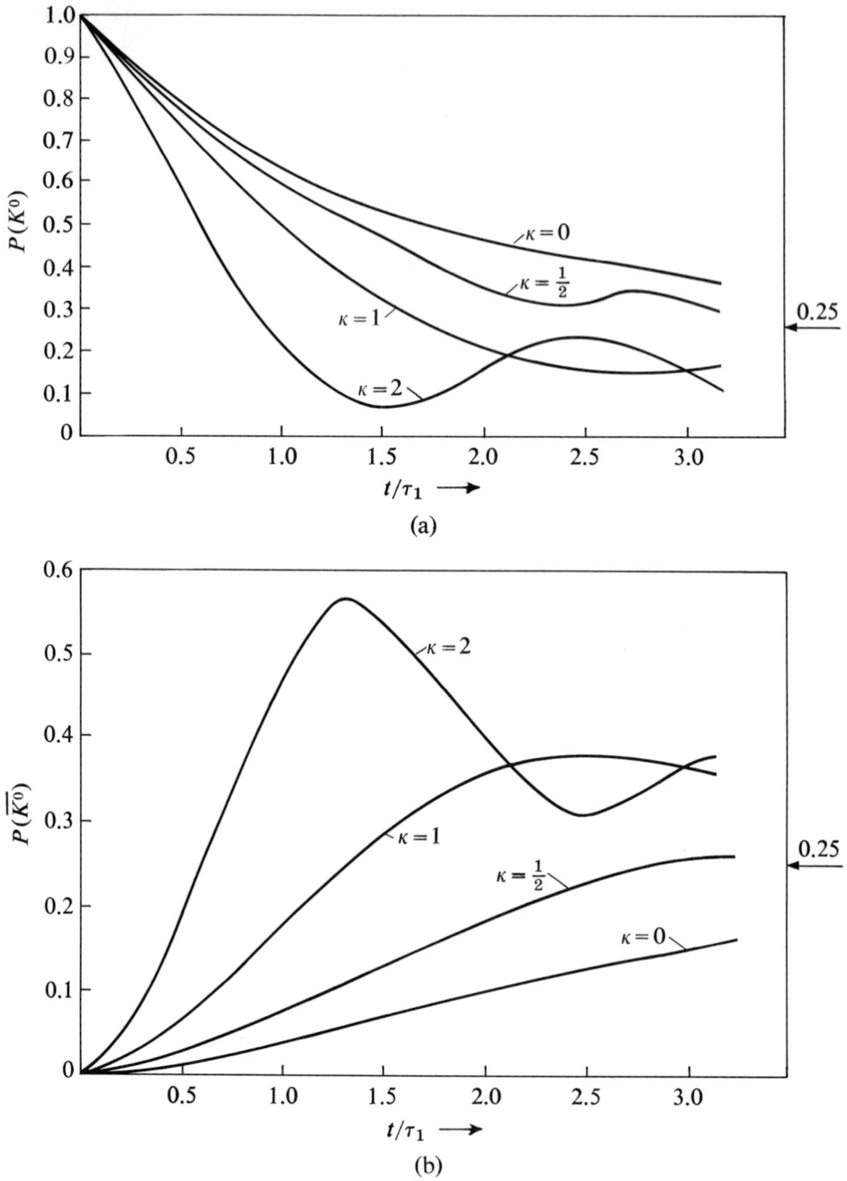

Figure 8.1 Probabilities of finding K^0 (a) and $\overline{K^0}$ (b) in an initially pure K^0 beam as a function of time of flight.

differences in the strong interactions of the K^0 and $\overline{K^0}$ (e.g., $K^0 + P \rightarrow K^+ + N$, $\overline{K^0} + P \rightarrow \pi^+ + \Lambda^0$, etc.) by observing the frequency of occurrence of such interactions in a thin "analyzer" as a function of the distance of the analyzer from the source. Both these methods are capable of yielding the magnitude of κ, but not its sign [see Equations (1a‴) and (1b‴)].

However, by far the most useful means of studying the details of the $K^0 \rightleftharpoons \overline{K^0}$ conversion has been through the observation in detail of the regeneration of K_1^0 in the passage of a pure K_2^0 beam through a slab of matter, as illustrated in Figure 8.2. A pure K_2^0 beam is easily obtained by permitting the K_1^0 component of a K^0 or $\overline{K^0}$ beam to decay in flight over a distance very large as compared to $v\tau_1$. In passing through the slab of matter, the K^0 and $\overline{K^0}$ components of the

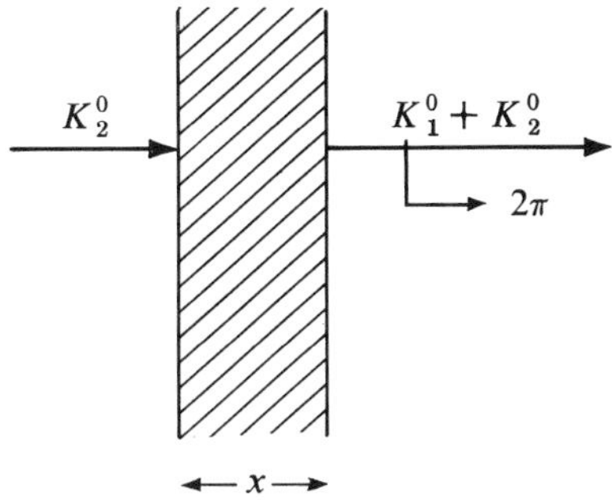

Figure 8.2 K_1^0 regeneration experiment.

K_2^0 undergo different strong interactions, and the emerging beam is no longer pure $K_2^0 = \sqrt{\tfrac{1}{2}}\,(K^0 - \overline{K^0})$, but rather a mixture of K_1^0 and K_2^0, the precise mixture being determined by the specific absorption and scattering properties of the material; the resulting K_1^0 component is easily detected by its rapid $K_1^0 \to \pi^+\pi^-$ decay.

Two types of strong interaction phenomena affect a $K^0(\overline{K^0})$ beam in its passage through matter: first, particles are removed from the beam (absorbed) as a result of both scattering and inelastic interactions; second, as a result of forward elastic scattering, the phase of the emerging beam is different from what it would have been if it had traversed the same distance in vacuum. Both these effects may be described in terms of a (complex) index of refraction, $n(\overline{n})$:[4]

$$|K^0(x)\rangle = |K^0(0)\rangle\, e^{inkx}$$
$$= |K^0(0)\rangle\, e^{-(\mathrm{Im}\, n)kx} e^{i(\mathrm{Re}\, n)kx}, \tag{4a}$$

$$|\overline{K^0}(x)\rangle = |\overline{K^0}(0)\rangle\, e^{-(\mathrm{Im}\, \overline{n})kx} e^{i(\mathrm{Re}\, \overline{n})kx}, \tag{4b}$$

where

$$n = 1 + \left(\frac{2\pi N}{k^2}\right) F(0). \tag{4c}$$

N is the density of nuclei and $F(0)$ is their forward scattering amplitude; by the optical theorem we have

$$\sigma_{\mathrm{tot}} = \frac{4\pi}{k}\, \mathrm{Im}\, F(0). \tag{4d}$$

[4] T. D. Lee and C. S. Wu, *Ann. Rev. Nucl. Sci., 16:* 511 (1966); for a simple derivation of the relationship between the scattering amplitude and the index of refraction, see E. Fermi, *Nuclear Physics,* University of Chicago Press, Chicago, Ill. (1950), p. 201.

The absorption coefficient in Equations (4a) and (4b), defined as

$$2k(\text{Im } n) = N\sigma_{\text{tot}} = \frac{1}{v\tau_a}, \tag{4e}$$

leads to an attenuation in the beam, while the (Re n) $= n_0$ leads only to a phase change.

In the absence of decay, the $K^0(\overline{K^0})$ amplitudes [Equations (4a) and (4b)] are described by the differential equations

$$\frac{d|K^0\rangle}{dx} = \left(-\frac{1}{2v\tau_a} + ikn_0\right)|K^0\rangle, \tag{4a'}$$

$$\frac{d|\overline{K^0}\rangle}{dx} = \left(-\frac{1}{2v\overline{\tau}_a} + ik\overline{n}_0\right)|\overline{K^0}\rangle, \tag{4b'}$$

from which, using Equation (1) to convert K^0 and $\overline{K^0}$ to K_1^0 and K_2^0, and putting in the decay properties through the differential equations leading to the solutions (3a) and (3b), we obtain for the equations governing the transmission through the slab:

$$\frac{d|K_1^0\rangle}{dx} = -\alpha|K_1^0\rangle + \gamma|K_2^0\rangle, \tag{5a}$$

$$\frac{d|K_2^0\rangle}{dx} = \gamma|K_1^0\rangle - \beta|K_2^0\rangle, \tag{5b}$$

with

$$\alpha = \frac{1}{2v}\left(\frac{1}{\tau_1} + \frac{1}{2\tau_a} + \frac{1}{2\overline{\tau}_a}\right) - \frac{ik}{2}(n_0 + \overline{n}_0), \tag{5c}$$

$$\beta = \frac{1}{2v}\left(\frac{1}{\tau_2} + \frac{1}{2\tau_a} + \frac{1}{2\overline{\tau}_a}\right) - \frac{ik}{2}\left(n_0 + \overline{n}_0 - \frac{2\kappa}{vk\tau_1}\right), \tag{5d}$$

$$\gamma = \frac{1}{4v}\left(\frac{1}{\overline{\tau}_a} - \frac{1}{\tau_a}\right) - \frac{ik}{2}(\overline{n}_0 - n_0). \tag{5e}$$

If the K^0 and $\overline{K^0}$ absorption and scattering properties of the material are known, the magnitude and sign of κ may be determined by measurement of the imaginary part of the parameter β [Equations (5b) and (5d)]. By observations of the $K_2^0 \to K_1^0$ conversion in slabs of different density and thickness, on the other hand, the nuclear properties may be determined as well. Such observations[5] have resulted in a measurement of the value of the K_2^0–K_1^0 mass difference, $\kappa = +0.469 \pm 0.015$.

[5] See Table 2.1; see also R. C. Casella, *Phys. Rev. Letters, 21:* 1128 (1968).

8.3 CP Noninvariance

Another application of the $K_2^0 \to K_1^0$ reconversion in matter has been in the elucidation of the relatively small CP-violating $K_2^0 \to 2\pi$ decays, first observed by Christenson, Cronin, Fitch, and Turlay[6] in the decay mode

$$K_2^0 \to \pi^+\pi^- . \tag{6a}$$

Subsequently,[7] the decay mode

$$K_2^0 \to \pi^0\pi^0 \tag{6b}$$

has also been observed.

The degree and form of the CP violation is characterized by the relative amplitudes

$$\eta_{+-} = \frac{A(K_2^0 \to \pi^+\pi^-)}{A(K_1^0 \to \pi^+\pi^-)} = |\eta_{+-}|\, e^{i\phi_{+-}}, \tag{6a$'$}$$

$$\eta_{00} = \frac{A(K_2^0 \to \pi^0\pi^0)}{A(K_1^0 \to \pi^0\pi^0)} = |\eta_{00}|\, e^{i\phi_{00}} . \tag{6b$'$}$$

Through the direct comparison of the 2π decays and other decays in a pure K_2^0 beam, one deduces the magnitudes $|\eta_{+-}|$ and $|\eta_{00}|$. To determine the phases, however, it is necessary to observe an interference between the 2π's from K_2^0 decay and from some other, coherent source of known phase. This may be accomplished by passing the K_2^0 beam through a thin slab of material of known nuclear properties, and subsequently observing the coherent superposition of the 2π's resulting from the decay of the regenerated K_1^0 [Equation (5a)] and those from the decay of the remaining K_2^0. In this way, combined with the direct $K_2^0 \to 2\pi$ observations, the values are

$$\begin{aligned} |\eta_{+-}| &= (1.90 \pm 0.05) \times 10^{-3}, \\ \phi_{+-} &= (40 \pm 6)^\circ, \end{aligned} \tag{6c}$$

while the measured values[8] of $|\eta_{00}|$ vary over the range $\sim (1\text{–}5) \times 10^{-3}$.

A number of possible origins have been suggested for the CP-violating decays. The simplest suggestion postulates a CP-violating term in the weak interaction Hamiltonian. Such a term could be of the usual form — i.e., exhibiting the usual $\Delta S = \Delta Q = \pm 1$, $\Delta t = \pm\frac{1}{2}$ selection rules, but with a coupling constant $\sim 10^{-3}\, G_w$; or it could arise from a new interaction[9] with the selection rule $\Delta S = \pm 2$, but

[6] *Phys. Rev. Letters, 13:* 138 (1964); for critical discussions of these observations and their consequences, see V. L. Fitch, *Comments on Nuclear and Particle Physics, 1:* 47 (1967) and *2:* 63 (1968); see also L. Wolfenstein, *Nuovo Cimento, 42A:* 17 (1966).

[7] Gaillard, *et al., Phys. Rev. Letters, 18:* 20 (1967); Cronin, *et al., Phys. Rev. Letters, 18:* 25 (1967).

[8] The early reported values were $|\eta_{00}| \approx 4 \times 10^{-3}$, $\phi_{00} \approx 50^\circ$ or 215°. However, the measurement on the $K_2^0 \to 2\pi^0$ decay has turned out to be subject to serious background problems, leading to large uncertainties [for a summary, see Casella, *Phys. Rev. Letters, 21:* 1128 (1968)]. The current situation is consistent with $\eta_{00} = \eta_{+-}$. (See Appendix 8.)

[9] This "superweak" interaction would lead to a direct — i.e., one-step — $K^0 \rightleftarrows \overline{K^0}$ conversion process [L. Wolfenstein, *Phys. Rev. Letters, 13:* 562 (1964)].

with coupling strength $\sim 10^{-9}\, G_w$. In either case, the effect would be to mix a small amount of $CP = -1$ term into the K_1^0 eigenstate of the weak interactions, and of $CP = +1$ into the K_2^0 eigenstate,[10]

$$K_1^0 = [2(1 + |\epsilon|^2)]^{-1/2}\{(K^0 + \overline{K^0}) + \epsilon(K^0 - \overline{K^0})\}$$
$$\cong \sqrt{\tfrac{1}{2}}\,\{(1 + \epsilon)\,K^0 + (1 - \epsilon)\,\overline{K^0}\}, \tag{7a}$$

$$K_2^0 \cong \sqrt{\tfrac{1}{2}}\,\{(K^0 - \overline{K^0}) + \epsilon(K^0 + \overline{K^0})\}$$
$$\cong \sqrt{\tfrac{1}{2}}\,\{(1 + \epsilon)\,K^0 - (1 - \epsilon)\,\overline{K^0}\}. \tag{7b}$$

The result of such a mixing would be

$$\eta = \frac{A(K_2^0 \to 2\pi)}{A(K_1^0 \to 2\pi)} = \epsilon \tag{7c}$$

for both decay modes.

However, it is also possible that the weak interaction Hamiltonian is, in fact, CP-invariant, but that the violation arises as a result of a violation of T and C in either the strong or electromagnetic interactions,[11] transmitted to the weak decays as a result of virtual strong or electromagnetic emission and absorption processes. An analysis of measurements of nuclear phenomena makes it extremely unlikely that a T violation of the required magnitude would have gone undetected in the strong interactions, but the same is not the case for the electromagnetic interactions.[12] Furthermore, the magnitude of the effect, $|\eta| \sim (\alpha/\pi)$, suggests that such an electromagnetic T violation, if present, could be an important feature of the electromagnetic interactions.

A likely form, in which such an electromagnetic effect would be manifested, would be in the $\Delta t = \frac{3}{2}$ amplitude for $K^0(\overline{K^0}) \to 2\pi$ decay. If such a term were present, either owing to an electromagnetic T violation or to some other cause more directly related to the weak interactions, we could write [see Section 7.4.3, Equations (33c)–(33d)]

$$A'(K^0) = (\mathrm{Re}\, A' + i\, \mathrm{Im}\, A')\, e^{i\delta_2}, \tag{8a}$$

$$\overline{A}'(\overline{K^0}) = (\mathrm{Re}\, A' - i\, \mathrm{Im}\, A')\, e^{i\delta_2}, \tag{8b}$$

in which the (Re A') leads to the CP-conserving $K_1^0 \to 2\pi$ decay component with $\Delta t = \frac{3}{2}$, and the (Im A') to the CP-violating $K_2^0 \to 2\pi$ decays. Taking into account the Clebsch–Gordan coefficients for the $\Delta t = \frac{3}{2}$ decays, and combining this $\Delta t = \frac{3}{2}$ with a CP-conserving $\Delta t = \frac{1}{2}$ K_1^0 decay amplitude, A [see Equation (7c)], we have

$$\eta_{+-} = \epsilon + \sqrt{\frac{1}{2}}\, i\, \frac{\mathrm{Im}\, A'}{A}\, e^{i(\delta_2 - \delta_0)} = \epsilon + \epsilon', \tag{8c}$$

---

[10] Since $|\epsilon| \sim 10^{-3}$, we henceforth neglect terms of order $|\epsilon|^2$. Note that ϵ is in general complex. Actually, one could be even more general and introduce two complex mixing constants, ϵ_1 in (7a) and ϵ_2 in (7b). However, in this case, TCP invariance requires $(\epsilon_1 - \epsilon_2) = 0$. In any event, this more general approach does not contribute anything new to the discussion of the $K_2^0 \to 2\pi$ decays.

[11] P is known to be conserved in both the strong and electromagnetic interactions to better than one part in $\sim 10^5$.

[12] J. Bernstein, G. Feinberg, and T. D. Lee, *Phys. Rev.*, *139:* B1650 (1965); S. Barshay, *Phys. Letters*, *17:* 78 (1965).

$$\eta_{00} = \epsilon - \sqrt{2}\, i \frac{\text{Im } A'}{A} e^{i(\delta_2 - \delta_0)} = \epsilon - 2\epsilon' . \tag{8d}$$

The phase angle of ϵ',

$$\arg \epsilon' = \frac{\pi}{2} + \delta_2 - \delta_0 \cong (37 \pm 15)° , \tag{8e}$$

is in principle directly obtainable from the difference of the S-wave π–π scattering phase shifts in the $t = 2$ and $t = 0$ states; however, owing to the indirect nature of the determination of these phase shifts, their uncertainties are rather large. (It should perhaps be noted that a direct determination of the phase of ϵ', through careful measurements of both η_{+-} and η_{00}, is probably the best available method for the experimental evaluation of $\delta_2 - \delta_0$.) In addition, the phase of ϵ may be shown[13] to be derivable from the masses and decay rates of the long-lived and short-lived K_1^0 and K_2^0:

$$\arg \epsilon \cong \tan^{-1} - 2 \left[\frac{m(K_2^0) - m(K_1^0)}{\Gamma(K_2^0) - \Gamma(K_1^0)}\right] \simeq 43° . \tag{8f}$$

The earliest experimental observations appeared to favor a large, if not dominant, $\Delta t = \frac{3}{2}$ component for the $K_2^0 \rightarrow 2\pi$ decays. However, considering the large uncertainties in the phases and, especially, in the value of $|\eta_{00}|$, such a conclusion would be somewhat premature. Actually, on the basis of the experimental values given above, a "best fit" solution[14] requires comparable values of ϵ and ϵ'.

Additional information on the CP-violating K_2^0 decay interaction has been obtained through the observation of a charge asymmetry in the semileptonic decays

$$K_2^0 \rightarrow \pi^{\mp} + l^{\pm} + \nu(\bar{\nu}) \tag{9}$$

for both the decays involving electrons[15] and muons.[16] Letting $R = N(l^+)/N(l^-)$ be the ratio of the decay rates involving the two lepton charges, we see that the assumption of CP violation [Equations (7a) and (7b)] coupled with the $\Delta S = \Delta Q$ rule,[17] requires

$$R = \left|\frac{1 + \epsilon}{1 - \epsilon}\right|^2 \cong 1 + 4 \text{ Re } \epsilon. \tag{9a}$$

---

[13] Lee and Wu, *Ann. Rev. Nucl. Sci., 16:* 511 (1966).
[14] L. D. Roper, private communication.
[15] Bennett, *et al., Phys. Rev. Letters, 19:* 993 (1967).
[16] Dorfan, *et al., Phys. Rev. Letters, 19:* 987 (1967).
[17] If $x = A(\Delta S = -\Delta Q)/A(\Delta S = \Delta Q)$ is the relative amplitude of the $(\Delta S = \Delta Q)$-violating K^0 and $\overline{K^0}$ decays, we have, instead,

$$R \cong 1 + 4 \left(\frac{1 - |x|^2}{|1 - x|^2}\right) \text{Re } \epsilon$$
$$\cong 1 + 4[1 + 2 \text{ Re } x + 2(\text{Re } x)^2 - 2(\text{Im } x)^2] \text{ Re } \epsilon. \tag{9a'}$$

[See L. Wolfenstein, *Nuovo Cimento, 42A:* 17 (1966) and *Phys. Rev. Letters, 13:* 562 (1964).]

The aforementioned experimental observations yield

$$R(e) - 1 = (4.48 \pm 0.72) \times 10^{-3}, \tag{9b}$$

$$R(\mu) - 1 = (8.1 \pm 2.7) \times 10^{-3}, \tag{9c}$$

for a weighted mean

$$\overline{R} - 1 = (4.7 \pm 0.7) \times 10^{-3}, \tag{9d}$$

which yields, from Equation (9a),

$$\text{Re}\ \epsilon = (1.42 \pm 0.17) \times 10^{-3}. \tag{9e}$$

This result would rule out a solution for which $\epsilon' \gg \epsilon$.

The most effective way of analyzing, simultaneously, all the data on the *CP*-violating K_2^0 decays is by use of the Wu–Yang diagram,[18] illustrated in Figure 8.3. (We have not attempted to represent the best values, since the uncertainties are too large. Actually, all of the data discussed above, with the exception of the value of $|\eta_{00}|$, are consistent with $\epsilon \gg \epsilon'$.)

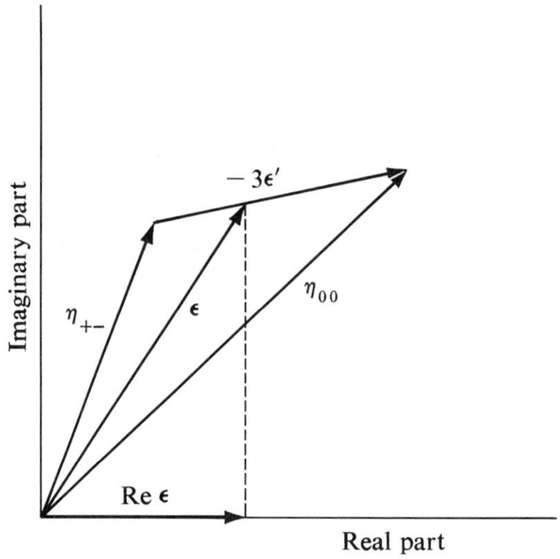

Figure 8.3 Wu–Yang diagram for analysis of *CP*-violating K_2^0 decays.

8.4 Other Possible Manifestations of *T* Violation

If, indeed, the *CP* violations arise from a virtual *T*-violating photon interaction (and not from a weak interaction effect), other manifestations should be observable in decays of similar origin. We have previously noted (Section 7.4.2) that the η-meson decays are probably of electromagnetic origin. Hence, in the decays $\eta^0 \to \pi^+\pi^-\pi^0$ or $\eta^0 \to \pi^+\pi^-\gamma$, an effect of a *T* violation might be observable

[18] T. T. Wu and C. S. Yang, *Phys. Rev. Letters, 13:* 180 (1964).

as a difference in the distributions of the π^+ and the π^-. However, careful observations place an upper limit of a few percent on any such effect.[19]

On the other hand, a T-violating weak interaction term should (if it were not solely confined to the K_2^0 decays) give rise to observable effects in other weak leptonic decays — e.g., β decay. Such an effect would manifest itself in a $\boldsymbol{\sigma} \cdot (\mathbf{p}_1 \times \mathbf{p}_2)$ term in the β-decay matrix element, where $\boldsymbol{\sigma}$ is the spin of one of the Fermions involved and $\mathbf{p}_1$, $\mathbf{p}_2$ are two of the independent momenta of the decay products. Such effects have, until now, not been observed.[20]

Finally, T violation can, if accompanied by P violation, give rise to a finite electric dipole moment in baryons (say, the neutron). The magnitude of the resulting dipole moment would, for an effect of electromagnetic origin, be roughly

$$\mu^E \approx \xi G_w M_{\mathfrak{N}} e \approx 2\xi \times 10^{-19}\, e \text{ cm}, \tag{10}$$

where ξ is a numerical factor which is expected to be $\sim \frac{1}{10}$, but which could, depending on the form of the T-violating interaction, be made smaller by some orders of magnitude. For a weak interaction origin of the T violation, the estimate [Equation (10)] should be reduced by the factor $\sim 10^{-3}$, while for a superweak interaction effect, the reduction would be by a factor $\sim 10^{-9}$. Recent measurements [21] have established the upper limit

$$\mu_N^E < 2 \times 10^{-22}\, e \text{ cm}, \tag{10a}$$

which is small enough to exclude a number of the proposed theories of the CP-violating interactions.

PROBLEMS

1. Devise and describe an experiment aimed at detecting T noninvariance in:
   (a) the strong (e.g., π–$\mathfrak{N}$) interactions;
   (b) the electromagnetic interactions, as manifested in pion photoproduction (assume the availability of polarized nucleon targets and/or polarized photon beams);
   (c) the weak, nonleptonic decays of the Σ hyperons;
   (d) nuclear β decay.
2. Let the $\Lambda^0 \to \mathfrak{N}\pi$ decay amplitude, $A_{S,P} = (\text{Re}\, A_{S,P} + i\, \text{Im}\, A_{S,P})\, e^{i\alpha_{S,P}}$, represent the T-violating amplitude for the $\Lambda \to \mathfrak{N}\pi$ decays. Using the data in Table 2.1, determine an experimental upper limit for the $\text{Im}\, A_{S,P}$ term.
3. Consider a system without spin. Let $P(\mathbf{r}, t)$ and $\pi(\mathbf{p}, t)$ represent, respectively, the probability densities in coordinate and momentum space. Show that, under the operation of time-reversal,

$$P_T(\mathbf{r}, t) = P(\mathbf{r}, -t),$$
$$\pi_T(\mathbf{p}, t) = \pi(-\mathbf{p}, -t).$$

---

[19] *Proceedings of the XVIII International Conference on High-Energy Physics,* University of California Press, Berkeley (1966), p. 63; however, see Gormley, *et al., Phys. Rev. Letters, 21:* 399 and 402 (1968).

[20] V. L. Fitch, *Comments on Nuclear and Particle Physics, 1:* 117 (1967).

[21] P. D. Miller, W. B. Dress, J. K. Baird, and N. F. Ramsey, *Phys. Rev. Letters, 19:* 381 (1967); C. G. Shull and R. Nathans, *Phys. Rev. Letters, 19:* 384 (1967).

9

Electron Scattering and Nucleon Form Factors

Just as the diffraction of X-rays and electrons has been a powerful tool for the determination of the structure of crystals and complex molecules, so has the study of the scattering of fast electrons yielded important information on the charge structure of nuclei and of the nucleons themselves. Considering that the wavelength of a fast electron of momentum p is $\lambda\!\!\!^- = \hbar/p = 1.0$ f for $p = 200$ MeV/c, and that nucleons have dimensions $\lesssim 10^{-13}$ cm $= 1$ f, the momentum of electrons required for investigating the nucleon charge structure is $p \gtrsim 200$ MeV/c. Intense monochromatic beams of electrons in this energy range have been available for over a decade from linear accelerators and synchrotrons, and they have been extensively and effectively utilized in such studies.[1]

The description of the scattering of fast electrons from nucleons utilizes the Rosenbluth formula

$$\frac{d\sigma}{d\Omega} = \left(\frac{d\sigma}{d\Omega}\right)_{\text{Mott}} R(\not{q}^2, \theta), \tag{1}$$

in which

$$\left(\frac{d\sigma}{d\Omega}\right)_{\text{Mott}} = \left(\frac{\alpha r_e}{2E}\right)^2 \left(\frac{(E'/E)\cos^2\theta/2}{\sin^4\theta/2}\right) \tag{1a}$$

is the differential cross section in the *lab* for scattering through the angle θ of an electron of initial energy E, final energy E', by a spin $\frac{1}{2}$ particle of point charge

[1] R. Hofstadter, ed., *Electron Scattering and Nuclear and Nucleon Structure,* W. A. Benjamin, New York (1963); R. Herman and R. Hofstadter, *High Energy Electron Scattering Tables,* Stanford University Press, Stanford, California (1960).

obeying the Dirac equation ($r_e = e^2/m_e c^2$ is the classical electron radius). The Rosenbluth factor $R(\not{q}^2, \theta)$, in which $\not{q}^2$ is the invariant 4-momentum transfer, $\not{q}^2 = (\mathbf{p} - \mathbf{p}')^2 - (p_0 - p_0')^2 \cong 2pp'(1 - \cos\theta)$, takes into account the charge distribution, through the Dirac form factor $F_1(\not{q}^2)$, with

$$F_1(\not{q}^2 = 0) = Q = (\tfrac{1}{2} + t_3), \qquad \text{for nucleons,} \tag{2a}$$

and the anomalous (Pauli) magnetic moment form factor $F_2(\not{q}^2)$, with

$$F_2(\not{q}^2 = 0) = 1. \tag{2b}$$

It is given by the expression

$$R(\not{q}^2, \theta) = F_1^2(\not{q}^2) + \tau\kappa^2 F_2^2(\not{q}^2) + 2\tau[F_1(\not{q}^2) + \kappa F_2(\not{q}^2)]^2 \tan^2\frac{\theta}{2}, \tag{1b}$$

where $\tau = \not{q}^2/4M^2$ (M is the mass of the target particle) and κ is the anomalous moment of the target (nucleon) in units of $\mu_{\mathfrak{N}} = e\hbar/2M_p c = e/2M_p$;

$$\kappa = \left(\frac{\mu}{\mu_{\mathfrak{N}}}\right) - Q. \tag{1c}$$

Note that $\kappa_p = 1.79$ for the proton and $\kappa_N = -1.91$ for the neutron.

EXAMPLE

Classically, the form factor is the Fourier transform of the charge density, $\rho(r)$ [or density of magnetization, $M(r)$],

$$F(q^2) = \int_0^\infty \rho(r)\,\frac{\sin qr}{qr}\,4\pi r^2\,dr, \tag{2c}$$

with, for a spherically symmetric charge density,

$$4\pi \int_0^\infty \rho(r)\,r^2\,dr = Q. \tag{2d}$$

The exact form of $F(q^2)$ depends, of course, on the form of $\rho(r)$; however, for small momentum transfers ($qR \ll 1$, where R is the "size" of the charge structure), the form factor depends on a single parameter, the mean-square charge radius

$$\langle r^2 \rangle = \frac{4\pi}{Q}\int_0^\infty \rho(r)\,r^4\,dr, \tag{2e}$$

with

$$F(q^2) \cong 1 - \tfrac{1}{6}\langle r^2 \rangle\, q^2. \tag{2f}$$

Some examples of charge distributions and the corresponding values of $\langle r^2 \rangle$ are given in Table 9.1.

The interpretation of the form factors as (three-dimensional) Fourier transforms of the densities of charge and magnetization is, of course, not

Table 9.1 Some Charge Distributions and Corresponding Values of $\langle r^2 \rangle$

Distribution, $\rho(r)$	$\langle r^2 \rangle$
Exponential: $e^{-r/R}$	$12R^2$
Hollow exponential: $r\, e^{-r/R}$	$20R^2$
Yukawa: $\dfrac{e^{-2\mu r}}{r^2}$	$\dfrac{1}{2\mu^2}$
Gaussian: e^{-r^2/r_0^2}	$\dfrac{3r_0^2}{2}$

Lorentz invariant. However, when viewed in the *cm*, in which $\not{q}^2 = \mathbf{q}^2 = 2p^2(1-\cos\theta)$, the form factors can indeed be interpreted in the classical fashion in terms of the appropriate spatial densities referred to the nucleon's rest frame.[2]

The experiments on the scattering of electrons by protons at low momentum transfer yield, from Equation (2f), the root-mean-square charge radius

$$\langle r^2 \rangle_P^{1/2} \cong 0.80 \text{ f.} \tag{2f$'$}$$

With increasing momentum transfer, some effects of the form of the charge distribution become manifest; a quite reasonable fit is provided by the exponential charge distribution, for which

$$F_{\text{exp}}(q^2) = (1 + R^2 q^2)^{-2}, \tag{2g}$$

with $R \cong 0.23$ f $= (865 \text{ MeV}/c)^{-1}$ (see Table 9.1).

Although the form factors F_1 and F_2 have a direct interpretation in terms of their origin in the Dirac equation, they have the disadvantage that they mix effects due to the distribution of charge and of magnetization. A more convenient pair of form factors may be defined[3] in terms of the components of the relativistically invariant 4-vector current density $[\mathbf{j}(\mathbf{r}), i\rho(\mathbf{r})]$:

$$\mathbf{j}(\mathbf{r}) = \frac{ie}{(2\pi)^3} \int d^3q\, (\boldsymbol{\sigma} \times \mathbf{q})\, G_M(\not{q}^2)\, e^{i\mathbf{q}\cdot\mathbf{r}}, \tag{3a}$$

$$\rho(\mathbf{r}) = \frac{e}{(2\pi)^3} \int d^3q\, G_E(\not{q}^2)\, e^{i\mathbf{q}\cdot\mathbf{r}}. \tag{3b}$$

G_E, the electric form factor, and G_M, the magnetic form factor, may be expressed in terms of F_1 and F_2:

$$G_M = F_1 + \kappa F_2, \tag{3a$'$}$$

$$G_E = F_1 - \kappa\tau F_2, \tag{3b$'$}$$

and the Rosenbluth factor [Equations (1) and (1b)] rewritten as

$$R(\not{q}^2, \theta) = \frac{G_E^2 + \tau G_M^2}{1+\tau} + 2\tau G_M^2 \tan^2 \frac{\theta}{2}. \tag{1d}$$

[2] R. G. Sachs, *Phys. Rev.*, *126:* 2256 (1962).
[3] *Ibid.*

The understanding of the form factors is facilitated by consideration of the Feynman diagram corresponding to electron-nucleon elastic scattering, Figure 9.1. A number of properties of the form factors follow:

1. The form factors clearly depend on the nature of the γ–$\mathfrak{N}$ vertex, which may be quite complex owing to the variety of strong interactions. The simplest kind of coupling would be through a direct γ-vector meson vertex, Figure 9.1(b),

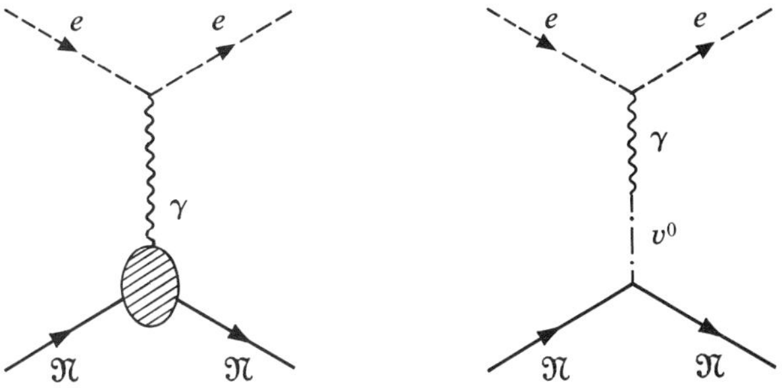

(a) (b)

Figure 9.1 Feynman diagrams for electron-nucleon scattering: (a) Basic diagram. (b) Diagram for the case of vector meson dominance.

this being possible by virtue of the fact that the γ and 1^--meson have the same quantum numbers (excepting mass). Such a coupling would lead to contributions to the form factors having a resonant behavior[4]

$$G = \left(1 + \frac{\not{q}^2}{m_v^2}\right)^{-1}, \tag{4a}$$

with the actual form factor being an appropriately weighted superposition of terms like (4a) corresponding to the different vector mesons (ω, ϕ, ρ) and their relative couplings to the γ and $\mathfrak{N}$.

2. The γ–$\mathfrak{N}$ or γ–v couplings have the properties of a combination of a scalar and a vector in isospin space. This enables us to express the proton and neutron form factors, G_E^P, G_M^P and G_E^N, G_M^N, in terms of another set of four, $G_{E,M}^{(s)}$ and $G_{E,M}^{(v)}$,

$$G_{E,M}^{\mathfrak{N}} = G_{E,M}^{(s)} + 2\tau_3 G_{E,M}^{(v)}, \tag{4b}$$

so that

$$\begin{aligned} G_{E,M}^{P} &= G_{E,M}^{(s)} + G_{E,M}^{(v)}, \\ G_{E,M}^{N} &= G_{E,M}^{(s)} - G_{E,M}^{(v)}, \end{aligned} \tag{4b'}$$

---

[4] The "resonance" occurs, of course, for $\not{q}^2 = -m_v^2$ (i.e., timelike 4-momentum transfer) which is a region not accessible to e–$\mathfrak{N}$ scattering. Also, in Equation (4a), we have neglected the finite width of the resonance, which is important in the timelike resonance region. It is interesting that the vector mesons were predicted on the basis of the early observations of the e–$\mathfrak{N}$ form factors. [W. R. Frazer and J. R. Fulco, *Phys. Rev.*, *117:* 1609 (1960)].

where the $G^{(s)}$ and $G^{(v)}$ would be given by the appropriate superposition of forms [Equation (4a)], in the case of dominating vector-meson coupling — e.g., $G^{(v)}$ would couple to ρ, $G^{(s)}$ to ω and ϕ. Note that the properties for $\not{q}^2 \to 0$ [Equations (2a) and (2b)] and the definitions of the G's [Equations (3a′) and (3b′)] require

$$\begin{aligned} G_E^P(0) &= 1, \qquad G_E^N(0) = 0, \\ G_E^{(s)}(0) &= G_E^{(v)}(0) = \tfrac{1}{2}, \end{aligned} \tag{4c}$$

$$\begin{aligned} G_M^P(0) &= 2.79, \qquad G_M^N(0) = -1.91, \\ G_M^{(s)}(0) &= 0.44, \qquad G_M^{(v)}(0) = 2.35. \end{aligned} \tag{4d}$$

3. Quantum electrodynamics requires

$$G_E(q^2 \to \infty) - G_M(q^2 \to \infty) \to 0, \tag{4e}$$

from which [according to Equations (3a′) and (3b′)] we deduce the requirement that $F_2(\not{q}^2 \to \infty) \to 0$ faster than τ^{-1}.

4. Figure 9.1, plus the analytical properties of reaction amplitudes, enables us to express the cross sections in the t-channel ($\mathfrak{N} + \overline{\mathfrak{N}} \rightleftharpoons e + \overline{e}$) in terms of the same form factors, but evaluated in the $\not{q}^2 < -4M^2$ region. Thus, if the form factors do, indeed, result from γ–v couplings, with the form of Equation (4a), we should be able to use these same forms to describe the annihilation reactions. In any event, whatever the forms of the G's, Equations (3a′) and (3b′) require, at $\tau = -1$ ($\not{q}^2 = -4M^2$),

$$\begin{aligned} G_E(\not{q}^2 = -4M^2) &= G_M(\not{q}^2 = -4M^2) \\ &= F_1(\not{q}^2 = -4M^2) + \kappa F_2(\not{q}^2 = -4M^2). \end{aligned} \tag{4f}$$

Note that $\not{q}^2 = -4M^2$ corresponds to nucleon-antinucleon annihilation at rest.

5. A further consequence of the vector-meson dominance model is that the same form factors that describe e–$\mathfrak{N}$ scattering should also describe e–π and e–K scattering, according to the diagrams shown in Figure 9.2, in which the only difference from Figure 9.1(b) is the substitution of the $\rho\pi\pi$ (a) and φKK (b) vertices for the $v\mathfrak{N}\mathfrak{N}$. Although the strength of these vertices is experimentally well known at only one value of $\not{q}^2 = -m_v^2$, through the decay widths $\Gamma(\rho \to 2\pi)$ and $\Gamma(\varphi \to K\overline{K})$, the value of the form factor (which should exhibit a Breit–Wigner form in the resonance region) can be measured directly through observation of the cross sections for the t-channel reactions (Figure 9.2)

$$e^+ + e^- \to \rho^0 \to 2\pi \tag{5a}$$

$$\to \varphi^0 \to K\overline{K} \tag{5b}$$

at electron energies now available in a number of laboratories for colliding-beam experiments. Recent results [5] give a resonant cross section, $\sigma_{\text{res}}(e^+e^- \to \rho^0) \simeq 1.2\ \mu$b, which corresponds to

$$\frac{\Gamma(\rho \to e^+e^-)}{\Gamma(\rho \to 2\pi)} \simeq 5 \times 10^{-5}, \tag{5c}$$

---

[5] 1967 *International Symposium on Electron and Photon Interactions at High Energies,* Stanford Linear Accelerator Center, Stanford, Calif. (1967).

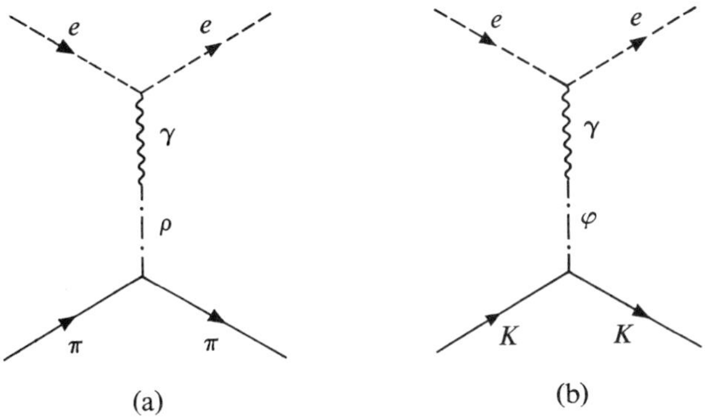

Figure 9.2 Feynman diagrams for (a) e–π and (b) e–K scattering according to the vector-meson dominance model.

a branching ratio in reasonable agreement with the results of the direct observation of the $\rho \to e^+e^-$ decay. Thus, observations on reactions relating to Figure 9.2(a) in the region of $\not{q}^2 \approx -m_\rho^2$ confirm the validity of the form of Equation (4a) for $G_E^{(v)}$.

6. Finally, some remarks are in order concerning the possibility of measuring electromagnetic form factors of unstable particles, such as the π and K, at arbitrary values of $\not{q}^2$. Let us consider the production of π-mesons by inelastic electron scattering on nucleons, according to the process illustrated in Figure 9.3.

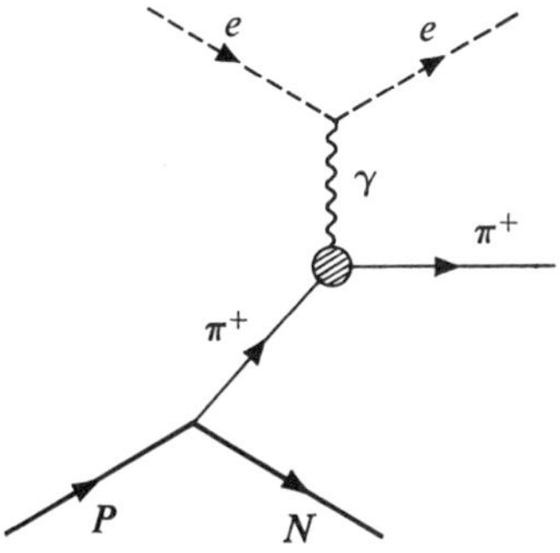

Figure 9.3 Feynman diagram for the electroproduction of π^+ on protons.

In such a sequence, the properties of all the vertices are known, except for the $\gamma\pi\pi$ vertex which, aside from purely kinematical factors, involves the electric form factor of the pion $G_\pi(\not{q}_\pi^2)$. Appropriate choice of the kinematical conditions (for example, variation of the direction of scattering for constant $\not{q}_\pi^2$) will then enable the determination of this form factor which should, if the vector-meson dominance model is appropriate, have a resonant form — i.e., Equation (4a).

The experimental observations on e–$\mathfrak{N}$ elastic scattering for small $\not{q}^2$, constrained as they are by Equations (4c) and (4d), serve primarily to determine the initial slopes of the form factors: $dG_E^N/d\not{q}^2(0) = (0.027 \pm 0.001)\,\mathrm{f}^2$, $dG_E^P/d\not{q}^2(0) = -(0.14 \pm 0.02)\,\mathrm{f}^2$. However, a quite unexpected result of the e–$\mathfrak{N}$ scattering measurements is that, over the entire range of $\not{q}^2$ measured [i.e., up to $\not{q}^2 \lesssim 600\,\mathrm{f}^{-2} \cong 25\,(\mathrm{GeV}/c)^2$], all the form factors may be expressed quite accurately in terms of one simple expression:[6]

$$G_E^P \cong \frac{G_M^P}{\mu_P} \cong \frac{G_M^N}{\mu_N} \cong \frac{G_E^N}{\tau\mu_N} \cong \left[1 + \frac{\not{q}^2}{0.71\,(\mathrm{GeV}/c)^2}\right]^{-2}. \tag{6}$$

One surprising aspect of this result is that the nucleons appear not to have any charged core, but rather to be describable in terms of a continuous (exponential) distribution of charge and magnetization. In addition, the form (6) corresponds to a universal "dipole" vector-meson coupling, rather than to any simple superposition of individual poles [Equation (4a)] corresponding to the known vector mesons. Although it appears possible to approximate the measured value of G_M^P (which is the most accurately measured form factor at the highest values of $\not{q}^2$) over a limited region by a superposition of simple poles, the behavior

$$G(\not{q}^2 \to \infty) \propto \not{q}^{-4} \tag{6a}$$

cannot result from any such superposition, but requires a dipole form. It is of great interest to know if, indeed, the behavior of Equation (6a) continues to prevail at even higher momentum transfers and, if so, to understand the origin[7] of the universal dipole form in Equation (6).

PROBLEM

Assume a proton charge density that is the sum of Yukawa terms

$$\rho(r) = \sum_i a_i \frac{e^{-2\mu_i r}}{r^2}.$$

Inverting the Fourier transform, Equation (3b), derive the electric form factor $G_E^P(\not{q}^2)$ and discuss the conditions under which this form factor could approximate the observed "dipole" form over the range of the observations.

---

[6] Note Equation (2g). However, there appear to be small, but experimentally significant, deviations from the simple "dipole" form of Equation (6) [Coward, *et al., Phys. Rev. Letters, 20:* 292 (1968)]. On the other hand, as $\not{q}^2 \to 0$, Equation (6) yields the observed values of $dG_E^{P,N}/d\not{q}^2$.

[7] S. D. Drell, *Comments on Nuclear and Particle Physics, 2:* 36 (1968). See also R. Wilson, *Comments on Nuclear and Particle Physics, 1:* 104 and 200 (1967). Equally interesting is the question of the form factors associated with inelastic electron scattering with isobar excitation, $e^- + \mathfrak{N} \to e^- + \mathfrak{N}^*$, for which some results are now becoming available [see C. Mistretta, *et al., Phys. Rev. Letters, 20:* 1070 (1968)]. In addition, there appears to be the interesting indication of a relatively constant form factor (i.e., point nucleon interaction) for scatterings corresponding to large inelastic excitations (of a few GeV). (W. K. H. Panofsky, *Report at the 15th International Conference on High Energy Physics,* Vienna, September 1968.)

10

Dispersion Relations

An approach of wide general applicability to the analysis of reactions is obtained by use of dispersion relations. These give rise to analytical connections between the amplitudes for scattering processes and their cross sections, whose origins are the wave nature of particle propagation (i.e., quantum mechanics) and the universal requirement of special relativity, that no signal can be propagated with a speed greater than c (*the principle of causality*).

Such relations have long been known in electromagnetic theory. They lead, for instance, to the connections (first derived by Lorentz) between the index of refraction of a medium and the amplitude for forward scattering of light by its atomic constituents and as a consequence, through connections between the index of refraction and the polarizability, to a relationship between the forward scattering and total cross section. We give, in the following, a number of examples of such dispersion relations.

10.1 The Weak Causality Relations of Wigner

To illustrate how the causality principle leads to useful conditions on the scattering phase shifts, we consider first the scattering of a particle — or a wave packet — by a center of finite range R. The incident wave packet has the form

$$\psi_{\text{in}} = \int d\omega\, g(\omega) \frac{e^{-i(kr+\omega t)}}{r}, \tag{1}$$

where $g(\omega)$ defines the size of the packet. We approximate this by a simple superposition of just two frequencies,

$$\psi_{\text{in}} \simeq \frac{1}{r} \{e^{-i(k+\delta k)r}\, e^{-i(\omega+\delta\omega)t} + e^{-i(k-\delta k)r}\, e^{-i(\omega-\delta\omega)t}\}, \tag{1a}$$

which is a wave packet whose center moves with the speed (group velocity)

$$v = -\frac{\delta\omega}{\delta k}. \tag{2}$$

Now, let the packet be scattered with a phase shift $\alpha(\omega)$. Then

$$\psi_{\text{out}} \simeq \frac{1}{r}\{e^{i(k+\delta k)r}\, e^{-i(\omega+\delta\omega)t}\, e^{2i(\alpha+\delta\alpha)} + e^{i(k-\delta k)r}\, e^{-i(\omega-\delta\omega)t}\, e^{2i(\alpha-\delta\alpha)}\}. \tag{1b}$$

The position of the center of the outgoing wave packet is now given by the condition

$$\begin{aligned} r\delta k - t\delta\omega + 2\delta\alpha &= 0, \\ r = \frac{\delta\omega}{\delta k}t - \frac{2\delta\alpha}{\delta k} &= v(t - \Delta t), \end{aligned} \tag{2a}$$

where

$$\Delta t = +\frac{2}{v}\frac{\delta\alpha}{\delta k} = 2\frac{\delta\alpha}{\delta\omega}. \tag{2b}$$

The causality condition simply states that if the wave is advanced in time ($\Delta t > 0$) as a result of the scattering, it cannot be advanced by more than $2R/v$, which is the maximum time saved by having a scatterer of range R rather than a point scatterer — i.e.,

$$\begin{aligned} \Delta t &\le \frac{2R}{v}, \\ R &\ge -\frac{\delta\alpha}{\delta k}, \\ \frac{\delta\alpha}{\delta k} &\ge -R. \end{aligned} \tag{3}$$

That is, for negative $\delta\alpha/\delta k$, the magnitude cannot exceed R.

Actually the situation is somewhat complicated by the fact that in practice we never have incident spherical waves, but rather plane waves. These can be analyzed as a sum of incident spherical waves; but the causality conditions are then different for each angular momentum. Wigner[1] has derived the causality conditions for S and P waves

$$\frac{d\alpha_0}{dk} \ge -R + \frac{\sin 2(\alpha_0 + kR)}{2k}, \tag{3a}$$

$$\frac{d\alpha_1}{dk} \ge -R + \frac{[1 - \cos 2(\alpha_1 + kR)]}{k^2 R} - \frac{\sin 2(\alpha_1 + kR)}{2k}. \tag{3b}$$

It follows directly from the forms of (3a) and (3b) that: (1) if $\alpha_0(kR \ll 1) = a_0(kR)^n$, then $n \ge 1$ if $a_0 > 0$ and $0 \le n \le 1$ if $a_0 < 0$; (2) taking $n = 1$, we have $a_0 \ge -1$ (which imposes an important restraint in the case of negative S-wave phase shifts); (3) if $\alpha_1(kR \ll 1) = a_1(kR)^n$, then $n \ge 3$ for $a_1 > 0$ and $0 \le n \le 3$ for $a_1 < 0$.

---

[1] E. P. Wigner, *Phys. Rev.*, *98:* 145 (1955).

10.2 The Dispersion Relations of Kramers and Kronig

In the following, we outline a simple derivation of the conventional dispersion relation. Consider scattering by a time-dependent potential

$$V(t) = 2\pi \int_{-\infty}^{\infty} V(\omega)\, e^{-i\omega t}\, d\omega. \tag{4a}$$

In general, the solution of the Schroedinger equation gives a scattered wave of amplitude

$$F(\omega) = K(\omega)\, V(\omega). \tag{4b}$$

Now, let the incident wave be represented by a δ function in space and let it be scattered by a point scatterer at the time $t = 0$. We may represent the time-dependent potential that gives rise to the scattering by

$$V(t) = \delta(0). \tag{4a$'$}$$

Then, *in the forward direction*,

$$F_0(t) = 0, \qquad \text{for all } t < 0. \tag{4b$'$}$$

However,

$$\begin{aligned} F_0(t) &= 2\pi \int_{-\infty}^{\infty} F_0(\omega)\, e^{-i\omega t}\, d\omega = 2\pi \int_{-\infty}^{\infty} K_0(\omega)\, V(\omega)\, e^{-i\omega t}\, d\omega \\ &= \int_{-\infty}^{\infty} K_0(\omega)\, e^{-i\omega t}\, d\omega \int_{-\infty}^{\infty} V(t')\, e^{i\omega t'}\, dt' \\ &= \int_{-\infty}^{\infty} K_0(\omega)\, e^{-i\omega t}\, d\omega. \end{aligned} \tag{4b$''$}$$

Hence,

$$\begin{aligned} F_0(\omega) = K_0(\omega) &= \int_{-\infty}^{\infty} F_0(t)\, e^{i\omega t}\, dt \\ &= \int_0^{\infty} F_0(t)\, e^{i\omega t}\, dt, \end{aligned} \tag{4c}$$

the last step being the consequence of *causality* as stated in Equation (4b$'$).

If we confine ourselves to problems in which the particles are represented by *real* wave packets [$F_0(t)$ real], we obtain

$$\text{Re } F_0(\omega) = \int_0^{\infty} F_0(t) \cos \omega t\, dt, \tag{4d}$$

$$\text{Im } F_0(\omega) = \int_0^{\infty} F_0(t) \sin \omega t\, dt, \tag{4e}$$

and using the relation

$$\cos \omega t = \frac{1}{\pi} \int_{-\infty}^{\infty} \frac{d\omega' \sin \omega' t}{\omega' - \omega}, \tag{4f}$$

we obtain

$$\operatorname{Re} F_0(\omega) = D(\omega) = \frac{1}{\pi}\int_{-\infty}^{\infty} \frac{d\omega' \operatorname{Im} F_0(\omega')}{\omega' - \omega}$$

$$= \frac{2}{\pi}\int_0^{\infty} d\omega' \frac{\omega' \operatorname{Im} F_0(\omega')}{\omega'^2 - \omega^2}, \tag{4d$'$}$$

since $\operatorname{Im} F_0(-\omega) = -\operatorname{Im} F_0(\omega)$. We may change (4d′) into a "once-subtracted" dispersion relation through the identity

$$\frac{1}{\omega'^2 - \omega^2} = \frac{\omega^2}{\omega'^2}\left(\frac{1}{\omega'^2 - \omega^2}\right) + \frac{1}{\omega'^2}, \tag{4g}$$

giving

$$D(\omega) - D(\omega = 0) = \frac{2\omega^2}{\pi}\int_0^{\infty} \frac{d\omega' \operatorname{Im} F_0(\omega')}{\omega'(\omega'^2 - \omega^2)}. \tag{4h}$$

Recalling the "optical theorem"

$$\operatorname{Im} F_0(\omega) = \frac{k}{4\pi}\,\sigma(\omega) = \frac{\omega}{4\pi c}\,\sigma(\omega), \tag{4i}$$

we finally obtain

$$D(\omega) - D(0) = \frac{\omega^2}{2\pi^2 c}\int_0^{\infty} \frac{d\omega'\,\sigma(\omega')}{\omega'^2 - \omega^2}. \tag{5}$$

From the Kramers–Kronig dispersion relation, Equation (5), we may derive a number of simple but useful relations for photon scattering. The most interesting ones arise from the *sum rule* that is obtained in the limit $\omega \to \infty$. Assuming that $\sigma(\omega)/\omega^2 \to 0$ faster than $1/\omega$, we obtain

$$D(\infty) - D(0) = -\frac{1}{2\pi^2 c}\int_0^{\infty} \sigma(\omega')\, d\omega'. \tag{6}$$

EXAMPLES[2]

1. *Compton scattering:* We have previously noted (Section 6.2.2) that for photon scattering by a *free charge,* independent of the energy,

$$D_c(\omega) = -\frac{e^2}{Mc^2} = D_c(0) = D_c(\infty). \tag{7a}$$

Accordingly,

$$\int_0^{\infty} \sigma_c(\omega)\, d\omega = 0. \tag{7b}$$

This vanishing of the integral cannot, of course, be absolutely true [since $\sigma_c(\omega) \geq 0$], but it is true at least to first order in the fine structure constant $\alpha = e^2/\hbar c$.

[2] For a general discussion, see M. Gell-Mann, M. L. Goldberger, and W. E. Thirring, *Phys. Rev., 95:* 1612 (1954).

2. *Photo-effect:* If the charged particle is bound, then, in the limit $\omega \to 0$, the scattering becomes Rayleigh ($\sigma \propto 1/\lambda^4 \propto \omega^4$):

$$D_b(0) = 0; \tag{8a}$$

at the high-energy limit, the binding is unimportant and

$$D_b(\infty) = D_c(\infty) = -\frac{e^2}{Mc^2}, \tag{8b}$$

whence

$$\int_0^\infty \sigma_b(\omega)\, d\omega = 2\pi^2 \frac{e^2}{Mc}. \tag{8c}$$

This is the well-known *dipole sum rule* of Thomas, Reiche, and Kuhn.

3. *Photon interactions with nuclei:* Consider a complex nucleus of charge Z and mass number A. We compare its scattering with that of Z free protons and $A - Z = N$ free neutrons. Let

$$\Delta_A = D_A(0) - D_A(\infty) = \frac{1}{2\pi^2 c} \int_0^\infty \sigma_A(\omega)\, d\omega, \tag{9a}$$

$$\Delta_p = Z[D_p(0) - D_p(\infty)] = \frac{Z}{2\pi^2 c} \int_0^\infty \sigma_p(\omega)\, d\omega, \tag{9b}$$

$$\Delta_n = N[D_n(0) - D_n(\infty)] = \frac{N}{2\pi^2 c} \int_0^\infty \sigma_n(\omega)\, d\omega. \tag{9c}$$

Now, from the previous discussion, we have

$$\begin{aligned} D_p(0) &= D_p(\infty) = -\frac{e^2}{Mc^2}, \\ D_n(0) &= D_n(\infty) = 0, \\ D_A(0) &= -\frac{Z^2 e^2}{AMc^2}, \\ D_A(\infty) &= Z D_p(\infty) + N D_n(\infty) = -\frac{Ze^2}{Mc^2}. \end{aligned} \tag{9d}$$

Hence,

$$\Delta_A - (\Delta_p + \Delta_n) = \frac{NZ}{A} \frac{e^2}{Mc^2} = \frac{1}{2\pi^2 c} \int [\sigma_A - Z\sigma_p - N\sigma_n]\, d\omega, \tag{9e}$$

and

$$\int_0^\infty \sigma_A(\omega)\, d\omega = 2\pi^2 \frac{NZ}{A} \frac{e^2}{Mc} + Z \int_0^\infty \sigma_p(\omega)\, d\omega + N \int_0^\infty \sigma_n(\omega)\, d\omega. \tag{9e$'$}$$

Now, to a first approximation,

$$\int_0^\infty \sigma_p(\omega)\, d\omega = \int_0^\infty \sigma_n(\omega)\, d\omega \simeq 0, \tag{9f}$$

since these are supposed to be free-particle cross sections. However, in actual fact both the proton and neutron are complex structures, involving bound

π-mesons, etc. If we were to make a simple model of a proton, as a neutral core with a single bound π^+-meson (mass m), then the second sum rule would give

$$\int \sigma_p(\omega)\, d\omega \simeq 2\pi^2 \frac{e^2}{mc} \times P, \tag{9g}$$

in which $0 \leq P \leq 1$ represents the probability that the real proton finds itself in the compound state as described above. On this crude model, the neutron (positive core plus π^--meson) would yield the same integral, and

$$Z \int \sigma_p(\omega)\, d\omega + N \int \sigma_n(\omega)\, d\omega \simeq P \times 2\pi^2 \frac{e^2}{mc} A, \tag{9h}$$

giving, finally,

$$\int_0^\infty \sigma_A(\omega)\, d\omega = 2\pi^2 \frac{NZ}{A} \frac{e^2}{Mc} \left(1 + \frac{A^2}{NZ} \frac{M}{m} P\right). \tag{9i}$$

This is the nuclear sum rule of Bethe and Levinger with, however, the correction $[(A^2/NZ)(M/m) P \approx \frac{1}{2}]$ expressed in a somewhat different form.

10.3 Dispersion Relations for Scattering of Particles of Finite Rest Mass

One encounters two types of problems in attempting to apply the dispersion relations, Equations (4d′) and (5), to particles of finite rest mass. The first arises directly from the finite mass, since the condition $\omega^2 = k^2 + m^2$ does not permit $\omega \to 0$ for $k \geq 0$. To define this problem more precisely, we consider the dispersion formula in the unsubtracted form, i.e., Equation (4d′). Substituting

$$\frac{1}{k'^2 - k^2} = \frac{1}{\omega'^2 - \omega^2} = \frac{k^2}{k'^2} \frac{1}{\omega'^2 - \omega^2} + \frac{1}{k'^2}, \tag{4g′}$$

we can express Equation (4h) as

$$\begin{aligned} D(k) - D(k=0) &= \frac{2k^2}{\pi} \int_0^\infty \frac{d\omega'\, \omega' \operatorname{Im} F_0(\omega')}{k'^2(\omega'^2 - \omega^2)} \\ &= \frac{k^2}{2\pi^2} \int_0^\infty \frac{d\omega'\, \omega'\, \sigma(\omega')}{k'(\omega'^2 - \omega^2)}. \end{aligned} \tag{5a}$$

In the region $0 \leq \omega' < m$, k' becomes imaginary and $\sigma(\omega')$ has no simple physical meaning. However, in this "nonphysical" region it is more convenient to describe the interaction (amplitude) in terms of the scattering length, which can be expressed as a sum of terms of the form

$$F_l \sim \frac{1}{k} e^{i\alpha_l} \sin \alpha_l. \tag{10}$$

In the nonphysical region, both k and α_l are imaginary; in this case, F_l becomes real, $\operatorname{Im} F_0(\omega' < m) = 0$, and the problem of the evaluation of Equation (5a) over the range $0 \leq \omega < m$ disappears. However, this situation is altered when a bound state of the system under consideration occurs in the nonphysical region. Under these circumstances, $F(\omega)$ has a pole at the bound state energy, $\omega = \omega_B < m$, and the pole results in a finite contribution to the dispersion integral. Equation (5a) then has the form

$$D(k) - D(0) = \lambda_B \left(\frac{k^2}{\omega + \omega_B}\right) + \frac{k^2}{2\pi^2} \int_m^\infty \frac{d\omega'\, \omega'\, \sigma(\omega')}{k'(\omega'^2 - \omega^2)}. \tag{5b}$$

The residue factor λ_B depends on the properties of the bound state.

The second difficulty is a consequence of the fact that the description of systems of charged particles requires the use of complex wave functions, so that our derivation breaks down at the stage of Equations (4d)–(4e). This difficulty can be circumvented by considering only those combinations of particles that can, indeed, be described by real wave functions. Thus, for example, considering the three-component pion field

$$\begin{aligned} \psi_{\pi^+} &= \psi_1 + i\psi_2\,, \\ \psi_{\pi^-} &= \psi_1 - i\psi_2\,, \end{aligned} \tag{11}$$

with ψ_1 and ψ_2 real, we can develop dispersion relations for the two combinations $\psi_{\pi^+} \pm \psi_{\pi^-}$, although for the second the relations (4d)–(4e) are inverted.

However, in considering such dispersion relations, it is not possible to separate the contributions of the two charges so that, for instance, the relations that can be derived have the form

$$D_\pm(\omega) - D_\pm(m) = f_\pm(\sigma_{\pi^+}, \sigma_{\pi^-}, \lambda_{B^+}, \text{etc.}), \tag{5c}$$

and it is necessary to utilize our knowledge of both σ_+ and σ_- to obtain information on either $D_+(\omega)$ or $D_-(\omega)$. In the case of the dispersion relations for pion-nucleon scattering this presents no great disadvantage, since both $\sigma_+(\pi^+P)$ and $\sigma_-(\pi^-P)$ are experimentally available. In other cases this may present more serious experimental problems, as for example in the case of the dispersion relations for nucleon-nucleon scattering, which require a knowledge of the cross sections for nucleon-antinucleon scattering as well as of $\sigma(\mathfrak{N}\mathfrak{N})$.

EXAMPLE

The pion-nucleon dispersion relations illustrate the problems raised in the preceding discussion. For simplicity, we may begin with the dispersion relations for π^0–P scattering, $\pi^0 P \to \pi^0 P$. Since the π^0 is described by the (real) wave functions, $\psi_{\pi^0} = \psi_3$, Equation (5b) is directly applicable. In this case there is a bound $\pi^0 P$ state — i.e., the proton — whose total *cm* energy is

$$\omega_\pi + \omega_P = \omega_B + M + \frac{k_B^2}{2M} = M, \tag{12a}$$

where

$$\omega_B = (k_B^2 + \mu^2)^{1/2}. \tag{12b}$$

Equations (12a) and (12b) have the solution (for $\mu/M \ll 1$)

$$\omega_B \approx \frac{\mu^2}{2M}, \tag{12c}$$

$$k_B^2 \approx -\mu^2. \tag{12d}$$

The evaluation of the residue factor requires the solution of the Yukawa equation for a bound state,[3]

$$\phi_{\pi^0} \approx \frac{e^{-\omega_B r}}{r}, \tag{12e}$$

and results in the value

$$\lambda_B = \frac{2f^2}{\mu^2}, \tag{12f}$$

so that the dispersion relation for $\pi^0 P$ elastic scattering becomes

$$D_0(k) = D_0(0) + \frac{2f^2}{\mu^2}\frac{k^2}{\omega + \mu^2/2M} + \frac{k^2}{2\pi^2}\int_\mu^\infty \frac{d\omega'\,\omega'\,\sigma_0(\omega')}{k'(\omega'^2 - \omega^2)}. \tag{12}$$

Although the $\pi^0 P$ cross section is not directly measurable, it can be related to the observed $\pi^+ P$, $\pi^- P$, and charge exchange ($\pi^- P \to \pi^0 N$) cross sections through isotopic-spin conservation (Section 7.1.2),

$$\sigma_0 = \tfrac{1}{2}(\sigma_+ + \sigma_- - \sigma_{\text{ex}}), \tag{13a}$$

thus permitting the evaluation of the dispersion integral in Equation (12). Furthermore, the unobservable forward scattering amplitude $D_0(k)$ can also be related to the observable $D_+(k)$ and $D_-(k)$ (see Table 7.4),

$$D_0 = \tfrac{1}{2}(D_+ + D_-), \tag{13b}$$

so that Equation (12) permits the evaluation of the sum.

The difference between D_+ and D_- relates to the amplitude for charge-exchange scattering

$$D_{\text{ex}} = \sqrt{\tfrac{1}{2}}\,(D_+ - D_-). \tag{13c}$$

Since the sum and difference of the charged pion fields are describable in terms of real field amplitudes [Equation (11)], dispersion relations can also be derived for these combinations. We cite below the final result of such a derivation:[4]

$$D_\pm(k) = \frac{1}{2}\left(1 + \frac{\omega}{\mu}\right) D_\pm(0) + \frac{1}{2}\left(1 - \frac{\omega}{\mu}\right) D_\mp(0) + 2\,\frac{f^2}{\mu^2}\frac{k^2}{\omega + \mu/2M}$$
$$+ \frac{k^2}{4\pi^2}\int_\mu^\infty \frac{d\omega'}{k'}\left\{\frac{\sigma_\pm(\omega')}{\omega' - \omega} + \frac{\sigma_\mp(\omega')}{\omega' + \omega}\right\}. \tag{14}$$

---

[3] M. L. Goldberger, H. Miyazawa, and R. Oehme, *Phys. Rev., 99:* 986 (1955).

[4] *Ibid.*

Equation (14) enables the writing of dispersion relations for π^+, π^-, and π^0 elastic scattering, or charge-exchange scattering, all in terms of dispersion integrals over the total cross sections for π^+P (σ_+) and π^-P (σ_-).

Alternatively, one may construct dispersion relations for the scattering amplitudes in the pure $t=\frac{3}{2}$ and $t=\frac{1}{2}$ π–$\mathfrak{N}$ states (D_3 and D_1, respectively); these are immediately obtained from Equation (14) and the relations

$$\begin{aligned} D_3 &= D_+, \\ D_1 &= \tfrac{3}{2}D_- - \tfrac{1}{2}D_+. \end{aligned} \tag{13d}$$

PROBLEM

Assume that the total cross section for π–$\mathfrak{N}$ scattering may be approximated by using only the contribution of the elastic $\mathfrak{N}^*(1236)$ resonance, with $t=\frac{3}{2}$, $j=\frac{3}{2}^+$. On this basis, obtain an expression for $D_0(k)$ [Equation (12)] and compare it with the expected contribution of the (3, 3) resonance to $D_0(k)$. What conclusions do you draw from this comparison? *Note:* The dispersion integral is always represented by its principal value.

11

Two-Body Reactions at High Energy

A number of approaches have been developed for describing the general two-body reaction

$$a + A \rightarrow a' + A' \tag{1}$$

in which the products may include short-lived hadron resonances as well as the relatively stable particles. Since a large fraction of multiproduct, high-energy strong interactions have been observed to proceed through a two-body intermediate state, the analysis of reactions of this type occupies an important segment of the high-energy physics effort.

Such reactions are characterized by their reaction amplitudes $A(E, \theta, \varphi)$ (the elements of the S- or T-matrix) most usefully expressed as a function of the two-body invariants, s, t, and u (see Section 3.4.2). In particular, the amplitude for elastic scattering ($a' = a$, $A' = A$),

$$A_{\text{sc}} = \sum_l \frac{e^{2i\delta_l} - 1}{2ik}, \tag{1a}$$

determines not only the differential cross section for elastic scattering, $d\sigma_{\text{el}}/d\Omega$ or $d\sigma_{\text{el}}/dt$, but, by virtue of the optical theorem, the value of its imaginary part at the forward angle, $\theta = t = 0$, yields the total cross section

$$\sigma_{(a+A\rightarrow\text{all possible products})} = \sigma_{\text{tot}} = \frac{4\pi}{k}\,\text{Im}\,A_{\text{sc}}(\theta = 0) \tag{1b}$$

as well.

General expressions for the reaction amplitudes, as well as their special forms for some specific values of the spins of the particles involved, have previously been given both in the conventional representation (Sections 6.2.1 and 6.2.2), in which the axis of angular momentum quantization is taken along the direction of the projectile's momentum, $\mathbf{k}_a = \mathbf{k}$, and in the helicity representation (Section 6.2.3), particularly well suited to the description of reactions whose mechanism involves exchange of a specific particle in the t-channel. Expressions have also been given for the density matrix, which describes the polarization states of the products and which, in particular, provides the basis for the description of the decay angular distributions of unstable reaction products and for the graphical analysis of final states in terms of Dalitz plots (Section 4.2.3).

In this chapter we consider a number of methods for parametrizing the s and t dependence of two-body reaction amplitudes in the high-energy limit. With respect to reactions (1), high energy is defined in terms of the parameters

$$kR,\ k'R \gg 1, \tag{2}$$

where k and k' are, respectively, the incident and product 3-momenta in the *cm* and R is a distance characterizing the range of the interaction responsible for (1). The high-energy condition (2) implies that many orbital angular momenta,

$$\begin{aligned} l &\lesssim kR, \\ l' &\lesssim k'R, \end{aligned} \tag{2a}$$

contribute to the reaction in question. Most high-energy approximations assume that the reaction amplitude may be considered to be a smoothly varying function of the orbital angular momentum — i.e., that the reaction is not dominated by just one or a few angular momentum values; the contrary situation, which would, for example, follow if the reaction proceeded mainly through a small number of resonances in the intermediate (s-channel) state, has been considered in Section 6.2. Another general procedure, in which the scattering amplitudes are described by means of dispersion relations, which is applicable at low as well as high energies, has been discussed in the preceding chapter.

11.1 Optical Approximations

Optical approximations are based on a number of assumptions, some physical and others mathematical.[1] The techniques of their application are best illustrated by starting with the least complicated example.

11.1.1 Elastic Scattering of Spinless Particles

Elastic scattering of spinless particles provides the simplest illustration of the optical approach. In the conventional representation, we may write for the scattering cross section

[1] Much of the material in this section is based on work carried out by the author during a stay at CERN, reported in the internal CERN reports 1114/TH.178 and 1700/TH.193 (1961), and developed further in collaboration with P. C. M. Yock ("High Energy Scattering at Low Momentum Transfer," Ph.D. thesis, M.I.T., 1965).

$$\frac{d\sigma}{d\Omega} = \frac{1}{k^2}\left|\sum_{l=0}^{\infty}\left(l+\frac{1}{2}\right)T_l(s)\,P_l(\cos\theta)\right|^2, \tag{3a}$$

where $T_l(s)$ is the numerator of one of the terms of Equation (1a).

Confining ourselves to the *cm*, the scattering angle θ is related to the 4-momentum transfer t and the (equal) *cm* 3-momenta of the reacting particles k_0:

$$\cos\theta = 1 + \frac{t}{2k_0^2} = 1 - \frac{\tau^2}{2k_0^2}. \tag{3b}$$

We now adopt the mathematical approximation of small angles ($\tau^2/k_0^2 \ll 1$) to replace the Legendre polynomials by Bessel's functions

$$P_l^{\nu}(\cos\theta) \cong (-1)^{\nu}\, l^{\nu} J_{\nu}\left(\frac{l\tau}{k_0}\right) \tag{3c}$$

and also introduce the physical assumption that the scattering amplitudes, $T_l(s)$, are smoothly and monotonically varying functions of l, which can be replaced by the continuous functions

$$T_l(s) \cong \overline{T}(l, s). \tag{3d}$$

This last assumption, coupled with the high-energy condition (2), permits[2] replacement of the summation in Equation (3a) by an integral:

$$\sum_{l=0}^{\infty}\left(l+\frac{1}{2}\right)T_l(s)\,P_l(\cos\theta) \cong \int_0^{\infty} l\,\overline{T}(l, s)\,J_0\left(\frac{l\tau}{k_0}\right)dl = F(s, \tau). \tag{3e}$$

Combining the expressions (3a)–(3e), we arrive at the optical approximation for the differential scattering cross section:

$$\frac{d\sigma}{dt} \cong \frac{\pi}{k_0^4}\,|F(s, t)|^2. \tag{4}$$

Adopting the same approximation (3d), the elastic scattering cross section becomes

$$\sigma_{\text{el}}(s) = \int \frac{d\sigma}{d\Omega}\,d\Omega \cong \frac{2\pi}{k_0^2}\int_0^{\infty} l\,|\overline{T}(l, s)|^2\,dl, \tag{4a}$$

and, from the optical theorem,

$$\sigma_{\text{tot}}(s) \cong \frac{4\pi}{k_0^2}\int_0^{\infty} l\,\text{Im}\,\overline{T}(l, s)\,dl. \tag{4b}$$

---

[2] The assumption (3d) is easily shown to lead to the confinement of appreciable $d\sigma/d\Omega$ within scattering angles $\theta < \theta_m \simeq (k_0 R)^{-1}$. Taking $R \approx (2m_\pi)^{-1}$ and assuming $k(lab) > M_p$, we have $k_0^2 \approx kM_p/2$ and $k_0^2R^2 \approx kM_p/8m_\pi^2 \approx k/m_\pi \gg 1$. Since, according to (3b), $\theta \cong \tau/k_0$ for small angles, the approximation (3c) is seen to be justified for $-t \ll k_0^2 \approx kM_p/2$. Since the second ($\frac{1}{2}$ as compared to l) term in Equation (3e) leads to an $F'(s, \tau) \sim (\tau/k_0)\,F(s, t)$, it may generally be neglected. It is also possible to apply the optical approximation to scattering in the backward direction, $\cos\theta \to -1$, corresponding to small values of the 4-momentum transfer in the u-channel. This can lead to (smaller) backward peaks in the differential cross section, an effect known in the optical case as "glory" scattering.

The problems of the optical approximation are thus reduced to the specification of the amplitude function $\overline{T}(l, s)$. It is at this point that the question becomes one of physics — of the dynamical features of the interaction that gives rise to the scattering process. Generally speaking, optical calculations assume that the phase of $\overline{T}$ can be taken as essentially constant, so that its form may be specified in terms of a single parameter. This parameter is variously given as the interaction range R or the equivalent mass m of a hypothetical particle whose exchange would give rise to an interaction of range $\hbar/mc$ ($m = R^{-1}$),[3] or the corresponding "cutoff" angular momentum $l_{\max} = k_0 R = k_0/m$. In the following, we normally adopt R as the parameter which, together with the specified shape function $\overline{T}(l, s)$, characterizes the scattering form factor $F(s, t)$.

Equation (4) may be still further simplified in the case where the range parameter is a constant, so that, expressing $\overline{T}(l, s)$ as a separable function of the parameters s and $x = l/l_{\max} = l/k_0 R$,

$$\overline{T}(l, s) = A(s)\,\overline{T}(x), \tag{3d$'$}$$

we have

$$\begin{aligned} F(s, \tau) &= k_0^2 R^2 A(s) \int_0^\infty \overline{T}(x) J_0(R\tau x)\, x\, dx \\ &= k_0^2 R^2 A(s)\, \mathfrak{F}(R\tau). \end{aligned} \tag{3e$'$}$$

The differential cross section now takes on the particularly simple form

$$\frac{d\sigma}{dt} \cong \pi R^4 |A(s)\, \mathfrak{F}(R\tau)|^2 . \tag{4$'$}$$

Many different shape functions have been used to describe a variety of scattering and reaction processes in many fields of physics. The most interesting ones from the point of view of high-energy interactions, and their resulting form factors, are listed in Table 11.1.

The form of the shape function $\overline{T}(l, s)$ thus determines the dependence of the differential cross section on the scattering angle or momentum transfer t. We note that the conventional diffraction pattern, with its recurring maxima and minima, results from a shape function with a sharp boundary, of which the step function is the classical example. As soon as one introduces forms with a diffuse boundary, say the Gaussian, the diffraction pattern is replaced by a monotonically decreasing form factor. On the other hand, some special forms, like the strongly absorbed Gaussian (useful for approximating a situation in which the scattering amplitudes corresponding to small l-values are suppressed) lead to form factors with one or a small number of zeros.

Other special physical situations may be described by combinations of the basic forms given in Table 11.1. Thus, for example, there is some evidence that high-energy nucleon-nucleon scattering is characterized by a superposition of

---

[3] We may also think of m as the "range" of the interaction in momentum space. Note that R (m) may in general be a function of the cm energy s.

Table 11.1 Some Convenient Amplitude Shape Functions and Their Resulting Form Factors

Description	$\overline{T}(x)\left[x \equiv \frac{l}{k_0 R}\right]$	$\mathfrak{F}(R\tau)$
Step function	$\begin{cases}\overline{T} = 1, \text{ for } x \leq 1 \\ \quad = 0, \text{ for } x > 1\end{cases}$	$\frac{2J_1(R\tau)}{R\tau}$
Gaussian	$e^{-x^2/2}$	$e^{-R^2\tau^2/2}$
Strongly absorbed Gaussian	$x\, e^{-x^2/2}$	$\sqrt{\frac{\pi}{2}}\, e^{-R^2\tau^2/2}\, F_1\left(-\frac{1}{2};\, 1;\, \frac{R^2\tau^2}{2}\right)$ [a]
Exponential	e^{-x}	$(1 + R^2\tau^2)^{-3/2}$
Yukawa	$\frac{e^{-x}}{x}$	$(1 + R^2\tau^2)^{-1/2}$
Power law I	$(1 + x^2)^{-n-1}$	$\frac{1}{m!}\left(\frac{R\tau}{2}\right)^n K_n(R\tau)$ [b]
Power law II	$\left(1 + \frac{x^4}{4}\right)^{-1/2}$	$2K_0(R\tau)J_0(R\tau)$

[a] F_1 is a confluent hypergeometric function of the first kind:

$$F_1(a;\, b;\, z) = 1 + \frac{a}{b}z + \frac{a(a+1)}{b(b+1)}\frac{z^2}{2!} + \cdots.$$

[b] The K_n are Bessel's functions of imaginary argument; see G. N. Watson, *A Treatise on the Theory of Bessel Functions*, 2d ed., Cambridge University Press, Cambridge, England (1944), p. 78.

Gaussian shape functions with different ranges. Another case of physical interest, mainly in describing some nuclear reactions, is the "surface" or peripheral interaction, whose shape function is usefully approximated by the difference between two exponentials of slightly different ranges.[4]

The value of the range parameter R determines the scale of the dependence of $d\sigma/dt$ on the 4-momentum transfer, while the form depends, of course, on the nature of the shape function. However, for small momentum transfers, $R^2\tau^2 \ll 1$, most differential cross sections may be approximated by a Gaussian function

$$\frac{d\sigma}{dt} \propto e^{at} \simeq 1 + at = 1 - a\tau^2\,, \tag{4''}$$

and the difference between the various shape functions is manifested in different numerical coefficients connecting a and R^2. Table 11.2 lists the values of a, corresponding to different assumed shape functions, as well as the values of σ_{sc} and σ_{tot} computed from Equations (4a) and (4b), respectively. One important observation is the strong dependence of the ratio σ_{tot}/σ_{sc} on the shape of the scattering amplitude; in fact, the familiar classical value of two for this ratio is seen to be a unique feature of the step function which is, after all, not the most realistic of the assumed forms.

[4] In such cases, where more than one value of the range parameter is involved, it is necessary to use the expression for the form factor given by Equation (3e) and the resulting Equation (4) for $d\sigma/dt$, rather than the corresponding primed forms.

Table 11.2 Properties of Cross Sections Derived from Different Shape Functions

Shape function	a	$\dfrac{\sigma_{el}}{\lvert A(s)\rvert^2}$ [a]	$\dfrac{\sigma_{tot}}{\text{Im}\,A(s)}$ [b]
Step function	$\dfrac{R^2}{4}$	πR^2	$2\pi R^2$
Gaussian	R^2	πR^2	$4\pi R^2$
Sum of two Gaussians	$\dfrac{\lvert A_1\rvert^2 R_1^2 + \lvert A_2\rvert^2 R_2^2 + \text{Re}\,A_1A_2^*(R_1^2+R_2^2)}{\lvert A_1\rvert^2 + \lvert A_2\rvert^2 + 2\,\text{Re}\,A_1A_2^*}$	$\pi\left\{\lvert A_1\rvert^2 R_1^2 + \lvert A_2\rvert^2 R_2^2 + 4\,\text{Re}\,A_1A_2^*\left(\dfrac{R_1^2R_2^2}{R_1^2+R_2^2}\right)\right\}$	$4\pi\{(\text{Im}\,A_1)R_1^2 + (\text{Im}\,A_2)R_2^2\}$
Strongly absorbed Gaussian	$\frac{3}{2}R^2$	πR^2	$4\pi\sqrt{\dfrac{\pi}{2}}\,R^2$
Exponential	$3R^2$	$\frac{1}{2}\pi R^2$	$4\pi R^2$
Peripheral (difference between two exponentials)	$\dfrac{3\{\lvert A_1\rvert^2 R_1^2 + \lvert A_2\rvert^2 R_2^2 - \text{Re}\,A_1A_2^*(R_1^2+R_2^2)\}}{\lvert A_1\rvert^2 + \lvert A_2\rvert^2 - 2\,\text{Re}\,A_1A_2^*}$	$\dfrac{\pi}{2}\left\{\lvert A_1\rvert^2 R_1^2 + \lvert A_2\rvert^2 R_2^2 - 8\,\text{Re}\,A_1A_2^*\left(\dfrac{1}{R_1}+\dfrac{1}{R_2}\right)^{-2}\right\}$	$4\pi\{(\text{Im}\,A_1)R_1^2 - (\text{Im}\,A_2)R_2^2\}$
Yukawa	R^2	∞	$4\pi R^2$
Power law I	$\dfrac{R^2}{2(n-1)}$	$\dfrac{\pi R^2}{(2n+1)}$	$\dfrac{2\pi R^2}{n}$
Power law II	—	$\pi^2 R^2$	∞

[a] Except for the two mixed cases, where we give σ_{el}.
[b] Except for the two mixed cases, where we give σ_{tot}. Note that it is generally assumed that $A(s) \cong i$ (pure imaginary) for high-energy scattering. This may be tested by verifying the relationship $(d\sigma/dt)(0) \overset{?}{=} (\sigma_{tot}^2/16\pi)$.

11.1.2 Effects of Spin; Reaction Cross Sections

The general two-body reaction (1), in which the products are not necessarily identical with the projectile and target, may be treated in a fashion quite similar to that developed in the preceding section on elastic scattering. There are a number of essential differences from the spinless elastic scattering situation, however. One difference derives from the kinematics of inelastic scattering: let μ and μ' be, respectively, the masses of a and a' in reaction (1); let k and k' be their *cm* momenta. Then the expression for the 4-momentum transfer [Equation (3b)] becomes

$$\cos\theta = 1 + \frac{t'}{2kk'} = 1 - \frac{\tau^2}{2k_0^2}, \tag{3b$'$}$$

where

$$-\tau^2 = t' = t + (k' - k)\left(\frac{\mu^2}{k} - \frac{\mu'^2}{k'}\right), \tag{3b$''$}$$

and we define $kk' \equiv k_0^2$. The k_0^4 in the denominator of Equation (4) is thus replaced by the product $k_0^2 k^2$.

The more important difference arises from the spins of the particles involved. In the conventional representation, the differential cross section corresponding to a given substate of the initial channel spin S and product channel spin S' with $\Delta m = m - m'$ is

$$k^2 \frac{d\sigma}{d\Omega}(\theta, \phi; S, m; S', m') = \left| \sum_{ll'j} \left[\left(l + \frac{1}{2}\right)\left(l' + \frac{1}{2}\right)\frac{(l' - \Delta m)!}{(l' + \Delta m)!}\right]^{1/2} \cdot C^{j,m}_{S,m;\, l,0} \cdot C^{j,m}_{S',m';\, l',\Delta m} \cdot T^{j}_{S,l;\, S',l'}(E) \cdot P^{\Delta m}_{l'}(\cos\theta)\right|^2, \tag{5a}$$

while in the helicity representation,

$$k^2 \frac{d\sigma}{d\Omega}(\theta, \varphi; \lambda_a, \lambda_A; \lambda_{a'}, \lambda_{A'}) = \left| \sum_j (j + \tfrac{1}{2})\, T^j_{\lambda_{a'},\lambda_{A'};\, \lambda_a,\lambda_A}(E) \cdot d^j_{\lambda_a - \lambda_A, \lambda_{a'} - \lambda_{A'}}(\theta, \varphi)\right|^2. \tag{5b}$$

Explicit expressions for Equations (5a) and (5b) for some specific values of the spins of a, A, a', A' are given in Appendix 5. However, adopting the usual assumptions of the optical approximation — i.e., neglecting terms of order unity as compared to $l \approx l'$, and replacing $P_l^\nu(\cos\theta)$ by $J_\nu(l\tau/k_0)$ according to Equation (3c), or using the equivalent ($\nu = \lambda_a - \lambda_A - \lambda_{a'} + \lambda_{A'} = \lambda - \mu$),

$$d^j_{\lambda,\mu}(\cos\theta) \cong J_\nu\left(\frac{j\tau}{k_0}\right), \tag{3c$'$}$$

we reduce the problem to the evaluation of summations of the form

$$\begin{aligned} F_\nu(s, \tau) &= \sum_{l=0}^{\infty} l^{(1-\nu)} T_{l,\nu}(s) P_l^\nu(\cos\theta) \\ &\cong (-1)^\nu \int_0^\infty l\,\overline{T}_\nu(s, l)\, J_\nu\left(\frac{l\tau}{k_0}\right) dl \\ &= k_0^2 R^2\, \mathfrak{F}_\nu(s, R\tau). \end{aligned} \tag{3e$''$}$$

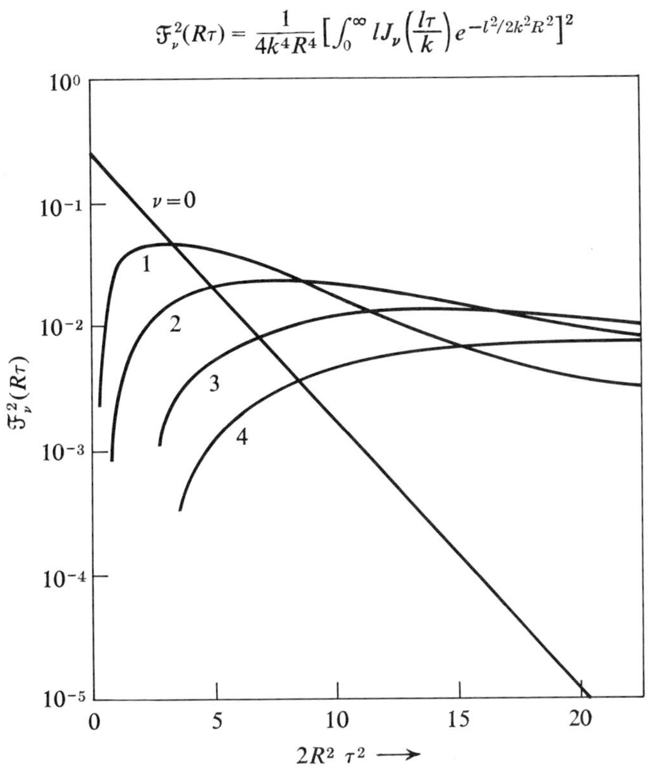

Figure 11.1 Comparison of absorption form factors corresponding to different spin changes for a Gaussian amplitude function.

The reaction form factors $\mathfrak{F}_\nu(s, R\tau)$ are thus determined by the absorption shape functions $\overline{T}_\nu(s, l/k_0R)$, which may, just as in the elastic scattering example, be chosen to have a variety of forms (see Table 11.1). The most widely used shape functions being the Gaussian and its derivatives, we give here expressions for the reaction form factors resulting from such forms.

1. The Gaussian shape function

$$\overline{T}_\nu\left(s, \frac{l}{k_0R}\right) = A_\nu(s)\, e^{-l^2/2k_0^2R^2} \tag{6}$$

yields

$$\mathfrak{F}_\nu(s, R\tau) = (-1)^\nu A_\nu(s) \left(\frac{R^2\tau^2}{2}\right)^{\nu/2} e^{-R^2\tau^2/2} \cdot \frac{\Gamma(1+\nu/2)}{\Gamma(\nu+1)}\, F_1\left(\frac{\nu}{2};\, \nu+1;\, \frac{R^2\tau^2}{2}\right), \tag{6a}$$

where the Γ's are the factorial functions

$$\Gamma(n+1) = n\Gamma(n), \tag{6b}$$

and the F_1's are confluent hypergeometric functions of the first kind, defined in Table 11.1.

Figure 11.1 compares the shapes of $\mathfrak{F}_\nu^2(R\tau)$ for $\nu \leq 4$. Note that in the region of small $R^2\tau^2 \lesssim 5$, the $\mathfrak{F}_\nu^2$'s decrease rapidly with increasing ν. For large values of $R^2\tau^2$, on the other hand, while $\mathfrak{F}_0$ is an unmodified Gaussian, the $\mathfrak{F}^2_{\nu\geq 1}$'s tend toward simple power functions:

$$\mathfrak{F}_{\nu\geq 1}(R\tau \gg 1) \approx (-1)^\nu A_\nu(s)\,\nu\,(2R\tau)^{-(\nu+2)}. \tag{6a$'$}$$

Thus, for Gaussian shape functions, provided some $A_{\nu\geq 1}$'s are comparable in importance to $A_0(s)$ for a given reaction, the zero spin approximation is reasonable only for values of $R^2\tau^2 \lesssim 5$.

2. The strongly absorbed Gaussian $[(d/dx)e^{-x^2/2}]$,

$$\overline{T}'_\nu\left(s, \frac{l}{k_0R}\right) = A'_\nu(s)\,\frac{l}{k_0R}\, e^{-l^2/2k_0^2R^2}, \tag{7}$$

results in

$$\mathfrak{F}'_\nu(s, R\tau) = (-1)^\nu \sqrt{2}\, A'_\nu(s) \left(\frac{R^2\tau^2}{2}\right)^{\nu/2} e^{-R^2\tau^2/2}$$
$$\cdot \frac{\Gamma(\nu/2 + 3/2)}{\Gamma(\nu+1)}\, F_1\left(\frac{\nu-1}{2};\, \nu+1;\, \frac{R^2\tau^2}{2}\right). \tag{7a}$$

EXAMPLE

$$0^- + \tfrac{1}{2}^+ \rightarrow 0^- + \tfrac{1}{2}^+.$$

This includes meson-nucleon scattering and charge exchange, associated production (e.g., $\pi^- + P \rightarrow K^0 + \Lambda^0$), etc. The differential cross section is given by

$$\frac{1}{\pi R^4}\frac{k^2}{k_0^2}\frac{d\sigma}{dt} = |f|^2 + |g|^2, \tag{8}$$

where f is the spin-nonflip amplitude

$$f = \frac{1}{k_0^2R^2}\sum_{l=0}^{\infty}\left(l + \frac{1}{2}\right) T_{l,0}(s)\, P_l(\cos\theta) \tag{8a}$$

with

$$(2l+1)\, T_{l,0} = (l+1)\, T_l^{j=l+1/2} + l T_l^{j=l-1/2}, \tag{8b}$$

and g is the spin-flip amplitude

$$g = \frac{1}{k_0^2R^2}\sum_{l=0}^{\infty} T_{l,1}(s)\, P_l^1(\cos\theta) \tag{8c}$$

with

$$2T_{l,1} = T_l^{j=l+1/2} - T_l^{j=l-1/2}. \tag{8d}$$

(a) Assuming Gaussian shape functions for both $\overline{T}_0(s, l/k_0R)$ and $\overline{T}_1(s, l/k_0R)$, we obtain

$$f = A_0 \, e^{-R^2\tau^2/2}, \tag{9a}$$

$$g = -\sqrt{\frac{\pi}{8}} A_1 \cdot (R\tau) \, e^{-R^2\tau^2/2} \cdot F_1\left(\frac{1}{2}; 2; \frac{R^2\tau^2}{2}\right). \tag{9b}$$

The shapes of $|f|^2$ and $|g|^2$ are shown in Figure 11.2(a), while the differential cross sections for various proportions of spin-flip to nonflip ($\xi = |A_1/A_0|$) are shown in Figure 11.2(b), for $\xi \leq 1$, and Figure 11.2(c), for $\xi \geq 1$.

(b) For strongly absorbed Gaussian shape functions, we have

$$f' = \sqrt{\frac{\pi}{2}} A_0' \, e^{-R^2\tau^2/2} \cdot F_1\left(-\frac{1}{2}; 1; \frac{R^2\tau^2}{2}\right), \tag{10a}$$

$$g' = -A_1' \cdot (R\tau) \, e^{-R^2\tau^2/2}. \tag{10b}$$

The corresponding shapes and differential cross sections are shown in Figures 11.3(a) and 11.3(b) and (c), respectively.

(c) A physically interesting approximation is one in which the nonflip amplitude is approximated by a strongly absorbed Gaussian shape function [Equation (10a)], while the spin-flip amplitude is approximated by a Gaussian shape function [Equation (9b)]. This model takes into account, in an approximate fashion, the "unitarity" requirement on the T_l's, which tends to reduce the amplitudes corresponding to small impact parameters, owing to the competition from the many reaction channels available to high-energy projectiles (see Section 5.1). For the spin-flip amplitude, on the other hand, since this results from a difference [Equation (8d)], the small l-values are expected to be most significant. Figure 11.4 shows the differential cross sections for this model corresponding to different relative strengths of the two contributions.

In general, the phases of f and g need not be equal:

$$\frac{A_1}{A_0} = \xi \, e^{i\delta}. \tag{11}$$

In this case, the product (spin $\frac{1}{2}$) baryon will be transversely polarized, with the degree of polarization given by

$$P_t = \frac{2 \operatorname{Im} fg^*}{|f|^2 + |g|^2}. \tag{11a}$$

We have plotted, in Figure 11.5, the value of $P/\sin\delta$ predicted for the mixed model for some values of $0.1 \leq \xi \leq 1.0$. (Note that we expect spin-nonflip to dominate at high energies.) It is seen that, provided $\sin\delta$ is appreciably different from 0, quite appreciable and characteristically shaped polarizations are expected.

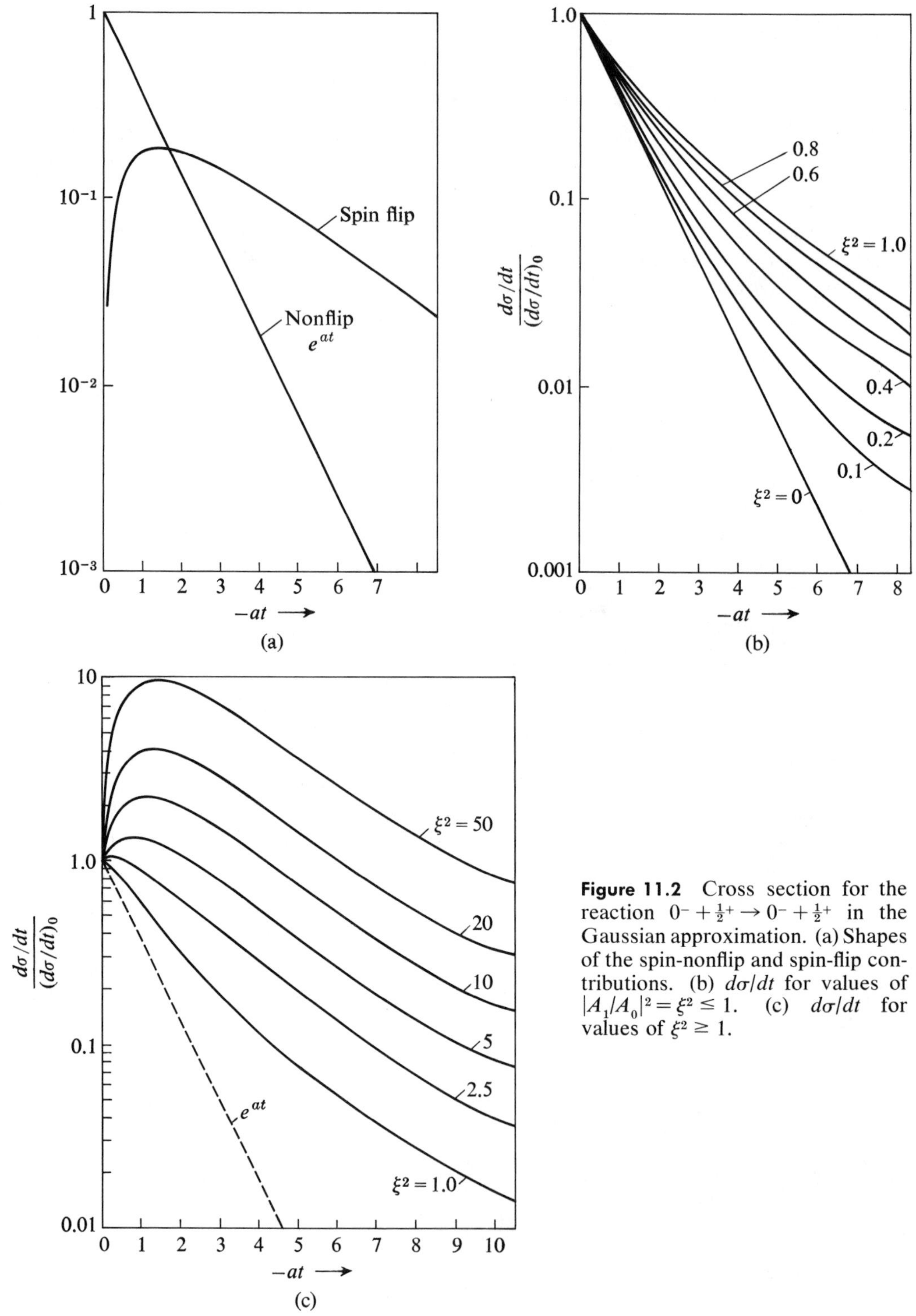

Figure 11.2 Cross section for the reaction $0^- + \frac{1}{2}^+ \rightarrow 0^- + \frac{1}{2}^+$ in the Gaussian approximation. (a) Shapes of the spin-nonflip and spin-flip contributions. (b) $d\sigma/dt$ for values of $|A_1/A_0|^2 = \xi^2 \leq 1$. (c) $d\sigma/dt$ for values of $\xi^2 \geq 1$.

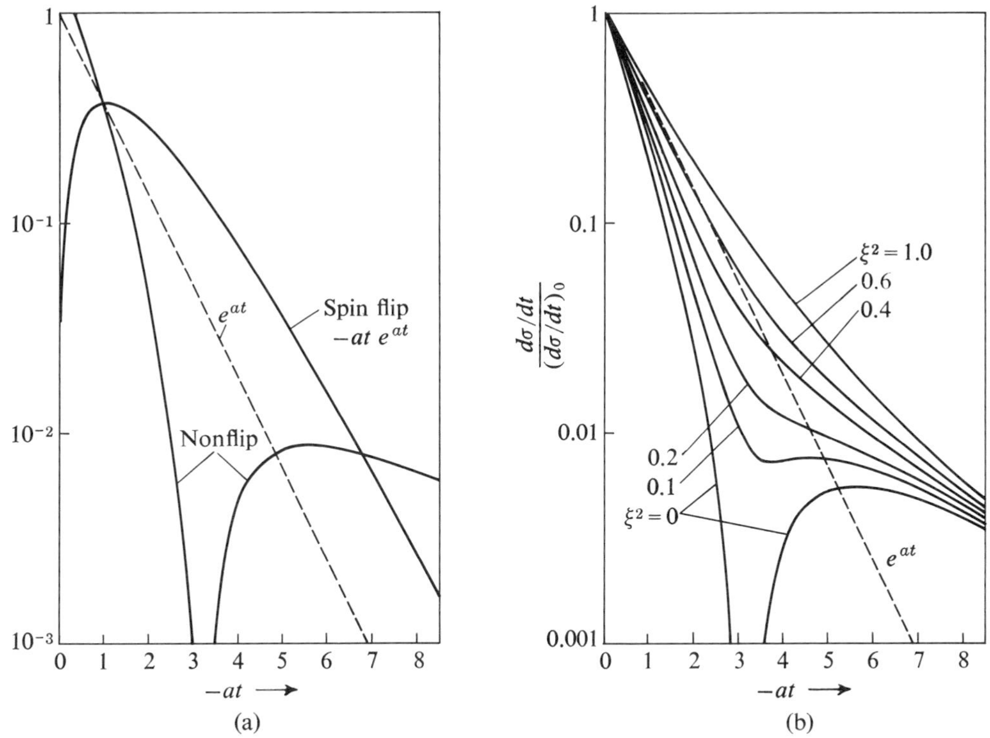

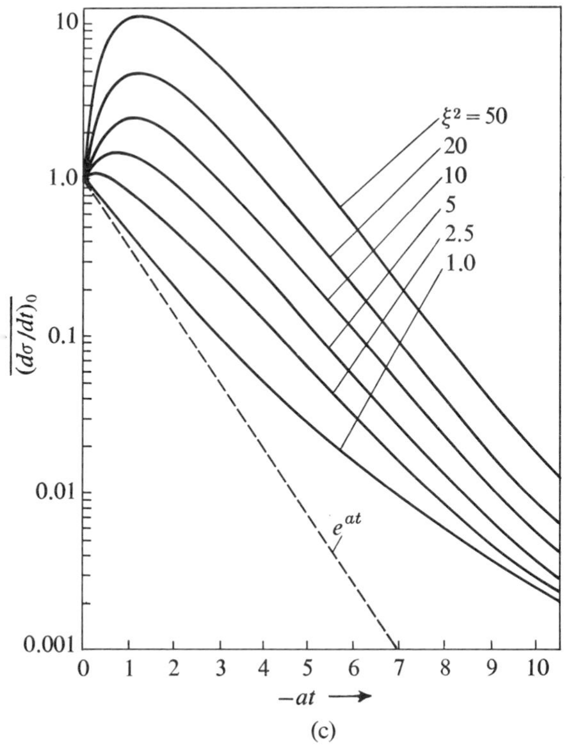

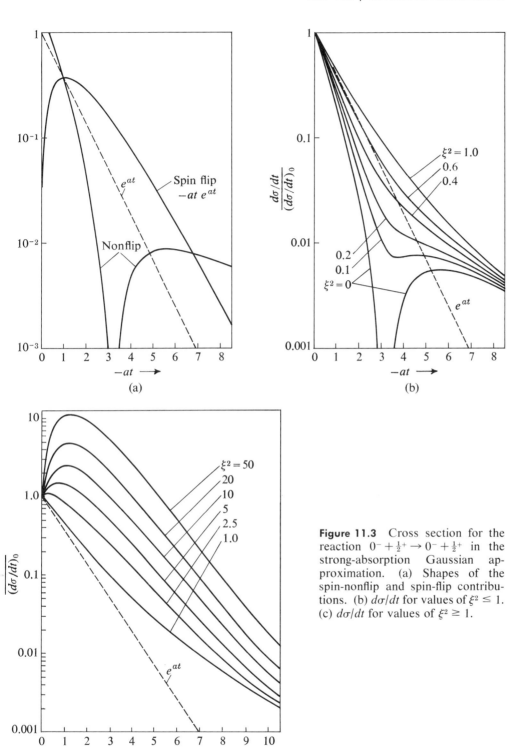

Figure 11.3 Cross section for the reaction $0^- + \frac{1}{2}^+ \rightarrow 0^- + \frac{1}{2}^+$ in the strong-absorption Gaussian approximation. (a) Shapes of the spin-nonflip and spin-flip contributions. (b) $d\sigma/dt$ for values of $\xi^2 \leq 1$. (c) $d\sigma/dt$ for values of $\xi^2 \geq 1$.

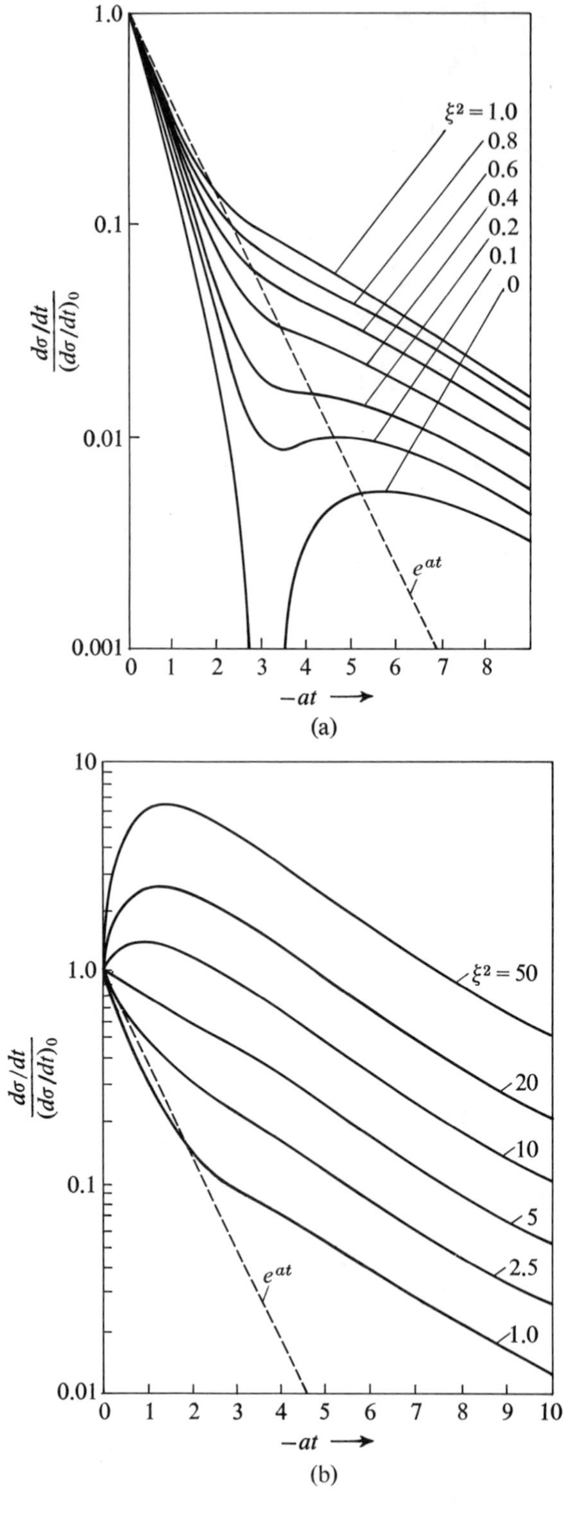

Figure 11.4 $d\sigma/dt$ for the reaction $0^- + \frac{1}{2}^+ \rightarrow 0^- + \frac{1}{2}^+$ in the mixed model. (a) $\xi^2 \leq 1$. (b) $\xi^2 \geq 1$.

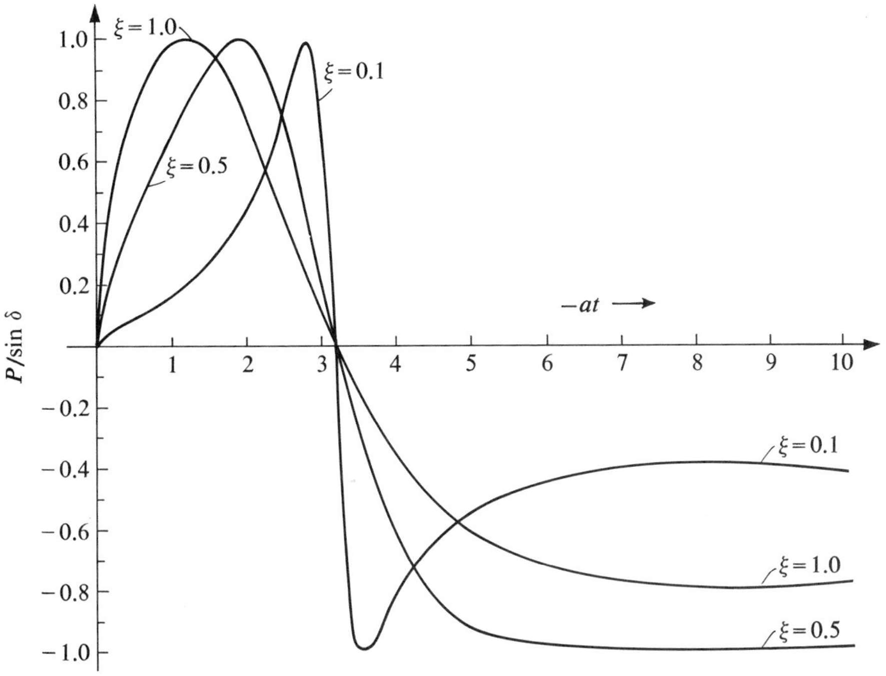

Figure 11.5 Product baryon polarization in $0^- + \frac{1}{2}^+ \to 0^- + \frac{1}{2}^+$ for the mixed Gaussian model ($\xi^2 \leq 1$).

11.1.3 Eikonal Approximations

Although the choice of shape functions, such as those used in the preceding section to describe the dependence on l of the scattering and reaction amplitudes, $T_l(s)$, was generally motivated by physical considerations, the selections were made on a somewhat *ad hoc* basis, with considerations of mathematical convenience playing an important role. However, it is possible to adopt a somewhat more physical approach, in which the $T_l(s)$'s are assumed to be proportional to the quantity of interacting matter traversed by the projectile on a classical trajectory whose impact parameter, $b = l/k$, corresponds to the orbital angular momentum under consideration; see Figure 11.6.

This is a semiclassical approach, known as the eikonal approximation;[5] its validity requires that the wavelength, $\lambda\!\!\!^{-} = k^{-1}$, be small compared to the dimensions, R, of the interacting system, which is precisely the condition of the optical approximations $kR \gg 1$. Referring to Figure 11.6, we thus have for the amplitude,

$$\overline{T}(l, s) = A(s) \int_{-\infty}^{\infty} \rho(r)\, dz, \tag{12}$$

where

$$z^2 + b^2 = r^2. \tag{12a}$$

[5] G. Moliere, *Z. Naturforsch.*, *2A*: 133 (1947).

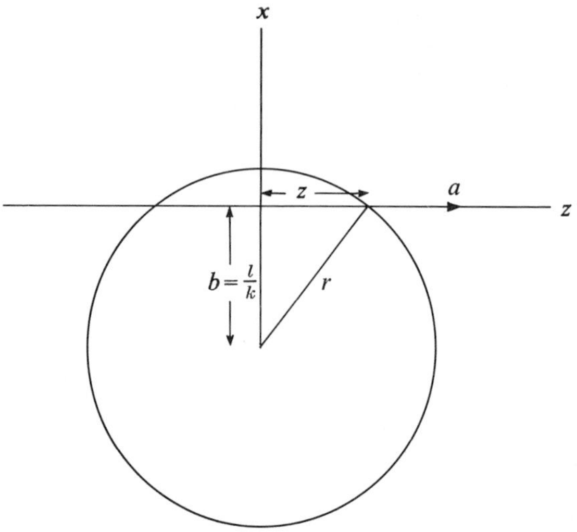

Figure 11.6 Geometrical relationships for the eikonal approximation.

Once the form of $\overline{T}(l, s)$ is determined, the computation of cross sections, etc., proceeds via the normal optical approximation.

We have assembled in Table 11.3 the characteristics of a number of density functions frequently used in the eikonal approximation. Among these, the step function has been used by Fernbach, Serber, and Taylor[6] in their pioneering work on the application of the eikonal approximation to the high-energy scattering of nucleons by complex nuclei. More recently, Serber[7] has been able to fit the data on elastic proton-proton scattering, for the range of 4-momentum transfers $0 < -t \lesssim 20\ (\text{GeV}/c)^2$ — over which the differential cross section decreases by a factor of $\sim 10^{12}$ — using a Yukawa density function at small impact parameters

$$\rho(r < 0.33\ \text{f}) = \frac{e^{-1.341r}}{r}, \tag{13a}$$

connecting smoothly onto a Gaussian density

$$\rho(r > 1.1\ \text{f}) = 0.567\ e^{-1.22r^2} \tag{13b}$$

(r is in fermis).

Strictly speaking, the $\rho(r)$ may be thought of as a density only in the case of the scattering of a "point" particle by an extended source; this is a reasonable approach, for example, in the case of high-energy electron or muon elastic scattering from nucleons or nuclei. For the case of strongly interacting particles, however, $\rho(r)$ should be thought of as a density overlap function[8] corresponding to two

---

[6] S. Fernbach, R. Serber, and T. B. Taylor, *Phys. Rev., 75:* 1352 (1949).
[7] R. Serber, *Rev. Mod. Phys., 36:* 649 (1964).
[8] An alternative approach is to note that Equation (12) is the form of the Born approximation solution of the Klein–Gordon equation describing the scattering of two particles interacting via the potential $\rho(r)$.

Table 11.3 Properties of Density Functions Employed in the Eikonal Approximation

$\rho(r)$	$\dfrac{\bar{T}(s, l/kR)}{A(s)}$	$\mathfrak{F}(R\tau)$	a	$\dfrac{\sigma_{sc}}{\lvert A(s)\rvert^2}$	$\dfrac{\sigma_{tot}}{\text{Im}\,A(s)}$
Step function: $\begin{cases} 1\ (r \le R) \\ 0\ (r > R) \end{cases}$	$\sqrt{1-\dfrac{l^2}{k^2R^2}}\ \left(\dfrac{l}{kR} \le 1\right)$; $0\ \left(\dfrac{l}{kR} > 1\right)$	$\dfrac{J_1(R\tau)}{R\tau}$	$\dfrac{R^2}{4}$	$\dfrac{\pi R^2}{2}$	$\dfrac{4\pi}{3}R^2$
Gaussian: $e^{-r^2/2R^2}$	$e^{-l^2/2k^2R^2}$	$e^{-R^2\tau^2/2}$	R^2	πR^2	$4\pi R^2$
Yukawa: $\dfrac{e^{-r/R}}{r/R}$	$K_0\left(\dfrac{l}{kR}\right)$	$\dfrac{2\pi}{(1+R^2\tau^2)}$	$2R^2$	πR^2	$4\pi R^2$

extended sources whose centers are separated by **r**. In this case, taking $\rho_i(r)$ as the density function for one of the particles involved, the effective absorption thickness is given by

$$D_i(x, y) = \int_{-\infty}^{\infty} \rho_i(x, y, z)\, dz, \tag{12b}$$

and, for a given impact parameter $b = l/k$,

$$\bar{T}(l, s) = A(s) \int_{-\infty}^{\infty}\!\!\int D_a(x, y)\, D_A(b - x, y)\, dx\, dy. \tag{12$'$}$$

Parenthetically, it should be noted that, in the case of elastic scattering, $\bar{T}(l, s)$ is generally associated with the imaginary part of the scattering phase shift, $\delta(l, s)$, so that the scattering amplitude [see Equation (1a)] is given by

$$A_{sc}(l, s) = \frac{1 - e^{-\bar{T}(l,s)}}{2ik}. \tag{12c}$$

The use of Gaussian density functions is especially helpful in this version of the eikonal approximation, since the folding of two Gaussians leads to another Gaussian, and since Gaussian overlap functions give rise to Gaussian form factors (Table 11.3).

Thus, Wu and Yang[9] suggest that, insofar as both the *e–P* scattering and the *P–P* scattering form factors depend on the density of matter comprising the physical proton, $\rho_P(r)$, these form factors should be connected by the simple relationship

$$\mathfrak{F}_{PP}(t) \cong [G_E^P(t)]^2 \tag{12d}$$

over the range of t in which the differential scattering cross sections can be approximated by sums of Gaussians. This conjecture provides a rough fit to the observations.

An important application of these approximations has been given by Chou and

[9] T. T. Wu and C. N. Yang, *Phys. Rev., 137:* B708 (1965); see also H. D. I. Abarbanel, S. D. Drell, and F. J. Gilman, *Phys. Rev. Letters, 20:* 280 (1968).

Yang,[10] who invert the observed e^{at} forms of the differential cross sections for nucleon-nucleon and pion-nucleon scattering at small t, to derive expressions for the nucleon and the pion density functions; in another application, Byers and Yang [11] derive the form of the charge exchange ($\pi^- P \to \pi^0 N$) cross section from eikonal considerations. General discussions of the eikonal approach may be found in articles by Glauber and by Adachi and Kotani.[12]

PROBLEMS

1. Consider the reaction

$$\gamma + P \to \rho^0 + P.$$

   (a) Derive an expression for the differential cross section at high energies in terms of helicity-nonflip and helicity-flip amplitudes. *Note:* the incident photon has helicity ± 1; the ρ^0 has $j = 1^-$.
   (b) Assuming Gaussian shape functions for these amplitudes, what will be the form of the differential cross section for an arbitrary ratio of flip to nonflip?

2. Answer (a) and (b) in Problem 1 for

$$\pi^- + P \to \mathfrak{N}^*(j = \tfrac{3}{2}^+) + \pi.$$

3. Consider, for simplicity, the spinless approximation for elastic scattering with

$$T_l(s) = e^{2i\alpha_l} - 1.$$

   Let $\alpha_l = \delta_l + i\gamma_l$, with

$$\delta_l \approx \delta f(l),$$
$$\gamma_l \approx \gamma f(l),$$

   and

$$f(l) \approx \left(1 - \frac{l^2}{l_0^2}\right)^{1/2},$$

   where $l_0 = kR = k/m$. (This is the classical form of the eikonal approximation.)

   (a) Obtain an expression for the differential scattering cross section where $l_0 \gg 1$.
   (b) From the high-energy data on π–$\mathfrak{N}$ scattering,[13] derive approximate values

---

[10] T. T. Chou and C. N. Yang, *High Energy Physics and Nuclear Structure,* North-Holland Press, Amsterdam (1967), p. 348; see also *Phys. Rev., 170:* 1591 (1968).

[11] N. Byers and C. N. Yang, *Phys. Rev., 142:* 976 (1966).

[12] R. J. Glauber, *High Energy Collision Theory, Lectures in Theoretical Physics,* Vol. *1,* Interscience Publishers, New York (1959); also in *Proceedings of the Conference on High-Energy Physics and Nuclear Structure,* G. Alexander, ed., North-Holland Press, Amsterdam (1967), p. 311; T. Adachi and T. Kotani, *Suppl. to Progr. Theoret. Phys.* (Kyoto), 316 (1965).

[13] See Foley, *et al., Phys. Rev. Letters, 11:* 425 (1963): S. J. Lindenbaum, *Proceedings of the Third Coral Gables Conference on Symmetry Principles at High Energy,* W. H. Freeman and Co., San Francisco (1966).

of the parameters γ and R (m). What can you say about the transparency of protons to pions?

(c) From the data on the ratio $\mathrm{Re}\,A(0)/\mathrm{Im}\,A(0)$, derive an approximate value of the parameter δ.

(d) Discuss the evidence for the validity of the spinless approximation in this case.

4. Krisch [14] has pointed out that all the data on proton-proton scattering for large momentum transfers can be represented by a "universal" curve of $d\sigma/dt$ versus $x^2 = \beta^2 p_t^2$, where β is the *cm* velocity and p_t is the transverse 3-momentum transfer to the scattered proton ($p_t = p \sin\theta$). Such a plot is shown in Figure 11.7. Discuss the physical meaning, if any, of the variable x, in the limits of both large and small momentum transfer, and speculate on what conclusions, if any, can be drawn from the shape of Krisch's universal curve.

11.2 Particle Exchange Mechanisms; Regge Poles

A large fraction of the observed two-body reactions [Equation (1)] exhibit a very similar behavior for small values of $-t$,

$$\frac{d\sigma}{dt} \propto e^{at}, \tag{4''}$$

the values of the range parameter a falling between the values $\sim$ 4–20 $(\mathrm{GeV}/c)^{-2}$, with some evidence [15] for a grouping of reactions about the a-values ~ 5, ~ 10 (these include most elastic scatterings), and ~ 15. This type of behavior is also exhibited in reactions where the product associated with the projectile (i.e., a') is emitted in the backward direction. For backward reactions, however, it is more convenient to use the variable u, the invariant 4-momentum transfer to A' (see Section 3.4.2); for small values of u, most backward reactions may be described by

$$\frac{d\sigma}{du} \propto e^{au}. \tag{4'''}$$

For such "backward diffraction" peaks, however, the values of a are generally considerably smaller: $a \approx$ 1–3 $(\mathrm{GeV}/c)^{-2}$. In addition, many reactions exhibit the phenomenon of shrinking diffraction peaks — i.e., increasing a with increasing incident momentum — in the 2–10 GeV/c range.

However, as we shall see in the following, the diffraction mechanism is not the only one that gives rise to an e^{at} behavior of $d\sigma/dt$ for small t. On the other hand, diffraction (in the optical sense) does have one distinctive feature (as compared, for example, to particle exchange processes): the cross section tends toward an essentially constant value at high energies. Most other reaction mechanisms lead to cross sections that fall off with increasing energy.

---

[14] *Phys. Rev. Letters, 19:* 1149 (1967).

[15] D. R. O. Morrison, *Review of Inelastic Two Body Reactions,* CERN/TC/Physics 66–20 (1966). For a number of reactions, however, $d\sigma/dt$ appears to peak at a small value of $-t$ and to descend towards 0 as $-t \to 0$, which is the type of behavior expected for reactions dominated by a spin-flip process.

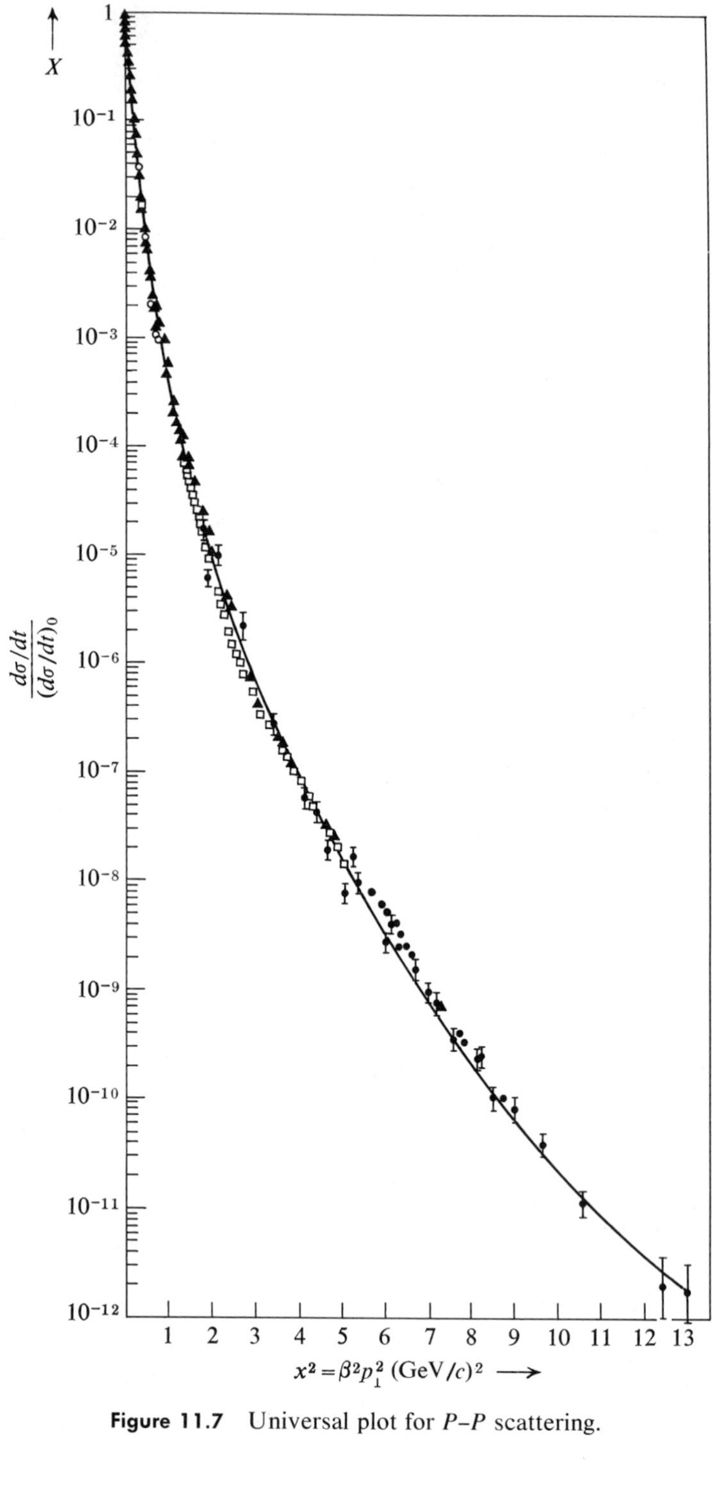

Figure 11.7 Universal plot for P–P scattering.

It has been observed[16] that this feature, of constant high-energy cross section, is common to a large number of two-body reactions, of which elastic scattering is but one example. Such reactions are generally distinguished by the fact that the products $a'(A')$ have the same "internal" quantum numbers (i.e., B, $\mathcal{Y}$ or S, t, G) as the incident particles $a(A)$ — only angular momentum is exchanged. Inelastic reactions that exhibit these features are frequently referred to as "diffraction dissociation" reactions.[17]

However, even in the case of reactions involving exchange of internal quantum numbers, the techniques developed in the preceding section are frequently very useful for their kinematical description and parametrization in terms of just a few empirical constants. In this case, the energy dependence is contained in the factor $A_\nu(s)$ [see Equation (6)].

11.2.1 One-Particle Exchange (OPE)

From the field-theoretical point of view, it is common to associate reactions involving small momentum transfers with the exchange of a single particle in the t-channel, as indicated in Figure 11.8(a), and to associate backward reactions with particle exchange in the u-channel, Figure 11.8(b). Since small momentum transfers correspond to large impact parameters, the shape of $d\sigma/dt$ for small $|t|$ is determined by the form of the reaction shape functions corresponding to large l-values, and the associated values of $a \approx R^2 = m^{-2}$ are determined by the masses of the lightest particles involved in the exchange processes. Thus, the aforementioned a-values observed for the forward peaks in two-body reactions correspond to exchange of particles ranging in mass from $m \sim 2m_\pi$ to $\sim m_\rho$, while the backward peaks correspond to the exchange of particles of baryonic mass.

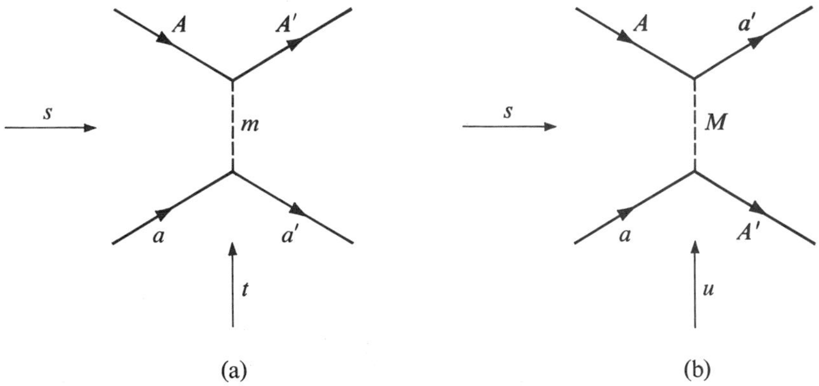

Figure 11.8 Feynman diagrams for particle exchange processes. (a) t-channel exchange. (b) u-channel exchange.

[16] For example, D. R. O. Morrison, *Phys. Rev.*, *165:* 1699 (1968). Morrison expresses reaction cross sections by $\sigma = \sigma_0 p_{lab}^{-n}$, with the value of n ($0 < n \lesssim 4$) generally characterizing the type of reaction (or particle exchanged). Diffractive reactions are characterized by $n \approx 0$.

[17] E. L. Feinberg and J. I. Pomeranchuk, *Suppl. Nuovo Cimento, 3:* 652 (1956); M. L. Good and W. D. Walker, *Phys. Rev.*, *120:* 1857 (1960).

To obtain the form of the reaction amplitude corresponding to a particle exchange process, consider the exchange of a scalar particle which, in Born approximation, gives rise to an effective potential [overlap function $\rho(r)$] of the Yukawa shape and correspondingly to an amplitude of the form (see Table 11.3)

$$\mathfrak{F}_{\text{ex}}^{(0)}(R\tau) = \frac{2\pi}{(1 + R^2\tau^2)} = \frac{2\pi m^2}{m^2 - t}. \tag{14}$$

More generally, the effect of the spin of the exchanged particle is to introduce an additional t dependence into Equation (14); thus, including the s dependence in the usual invariant form (Section 3.4.2) we may write as the general expression for the amplitude corresponding to the exchange of a particle of spin j and mass m:

$$A_{\text{ex}}^{(j)}(s, t) = \frac{s^{-1/2} f_j(t)}{m^2 - t}. \tag{14$'$}$$

The origin of the denominator in Equations (14) and (14′) is easily understood from the physical point of view: it is the resonant form corresponding to the t-channel reaction represented in Figure 11.8(a); thus, while $t \leq 0$ for an s-channel reaction, $t \rightarrow$ the cm (energy)^2 in the t-channel, and a resonance results when the incident t-channel energy equals the mass of the particle exchanged. In this regard, we note that for the exchange of an unstable particle of width $\Gamma(s)$, an appropriate modification of Equation (14′) would be

$$A_{\text{ex}}^{(j)}(s, t) = \frac{s^{-1/2} f_j(t)}{m^2 - t - im\Gamma(t)}. \tag{14$''$}$$

The application of the OPE model to a variety of two-body reactions at high energy has been explored by Gottfried and Jackson [18] and others. In general, reasonable agreement is found for reactions involving the exchange of a pion or kaon, while rather poorer results are obtained for reactions in which a vector meson is expected to be the particle exchanged. In both instances, however, the agreement between experiment and theory is greatly improved by modifying the simple OPE amplitude so as to reduce the importance of the contribution to (14″) of small l-values (small impact parameters).[19]

Physically, the suppression of the amplitudes corresponding to small l-values is required to preserve the unitarity of the corresponding S-matrix elements, $T_l(s)$, owing to the increasing competition of the many other inelastic channels (including multiparticle production) excited at the large momentum transfers associated with small impact parameters.[20]

---

[18] K. Gottfried and J. D. Jackson, *Nuovo Cimento, 33:* 309 (1964); J. D. Jackson and H. Pilkuhn, *Nuovo Cimento, 33:* 906 (1964).

[19] N. J. Sopkovitch, *Nuovo Cimento, 26:* 186 (1962); A. Dar, M. Kugler, Y. Dotham, and S. Nussinov, *Phys. Rev. Letters, 12:* 82 (1964); K. Gottfried and J. D. Jackson, *Nuovo Cimento, 34:* 735 (1964); J. D. Jackson, *Rev. Mod. Phys., 37:* 484 (1965).

[20] Unitarity of the S-matrix elements (Section 5.1) derives from the requirement that the total rate of absorption in a state of given l shall not exceed the portion of the incident flux corresponding to that l-value (i.e., contained between the impact parameters $b \approx l/k$ and $b + \Delta b$, $\Delta b \approx 1/k$). Hence, the absorption amplitudes A_l are limited in their magnitudes to $A_l \lesssim (l + \frac{1}{2})^{1/2}/k = (l + \frac{1}{2})^{1/2}\lambda\!\!\!^{-}$. This limitation

In addition to its successes in describing the t and s dependence of reaction cross sections, the OPEA (OPE with absorption) model has also been very useful in understanding the polarizations of the products (the ρ matrix), especially in reactions involving pion or kaon exchange.[21]

The choice of the appropriate particle to be exchanged in the reactions depicted in Figure 11.8 is governed, on the one hand, by the requirement that the conservation laws be satisfied for all the "internal" quantum numbers (B, $\mathcal{Y}$, C, G, etc.) at the exchange vertices and, on the other hand, by the dominance of exchange of particles of the smallest available mass in the small momentum transfer region. Thus, for example, while pion exchange might be expected to dominate in the reactions

$$\pi + \mathcal{N} \rightarrow \rho + \mathcal{N}', \tag{15a}$$

pions cannot be exchanged in the reactions

$$\pi + \mathcal{N} \rightarrow \pi' + \mathcal{N}', \tag{15b}$$

owing to the violation by a 3π vertex of G conservation; instead, the reactions (15b) are expected to be dominated by ρ exchange. Another case in point is the production of negative hyperons from protons, for example,

$$\pi^- + P \rightarrow K^+ + \Sigma^-, \tag{15c}$$

in which exchange of a doubly charged particle would be required in the t-channel. However, (15c) can proceed through exchange of, say, a Σ^0 in the u-channel, and its cross section would accordingly be expected to exhibit backward, but not forward, peaking. This is indeed the case for all observed reactions of this type.

The case of elastic nucleon-nucleon scattering is of special interest. Although one-pion exchange is permitted, this mechanism cannot be responsible for the diffraction peak observed at small momentum transfers since $f_\pi(t) = t$ in Equation (14″). This follows from the pseudoscalar nature of the pion, which has as a consequence that the $\mathcal{N}\mathcal{N}\pi$ vertex involves a spin-flip (as well as isospin-flip) process. More generally, if we assume that we are dealing with a pure diffraction process (i.e., "shadow" scattering) then in this reaction, if it is to be described as an exchange reaction, the only particles that can be exchanged are those that leave the quantum numbers of the projectile and target essentially unchanged, and consequently carry no isospin or strangeness and, furthermore, have $P = C = G = +1$ [for example, the spin 0^+ η_N (1070) or the spin 2^+ f(1260) or f' (1514)].[22]

---

is clearly the more severe the smaller the l-value, as well as becoming more stringent the greater the incident momentum $k = ƛ^{-1}$. Thus, a given reduction in the amplitudes for small l-values (absorption correction), which preserves unitarity at some given incident energy, may be inadequate at larger values of the energy. Furthermore, in the case of the production of particles of relatively large spin, S', the absorption (production) amplitude must be shared among the $(2S' + 1)$ final helicity states, thereby reducing further the maximum available to the individual A_l's as a consequence of the unitarity requirement.

[21] J. D. Jackson, *Rev. Mod. Phys., 37:* 484 (1965); Gottfried and Jackson, *Nuovo Cimento, 34:* 735 (1964).

[22] However, for the exchange of a particle with $j > 1$, there is the serious difficulty that OPE predicts $d\sigma/dt \propto s^{2j-2}$, which diverges as $s \rightarrow \infty$.

However, a 2π $(t=0)$ exchange in the spin states $0^+, 2^+, 4^+, \cdots$ is likely to have a longer effective range than the exchange of any one of these particles, so that we do not expect the simple OPE approach to hold in this case. Finally, for $\mathcal{N}$–$\mathcal{N}$ scattering, the exchange of a vector meson also leads to a forward peaking of $d\sigma/dt$, and this mechanism should therefore also be expected to contribute to the observed scattering, and in particular to any real part of the forward scattering amplitude (the amplitude for diffraction being pure imaginary).

We list in Table 11.4 some of the two-body reactions that have been studied at high energies, together with the most likely candidates for the responsible exchange mechanism.

Table 11.4 Candidates for Exchange in Some High-Energy, Two-Body Reactions

Reaction	*Exchanged particles*[a]
$\pi^\pm P \to \pi^\pm P$	$\rho(1^+1^-)$, $\eta_N(0^+0^+)$, $f(0^+2^+)$
$\pi^- P \to \pi^0 N$	ρ
$\pi^- P \to \eta^0 N$	$A_2(1^-2^+)$
$\pi P \to \rho \mathcal{N}$	$\pi(1^-0^-)$, $\omega(0^-1^-)$, $A_1(1^-1^+)$, A_2
$\pi P \to \omega P$	ρ, $B(1^+1^+)$
$K^\pm \mathcal{N} \to K^\pm \mathcal{N}$	η_N, ρ, ω, $\phi(0^-1^-)$, A_2, $f'(0^+2^+)$
$K^- P \to \overline{K^0} N$ }	ρ, A_2
$K^+ N \to K^0 P$ }	
$\mathcal{N}\mathcal{N}' \to \mathcal{N}\mathcal{N}'$ }	η_N, ρ, ω, ϕ, A_2, f
$\overline{\mathcal{N}}\mathcal{N}' \to \overline{\mathcal{N}}\mathcal{N}'$ }	
$PN \to NP$	ρ, A_2
$\pi\mathcal{N} \to \pi\mathcal{N}^*_{3/2}$	ρ
$\pi^- P \to K^0\Lambda$, $K\Sigma$	$K^*(\frac{1}{2}1^-)$, $K_N(\frac{1}{2}2^+)$
$\pi^+ P \to K^+\Sigma^+$	K^*, K_N
$\pi^- P \to K^{*0}\Lambda$	$K(\frac{1}{2}0^-)$, K^*
$K\mathcal{N} \to K^*\mathcal{N}$	π, $\eta(0^+0^-)$, $E(0^+0^-$ or $0^+1^+)$, ω, ρ, $\cdots$
$\pi\mathcal{N} \to \rho\mathcal{N}^*_{3/2}$	π, A_1, A_2
$\pi^+ P \to P\pi^+$	$\mathcal{N}$, $\mathcal{N}^*_{3/2}$
$\pi^- P \to P\pi^-$	$\mathcal{N}^*_{3/2}$
$\pi^+ P \to \Sigma^+ K^+$ }	Λ, Σ
$\pi^- P \to \Sigma^- K^+$ }	
$K^+ P \to P K^+$ }	
$K^- P \to \Xi^- K^+$ }	
$\gamma P \to \pi^+ N$	π
$\gamma P \to \pi^0 P$	ω

[a] Shown in parentheses, following the particle, are the values of the quantum numbers $(t^G j^P)$.

11.2.2 Regge Pole Exchange

Despite the successes of the one-particle exchange approach in correlating and describing the behavior of many two-body reactions at high energy, the difficulties encountered, especially in considering diffraction elastic scattering processes, have inspired interest in alternatives and modifications. The most promising alternative is the Regge pole approach which, although its theoretical basis and implications go far beyond this, was first applied to high-energy phenomena in order to explain an apparent shrinking with increasing energy of the width of the diffraction peak in nucleon-nucleon elastic scattering. Even though the shrinking phenomenon has since been found not to occur in most other elastic scattering reactions, the Regge pole method of analysis has been demonstrated to have wide and useful applicability, and it is today almost universally accepted as the basis for a comprehensive description of a wide range of high-energy reaction phenomena in terms of a small number of empirically deduced parameters.

The approach derives from an observation by Regge [23] in the realm of nonrelativistic potential scattering, treated on the basis of the Schroedinger equation. In the case of scattering by a central potential,[24] it is known that the scattering amplitude may be represented as a superposition of resonant contributions from a succession of virtual states, corresponding to the energy levels with increasing orbital angular momentum l, but having the same radial dependence of the wave function. For such a set of solutions, the level energy, E_l, increases monotonically with the l-value, and the scattering amplitude for a given incident energy, E, may be represented by a superposition of Breit–Wigner forms:

$$T(E, \cos\theta) = \frac{1}{2ik}\sum_l \frac{(2l+1)\,\Gamma_l(E)}{E - E_l + i\Gamma_l(E)}\,P_l(\cos\theta). \qquad (16a)$$

Regge started from the observation that an alternative representation [25] of the solution of the Schroedinger equation for the scattering problem is one in which l is treated as a complex variable, and E as a parameter. (Normally, the reverse approach is adopted because physically meaningful solutions occur only for integral l.) In this case, Equation (16a) may be put in the form

$$T(E, \cos\theta) = \frac{1}{2ik}\sum_l \frac{[2\alpha(E)+1]\,\gamma_l(E)}{\alpha(E) - l + i\gamma_l(E)}\,P_{\alpha(E)}(\cos\theta), \qquad (16b)$$

where $\alpha(E)$ is a continuous function of E which leads to resonances at $\mathrm{Re}\,\alpha(E_l) = l$, and the $P_\alpha(\cos\theta)$ are analytical continuations of the ordinary Legendre functions which take on the normal values at the poles, $P_{\alpha(E_l)} = P_l$. Equation (16b) may be put into an alternative form, which is more useful for its relativistic generalization:

$$T(E) = \frac{-i\pi}{2ik}\sum_i \frac{[2\alpha_i(E)+1]}{\sin\pi\alpha_i(E)}\,\beta_i(E)\,P_{\alpha_i(E)}(\cos\theta). \qquad (16b')$$

In going from Equation (16b′) to (16b), note that the widths arise from the small $\mathrm{Im}\,\alpha_i(E_l)$; the $\beta_i(E_l)$ are the residues at the poles, $\mathrm{Re}\,\alpha_i(E_l) = l$, of the "Regge trajectories," $\alpha_i(E)$.

---

[23] T. Regge, *Nuovo Cimento, 14:* 951 (1959); *18:* 947 (1960).

[24] The only requirement on the potential is that it should be a mathematically "nonpathological" function of r and not too strongly divergent as $r \to 0$. This permits a variety of forms, including the Yukawa potential, which has been the one most extensively studied.

[25] Known as the Watson–Sommerfeld representation.

To pass from Equation (16b′) to the usual high-energy form of the Regge amplitude involves a number of conjectures. First, it is conjectured that the same expression may be used in the relativistic realm to describe the particle exchange process [Figure 11.8(a)] in the *resonant t-channel*, by replacing the energy variable by t, and correspondingly [26] the momentum transfer variable, $\cos\theta$ [see Equation (3b)], by s. Second, we go to the limit of very large s and small $|t|$ which, although it corresponds to $\cos\theta \gg 1$ in the t-channel, represents the region of physical interest for the s-channel reactions under consideration. In this limit, the Legendre functions have an analytically simple form,

$$P_j(-z \to \infty) = \pm(-1)^j z^j .$$

Finally, we substitute for $T(E)$ the invariant amplitude, which has the effect of replacing the incident momentum and energy factors in $d\sigma/dt$ by a single factor s^{-1} [we incorporate all numerical factors into $\beta(t)$]. These conjectures lead to a Regge amplitude of the form [27]

$$A_R(s, t) = \frac{[2\alpha(t)+1]}{\Gamma(\alpha(t)+1)} \frac{[1 \pm e^{-i\pi\alpha(t)}]}{\sin \pi\alpha(t)} \beta(t) \left(\frac{s}{s_0}\right)^{\alpha(t)-1} . \tag{17}$$

Thus, the Regge amplitude is characterized by two parameters: the Regge trajectory $\alpha(t)$ and the residue function $\beta(t)$, which is usually assumed to be essentially constant for small t-values. [The constant s_0, introduced for the sole purpose of establishing the energy scale,[28] is usually taken approximately equal to the nucleon (mass)^2, $s_0 \simeq 1$ (GeV/c)^2.] In addition, a Regge trajectory is characterized by its "signature," which is the value of the sign [29] in the second bracket in Equation (17); trajectories of positive signature have poles corresponding to mesons with $(-1)^j$ positive or baryons with $(-1)^{j-1/2}$ positive, while those of negative signature have poles for meson trajectories at $(-1)^j$ negative, or $(-1)^{j-1/2}$ negative for baryon trajectories.

Equation (17) was derived for the case of spinless particles. For reactions involving particles with spin, the factor $[2\alpha(t)+1]\,\beta(t)$ is generally replaced by a set of factors $\beta_i(\alpha, t)$, depending in a more complicated fashion on the helicities, i, and on the trajectories, $\alpha(t)$, corresponding both to spin-nonflip and to spin-flip amplitudes.[30] For example, in the case of scattering of a particle of spin 0 by a

---

[26] Note that s and t are the total *cm* energy and 4-momentum transfer in the *s-channel*, for which we intend ultimately to obtain the form of the reaction amplitude.

[27] The factorial function $\Gamma(\alpha+1)$ is introduced to cause the amplitude to go to zero at unwanted (nonsense) integral values of $\alpha(t)$.

[28] Since $s - m_a^2 - m_A^2 = 2m_A E_a(lab)$ (Section 3.4.2), the energy variable $E_a(lab)$ is frequently used instead of s in Equation (17).

[29] Generally, an amplitude for a given two-body reaction can be written as a sum of two terms, one of positive and one of negative signature. In the special case of potential scattering, these correspond to potentials that are even and odd under space inversion. In any case, for both elastic and inelastic processes, the signature may be related to the so-called crossing symmetry in going from the s- to the u-channel representation; the positive signature terms in the amplitude remain the same, while the negative signature terms change sign, in going from the reaction $(a + A \to a' + A')$ to $(\bar{a}' + A \to \bar{a} + A')$.

[30] See, for example, R. Omnes and M. Froissart, *Mandelstam Theory and Regge Poles,* W. A. Benjamin, New York (1963); E. J. Squires, *Complex Angular Momenta and Particle Physics*, W. A. Benjamin, New York (1963); R. L. Omnes, *Ann. Rev. Nucl. Sci., 16:* 263 (1966).

spin $\frac{1}{2}$ nucleon (π–$\mathfrak{N}$), the simplest form of the spin-flip amplitude would involve replacing $(2\alpha+1)$ by α in Equation (17).

Assuming that the Regge trajectories correspond to the observed particles — i.e., they pass through the particle mass values at the appropriate spin values,

$$\alpha(t=m_i^2)=j_i, \tag{18}$$

we may attempt to plot the trajectories corresponding to various classes of particles, as in Figure 11.9. It is important to note, however, that the trajectories

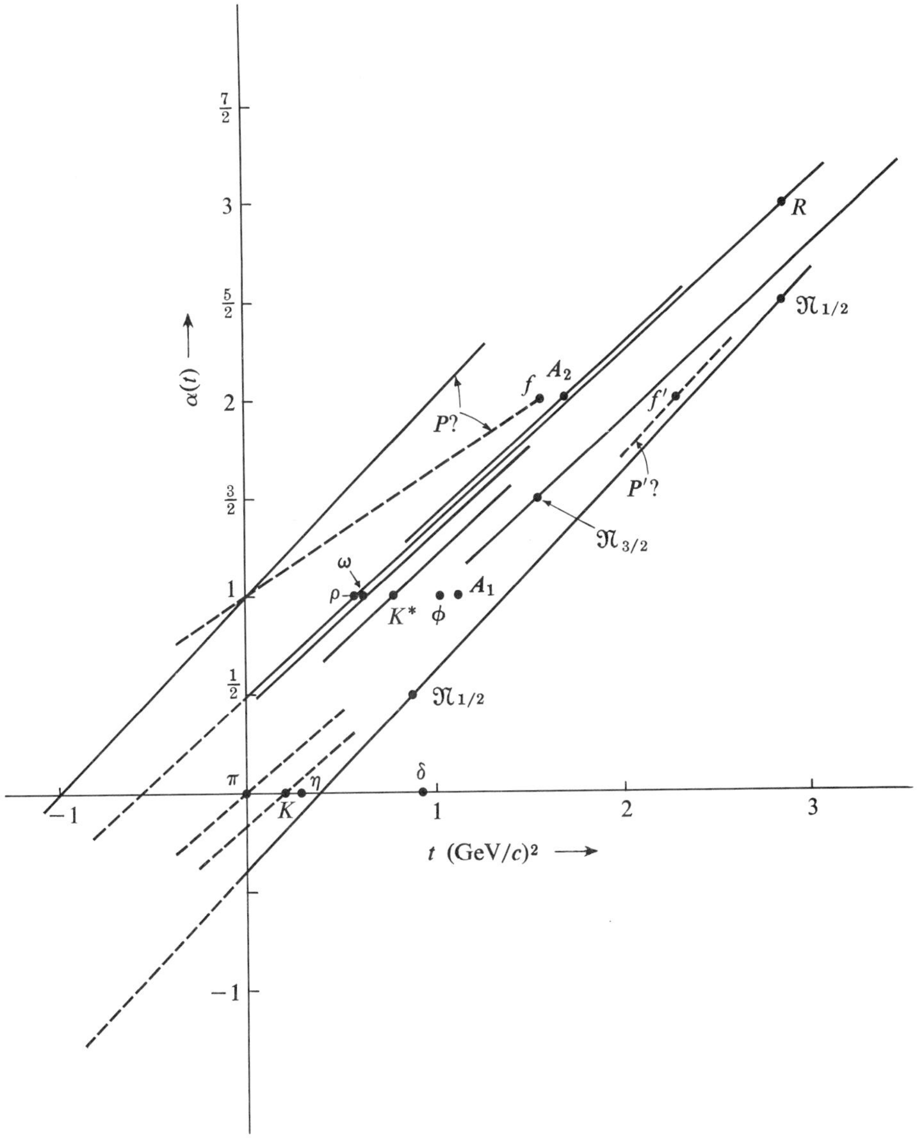

Figure 11.9 Regge trajectories.

are so determined only in the region $t > 0$, while the evaluation of the scattering amplitudes requires knowledge of $\alpha(t < 0)$. As a first approximation, we may attempt a linear extrapolation of $\alpha(t)$ into the $t < 0$ range, but it must be emphasized that eventually the shapes of the trajectories in the physical scattering range must be determined from the experimental behavior of the $d\sigma/dt$ corresponding to the exchange of the trajectory involved.

In the case of diffraction elastic scattering, the trajectories involved are the ones corresponding to mesons of $j = 0^+, 2^+, \cdots$, which presumably include the one labeled P (for Pomeranchuk) in Figure 11.9. Assuming that only the P trajectory were present, and that this trajectory has the value $\alpha(t = 0) \cong 1$, we would have

$$\alpha_P(t) - 1 \approx \alpha'_P t \tag{18a}$$

with

$$\alpha'_P \approx 1\ (\mathrm{GeV}/c)^{-2},$$

and correspondingly,

$$A_R^{(\mathrm{sc})}(s, t) \cong \frac{(2\alpha_P + 1)}{\Gamma(\alpha_P + 1)} \left(\frac{1 + e^{-i\pi\alpha_P}}{\sin \pi\alpha_P}\right) \beta_P(t)\, e^{\alpha'_P t \cdot \ln (s/s_0)}. \tag{17a}$$

Taking $\beta[0 > t \gtrsim -1\ (\mathrm{GeV}/c)^2] \simeq$ const,[31] we note that the width of the diffraction peak decreases with increasing s, since

$$\frac{d\sigma}{dt} \propto e^{at} \cong e^{2\alpha' \cdot \ln (s/s_0) \cdot t}. \tag{17a$'$}$$

Indeed, it was the observation of shrinking diffraction peaks in PP scattering[32] that called attention to the relevance of the Regge approach to high-energy processes. The fact that the phenomenon of shrinking diffraction peaks is not observed for other elastic scattering processes (i.e., $\pi^{\pm}P$, $K^{\pm}P$, $\bar{P}P$) led at the time to a certain amount of disillusion, but this fact need not be taken as a disproof of the Regge approach since (see Table 11.4) the coherent superposition of amplitudes corresponding to all possible Regge trajectories can lead to a cancellation, or in some cases even an inversion, of the shrinking phenomenon over a limited energy range.[33] However, it should be noted that in the asymptotic region ($s \to \infty$), the highest trajectory, presumably the Pomeranchuk trajectory, is expected to dominate, and the elastic scattering amplitudes should then all follow [Equation (17a)].[34]

---

[31] We could also take $\beta(t) = e^{a_0 t}$ without affecting the conclusion.

[32] K. J. Foley, S. J. Lindenbaum, W. A. Love, S. Ozaki, J. J. Russell, and L. C. L. Yuan, *Phys. Rev. Letters, 10:* 376, 543 (1963).

[33] W. Rarita, R. J. Riddall, Jr., C. B. Chiu, and R. J. N. Phillips, *Phys. Rev., 165:* 1615 (1968).

[34] Failure to observe elastic shrinking at even the highest available energies has led most authors to conclude that $\alpha'_P \approx 0$, $\alpha_P \simeq \text{const} \simeq 1$, for $0 > t \gtrsim -1\ (\mathrm{GeV}/c)^2$, which would make it difficult (but not impossible) to connect the Pomeranchuk trajectory with any known meson. However, the preceding arguments relating to shrinking peaks should apply to any process dominated by a single trajectory, α_i, for which $\alpha'_i > 0$. Thus, for example, in the reaction $\pi^- P \to \pi^0 N$, which should be dominated by the ρ trajectory (see Table 11.4), the expected behavior has been clearly demonstrated [G. Höhler, J. Baacke, H. Schlaile, and P. Sonderegger, *Phys. Letters, 20:* 79 (1966)].

One consequence of the asymptotic dominance of the P trajectory is that, in this limit, since the invariant forms of their amplitudes are the same,[35] reactions of the type

$$a + A \rightarrow a' + A' \tag{19}$$

and

$$\bar{a}' + A \rightarrow \bar{a} + A' \tag{19'}$$

should have the same cross sections. This is, of course, just a special case of the Pomeranchuk theorem, which requires $\sigma(\mathfrak{N}\mathfrak{N}) = \sigma(\bar{\mathfrak{N}}\mathfrak{N})$, $\sigma(\pi^+\mathfrak{N}) = \sigma(\pi^-\mathfrak{N})$, $\sigma(K\mathfrak{N}) = \sigma(\bar{K}\mathfrak{N})$, etc., as $s \rightarrow \infty$. On the other hand, even relatively small contributions from trajectories with negative signature (such as the ω trajectory for PP and $\bar{P}P$) can lead to appreciable differences between the cross sections for (19) and (19′), since the amplitudes add coherently. There remains, then, the important and unanswered question of how large a value of s is required to attain the asymptotic, Pomeranchuk limit.

Owing to the simultaneous influence of many Regge trajectories on most two-body reactions in the available energy range (Table 11.4), the Regge approach does not provide a unique solution, but rather it may be regarded as a convenient vehicle for parametrizing the observations through the introduction of the unknown functions $\beta_i(t)$ and $\alpha_i(t)$ characterizing the different possible Regge trajectories in the $t < 0$ region. In some cases, however, only one or two possible trajectories are involved, and such examples permit a much more stringent test of the Regge approach. An outstanding example is provided by the aforementioned charge-exchange reaction $\pi^- P \rightarrow \pi^0 N$, which is dominated by the ρ trajectory (Table 11.4). In the experiments on this reaction, the observation of a dip in $d\sigma/dt$ at $-t \simeq 0.6$ (GeV/c)^2 is accounted for[36] by the vanishing of the spin-flip amplitude, since $\alpha_\rho(-t \simeq 0.6) = 0$ (Figure 11.9). A similar effect may account for the dip in $d\sigma/du$ for backward π–P scattering as resulting from the vanishing of $[2\alpha(t) + 1]$ for the $\mathfrak{N}_{1/2}$ trajectory at small values of $-t$ [see Figures 11.8(b) and 11.9].

In other cases, it may be possible to isolate the effect of a single trajectory by consideration of an appropriate combination of cross sections.

EXAMPLE

Consider the set of reactions[37]

$$\pi^+ P \rightarrow \rho^+ P, \tag{19a}$$

$$\pi^- P \rightarrow \rho^- P, \tag{19b}$$

$$\pi^- P \rightarrow \rho^0 N, \tag{19c}$$

[35] The Mandelstam theorem, see Section 3.4.2.

[36] See, however, the example in Section 11.1.2 for another possible model capable of giving the observed dip in $(d\sigma/dt)(\pi^- P \rightarrow \pi^0 N)$.

[37] A. P. Contogouris, J. Tran Thanh Van, and H. J. Lubatti, *Phys. Rev. Letters, 19:* 1352 (1967).

for which the possible trajectories are π, ω, A_1, A_2 (Table 11.4). Of these, only the ω trajectory carries isospin 0 (and $C = -1$, while $C = +1$ for the other three). On the other hand, the reaction

$$\pi^0 P \to \rho^0 P \tag{19d}$$

involves the ω trajectory only, since a $\pi^0 \rho^0 x^0$ ($t = 1$) vertex is forbidden by isospin conservation. (Also, the $\pi^0 \rho^0$ combination has $C = -1$.) Reaction (19d) cannot be studied directly, but its cross section can be deduced from the other three by the application of isospin conservation. Let A_+, A_-, and A_0 be the amplitudes, respectively, for reactions (19a), (19b), and (19c); let A_{00} be the amplitude for (19d). Then

$$A_0 = \sqrt{\tfrac{1}{2}}\,(A_+ - A_-), \tag{19e}$$

$$A_{00} = \tfrac{1}{2}(A_+ + A_-). \tag{19f}$$

Thus, we have

$$|A_{00}|^2 = \tfrac{1}{2}(|A_+|^2 + |A_-|^2 - |A_0|^2), \tag{19g}$$

and

$$\frac{d\sigma}{dt}(\omega_{\text{ex}}) = \frac{d\sigma_{00}}{dt} = \frac{1}{2}\left(\frac{d\sigma_+}{dt} + \frac{d\sigma_-}{dt} - \frac{d\sigma_0}{dt}\right). \tag{19h}$$

Another useful property of the Regge approach, as applied to t-channel exchange reactions of the type in Figure 11.8(a), arises from the presumed factorizability of the residue function $\beta(t)$ into the product

$$\beta_{aA\to a'A'}(t) = \beta_{aa'}(t)\,\beta_{AA'}(t) \tag{20}$$

of residues corresponding to the two vertices. Equation (20) leads to connections between cross sections, for example,

$$\sigma^2(\pi\mathfrak{N}) = \sigma(\pi\pi)\,\sigma(\mathfrak{N}\mathfrak{N}), \tag{20a}$$

or

$$\frac{d\sigma(K\mathfrak{N})}{d\sigma(\pi\mathfrak{N})_{\text{spin-flip}}} = \frac{d\sigma(K\mathfrak{N})}{d\sigma(\pi\mathfrak{N})_{\text{spin-nonflip}}}, \tag{20b}$$

which appear to be satisfied (when measurable) at high energies.[38]

Another useful application of the Regge model has been in the description of multiparticle production processes,[39] in the limit of large $s_{ij} = (\not{p}_i + \not{p}_j)^2$ and small t_{ij} for the particles produced [see Figure 11.10(a)]. Finally, some success has recently been achieved in combining Regge exchange with a diffraction mecha-

---

[38] However, some doubts have recently been cast on the factorizability assumption owing to the failure to observe the expected vanishing of residues at so-called "crossover" points [see H. J. Lubatti, *Lectures at the International School of Physics, "Ettore Majorana,"* Erice, Sicily (1968)].

[39] H. F. Bali, G. F. Chew, and A. Pignotti, *Phys. Rev., 163:* 1572 (1967).

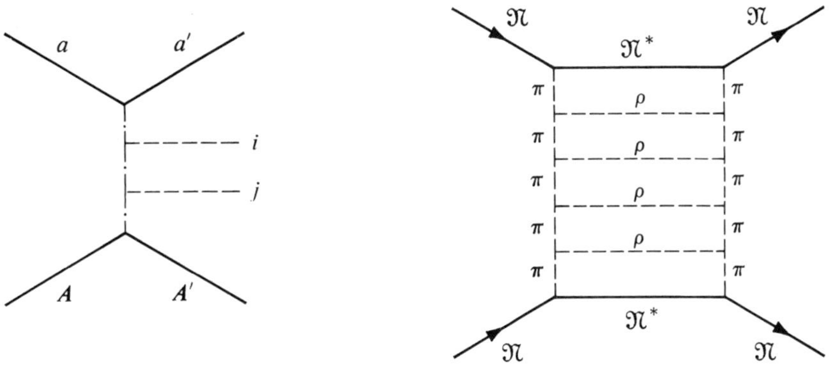

(a) (b)

Figure 11.10 Multiperipheral diagrams for Regge exchange. (a) Multiparticle production. (b) Ladder diagram for $\mathcal{N}$–$\mathcal{N}$ elastic scattering.

nism, either in the optical[40] or in the eikonal[41] approximation in a fashion similar to that used in the conventional OPEA computations discussed in the preceding section. This hybrid approach tries to take into account the totality of the strong interactions in the initial and final states by the modification of the usual Regge t-channel exchange diagram as shown in Figure 11.11. This has generally resulted in considerably better fits to observed high-energy, two-body reactions.

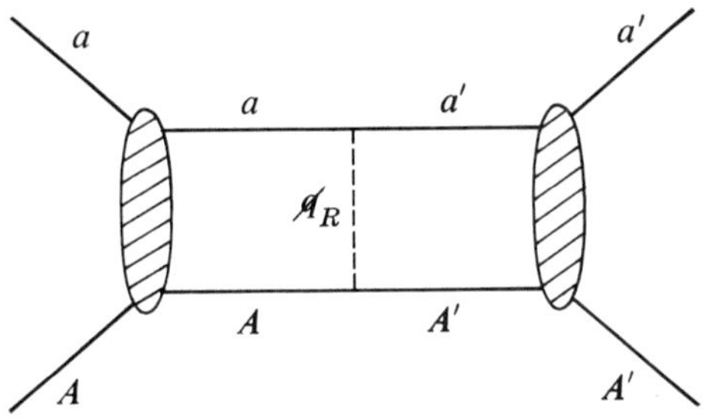

Figure 11.11 Hybrid Regge optical model for high-energy inelastic two-body reactions.

Although it has been successfully used to explain many aspects of observed high-energy interactions, the Regge pole model has encountered some difficulties in accounting for the observed polarizations of the product baryons in the $\pi\mathcal{N} \to \pi'\mathcal{N}'$ reactions.[42] Assumption of a single Regge trajectory predicts zero polarization, since the phases of the spin-nonflip and the spin-flip amplitudes are the same. Interference between two Regge trajectories can, however, lead to polarization of the products. Another ambiguous case is backward π–$\mathcal{N}$ scattering, where the observation of a series of relatively distinct peaks in $d\sigma/dt$ (180°) as a function

[40] G. Cohen-Tannoudji, A. Morel, and H. Navelet, *Nuovo Cimento, 48A:* 1075 (1967).
[41] C. B. Chiu and J. Finkelstein, *CERN Report*, TH 892 (1968).
[42] L. Van Hove, *Comments on Nuclear and Particle Physics, 1:* 19 (1967); *2:* 10 (1968).

of s appears to require the assumption of resonances in the s-channel coupled with the Regge exchange of the $\mathfrak{N}_{1/2}$ and $\mathfrak{N}^*_{3/2}$ trajectories in the t-channel. However, this type of explanation is in serious doubt, since it appears that the appropriate Regge representation of t-channel exchange trajectories should account, as well, for associated s-channel resonance effects (the problem of double counting).[43]

Generally speaking, as the data on high-energy reactions have increased and improved, it has become necessary to introduce further complications into the Regge description, so that much of the simplicity of the simple Regge approach has been lost.[44] Thus, for example, the parallel exchange of more than one Regge trajectory in the t-channel gives rise to "cuts" (i.e., moving branch points in the complex plane), which generally lead to a much more complicated behavior of the Regge amplitudes. Although such cuts can, in many cases, be approximated by a Regge-type behavior, they have the further unpleasant feature that the effective slopes of such quasi-trajectories are generally smaller than those of the most important particle trajectories [i.e., $\alpha' < 1$ (GeV/c)$^{-2}$; see Figure 11.9], so that their relative importance should increase with increasing s and $|t|$.

Another problem is associated with the analytical behavior of the Regge amplitudes for reactions involving particles of unequal mass as $t \to 0$. These amplitudes exhibit singularities, which can only be cancelled by the introduction of additional "daughter" trajectories — generally an infinite number of such — leading to the achievement of nonsingular behavior through devices known as "conspiracy" and "evasion." Since there is no evidence for actual particles associated with such daughter trajectories, their introduction must be regarded as a mathematical device for "patching up" an otherwise unsatisfactory theory. Associated with the daughter trajectories is a new quantum number, the Toller quantum number,[45] which serves to classify the types of new trajectories that must be introduced to cancel unwanted singularities.

Thus, the firm theoretical foundation of the Regge approach still remains to be established. In a number of cases, the form of the Regge amplitude, Equation (17), has been derived starting from a field-theoretical approach to elementary-particle dynamics.[46] In the case of elastic $\mathfrak{N}$–$\mathfrak{N}$ scattering, Amati, Fubini, and Stanghellini[47] have obtained Equation (17) from the summation of the "ladder" of particle exchange vertices shown in Figure 11.10(b). However, there is a school of thought that would consider the existence of particle trajectories, and the consequent properties of the S-matrix, as the more fundamental physical verity from which the observed properties of the so-called elementary

[43] R. Dolen, D. Horn, and C. Schmid, *Phys. Rev., 166:* 1768 (1968).

[44] See H. J. Lubatti, *Lectures at the International School of Physics, "Ettore Majorana,"* Erice, Sicily (1968). However, for a counter example, see G. Veneziano, *Nuovo Cimento, 57A:* 190 (1968).

[45] M. Toller, *Nuovo Cimento, 37:* 631 (1965).

[46] M. Gell-Mann and M. L. Goldberger, *Phys. Rev. Letters, 9:* 275 (1962); see also R. Blankenbecler and M. L. Goldberger, *Phys. Rev., 126:* 766 (1962) for the connections between the Regge approach and the eikonal approximation.

[47] D. Amati, S. Fubini, and A. Stanghellini, *Nuovo Cimento, 26:* 896 (1962).

particles and their interactions follow without the necessity of any field-theoretic superstructure.[48]

Whatever the answer, it is evident that the Regge approach can provide a large part, if not all, of the necessary kinematical framework for describing high-energy interactions.

PROBLEM

For the levels of the hydrogen atom, all the eigenstates that have the same number of nodes (zeros) in the radial wave function belong to the same Regge trajectory. What are the energies of the states belonging to the same trajectory? Plot an l versus E diagram for these trajectories.

---

[48] G. F. Chew, *S-Matrix Theory of Strong Interactions,* W. A. Benjamin, New York (1961); *The Analytic S-Matrix,* W. A. Benjamin, New York (1966).

PART II

The Use of Models

12

Early Models of Elementary Particles

The approach of Yukawa (see Section 1.1), in which the mesons are treated as quanta of a nucleonic force field, has been exceedingly fruitful, especially in providing an understanding of the forces between nucleons and of the pion-nucleon interactions. However, as the number of known baryonic states has been augmented by the discoveries of the strange baryons and the baryonic resonances, and as the number of known mesonic states has multiplied, the usefulness of the field-theoretic approach has been obscured by our ignorance of the relationships, if any, between the various possible fields arising out of the large number of possible baryon-meson combinations.

Furthermore, although the model of electromagnetic field theory has been quite instructive, accurate meson field-theoretic computations are considerably more complicated as a consequence of the much larger values of the baryon-meson coupling constants than the electromagnetic coupling ($e = 137^{-1/2}$); thus, perturbation techniques, which converge very rapidly in the electromagnetic case, are of rather doubtful utility for meson-field computations.

For these reasons, and also because of a common desire to seek simple, qualitative comprehension of complex phenomena before embarking on ambitious programs of difficult field-theoretical computations, it is useful to explore the relationships among the elementary particles in terms of simple models. The main purpose of such models is to seek, through simple approximations that embody the main features of known conservation principles, to explore and discover the relationships among the particles, to establish possible connections and hierarchies among them, and to provide the basis for an eventual and valid field-theoretic (or alternative) approach.

12.1 Fermi–Yang Model

Since we have no a priori basis for deciding which among the elementary particles are to be chosen as the fundamental constituents of all the others, we may as well begin by asking for the *minimum set* out of which the others can be constructed. Such a minimum set must be able to account for the following attributes:

1. *spin, s:* all possible spin values may be obtained from combinations of spin $\frac{1}{2}$ particles;
2. *isospin, t:* likewise, starting with particles of isospin $\frac{1}{2}$, we may construct all possible isospin states;
3. *nucleon (baryon) number, B:* starting with a baryon ($B = 1$), which also implies its antibaryon ($B = -1$), we may obtain all possible values of B;
4. *strangeness, S:* to provide for the strange particles, at least one of the fundamental constituents must carry the value $S = \pm 1$ of the strangeness quantum number.

If we disregard, for the moment, the strange particles, it is evident that the first three of the above requirements are satisfied by the nucleons (p, n) of spin and isospin $\frac{1}{2}$ and $B = 1$. This is the model of Fermi and Yang.[1] Not only are all atomic nuclei, and their excited states, made up of the various possible combinations of protons and neutrons, but the nonstrange mesons as well can be considered as combinations of a nucleon and an antinucleon (see Table 2.2).

Consider, for example, the π-mesons ($s = 0^-$, $t = 1$). These may be taken to be $\mathfrak{N}$–$\overline{\mathfrak{N}}$ combinations in the ${}^1S_0$ state,[2] with the charge combinations [3]

$$\begin{aligned} \pi^+ &= p\bar{n}, \\ \pi^0 &= \sqrt{\tfrac{1}{2}}\,(p\bar{p} - n\bar{n}), \\ \pi^- &= n\bar{p}. \end{aligned} \tag{1}$$

At the time Fermi and Yang first proposed this model, only the π-mesons were known. One of the immediate problems arising was the question of the possible existence of other bound $\mathfrak{N}$–$\overline{\mathfrak{N}}$ states, e.g., the isosinglet, ${}^1S_0$ state (spin 0^-, $t = 0$)

$$\pi^0_0 = \sqrt{\tfrac{1}{2}}\,(p\bar{p} + n\bar{n}), \tag{2}$$

or the $t = 1$ and $t = 0$ combinations in the ${}^3S_1$ state (spin 1^-). Since persistent search extending over a decade failed to reveal the existence of such mesons, at least not among the particles with relatively long mean lives, it was concluded that the forces are such that states other than those of the π-mesons are either unbound, or that their binding is considerably weaker than that in the ${}^1S_0$, $t = 1$ state — so that the resulting mesonic states must have masses large enough to permit their very rapid (strong) decay into two or more pions. The latter is in-

---

[1] E. Fermi and C. N. Yang, *Phys. Rev., 76:* 1739 (1949).

[2] Recall that $\mathfrak{N}$–$\overline{\mathfrak{N}}$ combinations have the parity $-(-1)^L$ owing to the opposite intrinsic parities of $\mathfrak{N}$ and $\overline{\mathfrak{N}}$.

[3] The minus sign in the symmetric ($t = 1$, $t_3 = 0$) π^0 charge combination arises from the conventional definition of the $\overline{\mathfrak{N}}$ doublet as $(-\bar{n}, \bar{p})$.

deed the case, and the other anticipated $\mathfrak{N}$–$\overline{\mathfrak{N}}$ mesonic combinations have since been found (see Table 2.2).

Calculations on the basis of the Fermi–Yang model are complicated by a number of factors: First, there is the problem of treating a system in which the binding energy is of the order of the total mass of the constituents (~ 2 GeV/c^2), resulting in a very small total energy ($E_0 \sim 137$ MeV) in the ground state. At first glance, this would appear to imply highly relativistic motion of the constituents. However, provided the range R of the interaction is sufficiently large, the average momenta in the ground state, $\langle p^2 \rangle \sim R^{-2}$, may be small enough so that relativistic effects are not decisive.

Second, there is the problem of describing the interaction in a relativistically invariant form, since what appears as a scalar interaction in one coordinate system [say, $V(r)$ for two nucleons at rest separated by the distance **r**] will have the nature of a 4-vector interaction when viewed in the rest frame of one of the nucleons. This problem has been treated in detail for the case of the electromagnetic interactions in simple atoms.[4]

Finally, the nucleons obey the Dirac equation, which introduces special complications when considering the angular momentum states. Thus, as is well known, a Dirac particle is described by a four-component spinor, in which the "large" and the "small" components have the same angular momentum but opposite parity; if the large components represent an $S_{1/2}$ state, then the small components of the wave function have the properties of a $P_{1/2}$ state. In the case of the two-nucleon problem, this has the effect of mixing the properties of 0^- and 0^+ states, of 1^- and 1^+ states, etc. If, however, the nature of the forces is such that the total spin value ($s = 0$ or 1) is conserved, then the ${}^1S_0(0^-)$ state is a pure one, which makes the computation somewhat simpler for the π- and η-mesons; for the 1^- mesons, on the other hand, the wave functions involve a mixture of ${}^3S_1$, ${}^3D_1(1^-)$, and ${}^3P_1(1^+)$.

Such complications notwithstanding, detailed computations have been carried out on the Fermi–Yang model.[5] However, as it turns out that the spatial extension of the pion is relatively large ($\langle r^2 \rangle^{1/2} \sim 1$ f, $\langle p^2 \rangle^{1/2} \sim 200$ MeV), it suffices for the purposes of orientation and qualitative understanding to use a nonrelativistic first approximation, neglecting the small components of the wave function and the "retardation" effects mentioned above.

As an example, let us consider the problem of the mass spectrum of the mesons: The simplest $\mathfrak{N}$–$\overline{\mathfrak{N}}$ interaction which is both charge and spin independent would have the form

$$H_{\overline{\mathfrak{N}}-\mathfrak{N}} = H_0(r) + H_1(r)\,\mathbf{s}_{\mathfrak{N}} \cdot \mathbf{s}_{\overline{\mathfrak{N}}} + H_2(r)\,\mathbf{t}_{\mathfrak{N}} \cdot \mathbf{t}_{\overline{\mathfrak{N}}}, \tag{3}$$

in which the main binding would arise from the first term, while the second and

[4] H. A. Bethe and E. E. Salpeter, "Quantum Mechanics of One- and Two-Electron Systems," *Encyclopedia of Physics, XXXV:* 88 (Springer, Berlin, 1957).

[5] Fermi and Yang, *Phys. Rev., 76:* 1739 (1949); R. E. Zier, "Fermi–Yang Model Applied to Unstable Mesons" (Ph.D. thesis, M.I.T., 1964); G. M. Fogelsong, "Investigation of the Model of the Λ and Σ Hyperons as Isospin Conserving Bound States of a Nucleon and an Antikaon" (Ph.D. thesis, M.I.T., 1962).

third would account for the splitting (fine structure) among the energies (masses) of the mesonic states of different spin and isospin through a spin-spin and isospin-isospin interaction, respectively. The resulting masses are obtained by computing the diagonal matrix elements of the total energy operator, $H_{\mathfrak{N}-\overline{\mathfrak{N}}}$, between $\mathfrak{N}$–$\overline{\mathfrak{N}}$ states which are eigenstates of both the total spin $\mathbf{s} = \mathbf{s}_1(\mathfrak{N}) + \mathbf{s}_2(\overline{\mathfrak{N}})$ and the total isospin $\mathbf{t} = \mathbf{t}_1(\mathfrak{N}) + \mathbf{t}_2(\overline{\mathfrak{N}})$:

$$\begin{aligned} M_{s,t} &= \langle \psi_{s,t}^{s_1,s_2;t_1,t_2}(r)^* | H_{\mathfrak{N}-\overline{\mathfrak{N}}} \psi_{s,t}^{s_1,s_2;t_1,t_2}(r) \rangle \\ &= \overline{H}_0 + \overline{H}_1 \langle \psi_{s,t}^* | \mathbf{s}_1 \cdot \mathbf{s}_2 \psi_{s,t} \rangle + \overline{H}_2 \langle \psi_{s,t}^* | \mathbf{t}_1 \cdot \mathbf{t}_2 \psi_{s,t} \rangle \\ &= \overline{H}_0 + \overline{H}_1 \langle \mathbf{s}_1 \cdot \mathbf{s}_2 \rangle + \overline{H}_2 \langle \mathbf{t}_1 \cdot \mathbf{t}_2 \rangle . \end{aligned} \tag{3a}$$

Recalling that

$$\begin{aligned} 2\langle \mathbf{s}_1 \cdot \mathbf{s}_2 \rangle &= \mathbf{s}^2 - \mathbf{s}_1^2 - \mathbf{s}_2^2 \\ &= s(s+1) - s_1(s_1+1) - s_2(s_2+2) \\ &= s(s+1) - \tfrac{3}{2}, \end{aligned} \tag{3b}$$

and

$$2\langle \mathbf{t}_1 \cdot \mathbf{t}_2 \rangle = t(t+1) - \tfrac{3}{2}, \tag{3c}$$

since $s_1 = s_2 = t_1 = t_2 = \frac{1}{2}$ for both $\mathfrak{N}$ and $\overline{\mathfrak{N}}$, and incorporating the constant terms into the $\overline{H}_0$ term, we note that the meson masses [Equation (3a)] are given by the expression

$$M_{s,t} = A + Bs(s+1) + Ct(t+1). \tag{3d}$$

When we attempt to apply Equation (3d) to the masses of the known mesons of spin 0^- and 1^-, shown in Table 12.1, we immediately encounter the problem that there are two isosinglet vector mesons, the ω and the ϕ. Actually, as may be seen immediately by comparing the mass differences $\eta - \pi$ with $\omega - \rho$ or $\phi - \rho$, Equation (3d) holds for neither choice, although the choice of ϕ leads to somewhat better agreement. In all this, we have neglected the problem of the X^0-meson (0^-, $t = 0$) of mass 958 MeV, which only makes things worse. We shall return to these problems in subsequent sections.

Table 12.1 Masses of the Nonstrange Mesons

Meson	s	t	*Mass* (MeV)
η	0^-	0	549
$\eta' = X^0$	0^-	0	958
π	0^-	1	138
ω	1^-	0	783
ϕ	1^-	0	1019
ρ	1^-	1	765

PROBLEMS

1. Can you improve matters, with respect to fitting the meson masses of Table 12.1, by adding a term $H_3(r)(\mathbf{s}_1 \cdot \mathbf{s}_2)(\mathbf{t}_1 \cdot \mathbf{t}_2)$ to the interaction Hamiltonian, Equation (3)?
2. Still using the Fermi–Yang model, how would you account for the existence of two mesons of $s=0^-$, $t=0$ (η and η') and two mesons of $s=1^-$, $t=0$ (ω and ϕ)?

12.2 Sakata Model

The Fermi–Yang model permits the construction of mesons and of other nonstrange baryonic states as well, e.g., $\mathfrak{N}\bar{\mathfrak{N}}\mathfrak{N}$, and so on. However, the introduction of the strangeness quantum number requires the addition of at least one more basic constituent. In the spirit of economy, the simplest way of accomplishing this is by adding an isosinglet λ^0 hyperon to the (p, n) pair. This was the proposal of Sakata,[6] and we shall refer to the resulting model as the Fermi–Yang–Sakata (F–Y–S) model.

12.2.1 Mesons

The major advantage of the F–Y–S model is that it allows for a completely uniform treatment of all mesons — strange as well as nonstrange. Out of the Sakata triplet (p, n, λ) and the corresponding antiparticles, taken in pairs, we may construct nine mesonic states, as demonstrated in Table 12.2. Note that there are three pairs with the same charge and strangeness ($p\bar{p}$, $n\bar{n}$, $\lambda\bar{\lambda}$) out of which it is possible to construct any number of groups of three orthogonal combinations. One of these (row 4) is determined by the requirement that it be the neutral ($t_3=0$) member of an isotriplet. However, the other two (rows 1 and 2) have identical quantum numbers. Thus, not only do we have room for two nonstrange mesons with $t=0$ for each spin value (ω^0–ϕ^0, η^0–X^0), but in fact the F–Y–S model requires that there be two rather than one such meson in each spin configuration!

However, in principle, the wave functions representing the two $S=t=0$ mesons need not have been those given in Table 12.2, but any set orthogonal to that of row 4; the most general pair of such wave functions may be written

$$\begin{aligned} \chi_1' &= a\chi_1 + b\chi_2 , \\ \chi_2' &= -b\chi_1 + a\chi_2 , \end{aligned} \tag{4}$$

with the normalization condition

$$|a|^2 + |b|^2 = 1. \tag{4a}$$

[6] S. Sakata, *Progr. Theoret. Phys.*, *16:* 686 (1956). Note that we use lower-case letters (p, n, λ) to denote the fundamental constituents, since these need not be identical in all respects with the observed (physical) baryons (P, N, Λ).

Table 12.2 Mesonic States in the F–Y–S *Model* [a]

S	t	t_3	χ Combination	0^- Meson	M (MeV)	M^2 (GeV^2)	1^- Meson	M (MeV)	M^2 (GeV^2)	2^+ Meson	M (MeV)	M^2 (GeV^2)
0	0	0	$\sqrt{\frac{1}{3}}\,(p\bar{p}+n\bar{n}+\lambda\bar{\lambda})$	X^0	958	0.918	ϕ	1019	1.039	f'	1514	2.29
0	0	0	$\sqrt{\frac{1}{6}}\,(p\bar{p}+n\bar{n}-2\lambda\bar{\lambda})$	η^0	549	0.301	ω	783	0.614	f	1260	1.57
0	1	1	pn	π^+	139.6	0.019	ρ^+	765	0.585	A_2^+	1305	1.70
		0	$\sqrt{\frac{1}{2}}\,(p\bar{p}-n\bar{n})$	π^0	135.0	0.018	ρ^0	770	0.593	A_2^0	1305	1.70
		-1	$n\bar{p}$	π^-	139.6	0.019	ρ^-	765	0.585	A_2^-	1305	1.70
1	$\frac{1}{2}$	$\frac{1}{2}$	$p\bar{\lambda}$	K^+	493.8	0.244	K^{*+}	892.4	0.796	K_N^+	1420	2.01
		$-\frac{1}{2}$	$n\bar{\lambda}$	K^0	497.7	0.248	K^{*0}	895.9	0.801	K_N^0	1420	2.01
-1	$\frac{1}{2}$	$\frac{1}{2}$	$\lambda\bar{n}$	$\overline{K^0}$	497.7	0.248	$\overline{K^{*0}}$	895.9	0.801	$\overline{K_N^0}$	1420	2.01
		$-\frac{1}{2}$	$\lambda\bar{p}$	K^-	493.8	0.244	K^{*-}	892.4	0.796	K_N^-	1420	2.01

[a] We list here only those combinations for which all the members are now experimentally well established, namely, those corresponding to the ${}^1S_0$, ${}^3S_1$, ${}^3P_2$ combinations. Some, but not all, of the members of the ${}^1P_1$, ${}^3P_0$, and ${}^3P_1$, as well as some possibly corresponding to larger internal angular momentum, are known. We reserve the discussion of these mesonic groups to Chapter 16.

Thus, for example, with $a = \sqrt{\frac{1}{3}}$, $b = -\sqrt{\frac{2}{3}}$, we would get

$$\chi_1' = \lambda\bar{\lambda},$$
$$\chi_2' = \sqrt{\tfrac{1}{2}}\,(p\bar{p} + n\bar{n}). \tag{5}$$

We have chosen the particular combinations shown in Table 12.2 because, in this case, the wave function χ_1 of row 1 has the greatest possible symmetry with respect to interchange of the constituents, $p \leftrightarrow n \leftrightarrow \lambda$; this choice then uniquely determines the combination χ_2. However, among the real mesons, it has been observed that while the combinations shown in Table 12.2 are most appropriate for representing the 0^- mesons, the combinations (5) are more appropriate for the case of the 1^- and 2^+ mesons.

A number of interesting observations may be made relating to the mass spectra. In the case of the F–Y–S model, the forces could be completely isospin independent, but the mass difference between π and η^0 could come about as a result of a difference between the $\mathfrak{N}$–$\bar{\mathfrak{N}}$ and λ–$\bar{\lambda}$ interaction, or simply as a result of the difference in intrinsic mass between λ and (p, n). Let us assume, for the moment, the latter possibility, taking

$$m(p) = m(n) = m(\lambda) - \Delta. \tag{6}$$

Then, from the wave functions in Table 12.2, column 4, we would have

$$m(\pi) = \mu,$$
$$m(\eta) = \mu + \frac{4\Delta}{3}, \tag{6a}$$

always assuming the identity of the $p\bar{p}$, $n\bar{n}$, and $\lambda\bar{\lambda}$ interactions; adding to this the identity of $p\bar{\lambda}$, etc. with the other interactions, we would have

$$m(K) = m(\bar{K}) = \mu + \Delta, \tag{6b}$$

leading to the interesting mass relationship

$$4m(K) = 4m(\bar{K}) = m(\pi) + 3m(\eta). \tag{7}$$

Equation (7) is quite well obeyed by the observed masses (Table 12.2, column 6) and even better still by the mass² values (column 7), which are the values generally considered as the more appropriate to use when considering meson mass spectra.[7]

However, we note that the X^0 does not fit into this scheme at all! Far from being the mean of the π and the η, it is much heavier than any other member of the 0^- F–Y–S nonet, seeming to lie quite separate from the other eight. This presents a problem for our model.

On the other hand, among the nine 1^- mesons, a different set of mass relationships seems to prevail; namely,

[7] The argument is that mass is a self-energy phenomenon which, in the case of a particle obeying Bose–Einstein statistics, and consequently described by a Klein–Gordon equation, always emerges from the theoretical computation in the quadratic form. Mass relations among fermions, on the other hand, always involve the masses themselves.

$$m(\rho) \cong m(\omega), \tag{8a}$$

$$2m(K^*) = 2m(\overline{K^*}) \cong m(\omega) + m(\phi) \cong 2[m(\rho) + \Delta]. \tag{8b}$$

Interestingly, these are exactly the relationships we would expect on the basis of the same crude and simple mass model used in the case of the 0^- mesons, but *provided the φ- and ω-mesons are in the charge states described by Equation (5).* The reason for this difference between the 0^- and 1^- mesons is just one of the problems of the F–Y–S model to which we shall return in a subsequent chapter.[8]

A final relation, based on the model for the mass spectra used above, connects all the meson groups, irrespective of the nature of the spin-dependent baryon–antibaryon interaction, namely,

$$m(K^*) - m(\rho) = m(K) - m(\pi) = m(K_N) - m(A_2) = \Delta. \tag{9}$$

This expression holds very poorly for the masses, but reasonably well for the m^2 values.

12.2.2 Baryons

In contrast to its successes in predicting the mesons, the problem of predicting the remaining baryons (e.g., Σ, Ξ, Ω) and of computing some of their more simple properties — e.g., mass spectrum — meets serious difficulties in the F–Y–S model. The simplest combinations that have baryonic number $B = 1$ are of two baryons plus one antibaryon, for example,

$$\begin{aligned} \mathcal{N}\bar{\mathcal{N}}\lambda &= \Sigma, \\ \lambda\bar{\mathcal{N}}\lambda &= \Xi. \end{aligned} \tag{10}$$

However, there are many more such combinations possible [twenty-seven in total, of which Equations (10) account for only five]; some can be thought of as representing excited baryonic states, e.g., $\mathcal{N}\bar{\mathcal{N}}\mathcal{N}$, $\mathcal{N}\bar{\lambda}\lambda$, or $\lambda\bar{\lambda}\lambda$. But others, such as $\mathcal{N}\bar{\lambda}\mathcal{N}$ (strangeness +1), are much more difficult to explain away.

Following Yamaguchi,[9] let us assume that the $B\bar{B}B$ combinations can be approximated as "linear triatomic molecules," in which the binding arises essentially from the relatively strong binding of $B\bar{B}$ pairs.[10] In this case, the difference in mass values between the Σ and Ξ hyperons would arise from the slightly stronger binding of $\mathcal{N}\bar{\mathcal{N}}$ as compared to $\lambda\bar{\mathcal{N}}$. However, on this assumption the $\mathcal{N}\bar{\lambda}\mathcal{N}$ ($S = +1$) combination should have roughly the same mass as the $\lambda\bar{\mathcal{N}}\lambda$ (Ξ), which would make it stable against strong decay into $\mathcal{N} + K$, and hence relatively

---

[8] The masses of the 2^+ mesons lie much closer to Equations (8a) and (8b) than Equation (7). However, in any case, it is evident that appropriate mixing parameters [a and b in Equation (4)] can be chosen to yield the observed masses, but in general the wave functions appropriate to the observed mesons are more complicated than either those shown in Table 12.2 or those of Equation (5).

[9] Y. Yamaguchi, *Progr. Theoret. Phys. Suppl.*, *11:* 1 (1959).

[10] The BB bindings can be neglected, being of order MeV as compared to the GeV binding energies of the BB combinations.

long-lived and observable.[11] Furthermore, in this case the $\mathcal{N}\overline{\mathcal{N}}\mathcal{N}$ (excited nucleon) should be the most strongly bound combination (but it could still decay rapidly into $\mathcal{N} + \pi$).

Another problem relates to the spin and parity of the $B\overline{B}B$ combinations. The masses of the mesons indicate that all $B\overline{B}$ combinations are by far most strongly bound in the $^1S_0$ state. Assuming this to be the case, we see that the lowest energy $B\overline{B}B$ combinations would all have spin $\frac{1}{2}$ *but negative parity* ($\frac{1}{2}^-$), owing to the intrinsic negative parity of the $\overline{B}$. But the Σ and Ξ hyperons have $s = \frac{1}{2}^+$. Of course, one can construct a three-body state with internal orbital angular momentum, which has $s = \frac{1}{2}^+$, but the necessity for doing this renders the Sakata–Yamaguchi model much less attractive.

We shall return to the Sakata model later (Chapter 15) and note how, by virtue of a simple but fundamental modification, practically all of the above-mentioned difficulties may be removed.

PROBLEMS

1. Referring to Equations (4) and (4a), we may define a mixing parameter θ, through

$$a = \cos\theta,$$
$$b = \sin\theta.$$

Starting from the masses and χ combinations given in Table 12.2, and assuming that the mass differences arise from a heavier λ [Equation (6)], compute the mixing angles appropriate to the 0^-, 1^-, and 2^+ nonets.

2. Using the Sakata–Yamaguchi model of the baryons, and assuming that all $B\overline{B}$ combinations are in relative S states, with a pairwise interaction of the form

$$H_{1\overline{2}} = H_0 + H_1 \mathbf{s}_1 \cdot \mathbf{s}_{\overline{2}} + H_2 \mathbf{t}_1 \cdot \mathbf{t}_{\overline{2}},$$

answer the following:

(a) What are the total spin and isospin values corresponding to the various possible $B\overline{B}B$ combinations? Write out the eigenfunctions for these combinations.

(b) Starting from the masses of some of the lower-lying baryons [e.g., $\mathcal{N}^*(1236)$, Σ, Ξ, Ω; see Table 2.1] predict the masses of all the rest of these combinations and compare them with the masses of observed baryon resonances, where known.

(c) Can you make a significant improvement by adding a term $H_3(\mathbf{s}_1 \cdot \mathbf{s}_{\overline{2}})(\mathbf{t}_1 \cdot \mathbf{t}_{\overline{2}})$ to the interaction? Or by assuming the λ mass greater than that of the p or n?

---

[11] Alternatively, the Ξ–Σ mass difference could arise in part from the greater mass of the λ than that of the $\mathcal{N}$. But in this case, the $\mathcal{N}\overline{\lambda}\mathcal{N}$ combination would be even lighter than the $\lambda\overline{\mathcal{N}}\lambda$, which only increases the difficulty. Admittedly, one should do the computation less crudely, taking into account, for instance, the possible differences in overlap integral of the different baryon-antibaryon combinations: but a more refined computation [Yamaguchi, *Progr. Theoret. Phys. Suppl. 11:* 1 (1959)] does not alter the general qualitative conclusions we are able to draw by crude arguments.

12.3 Atomic Models

Although the F–Y–S model provides the most economical and straightforward description of the known mesonic states, we have seen that it is not nearly so attractive when applied to the construction of the baryons. An alternative method of treating the baryons — namely to treat them as atomlike systems consisting of a nucleonic core surrounded by a cloud of one or more mesons — is suggested by Yukawa's field-theoretic approach.

Such models are generally less economical than the F–Y–S model in terms of the total number of elementary constituents required. Thus, a nonstrange meson is required for the construction of nucleonic states; and a strange meson is needed to provide for the strange baryons. The most natural choices for the mesonic constituents are the pion and the kaon.[12]

12.3.1 The Pion Atomic Model of the Nucleons

The meson field theory of Yukawa, discussed in Section 1.1, suggests a picture of the nucleons as a nucleonic core surrounded by a cloud of virtual pions. The cloud may have 0, 1, 2,... mesons present at any time, the relative probability for n mesons being proportional to the coupling constant f^{2n}. In the atomic model,[13] we represent this cloud by a single pion, treated as a real rather than as a virtual particle.

The nature of the Yukawa reaction requires that the stable pion-nucleon combination be in the $P_{1/2}$ state ($l=1$, $j=\frac{1}{2}^+$; $\mathbf{j}=\mathbf{s}+\mathbf{l}_\pi$), with isospin $t=\frac{1}{2}$. We may impose this requirement by assuming a pion-nucleon potential of the form[14]

$$H_{\pi-\mathfrak{N}}=f(\boldsymbol{\sigma}_{\mathfrak{N}}\cdot\mathbf{l}_\pi)(\mathbf{t}_{\mathfrak{N}}\cdot\mathbf{t}_\pi)\,V(r)\,\delta(l,1). \tag{11}$$

This interaction, with $V(r)<0$, is most strongly attractive in the $j=\frac{1}{2}$, $t=\frac{1}{2}$ state, since

$$\begin{Bmatrix}\boldsymbol{\sigma}_{\mathfrak{N}}\cdot\mathbf{l}_\pi\\ 2\mathbf{t}_{\mathfrak{N}}\cdot\mathbf{t}_\pi\end{Bmatrix}=\begin{matrix}-1, & \text{for } j,\ t=\frac{1}{2},\\ \frac{1}{2}, & \text{for } j,\ t=\frac{3}{2}.\end{matrix} \tag{11a}$$

It is repulsive in the $j=\frac{1}{2}$, $t=\frac{3}{2}$ and $j=\frac{3}{2}$, $t=\frac{1}{2}$ states, but again attractive in the

[12] We choose the pion rather than, say, the η^0 ($s=0^-$, $t=0$) since the isotopic spin 1 of the pion provides for the possibility of excited nucleonic states of $t>\frac{1}{2}$. However, in principle, the choice of mesons is not restricted to the π and K. For example, we could employ only the K's, constructing nonstrange mesonic states out of the various K–$\overline{K}$ combinations. However, our choice has a number of advantages. First, it permits us to treat the most important baryonic states as single-meson atoms. Second, it appears rather more natural to use as the basic mesons the lightest among the known mesons of strangeness 0 and 1, both because they are the most stable and also because, the range of a meson field being $\sim m^{-1}$, the structure of the outside and most readily accessible regions of the nucleons will be dominated by the lightest mesons.

[13] See B. T. Feld, *Ann. Phys.* (New York), *1:* 58 (1957).

[14] There are also interactions in the S state, too weak to lead to a bound state, which give rise to small S-wave pion-nucleon scattering phase shifts. The S-wave interaction is attractive in the $t=\frac{1}{2}$ and repulsive in the $t=\frac{3}{2}$ state and can be very roughly represented by the interaction Hamiltonian

$$H_S\approx f_S(\mathbf{t}_{\mathfrak{N}}\cdot\mathbf{t}_\pi)\,V_S(r), \tag{11'}$$

with $V_S(r)>0$.

$j = t = \frac{3}{2}$ state, although less so than in the ground state. This last feature provides the possibility of a virtual (resonant or isobar) state with $j = t = \frac{3}{2}$ and enables the atomic model to account, in considerable specific detail, for the resonance phenomena that are observed to dominate all pion-nucleon interactions in the low-energy range.[15]

Assuming, then, an interaction of form (11), the Schroedinger equation (or the Klein–Gordon) may be solved to obtain the wave function of the "physical" nucleon in the ground state. This will have the following features:

$$\begin{Bmatrix} P \\ N \end{Bmatrix}_{m=\pm 1/2} = \chi_{t_3} \psi_m F(r), \tag{12}$$

where χ_{t_3} represents the appropriate $t = \frac{1}{2}$ charge combination of a Dirac nucleon (p, n) and a pion (π^+, π^0, π^-)

$$\chi_{\pm 1/2} = \pm\sqrt{\frac{1}{3}} \begin{Bmatrix} p \\ n \end{Bmatrix} \pi^0 \mp \sqrt{\frac{2}{3}} \begin{Bmatrix} n\pi^+ \\ p\pi^- \end{Bmatrix}; \tag{12a}$$

ψ_m represents the $P_{1/2}$ angular momentum combination

$$\psi_{\pm 1/2} = \pm\sqrt{\frac{1}{3}} \begin{Bmatrix} \alpha \\ \beta \end{Bmatrix} Y_1^0(\theta_\pi, \varphi_\pi) \mp \sqrt{\frac{2}{3}} \begin{Bmatrix} \beta \\ \alpha \end{Bmatrix} Y_1^{\pm 1}(\theta_\pi, \varphi_\pi); \tag{12b}$$

and $F(r)$ is the spatial distribution of the pion, determined by the form of the pion-nucleon potential $V(r)$. A possibly reasonable choice for $F(r)$ is suggested by the solution of the Yukawa equation for a point nucleon (Section 1.1),

$$F_Y(r) = (1 + \kappa r) \frac{e^{-\kappa r}}{\kappa^2 r^2}, \tag{12c}$$

but other forms could be more appropriate for a phenomenological description of the observed physical nucleons.

For the $j = t = \frac{3}{2}$ isobar state, on the other hand, the appropriate wave functions are

$$\Delta_{t_3, m} = \chi'_{t_3} \psi'_m F'(r), \tag{13}$$

with

$$\begin{aligned} \chi'_{\pm 3/2} &= \begin{Bmatrix} p\pi^+ \\ n\pi^- \end{Bmatrix}, \\ \chi'_{\pm 1/2} &= \sqrt{\frac{2}{3}} \begin{Bmatrix} p \\ n \end{Bmatrix} \pi^0 + \sqrt{\frac{1}{3}} \begin{Bmatrix} n\pi^+ \\ p\pi^- \end{Bmatrix}, \end{aligned} \tag{13a}$$

and

$$\begin{aligned} \psi'_{\pm 3/2} &= \begin{Bmatrix} \alpha \\ \beta \end{Bmatrix} Y_1^{\pm 1}, \\ \psi'_{\pm 1/2} &= \sqrt{\frac{2}{3}} \begin{Bmatrix} \alpha \\ \beta \end{Bmatrix} Y_1^0 + \sqrt{\frac{1}{3}} \begin{Bmatrix} \beta \\ \alpha \end{Bmatrix} Y_1^{\pm 1}. \end{aligned} \tag{13b}$$

---

[15] B. T. Feld, *Ann. Phys.* (New York), *4:* 189 (1958).

These wave functions will be employed in Chapter 13 in computing some of the properties of nucleons and of the (3, 3) isobar on the basis of the atomic model.

In principle, the higher nucleonic excited states can be constructed by the addition of mesons to the nucleonic atom. If one could neglect the meson-meson forces, the problem would be straightforward: the lowest n-meson state would be one in which all n-mesons tend as much as possible to be in the $j=\frac{1}{2}$, $t=\frac{1}{2}$ state with respect to the nucleon, a situation that is permitted by the Bose–Einstein statistics obeyed by the pions. Hence, we would have a succession of even-parity ground and excited states corresponding to 1, 2, 3, . . . mesonic atoms.

However, the effects of the meson-meson forces not only will complicate the computations of multimesonic atomic energy levels, but also could lead to the binding of mesons in other than P states. The binding of an odd number of mesons in the S state will give rise to odd-parity nucleonic states, and could account for the relatively low-lying $\frac{3}{2}^-$ and $\frac{1}{2}^-$ nucleon isobars (Table 2.1).

In view of the obvious complexity of the multimeson problem,[16] and of the crudity of the model, we shall not attempt any detailed calculation of pionic atoms with $n > 1$.

A final remark concerning the applicability of the model: All of the nucleon isobars tend to decay through the emission of pions. However, this should not be interpreted to mean that a state B, which decays to the state A via $B \to A + \pi$, must necessarily be represented in the model as containing one pion more than A. Although the model treats the mesons in the atomic system as real particles, the pion remains the quantum of the Yukawa field and, as such, still can be created and annihilated by the nucleonic source. Thus, as far as pion absorptions and decays are concerned, the Yukawa process still can and often must be evoked in the atomic model. This is especially important to recall in considering the decay or production of the (3, 3) isobar, $\Delta \rightleftharpoons \mathfrak{N} + \pi$, in which, on the basis of the atomic model, the rearrangement of the single-pion orbit (nucleon spin-flip) is accompanied by the creation or annihilation of a Yukawa meson.

12.3.2 The Goldhaber Model of the Hyperons

If, instead of using pions, one uses the antikaon doublet ($\overline{K^0}$, K^-) to construct nucleonic atoms, one obtains the hyperons. This is the model of Goldhaber.[17]

The $\overline{K}$, having the same spin 0^- as the pion, must also be bound to the nucleon in a $P_{1/2}$ state, since the Λ, Σ, and Ξ have spin $\frac{1}{2}^+$. However, in the hyperon case, both isotopic-spin states are bound, $t=0$ for the Λ^0 and $t=1$ for the Σ, with the Λ^0 being bound somewhat more strongly. Note also that no $\mathfrak{N}$–K (strangeness +1) bound states are observed. These conditions suggest an interaction Hamiltonian of the form

$$H_{K-\mathfrak{N}} = f_K\{A\,\delta(j, \tfrac{1}{2}^+) - B(\mathbf{t}_{\mathfrak{N}} \cdot \mathbf{t}_K)\}\mathcal{Y}\,V_K(r), \tag{14}$$

[16] G. Costa and B. T. Feld, *Ann. Phys.* (New York), *9:* 354 (1960).
[17] M. Goldhaber, *Phys. Rev., 101:* 437 (1953).

with $A > B > 0$, $V_K(r) > 0$. The strangeness factor or hypercharge ($\mathcal{Y} = S = +1$ for K, -1 for $\bar{K}$, and 0 for π), together with the choice of positive signs for all the constants, assures that the binding energy $(-\langle H_{\bar{K}-\mathfrak{N}}\rangle)$ is positive for the $\mathfrak{N}$–$\bar{K}$ system (bound) and negative for the $\mathfrak{N}$–K (unbound).

The eigenstates, $\psi_{j,t}(r)$ of Equation (14), have $j = \frac{1}{2}^+$, $t = 1$, or 0 ($t_{\mathfrak{N}} = t_K = \frac{1}{2}$), with $\langle \mathbf{t}_{\mathfrak{N}} \cdot \mathbf{t}_K \rangle = \frac{1}{4}$ or $-\frac{3}{4}$, respectively [see Section 12.1, Equation (3c)]; the charge combinations corresponding to the two bound eigenstates are, for the Λ^0 ($t = 0$),

$$\chi_{\Lambda^0} = \sqrt{\tfrac{1}{2}}\,(pK^- - n\overline{K^0}), \tag{14a}$$

and, for the Σ ($t = 1$),

$$\begin{aligned} \chi_{\Sigma^+} &= p\overline{K^0}, \\ \chi_{\Sigma^0} &= \sqrt{\tfrac{1}{2}}\,(pK^- + n\overline{K^0}), \\ \chi_{\Sigma^-} &= nK^-; \end{aligned} \tag{14b}$$

and the respective energies (masses) are

$$M(\Lambda^0) = M_0 - (\bar{A} + \tfrac{3}{4}\bar{B}), \tag{14a$'$}$$

$$M(\Sigma) = M_0 - (\bar{A} - \tfrac{1}{4}\bar{B}). \tag{14b$'$}$$

[$M_0 = M_{\mathfrak{N}} + M_K = 1435$ MeV; $\bar{A}(\bar{B})$ is the mean interaction energy $f_K A(B) \cdot \int \psi^* V(r)\, \psi\, d^3\mathbf{r}$.] Using the observed masses, we deduce $\bar{A} = 261$ MeV, $\bar{B} = 77.6$ MeV.

The cascade hyperon doublet $\Xi^{0,-}$, having $S = -2$, requires two $\bar{K}$. However, the form of the $\mathfrak{N}$–$2\bar{K}$ atomic wave function depends in detail on the state in which the two $\bar{K}$ are bound, which, in turn, depends on the $\bar{K}$–$\bar{K}$ interaction. We may try two different assumptions:

1. The two $\bar{K}$, both in $l = 1$ states with respect to the nucleon, have $L = 1$ and are therefore in an odd space configuration. Since the two $\bar{K}$ are bosons, this requires the odd charge state, i.e., $t = 0$,

$$\chi_0(2\bar{K}) = \sqrt{\tfrac{1}{2}}\,(\overline{K_1^0}K_2^- - K_1^-\overline{K_2^0}), \tag{15a}$$

giving for the charge states of the Ξ's,

$$\chi(\Xi^{0,-}) = \begin{Bmatrix} p \\ n \end{Bmatrix} \chi_0(2\bar{K}), \tag{15a$'$}$$

and for the energy (mass) of the cascade [using Equation (14) with $\mathbf{t}_{2\bar{K}} = \mathbf{t}_{K_1} + \mathbf{t}_{K_2} = 0$],

$$M^{(0)}(\Xi) = M_{\mathfrak{N}} + 2M_K - 2\bar{A}. \tag{15b}$$

Equations (14a′), (14b′), and (15b) lead to a simple relationship between the nucleon and hyperon masses,

$$\underset{(1128.5\text{ MeV})}{\frac{M(\mathfrak{N}) + M(\Xi)}{2}} = \underset{(1173.8\text{ MeV})}{\frac{3M(\Sigma) + M(\Lambda)}{4}}, \tag{15c}$$

which, as may be seen from the figures in parentheses, is not very well satisfied. [Equation (15b), using $\overline{A}=261$ MeV, predicts $M(\Xi)=1409$ MeV, which is ~ 90 MeV too large.]

2. If the $2\overline{K}$ are in identical $l=1$ states, their space configuration may be even (say, $L=0$) and the charge configuration must then also be even, i.e., $t=1$,

$$\begin{aligned} \chi_1^1(2\overline{K}) &= \overline{K}_1^0\overline{K}_2^0, \\ \chi_1^0 &= \sqrt{\tfrac{1}{2}}\,(\overline{K}_1^0K_2^- + K_1^-\overline{K}_2^0), \\ \chi_1^{-1} &= K_1^-K_2^-, \end{aligned} \tag{16a}$$

leading to the Ξ charge combinations,

$$\chi(\Xi^{0,-}) = \pm\sqrt{\frac{1}{3}}\begin{Bmatrix} p \\ n \end{Bmatrix}\chi_1^0\,(2\overline{K}) \mp \sqrt{\frac{2}{3}}\begin{Bmatrix} n \\ p \end{Bmatrix}\chi_1^{\pm 1}\,(2\overline{K}). \tag{16b}$$

In this case, application of Equation (14) with $t_{2\overline{K}}=1$, $t_{\mathfrak{N}+2\overline{K}}=\frac{1}{2}$, gives

$$M^{(1)}(\Xi) = M_{\mathfrak{N}} + 2M_K - 2\overline{A} - \overline{B} \tag{16c}$$

and leads to the interesting relationship

$$\underset{(1128.5\text{ MeV})}{\frac{M(\mathfrak{N})+M(\Xi)}{2}} = \underset{(1135.0\text{ MeV})}{\frac{3M(\Lambda)+M(\Sigma)}{4}}, \tag{16d}$$

which is *remarkably* well satisfied by the masses. However, corresponding to the same space and isospin $2\overline{K}$ combinations, there would be another $2\overline{K}$ atom with $t=\frac{3}{2}$, whose mass,

$$M^{(1)}(\Xi^*) = M_{\mathfrak{N}} + 2M_K - 2\overline{A} + \tfrac{1}{2}\overline{B}, \tag{16e}$$

is greater than that of the Ξ by only $3\overline{B}/2 \cong 116$ MeV, not quite (but almost) large enough to decay rapidly via the process $\Xi^* \rightarrow \Xi + \pi$. However, no $t=\frac{3}{2}$, Ξ-like hyperon has been observed — neither rapidly nor slowly decaying.

12.3.3 Frisch's Symmetrical Model

There is no a priori reason for using the nucleon, rather than one of the other spin $\frac{1}{2}$ baryons, as the core of the mesonic atoms. In fact, as we have seen in the preceding sections, this assumption introduces a rather disagreeable asymmetry in the treatment of the Λ, Σ, and the Ξ hyperons. A much more symmetrical scheme, explored by Frisch,[18] uses the Λ^0 hyperon as the atomic core. In this case, the nucleon and cascade are treated quite symmetrically,

$$\mathfrak{N} = \Lambda K, \tag{17a}$$

$$\Xi = \Lambda\overline{K}, \tag{17b}$$

[18] D. H. Frisch, *Nuovo Cimento, 15:* 757 (1960).

as doublets resulting from the combination of the $t=0$ core with the K and $\overline{K}$ doublets. The Σ hyperon, in this case, is simply a combination of the core and a pion,

$$\Sigma = \Lambda\pi. \tag{18}$$

The Λ-kaon and Λ-pion interactions may be assumed to have the form

$$H_{\Lambda-K,\pi} = -A'_{K,\pi}(r)\ \delta(j=\tfrac{1}{2}^{+}) - \mathcal{Y} B'(r), \tag{19}$$

in which the second term, proportional to the meson strangeness or hypercharge, $\mathcal{Y}$, is required to account for the Ξ–N mass difference. On this assumption, the hyperon masses are

$$M(\Sigma) = M_\Lambda + M_\pi - \overline{A}'_\pi, \tag{19a}$$

$$M(\mathfrak{N}) = M_\Lambda + M_K - \overline{A}'_K - \overline{B}', \tag{19b}$$

$$M(\Xi) = M_\Lambda + M_K - \overline{A}'_K + \overline{B}'. \tag{19c}$$

With three masses and three arbitrary constants, the most we can do is determine the values of the constants: $\overline{A}'_\pi = 60.4$ MeV, $\overline{A}'_K = 482.8$ MeV, $\overline{B}' = 189.5$ MeV.

PROBLEMS

1. Consider the two-pion states in the pion atomic model of the nucleons. Assume a π–π interaction which favors the value $j = 1^-$ for the internal angular momentum of the two pions (i.e., the ρ-meson).
   (a) What is the consequent value of the isospin of the two-pion system? What are the corresponding charge eigenstates?
   (b) Assuming an effective interaction proportional to $\mathbf{t}_{\mathfrak{N}} \cdot \mathbf{t}_\pi$, what are the resulting charge eigenstates of the nucleonic ($\mathfrak{N} + 2\pi$) system?
   (c) Putting each of the pions into an $l = 1$, $j = \frac{1}{2}$ state with respect to the nucleon (assumed of infinite mass — i.e., fixed in space), compute the amplitudes corresponding to the internal angular momentum $L = 1$ for the two-pion system in the various possible states of total angular momentum $\frac{1}{2} \leq j \leq \frac{5}{2}$. *Hint:* Use the addition theorem of spherical harmonics (Appendix 1).
2. Discuss the 2π, $2K$, $K\overline{K}$, and $2\overline{K}$ states of Frisch's symmetrical atomic model.

12.4 Dynamical Symmetries: the Doublet Model of Schwinger

The different models discussed in the preceding sections are suggested by different views of the form of the basic interactions among the hadrons; in essence, in choosing certain particles as being more basic than others, we are suggesting certain priorities among the various possible fields and their interactions.

However, perhaps the most striking aspect of the best-known groups of baryons and mesons is the symmetry among their members, an aspect that rather suggests the impossibility of choosing some among them as being more basic than others. This symmetry is perhaps most strikingly illustrated in Table 12.3, in which the $\frac{1}{2}^+$ baryons and the 0^- mesons (or the 1^- mesons) are distributed according to the values of the baryon number B and hypercharge $\mathcal{Y} = (B + S)$.

Owing to the relationship between charge, hypercharge, and isospin,

$$Q = t_3 + \frac{\mathcal{Y}}{2}, \tag{20}$$

the particles in the first and third rows have odd half-integral isospin (doublets) while those with $\mathcal{Y} = 0$ have integral isospin (singlets and triplets). One is tempted to seek models in which this basic symmetry is either assumed or deduced.

It was Schwinger who first suggested that the observed symmetries among the hadrons should be regarded as the dynamical result of the symmetrical form of the basic interactions between them.[19] Although the particular symmetry suggested by Schwinger — the doublet symmetry — turns out not to lead to the actual relationships observed among the hadrons, the scheme is worth reviewing as the early and elegant prototype of the more successful symmetry schemes of more recent origin.

Table 12.3 Symmetrical Plot of Baryons and Mesons

$\mathcal{Y}$ \ B	1	0	−1
1	$\mathfrak{N}$	$K(K^*)$	$\overline{\Xi}$
0	Σ, Λ	$\pi, \eta\ (\rho, \omega)$	$\overline{\Sigma}, \overline{\Lambda}$
−1	Ξ	$\overline{K}(\overline{K^*})$	$\overline{\mathfrak{N}}$

12.4.1 "Global" Pion Interaction

The doublet symmetry[20] follows from the assumption of a universal Yukawa interaction between pions and all baryons (or, rather, a basic baryon doublet capable of taking on different values of the hypercharge quantum number $\mathcal{Y}$). Consider a baryon doublet $B = \begin{pmatrix} b_1 \\ b_2 \end{pmatrix}$ subject to the fundamental Yukawa reaction

$$\begin{pmatrix} b_1 \\ b_2 \end{pmatrix} \rightleftharpoons \pm \begin{pmatrix} b_1 \\ b_2 \end{pmatrix} \pi^0 \mp \sqrt{2} \begin{pmatrix} b_2 \pi^+ \\ b_1 \pi^- \end{pmatrix}, \tag{21}$$

which may be abbreviated

$$B \rightleftharpoons \boldsymbol{\tau} \cdot \boldsymbol{\pi} B, \tag{21'}$$

[19] J. Schwinger, *Ann. Phys.* (New York), *2:* 407 (1957).

[20] There are two kinds of doublet symmetries: one based on the assumption of universality of the pion interactions, called "global" [M. Gell-Mann, *Phys. Rev.*, *106:* 1296 (1957)], and a second, called "cosmic," based on the universality of the kaon interactions [J. J. Sakurai, *Phys. Rev.*, *113:* 1679 (1959)]. We shall consider both, in the order mentioned.

with τ the Pauli spin matrices for isospin $\frac{1}{2}$

$$\tau_x = \begin{pmatrix} 0 & 1 \\ 1 & 0 \end{pmatrix}, \qquad \tau_y = \begin{pmatrix} 0 & -i \\ i & 0 \end{pmatrix}, \qquad \tau_z = \begin{pmatrix} 1 & 0 \\ 0 & -1 \end{pmatrix}, \tag{21a}$$

and π the pion creation operator, defined as

$$\begin{aligned} \pi^{\pm} &= \mp\tfrac{1}{2}(\pi_x \pm i\pi_y), \\ \pi^0 &= \pi_z . \end{aligned} \tag{21b}$$

Thus, the meson creation operator becomes

$$\boldsymbol{\tau} \cdot \boldsymbol{\pi} = \begin{pmatrix} \pi^0 & -\sqrt{2}\,\pi^+ \\ \sqrt{2}\,\pi^- & -\pi^0 \end{pmatrix}, \tag{21c}$$

which, when multiplying the baryon doublet vector B [Equation (21′)], reproduces the results of Equation (21).

Now, the interaction term in a Lagrangian representing the Yukawa reaction (21) has the form[21]

$$\mathcal{L}_i = \mathcal{G}_i B_i^{\dagger}\, \boldsymbol{\tau} \cdot \boldsymbol{\pi}\, B_i . \tag{22}$$

The "global" pion-baryon interaction follows on the assumption of a Lagrangian of the form

$$\mathcal{L}_\pi = \mathcal{G}_\pi \sum_{i=1}^{4} B_i^{\dagger}\, \boldsymbol{\tau} \cdot \boldsymbol{\pi}\, B_i , \tag{22a}$$

where the four global baryon doublets are

$$B_1 = \begin{pmatrix} P \\ N \end{pmatrix} \qquad \text{with } \mathcal{Y} = 1, \tag{22b}$$

$$B_2 = \begin{pmatrix} \Sigma^+ \\ Y^0 \end{pmatrix} \qquad \text{with } \mathcal{Y} = 0, \tag{22c}$$

$$B_3 = \begin{pmatrix} Z^0 \\ \Sigma^- \end{pmatrix} \qquad \text{with } \mathcal{Y} = 0, \tag{22d}$$

$$B_4 = \begin{pmatrix} \Xi^0 \\ \Xi^- \end{pmatrix} \qquad \text{with } \mathcal{Y} = -1. \tag{22e}$$

The neutral $\mathcal{Y} = 0$ states are combinations of the Σ^0 and Λ^0 baryons:

$$\begin{aligned} Y^0 &= \sqrt{\tfrac{1}{2}}\,(\Sigma^0 - \Lambda^0), \\ Z^0 &= \sqrt{\tfrac{1}{2}}\,(\Sigma^0 + \Lambda^0). \end{aligned} \tag{22f}$$

---

[21] We suppress the factor $\boldsymbol{\sigma} \cdot \boldsymbol{\nabla}$ which leads to the emission of pseudoscalar mesons in the $P_{1/2}$ state, and is henceforth to be understood as universally present in all baryon-pion and baryon-kaon interactions.

EXAMPLE

Demonstration of the global character of the pion-baryon interaction (22a): For the nucleons and the Ξ hyperons, Equation (22) yields immediately the expected Yukawa reactions

$$\mathfrak{N} \rightleftharpoons \boldsymbol{\tau} \cdot \boldsymbol{\pi}\, \mathfrak{N}, \tag{23a}$$

$$\Xi \rightleftharpoons \boldsymbol{\tau} \cdot \boldsymbol{\pi}\, \Xi, \tag{23b}$$

while Equation (22a) simply states that they have the same interaction strength (coupling constant $\mathcal{G}_\pi$). For the Σ and Λ, Equation (22a) implies the following:

$$\Sigma^+ \rightleftharpoons \pi^0\Sigma^+ - \sqrt{2}\,\pi^+ Y^0 = \pi^0\Sigma^+ - \pi^+\Sigma^0 + \pi^+\Lambda^0, \tag{23c}$$

$$\Sigma^- \rightleftharpoons -\pi^0\Sigma^- + \sqrt{2}\,\pi^- Z^0 = -\pi^0\Sigma^- + \pi^-\Sigma^0 + \pi^-\Lambda^0, \tag{23d}$$

$$\Sigma^0 - \Lambda^0 \rightleftharpoons -\pi^0(\Sigma^0 - \Lambda^0) + 2\pi^-\Sigma^+ = -\pi^0\Sigma^0 + 2\pi^-\Sigma^+ + \pi^0\Lambda^0, \tag{23e}$$

$$\Sigma^0 + \Lambda^0 \rightleftharpoons \pi^0(\Sigma^0 + \Lambda^0) - 2\pi^+\Sigma^- = \pi^0\Sigma^0 - 2\pi^+\Sigma^- + \pi^0\Lambda^0. \tag{23f}$$

Combining (23e) and (23f), we obtain

$$\Sigma^0 \rightleftharpoons \pi^-\Sigma^+ - \pi^+\Sigma^- + \pi^0\Lambda^0, \tag{23e$'$}$$

$$\Lambda^0 \rightleftharpoons \pi^0\Sigma^0 - \pi^-\Sigma^+ - \pi^+\Sigma^-. \tag{23f$'$}$$

Accordingly, we may write, in terms of the observed Σ triplet and Λ^0 singlet,

$$\begin{pmatrix} \Sigma^+ \\ \Sigma^0 \\ \Sigma^- \end{pmatrix} \rightleftharpoons \begin{pmatrix} \pi^0 & -\pi^+ & 0 \\ \pi^- & 0 & -\pi^+ \\ 0 & \pi^- & -\pi^0 \end{pmatrix} \begin{pmatrix} \Sigma^+ \\ \Sigma^0 \\ \Sigma^- \end{pmatrix} + \Lambda^0 \begin{pmatrix} \pi^+ \\ \pi^0 \\ \pi^- \end{pmatrix},$$

$$\boldsymbol{\Sigma} \rightleftharpoons (\mathbf{t} \cdot \boldsymbol{\pi})\,\boldsymbol{\Sigma} + \boldsymbol{\pi}\,\Lambda^0, \tag{24a}$$

and

$$\Lambda^0 \rightleftharpoons (-\pi^- \;\; \pi^0 \;\; -\pi^+) \begin{pmatrix} \Sigma^+ \\ \Sigma^0 \\ \Sigma^- \end{pmatrix} = \boldsymbol{\pi}^* \cdot \boldsymbol{\Sigma}. \tag{24b}$$

We have thus demonstrated that the global interaction (22a) is equivalent to a universal pion-hyperon coupling between the pions and the actual Σ triplet and Λ^0 singlet, with the common coupling constant $\mathcal{G}_\pi$.

For the K-baryon interaction not to destroy the doublet symmetry imposed by the universal π–B interaction, it must have a very special form. In particular, in normal charge-independent Yukawa reactions such as

$$\begin{aligned} P &\rightleftharpoons a(K^+\Sigma^0 - \sqrt{2}\,K^0\Sigma^+) + bK^+\Lambda^0, \\ N &\rightleftharpoons a(-K^0\Sigma^0 + \sqrt{2}\,K^+\Sigma^-) + bK^0\Lambda^0, \end{aligned} \tag{25a}$$

the B_2 and B_3 doublets are inextricably mixed and such an interaction would therefore destroy the doublet symmetry. Since the global doublets are, in fact, not found in nature, such interactions could in fact exist; but if the global symmetry scheme is to have any physical meaning, the symmetry-violating interactions must be weaker than the universal pion interaction, Equation (22a).

However, before considering the effects of the symmetry-breaking kaon interactions, we should note that there is one form of K–B interaction that could be present without disturbing the global doublet scheme.[22] Such an interaction would have a Lagrangian of the form

$$\mathcal{L}_K = \sqrt{2}\,\mathcal{G}_K\{B_1^\dagger K^0 B_2 + B_1^\dagger K^+ B_3 + B_2^\dagger K^+ B_4 + B_3^\dagger K^0 B_4 + \text{hermitian conjugates}\}. \tag{26}$$

In effect, this interaction treats the K^0 and K^+ (or $\overline{K^0}$ and K^-) as unconnected particles, rather than as members of isospin doublets, and would result in a Yukawa reaction of the form

$$\begin{aligned} P &\rightleftharpoons \sqrt{2}\,K^0\Sigma^+ + K^+\Sigma^0 + K^+\Lambda^0, \\ N &\rightleftharpoons \sqrt{2}\,K^+\Sigma^- + K^0\Sigma^0 - K^0\Lambda^0, \end{aligned} \tag{25b}$$

which cannot be obtained from (25a) because of the relative signs of the $K\Sigma$ terms. However, a more important consequence of (26) is that it would prohibit reactions of the form

$$\begin{aligned} \pi^+ + P &\rightarrow K^+ + \Sigma^+, \\ K^- + P &\rightarrow \overline{K^0} + N, \end{aligned} \tag{25c}$$

since the necessary Yukawa processes corresponding to reactions (25c) are not present in the interaction Lagrangian (26). Yet such reactions are in fact observed and, unfortunately for the global symmetry scheme, have strengths quite comparable to reactions allowed by (26).

So far, the interactions postulated, Equations (22a) and (26), have treated all the baryons in a completely symmetrical fashion, and would thus result in equal baryon masses (self-energies). It is necessary now to introduce a symmetry-breaking interaction that would have two effects: to split the baryon masses, and to separate the two $\mathcal{Y} = 0$ doublets, B_2 and B_3, into the observed Σ triplet and Λ singlet. This can be achieved as follows: a charge-independent π–B interaction which depends, however, on the value of the hypercharge quantum number,

$$\mathcal{L}'_\pi = \mathcal{G}'_\pi \sum_{i=1}^{4} \mathcal{Y}_i B_i^\dagger \boldsymbol{\tau}\cdot\boldsymbol{\pi} B_i, \tag{27a}$$

would result in $M(B_1) \neq M(B_4) \neq M(B_2) = M(B_3)$; a charge-independent K–B interaction which treats the Λ^0 and the Σ as isosinglet and isotriplet, respectively,

$$\mathcal{L}'_K = \mathcal{G}'_K\{N^\dagger(\Lambda + \boldsymbol{\tau}\cdot\boldsymbol{\Sigma})K + \Xi^\dagger(\Lambda + \boldsymbol{\tau}\cdot\boldsymbol{\Sigma})\overline{K} + \text{hermitian conjugates}\}, \tag{27b}$$

where $K = \begin{pmatrix} K^+ \\ K^0 \end{pmatrix}$, $\overline{K} = \begin{pmatrix} \overline{K^0} \\ K^- \end{pmatrix}$, and

[22] A. Pais, *Phys. Rev., 110:* 574 (1958); *Phys. Rev., 112:* 624 (1958).

$$\boldsymbol{\tau} \cdot \boldsymbol{\Sigma} = \begin{pmatrix} \Sigma^0 & -\sqrt{2}\,\Sigma^+ \\ \sqrt{2}\,\Sigma^- & -\Sigma^0 \end{pmatrix}, \tag{27c}$$

separates the singlet from the triplet.

The effect of (27a) and (27b) is to yield a mass spectrum of the form[23]

$$M = M_0 + A\mathcal{Y} + B(\mathbf{t}_{\mathfrak{N}} \cdot \mathbf{t}_K)\,\delta(\mathcal{Y} = 0), \tag{28}$$

resulting in the mass equation

$$\frac{M(\mathfrak{N}) + M(\Xi)}{2} = \frac{3M(\Sigma) + M(\Lambda)}{4}, \tag{28a}$$

$$(1128.5 \text{ MeV}) \quad (1173.8 \text{ MeV})$$

which, as noted in Section 12.3.2, is in rather poor agreement with the observed mass spectrum.

12.4.2 "Cosmic" Kaon Interaction

An alternative approach would be to assume that the dominant interaction is the B–K interaction, and that the symmetry is broken by the pions. In this case,[24] the Lagrangian (27b) would describe the universal K–B interaction, and again this could be written as a universal interaction among four baryon doublets, B_i',

$$\mathcal{L}_K' = -\sqrt{2}\,\mathcal{G}_K'\{B_1'^{\dagger}(\boldsymbol{\tau} \cdot \tilde{\mathbf{K}})B_2' + B_4'^{\dagger}(\boldsymbol{\tau} \cdot \tilde{\mathbf{K}})B_3' + \text{hermitian conjugates}\}, \tag{29}$$

where

$$B_1' = \begin{pmatrix} P \\ \Xi^0 \end{pmatrix}, \tag{29a}$$

$$B_2' = \begin{pmatrix} \Sigma^+ \\ Z^0 \end{pmatrix}, \tag{29b}$$

$$B_3' = \begin{pmatrix} Y^0 \\ \Sigma^- \end{pmatrix}, \tag{29c}$$

$$B_4' = \begin{pmatrix} N \\ \Xi^- \end{pmatrix}, \tag{29d}$$

and

$$\boldsymbol{\tau} \cdot \tilde{\mathbf{K}} = \begin{pmatrix} K^0 & -K^+ \\ K^- & -\overline{K^0} \end{pmatrix}. \tag{29e}$$

---

[23] J. Schwinger, *Ann. Phys.* (New York), *2:* 407 (1957).

[24] The demonstration of the equivalence of Equations (27b) and (29) follows along the same lines as the previous demonstration of the equivalence of Equations (22) and (24). It is left as an exercise for the reader.

To preserve the cosmic symmetry, the pion interaction terms would have to be of the form $B_i'^{\dagger} \pi^0 B_i'$, $B_1'^{\dagger} \pi^+ B_4'$, $B_2'^{\dagger} \pi^+ B_3'$, which would be inconsistent with treating the pion as an isotriplet. Introduction of charge-independent symmetry-breaking terms of the form of Equations (23) would then lead to the same form of mass splitting as Equation (28a), and to a redistribution of the baryons into the observed N, Ξ, Σ, Λ multiplets.

The problems encountered in the universal doublet symmetry schemes, described above, stem from the magnitude of the symmetry-breaking interactions required to account for the observed mass splittings, and especially from the observed violations, involving meson production and absorption processes, of the selection rules which follow from the basic symmetry. If, as appears to be necessary, the symmetry-breaking terms are of roughly the same strength as the symmetry-conserving terms in the Lagrangian, then the original symmetry loses all but pedagogic meaning. Nevertheless, these schemes serve as an illuminating demonstration of an approach that attempts to describe multiplets of similar hadrons in terms of representations of corresponding mathematical symmetry groups, an approach that has proved to be extremely fruitful. The problem becomes one of discovering the appropriate groups for representing the observed hadrons.

PROBLEM

Discuss the symmetry properties of the mesons, assumed to be bound $B_i\overline{B}_j$ states, on the basis of the doublet symmetry schemes and possible symmetry-breaking interactions.

13

Computation of Static Hadron Properties

The test of a model is its ability to reproduce the observed hadron characteristics. Among the hadron properties of interest, the most obvious is the mass spectrum of related multiplets, which is in the nature of a "fine structure" in the spectrum of similar particles (i.e., the spin $\frac{1}{2}^+$ baryons, 0^- or 1^- mesons, and so on). We have seen in Chapter 12 how different models lead to different predictions for the baryon and meson mass spectra and, in fact, we have found some of the models lacking in this respect. For the baryon spectrum, we have noted that the relationship

$$\frac{M(\mathcal{N}) + M(\Xi)}{2} = \frac{3M(\Lambda) + M(\Sigma)}{4},$$

so well satisfied by the observed masses, is predicted by the Goldhaber model. It is most interesting to note, and could hardly be coincidental, that the same mass formula above, with the substitution $N \to K$, $\Xi \to \overline{K}$, $\Lambda^0 \to \eta^0$, $\Sigma \to \pi$ (i.e., same values of the isospin and $\mathcal{Y}$), holds for the pseudoscalar mesons, although the agreement is much better if we use the values of the $(\text{mass})^2$ of the mesons. For the 1^- mesons, of which there are nine, the situation is somewhat different although, as we have seen, the F–Y–S model provides the possibility of describing the mass spectra in both instances (Section 12.2.1).

However, other properties of the hadrons serve equally well to test the adequacy of the models under consideration. We give some examples of such computations in this chapter.

13.1 Mass Splittings within Multiplets: Hyperfine Structure of Mass Spectra [1]

In all models considered, the strong interaction forces are charge independent, and, consequently, the members of a given isospin multiplet, differing only in their values of t_3, have the same mass. However, there are weaker forces among the elementary particles that are charge dependent — in particular, the electromagnetic forces — and these give rise to additional interaction energies which, differing from member to member of a given isospin multiplet, result in a hyperfine structure of the mass spectra of multiplets.

Table 13.1 summarizes the known values of the hyperfine mass differences among mesons and baryons. It should be emphasized that the measurement of mass differences among highly unstable particles is exceedingly difficult, owing to the large natural widths of the particle masses, and subject to large systematic errors that are not always reflected in the uncertainties quoted in the table.

Nevertheless, a number of interesting regularities that are worthy of comment

---

[1] Although we have adopted the nomenclature of atomic spectroscopy, the origins of the level energies and their fine and hyperfine structure are, of course, quite different for the hadrons than for atoms. In the atomic case, the level energies and their splittings are all of electromagnetic origin: the level energies are electrostatic in origin, being typically

$$E \approx \frac{e^2}{r_0},$$

with r_0, the Bohr radius,

$$r_0 = \frac{\hbar^2}{me^2} = \left(\frac{\hbar}{mc}\right)\left(\frac{\hbar c}{e^2}\right) = 137\left(\frac{\hbar}{mc}\right) \approx \frac{1}{2} \times 10^{-8}\text{ cm},$$

giving

$$E \approx \left(\frac{e^2}{\hbar c}\right)^2 mc^2 = (137)^{-2}\left(\frac{1}{2}\text{ MeV}\right) \approx 25\text{ eV}.$$

The atomic fine structure arises from a magnetic spin-orbit interaction,

$$E_1 \approx \frac{\mu_0\mu_s}{r_0^3} \approx \left(\frac{e^2}{r_0}\right)\left(\frac{e^2}{\hbar c}\right)^2 \approx 10^{-3}\text{ eV},$$

since

$$\mu_0 \sim \mu_s \sim \frac{e\hbar}{mc},$$

while the atomic hyperfine structure arises from a magnetic interaction between the nuclear and electron magnetic dipole moments

$$E_2 \approx \frac{\mu_{\mathfrak{N}}\mu_s}{r_0^3} \approx \left(\frac{2m}{M}\right)E_1 \approx 10^{-6}\text{ eV}.$$

For the hadronic case, on the other hand, the typical level energies are

$$E \approx Mc^2 \approx 1\text{ GeV}.$$

The level splittings (fine structure) arise from the different orientations of the meson (pion) field

$$E_1 \approx \mu c^2 \approx \left(\frac{\mu}{M}\right)E \approx 137\text{ MeV},$$

while the hyperfine splittings, assumed electromagnetic in origin, are typically

$$\frac{e^2}{R} \approx \frac{e^2}{(\hbar/\mu c)} = \left(\frac{e^2}{\hbar c}\right)\mu c^2 \approx 1\text{ MeV}.$$

Table 13.1 Hyperfine Mass Splittings[a]

Difference	δ (MeV)
Mesons	
$\pi^{\pm}-\pi^0$	4.604 ± 0.004
$K^{\pm}-K^0$	-3.94 ± 0.13
$\rho^{\pm}-\rho^0$	-3 ± 9
$K^{*\pm}-K^{*0}$	-6.3 ± 4.1
Baryons with spin $\frac{1}{2}^+$	
$N-P$	1.2933 ± 0.0001
$\Sigma^--\Sigma^+$	8.00 ± 0.18
$\Sigma^--\Sigma^0$	4.87 ± 0.07
$\Sigma^0-\Sigma^+$	3.13 ± 0.19[b]
$\Xi^--\Xi^0$	6.6 ± 0.7
Baryons with spin $\frac{3}{2}^+$[c]	
$\Delta^--\Delta^{++}$	7.9 ± 6.8
$\Delta^0-\Delta^{++}$	0.45 ± 0.85
$\Delta^--\Delta^0$	7.4 ± 6.9[b]
${}_\Delta Y^- - {}_\Delta Y^+$	5.8 ± 3.1
${}_\Delta \Xi^- - {}_\Delta \Xi^0$	4.9 ± 2.2

[a] See Table 2.1.
[b] This is not an independent measurement, but deduced from the preceding two.
[c] We use the following notation: Δ for $N^*(1236)$, ${}_\Delta Y$ for $Y_1^*(1385)$, ${}_\Delta\Xi$ for $\Xi^*(1530)$. These have, respectively, $t = \frac{3}{2}$, 1, and $\frac{1}{2}$.

appear. Among the mesons, note the similarity of mass differences for corresponding multiplets of the 0^- and 1^- mesons. However, note the reversal in sign of the mass difference between π's and K's! Among the baryons, both of spin $\frac{1}{2}^+$ and spin $\frac{3}{2}^+$, note the monotonic increase of mass, in every multiplet, in going from the most positively to the most negatively charged member.

The correct treatment of such electromagnetic self-energies is an extremely complicated field-theoretical problem,[2] involving the summation of contributions from all possible virtual photon emission and reabsorption (Compton) processes from all possible virtual intermediate states (the blob in Figure 13.1) of the hadron in question, as illustrated in the associated Feynman diagram, Figure 13.1. We shall not attempt to reproduce these computations here. Rather, we present some qualitative, nonrelativistic estimates, using our models in perhaps too literal a sense; these estimates will, however, be useful in indicating the sources of such hyperfine mass splittings and in understanding the magnitudes of the splittings involved.

Hyperfine mass effects can be considered as arising from three causes:

[2] R. P. Feynman and G. Speisman, *Phys. Rev., 94:* 500 (1954); A. Peterman, *Helv. Phys. Acta, 27:* 441 (1954); recently, there has been some progress in the solution of this problem, resulting from the application of more sophisticated dispersion techniques; see W. N. Cottingham, *Ann. Phys.* (New York), *25:* 424 (1963) and H. Harari, *Phys. Rev. Letters, 17:* 1303 (1966). For a summary of recent progress, see S. D. Drell, *Comments on Nuclear and Particle Physics, 1:* 94 (1967).

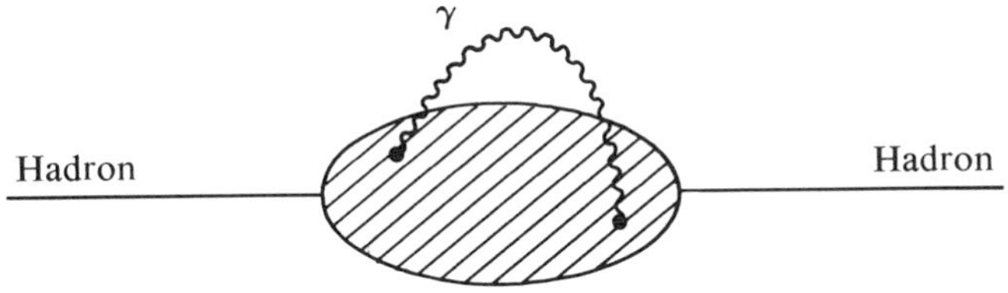

Figure 13.1 Feynman diagram for the electromagnetic self-energy of a hadron.

1. *Intrinsic mass differences* among the elementary constituents. Thus, for example, in models that use the p–n doublet as elementary constituents, we assume an intrinsic mass difference

$$\delta_1(p-n) = M(p) - M(n); \tag{1}$$

δ_1 is itself presumably of electromagnetic origin and not necessarily equal to the mass difference between the physical proton and neutron. In fact, if we consider the nucleon core in atomic models to be the "unclothed" Dirac proton and neutron, we would expect the difference

$$\delta_1(p-n) \approx \frac{e^2}{R_p} \approx \frac{e^2}{(\hbar/M_p c)} = \frac{e^2}{\hbar c} M_p c^2 \doteq \frac{938}{137} = 6.8 \text{ MeV}, \tag{1a}$$

which is simply the energy in the electric field of the Dirac proton, and both considerably larger than and opposite in sign to the physical P–N mass difference.

However, in models such as the F–Y–S model it is not obvious whether we should adopt the physical or the Dirac nucleons as the elementary constituents.[3]

For the mesons, the most reasonable assumption is to use the values in Table 13.1, although we might hope to understand these on the basis of the F–Y–S model.

2. *Electrostatic interaction energy* between the elementary constituents. For a model involving n constituents, this mass shift is

$$\delta_2 = \frac{1}{2} \sum_{i \neq j = 1}^{n} Q_i Q_j \left\langle \frac{1}{r_{ij}} \right\rangle. \tag{2}$$

3. *Magnetic interaction energy:* In the models under consideration we shall consider two possible forms of magnetic self-energy, in strict analogy to the magnetic interactions that account for the atomic fine and hyperfine level splittings:[4]

(a) Particles with spins s_i (and magnetic dipole moments μ_i) bound in an S state. For this case, the Fermi–Segre formula is applicable:

$$\delta_3^{(S)}(i, j) = -\frac{8\pi}{3} \left(\frac{\mu_i}{s_i}\right) \left(\frac{\mu_j}{s_j}\right) |\psi_{i,j}(0)|^2 \, \mathbf{s}_i \cdot \mathbf{s}_j \,, \tag{3a}$$

---

[3] The Λ–$\mathfrak{N}$ mass difference Δ, assumed in our discussion of the F–Y–S model (Section 12.2.1) to account for the meson mass fine structure, does not enter into the hyperfine structure.

[4] See H. Kopfermann, *Kernmomente* (2d ed.), Akad. Verlagsges., Frankfort/Main (1956).

in which $\psi_{i,j}(0)$ is the value of the wave function for $r_{ij}=0$. Taking, for example, $\psi(r) \propto e^{-\kappa r}/r$ gives $|\psi(0)|^2 = \kappa^3/2\pi$, approximately the inverse of the interaction volume for an interaction range, $R=\kappa^{-1}$. Equation (3a) has its origin in the magnetic dipole-dipole interaction ($\propto \boldsymbol{\mu}_i \cdot \boldsymbol{\mu}_j/r_{ij}^3$) for particles in a relative S state which classically averages out to zero as long as the two dipoles have a finite separation, owing to the isotropic distribution of the S-state wave function. However, the dipole-dipole interaction energy has a pole at $r_{ij}=0$ which gives rise, on integration over the wave function, to a term $\propto \delta(r_{ij}=0)$; this leads to the $|\psi_{i,j}(0)|^2$ dependence of $\delta_3^{(S)}$.

(b) Magnetic spin-orbit interaction for charged particle orbits with $l>0$, given by the well-known expression

$$\delta_3^{(l)} = -\left(\frac{\mu_s}{s}\right)(\mu_l)\left\langle\frac{1}{r^3}\right\rangle(\mathbf{l}\cdot\mathbf{s}), \tag{3b}$$

with $\mu_l = e\hbar/2mc$ being the orbital magnetic g-factor corresponding to a particle of mass m, charge e. In mesic atomic models the entire magnetic interaction energy comes from (3b), which may be derived from classical consideration of the energy of interaction ($-\boldsymbol{\mu}_s \cdot \mathbf{H}_l$) of the baryon magnetic dipole moment in the magnetic field $\mathbf{H}_l$ arising from the orbital motion to the meson.

In either case, the order of magnitude of the magnetic interaction is

$$|\delta_3(i,j)| \sim \frac{|e_i e_j|}{M_i M_j}\left\langle\frac{1}{r_{ij}^3}\right\rangle. \tag{3c}$$

Clearly, the relative importance of the magnetic and electrostatic terms depends on the dimensions of the compound system.[5] In particular, for systems with dimensions of the pion Compton wavelength, $R \sim m_\pi^{-1}$,

$$\frac{\delta_3}{\delta_2} \sim \frac{m_\pi^2}{M_i M_j}, \tag{4}$$

which ranges between $\frac{1}{50}$ for $M_i = M_j = M_P$ (F–Y–S model) and $\frac{1}{7}$ for $M_i = M_P$, $M_j = m_\pi$ (pion atomic model). For systems of dimension $R \sim M_P^{-1}$, on the other hand, the magnetic self-energy begins to exceed the electrostatic.

EXAMPLES

1. *Pions and kaons.* Treated as elementary particles, with no internal structure, charged pions carry an electric field and are therefore heavier than the π^0 by an amount

$$\delta_1(\pi^{\pm}-\pi^0) \sim \frac{e^2}{R_\pi}, \tag{5a}$$

which has the right sign, but requires $R_\pi \sim 1/5m_\pi$, a rather small size for an

[5] The magnetic terms can be further enhanced if the magnetic moments of the physical nucleons ($\mu_P = 2.79\mu_0$, $\mu_N = -1.91\mu_0$, with $\mu_0 = e\hbar/2M_Pc$) are taken instead of the Dirac values ($\mu_p = \mu_0$, $\mu_n = 0$).

elementary particle of mass m_π. But such a naive treatment would give the wrong sign for $\delta_1(K^\pm - K^0)$.

However, although the pion can be treated as an elementary particle, it is easy to demonstrate that such treatment is not reasonable for the K. Consider the relativistic 4-vector generalization of the Gell-Mann–Nishijima relationship

$$\mathcal{J}(r) = \mathcal{J}_1(r)\, t_3 + \mathcal{J}_2(r)\frac{\mathcal{Y}}{2}, \tag{6}$$

in which the charge, $Q = \int \rho(r)\, dV$, is obtained by integrating Equation (6) for the fourth component (charge density) over all space, with the condition

$$\int \rho_1(r)\, dV = \int \rho_2(r)\, dV = 1. \tag{6a}$$

In the case of the pion, $\mathcal{Y} = 0$, and we may choose a system in which $j_{1x} = j_{1y} = j_{1z} = 0$, so that the entire mass difference comes from the electric field of the charged pions. In any case $\mathcal{J}(r)_{\pi^0} = 0$, which is as elementary as can be.

For the kaons, on the other hand,

$$\mathcal{J}_{K^\pm} = \pm\tfrac{1}{2}[\mathcal{J}_1(r) + \mathcal{J}_2(r)], \tag{6b}$$

$$\mathcal{J}_{K^0, \overline{K^0}} = \mp\tfrac{1}{2}[\mathcal{J}_1(r) - \mathcal{J}_2(r)], \tag{6c}$$

which permits an arbitrary mass difference of either sign, depending on the model. Thus, considering the F–Y–S model with Dirac baryons in the $^1S_0$ state, $K^+ = p\bar{\lambda}$, $K^0 = n\bar{\lambda}$, the entire mass difference comes from the intrinsic p–n difference

$$\delta(K^+ - K^0) = \delta_1(p-n) > 0, \tag{6d}$$

since the Dirac n and λ have neither charge nor magnetic moment. Assuming, however, physical baryons $K^+ = P\bar{\Lambda}$, $K^0 = N\bar{\Lambda}$, we have

$$\delta(K^+ - K^0) = \delta_1(P-N) + \delta_3^{(S)}(P-\bar{\Lambda}) - \delta_3^{(S)}(N-\bar{\Lambda}). \tag{6e}$$

The first term is already < 0, but only by 1.3 MeV, so the remainder of the difference (−2.6 MeV; see Table 13.1) must come from the magnetic terms given by Equation (3a). Since $\mu_P > 0$, $\mu_N < 0$, both magnetic terms in (6e) contribute in the same direction; a negative contribution requires $\mu_{\bar{\Lambda}} < 0$ or $\mu_\Lambda > 0$. Although lack of knowledge of the pion's dimensions prevents prediction of the magnitude of the magnetic contribution, the requirement that it be negative is already a serious blow to the F–Y–S model, since the observed Λ moment is negative.

2. *Nucleons and* Δ. At first glance, it may appear strange that the neutron is heavier than the proton, the latter being charged; but the pion atomic model provides some indication of how such a result could come about. For the evaluation of the various effects, we recall that this model adopts as the charge states of the physical proton and neutron

$$\begin{Bmatrix} P \\ N \end{Bmatrix} = \pm \sqrt{\frac{1}{3}} \begin{Bmatrix} p \\ n \end{Bmatrix} \pi^0 \mp \sqrt{\frac{2}{3}} \begin{Bmatrix} n\pi^+ \\ p\pi^- \end{Bmatrix}, \tag{7a}$$

so that it exhibits the somewhat surprising feature that the physical $P(N)$ is composed of only $\frac{1}{3}$ of a Dirac $p(n)$ and $\frac{2}{3}$ of a Dirac $n(p)$, whence

$$\delta_1(P-N) = -\tfrac{1}{3}\delta_1(p-n) \approx -2.3 \text{ MeV}. \tag{7b}$$

To this we must add the electrostatic attraction [Equation (2)] in the $(p\pi^-)$ state of the N, which tends to make the N lighter than the P,

$$\delta_2(P-N) = \frac{2}{3} e^2 \left\langle \frac{1}{r} \right\rangle \approx \frac{2}{3} e^2 m_\pi = 0.7 \text{ MeV}, \tag{7c}$$

and the magnetic spin-orbit interaction of $p\pi^-$ in the $P_{1/2}$ state [Equation (3b)], again attractive but much smaller

$$\delta_3(P-N) \approx \frac{2}{3} \frac{e^2}{M_p m_\pi} (m_\pi^3) = 0.1 \text{ MeV}. \tag{7d}$$

The net result

$$\delta(P-N) \approx -1.5 \text{ MeV} \tag{7e}$$

is remarkably close to the truth.

However, this result is possibly fortuitous, as may be seen when we apply exactly the same considerations to the $t = \frac{3}{2}$ Δ's, assuming the same dimensions for the $P_{3/2}$ pion as in the $P_{1/2}$ state. In this case, we obtain the results

$$\delta(\Delta^- - \Delta^{++}) \approx -7.7 \text{ MeV}, \qquad \delta(\Delta^0 - \Delta^{++}) \approx -8.8 \text{ MeV}, \tag{7f}$$

in appalling disagreement with the values given in Table 13.1.

3. *Σ and Ξ.* Generally speaking, the simple models considered in the previous chapter have great difficulty in reproducing, even qualitatively, the hyperfine mass splittings shown in Table 13.1. Consider the Goldhaber model for the Σ hyperons, in which the charge states are given by

$$\begin{aligned} \Sigma^+ &= p\overline{K^0}, \\ \Sigma^0 &= \sqrt{\tfrac{1}{2}}(pK^- + n\overline{K^0}), \\ \Sigma^- &= nK^-. \end{aligned} \tag{8}$$

To avoid, for the moment, effects of the intrinsic masses, consider the combination

$$\delta(\Sigma^+ + \Sigma^- - 2\Sigma^0) \cong e^2 \left\langle \frac{1}{r} \right\rangle + (\mu_p - \mu_n)\, \mu_{lK} \left\langle \frac{1}{r^3} \right\rangle. \tag{8a}$$

(We have left open the possibility that the neutron and proton cores may have anomalous moments.) Experimentally, the value is +1.79 MeV (Table 13.1), which is easily satisfied by taking $\langle 1/r \rangle \approx 1$–$2\ m_\pi$, using either the Dirac or the physical nucleon moments in (8a). However, this triumph is short-lived when we consider differences involving the intrinsic masses of the constituents. For example,

$$\delta(\Sigma^- - \Sigma^+) = -\delta_1(p-n) - \delta_1(\overline{K^0} - K^-) - \mu_n \mu_{lK} \left\langle \frac{1}{r^3} \right\rangle. \tag{8b}$$

For Dirac nucleons, Equation (8b) predicts $\delta(\Sigma^- - \Sigma^+) \approx -10$ MeV, compared to the experimental value of +8 MeV. The assumption of physical nucleons for the core helps somewhat, giving

$$\delta(\Sigma^- - \Sigma^+) = -2.76 + 1.91 \mu_0 \mu_{lK} \left\langle \frac{1}{r^3} \right\rangle. \tag{8b$'$}$$

However, making $\langle 1/r^3 \rangle$ large enough to yield the experimental value of $\delta(\Sigma^- - \Sigma^+)$ would hopelessly spoil the possibility of agreement in Equation (8a) for $\delta(\Sigma^+ + \Sigma^- - 2\Sigma^0)$.

Symmetrical models, such as that of Frisch or the doublet symmetry scheme of Schwinger, suffer from other difficulties. In general, if we neglect anomalous magnetic moment effects, these lead to the predictions

$$\begin{aligned} \delta(\Sigma^- - \Sigma^+) &= 0, \\ \delta(\Sigma^\pm - \Sigma^0) &> 0, \end{aligned} \tag{9a}$$

owing to the positive self-energy of the charged Σ's (or alternatively, to the electrostatic and magnetic attraction of such combinations as $\Sigma^+\pi^-$, $\Sigma^-\pi^+$, K^-p, $K^+\Xi^-$, which occur in the Σ^0 structure). If we introduce an anomalous core magnetic moment, say in the Frisch model, we obtain the possibility of separating the Σ^- and Σ^+ masses; however, due to the symmetry, the magnetic effects cancel in computing $\delta(\Sigma^+ + \Sigma^- - 2\Sigma^0)$, and the Frisch model gives

$$\delta(\Sigma^+ + \Sigma^- - 2\Sigma^0) = 2\delta_1(\pi^\pm - \pi^0) \approx 9 \text{ MeV}, \tag{9b}$$

much too large a value if we use the observed $\delta(\pi^\pm - \pi^0)$.

Furthermore, such symmetrical models, neglecting anomalous magnetic moments, predict

$$\delta(\Xi^- - \Xi^0) \cong \delta(P-N), \tag{9c}$$

which is woefully wrong, both in magnitude and in sign.[6]

In summary, the hyperfine mass splittings within meson and baryon multiplets, arising from charge-dependent electromagnetic interactions, provide a crucial testing ground for the simple models described in Chapter 12. When put to this

---

[6] Note that an anomalous magnetic moment $\mu_\Lambda < 0$ in the Frisch model would yield

$$\begin{aligned} \delta(P-N) &= \delta_1(K^\pm - K^0) - \delta_3, \\ \delta(\Xi^- - \Xi^0) &= \delta_1(K^\pm - K^0) + \delta_3, \end{aligned} \tag{9d}$$

and could work, but only for $\delta_1(K^\pm - K^0) \cong +2.6$ MeV, instead of the observed value of -3.93 MeV.

test, all of these models are found to be wanting in some respect. However, some insights into the origin of these mass splittings have been provided, and the magnitudes of the effects predicted are generally in accord with those observed.

PROBLEM

Assuming a common $B\bar{B}B$ structure for the $\frac{1}{2}^+$ and $\frac{3}{2}^+$ baryons, on the basis of the Sakata–Yamaguchi model, compute the hyperfine mass splittings and compare them with the experimental values given in Table 13.1. Consider the values of $\langle 1/r_{ij} \rangle$ and $|\psi_{i,j}(0)|^2$ as parameters. Perform the computations for

(a) Dirac baryon constituents (p, n, λ), and
(b) physical baryon constituents (P, N, Λ).

13.2 Magnetic Dipole Moments

Not many magnetic dipole moments have been measured among the hadrons — only four, in fact, whose values are given in Table 13.2. However, these measurements already permit rather stringent tests of various models, and more measurements are certainly to be expected in the future.[7]

Table 13.2 Measured Baryon Magnetic Dipole Moments [a]

Baryon	Moment/$\mu_0 = \dfrac{e\hbar}{2M_p c}$
P	$2.793 \pm 10^{-3}\%$
N	$-1.913 \pm 3 \times 10^{-2}\%$
Σ^+	2.5 ± 0.7
Λ^0	-0.73 ± 0.16

[a] See Table 2.1.

[7] The measurement of the static magnetic moments of unstable particles presents formidable difficulties. The most direct way of measuring the moment is by observing the rate of its precession in a known magnetic field. This requires, first, the production of polarized particles and, second, a means of detection of the direction of their polarization. Fortunately, in the cases of the Λ and Σ, many production reactions give rise to appreciable transverse polarizations (i.e., in the direction normal to the production plane); and, owing to parity nonconservation in the weak decays, the direction of emission of the weak decay products is correlated with the polarization direction. Finally, there is the problem of providing magnetic fields sufficiently strong to produce an observable precession in the extremely short lifetimes, τ, of these particles. Given a moment $\mu \approx \mu_0$, a magnetic field B, and the time $\tau \approx 10^{-10}$ sec, the precession angle,

$$\theta = \frac{\mu_0 B \tau}{\hbar}, \tag{10}$$

becomes ≈ 1 rad for $B \approx 2 \times 10^6$ gauss. Fortunately, such strong fields are required for only a very short time, $\sim \tau$, and the total energy involved in their production need not be prohibitive. But the problems remain formidable.

13.2.1 Values

The computation of the magnetic moment of a compound system (spin j) requires the summation of the contributions of its constituents,

$$\boldsymbol{\mu} = \sum \boldsymbol{\mu}_i = \sum (g_{si}\mathbf{s}_i + g_{li}\mathbf{l}_i)\,\mu_0, \tag{11}$$

and is obtained by taking the expectation value of μ_z in the state of the compound system with $m_j = j$,

$$\mu = \langle \Psi_j^{j\,*} | \sum \mu_{iz} \Psi_j^j \rangle. \tag{12}$$

The values of the spin g-factors, g_{si}, depend, of course, on the particle involved; on the assumption of Dirac moments, we would have for a given spin $\frac{1}{2}$ baryon of charge $Q_i e$,

$$g_{si} = 2Q_i. \tag{11a}$$

However, we need not exclude anomalous moments. In the case of the nucleon doublet, we may provide for anomalous values of g_p and g_n by using the expression

$$\begin{aligned} g_s &= g_p(t_3 + \tfrac{1}{2}) - g_n(t_3 - \tfrac{1}{2}) \\ &= (g_p - g_n)\,t_3 + \tfrac{1}{2}(g_p + g_n). \end{aligned} \tag{11b}$$

For the orbital g-factor, g_l, we may simply write

$$g_{li} = \frac{M_P}{m_i} Q_i, \tag{11c}$$

which, for the case of a meson of mass m and hypercharge $\mathcal{Y}$, becomes

$$g_l = \frac{M_P}{m}\left(t_3 + \frac{\mathcal{Y}}{2}\right). \tag{11d}$$

The use of Equations (11) and (12) is best demonstrated by some examples.

EXAMPLES

1. *The nucleons.* Let us adopt the pion atomic model (neglecting the internal motion of the nucleon core — i.e., assuming a fixed nucleon at the center of the pion orbit). Then, for the nucleon,

$$\frac{\boldsymbol{\mu}_{\mathfrak{N}}}{\mu_0} = g_s\,\mathbf{s}, \tag{11b$'$}$$

   and for the pion,

$$\frac{\boldsymbol{\mu}_\pi}{\mu_0} = \frac{M}{m} t_{\pi 3}\mathbf{l} = g_l\,\mathbf{l}. \tag{11d$'$}$$

First, we evaluate the effects of the spin-orbit factor[8] in Equation (12):

$$\langle(\sqrt{\tfrac{1}{3}}\,\alpha Y_1^0 - \sqrt{\tfrac{2}{3}}\,\beta Y_1^1)^* | (g_s s_3 + g_l l_3)(\sqrt{\tfrac{1}{3}}\,\alpha Y_1^0 - \sqrt{\tfrac{2}{3}}\,\beta Y_1^1)\rangle = -\tfrac{1}{6} g_s + \tfrac{2}{3} g_l, \tag{12a}$$

and then the effects of the nucleon charge distributions,

$$\chi_{t=1/2}^{t_3=\pm 1/2} = \pm\sqrt{\frac{1}{3}}\begin{Bmatrix} p \\ n \end{Bmatrix}\pi^0 \mp \sqrt{\frac{2}{3}}\begin{Bmatrix} n\pi^+ \\ p\pi^- \end{Bmatrix}, \tag{12a$'$}$$

giving

$$\begin{aligned} \langle \chi_P^* | g_s \chi_P \rangle &= \tfrac{1}{3}(g_p + 2g_n), \\ \langle \chi_N^* | g_s \chi_N \rangle &= \tfrac{1}{3}(2g_p + g_n), \\ \langle \chi_{P,N}^* | g_l \chi_{P,N} \rangle &= \pm \frac{2}{3}\frac{M}{m}, \end{aligned} \tag{12b}$$

to yield, on combination,

$$\begin{aligned} \frac{\mu_P}{\mu_0} &= -\frac{1}{18}(g_p + 2g_n) + \frac{4}{9}\frac{M}{m}, \\ \frac{\mu_N}{\mu_0} &= -\frac{1}{18}(2g_p + g_n) - \frac{4}{9}\frac{M}{m}. \end{aligned} \tag{12c}$$

The main contributions in this case arise from the pion orbital moment, which yields $\approx \pm 3\mu_0$ for the moments of the physical proton and neutron. This result is not significantly changed by taking into account the nucleon g-factors, either through the Dirac moments ($g_p = 2$, $g_n = 0$) or by using the anomalous values ($g_{p,n} = 2\mu_{P,N}$ from Table 13.2); nor does correcting for the nucleon orbital motion, due to the finite nucleon mass, seriously affect the answer.

The results (12c), while perhaps not a great triumph for the pion atomic model, serve very well to indicate the origins of the magnetic moments of the physical nucleons, and of the approximate equality of the magnitudes of the anomalous moments.

Equation (12a) holds, in general, for all the atomic models with, of course, values of g_s and g_l appropriate to the model under consideration. Thus, for example, the Frisch model ($P = \Lambda^0 K^+$, $N = \Lambda^0 K^0$) immediately yields

$$\begin{aligned} \frac{\mu_P}{\mu_0} &= -\frac{1}{6} g_\Lambda + \frac{2}{3}\frac{M}{m_K}, \\ \frac{\mu_N}{\mu_0} &= -\frac{1}{6} g_\Lambda = -\frac{1}{3}\frac{\mu_\Lambda}{\mu_0}. \end{aligned} \tag{13}$$

Note that neither the Dirac value ($\mu_\Lambda = 0$) nor the observed physical value ($\mu_\Lambda \approx \mu_N/2$) comes anywhere near giving the observed values of μ_P and μ_N through Equation (13).

---

[8] Equation (12a), of course, is simply half the Landé g-factor for a $P_{1/2}$ state.

2. *Σ and Λ on the Goldhaber model.* The charge states of Σ and Λ being, according to the Goldhaber model,

$$\begin{aligned} \Sigma^+ &= p\overline{K^0}, \\ \Sigma^0 &= \sqrt{\tfrac{1}{2}}\,(pK^- + n\overline{K^0}), \\ \Sigma^- &= nK^-, \\ \Lambda^0 &= \sqrt{\tfrac{1}{2}}\,(pK^- - n\overline{K^0}), \end{aligned} \tag{14a}$$

the values of g_s and g_l appropriate to Equation (12) are

$$\begin{aligned} g_s^+ &= g_p, \\ g_s^- &= g_n, \\ g_s^0 &= \tfrac{1}{2}(g_p + g_n), \end{aligned} \tag{14a$'$}$$

and

$$g_l(\mathfrak{N}, K) = \left(\frac{M}{M+m_K}\right)\frac{M}{m_K}\,Q_K + \left(\frac{m_K}{M+m_K}\right)Q_{\mathfrak{N}}\,. \tag{14b$'$}$$

Equation (14b′) is the corrected version of (11c), taking into account the finite nucleon mass M. The results for the Σ and Λ magnetic moments are summarized in Table 13.3, in which the moments are computed on the assumption both of Dirac and of physical moments for the nucleons.

Table 13.3 Σ and Λ Magnetic Moments According to the Goldhaber Model

Particle	μ/μ_0	
	Dirac μ_s	Physical μ_s
Σ^+	−0.10	−0.70
Σ^0	−0.47	−0.45
Σ^-	−0.83	−0.20
Λ^0	−0.47	−0.45

13.2.2 Sum Rules

Irrespective of the details of our models, there are certain general relations among magnetic moments that follow from general properties of the electromagnetic interactions, while others are more specific consequences of the symmetry properties assumed. Thus, in general, since the internal electromagnetic 4-currents within a given multiplet take on the form

$$\mathcal{J}_i(r) = \mathcal{J}_1(r)\,t_3 + \mathcal{J}_2(r)\,\frac{\mathcal{Y}}{2}, \tag{15}$$

we have for the magnetic moments within a given multiplet

$$\mu_i = \mu_{1i}\,t_{3i} + \mu_{2i}\,. \tag{15a}$$

For isosinglets and doublets, Equation (15a) tells us nothing new. For isotriplets, however, such as the Σ's, Equation (15a) leads immediately to the sum rule

$$\mu(\Sigma^+) + \mu(\Sigma^-) = 2\mu(\Sigma^0), \tag{15b}$$

which must hold for all models.

Equation (15) is a special case of the general relationship involving the baryon number B and strangeness S,

$$\mathcal{J}(r) = \mathcal{J}_1(r)\, t_3 + \tfrac{1}{2}\mathcal{J}_2(r)\, B + \tfrac{1}{2}\mathcal{J}_3(r)\, S, \tag{15'}$$

where the $\mathcal{J}_{1,2,3}$ may in general also depend on the isotopic spin t, with only the condition on the fourth components (charge densities)

$$\int \rho_i(r)\, dV = 1. \tag{15'a}$$

Special symmetry assumptions imply special relationships among the $\mathcal{J}_i(r)$ in (15′) and, accordingly, relationships between the magnetic moments, which are proportional to the spatial part of the current, $\mathbf{j}(r)$. Thus, for example, a model in which the strong interactions depend only on $\mathcal{Y} = B + S$ (e.g., the Frisch model or the doublet symmetry) immediately yields $\mathcal{J}_2 = \mathcal{J}_3$, and

$$\begin{aligned} \mathbf{j}_P &= \tfrac{1}{2}[\mathbf{j}_1(r) + \mathbf{j}_2(r)], \\ \mathbf{j}_{\Xi^-} &= -\tfrac{1}{2}[\mathbf{j}_1(r) + \mathbf{j}_2(r)]. \end{aligned} \tag{15'b}$$

Accordingly,

$$\mu_{\Xi^-} = -\mu_P, \tag{15'c}$$

and, by the same argument,

$$\mu_{\Xi^0} = -\mu_N. \tag{15'd}$$

The doublet symmetry scheme of Schwinger goes still farther: Assuming universal pion and kaon interactions, we note that the currents are the same for all doublets (except for possible sign reversals) and, accordingly,[9]

$$\begin{aligned} \mu_{\Sigma^+} &= \mu_P, \\ \mu_{\Sigma^-} &= \mu_{\Xi^-} = -\mu_P, \\ \mu_{Y^0} &= \mu_N, \\ \mu_{Z^0} &= \mu_{\Xi^0} = -\mu_N. \end{aligned} \tag{15'e}$$

The last two of (15′e) permit us to obtain μ_{Σ^0} and μ_{Λ^0}, since

$$\begin{aligned} \mu_{Y^0} &= \langle Y^{0*} | \mu Y^0 \rangle = \tfrac{1}{2}(\mu_{\Sigma^0} + \mu_{\Lambda^0}) - \mu_{\Sigma-\Lambda}, \\ \mu_{Z^0} &= \langle Z^{0*} | \mu Z^0 \rangle = \tfrac{1}{2}(\mu_{\Sigma^0} + \mu_{\Lambda^0}) + \mu_{\Sigma-\Lambda}, \\ \mu_{Z^0-Y^0} = 0 &= \langle Z^{0*} | \mu Y^0 \rangle = \tfrac{1}{2}(\mu_{\Sigma^0} - \mu_{\Lambda^0}), \end{aligned} \tag{15'f}$$

[9] Of course, the symmetry-breaking interactions will violate these rules. However, since these couplings should be small, and since they involve K-meson couplings, with typical moments $\sim M/m_K$ as compared to M/m_π for the stronger pion couplings, we expect relatively small deviations from these relationships if the global Schwinger scheme is valid.

giving

$$\mu_{\Sigma^0} = \mu_{\Lambda^0} = 0, \tag{15'g}$$

$$\mu_{\Sigma-\Lambda} = -\mu_N. \tag{15'h}$$

[Note that Equation (15b) is satisfied.] The last condition in (15′f) arises from the assumption that the electromagnetic interactions maintain the doublet symmetry (i.e., no mixing of Y^0 and Z^0).

Equation (15′g) ($\mu_{\Lambda^0} = 0$) is rather discouraging in view of Table 13.2. The second result, Equation (15′h), $\mu_{\Sigma-\Lambda} = -\mu_N$, represents the transition moment, or off-diagonal magnetic dipole matrix element, leading to the decay by $M1$ photon emission

$$\Sigma^0 \to \Lambda^0 + \gamma. \tag{16}$$

A more general sum rule is sometimes useful: Consider a related set of multiplets that are symmetrically placed with respect to t_3 and $\mathcal{Y}$, as are, for example, the 8 baryons, N, Σ, Λ, Ξ. Then Equation (15′) with $\mathcal{J}_2 = \mathcal{J}_3$ (i.e., using $\mathcal{Y} = B + S$ as the appropriate quantum number for the electromagnetic interactions) implies

$$\sum_{i=1}^{8} \mu_i = 0, \tag{15'i}$$

which is satisfied by, but is also much more general than, the relations in (15′e).

13.2.3 Transition Moments

Although for relatively stable particles, such as the Λ^0 or $\Sigma^{\pm}$, it is possible to contemplate direct measurement of the magnetic dipole moments, such measurements are not possible — at least not using available techniques — for particles whose decays are governed by the electromagnetic or strong interactions. However, as we have noted in the section immediately preceding, we may utilize the electromagnetic decay rates in some cases, e.g., $\Sigma^0 \to \Lambda^0 + \gamma$, to measure the off-diagonal magnetic dipole matrix elements between two related states.

Consider the general $M1$ decay

$$A \to B + \gamma \tag{17}$$

for which the selection rule is

$$\Delta j = 0, \pm 1 \qquad \text{(no parity change, no } 0 \to 0\text{)}. \tag{17a}$$

Transitions come about by virtue of the dipole operator

$$\begin{aligned} \boldsymbol{\mu} &= g_s \mathbf{s} + g_l \mathbf{l} \\ &= \mu_+ \boldsymbol{\epsilon}_- + \mu_- \boldsymbol{\epsilon}_+ + \mu_3 \boldsymbol{\epsilon}_3, \end{aligned} \tag{17b}$$

where

$$\begin{aligned} \mu_{\pm} &= \sqrt{\tfrac{1}{2}}\,(\mu_x \pm i\mu_y), \qquad & \mu_3 &= \mu_z, \\ \boldsymbol{\epsilon}_{\pm} &= \sqrt{\tfrac{1}{2}}\,(\mathbf{x}_0 \pm i\mathbf{y}_0), \qquad & \boldsymbol{\epsilon}_3 &= \mathbf{z}_0, \end{aligned} \tag{17c}$$

through the interaction with the vacuum electromagnetic field

$$H_{\text{int}} = \boldsymbol{\mu} \cdot \mathbf{A}. \tag{17d}$$

The three terms in Equation (17b) lead, respectively, to the emission of left circularly polarized ($m_f = m_i + 1$), right circularly polarized ($m_f = m_i - 1$), and unpolarized ($m_f = m_i$) $M1$ photons.

In terms of the matrix elements between the substates of A and B,

$$\boldsymbol{\mu}_{f,i} = \langle B_f^* | \boldsymbol{\mu} A_i \rangle, \tag{18}$$

the transition rate[10] (width) for the decay (17)

$$\Gamma_{A \to B} = \textstyle\sum_f \Gamma_{f,i} \tag{18a}$$

is given by

$$\Gamma_{f,i} = \tfrac{4}{3} \mu_{f,i}^2 k_\gamma^3, \tag{18b}$$

where $k_\gamma = \lambda\!\!\!^{-}{}_\gamma^{-1}$ is the photon wave number ($\hbar k_\gamma = p_\gamma$). In the rest frame of the initial particle, A, we have

$$k_\gamma = \frac{M_A^2 - M_B^2}{2M_A}, \tag{18c}$$

and expressing $\mu_{f,i}$ in units of $\mu_0 = e/2M_P$, we may write

$$\Gamma_{f,i} = 0.286 \left(\frac{\mu_{f,i}}{\mu_0}\right)^2 \left(\frac{M_A^2 - M_B^2}{M_P M_A}\right)^3 \text{MeV}. \tag{18d}$$

EXAMPLES

1. *The decay* $\Sigma^0 \to \Lambda^0 + \gamma$. The transaction moment $\mu_{\Sigma-\Lambda} = -\mu_N = 1.913\,\mu_0$, derived from Schwinger's doublet approximation, corresponds to the operator μ_3, or to the transition $m_\Sigma = \pm\frac{1}{2} \to m_\Lambda = \pm\frac{1}{2}$. In addition we require the $\mu_\pm$ matrix elements, corresponding to $m_\Sigma = \pm\frac{1}{2} \to m_\Lambda = \mp\frac{1}{2}$; these are readily shown to be $\mu_{\Sigma-\Lambda}^{\pm} = \mp\sqrt{2}\,\mu_N$, so that

$$\Gamma_{\Sigma \to \Lambda} = 3 \times 0.286 \times (1.913)^2 \left\{\frac{(1192.6)^2 - (1115.6)^2}{938.3 \times 1192.6}\right\}^3 \text{MeV}$$
$$= 13 \text{ keV},$$
$$\left(\tau_{\Sigma \to \Lambda} = \frac{\hbar}{\Gamma_{\Sigma \to \Lambda}} \cong 5 \times 10^{-20} \text{ sec}\right).$$

Experimentally, all that is available is an upper limit, $\tau < 10^{-14}$ sec.

2. *The decay* $\Delta^+ \to P + \gamma$. The pion atomic model provides us with wave functions for the Δ^+ and P substates (Section 12.3.1) which we may use to compute the $M1$ matrix elements between appropriate substates. Consider the transi-

[10] The value of $\Gamma_{A \to B}$ must be independent of the initial substate i; if this were not so, then starting from an initially unpolarized A, we would find that the product B would be polarized.

tion between the substates $\Delta^+_{1/2} \to P_{\pm 1/2}$, for which the matrix elements are

$$\mu_{1/2,1/2} = \langle \Delta^{+*}_{1/2} | \mu_3 P_{1/2} \rangle = \frac{2}{9}\left(g_p - g_n + \frac{M}{m}\right) F\mu_0, \tag{19a}$$

$$\mu_{-1/2,1/2} = \sqrt{\tfrac{1}{2}}\, \mu_{1/2,1/2}, \tag{19b}$$

in which $F \lesssim 1$ is the overlap integral of the spatial dependence of the Δ and P wave functions. Substitution into Equations (18d) and (18a) yields (using $g_p = 2$, $g_n = 0$, the Dirac moments)

$$\Gamma_{\Delta^+ \to P} = 0.3F^2 \text{ MeV}. \tag{19c}$$

[Use of the physical moments raises the 0.3 to around 1.0 in Equation (19c).]

The experimental value of $\Gamma_{\Delta^+ \to P}$ may be obtained from the measurement of the cross section $\sigma(\gamma + P \to P + \pi^0)$ at the resonance energy, where it may be reasonably assumed that the observed cross section arises almost entirely from resonant $M1$ absorption. On this assumption [11]

$$\sigma_{\text{res}}(\gamma P \to P\pi^0) = \frac{8\pi}{3} \lambda\!\!\!^{-2}_\gamma \frac{\Gamma_\gamma}{\Gamma}, \tag{20}$$

and using the experimental values of ≈ 230 μb for the resonant cross section and 120 MeV for the total width Γ, we obtain from (20)

$$\Gamma^{(\text{exp})}_{\Delta^+ \to P} = 0.58 \text{ MeV}. \tag{19c$'$}$$

The agreement, to within a factor ~ 2, is not bad for a crude model.

3. *The decays ω, $\rho \to \pi + \gamma$ according to the Fermi–Yang model.* In the model of Fermi and Yang (Section 12.1), the ω and ρ are $\mathfrak{N}\overline{\mathfrak{N}}$ combinations in the $^3S_1$ state, with $t = 0$ and 1, respectively, while the π's are $\mathfrak{N}\overline{\mathfrak{N}}$ combinations in the $^1S_0$, $t = 1$ state. The magnetic moment operator is

$$\boldsymbol{\mu} = (g_{\mathfrak{N}} \mathbf{s}_{\mathfrak{N}} + g_{\overline{\mathfrak{N}}} \mathbf{s}_{\overline{\mathfrak{N}}})\, \mu_0 \tag{21}$$

with $g_p = -g_{\bar{p}}$, $g_n = -g_{\bar{n}}$. It is easily shown that for the π's ($s = 0$) or for the neutral ω^0 and ρ^0 ($t_3 = 0$), the static moments are zero, while for the charged ρ's

$$\begin{aligned} \mu_{\rho^\pm} &= \left\langle \begin{Bmatrix} p \\ n \end{Bmatrix} \begin{Bmatrix} \bar{n} \\ \bar{p} \end{Bmatrix} \alpha_{\mathfrak{N}} \alpha_{\overline{\mathfrak{N}}} \middle| \mu_3 \begin{Bmatrix} p \\ n \end{Bmatrix} \begin{Bmatrix} \bar{n} \\ \bar{p} \end{Bmatrix} \alpha_{\mathfrak{N}} \alpha_{\overline{\mathfrak{N}}} \right\rangle \\ &= \pm \tfrac{1}{2}(g_p + g_{\bar{n}})\, \mu_0 \\ &= \pm (g_p - g_n)\, \mu_0, \end{aligned} \tag{21a}$$

where α is the spin wave function corresponding to $m_s = \frac{1}{2}$. For Dirac nucleons, this yields

$$\mu_{\rho^\pm} = \pm \mu_0. \tag{21a$'$}$$

However, for a model using physical nucleons,

---

[11] The factor $\frac{8}{3}$ arises from the statistical factor $(2j + 1)/2(2s + 1) = 1$ for resonance formation times the probability $\frac{2}{3}$ of the decay $\Delta^+ \to P\pi^0$ (i.e., $\frac{1}{3}$ for the decay $\Delta^+ \to N\pi^+$).

$$\mu_{\rho^\pm} = \pm 4.71 \mu_0 . \tag{21a''}$$

A more interesting test relates to the matrix elements determining the decays

$$\rho^{+,-,0} \rightarrow \pi^{+,-,0} + \gamma, \tag{22a}$$

$$\omega^0 \rightarrow \pi^0 + \gamma. \tag{22b}$$

Since the $M1$ matrix elements from all ρ substates to the appropriate pion substates are equal, we demonstrate by computing the matrix element

$$\begin{aligned}\frac{\mu_{\rho,\pi}}{\mu^0} &= \left\langle \pi^0_{m=0} \middle| \frac{\mu_3}{\mu_0} \rho^0_{m=0} \right\rangle \\ &= \frac{1}{4} \left\langle (p\bar{p} - n\bar{n})(\alpha_{\mathfrak{N}}\beta_{\bar{\mathfrak{N}}} - \beta_{\mathfrak{N}}\alpha_{\bar{\mathfrak{N}}}) \middle| (g_{\mathfrak{N}} s_{\mathfrak{N}3} + g_{\bar{\mathfrak{N}}} s_{\bar{\mathfrak{N}}3})(p\bar{p} - n\bar{n})(\alpha_{\mathfrak{N}}\beta_{\bar{\mathfrak{N}}} + \beta_{\mathfrak{N}}\alpha_{\bar{\mathfrak{N}}}) \right\rangle \\ &= \frac{1}{4}[(g_p - g_{\bar{p}}) + (g_n - g_{\bar{n}})] = \frac{1}{2}(g_p + g_n).\end{aligned} \tag{21b}$$

The corresponding $\omega \rightarrow \pi$ matrix element differs only in the sign of the $(p\bar{p} + n\bar{n})$ factor in the ω wave function, yielding

$$\mu_{\omega^0,\pi^0} = \tfrac{1}{2}(g_p - g_n)\,\mu_0 . \tag{21c}$$

The corresponding decay widths are obtained from Equation (18d) and summarized in Table 13.4, in which values are computed both for Dirac nucleon moments and for the observed moments of the physical nucleons (columns 3 and 4), and compared with the experimental values (column 5).

Again in this case, the comparison favors the use of physical nucleons in the F–Y model, but the agreement[12] is only within a factor of ~ 3.

Table 13.4 Decay Widths (in MeV) of ρ and ω for $M1$ Photon Emission According to the Model of Fermi and Yang

Decay	$\mu_{f,i}$	$\Gamma_{\text{(Dirac)}}$	$\Gamma_{\text{(physical)}}$	$\Gamma_{\text{(exp)}}$
$\rho^\pm \rightarrow \pi^\pm + \gamma$	$\frac{1}{2}(g_p + g_n)$	0.15	0.12	—
$\rho^0 \rightarrow \pi^0 + \gamma$	$\frac{1}{2}(g_p + g_n)$	0.15	0.12	<0.6
$\omega^0 \rightarrow \pi^0 + \gamma$	$\frac{1}{2}(g_p - g_n)$	0.15	3.30	1.16 ± 0.17

PROBLEMS

1. Compute the values of the nucleon magnetic dipole moments on the basis of the pion atomic model, taking into account:

   (a) corrections to g_l resulting from the finite mass of the nucleon core, and
   (b) the anomalous nucleon core moments, on the assumption that the nucleonic core particles are the physical nucleons.

[12] The predicted decay widths will be reduced if the spatial distributions of the ρ, ω^0 and π are appreciably different.

2. Compute the baryon magnetic moments on the basis of the Sakata–Yamaguchi model. Check the validity of the sum rule (15′i) for appropriate sets of baryons.
3. Using the pion atomic model, do the following:
   (a) Show by direct computation that the matrix element for the decay

$$\Delta^+_{3/2} \to P_{1/2} + \gamma$$

   leads to the same width $\Gamma_{\Delta^+ \to P}$ as that computed in the text (Equation 19c).
   (b) What are the values of the decay widths for

$$\Delta^+ \to P + \gamma,$$
$$\Delta^0 \to N + \gamma,$$

   computed with the anomalous nucleon moments?
4. Compute the decay widths for the transitions $\omega, \rho, \phi \to \eta^0 + \gamma$ on the basis of the F–Y–S model. (Try using both the Dirac and the physical nucleon moments.)

13.3 Form Factors, etc.

If a model is specific enough, it should be possible to compute all the moments of the charge and current density of a given compound particle and, correspondingly, the electric and magnetic form factors. Such is the case, for example, with the atomic models. However, although such models are specific enough, it is clear that they are only to be taken seriously, if at all, in their predictions relating to the outer regions, where the mesonic structure dominates; in the region of the core we expect to encounter difficulties, owing not only to the unknown core structure itself but also to the effects of virtual states consisting of heavier mesons and baryons (e.g., $P \rightleftharpoons \Lambda K^+$, etc.). However, confining ourselves to effects arising mainly from the properties of the outer mesonic cloud,[13] it is of interest to see what the models predict.

13.3.1 Charge Distributions

For example, we may compute the rms charge radius of the physical proton using the atomic model:

$$\langle r^2 \rangle_P^E = \iiint \langle P^* | (t_3 + \tfrac{1}{2}) r^2 P \rangle \, r^2 \, dr \, d\Omega. \tag{23}$$

The relevant factors in the proton wave function are the isospin (charge) factor, $\chi_P = \sqrt{\tfrac{1}{3}}\, p\pi^0 - \sqrt{\tfrac{2}{3}}\, n\pi^+$, and the radial distribution of the p and π^+ charges, $R_p(r)$ and $R_\pi(r)$.

$$\langle r^2 \rangle_P^E = \tfrac{1}{3} \langle r^2 \rangle_p + \tfrac{2}{3} \langle r^2 \rangle_\pi , \tag{23a}$$

[13] Clearly, for the moments $\langle r^n \rangle$, with $n > 1$, the effects of the outermost structure will dominate.

where

$$\langle r^2 \rangle_{p,\pi} = \frac{\int_0^\infty R^2_{p,\pi}(r)\, r^4\, dr}{\int_0^\infty R^2_{p,\pi}(r)\, r^2\, dr}. \tag{23b}$$

The main contribution to (23a) clearly comes from the more extended pion cloud. Adopting a Yukawa form for $R_\pi(r)$,

$$R_\pi(r) = N \frac{e^{-\kappa r}}{r}, \tag{23c}$$

we obtain, from (23b),

$$\langle r^2 \rangle_\pi = (2\kappa^2)^{-1} \cong (2m_\pi^2)^{-1}. \tag{23d}$$

Thus, neglecting the contribution of the core,[14]

$$\langle r^2 \rangle_P^E \cong (3m_\pi^2)^{-1} = (0.81 \text{ f})^2, \tag{23e}$$

which is in excellent accord with the low-energy electron-proton scattering measurements.

Since the neutron charge state $\chi_N = -\sqrt{\frac{1}{3}}\, n\pi^0 + \sqrt{\frac{2}{3}}\, p\pi^-$ contains the same pion distribution, but opposite charge, its charge radius should be essentially the same as that of the proton,

$$\langle r^2 \rangle_N^E = \tfrac{2}{3} \langle r^2 \rangle_p - \tfrac{2}{3} \langle r^2 \rangle_\pi \simeq - \langle r^2 \rangle_P^E. \tag{24}$$

(The meaning of a negative $\langle r^2 \rangle^E$ is simply that the negative charge dominates.) Just as in the case of the proton, for which $\langle r^2 \rangle_P^E$ may be measured by observing the electric form factor for electron-proton scattering at low-momentum transfer.

$$G_E^P(\not{q}^2) \simeq 1 - \langle r^2 \rangle_P^E \frac{\not{q}^2}{6}, \tag{25a}$$

so, in the case of the neutron

$$G_E^N(\not{q}^2) \simeq \frac{2}{3}\left[\left(1 - \langle r^2 \rangle_p \frac{\not{q}^2}{6}\right) - \left(1 - \langle r^2 \rangle_\pi \frac{\not{q}^2}{6}\right)\right]$$

$$\simeq - \langle r^2 \rangle_N^E \frac{\not{q}^2}{6}. \tag{25b}$$

Although the neutron form factor vanishes as $\not{q}^2 \to 0$, the value of $\langle r^2 \rangle_N^E$ may be

---

[14] Assuming a uniformly charged sphere of radius R, $\langle r^2 \rangle_p = \frac{3}{5} R^2$ and Equation (23a) would become

$$\langle r^2 \rangle_P^E = \tfrac{2}{3} \langle r^2 \rangle_\pi (1 + \tfrac{3}{5} m_\pi^2 R^2). \tag{23a'}$$

Even taking R several times the proton Compton wavelength, $M_P^{-1} \sim (7m_\pi)^{-1}$, the core contribution would have a very small effect on $\langle r^2 \rangle_P^E$. However, one difficulty presented by the experimental observations (Chapter 9) is that they provide no evidence whatsover of a charged core in the physical proton.

obtained from its derivative for small $\not{q}^2$,

$$-\langle r^2\rangle_N^E = 6\,\frac{dG_E^N}{d\not{q}^2}\,(\not{q}^2 \to 0). \tag{25c}$$

Experimentally (Chapter 9), the low-energy e-deuteron and e-proton scattering data yield

$$\begin{aligned} \frac{dG_E^N}{d\not{q}^2}(0) &= (0.027 \pm 0.001)\ \mathrm{f}^2, \\ \frac{dG_E^P}{d\not{q}^2}(0) &= -(0.14 \pm 0.02)\ \mathrm{f}^2, \end{aligned} \tag{25}$$

from which we deduce

$$\begin{aligned} \langle r^2\rangle_N^E &= -(0.41 \pm 0.02\ \mathrm{f})^2, \\ \langle r^2\rangle_P^E &= (0.91 \pm 0.13\ \mathrm{f})^2. \end{aligned} \tag{25'}$$

The rms charge radius of the neutron thus appears to come out too small. However, it must be noted that the determination of the limiting slope of the form factor is difficult, because of the small values of $G_E^N(\not{q}^2 \to 0)$.

Another measurement of $\langle r^2\rangle_N^E$ may be obtained through the observation of the S-wave scattering of neutrons by electrons at extremely low ("cold") neutron energies, which may be accomplished by observing the interference between scattering from the nucleus and from the electron cloud in heavy atoms. The value so determined is $\langle r^2\rangle_N^E = -(0.35 \pm 0.01\ \mathrm{f})^2$, in essential agreement with the value deduced from e–D scattering, and still substantially smaller than the value of the charge radius of the proton.

EXAMPLE

Demonstration of evaluation of $\langle r^2\rangle_N^E$ from the N–e scattering cross section at zero energy: Let $U(r)$ be the electrostatic e–N interaction energy,

$$U(r) = -e\int_r^\infty E(r')\,dr' = -e\int_r^\infty \frac{Q(r')}{r'^2}\,dr', \tag{25d}$$

where

$$Q(r) = 4\pi\int_0^r \rho(r')\,r'^2\,dr' \tag{25e}$$

is the charge in a sphere of radius r. Note, for the neutron, $Q(r \to \infty) = 0$. We now form the integral

$$B = 4\pi\int_0^\infty U(r)\,r^2\,dr = -\frac{2\pi e^2}{3}\langle r^2\rangle_N^E, \tag{25f}$$

and evaluate it by two integrations by parts. In the Born approximation, B is proportional to the amplitude for e–N S-wave scattering:

$$\sigma(e\text{–}N) = \frac{M_N^2 |B|^2}{\pi \hbar^4}. \tag{25g}$$

Taking $\langle r^2 \rangle_N^E \simeq -(0.8 \text{ f})^2$, we would obtain $\sigma(e\text{–}N) \simeq 0.022$ mb, which is considerably larger than the value deduced from the experiments.[15]

13.3.2 Electric Quadrupole Moments and E2 Transitions

For composite particles of spin $s \geq 1$, the system may also exhibit an electric quadrupole moment

$$Q = \langle (3z^2 - r^2) \rangle_{m=s}, \tag{26}$$

averaged over the charge distribution in the magnetic substate with $m = s$. Since

$$(3z^2 - r^2) = (3 \cos^2 \theta - 1)\, r^2 = \left(\frac{16\pi}{5}\right)^{1/2} Y_2^0(\theta, \varphi)\, r^2, \tag{26a}$$

it is evident that the value of Q also depends on the value of $\langle r^2 \rangle^E$. Consider, for example, the different charge substates, χ'_{t_3}, of the (3, 3) isobar Δ:

$$\chi'_{\pm 3/2} = \begin{Bmatrix} p\pi^+ \\ n\pi^- \end{Bmatrix}, \tag{27a}$$

$$\chi'_{\pm 1/2} = \sqrt{\frac{2}{3}} \begin{Bmatrix} p \\ n \end{Bmatrix} \pi^0 + \sqrt{\frac{1}{3}} \begin{Bmatrix} n\pi^+ \\ p\pi^- \end{Bmatrix}. \tag{27b}$$

The values of the quadrupole moments are

$$\begin{aligned} Q_{t_3} &= \langle \chi'_{t_3} | t_{\pi 3} \chi'_{t_3} \rangle \int_0^\infty R'^2_\pi(r)\, r^4\, dr \int Y_1^{1*}(\theta, \varphi)(3\cos^2\theta - 1)\, Y_1^1(\theta, \varphi)\, d\Omega \\ &= -\langle \chi'_{t_3} | t_{\pi 3} \chi'_{t_3} \rangle \cdot \tfrac{2}{5} \langle r^2 \rangle_\pi . \end{aligned} \tag{27c}$$

The charge factor $\langle \chi'_{t_3} | t_{\pi 3} \chi'_{t_3} \rangle$ is, respectively, $1, \frac{1}{3}, -\frac{1}{3}, -1$ for Δ^{++}, Δ^+, Δ^0, and Δ^-. Note that the meaning of a negative Q is that the spheroid (if positively charged) is oblate — i.e., flattened at the poles. The magnitude of the intrinsic quadrupole moment, $\frac{2}{5}\langle r^2 \rangle_\pi \approx 4 \times 10^{-27}$ cm^2, is not inappreciable.

However, the most important effect of a nonvanishing matrix element of the quadrupole operator,

$$Q_m = t_{\pi 3}\, r^2\, Y_2^m(\theta_\pi, \varphi_\pi), \tag{28}$$

is that it gives rise to radiative transitions between Δ^+ and P (or Δ^0 and N), with the emission of electromagnetic $E2$ radiation, in competition with the $M1$ transi-

---

[15] See, for example, B. T. Feld, "The Neutron," in *Experimental Nuclear Physics, 2,* E. Segré, ed., John Wiley and Sons, New York (1953), p. 240; see also, R. R. Wilson and J. S. Levinger, *Ann. Rev. Nucl. Sci., 14:* 135 (1964).

tions considered in the preceding section. For the $E2$ case, the transition rate is [16]

$$\Gamma_{f,i}^{(E2)} = \frac{4\pi e^2 k_\gamma^5}{75} |Q_{f,i}|^2. \tag{28a}$$

A straightforward evaluation, utilizing the pion atomic model wave functions for Δ^+ and P, gives

$$\langle P_{1/2}^+ | Q_0 \Delta_{1/2}^+ \rangle = \sqrt{\frac{1}{45\pi}} \langle r^2 \rangle_\pi', \tag{28b}$$

and

$$\langle P_{-1/2}^+ | Q_{-1} \Delta_{1/2}^+ \rangle = \sqrt{\frac{1}{30\pi}} \langle r^2 \rangle_\pi', \tag{28c}$$

where

$$\langle r^2 \rangle_\pi' = \int_0^\infty R_\pi(r) R_\pi'(r) r^4 \, dr. \tag{28d}$$

Taking $\langle r^2 \rangle_\pi' = \langle r^2 \rangle_\pi F \simeq (2m_\pi^2)^{-1} F$, where $F \lesssim 1$ is a spatial overlap factor, we see that substitution in (28a) and summing over final substates yields

$$\Gamma_\gamma^{(E2)} = \frac{2e^2}{675} \frac{k_\gamma^5}{(4m_\pi^4)} F^2 = 0.02 \; F^2 \text{ MeV}. \tag{28a$'$}$$

This is no more than a few percent of $\Gamma_\gamma^{(M1)}$ but, provided the factor F^2 is not too small, it might still be observable in the pion photoproduction experiments through $M1$–$E2$ interference effects on the angular distribution. The experimental situation is somewhat uncertain on this point.[17]

13.3.3 Scattering and Reaction Cross Sections

A model that postulates simple relations among the interactions of the elementary particles will correspondingly predict connections among their cross sections. However, in some cases the details of the computations may be complicated, laborious, and uncertain, as in the case of the use of the Goldhaber model to compute associated hyperon-kaon production, which requires consideration of a two-stage process, e.g.,

$$\pi + \mathfrak{N} \rightarrow \pi + \mathfrak{N} + \overline{K} + K \rightarrow Y + K. \tag{29}$$

However, for this model, processes like K–$\mathfrak{N}$ scattering and $\overline{K}\mathfrak{N} \rightarrow Y\pi$ are directly computable, given an assumed K, $\overline{K}$–nucleon potential.[18]

---

[16] J. M. Blatt and V. F. Weisskopf, *Theoretical Nuclear Physics*, Chapter 12, John Wiley and Sons, New York (1952).

[17] B. T. Feld, *Ann. Phys.* (New York), *4:* 189 (1958).

[18] R. F. Christy, *Proc. of the 7th Annual Rochester Conf.*, Interscience, New York (1957). Note that the computation of reactions like Equation (29) is further complicated by the fact that the direct conversion $\pi \rightarrow K + \overline{K}$ is forbidden by parity conservation.

Another example is the treatment of low-energy pion-nucleon scattering, using the pion atomic model,[19] in a fashion analogous to the treatment of the scattering of electrons by atomic hydrogen. This approach gives reasonable results for the low-energy phase shifts, reproducing, in particular, the resonant scattering in the $j = t = \frac{3}{2}$ state.[20]

On the other hand, there are some general relationships among cross sections which are less dependent on model details and which, therefore, provide more stringent tests. An example is the theorem of Pomeranchuk[21] which, on the basis of general considerations, concludes that in the asymptotic limit of high energies, the total cross sections of like particles should tend to become independent of all subsidiary quantum numbers (i.e., spin, isospin, B) and consequently equal. Thus, Pomeranchuk predicts, in the asymptotic region (considering only observable processes),

$$\sigma(\overline{P}P) = \sigma(\overline{N}P) = \sigma(PP) = \sigma(NP), \tag{30a}$$

$$\sigma(\pi^+P) = \sigma(\pi^-P) = \sigma(\pi^+N) = \sigma(\pi^-N), \tag{30b}$$

$$\sigma(K^+P) = \sigma(K^+N) = \sigma(K^-P) = \sigma(K^-N), \tag{30c}$$

and consequently, at the same asymptotic limit, the vanishing of charge exchange reactions

$$\sigma(\overline{P}P \to \overline{N}N) = \sigma(\pi^-P \to \pi^0N) = \sigma(K^-P \to \overline{K^0}N) = \sigma(K^+N \to K^0P) \to 0. \tag{30d}$$

A plot of the observed total cross sections for the various available combinations of elementary particles, Figure 13.2, indicates that these cross sections appear to be tending toward their Pomeranchuk limits, but have not yet attained them at even the highest available projectile energies of $\gtrsim 20$ GeV.

On the assumption that, at sufficiently high energies, at which a large number of inelastic (reaction) channels are available for the interactions among elementary particles, the inelastic reactions will overwhelm in importance the single channel corresponding to the elastic re-emission of the projectile (potential elastic scattering), the total cross section is related to the differential cross section for elastic scattering in the forward direction through the optical theorem[22]

$$\sigma_{\text{tot}} = \frac{4\pi}{k_i} \operatorname{Im} f(0) \cong \frac{4\pi}{k_i} \left[\frac{d\sigma}{d\Omega}(\theta = 0)\right]^{1/2}. \tag{31}$$

---

[19] G. Costa and B. T. Feld, *Ann. Phys.* (New York), *9:* 354 (1960).

[20] This is easy to understand qualitatively: the incident pion prefers to occupy the same $j = t = \frac{1}{2}$ ($l = 1$) state as the pion in the physical nucleon. Hence the two pions tend to align themselves both in ordinary and in isospin space, with their angular momenta and isospins opposing those of the nucleon core — i.e., in the state of total $j = t = \frac{3}{2}$. The details, of course, require the solution of a three-body problem, with the two pions obeying Bose statistics.

[21] I. Ia. Pomeranchuk, *JETP* (U.S.S.R.), *30:* 423 (1956) [transl. *Sov. Phys. JETP, 3:* 306 (1956)]; *34:* 725 (1958) [transl. *7:* 499 (1958)].

[22] Classically, for a perfectly absorbing (black) sphere of radius R, the cross section for a projectile of $\lambda\!\!\!^{-} \ll R$ is equally divided between absorption and shadow (diffraction) elastic scattering

$$\sigma_{\text{abs}} = \sigma_{\text{el}} = \tfrac{1}{2}\sigma_{\text{tot}} = \pi R^2. \tag{31a}$$

This relation between σ_{tot} and the forward elastic scattering amplitude permits additional, model-dependent predictions for σ_{tot} through an approach due to Okun and Lipkin.[23]

Consider the total cross section for particles $A + B$, in which A is a composite particle, $A = a_1 + a_2 + \cdots$. Then, for forward elastic scattering, in which there is no momentum transfer, the total forward scattering amplitude may be taken as the sum of the scattering amplitudes of the components [24]

$$f(0)_{A+B} \cong f(0)_{a_1+B} + f(0)_{a_2+B} + \cdots. \tag{32a}$$

Equation (32a) holds also for the imaginary parts, thus leading to the same relationship for the total cross sections

$$\sigma_{tot}(A + B) \rightarrow \sigma_{tot}(a_1 + B) + \sigma_{tot}(a_2 + B) + \cdots. \tag{32b}$$

Consider for example the F–Y–S model. Using the Okun–Lipkin *ansatz,* we see that the model gives

$$\sigma(\pi\mathfrak{N}) \rightarrow \sigma(\mathfrak{N}\mathfrak{N}) + \sigma(\overline{\mathfrak{N}}\mathfrak{N}), \tag{32c}$$

$$\sigma(K\mathfrak{N}) \rightarrow \sigma(\mathfrak{N}\mathfrak{N}) + \sigma(\overline{\Lambda}\mathfrak{N}). \tag{32d}$$

Both (32c) and (32d) are extremely wide of the mark.[25] However, a series of sum rules, which may be derived on the basis of the F–Y–S model,

$$\sigma(K^-P) - \sigma(K^-N) + \sigma(K^+N) - \sigma(K^+P) = \sigma(\pi^-P) - \sigma(\pi^+P), \tag{32e}$$

$$\sigma(K^+N) - \sigma(K^+P) = \sigma(NP) - \sigma(PP), \tag{32f}$$

$$\sigma(K^-P) - \sigma(K^-N) = \sigma(\overline{P}P) - \sigma(\overline{P}N), \tag{32g}$$

are borne out very well in the high-energy limit (say, $\gtrsim$ 10 GeV). Of these, (32e) is independent of whether or not the elements in the F–Y–S triplet are the physical nucleons;[26] on the other hand, Equations (32f) and (32g) depend on the assumption that the constituents of the mesons are the physical P and N.

If we consider elastic scattering in directions other than forward, the differential cross section may be written[27]

$$\frac{d\sigma}{dt} = \left.\frac{d\sigma}{dt}\right)_0 F^2(t), \tag{33}$$

where $(-t)$ is the invariant 4-momentum transfer and $F(t)$ is a scattering form

---

[23] L. B. Okun, *Seminar on High Energy Physics,* Int. Atomic Energy Agency, Trieste, Italy (1965); H. J. Lipkin and F. Scheck, *Phys. Rev. Letters, 16:* 71 (1966); E. M. Levin and L. L. Frankfort, *JETP Letters, 2:* 65 (1965).

[24] This is easily generalized to the case where B is also composite, $B = b_1 + b_2 + \cdots$.

[25] But if the elements of the F–Y–S model were not the physical nucleons (for instance, Dirac nucleons), then (32c) and (32d) would present no contradictions.

[26] Equation (32e) is a weaker version of a set of relationships derived on the basis of $SU(6)$ symmetry by K. A. Johnson and S. B. Treiman, *Phys. Rev. Letters, 14:* 189 (1965) (see Chapter 17).

[27] Strictly speaking, Equation (33) can be considered to apply only over a limited range of incident energies. Otherwise, F depends both on the total *cm* energy, $s^{1/2}$, and on t. Correspondingly, we may consider the constant a [Equation (33a)] to be a slowly varying function of s.

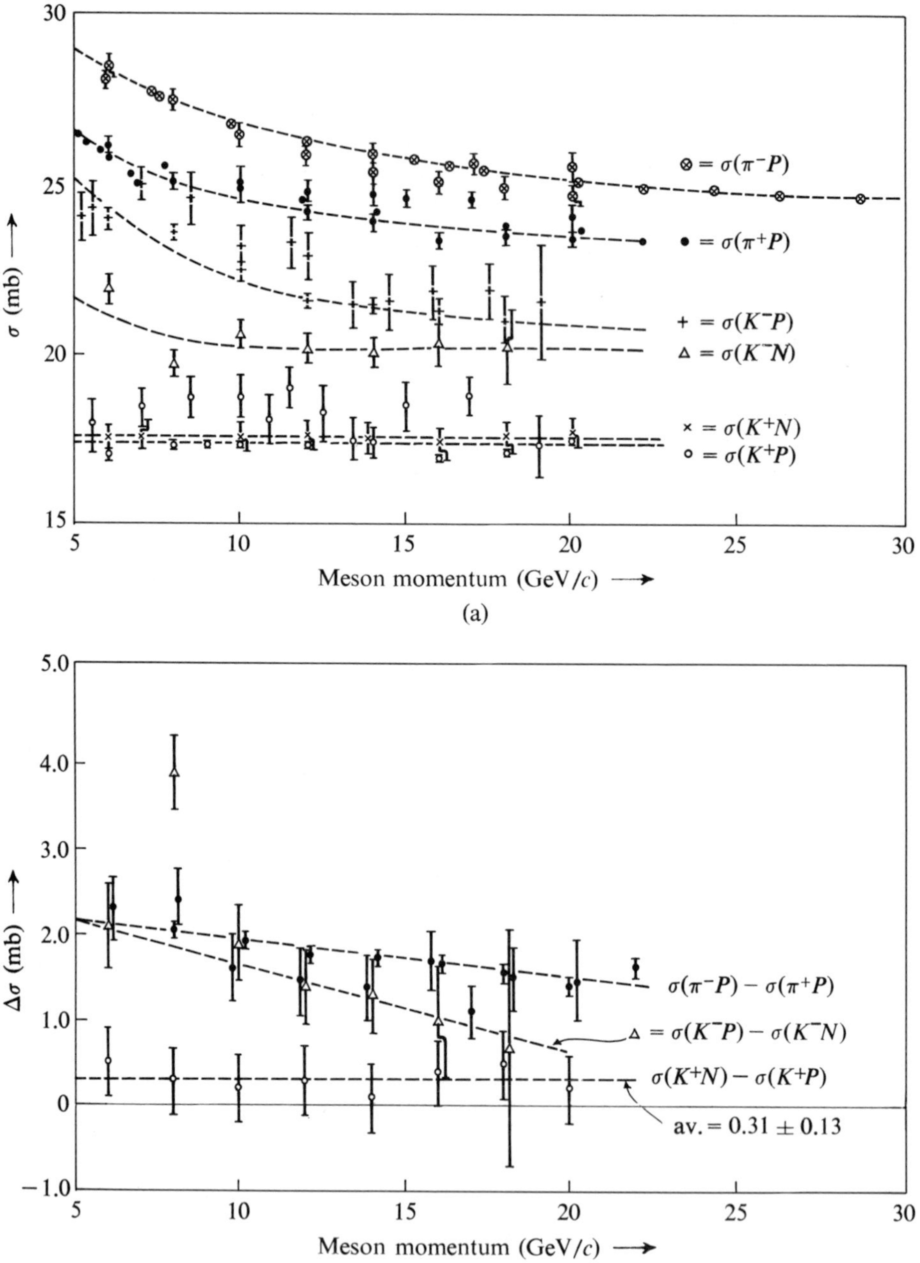

Figure 13.2 Total cross sections for (a) meson + nucleon and (c) nucleon or antinucleon + nucleon, and their differences (b) and (d).

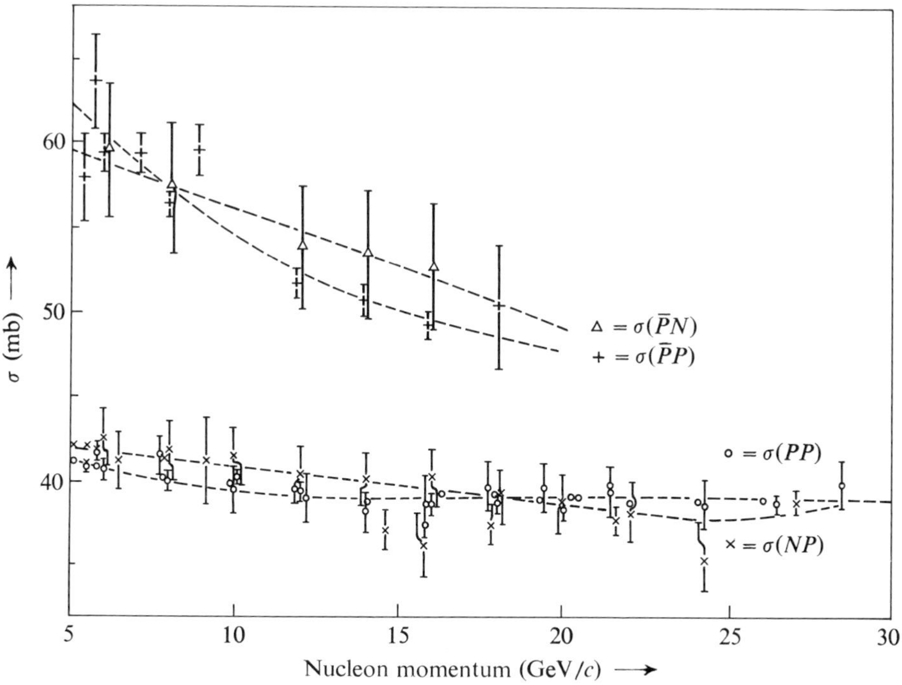
σ (mb) →
60
50
40
5
10
15
20
25
30
Nucleon momentum (GeV/c) →
△ = σ(P̄N)
+ = σ(P̄P)
○ = σ(PP)
× = σ(NP)

(c)

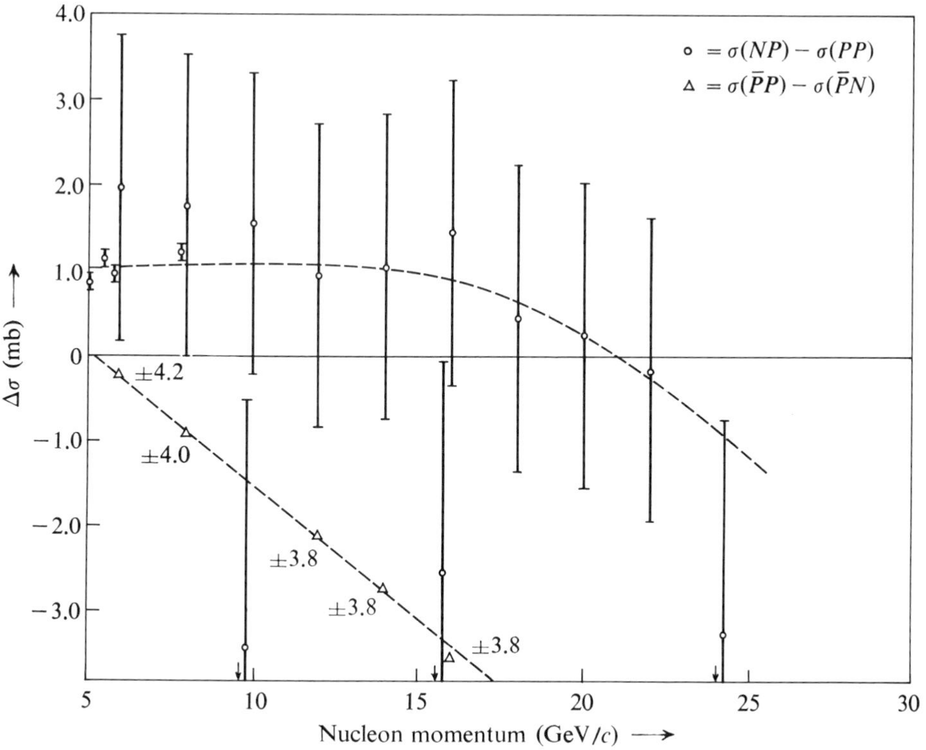
Δσ (mb) →
4.0
3.0
2.0
1.0
0
−1.0
−2.0
−3.0
5
10
15
20
25
30
Nucleon momentum (GeV/c) →
○ = σ(NP) − σ(PP)
△ = σ(P̄P) − σ(P̄N)
±4.2
±4.0
±3.8
±3.8
±3.8

(d)

factor. Generally, over a relatively wide range (but up to not too large values of $|t|$),

$$F^2(t) \cong e^{at}, \tag{33a}$$

where a is related to the mean square scattering (strong interaction) radius

$$3a \cong \langle r^2 \rangle^{(s)}. \tag{33b}$$

For both π–P and P–P elastic scattering, $a \simeq 10\ (\text{GeV}/c)^{-2}$, which gives

$$[\langle r^2 \rangle^{(s)}]^{1/2} \simeq 1.1 \text{ f} \approx \sqrt{2}\,(0.8) \text{ f}, \tag{33b$'$}$$

a result to be expected if both the pion and the physical nucleon are extended structures, with $\langle r^2 \rangle_\pi^{1/2} \approx \langle r^2 \rangle_P^{1/2} \approx 0.8$ f, and assuming additivity of the (relatively) forward scattering amplitudes of the components.

A careful analysis of high-energy scattering would contain many more subtleties than indicated in the preceding crude, qualitative discussion. Nevertheless, the study of the properties of elastic and inelastic differential cross sections, at high energy and relatively small momentum transfer, sheds considerable light on proposed models of elementary particle structure. We shall return to these questions in greater detail in Chapter 17.

PROBLEMS

1. Consider the pion atomic model of the nucleons with

$$R_{p,\pi}(r) = A \exp\,[-r^2/2R_{p,\pi}^2].$$

Compute the values of $\langle r^2 \rangle_{P,N}^E$, and estimate $R_{p,\pi}$ from the observed values of $G_E^{P,N}(q\!\!\!/^2 \to 0)$.

2. Assume, on the basis of the F–Y–S model of the mesons, that the ρ and ω mesons are a mixture of $^3S_1$ and $^3D_1$ $\mathfrak{N}\overline{\mathfrak{N}}$ states with relative amplitude $\xi = |a_D/a_S| \ll 1$, $(|a_D|^2 + |a_S|^2 = 1)$.
   (a) Considering the decays $\rho, \omega \to \pi + \gamma$, how could you measure the rate of $E2$ decay relative to that of $M1$?
   (b) Derive an expression for $\Gamma^{(E2)}/\Gamma^{(M1)}$ in terms of ξ and the spatial distributions of the $\mathfrak{N}\overline{\mathfrak{N}}$ wave functions.

3. One way of obtaining the asymptotic (Pomeranchuk) limits of the total hadron-hadron cross sections (Figure 13.2) is to plot them versus $s^{-1/2}$, and to attempt a smooth extrapolation to the limit $s^{-1/2} \to 0$. Using this method, compare the asymptotic limits of the cross sections with the Pomeranchuk predictions [Equations (30)] and with those of the F–Y–S model [Equations (32)]. What is the *lab* energy to which hadronic projectiles would need to be accelerated in order to arrive at observed cross sections which differ from the asymptotic ($s^{-1/2} \to 0$) limits by less than 1 percent?

PART III

Unitary Symmetry and Quark Models

14

$SU(3)$

Of the various models considered in preceding chapters, the doublet-symmetry scheme (Section 12.4) is perhaps the most appealing owing to the general nature of the approach, in which members of baryon and/or meson groups with common intrinsic properties are treated on an equal footing, the group structure being determined by the dynamical symmetries governing the basic strong interactions. According to this approach, the distinctions between the observed particles arise from the dependence of the symmetry-breaking interactions (assumed less strong than the basic interaction) on the values of a subset of the intrinsic quantum numbers — e.g., isotopic spin (t, t_3) and hypercharge ($\mathcal{Y}$).

Although the doublet-symmetry scheme was not successful, it did inspire a search for a more appropriate symmetry or group structure into which the observed multiplets of mesons and baryons could be imbedded. This search came to fruition with the discovery by Gell-Mann and Ne'eman [1] that the major (spin $\frac{1}{2}^+$) baryons and the pseudoscalar mesons could be fitted into the octet representation of $SU(3)$ — the symmetric unitary group of dimension three. In this chapter, we shall explore the meaning and implications of this statement.[2]

Before considering $SU(3)$ and its consequences, we illustrate the approach by reviewing briefly the symmetry or group properties associated with angular momentum, or isotopic spin, and its combinations. It is well known that all angular momenta can be built up out of combinations of systems of spin $\frac{1}{2}$ (doublets). Thus, the combination of two spin $\frac{1}{2}$ systems yields a spin 0 (singlet) and

[1] M. Gell-Mann and Y. Ne'eman, eds., *The Eightfold Way*, W. A. Benjamin, New York (1964).

[2] For a general discussion of the material of this chapter and Chapter 15, see V. F. Weisskopf, "$SU(2) \rightarrow SU(3) \rightarrow SU(6)$," *CERN Report*, 66–19 (1966).

a spin 1 (triplet), with the associated eigenfunctions of the combinations being, respectively, antisymmetric and symmetric with respect to interchange of the two constituents. Likewise, combining spin $\frac{1}{2}$ with spin 1 yields the spins $\frac{1}{2}$ and $\frac{3}{2}$; in this case the (four) eigenfunctions of the spin $\frac{3}{2}$ system are symmetric, while those of the spin $\frac{1}{2}$ have mixed symmetry.

In the language of group theory, the spin $\frac{1}{2}$ system corresponds to the basic representation of the symmetric unitary group of dimension two, $SU(2)$, while the product

$$2 \otimes 2 = 1 \oplus 3 \tag{1a}$$

gives rise to combinations corresponding to representations of $SU(2)$ of multiplicity 1 (singlet) and 3 (triplet). Likewise,

$$2 \otimes 3 = 2 \oplus 4 \tag{1b}$$

describes, in group-theoretic language, the representations resulting from the product of an $SU(2)$ doublet and triplet. Thus, the various spins that can result from all the possible combinations of spin $\frac{1}{2}$ systems are in one-to-one correspondence with the different possible representations of the $SU(2)$ group.

The algebra of spin $\frac{1}{2}$ combination requires the use of the 2×2 Pauli spin matrices, τ_x, τ_y, τ_z, or, alternatively, τ_+, τ_-, τ_3, which are referred to as the "generators" of the $SU(2)$ group.

The components of the representations of $SU(2)$ can be given a geometrical description by means of diagrams such as those depicted in Figure 14.1, in which the members of the spin multiplets are plotted on a *linear* scale, with the distance from the origin proportional to the m-value or third component of the spin. The assumed (dynamical) $SU(2)$ symmetry of the interaction between the basic doublets requires that the corresponding properties of the members of the resulting spin multiplets be invariant with respect to reflection about an axis normal to the t_3 axis and passing through its origin.

However, the $SU(2)$ group is inadequate for representing the observed meson and baryon multiplets for at least two reasons. First, as we have already noted (Section 12.2), these require at least three basic constituents (the Sakata model

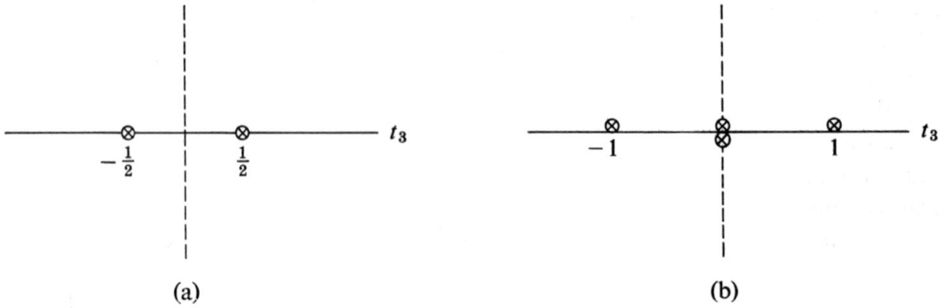

Figure 14.1 Geometrical description of representations of the $SU(2)$ group. (a) The basic doublet. (b) $2 \otimes 2 = 1 \oplus 3$.

shows the necessity for adding the λ to the basic p–n isotopic doublet in order to introduce the hypercharge quantum number $\mathcal{Y}$). Second, the lowest-lying mesonic states contain eight or nine members ($\pi^+\pi^-\pi^0$, η, K^+K^0, $\overline{K^0}K^-$, and η' for the pseudoscalars; $\rho^+\rho^0\rho^-$, ω, φ, $K^{*+}K^{*0}$, $\overline{K^{*0}}\,K^{*-}$ for the vectors), and the low-lying baryon states comprise an octet (PN, Λ, $\Sigma^+\Sigma^0\Sigma^-$, $\Xi^0\Xi^-$ for $\frac{1}{2}^+$) and a decimet ($\Delta^{++}\Delta^+\Delta^0\Delta^-$, $Y_1^{*+}Y_1^{*0}Y_1^{*-}$, $\Xi^{*0}\Xi^{*-}$, Ω^- for $\frac{3}{2}^+$). The important step taken by Gell-Mann and Ne'eman was that of associating these multiplets with representations of the $SU(3)$ group and, in particular, of adopting the $\frac{1}{2}^+$ baryon octet as the basic representation from which the other multiplets may be derived by appropriate combination.

In the following, we derive the most important aspects of the $SU(3)$ model by use, mainly, of the geometrical approach, in which the symmetry properties of the various representations are exhibited through diagrams where the multiplet members are represented by points on a *plane*, the abscissa being the value of t_3 and the ordinate that of $\mathcal{Y}$. We also take advantage of the explicit symmetries exhibited by the combination eigenfunctions for deriving the properties of the representations resulting from various combinations. For a discussion of the mathematical tools of group theory, the reader is referred to the standard texts.[3]

14.1 The Basic Octets and Their Combination

As noted, the basic baryon multiplet consists of an octet (eight) of members: the nucleon and Ξ isodoublets ($\mathcal{Y} = 1$ and -1, respectively), the Σ isotriplet and the Λ isosinglet (both $\mathcal{Y} = 0$); for the pseudoscalar mesons, the analogous octet corresponds exactly to that of the baryons with the members being K, $\overline{K}$, π, η. The symmetry inherent in these octets is illustrated in Figure 14.2, in which the members of the multiplets are plotted on a plane whose x axis is the value of t_3, and whose y axis is the value of the hypercharge $\mathcal{Y}$. We note that two members of each octet (Σ^0–Λ^0 or π^0–η^0) occupy the same position on the t_3–$\mathcal{Y}$ diagram. Note, also, that the charge of any member is given by the usual relationship

$$Q = t_3 + \frac{\mathcal{Y}}{2}, \tag{2}$$

which means that points of equal charge lie on parallel straight lines in the t_3–$\mathcal{Y}$ plane.

Now, the characteristic feature of $SU(3)$ symmetry is the invariance of such diagrams with respect to rotations of the axes by 120°. In particular, the axis obtained by a counterclockwise rotation of $\mathcal{Y}$ by 120° in Figure 14.2 corresponds to the charge ($-Q$); the diagram is invariant with respect to reflection across this axis, in that the reflected position corresponds to another member of the octet whose charge is the same as that of the original. Furthermore, the multiplicity (number of values of U_3, the "third component" of a new physical $SU(3)$ invariant,

[3] For example, M. Hamermesh, *Group Theory*, Addison-Wesley, Reading, Mass. (1962); H. Weyl, *The Classical Groups*, Princeton University Press, Princeton, N.J. (1946); E. P. Wigner, *Group Theory*, Academic Press, New York (1959).

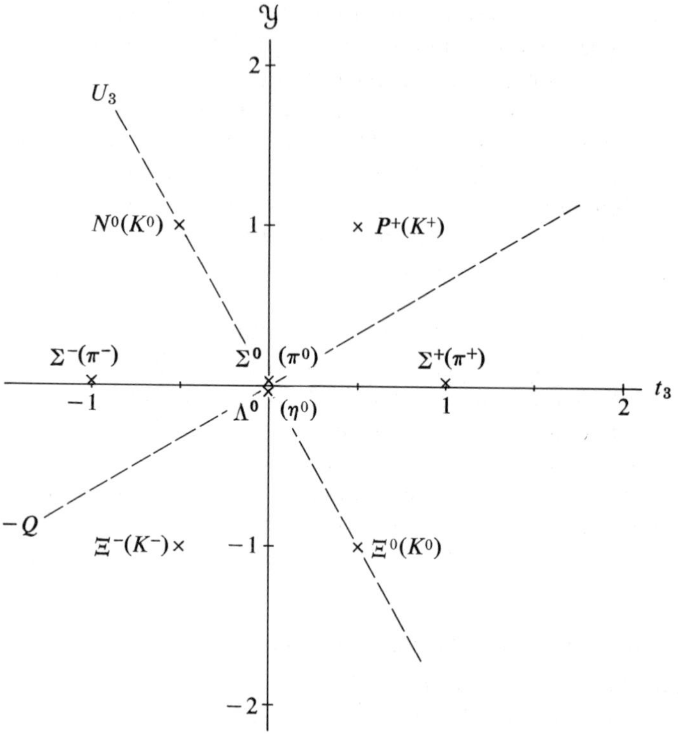

Figure 14.2 The basic $SU(3)$ octets.

which we call the U spin) of the sets of particles of equal charge is in one-to-one correspondence with the isotopic-spin multiplicities present in the original t_3–$\mathcal{Y}$ diagram.

These features are common to all $SU(3)$ multiplets and, while deferring until Section 14.2 the exploration of the physical meaning and consequences of these invariance properties, we may take advantage of them for deriving the combinatorial properties of $SU(3)$ multiplets.

EXAMPLE

The combination of two octets leads to $8 \times 8 = 64$ members, which divide into six $SU(3)$ multiplets according to the symmetry in isotopic-spin space of the product wave functions. Mathematical group-theoretic methods[4] lead to the following decomposition:

$$8 \otimes 8' = 1 \oplus 8_1 \oplus 8_2 \oplus 10 \oplus \overline{10} \oplus 27; \tag{3}$$

but it is of interest to see how this result can be obtained by straightforward combinatorial techniques, making use of the invariance properties noted above.

[4] J. J. de Swart, *Rev. Mod. Phys., 35:* 916 (1963).

In Table 14.1, which lists all the possible combinations of the members of the octets 8 and 8′, we show the initial values of $\mathcal{Y}$ and t (columns 1–4) and their combined values (columns 5 and 6), the number of independent product wave functions $(2t+1)$ corresponding to each combination (column 7), and their symmetry in t space (columns 8 and 9). The problem is to find the appropriate $SU(3)$ representations to which these products belong (column 10).

We adopt a stepwise approach with the aid of Figure 14.3. Starting with the unique $\mathcal{Y}=2$ triplet ($t=1$), row 1 of Table 14.1, we plot its members as open circles, ○, on the t_3–$\mathcal{Y}$ diagram in Figure 14.3(a). Reflection of these three points about the Q axis yields the crosses, ×, from which, making use of the requirement that every isotopic multiplet be complete ($t \leq t_3 \leq -t$ in unit

Table 14.1 Combinations Resulting from 8 ⊗ 8′

$\mathcal{Y}_8$	t_8	$\mathcal{Y}_{8'}$	$t_{8'}$	$\mathcal{Y}$	t	$(2t+1)$	Symmetry		Multiplet assignment
1	$\frac{1}{2}$	1	$\frac{1}{2}$	2	1	3	+		27
1	$\frac{1}{2}$	1	$\frac{1}{2}$	2	0	1	−		$\overline{10}$
1	$\frac{1}{2}$	0	1	1	$\frac{3}{2}$	4		+	27
0	1	1	$\frac{1}{2}$	1	$\frac{3}{2}$	4		−	10
1	$\frac{1}{2}$	0	1	1	$\frac{1}{2}$	2		(+)	8_1
0	1	1	$\frac{1}{2}$	1	$\frac{1}{2}$	2		−	$\overline{10}$
1	$\frac{1}{2}$	0	0	1	$\frac{1}{2}$	2		(−)	8_2
0	0	1	$\frac{1}{2}$	1	$\frac{1}{2}$	2		+	27
0	1	0	1	0	2	5	+		27
0	1	0	1	0	1	3		(−)	8_2
0	1	0	0	0	1	3		(+)	8_1
0	0	0	1	0	1	3		−	$\overline{10}$
1	$\frac{1}{2}$	−1	$\frac{1}{2}$	0	1	3		−	10
−1	$\frac{1}{2}$	1	$\frac{1}{2}$	0	1	3		+	27
0	1	0	1	0	0	1		+	27
0	0	0	0	0	0	1		(−)	8_2
1	$\frac{1}{2}$	−1	$\frac{1}{2}$	0	0	1		(+)	8_1
−1	$\frac{1}{2}$	1	$\frac{1}{2}$	0	0	1		−	1
0	0	−1	$\frac{1}{2}$	−1	$\frac{1}{2}$	2		+	27
−1	$\frac{1}{2}$	0	0	−1	$\frac{1}{2}$	2		(−)	8_2
0	1	−1	$\frac{1}{2}$	−1	$\frac{1}{2}$	2		−	10
−1	$\frac{1}{2}$	0	1	−1	$\frac{1}{2}$	2		(+)	8_1
0	1	−1	$\frac{1}{2}$	−1	$\frac{3}{2}$	4		−	$\overline{10}$
−1	$\frac{1}{2}$	0	1	−1	$\frac{3}{2}$	4		+	27
−1	$\frac{1}{2}$	−1	$\frac{1}{2}$	−2	0	1	−		10
−1	$\frac{1}{2}$	−1	$\frac{1}{2}$	−2	1	3	+		27

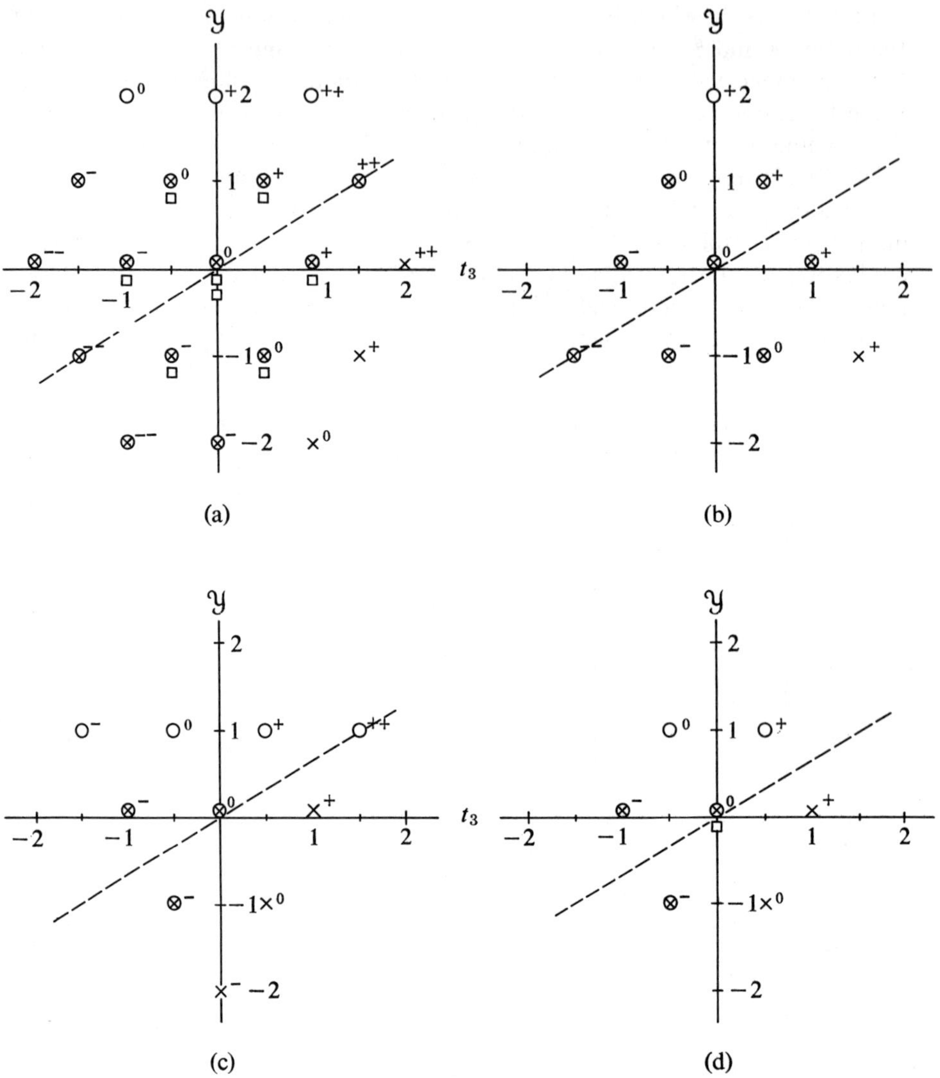

Figure 14.3 $SU(3)$ multiplets resulting from $8 \otimes 8'$. (a) "27." (b) "$\overline{10}$." (c) "10." (d) "8."

steps) and of the correspondence between isospin and U spin multiplets, we are able to deduce the rest of the members depicted by the circled crosses, $\otimes$, in Figure 14.3(a). This procedure immediately accounts for 19 members of the "27-plet"; we shall shortly see how to fill in the remaining 8.

We turn next to the antisymmetric $\mathcal{Y}=2$, $t=0$ combination, which is also unique. Plotting this as the open circle in Figure 14.3(b), its Q-reflected point as $\times$, we may similarly fill in the rest of the members as $\otimes$. (It is remarkable that this entire multiplet of ten is obtained, starting from just one member, by straightforward application of invariance and symmetry.)

A similar multiplet of ten members, but inverted with respect to the t_3 axis, could be obtained starting with the $\mathcal{Y} = -2$, $t = 0$ combination; instead, we have chosen to start, in Figure 14.3(c), with the antisymmetric $\mathcal{Y} = 1$, $t = \frac{3}{2}$ combination (orthogonal to the symmetric combination belonging to the 27-plet), but the result is identical.

With the combinations already identified, indicated by the ○, ×, and ⊗ in Figures 14.3(a), (b), and (c), we have exhausted most of the available combinations. There remain to be accounted for (Table 14.1): three each with $\mathcal{Y} = \pm 1$, $t = \frac{1}{2}$, three with $\mathcal{Y} = 0$, $t = 1$, and four with $\mathcal{Y} = 0$, $t = 0$. Evidently, as illustrated in Figure 14.3(d), starting with any combination but the last, one obtains seven members of an octet (Figure 14.2), so that a singlet must be added to complete each octet configuration [the □ in Figure 14.3(d)]. This gives us three octets, and finally leaves a lone (antisymmetric) singlet. However, among the various possible combinations making up the three octets, one set has the complete symmetry characteristic of the 27-plet (see Table 14.1) and should therefore be added to the 19 previously identified, to complete the group of 27 [□ in Figure 14.3(a)]. The remaining two octets have mixed symmetries, inappropriate[5] to either the $\overline{10}$ or the 10. We are thus finally left with exactly those combinations given by Equation (3).

Starting with the baryon and pseudoscalar meson octets, we would hope to identify the rest of the observed baryons as belonging to multiplets resulting from their combination

$$B' = B_8 \otimes m_8 . \tag{3a}$$

Indeed, among the known baryon states of mass ≤ 2.2 GeV, there are a number of clear candidates, as indicated in Table 14.2.

However, the most striking illustration of the usefulness of this approach is in the identification of the Δ decimet of (ten) spin $\frac{3}{2}^+$ baryons,[6] $N^*_{3/2}(1236)$, $Y^*_1(1385)$, $\Xi^*_{1/2}(1530)$, and $\Omega^-_0(1672)$, with the representation "10" of $SU(3)$, as depicted in Figure 14.3(c). Indeed, the discovery[7] of the Ω^-, as predicted by Gell-Mann on the basis of $SU(3)$, was a most convincing confirmation of the applicability of this symmetry to the observed baryons.

Nevertheless, the question arises as to the reasons for the absence of the "27" and "$\overline{10}$" multiplets from the observed baryon configurations. In principle, one

---

[5] Note that the doublets and triplets belonging to the $\overline{10}$ and 10 groups differ from those of the octets in that one member of each of the former belongs to a quartet of charge states ($\frac{3}{2} \geq U_3 \geq -\frac{3}{2}$), while the charged members of octets all belong to charge doublets ($\frac{1}{2} \geq U_3 \geq -\frac{1}{2}$). The product wave functions for the $\overline{10}$ or 10 can be distinguished from those of the 8 on this basis.

[6] Henceforth denoted by Δ, $_\Delta Y$, $_\Delta \Xi$, and Ω.

[7] V. E. Barnes, *et al., Phys. Rev. Letters, 12:* 204 (1964). Note that as long ago as 1954, Y. Eisenberg (*Phys. Rev., 96:* 541) observed an unstable particle, in a nuclear emulsion exposed to cosmic rays, whose mass he measured as 1650 ± 360 MeV, and which he interpreted as possibly $\Omega^- \rightarrow (\Lambda^0 \text{ or } \Sigma^0) + K^-$.

Table 14.2 Groups of Excited Baryonic States and Their Possible SU(3) Identification

	Mass (MeV)						
Spin[a]	$N^*_{1/2}$	$N^*_{3/2}$	Y^*_0	Y^*_1	$\Xi^*_{1/2}$	Ω^-_0	$SU(3)$ multiplet
$\frac{1}{2}^+$	1470						8?
	1750	1930	(1745)				1, 8, 10 ?
$\frac{1}{2}^-$			1405				1
	1550		1670	(1610)			8
		1640					10
	1710		(1750)	(1700)			8
$\frac{3}{2}^+$		1236		1385	1530	[1677] (1672)	10
$\frac{3}{2}^-$			1520				1
	1520		1700	1660	[1860]		8
		1690			1820		10
$\frac{5}{2}^+$	1690		1815	1910	[1987] 2030		8
$\frac{5}{2}^-$	1680		1830	1765	[1947] 1930		8
$\frac{7}{2}^+$		1950		2030	[2110]	[2190]	10
$\frac{7}{2}^-$	2190		2100				8?

[a] For those mesons listed in parentheses, the spin has not yet been independently verified; the values in brackets are computed from the $SU(3)$ mass formula (to be derived) for those multiplets in which the other members are identified in the table.

may postulate a strong dependence of the B_8–m_8 interaction on the isotopic symmetry of the product wave functions such as to lead to either a weak, nonresonant interaction or even a repulsion in the unobserved states; still, the scheme for the excited baryons, represented by Equation (3a), does appear to be a somewhat uneconomical one.

The same questions arise in consideration of the multiplets of mesons heavier than the pseudoscalars: the vector (1^-) and tensor (2^+) nonets, as well as others, still incompletely identified (Table 2.1). One might postulate these as basic octets and singlets, or one might attempt to regard them as B–$\overline{B}$ combinations according to the scheme

$$m = B_8 \otimes \overline{B}_8 \tag{3b}$$

in the spirit of the F–Y–S approach. Here, again, the predictions [Equation (3)] are much too rich in comparison with the observations; only singlets and octets have thus far been unambiguously observed among the mesons.

We shall return to these questions at the end of this chapter.

PROBLEM

Consider an F–Y–S type of model in which the mesons are

$$m = B_{10} \otimes \overline{B}_{10}.$$

(a) What are the resulting meson multiplets?
(b) Does this work any better than $B_8 \otimes \overline{B}_8$?

14.2 *I* Spin, *U* Spin, *V* Spin

We have noted in Section 14.1 the invariance property of the $SU(3)$ multiplets with respect to rotation of the t_3–$\mathcal{Y}$ axes by 120°. Considering the diagrams of the baryon octet and decimet with respect to the rotated axes U_3 and Q as shown in Figure 14.4, we note that the same set of multiplets appears as in the original t_3–$\mathcal{Y}$ diagrams (Figures 14.2 and 14.3), except that the multiplets are here characterized by the same value of the charge Q rather than the hypercharge $\mathcal{Y}$.

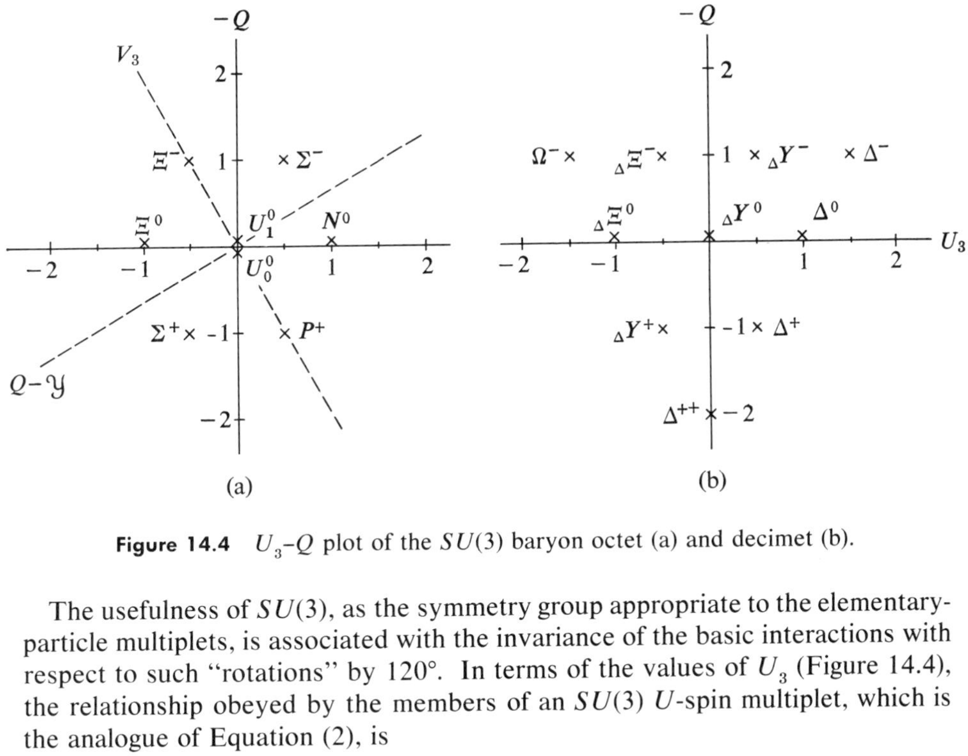

Figure 14.4 U_3–Q plot of the $SU(3)$ baryon octet (a) and decimet (b).

The usefulness of $SU(3)$, as the symmetry group appropriate to the elementary-particle multiplets, is associated with the invariance of the basic interactions with respect to such "rotations" by 120°. In terms of the values of U_3 (Figure 14.4), the relationship obeyed by the members of an $SU(3)$ U-spin multiplet, which is the analogue of Equation (2), is

$$\mathcal{Y} = U_3 + \frac{Q}{2}. \tag{2'}$$

Thus, U_3 may be regarded as the third component of another invariant vector, **U**, whose length is conserved in all interactions that are $SU(3)$-invariant. As in the case of the I spin, the components of $\mathbf{U}$ obey the commutation relation

$$(U_i, U_j) = iU_k, \tag{2a}$$

and we may define the "raising" and "lowering" operators

$$U_\pm = (U_1 \pm iU_2), \tag{2b}$$

which have the property

$$U_\pm |U, U_3\rangle = \sqrt{U(U+1) - U_3(U_3 \pm 1)}\,|U, U_3 \pm 1\rangle. \tag{2c}$$

In particular, referring to Figure 14.4(a), we require the particular combinations of Σ^0 and Λ^0 corresponding to ($U=1$, $U_3=0$) and ($U=0$, $U_3=0$), where

$$U_+\Xi^0 = \sqrt{2}\,U_1^0, \tag{2d}$$

$$\langle U_1^0 | U_0^0 \rangle = 0. \tag{2e}$$

The simplest way [8] of obtaining these is to note that the transformation from the t_3–$\mathcal{Y}$ diagram (Figure 14.2) to the U_3–Q diagram [Figure 14.4(a)] involves a geometric rotation by $-120°$, so that we may apply the rotation matrix

$$\begin{pmatrix} U_1^0 \\ U_0^0 \end{pmatrix} = -\begin{pmatrix} \cos\dfrac{2\pi}{3} & \sin\dfrac{2\pi}{3} \\ -\sin\dfrac{2\pi}{3} & \cos\dfrac{2\pi}{3} \end{pmatrix} \begin{pmatrix} \Sigma^0 \\ \Lambda^0 \end{pmatrix}$$

$$= \begin{pmatrix} \dfrac{1}{2} & -\dfrac{\sqrt{3}}{2} \\ \dfrac{\sqrt{3}}{2} & \dfrac{1}{2} \end{pmatrix} \begin{pmatrix} \Sigma^0 \\ \Lambda^0 \end{pmatrix}$$

$$= \begin{pmatrix} \left(\dfrac{1}{2}\Sigma^0 - \dfrac{\sqrt{3}}{2}\Lambda^0\right) \\ \left(\dfrac{\sqrt{3}}{2}\Sigma^0 + \dfrac{1}{2}\Lambda^0\right) \end{pmatrix}. \tag{2f}$$

In the case of the Δ decimet [Figures 14.3(c) and 14.4(b)], there is only one baryon at the central position, so that the ${}_\Delta Y^0$ is at the same time the ($t=1$, $t_3=0$) and ($U=1$, $U_3=0$) member. For the pseudoscalar meson octet (Figure 14.2) the central members are the same as in the case of the baryon octet, with the substitution $\Sigma^0 \to \pi^0$, $\Lambda^0 \to \eta^0$. The vector meson octet, however, requires special consideration, in view of the fact that the $\mathcal{Y}=0$, $t=0$ member is a linear combination of the observed ω^0 and the ϕ^0; we return to this question in Section 14.3.

[8] The transformation is also obtained in a natural fashion when we regard the baryons and mesons as compounds, consisting of the appropriate combinations of basic octets, and we apply Equation (2d) to the appropriate product wave function for the Ξ^0 or the K^0. However, this becomes easier to do in the quark model; see Chapter 15.

The $SU(3)$ symmetry being invariant with respect to 120° rotations of the t_3–$\mathcal{Y}$ axes, the invariance applies also to a second 120° rotation, as illustrated in Figure 14.4(a). For this new set of axes, the ordinate corresponds to the combination $(Q-\mathcal{Y})$, and the abscissa corresponds to the third component, V_3, of a third invariant vector **V**, with

$$-\mathcal{Y}=V_3+\frac{(Q-\mathcal{Y})}{2}. \tag{4}$$

When we perform this second rotation, the appropriate central members of the baryon octet in the V_3–$(Q-\mathcal{Y})$ plane become[9]

$$\begin{pmatrix} V_1^0 \\ V_0^0 \end{pmatrix}=\begin{pmatrix} \frac{1}{2} & -\frac{\sqrt{3}}{2} \\ \frac{\sqrt{3}}{2} & \frac{1}{2} \end{pmatrix}\begin{pmatrix} U_1^0 \\ U_0^0 \end{pmatrix}=-\begin{pmatrix} \left(\frac{1}{2}\Sigma^0+\frac{\sqrt{3}}{2}\Lambda^0\right) \\ \left(-\frac{\sqrt{3}}{2}\Sigma^0+\frac{1}{2}\Lambda^0\right) \end{pmatrix}. \tag{4a}$$

However, in general, V-spin conservation does not add any new consequences to the $SU(3)$ symmetry, owing to the fact that Equations (2), (2′), and (4) are not linearly independent, but are connected by the condition

$$t_3+U_3+V_3=0. \tag{5}$$

PROBLEM

In the t_3–$\mathcal{Y}$ diagram of the "27-plet" (Figure 14.3), a number of places are occupied by two members, while one spot ($t_3=\mathcal{Y}=0$) is occupied by three. Find the appropriate combinations of the $(t, t_3, \mathcal{Y})$ eigenstates in the (U, U_3, Q) representation. *Note:* Unless you are more clever than I, you will probably need to use the properties of the $U_\pm$ operators and the appropriate $8\otimes 8'$ combinations.

14.3 Some Consequences of *SU*(3) Symmetry; the Symmetry-Breaking Interactions

The utility of $SU(3)$ derives from the invariance of the basic strong interaction among the hadrons with respect to the operations (rotations in t_3–$\mathcal{Y}$ space) described in Section 14.2; this interaction determines the multiplet structure of the various hadron groups. Thus, if we describe the interactions among the hadrons in terms of an interaction Hamiltonian, the leading term in this Hamiltonian must behave as a scalar in t space, U space, and V space; we refer to this as the "very strong interaction," or VSI.

Now, in the absence of any other interaction terms, all the members of a given $SU(3)$ multiplet would be degenerate in mass, since there would be no difference between their total energies. The mass splittings that separate the different I-spin

---

[9] Note that a third rotation brings us back to the original $\begin{pmatrix} \Sigma^0 \\ \Lambda^0 \end{pmatrix}$, as it should.

multiplets[10] within a given $SU(3)$ multiplet, and which are relatively large (i.e., comparable to their masses in some cases), must result from a term in the Hamiltonian that is at least a "moderately strong interaction" (MSI). However, since isotopic spin is conserved in the MSI, this interaction term must still behave as a scalar in t space; the symmetry breaking must therefore arise as a consequence of either U-spin or V-spin nonconservation, or both.[11]

On the other hand, the term in the Hamiltonian corresponding to the electromagnetic interaction (EMI) is manifestly charge dependent (I-spin nonconserving), while it is most natural to assume that it conserves U spin since all the members of a given U-spin multiplet have the same charge.

As for the weak interactions (WI), they violate both I-spin and U-spin conservation, albeit in a special fashion (note the $\Delta t = \frac{1}{2}$ and $\Delta S = \Delta Q$ selection rules).

We consider, in this section, some of the consequences of such a hierarchy of terms in the interaction Hamiltonian, leaving the question of the form of the WI for Chapter 18, however.

14.3.1 The MSI and the Mass "Fine Structure"

Let us adopt the simplest useful assumption for the MSI — that it behaves as a scalar in t space and as a vector in U space. If we define the mass operator

$$O_M = H_{\text{VSI}} + H_{\text{MSI}}, \tag{6a}$$

$$O_M \psi_i = M_i \psi_i, \tag{6b}$$

this operator will have the form[12]

$$O_M = M_0 + AU_3, \tag{6c}$$

where both M_0 and A are assumed to behave as scalars in both t space and U space.

The Baryons • We now apply O_M to the members of the $U = 1$ ($Q = 0$) baryon triplet [Figure 14.4(a)]

$$M_{\Xi^0} = \langle \Xi^0 | O_M \Xi^0 \rangle = M_0 - A, \tag{7a}$$

$$M_{N^0} = \langle N^0 | O_M N^0 \rangle = M_0 + A, \tag{7b}$$

$$M_{U_1^0} = \left\langle \left(\frac{1}{2} \Sigma^0 - \frac{\sqrt{3}}{2} \Lambda^0 \right) \middle| O_M \left(\frac{1}{2} \Sigma^0 - \frac{\sqrt{3}}{2} \Lambda^0 \right) \right\rangle$$

$$= \frac{1}{4} M_{\Sigma^0} + \frac{3}{4} M_{\Lambda^0} = M_0. \tag{7c}$$

---

[10] We use the term I spin as an abbreviation for the isotopic spin; however, since the symbol **I** is conventionally used to represent the (ordinary) spin of a nucleus, we prefer to use the symbol **t** for the isotopic-spin vector. We apologize for any confusion resulting.

[11] Actually, because of their interdependence [see Equation (5)] the invariance properties of the Hamiltonian with respect to I spin and U spin determine the behavior with respect to the V spin. Hence, in what follows, we consider only the first two.

[12] Equation (6c) is obviously not the most general U-spin noninvariant form. However, it is the simplest and, furthermore, one that leads to matrix elements only between states with $\Delta U = 0, \pm 1$, which reflects the vector nature of the U-spin violation.

Note that $\langle \Sigma^0 | O_M \Lambda^0 \rangle = 0$ as a consequence of the *I*-spin conserving nature of O_M. Combining Equations (7a)–(7c), we obtain the famous mass formula[13]

$$\frac{M_\Xi + M_{\mathfrak{N}}}{2} = \frac{M_\Sigma + 3M_\Lambda}{4}, \tag{7}$$

which we know holds to an accuracy of better than 1 percent.

The same considerations may be applied to the members of the $Q = -1$, $U = \frac{3}{2}$ quartet of the Δ decimet [Figure 14.4(b)]:

$$\begin{aligned} M_\Delta &= M_0' + \tfrac{3}{2}A', \\ M_{\Delta Y} &= M_0' + \tfrac{1}{2}A', \\ M_{\Delta\Xi} &= M_0' - \tfrac{1}{2}A', \\ M_\Omega &= M_0' - \tfrac{3}{2}A', \end{aligned} \tag{8a}$$

leading to the equal-spacing rule for the decimet,

$$M_{\Delta Y} - M_\Delta = M_{\Delta\Xi} - M_{\Delta Y} = M_\Omega - M_{\Delta\Xi}, \tag{8}$$

which may be compared with the experimental values 149, 146, and 141 MeV, respectively. Indeed, it was on the basis of the equal-spacing rule, derived under the assumptions stated above, that Gell-Mann predicted the mass of the Ω^-; its discovery may thus be regarded as a major triumph of the $SU(3)$ scheme (together with the assumption as to the nature of the symmetry-violating MSI) and a confirmation of the assignment of the $\frac{3}{2}^+$ baryons to its decimet representation.

Generalized Mass Formula • Equations (7) and (8) are special cases of a general $SU(3)$ mass relation, derived by Gell-Mann and Okubo[14] on the assumption of the vector form of the *U*-spin violating interaction. We present here a plausible outline (*not* a rigorous demonstration) of the form of the Gell-Mann–Okubo mass formula.

Let us consider in greater detail the form of the mass operator M_0 in Equation (6c),

$$M_0 = M_0(U^2, t^2, \mathcal{Y}^2), \tag{9a}$$

recalling that it must behave as a scalar in both *t* space and *U* space. In particular, within a given *U*-spin multiplet, the form of M_0 must be such that Equation (6c) yields the equal-spacing rule for the members of the multiplet. Furthermore, Equation (6c) may be rewritten [see Equation (2′)] as

$$O_M = M_0 + AU_3 = \left(M_0 - \frac{AQ}{2}\right) + A\mathcal{Y} = M_0' + A\mathcal{Y}, \tag{9b}$$

[13] Since Equation (6a) behaves as an isotopic scalar, all members of the same *I*-spin multiplet automatically have the same mass.

[14] M. Gell-Mann and Y. Ne'eman, *The Eightfold Way;* S. Okubo, *Progr. Theoret. Phys. 27:* 949 (1962).

where, for a given U-spin multiplet, M'_0 again depends on t^2 and $\mathcal{Y}^2$ only (Q is constant within a given multiplet). Now, taking advantage of (9a), we surmise, as the simplest form with the minimum number of arbitrary constants,

$$M'_0 = M + Bt(t+1) + C\mathcal{Y}^2, \tag{9c}$$

$$O_M = M + A\mathcal{Y} + Bt(t+1) + C\mathcal{Y}^2. \tag{9d}$$

We have now only to determine the appropriate relative values for B and C to insure equal spacing between members of any U-spin multiplet. For this purpose, for example, we may apply O_M, Equation (9d), to the members of the $U=1$ triplet in the decimet [Figure 14.4(b)]:

$$\begin{aligned} M_{\Delta^0} &= M + A + \tfrac{15}{4}B + C, \\ M_{\Delta Y^0} &= M + 2B, \\ M_{\Delta\Xi^0} &= M - A + \tfrac{3}{4}B + C; \end{aligned} \tag{9e}$$

setting $M_{\Delta\Xi^0} - M_{\Delta Y^0} = M_{\Delta Y^0} - M_{\Delta^0}$, we obtain

$$C = -\frac{B}{4}, \tag{9f}$$

thereby obtaining the generalized $SU(3)$ mass formula of Gell-Mann and Okubo:

$$M_i = M + A\mathcal{Y}_i + B\left[t_i(t_i+1) - \frac{\mathcal{Y}_i^2}{4}\right]. \tag{9}$$

Equation (9) contains Equations (7) and (8) as special cases and, indeed, the mass relationships appropriate to all representations of $SU(3)$, *provided* the mass fine structure is the consequence of an MSI which behaves as a vector in U space.

The Mesons • We have previously noted that the pseudoscalar meson octet (π, η, K, $\overline{K}$) approximately satisfies the octet mass relationship[15]

$$4m_K^2 = 3m_\eta^2 + m_\pi^2, \tag{10}$$

but with a discrepancy of ~ 6 percent (as compared to less than 1 percent for the $\frac{1}{2}^+$ baryon octet). For any of the other identified meson groups (1^-, 2^+), on the other hand, the analogue of Equation 10 fails by a very wide margin.

Accepting that the mass relationships for mesons should be applied to the squares of the masses, rather than to the masses themselves, as suggested by field-theoretic arguments, we note that the major problem lies in the separation of the observed meson nonets into octets plus singlets — i.e., in the identification of the appropriate $t = \mathcal{Y} = 0$ member of the octet. Indeed, if the MSI violates $SU(3)$ symmetry, it can equally well lead to a mixing of the $SU(3)$ singlet with that member of the $SU(3)$ octet having identical values of $\mathcal{Y} = t = 0$ — namely, η–$\eta'(X^0)$ for the 0^- nonet, ω–ϕ for 1^-, and f–f' for 2^+. However, assuming the validity of the octet mass relationship [Equation (10)], we may invert the problem

---

[15] $m_K = m_{\overline{K}}$ as a consequence of TCP invariance.

and attempt to determine the degree of mixing of the octet and singlet in the observed $\mathcal{Y} = t = 0$ mesons.

Let π, K, η, η' symbolize the wave functions of the corresponding observed members of any one of the meson nonets, with masses m_π, m_K, m_η, $m_{\eta'}$, respectively. The isosinglet states η and η' are (orthogonal) linear combinations of the pure octet and singlet mesons, which we denote by η_8 and η_1. In terms of the meson mass (squared) operator, O_m, which contains terms from both the VSI and MSI,

$$O_m \begin{pmatrix} \eta \\ \eta' \end{pmatrix} = \begin{pmatrix} m_\eta^2 & 0 \\ 0 & m_{\eta'}^2 \end{pmatrix} \begin{pmatrix} \eta \\ \eta' \end{pmatrix}, \tag{11a}$$

since the observed particles are eigenstates of O_m. On the other hand, O_m mixes η_8 and η_1, so that we may write

$$O_m \begin{pmatrix} \eta_8 \\ \eta_1 \end{pmatrix} = \begin{pmatrix} m_8^2 & m_{18}^2 \\ m_{18}^2 & m_1^2 \end{pmatrix} \begin{pmatrix} \eta_8 \\ \eta_1 \end{pmatrix}. \tag{11b}$$

The problem is now reduced to the conventional one of finding the unitary matrix which will diagonalize Equation (11b), i.e., achieve its transformation into Equation (11a). Let

$$\begin{pmatrix} \eta \\ \eta' \end{pmatrix} = \begin{pmatrix} \cos\theta & \sin\theta \\ -\sin\theta & \cos\theta \end{pmatrix} \begin{pmatrix} \eta_8 \\ \eta_1 \end{pmatrix}, \tag{11c}$$

where θ is the "mixing angle." The appropriate unitary transformation is [16]

$$\begin{pmatrix} \cos\theta & -\sin\theta \\ \sin\theta & \cos\theta \end{pmatrix} \begin{pmatrix} m_\eta^2 & 0 \\ 0 & m_{\eta'}^2 \end{pmatrix} \begin{pmatrix} \cos\theta & \sin\theta \\ -\sin\theta & \cos\theta \end{pmatrix} = \begin{pmatrix} m_8^2 & m_{18}^2 \\ m_{18}^2 & m_1^2 \end{pmatrix}, \tag{11d}$$

from which, equating terms, we obtain

$$m_1^2 + m_8^2 = m_\eta^2 + m_{\eta'}^2, \tag{12a}$$

$$m_1^2 m_8^2 - m_{18}^4 = m_\eta^2 m_{\eta'}^2, \tag{12b}$$

$$\sin^2\theta = \frac{m_\eta^2 - m_8^2}{m_\eta^2 - m_{\eta'}^2}. \tag{12c}$$

However, Equations (12a) through (12c) are insufficient to determine the four unknowns (m_8^2, m_1^2, m_{18}^2, θ) without a further condition; it is at this point that we may take advantage of the octet mass relationship, Equation (10), to write

$$m_8^2 = \frac{4m_K^2 - m_\pi^2}{3} = m_K^2 + \frac{m_K^2 - m_\pi^2}{3}. \tag{12d}$$

---

[16] Alternatively, we may solve the eigenvalue equation

$$\begin{vmatrix} m_8^2 - \lambda & m_{18}^2 \\ m_{18}^2 & m_1^2 - \lambda \end{vmatrix} = 0,$$

with λ having the two solutions m_η^2 and $m_{\eta'}^2$. There remains an ambiguity as to which of the observed $\mathcal{Y} = t = 0$ mesons we call η and which η', which we resolve by identifying the η with that meson whose mass value lies closer to m_8.

Equations (12a) through (12d) have been used, together with the observed meson mass values,[17] to determine the masses and mixing parameters for the known meson nonets as given in Table 14.3.

These results demonstrate the relative purity of the pseudoscalar octet as compared to the other two. Furthermore, we note that the mixing angles θ for the 1^- and 2^+ nonets lie rather close to the value predicted by the particular form of the F–Y–S model discussed in Section 12.2.1, for which $\sin^2\theta = \frac{1}{3}$, ($\theta = 35.3°$).

Table 14.3 Masses and SU(3) Mixing Parameters for the $t = \mathcal{Y} = 0$ Mesons in Observed Meson Nonets

Multiplet	0^-	1^-	2^+
$m^2_{1,0}$ $(\mathrm{GeV}/c^2)^2$	0.018 (π^0)	0.593 (ρ^0)	1.72 (A_2)
$m^2_{1/2,\pm 1}$ $(\mathrm{GeV}/c^2)^2$	0.248 (K^0)	0.796 (K^{*0})	2.008 (K_N)
$m^2_{0,0}$ $(\mathrm{GeV}/c^2)^2$	0.301 (η)	1.039 (φ)	2.29 (f')
$m^2_{0,0}$ $(\mathrm{GeV}/c^2)^2$	0.918 (η')	0.614 (ω)	1.57 (f)
m^2_8 $(\mathrm{GeV}/c^2)^2$	0.325	0.864	2.10
m^2_1 $(\mathrm{GeV}/c^2)^2$	0.894	0.789	1.76
m^2_{18} $(\mathrm{GeV}/c^2)^2$	0.119	0.209	0.315
$\sin^2\theta$	0.033 ± 0.001	0.414 ± 0.013	0.26 ± 0.06
m_8 (MeV/c^2)	566.8 ± 0.2	928.4 ± 3.0	1450
m_1 (MeV/c^2)	946	888	1325
θ	10.4°	40.1°	30.5°

PROBLEM

What would be the appropriate $SU(3)$ mass formulas if the MSI behaved as a scalar in t space and a vector in V space?

14.3.2 Electromagnetic Effects

Both the VSI and the MSI are I-spin conserving interactions, so that any operator (such as the O_M) that has this invariance property cannot distinguish between members of a given I-spin multiplet. However, as we have noted in Section 13.1, all the multiplets exhibit "hyperfine" mass splittings, which are generally assumed to be electromagnetic in origin. In addition, the different members of an I-spin multiplet have, in general, different magnetic dipole moments, another manifestation of electromagnetic effects.

Assuming that the above-mentioned effects arise from the EMI, we may examine the obvious and simple assumption that the EMI behaves as a scalar in U space (i.e., all members of a given U-spin multiplet, having the same charge, have the same EMI), but that the $SU(3)$ violation is manifested by the behavior of the EMI as a vector in t space.

[17] We adopt, for the appropriate masses of the I-spin multiplets, the masses of the neutral members; this procedure differs somewhat from that adopted by Rosenfeld, *et al.*, *Rev. Mod. Phys.*, *39:* 1(1967).

The Hyperfine Mass Splittings • The properties of the hyperfine mass operator are rather complex, since the electromagnetic self-energies depend on the squares of the electric and magnetic fields, and consequently contain significant interference terms between components of the charge density of different origin. However, we may take advantage of the scalar nature of the EMI in U space to equate the hyperfine mass shifts of members of the same U-spin multiplet. In the case of the baryon $\frac{1}{2}^+$ octet [Figure 14.4(a)] this gives

$$\begin{aligned} \delta M(P^+) &= \delta M(\Sigma^+), \\ \delta M(\Sigma^-) &= \delta M(\Xi^-), \\ \delta M(\Xi^0) &= \delta M(N^0), \end{aligned} \tag{13a}$$

which, by addition and rearrangement of terms, yields

$$\begin{aligned} (M_{\Sigma^-} - M_{\Sigma^+}) - (M_N - M_P) &= (M_{\Xi^-} - M_{\Xi^0}), \\ (8.00 \pm 0.18) - 1.29 \quad &\stackrel{?}{=} (6.6 \pm 0.7), \qquad \text{in MeV}, \end{aligned} \tag{13}$$

in excellent agreement with the observed values (Table 13.1).

Among the members of the baryon $\frac{3}{2}^+$ decimet [Figure 14.4(b)], the same considerations give

$$\begin{aligned} (M_{\Delta\Xi^-} - M_{\Delta\Xi^0}) = (M_{\Delta Y^-} - M_{\Delta Y^0}) &= (M_{\Delta^-} - M_{\Delta^0}), \\ (4.9 \pm 2.2\ \text{MeV}) \qquad\qquad &(7.4 \pm 6.8\ \text{MeV}) \end{aligned} \tag{14a}$$

$$(M_{\Delta Y^0} - M_{\Delta Y^+}) = (M_{\Delta^0} - M_{\Delta^+}), \tag{14b}$$

in which the relevant experimental splittings (summarized in Table 13.1) are again indicated in parentheses. The measurement of the hyperfine mass splittings of the members of the decimet is much more difficult than for the $\frac{1}{2}^+$ baryons, owing to the large widths ($\sim$ 10–100 MeV) of these highly unstable particles, and the experimental uncertainties are correspondingly larger.

In the case of the meson nonets, the analogues of Equations (13) are devoid of any new information, owing to the TCP requirement of equal masses for particles and their antiparticles, e.g., $m_{K^+} = m_{K^-}$, $m_{K^0} = m_{\overline{K^0}}$, $m_{\pi^+} = m_{\pi^-}$.

Magnetic Dipole Moments • Owing to the linear dependence of the magnetic moment on the current densities, we may now take advantage of the vector nature in t space of the magnetic moment operator $\mu = \mu_3$.

Consider the baryon $\frac{1}{2}^+$ octet: starting with the U-spin scalar property of μ, we have

$$\mu(\Xi^-) = \langle \Xi^- | \mu \Xi^- \rangle = \mu(\Sigma^-), \tag{15a}$$

$$\mu(\Sigma^+) = \mu(P), \tag{15b}$$

$$\begin{aligned} \mu(N) &= \mu(\Xi^0) = \mu(U_1^0) \\ &= \left\langle \left(\frac{1}{2}\Sigma^0 - \frac{\sqrt{3}}{2}\Lambda^0\right) \middle| \mu \left(\frac{1}{2}\Sigma^0 - \frac{\sqrt{3}}{2}\Lambda^0\right) \right\rangle \\ &= \frac{1}{4}\mu(\Sigma^0) + \frac{3}{4}\mu(\Lambda^0) - \frac{\sqrt{3}}{2}\mu(\Sigma^0\text{–}\Lambda^0), \end{aligned} \tag{15c}$$

where $\mu(\Sigma^0\text{–}\Lambda^0)$ is the magnetic dipole $\Sigma^0\text{–}\Lambda^0$ transition matrix element. We may eliminate $\mu(\Sigma^0\text{–}\Lambda^0)$ by taking advantage of the U-spin conserving property of the μ operator

$$\langle U_1^0|\mu U_0^0\rangle = \frac{\sqrt{3}}{4}\,\mu(\Sigma^0) - \frac{\sqrt{3}}{4}\,\mu(\Lambda^0) - \frac{1}{2}\,\mu(\Sigma^0\text{–}\Lambda^0) = 0. \tag{15d}$$

Combining (15c) and (15d), we obtain

$$\mu(N) = \mu(\Xi^0) = -\tfrac{1}{2}\mu(\Sigma^0) + \tfrac{3}{2}\mu(\Lambda^0). \tag{15c'}$$

Having now exhausted the consequences of U-spin conservation, we turn to the effects of I spin, which may be expressed by the statement that, for a given I-spin multiplet, the μ operator has the form

$$\mu_t = \mu_0 + \mu_1 t_3\,. \tag{15e}$$

Applying (15e) to the Σ triplet gives

$$2\mu(\Sigma^0) = \mu(\Sigma^+) + \mu(\Sigma^-). \tag{15e'}$$

Finally, we take advantage of the symmetrical nature of the octet in t_3–$\mathcal{Y}$ space (Figure 14.2), which gives rise to the sum rule (or cloture condition)

$$\sum_{i=1}^{8} \mu_i = 0. \tag{15f}$$

Equations (15a) through (15f) may be combined to obtain the following relations:

$$\mu(\Lambda^0) = -\mu(\Sigma^0) = -\sqrt{\tfrac{1}{3}}\,\mu(\Sigma^0\text{–}\Lambda^0) = \tfrac{1}{2}\mu(N) = \tfrac{1}{2}\mu(\Xi^0), \tag{16a}$$

$$\mu(\Xi^-) = \mu(\Sigma^-) = -[\mu(P) + \mu(N)], \tag{16b}$$

$$\mu(P) = \mu(\Sigma^+) = -[\mu(\Xi^0) + \mu(\Xi^-)]. \tag{16c}$$

The observed baryon moments, summarized in Table 13.2, are in excellent accord with these predictions. However, we may note that Equations (16a) through (16c) are incomplete insofar as they do not lead to any prediction for the relative values of the magnetic moments of P and N (or Ξ^0 and Ξ^-).

Similar considerations may be used to derive relationships among the moments of the members of the $\frac{3}{2}^+$ baryon decimet, or the various meson nonets. However, we have no experimental information on these moments, while the observable values of the transition moments between members of the baryon octet and decimet, or between the vector and pseudoscalar mesons, cannot be predicted on the basis of $SU(3)$ symmetry alone.

The Photon and the Vector-Meson Dominance Hypothesis • In considering reactions involving photons, the question immediately arises of the properties of the photon under $SU(3)$. It is clear that since the EMI behaves as a scalar in U space, so must the photon. On the other hand, since photon interactions exhibit the selection rules $\Delta t = 0$ or ± 1, $\Delta S = 0$, the photon, a boson, must also carry the properties of the $Q=0$ members of both an I-spin singlet and triplet with $\mathcal{Y}=B=0$. Among the simplest $SU(3)$ representations (see Figure 14.3), the most natural choice is the U_0^0 member of a meson octet. Furthermore, the photon has spin 1 and charge conjugation number $C=-1$, which corresponds exactly to the neutral, nonstrange vector mesons.

All the required properties, then, are precisely those of the U_0^0 member of the vector-meson octet, which is a specified combination of ρ^0, ω, ϕ:

$$\begin{aligned}\gamma &\to \frac{\sqrt{3}}{2}\rho^0 + \frac{1}{2}\omega_8 \\ &= \frac{\sqrt{3}}{2}\rho^0 + \frac{1}{2}(\omega \sin\theta_v + \varphi \cos\theta_v), \end{aligned} \tag{17}$$

in which the value of the mixing angle, $\theta_v \approx 40°$, may be obtained from Table 14.3. Equation (17) may be interpreted as giving the relative amplitudes for ρ^0, ω, and φ production in processes involving the direct (virtual) conversion of a photon into a vector meson. A number of examples of such processes have been discussed in Chapter 9.

One of the most straightforward observations of such a direct $\gamma \to$ vector meson conversion is in the reaction[18]

$$e^+ + e^- \to v \tag{18}$$

utilizing colliding beams; this process is illustrated in Figure 14.5. Treating

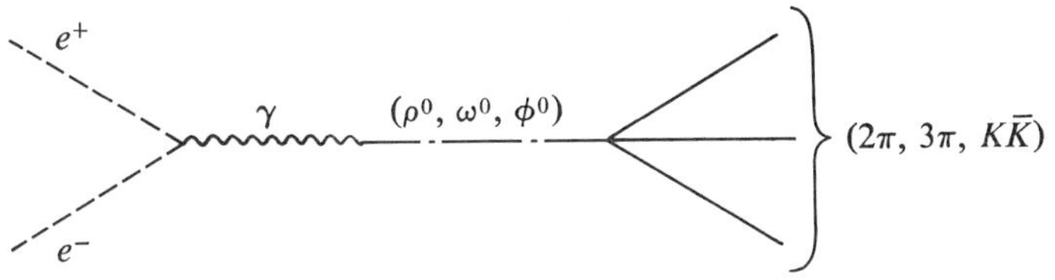

Figure 14.5 Direct $\gamma \to$ vector meson conversion process.

reaction (18) as a resonant reaction, the cross section is given by the Breit–Wigner formula

$$\sigma = \pi \lambda\!\!\!^-{}_e^2 \frac{(2J+1)}{4} \frac{\Gamma_{\text{in}}\Gamma}{(2E_e - m_v)^2 + \Gamma^2/4}, \tag{18a}$$

with $J=1$, which, at resonance ($E_e \cong p_e \cong \lambda\!\!\!^-{}_e^{-1} = m_v/2$), gives

$$\sigma_{\text{res}} = \frac{12\pi}{m_v^2} \frac{\Gamma(v \to e^+e^-)}{\Gamma_{\text{tot}}}. \tag{18b}$$

[18] The inverse of reaction (18), the direct decays of vector mesons into lepton pairs, has also been observed.

Assuming the mechanism of Figure 14.5, the values of $\Gamma(v_i \to e^+e^-)$ are proportional to the squares of the coefficients[19] of the corresponding v_i in Equation (17); using the value of θ_v from Table 14.3 and correcting for the phase space available[20] to the product lepton pair, these give

$$\Gamma(\rho^0 \to e^+e^-):\Gamma(\omega \to e^+e^-):\Gamma(\phi \to e^+e^-) = 9:1.27:2.35. \tag{17a}$$

Experimentally, these ratios are $9:(1.0 \pm 0.3):(2.1 \pm 0.6)$.[21]

The same $\gamma \to v$ conversion is assumed in the vector-dominance model of the nucleon form factors, Figure 9.1(b), as well as in the "diffraction" model of vector-meson photoproduction as shown in Figure 14.6. However, in these cases, the amplitudes depend both on the relative $\gamma \to v$ amplitudes and on the relative strengths of the v–$\mathfrak{N}$ vertices (absorption in the case of the form factors, scattering in the case of the photoproduction), which are in general not predictable on the basis of $SU(3)$ alone. (See Section 14.3.3.)

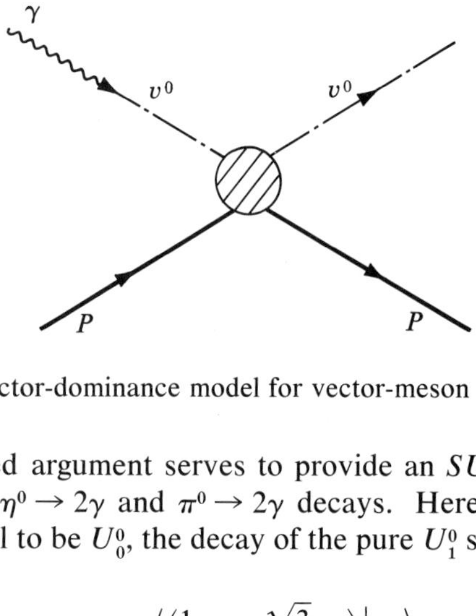

Figure 14.6 Vector-dominance model for vector-meson photoproduction.

A somewhat related argument serves to provide an $SU(3)$ prediction for the relative rates of the $\eta^0 \to 2\gamma$ and $\pi^0 \to 2\gamma$ decays. Here, the final state being assumed by the model to be U_0^0, the decay of the pure U_1^0 state into photons must be forbidden:

$$\langle U_1^0|\gamma\gamma\rangle = \left\langle\left(\frac{1}{2}\pi^0 - \frac{\sqrt{3}}{2}\eta^0\right)\middle|\gamma\gamma\right\rangle = 0,$$
$$\langle \pi^0|\gamma\gamma\rangle = \sqrt{3}\,\langle \eta^0|\gamma\gamma\rangle. \tag{17b}$$

Hence, the relative decay rates are

$$\frac{\Gamma(\eta^0 \to 2\gamma)}{\Gamma(\pi^0 \to 2\gamma)} = \frac{1}{3}\left(\frac{m_\eta}{m_\pi}\right)^3 = 22.4, \tag{17c}$$

---

[19] The simple F–Y–S model, Section 12.2.1, predicts $\sin^2\theta_v = \frac{1}{3}$, leading to a ratio of 9:1:2 in Equation (17a). These are the values usually quoted as the $SU(3)$ predictions.

[20] We have used the invariant two-body phase-space formula, which gives the correction factor (m_v/m_ρ). However, we should note that there is some disagreement concerning the appropriate kinematical correction factor, which could change the predicted $\varphi \to l^+l^-$ decay rate by as much as a factor $(m_\rho/m_\varphi)^2 \simeq \frac{1}{2}$.

[21] S. C. C. Ting, *Proceedings of the XIV International Conference on High Energy Physics,* Vienna (September 1968).

the mass factor in (17c) arising from the combined phase-space and *P*-wave angular momentum barrier factors. In addition to the assumption of the *U*-spin scalar nature of the photon, Equation (17c) also depends on the purity of the pseudoscalar octet, with the isosinglet member being the assumed pure η^0 (see Table 14.3). Experimentally, from Table 2.1, the ratio (17c) is $\approx$ 100.

PROBLEMS

1. Derive the $SU(3)$ relations among the magnetic dipole moments of members of the $s=\frac{3}{2}^+$ decimet.
2. What is the value of the decay mean life for

$$\Sigma^0 \to \Lambda^0 + \gamma$$

predicted by $SU(3)$?
3. Predict the values of $\sigma_{\text{res}}(e^+ + e^- \to v)$ for $v = \rho^0, \omega^0, \phi^0$.
4. Using the mixing parameters of Table 14.3 for the η and η', compute the expected values of $\Gamma(\eta, \eta' \to 2\gamma)/\Gamma(\pi^0 \to 2\gamma)$ on the basis of the assumed U_0^0 nature of the photon.

14.3.3 Selection Rules

Strong Interactions • When members of two $SU(3)$ multiplets interact, the combinations (i.e., the intermediate states in the *s*-channel) must belong to one of the $SU(3)$ representations accessible to the product of the two original representations. Using the methods outlined in Section 14.1, or the techniques of conventional group theory,[22] we may show that the $SU(3)$ decompositions of the products of representations of interest are

$$8 \otimes 8 = 1 \oplus 8_1 \oplus 8_2 \oplus 10 \oplus \overline{10} \oplus 27, \tag{19a}$$

$$8 \otimes 10 = 8 \oplus 10 \oplus 27 \oplus 35, \tag{19b}$$

$$8 \otimes 27 = 8 \oplus 10 \oplus \overline{10} \oplus 27_1 \oplus 27_2 \oplus 35 \oplus \overline{35} \oplus 64, \tag{19c}$$

$$10 \otimes 10 = \overline{10} \oplus 27 \oplus 28 \oplus 35, \tag{19d}$$

$$10 \otimes \overline{10} = 1 \oplus 8 \oplus 27 \oplus 64. \tag{19e}$$

Of course, the individual interacting particles have specific values of the hypercharge, isotopic spin, and charge (t_3), and since these quantities are conserved in both the VSI and the MSI, we must have $\mathcal{Y} = \mathcal{Y}_1 + \mathcal{Y}_2$, $t_1 + t_2 \geq t \geq |t_1 - t_2|$, $t_3 = t_{1,3} + t_{2,3}$ for the combined state. But, if we consider the VSI alone, which is $SU(3)$ conserving, the combined states must also conserve U and U_3 (as well as V and V_3). In this case, the properties of the **t**, **U**, and **V** operators may be used to derive the combination coefficients that determine the weights of the various final states (defined by the multiplicity of the representation, $\mathcal{Y}$, and t) permitted to a given combining pair; these coefficients are strictly analogous to the Clebsch–

[22] J. J. de Swart, *Rev. Mod. Phys.*, *35*: 916 (1963).

Gordan coefficients for the combinations of angular momentum or I spin, in which case the angular momentum multiplets are representations of the $SU(2)$ group.

Such a table of $SU(3)$ combination coefficients has been derived by de Swart [23] and is reproduced in Appendix 6. Note that these coefficients do not yet take into specific account the effects of charge independence, and do not distinguish between charge states with the same value of $(\mathcal{Y}, t)$; the effects of (t, t_3) conservation must be superimposed on the table by multiplication by the appropriate Clebsch–Gordan coefficient for the isospin combination in question. Thus, for example, the combination $P + \pi^- \to \Delta^0$ would have the coefficient $-\sqrt{2}/2 \times \sqrt{\frac{1}{3}} = -\sqrt{\frac{1}{6}}$, where the first factor arises from the $8 \otimes 8 = 10$ combination $(t_1 = \frac{1}{2}, \mathcal{Y}_1 = 1; t_2 = 1, \mathcal{Y}_2 = 0 | t = \frac{3}{2}, \mathcal{Y} = 1)$ in the tables of de Swart, and the second is

$$C^{t=3/2,\, t_3=-1/2}_{t_1=1/2,\, t_{1,3}=1/2;\ t_2=1,\, t_{2,3}=-1} = \sqrt{\tfrac{1}{3}}.$$

We give, in the following, a number of consequences of the application of these combination coefficients to the strong interactions, which we assume to be dominated by the VSI.

DECAYS: Consider the general decay

$$A \to B + C \tag{20}$$

in which each component is a member of a definite $SU(3)$ multiplet. Then the decay matrix element is proportional to the corresponding combination coefficient.

Even without looking at any details, we may immediately note certain decay selection rules, which follow from the product decompositions summarized in Equations (19). Thus, for example, suppose A is a baryon whose $SU(3)$ representation is not known, which decays into a B_8 and m_8. We may immediately conclude that it is *not* a member of either the 35- or 64-plet representations. On the other hand, if it decays into $B_{10} + m_8$, then it is neither a singlet, a $\overline{10}$, nor a 64-plet.

Beyond such general selection rules, the specific coefficients should give the relative rates of alternative decay modes within the same combination of representations, after corrections are applied for relative phase-space and angular momentum barrier factors.

EXAMPLES

1. Consider the observed strong decays, $B_{10} \to B_8 + m_8$, as summarized in column 1 of Table 14.4, whose decay widths are given in column 2, and for which the momenta of the decay pions (in the B_{10} rest frame) are shown in column 3. Since this decay, $\frac{3}{2}^+ \to \frac{1}{2}^+ + 0^-$, requires P-wave pion emission, the decay rate should be $\propto p^{2l+1} = p^3$. Hence the ratio Γ/p^3 should be proportional to the square of the $SU(3)$ combination coefficients,[24] which we may obtain

---

[23] *Ibid.*

[24] This is, strictly speaking, only the case in a nonrelativistic approximation. We neglect relativistic effects in this crude comparison, and therefore ignore variations of a factor ~ 2 arising from the mass differences among the baryons in question.

from Table A6.1. Columns 4 and 5 of Table 14.4 give such a comparison (we have normalized to the mean of the $\Lambda\pi$ and $\Xi\pi$ predictions). Considering that the observed widths vary over a factor ~ 40, the agreement with the $SU(3)$ predictions is quite satisfactory.

Table 14.4 Decay Properties and SU(3) Predictions for $B_{10} \to B_8 + \pi_8$

Decay	Γ (MeV)	p_{cm} (MeV/c)	$\Gamma/3p^3$ ($\times 10^6$)	(Isoscalar factor)^2
$\Delta \to \mathfrak{N}\pi$	120	231	3.2	2
$_\Delta Y \to \Lambda\pi$	33.7	208	1.25	1
$\to \Sigma\pi$	3.3	117	0.69	$\frac{2}{3}$
$_\Delta\Xi \to \Xi\pi$	7.3	145	0.80	1

2. There are a number of $\mathcal{Y} = t = 0$ baryons (Y_0^*) whose multiplet assignments are in doubt (see Table 14.2). One way of checking a possible assignment is to compare the relative decay rates into members of the same $SU(3)$ multiplets. Table 14.5 lists the possible decay modes of a Y_0^* (always assuming the mass is sufficiently large) into $B_8 \otimes m_8$ or $B_{10} \otimes m_8$ for the different possible assumptions as to the parentage of the Y_0^*, and the corresponding coefficients from the de Swart tables (Appendix 6). Consider, for example, the assumed $\frac{3}{2}^-$ octet, whose members could include the $\mathfrak{N}^*(1520)$, $Y_0^*(1520$ or $1700)$, and $Y_0^*(1660)$. Our choice of the $Y_0^*(1700)$ is mainly based on the relative strength of the $\Sigma\pi$ as compared to the $\mathfrak{N}\bar{K}$ decay, which is ~ 1.3 for the $Y_0^*(1520)$ and ~ 2 for the $Y_0^*(1700)$; Table 14.5 predicts [25] the value $\frac{1}{6}$ for a member of the 27-plet, 1.5 for a singlet, but the relative decay rate is, however, undetermined for an octet

Table 14.5 SU(3) Weight Factors for the Possible Decays of a Y_0^*

Decay mode	Weight factor 1	8_1	8_2	27
$Y_0^* \to \mathfrak{N}\bar{K}$	$1/2$	$\sqrt{1/10}$	$\sqrt{1/2}$	$\sqrt{15}/10$
$\Sigma\pi$	$\sqrt{6}/4$	$-\sqrt{3/5}$	0	$-\sqrt{10}/20$
$\Sigma\eta$	forbidden by I spin			
$\Lambda\pi$	forbidden by I spin			
$\Lambda\eta$	$-\sqrt{2}/4$	$-\sqrt{1/5}$	0	$3\sqrt{30}/20$
ΞK	$-1/2$	$-\sqrt{1/10}$	$\sqrt{1/2}$	$-\sqrt{15}/10$
$Y_0^* \to \Delta\bar{K}$	forbidden by I spin			
$_\Delta Y\pi$	0	$-\sqrt{3/5}$	—	$\sqrt{2/5}$
$_\Delta Y\eta$	forbidden by I spin			
$_\Delta\Xi K$	0	$-\sqrt{2/5}$	—	$-\sqrt{3/5}$

[25] This neglects phase-space corrections which, although not expected to be large, would tend to raise the predicted $\Sigma\pi/\mathfrak{N}\bar{K}$ ratios for $Y_0^*(1520)$ and lower them for $Y_0^*(1700)$.

owing to the two interfering octet amplitudes for the $\mathfrak{N}\bar{K}$ decay. Thus we see that, in this case, the argument from $SU(3)$ is not too conclusive.

TWO-BODY REACTIONS: Consider the reactions

$$m_8 + B_8 \rightarrow m_8' + B_8'. \tag{21}$$

According to Equation (19a), the combination $m_8 \otimes B_8$ has six possible intermediate states in the s-channel, each of which, in turn, can decay into $m_8' \otimes B_8'$. Accordingly, the matrix elements are proportional to the products of the appropriate combination coefficients from Table A6.1, multiplied in turn by the appropriate Clebsch–Gordan coefficients for the isotopic-spin combinations. In addition, for the case under consideration, there is one additional amplitude, arising from the interference between the two intermediate octet representations. Thus, each possible reaction amplitude is a sum of seven terms, whose coefficients are given in Table 14.6 for the case[26] $0^- + \frac{1}{2}^+ \rightarrow 0^- + \frac{1}{2}^+$.

As an illustration, we derive the coefficient of A_{27} for the reaction amplitude $(\pi^-P|K^+\Sigma^-)$: the initial state is a mixture of $t=\frac{3}{2}$ and $t=\frac{1}{2}$, with weights $\sqrt{\frac{1}{3}}$ and $-\sqrt{\frac{2}{3}}$, respectively; the final state contains the same mixture of I spins. Thus, we need the factors ($t=1, \mathcal{Y}=0; t=\frac{1}{2}, \mathcal{Y}=1 \mid t=\frac{3}{2}, \mathcal{Y}=1$) and $(1, 0; \frac{1}{2}, 1 \mid \frac{1}{2}, 1)$; referring to Table A6.1, the required combination is

$$(\sqrt{\tfrac{1}{3}} \cdot \sqrt{\tfrac{1}{2}})^2 + (-\sqrt{\tfrac{2}{3}})^2 (-\tfrac{1}{2}\sqrt{\tfrac{1}{5}})^2 = \tfrac{1}{6} + \tfrac{1}{30} = \tfrac{1}{5}\cdot$$

Aside from the usual triangular relationships, derivable from isotopic-spin conservation, e.g.,

$$(K^-P|\pi^-\Sigma^+) + (K^-P|\pi^+\Sigma^-) + 2(K^-P|\pi^0\Sigma^0) = 0, \tag{21a}$$

Table 14.6 leads only to two interesting new predictions:

$$(K^-P|\pi^+\Sigma^-) = (K^-P|K^0\Xi^0), \tag{21b}$$

$$(\pi^-P|K^+\Sigma^-) = (K^-N|K^0\Xi^-). \tag{21c}$$

The same considerations may be applied to the reaction

$$m_8 + B_8 \rightarrow m_8' + B_{10}. \tag{22}$$

In this case, there are only four overlapping representations (27, 10, 8_1, and 8_2), and there is no interference term since the final state combination $8 \otimes 10$ leads to only one octet [Equation (19b)]. Table 14.7 summarizes the coefficients of the amplitudes for reactions (22). We have also listed, in column 6, the relationships derivable on the basis of I-spin and U-spin conservation.

Table 14.7 leads to many connections among the cross sections for the 38 reactions listed, since they are all expressed in terms of only four (complex) amplitudes. Many of these relationships follow directly from the simplest I-spin

[26] These same amplitudes apply in the t-channel, for the reactions $B_8 + \bar{B}_8' \rightarrow \bar{m}_8 + m_8'$ with the appropriate substitutions in Table 14.6 of the analogous $m_8 \rightarrow \bar{B}_8'$, $B_8' \rightarrow \bar{m}_8$. In the case of elastic meson-baryon scattering, the t-channel representation, in fact, may be the more useful one. [S. Meshkov and G. B. Yodh, *Phys. Rev. Letters, 19:* 603 (1967).]

Table 14.6 Reaction Amplitudes for $m_8 + B_8 \to m'_8 + B'_8$ Through the Various Possible Intermediate States[a]

Intermediate state	27	8_1	8_2	10	$\overline{10}$	1	$8_1/8_2$	$8'_1$	$8'_2$	$8'_1/8'_2$
1. $(K^-N\|K^-N)$	$\frac{1}{5}$	$\frac{3}{10}$	$\frac{1}{6}$	$\frac{1}{6}$	$\frac{1}{6}$	0	$-1/\sqrt{5}$	0	$\frac{7}{15}$	0
2. $(\pi^-P\|\pi^-P)$	$\frac{1}{5}$	$\frac{3}{10}$	$\frac{1}{6}$	$\frac{1}{6}$	$\frac{1}{6}$	0	$1/\sqrt{5}$	$\frac{3}{7}$	$\frac{4}{105}$	$4/7\sqrt{5}$
3. $(K^-N\|K^0\Xi^-)$	$\frac{1}{5}$	$\frac{3}{10}$	$-\frac{1}{6}$	$-\frac{1}{6}$	$-\frac{1}{6}$	0	0	0	$\sqrt{\frac{2}{15}}$	0
4. $(\pi^-P\|K^+\Sigma^-)$	$\frac{1}{5}$	$\frac{3}{10}$	$-\frac{1}{6}$	$-\frac{1}{6}$	$-\frac{1}{6}$	0	0	0	$\sqrt{\frac{2}{15}}$	0
5. $(\pi^+P\|\pi^+P)$	$\frac{1}{2}$	0	0	$\frac{1}{2}$	0	0	0	0	0	0
6. $(\pi^+P\|K^+\Sigma^+)$	$\frac{1}{2}$	0	0	$-\frac{1}{2}$	0	0	0	0	0	0
7. $(K^+N\|K^0P)$	$\frac{1}{2}$	0	0	0	$-\frac{1}{2}$	0	0	0	0	0
8. $(K^+N\|K^+N)$	$\frac{1}{2}$	0	0	0	$\frac{1}{2}$	0	0	0	0	0
9. $(K^-P\|K^-P)$	$\frac{7}{40}$	$\frac{1}{5}$	$\frac{1}{3}$	$\frac{1}{12}$	$\frac{1}{12}$	$\frac{1}{8}$	0	$\frac{2}{7}$	$\frac{26}{105}$	$-2/7\sqrt{5}$
10. $(K^-P\|\overline{K^0}N)$	$\frac{1}{40}$	$\frac{1}{10}$	$-\frac{1}{6}$	$\frac{1}{12}$	$\frac{1}{12}$	$-\frac{1}{8}$	$-1/\sqrt{5}$	$-\frac{2}{7}$	$-\frac{23}{105}$	$2/7\sqrt{5}$
11. $(K^-P\|\pi^-\Sigma^+)$	$\frac{1}{40}$	$\frac{1}{10}$	$-\frac{1}{6}$	$\frac{1}{12}$	$\frac{1}{12}$	$-\frac{1}{8}$	$1/\sqrt{5}$	$\frac{1}{7}$	$-\frac{22}{105}$	$6/7\sqrt{5}$
12. $(K^-P\|\pi^+\Sigma^-)$	$\frac{1}{40}$	$\frac{1}{10}$	$\frac{1}{6}$	$-\frac{1}{12}$	$-\frac{1}{12}$	$-\frac{1}{8}$	0	$\frac{1}{7}$	$\frac{13}{105}$	$-1/7\sqrt{5}$
13. $(K^-P\|K^0\Xi^0)$	$\frac{1}{40}$	$\frac{1}{10}$	$\frac{1}{6}$	$-\frac{1}{12}$	$-\frac{1}{12}$	$-\frac{1}{8}$	0	$\frac{1}{7}$	$\frac{13}{105}$	$-1/7\sqrt{5}$
14. $(K^-P\|\pi^0\Sigma^0)$	$\frac{1}{40}$	$\frac{1}{10}$	0	0	0	$-\frac{1}{8}$	$-1/2\sqrt{5}$	$-\frac{1}{7}$	$\frac{3}{70}$	$-5/14\sqrt{5}$
15. $(K^-P\|\pi^0\Lambda^0)$	$\sqrt{3}/10$	$-\sqrt{3}/10$	0	$1/4\sqrt{3}$	$-1/4\sqrt{3}$	0	$1/2\sqrt{15}$	0	$\sqrt{3}/10$	$-1/2\sqrt{15}$
16. $(\pi^-P\|K^0\Lambda^0)$	$-\frac{1}{10}\sqrt{\frac{3}{2}}$	$\frac{1}{10}\sqrt{\frac{3}{2}}$	$1/2\sqrt{6}$	0	$-1/2\sqrt{6}$	0	$\sqrt{\frac{2}{15}}$	$\sqrt{6}/7$	$\frac{1}{35}\sqrt{\frac{2}{3}}$	$1/\sqrt{30}$
17. $(\pi^-P\|\pi^0N)$	$\frac{3}{10}\sqrt{\frac{1}{2}}$	$-\frac{3}{10}\sqrt{\frac{1}{2}}$	$-1/6\sqrt{2}$	$1/3\sqrt{2}$	$-1/6\sqrt{2}$	0	$-\sqrt{\frac{1}{10}}$	$-\sqrt{3}/7$	$-2\sqrt{2}/105$	0

[a] C. A. Levinson, H. J. Lipkin, and S. Meshkov, *Phys. Letters, 1:* 44 (1962). The existence of two intermediate octets means that there are off-diagonal (mixing) elements, as shown in column 8. An alternative mixing for the two octets is given in the last three columns.

Table 14.7 Amplitudes for Reactions $m_8 + B_8 \rightarrow m'_8 + B_{10}$

Reaction	Intermediate states				Companion reaction
	27	10	8_1	8_2	
1. $\langle K^+P\|K^0\Delta^{++}\rangle$	$-\sqrt{3}/2$				$-\sqrt{3}\,\langle K^+P\|K^+\Delta^+\rangle$
2. $\langle K^+N\|K^0\Delta^+\rangle$	$-\frac{1}{2}$				$-\langle K^+N\|K^+\Delta^0\rangle$
3. $\langle \pi^+P\|\pi^0\Delta^{++}\rangle$	$-\sqrt{6}/8$	$\sqrt{3}/4$			$-\langle \pi^-N\|\pi^0\Delta^-\rangle$
4. $\langle \pi^+P\|\pi^+\Delta^+\rangle$	$\frac{1}{4}$	$-\sqrt{2}/4$			$-\langle \pi^-N\|\pi^-\Delta^0\rangle$
5. $\langle \pi^+P\|\eta^0\Delta^{++}\rangle$	$-3\sqrt{2}/8$	$-\frac{1}{4}$			$\langle \pi^-N\|\eta^0\Delta^-\rangle$
6. $\langle \pi^+P\|K^+{}_\Delta Y^+\rangle$	$\frac{1}{4}$	$\sqrt{2}/4$			$\langle \pi^-N\|K^0{}_\Delta Y^-\rangle$
7. $\langle \pi^-P\|\pi^+\Delta^-\rangle$	$\sqrt{3}/20$	$-\sqrt{6}/12$	$\sqrt{3}/5$	$-\sqrt{15}/15$	$-\langle \pi^+N\|\pi^-\Delta^{++}\rangle$
8. $\langle \pi^-P\|\pi^0\Delta^0\rangle$	$3\sqrt{2}/40$	$-\frac{1}{12}$	$-\sqrt{2}/5$	$\sqrt{10}/15$	$-\langle \pi^+N\|\pi^0\Delta^+\rangle$
9. $\langle \pi^-P\|\pi^-\Delta^+\rangle$	$-\frac{1}{5}$	$\sqrt{2}/6$	$\frac{1}{5}$	$-\sqrt{5}/15$	$-\langle \pi^+N\|\pi^+\Delta^0\rangle$
10. $\langle \pi^-P\|\eta^0\Delta^0\rangle$	$-\sqrt{6}/8$	$-\sqrt{3}/12$			$-\langle \pi^+N\|\eta^0\Delta^+\rangle$
11. $\langle \pi^-P\|K^+{}_\Delta Y^-\rangle$	$-\frac{1}{20}$	$\sqrt{2}/12$	$-\frac{1}{5}$	$\sqrt{5}/15$	$\langle \pi^+N\|K^0{}_\Delta Y^+\rangle$
12. $\langle \pi^-P\|K^0{}_\Delta Y^0\rangle$	$3\sqrt{2}/20$	$\frac{1}{6}$	$\sqrt{2}/10$	$-\sqrt{10}/30$	$\langle \pi^+N\|K^+{}_\Delta Y^0\rangle$
13. $\langle K^-P\|K^-\Delta^+\rangle$	$\frac{1}{20}$	$\sqrt{2}/12$	$\frac{1}{5}$	$\sqrt{5}/15$	$\langle K^-N\|K^-\Delta^0\rangle$
14. $\langle K^-P\|\overline{K^0}\Delta^0\rangle$	$-\frac{1}{20}$	$-\sqrt{2}/12$	$-\frac{1}{5}$	$-\sqrt{5}/15$	$\sqrt{\frac{1}{3}}\,\langle K^-N\|\overline{K^0}\Delta^-\rangle$
15. $\langle K^-P\|\pi^-{}_\Delta Y^+\rangle$	$-\frac{1}{4}$	$\sqrt{2}/12$		$-2\sqrt{5}/15$	
16. $\langle K^-P\|\pi^+{}_\Delta Y^-\rangle$	$\frac{1}{20}$	$-\sqrt{2}/12$	$\frac{1}{5}$	$-\sqrt{5}/15$	$-\langle K^-P\|K^+{}_\Delta\Xi^-\rangle$
17. $\langle K^-P\|\pi^0{}_\Delta Y^0\rangle$	$\frac{1}{10}$		$-\frac{1}{10}$	$\sqrt{5}/10$	
18. $\langle K^-P\|\eta^0{}_\Delta Y^0\rangle$	$-\sqrt{3}/10$		$\sqrt{3}/10$	$\sqrt{15}/30$	$\sqrt{\frac{1}{2}}\,\langle K^-N\|\eta^0{}_\Delta Y^-\rangle$
19. $\langle K^-P\|K^0{}_\Delta\Xi^0\rangle$	$\frac{1}{4}$	$\sqrt{2}/12$		$-2\sqrt{5}/15$	
20. $\langle K^-N\|\pi^0{}_\Delta Y^-\rangle$	$3\sqrt{2}/20$	$-\frac{1}{6}$	$\sqrt{2}/10$	$\sqrt{10}/30$	$-\langle K^-N\|\pi^-{}_\Delta Y^0\rangle$
21. $\langle K^-N\|K^0{}_\Delta\Xi^-\rangle$	$\frac{1}{5}$	$\sqrt{2}/6$	$-\frac{1}{5}$	$-\sqrt{5}/15$	

and U-spin conservation considerations, and most of these are already noted in the table. The most interesting new result is a set of identities among the amplitudes

$$(\pi^-P|K^+{}_\Delta Y^-) = (K^-P|K^+{}_\Delta\Xi^-) = -(K^-P|\pi^+{}_\Delta Y^-) = -\sqrt{\tfrac{1}{3}}\,(\pi^-P|\pi^+\Delta^-). \quad (22a)$$

It is also possible to derive relationships among the amplitudes squared, which can be compared to observed cross sections, e.g.,

$$|(K^+P|K^0\Delta^{++})|^2 + 3|(\pi^+P|K^+{}_\Delta Y^+)|^2 = |(\pi^+P|\pi^0\Delta^{++})|^2 + 3|(\pi^+P|\eta^0\Delta^{++})|^2. \quad (22b)$$

However, most of the relationships that can be obtained are algebraic connections among various complex amplitudes, of which we cite just two examples:

$$(K^-P|K^-\Delta^+) + (K^-P|\pi^-{}_\Delta Y^+) - (\pi^-P|\pi^-\Delta^+) = 0, \quad (22c)$$

$$2(\pi^+P|K^+{}_\Delta Y^+) + \sqrt{2}\,(\pi^+P|\eta^0\Delta^{++}) + (\pi^+P|\pi^+\Delta^+) = 0. \quad (22d)$$

The usefulness of such connections is that they provide triangular inequalities among the absolute values of the amplitudes, or the (cross sections)$^{1/2}$. Thus, from Equation (22d), we may derive three sets of such inequalities, of the form

$$\begin{aligned} 2|(\pi^+P|K^+{}_\Delta Y^+)| &\leq \sqrt{2}\,|(\pi^+P|\eta^0\Delta^{++})| + |(\pi^+P|\pi^+\Delta^+)| \\ &\geq \big|\sqrt{2}|(\pi^+P|\eta^0\Delta^{++})| - |(\pi^+P|\pi^+\Delta^+)|\big|. \end{aligned} \quad (22d')$$

However, in order to check relationships such as Equations (22a) through (22d′) against the measured cross sections, it is necessary to take into account the differences in the masses of members of the same multiplets. Of course, these are a reflection of the MSI which can give rise to violations of the connections between amplitudes discussed above. We shall consider the effects of $SU(3)$-breaking in the next section; but even neglecting such effects, it is still necessary to take into account the kinematical consequences of the mass differences. The conventional procedure for applying the kinematical corrections[27] is to compare all cross sections at the same Q-value,

$$Q = E_{cm} - M_1 - M_2, \tag{23a}$$

where M_1 and M_2 are, respectively, the masses of the incident m_8 and B_8; and to obtain the corresponding matrix elements (amplitudes) by dividing the cross section by an invariant phase-space factor

$$|M_{f,i}|^2 = \frac{E_{cm}^2 p_{\text{in}}}{p_{\text{out}}} \sigma_{f,i} = F\sigma, \tag{23b}$$

where p_{in} and p_{out} are, respectively, the cm momenta in the initial and the final states. Thus, Equation (22d′) becomes

$$[4F\sigma(\pi^+P \to K^+{}_\Delta Y^+)]^{1/2} \le [2F\sigma(\pi^+P \to \eta^0\Delta^{++})]^{1/2} + [F\sigma(\pi^+P \to \pi^+\Delta^+)]^{1/2}. \tag{22d''}$$

Taking into account such kinematical corrections, it is observed that all of the above relationships, with the exception of (21b), seem to be reasonably well satisfied.

U-SPIN CONSIDERATIONS: Many of the $SU(3)$ combinatorial properties, considered in the preceding discussion, may be derived as a straightforward consequence of I- and U-spin conservation. Consider, for example, the relationships in (22a). In the initial state, the mesons (π^-, K^-) belong to a U-spin doublet, as does the proton, (P, Σ^+); these doublets can combine to give $U = 1$ and 0. On the other hand, the final-state mesons (K^+, π^+) have $U_{m'} = \frac{1}{2}$, while the final baryons belong to $U_{B'} = \frac{3}{2}$ $(\Delta^-, {}_\Delta Y^-, {}_\Delta\Xi^-, \Omega^-)$; these combine to give $U = 2$ and 1. Conservation of U spin permits only the $U = 1$ intermediate state, so that all the matrix elements involved in (22a) depend on one amplitude, $A(U = 1)$, with the proportionality constant given by the product of the initial- and final-state Clebsch–Gordan coefficients

$$A_{f,i} = C^{1,U_3}_{1/2,U_{3m'};\ 3/2,U_{3B'}} \cdot C^{1,U_3}_{1/2,U_{3m};\ 1/2,U_{3B}} \cdot A(U = 1), \tag{22a'}$$

which leads directly to (22a).

As another example, consider the reactions[28]

$$P\overline{P} \to B_{10}^- \overline{B_8^-}, \tag{24}$$

[27] S. Meshkov, G. A. Snow, and G. Yodh, *Phys. Rev. Letters, 12:* 87 (1964).

[28] The reactions $P\overline{P} \to B_8^- \overline{B_{10}^-}$ are related to (24) by charge-conjugation invariance.

of which there are just two $\mathcal{Y}$-conserving possibilities:

$$P\overline{P} \to {}_{\Delta}Y^{-}\overline{\Sigma^{-}}, \tag{24a}$$

$$P\overline{P} \to {}_{\Delta}\Xi^{-}\overline{\Xi^{-}}. \tag{24b}$$

The initial state has values $U = 1$ and 0 and the final state, being a combination of $U_{10} = \frac{3}{2}$ and $U_{\overline{8}} = \frac{1}{2}$, has $U = 2$ and 1, with only $U = 1$ overlapping; hence, reactions (24a) and (24b) are given by a single amplitude and have, in fact, equal matrix elements [see Equation (22a′)].

A somewhat less trivial example is provided by the reactions

$$P\overline{P} \to B_{10}\overline{B_{10}}. \tag{25}$$

In this case, we are combining $8 \otimes \overline{8}$ in the initial state and $10 \otimes \overline{10}$ in the final state. According to Equations (19a) and (19e), there are four overlapping representations (1, 8_1, 8_2, and 27), and, accordingly, four arbitrary amplitudes. However, if we confine ourselves only to those reactions involving $U_{10} = U_{\overline{10}} = \frac{3}{2}$ in the final state, i.e.,

$$P\overline{P} \to \Delta^{-}\overline{\Delta^{-}} \tag{25a}$$

$$\to {}_{\Delta}Y^{-}\,\overline{{}_{\Delta}Y^{-}} \tag{25b}$$

$$\to {}_{\Delta}\Xi^{-}\,\overline{{}_{\Delta}\Xi^{-}} \tag{25c}$$

$$\to \Omega^{-}\overline{\Omega^{-}}, \tag{25d}$$

the matrix elements may all be expressed in terms of just two independent combinations, corresponding to $U = 1$ and 0, since these are the only U-spin values accessible to the $P\overline{P}$ combination. In this case, the appropriate combination of Clebsch–Gordan coefficients leads to the relationship

$$F\sigma(P\overline{P} \to \Omega^{-}\overline{\Omega^{-}}) - F\sigma(P\overline{P} \to \Delta^{-}\overline{\Delta^{-}})$$
$$= 3[F\sigma(P\overline{P} \to {}_{\Delta}\Xi^{-}\,\overline{{}_{\Delta}\Xi^{-}}) - F\sigma(P\overline{P} \to {}_{\Delta}Y^{-}\,\overline{{}_{\Delta}Y^{-}})]. \tag{25′}$$

Sometimes, U-spin considerations are especially useful for deriving relationships among reactions with three particles in the final state. Consider the set of reactions

$$K^{-}P \to \Omega^{-}K^{+}K^{0} \qquad [\sigma(\Omega^{-})] \tag{26a}$$

$$\left.\begin{aligned} &\to {}_{\Delta}\Xi^{-}K^{+}\pi^{0} \\ &\to {}_{\Delta}\Xi^{-}K^{+}\eta^{0} \\ &\to {}_{\Delta}\Xi^{-}K^{0}\pi^{+} \end{aligned}\right\} \qquad [\sigma({}_{\Delta}\Xi^{-})] \tag{26b}$$

$$\left.\begin{aligned} &\to {}_{\Delta}Y^{-}\pi^{+}\pi^{0} \\ &\to {}_{\Delta}Y^{-}\pi^{+}\eta^{0} \\ &\to {}_{\Delta}Y^{-}K^{+}\overline{K^{0}} \end{aligned}\right\} \qquad [\sigma({}_{\Delta}Y^{-})] \tag{26c}$$

$$\to \Delta^{-}\overline{K^{0}}\pi^{+} \qquad [\sigma(\Delta^{-})]. \tag{26d}$$

Here, again, there are two possible initial U-spin channels, $U = 1$ and 0. The final states are made up out of a member of a U-spin quartet (B_{10}) and two octet mesons, one of which is a member of a U-spin doublet and the second of a U-spin triplet or singlet; these combine into a $(U_{m_1}=\frac{1}{2})+(U_{m_2}=1)$ quartet and doublet plus a $(U_{m_1}=\frac{1}{2})+(U_{m_2}=0)$ doublet. There are four independent amplitudes: three with $U=1$ ($U_B=\frac{3}{2}$, $U_m=\frac{3}{2}$; $U_B=\frac{3}{2}$, $U_m=\frac{1}{2}$; $U_B=\frac{3}{2}$, $U'_m=\frac{1}{2}$) and one with $U=0$ ($U_B=\frac{3}{2}$, $U_m=\frac{3}{2}$). However, when the amplitudes appropriate to reactions (26) are squared, they may be combined to yield

$$F\sigma(\Omega^-)-F\sigma(\Delta^-)=3[F\sigma({}_\Delta\Xi^-)-F\sigma({}_\Delta Y^-)]. \tag{26}$$

Clearly, the use of U-spin conservation is a powerful tool for deriving such connections and others.[29] However, in addition, we may use the properties of the U-spin operators to describe the effects of the MSI — the U-spin violating interactions. Assuming that the MSI behaves as a vector in U space, we may consider the properties of the $SU(3)$ violation in a fashion strictly analogous to the description of the I-spin violation resulting from the EMI (Section 7.2). We illustrate by considering the relative strengths of the possible decay modes of a hypothetical $SU(3)$ singlet baryon,[30] Y_0^0 ($\mathcal{Y}=t=U=V=0$), of mass sufficiently great to allow all possible decay modes into a $\frac{1}{2}^+$ baryon (B_8) and a pseudoscalar meson (m_8). In Table 14.8, column 1 lists the possible (B_8+m_8) decay modes, while columns 2–4 summarize the consequences of I-spin conservation. To apply U-spin conservation (columns 5–7) we must use the appropriate U_1^0 and U_0^0 combinations of the neutral $\mathcal{Y}=0$ members. The simultaneous conservation of both I and U spin leads to the relative amplitudes of column 8; in this approximation all permitted decay modes have equal matrix elements.

The U-spin violating, MSI Hamiltonian may be written in the form

$$H'=\alpha'+\beta U_{B3}+\gamma U_{m3}\,. \tag{27}$$

Its consequences may be derived by consideration of the $(U_B=1)\,(U_m=1)$ combination leading to $U=0$, and, at the same time, satisfying I-spin conservation; the appropriate combination may be derived from column 8,

$$U^0(1+1)=\tfrac{1}{2}(-N\overline{K^0}+\Sigma^0\pi^0+\Lambda^0\eta^0-\Xi^0K^0), \tag{27a}$$

and the appropriate matrix elements,

$$M'=\langle U^0|H'U^0\rangle, \tag{27b}$$

are listed in column 9, with $\beta'=\beta-\gamma$. Then, I-spin conservation (by definition also satisfied by the MSI) permits us to supply the rest of the entries.[31] Thus, the relative values of the phase-space corrected decay widths become

---

[29] Thus, for example, the combinations $B_8\otimes B_8$ may be used to derive relations between the nucleon-nucleon forces and the Λ–$\mathfrak{N}$ forces appropriate to the discussion of hypernuclei (i.e., nuclei where one of the neutrons is substituted by a Λ^0).

[30] The $Y_0^*(1405)$ is generally assumed to be an $SU(3)$ singlet. However, its mass is too small to permit any of the possible decay modes except the $\Sigma\pi$. See Table 14.5 for the relative decay amplitudes in the case of strict $SU(3)$ invariance (VSI only).

[31] We obtain the same results by applying H', Equation (27), to the $U^0(\frac{1}{2}+\frac{1}{2})$ combinations.

Table 14.8 Amplitudes for the Decay of an SU(3) Singlet Y_0^0

Final state	(t_B, t_{B3})	(t_m, t_{m3})	I Spin (0, 0) amplitude	$(U_B, U_{B3})^a$	$(U_m, U_{m3})^a$	U Spin (0, 0) amplitude	$SU(3)$ amplitude	MSI violation
1. PK^-	$(\frac{1}{2}, \frac{1}{2})$	$(\frac{1}{2}, -\frac{1}{2})$	$\sqrt{\frac{1}{2}}A$	$(\frac{1}{2}, \frac{1}{2})$	$(\frac{1}{2}, -\frac{1}{2})$	$\sqrt{\frac{1}{2}}A'$	α	$-\alpha' - \beta'$
2. $N\bar{K}^0$	$(\frac{1}{2}, -\frac{1}{2})$	$(\frac{1}{2}, \frac{1}{2})$	$-\sqrt{\frac{1}{2}}A$	$(1, 1)$	$(1, -1)$	$\frac{1}{3}B'$	$-\alpha$	$\alpha' + \beta'$
3. $\Sigma^+\pi^-$	$(1, 1)$	$(1, -1)$	$\frac{1}{3}B$	$(\frac{1}{2}, -\frac{1}{2})$	$(\frac{1}{2}, \frac{1}{2})$	$-\sqrt{\frac{1}{2}}A'$	$-\alpha$	$-\alpha'$
4. $\Sigma^-\pi^+$	$(1, -1)$	$(1, 1)$	$\frac{1}{3}B$	$(\frac{1}{2}, \frac{1}{2})$	$(\frac{1}{2}, -\frac{1}{2})$	$\sqrt{\frac{1}{2}}D'$	$-\alpha$	$-\alpha'$
5. $\Sigma^0\pi^0$	$(1, 0)$	$(1, 0)$	$-\frac{1}{3}B$	$(1, 0)$	$(1, 0)$	$-\frac{1}{3}B'$	α	α'
6. $\Sigma^0\eta^0$	$(1, 0)$	$(0, 0)$	0	$(1, 0)$	$(0, 0)$	0	0	0
7. $\Lambda^0\pi^0$	$(0, 0)$	$(1, 0)$	0	$(0, 0)$	$(1, 0)$	0	0	0
8. $\Lambda^0\eta^0$	$(0, 0)$	$(0, 0)$	C	$(0, 0)$	$(0, 0)$	C'	α	α'
9. Ξ^-K^+	$(\frac{1}{2}, -\frac{1}{2})$	$(\frac{1}{2}, \frac{1}{2})$	$-\sqrt{\frac{1}{2}}D$	$(\frac{1}{2}, -\frac{1}{2})$	$(\frac{1}{2}, \frac{1}{2})$	$-\sqrt{\frac{1}{2}}D'$	α	$-\alpha' + \beta'$
10. Ξ^0K^0	$(\frac{1}{2}, \frac{1}{2})$	$(\frac{1}{2}, -\frac{1}{2})$	$\sqrt{\frac{1}{2}}D$	$(1, -1)$	$(1, 1)$	$\frac{1}{3}B'$	$-\alpha$	$\alpha' - \beta'$

[a] The states U_1^0 and U_0^0 referred to in these columns are the combinations

$$U_{B1}^0 = \tfrac{1}{2}\Sigma^0 - (\sqrt{3}/2)\,\Lambda^0,$$
$$U_{B0}^0 = (\sqrt{3}/2)\,\Sigma^0 + \tfrac{1}{2}\Lambda^0,$$
$$U_{m1}^0 = \tfrac{1}{2}\pi^0 - (\sqrt{3}/2)\,\eta^0,$$
$$U_{m0}^0 = (\sqrt{3}/2)\,\pi^0 + \tfrac{1}{2}\eta^0.$$

For the purposes of this computation, it is assumed that the η^0 is the pure $SU(3)$, $t = 0$ member of the pseudoscalar octet (see Table 14.3).

$$F\Gamma(Y_0^0 \to \mathfrak{N}\bar{K}):F\Gamma(Y_0^0 \to \Sigma\pi):F\Gamma(Y_0^0 \to \Lambda\eta):F\Gamma(Y_0^0 \to \Xi K)$$
$$= |\alpha - \alpha' - \beta'|^2 : |\alpha + \alpha'|^2 : |\alpha + \alpha'|^2 : |\alpha - \alpha' + \beta'|^2. \quad (28)$$

Photon Interactions • Interactions involving photons provide a most useful field for the application of U-spin conservation owing to the $U_\gamma = 0$ character of the photon.[32] Consider the decays

$$B_{10} \to B_8 + \gamma. \quad (29)$$

U-spin conservation immediately yields a selection rule forbidding the B_{10}^- decays

$$\langle_\Delta\Xi^-|\Xi^-\gamma\rangle = \langle_\Delta Y^-|\Sigma^-\gamma\rangle = 0, \quad (29a)$$

owing to the $U = \frac{3}{2}$ of the B_{10}^-. On the other hand,

$$\langle_\Delta Y^+|\Sigma^+\gamma\rangle = \langle\Delta^+|P\gamma\rangle \neq 0, \quad (29b)$$

while, for the members of the B_{10}^0 triplet,

$$\langle\Delta^0|N\gamma\rangle = \langle_\Delta\Xi^0|\Xi^0\gamma\rangle = 2\langle_\Delta Y^0|\Sigma^0\gamma\rangle = -\frac{2}{\sqrt{3}}\langle_\Delta Y^0|\Lambda^0\gamma\rangle, \quad (29c)$$

the last two equalities deriving directly from the mixture $U_1^0 = [\frac{1}{2}\Sigma^0 - (\sqrt{3}/2)\Lambda^0]$.

In the same way, we may derive relations among the matrix elements for the decay of a vector meson into a photon and a pseudoscalar:

$$8_v \to 8_p + \gamma. \quad (30)$$

For the charged members, we have

$$\langle K^{*\pm}|K^\pm\gamma\rangle = \langle\rho^\pm|\pi^\pm\gamma\rangle. \quad (30a)$$

However, the relations pertaining to the neutral members are more complicated, not only owing to the mixing in the octet of ρ^0 and ω_8, appropriate to the U_1^0 and U_0^0 combinations, but also because of the mixing of the octet member ω_8 and the singlet $\omega_1 = U_0'^0$ in the observed neutral mesons [Equation (11c) and Table 14.3]. Defining the following matrix elements,[33]

$$\begin{aligned} A &= \langle U_{1v}^0|\gamma U_{1p}^0\rangle, \\ B &= \langle U_{0v}^0|\gamma U_{0p}^0\rangle, \\ C &= \langle U_{0v}^0|\gamma U_{0p}'^0\rangle = \langle U_{0v}'^0|\gamma U_{0p}^0\rangle, \\ D &= \langle U_{0v}'^0|\gamma U_{0p}'^0\rangle, \end{aligned} \quad (30b)$$

we exhibit in Table 14.9 the combinations of amplitudes appropriate to the photon decays of the physical meson states. The combinations in the last column correspond to the approximation of the F–Y–S model, in which the observed pseudoscalar mesons are taken to be pure octet and singlet, while the vector mesons are mixed according to the prescription given in Section 12.2.1 ($\sin^2\theta_v = \frac{1}{3}$).

[32] The EMI can mix $SU(3)$ multiplets, since the photon carries with it the properties of the U_0^0 member of an octet. Thus, the $SU(3)$ selection rules for photon interactions are governed by Equations (19a) through (19c).

[33] Note that the decay $\omega_1 \to \eta_1' + \gamma$ violates $SU(3)$, since $1 \otimes 8 \neq 1$, so that we expect $D \ll A, B, C$.

Table 14.9 Matrix Elements for the Decays $v^0 \rightarrow p^0 + \gamma$

Decay [a]	$\langle v^0 \vert p^0\gamma \rangle$	$\langle v^0 \vert p^0\gamma \rangle$ for $\theta_p = 0$, $\theta_v = \sin^{-1}\sqrt{\frac{1}{3}}$
$\rho^0 \rightarrow \pi^0\gamma$	$\frac{1}{4}(A+3B)$	$\frac{1}{4}(A+3B)$
$\rightarrow \eta\gamma$	$(\sqrt{3}/4)\cos\theta_p(-A+B)-(\sqrt{3}/2)\sin\theta_p C$	$(\sqrt{3}/4)(-A+B)$
$\rightarrow \eta'\gamma$	$(\sqrt{3}/4)\sin\theta_p(-A+B)+(\sqrt{3}/2)\cos\theta_p C$	$(\sqrt{3}/2)C$
$\phi \rightarrow \pi^0\gamma$	$(\sqrt{3}/4)\cos\theta_v(-A+B)-(\sqrt{3}/2)\sin\theta_v C$	$(\sqrt{2}/4)(-A+B)-\frac{1}{2}C$
$\rightarrow \eta\gamma$	$\frac{1}{4}\cos\theta_v\cos\theta_p(3A+B)-\frac{1}{2}\sin(\theta_v+\theta_p)C+\sin\theta_v\sin\theta_p D$	$(\sqrt{6}/12)(3A+B)-(\sqrt{3}/6)C$
$\rightarrow \eta'\gamma$	$\frac{1}{4}\cos\theta_v\sin\theta_p(3A+B)+\frac{1}{2}\cos(\theta_v+\theta_p)C-\sin\theta_v\cos\theta_p D$	$\sqrt{\frac{1}{6}}C-\sqrt{\frac{1}{3}}D$
$\omega \rightarrow \pi^0\gamma$	$(\sqrt{3}/4)\sin\theta_v(-A+B)+(\sqrt{3}/2)\cos\theta_v C$	$\frac{1}{4}(-A+B)+\sqrt{\frac{1}{2}}C$
$\rightarrow \eta\gamma$	$\frac{1}{4}\sin\theta_v\cos\theta_p(3A+B)+\frac{1}{2}\cos(\theta_v+\theta_p)C-\cos\theta_v\sin\theta_p D$	$(\sqrt{3}/12)(3A+B)+\sqrt{\frac{1}{6}}C$
$\rightarrow \eta'\gamma$	$\frac{1}{4}\sin\theta_v\sin\theta_p(3A+B)+\frac{1}{2}\sin(\theta_v+\theta_p)C+\cos\theta_v\cos\theta_p D$	$\frac{1}{2}\sqrt{\frac{1}{3}}C+\sqrt{\frac{2}{3}}D$

[a] Owing to the relative masses $M_\phi > M_{\eta'} > M_\rho \approx M_\omega$ the decays of the third and ninth rows should be reversed. While the matrix elements are independent of this inversion, the decay rates for the η' decays are proportional to $3|\langle \eta' | v^0\gamma \rangle|^2$, owing to the three possible spin substates ($m = 1, 0, -1$) or the product v^0.

U-spin conservation also leads to some interesting predictions for photon-induced reactions. Thus, by a straightforward comparison of Clebsch–Gordan coefficients, we obtain

$$\frac{\langle \gamma P|\Delta^0\pi^+\rangle}{\langle \gamma P|{}_\Delta Y^0K^+\rangle}=\frac{\langle \gamma P|\Delta^0\rho^+\rangle}{\langle \gamma P|{}_\Delta Y^0K^{*+}\rangle}=-\sqrt{2}, \tag{31a}$$

$$\frac{\langle \gamma N|\Delta^-\pi^+\rangle}{\langle \gamma N|{}_\Delta Y^-K^+\rangle}=\frac{\langle \gamma N|\Delta^-\rho^+\rangle}{\langle \gamma N|{}_\Delta Y^-K^{*+}\rangle}=-\sqrt{3}, \tag{31b}$$

$$\langle \gamma P|\Sigma^0K^+\rangle-\sqrt{3}\,\langle \gamma P|\Lambda^0K^+\rangle+\sqrt{2}\,\langle \gamma P|N\pi^+\rangle=0. \tag{31c}$$

Another fine example of the application of U-spin considerations is that of the special set of three-body photoreactions

$$\gamma+P\rightarrow B^-_{10}+2m^+_8; \tag{32}$$

for example,[34]

$$\begin{aligned}\gamma+P&\rightarrow \Delta^-\pi^+\pi^+\\ &\rightarrow {}_\Delta Y^-\pi^+K^+ + {}_\Delta Y^-K^+\pi^+\\ &\rightarrow {}_\Delta\Xi^-K^+K^+,\end{aligned} \tag{32a}$$

in which the two $U=\frac{1}{2}$ mesons must always be in the $U=1$ state if they are to combine with $U=\frac{3}{2}$ baryons to give a total $U=\frac{1}{2}(\gamma P)$; consequently, there is only one amplitude and

$$\begin{aligned}\langle \gamma P|\Delta^-\pi^+\pi^+\rangle&=-\sqrt{3}\,\langle \gamma P|{}_\Delta Y^-\pi^+K^+\rangle=-\sqrt{3}\,\langle \gamma P|{}_\Delta Y^-K^+\pi^+\rangle\\ &=\sqrt{3}\,\langle \gamma P|{}_\Delta\Xi^-K^+K^+\rangle,\end{aligned} \tag{32b}$$

giving

$$F\sigma(\Delta^-):F\sigma({}_\Delta Y^-):F\sigma({}_\Delta\Xi^-):F\sigma(\Omega^-)=3:2:1:0. \tag{32c}$$

PROBLEMS

1. Referring to Table 14.2, justify (or contradict) the assignment of the $\Xi^*(1820)$ to a $\frac{3}{2}^-$ decimet on the basis of its observed decays.
2. Derive the reaction amplitude relation (22c) by use of U-spin conservation.
3. Show that the $SU(3)$ selection rules imply:

(a) $F\sigma(P\overline{P}\rightarrow {}_\Delta Y^-\overline{\Sigma^-})=F\sigma(P\overline{P}\rightarrow {}_\Delta\Xi^-\overline{\Xi^-})$,

(b) $$\begin{aligned}[F\sigma(P\overline{P}\rightarrow \Omega^-\overline{\Omega^-})]^{1/2}&\geq |2[F\sigma(P\overline{P}\rightarrow \Delta^-\overline{\Delta^-})]^{1/2}-3[F\sigma(P\overline{P}\rightarrow {}_\Delta Y^-{}_\Delta\overline{Y^-})]^{1/2}|\\ &\geq |\tfrac{1}{2}[F\sigma(P\overline{P}\rightarrow \Delta^-\overline{\Delta^-})]^{1/2}-\tfrac{3}{2}[F\sigma(P\overline{P}\rightarrow {}_\Delta\Xi^-{}_\Delta\overline{\Xi^-})]^{1/2}|\\ &\geq |[F\sigma(P\overline{P}\rightarrow {}_\Delta Y^-{}_\Delta\overline{Y^-})]^{1/2}-2[F\sigma(P\overline{P}\rightarrow {}_\Delta\Xi^-{}_\Delta\overline{\Xi^-})]^{1/2}|,\end{aligned}$$

(c) $$\begin{aligned}[F\sigma(K^-P\rightarrow K^0K^+\Omega^-)]^{1/2}\geq |&[3F\sigma(\pi^-P\rightarrow K^0K^+{}_\Delta\Xi^-)]^{1/2}\\ &-[F\sigma(K^-P\rightarrow \overline{K^0}\pi^+\Delta^-]^{1/2}|,\end{aligned}$$

(d) $F\sigma(PP\rightarrow \Delta^{++}\Delta^0)=2F\sigma(\Sigma^+P\rightarrow \Delta^{++}{}_\Delta Y^0)$,

(e) $F\Gamma(\rho^0\rightarrow K^0\overline{K^0}):F\Gamma(\omega^0\rightarrow K^0\overline{K^0}):F\Gamma(\phi^0\rightarrow K^0\overline{K^0})=1:3\sin^2\theta_v:3\cos^2\theta_v$,

[34] Note that $\gamma P\rightarrow \Omega^-+2m^+_8$ is impossible, owing to $\mathcal{Y}$ conservation.

and that, therefore,

$$F\sigma(K^-P \to \rho^0\Lambda^0):F\sigma(K^-P \to \omega^0\Lambda^0):F\sigma(K^-P \to \phi^0\Lambda^0) = 1:3\sin^2\theta_v:3\cos^2\theta_v,$$

provided that this set of reactions proceeds through a one-kaon exchange mechanism. (Draw the Feynman diagrams.)

4. Consider the decays of the 2^+-mesons

(a) $2^+ \to 1^- + 0^-$:

$$\begin{array}{ll} A_2 \to \rho\pi, & K_2 \to K^*\pi \\ f' \to K^*K, & \quad\;\; \to \rho K \\ & \quad\;\; \to \omega K. \end{array}$$

(b) $2^+ \to 0^- + 0^-$:

$$\begin{array}{ll} A_2 \to K\overline{K} & K_2 \to K\pi \\ \quad\;\; \to \eta\pi, & \quad\;\; \to K\eta, \\ f' \to \pi\pi & f \to \pi\pi \\ \quad\;\; \to K\overline{K} & \quad\;\; \to K\overline{K} \\ \quad\;\; \to \eta\eta, & \quad\;\; \to \eta\eta. \end{array}$$

Derive the relative values of the matrix elements for these decays based on $SU(3)$ and the mixing of the octet and singlet $\mathcal{Y} = t = 0$ members of the nonets, in terms of the mixing angles θ_v and θ_{psc}. How does conservation of angular momentum enter into the determination of the relative decay rates?

5. Using U-spin invariance and the I-spin properties of the EMI, derive the consequent connections among the cross sections for the reactions

$$\gamma P \to m_8 B_8.$$

6. Show that

$$[F\sigma(\gamma P \to K^0K^+K^+\Omega^-)]^{1/2} \geq |[3F\sigma(\gamma P \to K^0\pi^+\pi^+{}_\Delta Y^-)]^{1/2} - [3F\sigma(\gamma P \to \overline{K^0}K^+K^+{}_\Delta Y^-)]^{1/2}|.$$

14.4 Sakata Model in SU(3)

As previously noted, if one starts out with the baryon octet, B_8, as the basic elementary multiplet, the construction of the mesons according to an octet F–Y model, $m = B_8 \otimes \overline{B}_8$, yields many more multiplets than can be accounted for among the observed mesons. On the other hand, accepting both the $\frac{1}{2}^+$ baryons and the mesons as basic, the resulting excited baryonic states, $B' = B_8 \otimes (m_8 \oplus m_1)$, are also overabundant in unobserved or redundant $SU(3)$ representations.

However, it is noteworthy that the Sakata triplet (P, N, Λ) itself belongs to a representation of $SU(3)$ (see Figure 14.7) — the triplet representation which is, in fact, the simplest one out of which all others can be constructed. Accordingly, it is irresistibly tempting to try to construct an $SU(3)$ F–Y–S model, in which we take for the mesons,

$$m = B_3 \otimes \overline{B}_3, \tag{33a}$$

and for the baryons,

$$B = m \otimes B_3 = B_3 \otimes \overline{B}_3 \otimes B_3. \tag{33b}$$

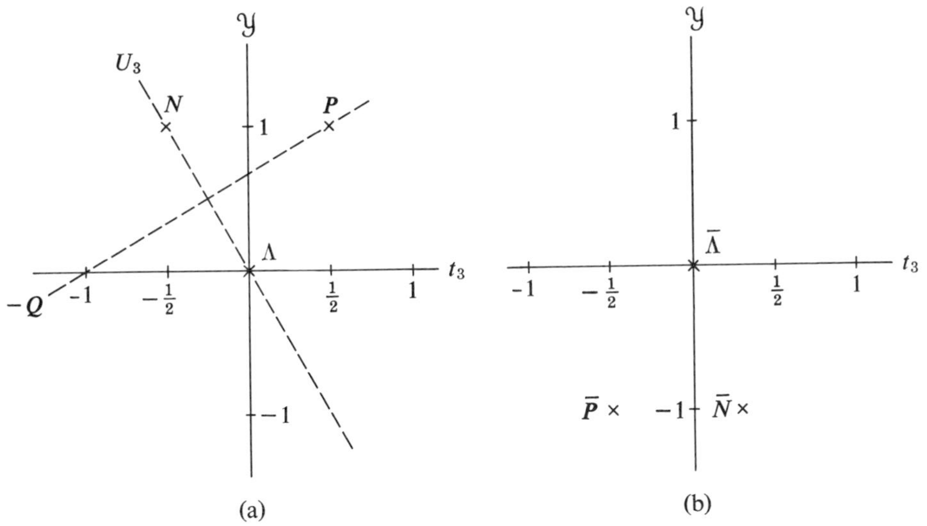

Figure 14.7 $SU(3)$ diagrams for the Sakata triplet. (a) B_3. (b) $\bar{B}_3$.

As far as the mesons are concerned, we have already demonstrated (Section 12.2.1, Table 12.2) the decomposition

$$3 \otimes \bar{3} = 1 \oplus 8, \tag{34}$$

the singlet, η_1, corresponding to the completely symmetrical combination

$$\chi_0^0 = \sqrt{\tfrac{1}{3}}\,(P\bar{P} + N\bar{N} + \Lambda\bar{\Lambda}), \tag{34a}$$

which, being invariant with respect to rotations in the t_3–$\mathcal{Y}$ plane, has the properties $\mathcal{Y} = t = U = V = 0$. The wave function of the octet meson with $\mathcal{Y} = t = 0$, η_8, is then specified (Table 12.2, row 2); the singlet-octet mixing must arise from the symmetry-breaking MSI. An example of such an interaction, which could account for the ω–ϕ mixing in the vector meson octet, was given in Section 12.2.1, but we were still left with the problem of explaining the great difference between the 0^- and 1^- nonets in this regard.

The model for the baryons [Equation (33b)] being essentially that of Yamaguchi, we might expect to encounter difficulties similar to those exposed in Section 12.2.2. This is indeed the case, but their origin (and possible means of elimination) is more clearly understood when we consider the group properties of the decomposition

$$3 \otimes \bar{3} \otimes 3 = 3 \oplus 3' \oplus 6 \oplus 15. \tag{35}$$

EXAMPLE

Equation (35) may be derived as follows:

$$\begin{aligned} 3 \otimes (\bar{3} \otimes 3) &= 3 \otimes (1 \oplus 8) = (3 \otimes 1) \oplus (3 \otimes 8) \\ &= 3 \oplus (3 \oplus 6 \oplus 15). \end{aligned} \tag{35a}$$

Table 14.10 SU(3) Decomposition of 3 ⊗ 8

$\mathcal{Y}_1$	t_1	$\mathcal{Y}_2$	t_2	$\mathcal{Y}$	t	Symmetry	Multiplet
1	$\frac{1}{2}$	1	$\frac{1}{2}$	2	1	+	15
				2	0	−	6
1	$\frac{1}{2}$	0	1	1	$\frac{3}{2}$	+	15
				1	$\frac{1}{2}$ }	+	15
		0	0	1	$\frac{1}{2}$ }	−	6
0	0	1	$\frac{1}{2}$	1	$\frac{1}{2}$ }	mixed	3
0	0	0	1	0	1 }	+	15
1	$\frac{1}{2}$	−1	$\frac{1}{2}$	0	1 }	−	6
				0	0 }	+	15
0	0	0	0	0	0 }	mixed	3
0	0	−1	$\frac{1}{2}$	−1	$\frac{1}{2}$	+	15

We now use the technique developed in Section 14.1 for the decomposition of the 3 ⊗ 8. The permitted combinations are listed in Table 14.10, and developed in Figure 14.8. The combinations listed in the first two rows, having different symmetry, belong to two different representations; these are shown as crosses (×) in Figure 14.8. Using the symmetry with respect to reflection about the $\mathcal{Y}$ and $-Q$ axes (and noting, from Figure 14.7, that the origin of the U_3–Q axes is displaced from the origin of the t_3–$\mathcal{Y}$) we immediately identify all but four of the remaining combinations as belonging to other members of these representations, shown as ⊗ in Figure 14.8. There remain two triplets [see Figure

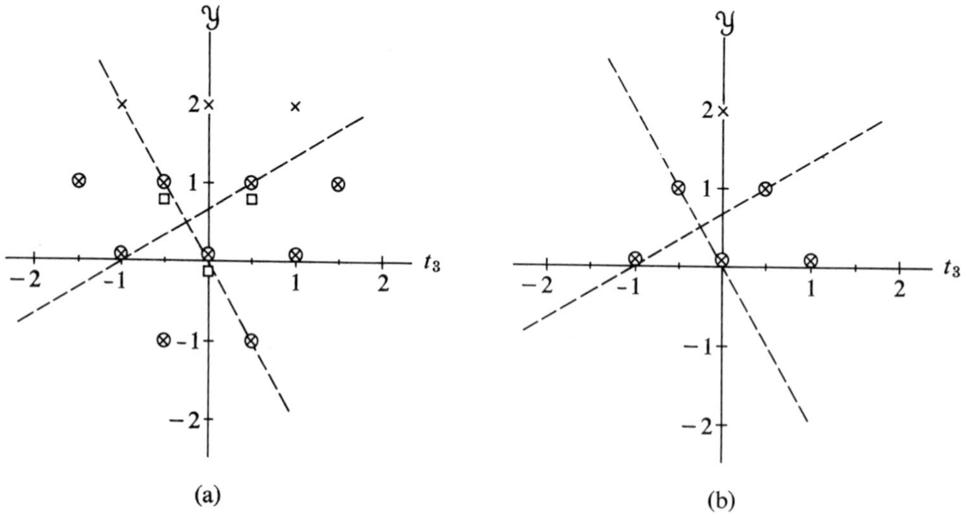

Figure 14.8 Decomposition of 3 ⊗ 8 = 3 ⊕ 6 ⊕ 15. (a) "15." (b) "6."

14.7(a)] of which one shares the symmetry of the 15-plet and is shown as □ in Figure 14.8(a). The remaining three combinations belong to a separate triplet. Q.E.D.

It is instructive to inquire into the reasons for the disappointing failure of the $SU(3)$–Sakata model to yield the observed baryon (octet and decimet) multiplets, and to see what modifications, if any, might serve to repair this deficiency. The first problem lies with the combinatorial properties of $SU(3)$ — i.e., Equation (35); one way to overcome this would be to add to the fundamental particles, so that the baryons might be arrived at through different $SU(3)$ combinations. Thus, it is possible[35] to add a baryon singlet, B_1 ($\mathcal{Y}=t=U=V=0$), to the Sakata triplet, B_3. The mesons would still be given by $B_3 \otimes \overline{B_3} = m_1 \oplus m_8$ (also, $B_1 \otimes \overline{B_1} = m_1'$), while the baryon octet would be obtained by $B_3 \otimes \overline{B_3} \otimes B_1 = B_1 \oplus B_8$; the rest of the baryons could then be constructed according to the conventional prescription, $B' = B_8 \otimes m_8$ (Section 14.1), which would still yield the superfluous $\overline{10}$ and 27 baryon representations.

An alternative version starts with a fundamental *meson* triplet, m_3, and a baryon singlet, B_1. Then, $m_3 \otimes \overline{m_3} = m_1 \oplus m_8$; $B_1 \otimes \overline{B_1} = m_1'$; $m_8 \otimes B_1 = B_8$, etc. In the more general case,[36] the fundamental baryon triplet, B_3, is combined with a boson triplet, b_3, which can carry baryon number 0 or 2; the first gives $B_3 \otimes \overline{b_3}^{(0)} = B_1 \oplus B_8$, while the second gives $\overline{B_3} \otimes b_3^{(2)} = B_1 \oplus B_8$. In either case, $B_8 \otimes b_3^{(0)}(\overline{B_8} \otimes b_3^{(2)}) = B_3 \oplus B_6 \oplus B_{15}$ (Table 14.10), which does not help with the excited baryon states, and still lacks the $\frac{3}{2}^+$ decimet.

However, the introduction of bosons with baryon number 2 opens up a new possibility, which arises out of the $SU(3)$ combinatorial property:[37]

$$\begin{aligned} 3 \otimes 3 \otimes 3 &= 3 \otimes (3 \otimes 3) = 3 \otimes (\overline{3} \oplus 6) = (3 \otimes \overline{3}) \oplus (3 \otimes 6) \\ &= 1 \otimes 8 \otimes 8' \oplus 10. \end{aligned} \tag{36}$$

Of course, if the "3" in Equation (36) refers to the Sakata B_3, the products could not be the observed baryons, since the product representations would correspond to baryon number 3, the corresponding groups would be displaced upward on the t_3–$\mathcal{Y}$ diagrams by $\Delta\mathcal{Y} = 2$ units from the corresponding diagrams for the observed baryon multiplets (Figures 14.2 and 14.3), and the particle charges would be one greater than for the observed baryon multiplets. However, introduction of a boson (even-spin) singlet of baryon number 2, $\mathcal{Y}=2$, $t=0$, $Q=1$ (i.e., $b_1^{+(2)}$) permits the formation of the desired baryon multiplets through[38]

$$(B_3 \otimes B_3 \otimes B_3) \otimes \overline{b_1^{+(2)}} = B_1 \oplus B_8 \oplus B_8' \oplus B_{10}. \tag{36a}$$

---

[35] Z. Maki, *Progr. Theoret. Phys.*, *31:* 331 (1964); Y. Hara, *Phys. Rev.*, *134:* B701 (1964).

[36] F. Gürsey, T. D. Lee, and M. Nauenberg, *Phys. Rev.*, *135:* B467 (1964); J. Schwinger, *Phys. Rev.*, *135:* B816 (1964).

[37] The derivation of Equation (36), using the techniques developed in this chapter, is left as an exercise to the reader.

[38] The alternative is

$$B_{1,8,8',10} = (b_3^{(0)} \otimes b_3^{(0)} \otimes b_3^{(0)}) \otimes B_1^-, \tag{36b}$$

with B_1^- having baryon number 1, $\mathcal{Y} = -2$, $t = 0$ (i.e., the quantum numbers of the Ω^-).

There is, however, a serious difficulty associated with this solution: the displaced isotopic singlet $b_{\bar{1}}^{+(2)}$ (or $B_{\bar{1}}^{-}$) cannot exhibit $SU(3)$ invariance with respect to rotations in the t_3–$\mathcal{Y}$ plane since it cannot have, at the same time, $U = V = 0$ (see Section 14.2). To circumvent this difficulty, it is necessary to redefine the hypercharge $\mathcal{Y}$ for displaced $SU(3)$ multiplets (i.e., multiplets whose "center of gravity" does not lie at the origin of the t_3–$\mathcal{Y}$ coordinate system) by the introduction of an additional conserved and additive quantum number, called the "triality" number D.

We illustrate the idea of triality by considering a modification of the above scheme,[39] in which there are two basic baryon triplets, $B_3^{(1)}$ and $B_3^{(2)}$, both symmetrically disposed with respect to the t_3–$\mathcal{Y}$ axes, whose properties are summarized in Table 14.11. Defining the triality number as

$$D = \sum_{i=1}^{3} Q_i, \tag{37}$$

we now have for the basic $SU(3)$ relations

$$Q = t_3 + \frac{\mathcal{Y}}{2} + \frac{D}{3} = t_3 + \frac{\mathcal{Y}'}{2}, \tag{37a}$$

$$\mathcal{Y}' = U_3 + \frac{Q}{2}, \tag{37b}$$

$$0 = t_3 + U_3 + V_3, \tag{37c}$$

and the observed meson and baryon multiplets

$$B_3^{(1)} \otimes \overline{B_3^{(1)}} = m_1 \oplus m_8, \tag{38a}$$

$$B_3^{(2)} \otimes \overline{B_3^{(2)}} = m_1' \oplus m_8', \tag{38b}$$

$$B_3^{(1)} \otimes B_3^{(1)} \otimes \overline{B_3^{(2)}} = B_1 \oplus B_8 \oplus B_8' \oplus B_{10}. \tag{38c}$$

Note that the members of the elementary baryon triplets have nonintegral values of hypercharge $\mathcal{Y}$ and strangeness S, and, therefore, they can be produced only

Table 14.11 Properties of the Baryon Triplets of Bacry, Nuyts, and Van Hove

	$B_3^{(1)}$			$B_3^{(2)}$		
	p	n	λ	p'	n'	λ'
Q	1	0	0	0	1	1
t	$\frac{1}{2}$	$\frac{1}{2}$	0	$\frac{1}{2}$	$\frac{1}{2}$	0
t_3	$\frac{1}{2}$	$-\frac{1}{2}$	0	$-\frac{1}{2}$	$\frac{1}{2}$	0
$\mathcal{Y}$	$\frac{1}{3}$	$\frac{1}{3}$	$-\frac{2}{3}$	$-\frac{1}{3}$	$-\frac{1}{3}$	$\frac{2}{3}$
S	$-\frac{2}{3}$	$-\frac{2}{3}$	$-\frac{5}{3}$	$-\frac{4}{3}$	$-\frac{4}{3}$	$-\frac{1}{3}$
D	1	1	1	2	2	2

[39] H. Bacry, J. Nuyts, and L. Van Hove, *Phys. Letters, 9:* 279 (1964).

in the hypercharge-conserving strong and electromagnetic interactions in groups for which $\Sigma_i \mathcal{Y}_i$ is integral. Since Q, t_3, B, and S (and consequently, $\mathcal{Y}$) are all conserved in the strong and electromagnetic interactions, so also the triality number D must be conserved.

However, there is a way to avoid the introduction of the unobserved and superfluous triality, provided one is prepared to accept, for the members of the Sakata triplet, nonintegral values, not only of the strangeness and hypercharge, but of the absolutely conserved charge and baryon numbers themselves. Once one is prepared to go this far, one may define the Sakata triplet as having baryon number $\frac{1}{3}$, so that

$$B_3^{(1/3)} \otimes B_3^{(1/3)} \otimes B_3^{(1/3)} = B_1 \oplus B_8 \oplus B_8' \oplus B_{10} \tag{39a}$$

yields all three required baryon multiplets without further ado; this modification makes absolutely no difference for the mesons

$$B_3^{(1/3)} \otimes \overline{B_3^{(1/3)}} = m_1 \otimes m_8. \tag{39b}$$

The $B_3^{(1/3)}$ triplet must have a symmetric t_3–$\mathcal{Y}$ plot, since the resulting baryons [Equation (39a)] must be symmetric; this requires the same $\mathcal{Y}$ assignments as for $B_3^{(1)}$ in Table 14.11. But now we have no additional quantum numbers, so that

$$Q = t_3 + \frac{\mathcal{Y}}{2} \tag{39c}$$

requires nonintegral values of Q.

These are the quarks of Gell-Mann and Zweig.[40] Their properties are summarized in Table 14.12, and will be discussed in detail in Chapter 15.

Table 14.12 The Quarks, q or $B_3^{(1/3)}$, of Gell-Mann and Zweig

	p	n	λ
t	$\frac{1}{2}$	$\frac{1}{2}$	0
t_3	$\frac{1}{2}$	$-\frac{1}{2}$	0
B	$\frac{1}{3}$	$\frac{1}{3}$	$\frac{1}{3}$
S	0	0	-1
$\mathcal{Y}$	$\frac{1}{3}$	$\frac{1}{3}$	$-\frac{2}{3}$
Q	$\frac{2}{3}$	$-\frac{1}{3}$	$-\frac{1}{3}$

PROBLEMS

1. Derive the $q = (p, n, \lambda)$ combinations corresponding to

$$q \otimes q \otimes q = B_1 \oplus B_8 \oplus B_8' \oplus B_{10}.$$

2. Using the model of Bacry, Nuyts, and Van Hove for the baryons [Equation

[40] M. Gell-Mann, *Phys. Letters, 8:* 214 (1964); G. Zweig, *CERN Reports,* TH 401 and 412 (1964).

(38c)], and assuming an invariant B_iB_j interaction, show that the octet and decimet baryon mass formulas follow from the assumption of four separate basic baryon masses:

$$M(p_1) = M(n_1) = M_1,$$
$$M(\lambda_1) = M_1 + \Delta_1,$$
$$M(p_2) = M(n_2) = M_2,$$
$$M(\lambda_2) = M_2 + \Delta_2.$$

14.5 Some Group-Theoretical Considerations

Although, up to this point, we have been able to derive the relevant properties of the $SU(3)$ group without explicit resort to formal group theory, it is useful to review[41] very briefly some of the general properties of the unitary groups of n dimensions, $U(n)$, and particularly of the symmetric subgroups, $SU(n)$, which are the ones most relevant to particle theory. Any representation of the group $U(n)$ may be characterized by n integers:

$$q_1 \geq q_2 \geq q_3 \geq \cdots \geq q_{n-1} \geq q_n, \tag{40}$$

or by the equivalent Young tableaux:

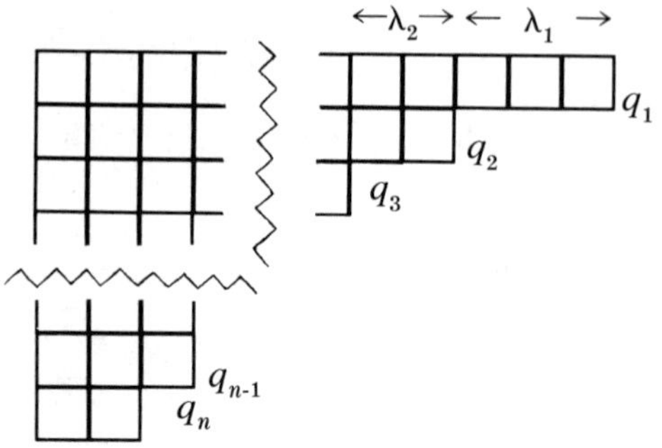

(40a)

For the symmetrical group $SU(n)$ we have $q_n = 0$, and we require only $n-1$ integers, which are generally listed as the set of differences

$$\begin{aligned}(\lambda_1 = q_1 - q_2,\ \lambda_2 = q_2 - q_3,\ \cdots,\ \lambda_j = q_j - q_{j+1},\ \cdots)\\ = D_n^N(\lambda_1, \lambda_2, \cdots, \lambda_{n-1} = q_{n-1}),\end{aligned} \tag{40b}$$

where N is the dimension of the representation. The rank of the representation is given by

$$R_n = \sum_{i=1}^{n} q_i \tag{40c}$$

---

[41] See Y. Ne'eman, *Algebraic Theory of Particle Physics*, W. A. Benjamin, New York (1967); E. P. Wigner, *Group Theory and its Application to the Quantum Mechanics of Atomic Spectra*, Academic Press, New York (1959).

In particular, for the group $U(3)$, a given representation is characterized by q_1, q_2, q_3, or $\lambda_1 = \lambda = q_1 - q_2$, $\lambda_2 = \mu = q_2 - q_3$, and

$$D_3^N(\lambda, \mu) = \{\lambda, \mu\} \tag{41a}$$

represents a given N-dimensional representation of $SU(3)$, with

$$N = \tfrac{1}{2}(q_1 - q_2 + 1)(q_1 - q_3 + 2)(q_2 - q_3 + 1) \rightarrow \tfrac{1}{2}(\lambda + 1)(\lambda + \mu + 2)(\mu + 1), \tag{41b}$$

$$R_3 = q_1 + q_2 + q_3 \rightarrow \lambda + 2\mu. \tag{41c}$$

We collect, in Table 14.13, the combinations corresponding to the simplest representations of $SU(3)$ and their corresponding Young tableaux. It may be

Table 14.13 Properties of the Simplest Representations of SU(3)

Representation[a]			
(q_1, q_2)	$\{\lambda, \mu\}$	Dimension (N)	Young tableaux
1, 1, 1 or 0, 0	0, 0	1	
1, 0	1, 0	3	
1, 1	0, 1	$\overline{3}$	
2, 0	2, 0	6	
2, 2	0, 2	$\overline{6}$	
2, 1	1, 1	8	
3, 0	3, 0	10	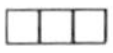
3, 3	0, 3	$\overline{10}$	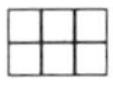
3, 1	2, 1	15	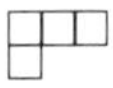
3, 2	1, 2	$\overline{15}$	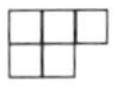
4, 1	3, 1	24	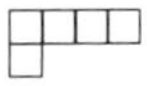
4, 3	1, 3	$\overline{24}$	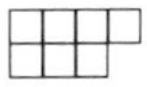
4, 2	2, 2	27	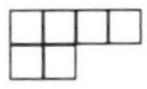
6, 0	6, 0	28	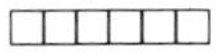
6, 6	0, 6	$\overline{28}$	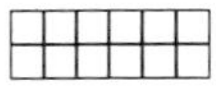
5, 1	4, 1	35	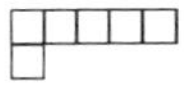
5, 4	1, 4	$\overline{35}$	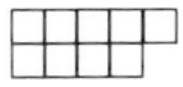
5, 2	3, 2	42	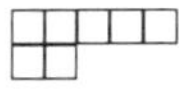
5, 3	2, 3	$\overline{42}$	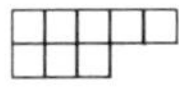
6, 3	3, 3	64	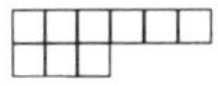

[a] Except for the $N = 1$ representation, we take $q_3 = 0$.

noted that, in the association of $SU(3)$ with the known mesons and baryons, the hypercharge of the particle with largest isotopic-spin multiplicity (i.e., Σ in the baryon octet, $\mathfrak{N}^*_{3/2}$ or Δ in the baryon decimet) is given by

$$\mathcal{Y}(I_{\text{max}}) = \frac{\lambda - \mu}{3}. \tag{41d}$$

Thus, the known particles can be associated only with $SU(3)$ representations with

$$\lambda - \mu = 3i, \qquad (i = 0, 1, 2, \cdots). \tag{41d$'$}$$

The basic representation $\{1, 0\}$ corresponds, then, to particles of $\frac{1}{3}$ integral hypercharge, i.e., quarks.

Multiplets with $\lambda = \mu$ are self-conjugate, in the sense that the contragradient representation

$$D_n^{\overline{N}} = \{-f_n, -f_{n-1}, \cdots, -f_1\} \tag{42}$$

leads to the same representation.

Now the representation $D_n^N(\lambda_1, \cdots, \lambda_{n-1})$ may generally be described by a set of tensors of dimension N. These may then be combined into invariant forms, of which the isotopic spin and its z component are the prototypes for the group $SU(2)$. For $SU(3)$ there are three such forms:

$$F_3 = -R_3 = -(\lambda + 2\mu), \tag{42a}$$

$$\begin{aligned} F^2 &= (q_1^2 + q_2^2 + q_3^2) + 2(q_1 - q_3) + F_3 \\ &= (\lambda + \mu)^2 + \mu^2 + \lambda, \end{aligned} \tag{42b}$$

$$\begin{aligned} \overline{F^3} = &-(q_1^3 + q_2^3 + q_3^3) \\ &+ (-\tfrac{3}{2}q_1^2 + \tfrac{3}{2}q_2^2 + \tfrac{9}{2}q_3^2) \\ &- \tfrac{1}{2}(q_1 + q_2 + q_3)^2 + (2q_1 + 2q_2 - 4q_3), \end{aligned} \tag{42c}$$

where F is sometimes referred to as the unitary spin. We summarize, in Table 14.14, the values of F_3, F^2, and $\overline{F^3}$ for the representations of greatest interest for particle applications.

Table 14.14 Unitary-Spin Invariants for Representations of SU(3)

Representation $\{\lambda, \mu\}$	Dimension (N)	$-F_3$	F^2	$-\overline{F^3}$
0, 0	1	0	0	0
1, 1	8	3	6	12
3, 0	10	3	12	39
0, 3	$\overline{10}$	6	18	60
2, 2	27	6	22	96
4, 1	35	6	30	168
1, 4	$\overline{35}$	9	42	225
3, 3	64	9	48	306

Finally, we note that the Young tableaux may be used directly to construct the representations corresponding to the direct product of two specified representations of a group, simply by geometrical addition as illustrated in Figure 14.9.

$$3 \otimes 3 \otimes 3 = 3 \otimes (3 \otimes 3) = 3 \otimes (\bar{3} \oplus 6) = (3 \otimes \bar{3}) \oplus (3 \otimes 6) = 1 \oplus 8 \oplus 8 \oplus 10$$

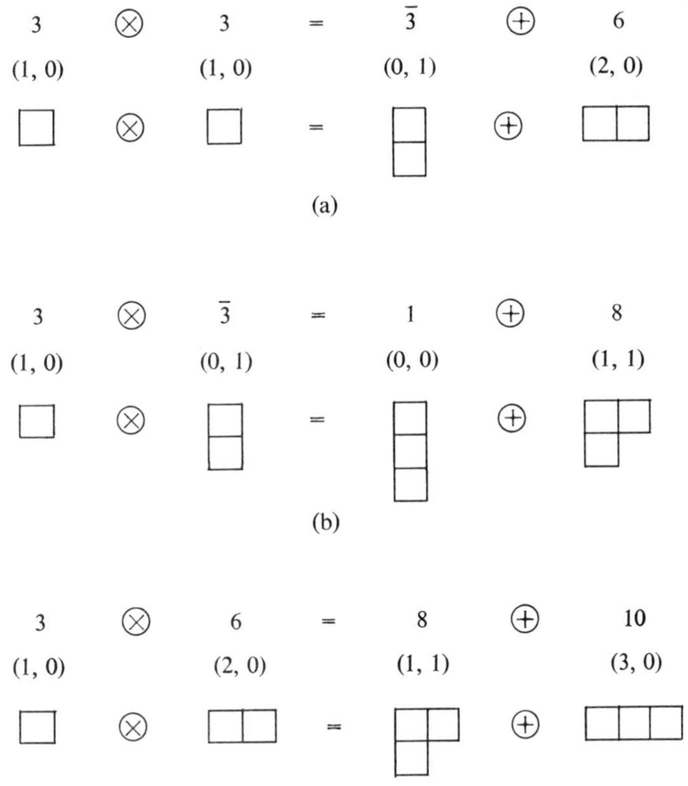

Figure 14.9 Product of $3 \otimes 3 \otimes 3$ in $SU(3)$, using the Young tableaux.

PROBLEM

Using the method of addition of Young tableaux, show how

$$\begin{aligned} 8 \otimes 8 &= 8 \otimes [(3 \otimes \bar{3}) \ominus 1] = [(8 \otimes 3) \otimes \bar{3}] \ominus (8 \otimes 1) \\ &= [(15 \oplus \bar{6} \oplus 3) \otimes \bar{3}] \ominus (8 \otimes 1) \\ &= (27 \oplus 10 \oplus 8) \oplus (\overline{10} \oplus 8) \oplus (1 \oplus 8) \ominus 8. \end{aligned}$$

15

The Quark Model and $SU(6)$

15.1 Quarks: Their Combination and Their Properties

Of all the suggestions aimed at finding a more fundamental basis for an $SU(3)$ model of the hadrons, discussed at the end of Chapter 14, the quark model of Gell-Mann and Zweig is, at the same time, the simplest and the most drastic. Its simplicity lies in its retention of the Sakata triplet, as shown in Figure 15.1,

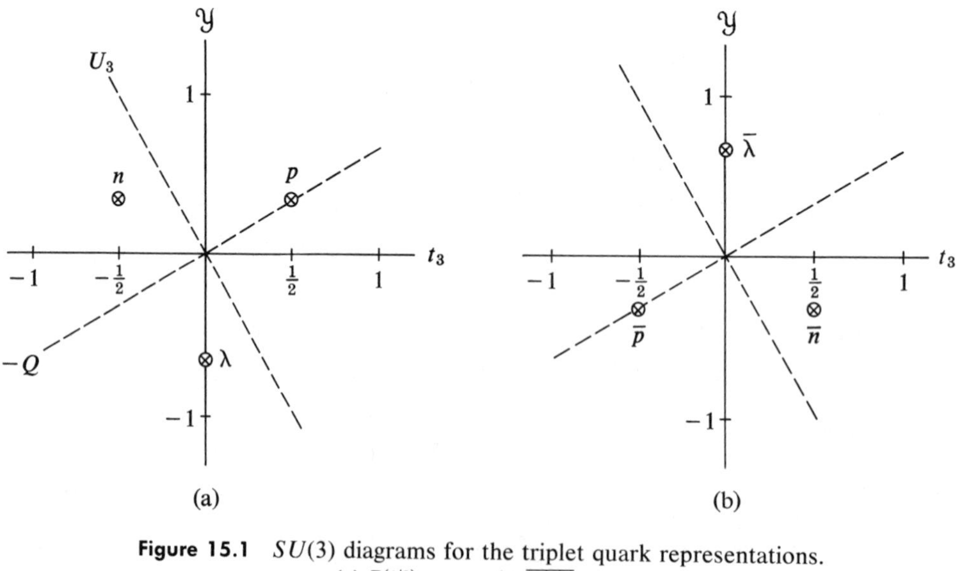

Figure 15.1 $SU(3)$ diagrams for the triplet quark representations. (a) $B_3^{(1/3)} \equiv q$. (b) $\overline{B_3^{(1/3)}} \equiv \bar{q}$.

with no additional building blocks or quantum numbers required, as the fundamental basis of all other $SU(3)$ representations, and in symmetrizing this triplet with respect to the t_3–$\mathcal{Y}$ axes (and consequently, in the U- and V-spin planes as well); this insures the symmetry of the product representations. Furthermore, it permits the most economical construction of the observed baryon singlets, octets, and decimets (with no additional multiplets) out of $3 \otimes 3 \otimes 3$.

The drastic nature of the quark assumption is clearly seen in Table 14.12 and Figure 15.1 — it requires the introduction of a triplet of particles $q = \{p, n, \lambda\}$ which, although otherwise resembling the physical P, N, and Λ, have third-integral baryon number and charges. Reserving for later the question of whether such particles exist in nature, we may nevertheless explore the consequences of the model for the properties of the mesons and baryons.

As far as the mesons are concerned, the product

$$q \otimes \bar{q} = m_1 \oplus m_8 \tag{1}$$

yields precisely the same combinations as have previously been discussed for the F–Y–S model (Section 12.2.1), with the same consequences arising from the $SU(3)$ symmetry as have been derived in Chapter 14. For the baryons, we have

$$q \otimes q \otimes q = 3 \otimes (\bar{3} \oplus 6) = (3 \otimes \bar{3}) \oplus (3 \otimes 6) = B_1 \oplus B_{8'} \oplus B_8 \oplus B_{10}, \tag{2}$$

as indicated in Figure 15.2. The three-quark combinations appropriate to these baryon multiplets are given in Table 15.1.

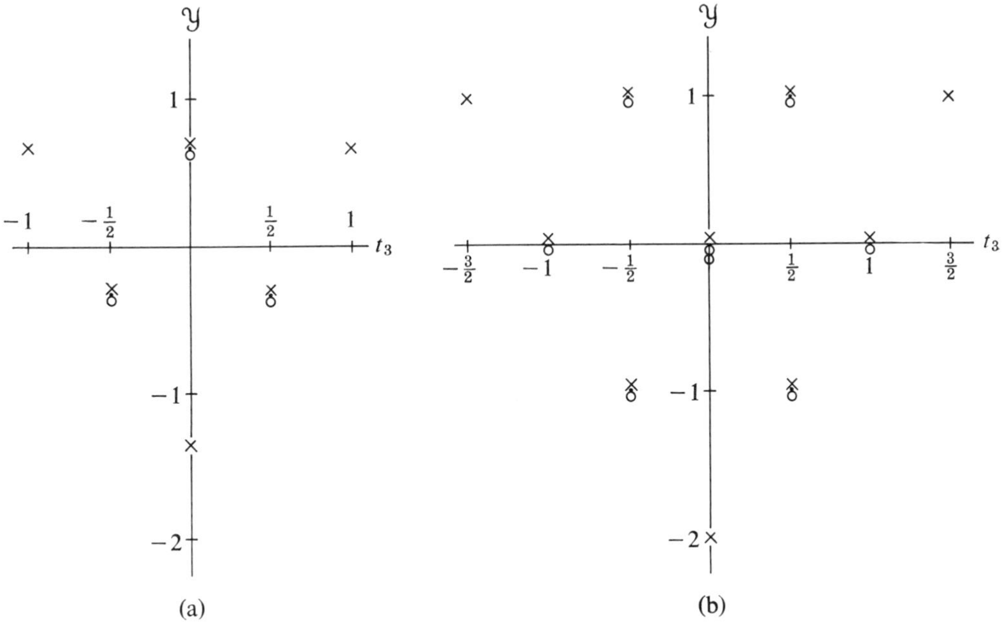

Figure 15.2 $SU(3)$ diagrams for quark combinations. (a) $q \otimes q = \bar{3}(\bigcirc) \oplus 6(\times)$. (b) $q \otimes 6 = B_8(\bigcirc) \oplus B_{10}(\times)$.

Table 15.1 Quark Combinations Resulting from $q \otimes q \otimes q = B_1 \oplus B_{8'} \oplus B_8 \oplus B_{10}$

$(\mathcal{Y}_1\ t_1)$	$(\mathcal{Y}_2\ t_2)$	$(\mathcal{Y}\ t)$	t_3	Quark combination
(a) $q \otimes q = 6$ (*symmetric*)				
$(\frac{1}{3}\ \frac{1}{2})$	$(\frac{1}{3}\ \frac{1}{2})$	$(\frac{2}{3}\ 1)$	1	pp
			0	$\sqrt{\frac{1}{2}}\,(pn + np)$
			-1	nn
$(\frac{1}{3}\ \frac{1}{2})$	$(-\frac{2}{3}\ 0)$	$(-\frac{1}{3}\ \frac{1}{2})$	$\frac{1}{2}$	$\sqrt{\frac{1}{2}}\,(p\lambda + \lambda p)$
$(-\frac{2}{3}\ 0)$	$(\frac{1}{3}\ \frac{1}{2})$		$-\frac{1}{2}$	$\sqrt{\frac{1}{2}}\,(n\lambda + \lambda n)$
$(-\frac{2}{3}\ 0)$	$(-\frac{2}{3}\ 0)$	$(-\frac{4}{3}\ 0)$	0	$\lambda\lambda$
(b) $q \otimes q = \overline{3}$ (*antisymmetric*)				
$(\frac{1}{3}\ \frac{1}{2})$	$(\frac{1}{3}\ \frac{1}{2})$	$(\frac{2}{3}\ 0)$	0	$\sqrt{\frac{1}{2}}\,(pn - np)$
$(\frac{1}{3}\ \frac{1}{2})$	$(-\frac{2}{3}\ 0)$	$(-\frac{1}{3}\ \frac{1}{2})$	$\frac{1}{2}$	$\sqrt{\frac{1}{2}}\,(p\lambda - \lambda p)$
$(-\frac{2}{3}\ 0)$	$(\frac{1}{3}\ \frac{1}{2})$		$-\frac{1}{2}$	$\sqrt{\frac{1}{2}}\,(n\lambda - \lambda n)$
(c) $q \otimes 6 = B_{10}$ (*symmetric*)				
$(\frac{1}{3}\ \frac{1}{2})$	$(\frac{2}{3}\ 1)$	$(1\ \frac{3}{2})$	$\frac{3}{2}$	$\chi_{1/2}^{1/2}\chi_1^1 = ppp$
			$\frac{1}{2}$	$\sqrt{\frac{2}{3}}\,\chi_{1/2}^{1/2}\chi_1^0 + \sqrt{\frac{1}{3}}\,\chi_{1/2}^{-1/2}\chi_1^1 = \sqrt{\frac{1}{3}}\,(ppn + pnp + npp)$
			$-\frac{1}{2}$	$\sqrt{\frac{1}{3}}\,(npn + nnp + pnn)$
			$-\frac{3}{2}$	nnn
$(\frac{1}{3}\ \frac{1}{2})$	$(-\frac{1}{3}\ \frac{1}{2})$	$(0\ 1)$	1	$\sqrt{\frac{2}{3}}\,\chi_{1/2}^{1/2}\chi_{1/2}^{1/2} + \sqrt{\frac{1}{3}}\,\chi_0^0\chi_1^1 = \sqrt{\frac{1}{3}}\,(pp\lambda + p\lambda p + \lambda pp)$
$(-\frac{2}{3}\ 0)$	$(\frac{2}{3}\ 1)$		0	$\sqrt{\frac{2}{3}}\sqrt{\frac{1}{2}}\,(\chi_{1/2}^{1/2}\chi_{1/2}^{-1/2} + \chi_{1/2}^{-1/2}\chi_{1/2}^{1/2}) + \sqrt{\frac{1}{3}}\,\chi_0^0\chi_1^0$
				$= \sqrt{\frac{1}{6}}\,(pn\lambda + p\lambda n + np\lambda + n\lambda p + \lambda pn + \lambda np)$
			-1	$\sqrt{\frac{1}{3}}\,(nn\lambda + n\lambda n + \lambda nn)$
$(\frac{1}{3}\ \frac{1}{2})$	$(-\frac{4}{3}\ 0)$	$(-1\ \frac{1}{2})$	$\frac{1}{2}$	$\sqrt{\frac{1}{3}}\,\chi_{1/2}^{1/2}\chi_0^0 + \sqrt{\frac{2}{3}}\,\chi_0^0\chi_{1/2}^{1/2} = \sqrt{\frac{1}{3}}\,(p\lambda\lambda + \lambda p\lambda + \lambda\lambda p)$
$(-\frac{2}{3}\ 0)$	$(-\frac{1}{3}\ \frac{1}{2})$		$-\frac{1}{2}$	$\sqrt{\frac{1}{3}}\,(n\lambda\lambda + \lambda n\lambda + \lambda\lambda n)$
$(-\frac{2}{3}\ 0)$	$(-\frac{4}{3}\ 0)$	$(-2\ 0)$	0	$\lambda\lambda\lambda$
(d) $q \otimes 6 = B_8$ (*mixed*)				
$(\frac{1}{3}\ \frac{1}{2})$	$(\frac{2}{3}\ 1)$	$(1\ \frac{1}{2})$	$\frac{1}{2}$	$\sqrt{\frac{1}{3}}\,\chi_{1/2}^{1/2}\chi_1^0 - \sqrt{\frac{2}{3}}\,\chi_{1/2}^{-1/2}\chi_1^1 = \sqrt{\frac{1}{6}}\,(ppn + pnp - 2npp)$
			$-\frac{1}{2}$	$-\sqrt{\frac{1}{6}}\,(npn + nnp - 2pnn)$
$(\frac{1}{3}\ \frac{1}{2})$	$(-\frac{1}{3}\ \frac{1}{2})$	$(0\ 1)$	1	$\sqrt{\frac{1}{3}}\,\chi_{1/2}^{1/2}\chi_{1/2}^{1/2} - \sqrt{\frac{2}{3}}\,\chi_0^0\chi_1^1 = \sqrt{\frac{1}{6}}\,(pp\lambda + p\lambda p - 2\lambda pp)$
$(-\frac{2}{3}\ 0)$	$(\frac{2}{3}\ 1)$		0	$\sqrt{\frac{1}{3}}\sqrt{\frac{1}{2}}\,(\chi_{1/2}^{1/2}\chi_{1/2}^{-1/2} + \chi_{1/2}^{-1/2}\chi_{1/2}^{1/2}) - \sqrt{\frac{2}{3}}\,\chi_0^0\chi_0^0$
				$= \sqrt{\frac{1}{12}}\,(pn\lambda + p\lambda n + np\lambda + n\lambda p - 2\lambda pn - 2\lambda np)$
			-1	$-\sqrt{\frac{1}{6}}\,(nn\lambda + n\lambda n - 2\lambda nn)$
$(\frac{1}{3}\ \frac{1}{2})$	$(-\frac{1}{3}\ \frac{1}{2})$	$(0\ 0)$	0	$\sqrt{\frac{1}{2}}\,(\chi_{1/2}^{1/2}\chi_{1/2}^{-1/2} - \chi_{1/2}^{-1/2}\chi_{1/2}^{1/2}) = \frac{1}{2}\,(pn\lambda + p\lambda n - np\lambda - n\lambda p)$
$(\frac{1}{3}\ \frac{1}{2})$	$(-\frac{4}{3}\ 0)$	$(-1\ \frac{1}{2})$	$\frac{1}{2}$	$\sqrt{\frac{2}{3}}\,\chi_{1/2}^{1/2}\chi_0^0 - \sqrt{\frac{1}{3}}\,\chi_0^0\chi_{1/2}^{1/2} = \sqrt{\frac{1}{6}}\,(2p\lambda\lambda - \lambda p\lambda - \lambda\lambda p)$
$(-\frac{2}{3}\ 0)$	$(-\frac{1}{3}\ \frac{1}{2})$		$-\frac{1}{2}$	$\sqrt{\frac{1}{6}}\,(-2n\lambda\lambda + \lambda n\lambda + \lambda\lambda n)$

Table 15.1 (continued)

$(\mathcal{Y}_1\ t_1)$	$(\mathcal{Y}_2\ t_2)$	$(\mathcal{Y}\ t)$	t_3	Quark combination
(e) $q \otimes \overline{3} = B_{8'}$ *(mixed)*				
$(\frac{1}{3}\ \frac{1}{2})$	$(\frac{2}{3}\ 0)$	$(1\ \frac{1}{2})$	$\frac{1}{2}$	$\chi_{1/2}^{1/2}\chi_0^0 = \sqrt{\frac{1}{2}}\,(ppn - pnp)$
			$-\frac{1}{2}$	$\sqrt{\frac{1}{2}}\,(npn - nnp)$
$(\frac{1}{3}\ \frac{1}{2})$	$(-\frac{1}{3}\ \frac{1}{2})$	$(0\ 1)$	1	$\chi_{1/2}^{1/2}\chi_{1/2}^{1/2} = \sqrt{\frac{1}{2}}\,(pp\lambda - p\lambda p)$
			0	$\sqrt{\frac{1}{2}}\,(\chi_{1/2}^{1/2}\chi_{1/2}^{-1/2} + \chi_{1/2}^{-1/2}\chi_{1/2}^{1/2}) = \frac{1}{2}\,(pn\lambda - p\lambda n + np\lambda - n\lambda p)$
			-1	$\sqrt{\frac{1}{2}}\,(nn\lambda - n\lambda n)$
$(\frac{1}{3}\ \frac{1}{2})$ $(-\frac{2}{3}\ 0)$	$(-\frac{1}{3}\ \frac{1}{2})$ $(\frac{2}{3}\ 0)$	$(0\ 0)$	0	$\sqrt{\frac{1}{3}}\sqrt{\frac{1}{2}}\,(\chi_{1/2}^{1/2}\chi_{1/2}^{-1/2} - \chi_{1/2}^{-1/2}\chi^{1/2}) - \sqrt{\frac{2}{3}}\,\chi_0^0\chi_0^0$ $= \sqrt{\frac{1}{12}}\,(pn\lambda - p\lambda n - np\lambda + n\lambda p - 2\lambda pn + 2\lambda np)$
$(-\frac{2}{3}\ 0)$	$(-\frac{1}{3}\ \frac{1}{2})$	$(-1\ \frac{1}{2})$	$\frac{1}{2}$	$\chi_0^0\chi_{1/2}^{1/2} = \sqrt{\frac{1}{2}}\,(\lambda p\lambda - \lambda\lambda p)$
			$-\frac{1}{2}$	$\sqrt{\frac{1}{2}}\,(\lambda n\lambda - \lambda\lambda n)$
(f) $q \otimes \overline{3} = B_1$ *(antisymmetric)*				
$(\frac{1}{3}\ \frac{1}{2})$ $(-\frac{2}{3}\ 0)$	$(-\frac{1}{3}\ \frac{1}{2})$ $(\frac{2}{3}\ 0)$	$(0\ 0)$	0	$\sqrt{\frac{2}{3}}\sqrt{\frac{1}{2}}\,(\chi_{1/2}^{1/2}\chi_{1/2}^{-1/2} - \chi_{1/2}^{-1/2}\chi_{1/2}^{1/2}) + \sqrt{\frac{1}{3}}\,\chi_0^0\chi_0^0$ $= \sqrt{\frac{1}{6}}\,(pn\lambda - p\lambda n - np\lambda + n\lambda p + \lambda pn - \lambda np)$

EXAMPLE

Derivation of the baryon qqq combinations corresponding to the multiplets given by Equation (2) (Table 15.1): the qq combinations immediately divide into a symmetric sextet (6) and an antisymmetric triplet ($\overline{3}$), as indicated in parts (a) and (b) of the table. The combination $q \otimes 6$ leads to one completely symmetric set of qqq combinations, which corresponds to the baryon decimet, part (c). Thus, for example, the weight factors corresponding to the two possible combinations which can lead to the $\mathcal{Y} = 0$, $t = 1$ or the $\mathcal{Y} = -1$, $t = \frac{1}{2}$ states are uniquely determined by the requirement of symmetry — i.e., that the wave function be symmetrical with respect to all possible quark permutations. The other $q \otimes 6$ combinations corresponding to the octet, part (d), have mixed symmetry; the appropriate weight factors are determined both by the Clebsch–Gordan coefficients for the isospin combinations involved and, in the cases where the same final state is obtained from two different combinations, by the requirement that the octet wave functions be orthogonal to the decimet wave functions corresponding to the same $(\mathcal{Y}, t)$. For the second octet, derived from $q \otimes \overline{3}$, part (e), except for the case $\mathcal{Y} = t = 0$, the combinations are again uniquely determined by the Clebsch–Gordan coefficients for the isospin combinations involved. The (0, 0) state is the only one requiring special attention, since it derives from two different sets of parents. Here, it is simpler to start with the completely antisymmetric combination which, being unique, corresponds to the baryon singlet, part (f); the other (0, 0) combination, orthogonal to that of the singlet, must then be assigned to the 8′.

With respect to the symmetry of the qqq combinations, some features are worth noting. Consider the decimet: in all cases, the total isotopic spin of any pair of nucleonic quarks (p and n) is 1; of course, this is necessary if the total isotopic spin of the qqq combination is to have its maximum possible value. Now, consider the octet associated with the decimet [Table 15.1 (d)]: here, for example, in the combinations corresponding to the P or N (i.e., $\mathcal{Y}=1$, $t=\frac{1}{2}$), the isotopic spin of the (pn) combinations has the value 0 in two of the three possible permutations, and the value 1 only in the third. For the octet arising from $3 \otimes \overline{3}$, on the other hand, the (pn) pairs in the P and N combinations are always in the 0 isospin state.

One additional property of the qqq baryon combinations is noteworthy, as well as providing a useful means of checking the consistency of the combinations derived in Table 15.1. The wave functions corresponding to the same values of $\mathcal{Y}$ and t_3 (irrespective of t) must all be orthogonal; in the case of $\mathcal{Y}=0$, $t_3=0$, there are six such combinations, and their mutual orthogonality is easily checked.

So far, the quark model as outlined above is completely $SU(3)$-invariant, and provides a more economical method for obtaining the observed meson and excited baryon multiplets than the original octet model of Gell-Mann and Ne'-eman, which derived then from $8 \otimes \overline{8}$ and $8 \otimes 8$, respectively. All the results derived in Chapter 14, relating to the consequences both of the symmetry-preserving and symmetry-breaking interactions, apply to the quark version of $SU(3)$. In addition, the quark model provides a set of specific $q\overline{q}$ and qqq combinations, respectively, for the meson and baryon states. These enable the direct interpretation of some of the observed hadron properties in terms of the specific quark combinations assumed.

For the mesons, the quark-model wave functions are precisely those derived in Section 12.2.1 for the F–Y–S model, and the consequences of the models are accordingly identical, *with the exception* of those properties that depend on the quark charges, which are $\{\frac{2}{3}, -\frac{1}{3}, -\frac{1}{3}\}$ instead of the values $\{1, 0, 0\}$ assumed in the F–Y–S model.[1] The baryons present a problem, however, since we have no a priori reason for choosing between the B_8 and $B_{8'}$ (or some linear combination) as the appropriate representation of the $\mathfrak{N}$–Σ–Λ–Ξ baryon octet.

We shall resolve this problem in Section 15.2. However, at this point, we may already obtain some interesting general consequences of the quark model that depend only on the basic assumption that the mesons may be represented by $q\overline{q}$ and the baryons by qqq combinations. Thus, let us consider the asymptotic (i.e., very high-energy) relations among the meson-nucleon and nucleon-nucleon cross sections, based on the hypothesis of Lipkin and Okun, that the forward scattering amplitudes for real particles may be taken as the sum of the individual quark-quark amplitudes, taken in pairs, and on the optical theorem that relates the total cross section to the imaginary part of the forward elastic scattering amplitude (Section 13.3.3).

If we combine $SU(3)$ symmetry for the quark-quark interactions with the Pomeranchuk theorem — i.e., assume that all q–q and $\overline{q}$–q scattering amplitudes

[1] This will also affect the magnetic dipole moments; see Section 13.2.

are asymptotically equal — then we obtain immediately

$$\sigma(\overline{\mathfrak{N}}\mathfrak{N}) = \sigma(\mathfrak{N}\mathfrak{N}) = \tfrac{3}{2}\,\sigma(\pi\mathfrak{N}) = \tfrac{3}{2}\,\sigma(\overline{K}\mathfrak{N}) = \tfrac{3}{2}\,\sigma(K\mathfrak{N}), \tag{3}$$

since there are nine qqq–qqq pairs as compared to six $q\bar{q}$–qqq pairs. Referring to Figure 13.2, it is seen that at the highest available energies, ~ 20 GeV, Equations (3) are well satisfied in some cases and poorly in others.[2] The rather extreme Pomeranchuk assumption may, however, be relaxed, by assuming that the q–q and q–$\bar{q}$ scattering amplitudes differ and that they can depend on the isotopic spin or on the spin, or both, leading to specific relations among the individual cross sections. We shall, however, reserve the discussion of these relations for Chapter 17, since we have still to inject the quark spins into our considerations.

Another useful application of the quark model is in the direct derivation of the appropriate combinations of the $\mathcal{Y}=0$, $t_3=0$ members in the U-spin singlet and triplet, U_0^0 and U_1^0. Consider the action of the U-spin lowering operator,[3] $\mathbf{U}^-$, on the U_1^1 member of the meson octet:

$$\begin{aligned}\mathbf{U}^-U_1^1 &= \sqrt{2}\,U_1^0 = \mathbf{U}^-K^0 = \mathbf{U}^-(n\bar{\lambda})\\ &= (\mathbf{u}^- + \bar{\mathbf{u}}^-)(n\bar{\lambda}) = (\lambda\bar{\lambda} - n\bar{n}).\end{aligned} \tag{4a}$$

Since

$$\begin{aligned}\pi^0 &= \sqrt{\tfrac{1}{2}}\,(p\bar{p} - n\bar{n}),\\ \eta^0 &= \sqrt{\tfrac{1}{6}}\,(p\bar{p} + n\bar{n} - 2\lambda\bar{\lambda}),\end{aligned} \tag{4b}$$

we have

$$U_1^0 = \tfrac{1}{2}(\pi^0 - \sqrt{3}\,\eta^0), \tag{4c}$$

and, by orthogonality,

$$U_0^0 = \tfrac{1}{2}(\sqrt{3}\,\pi^0 + \eta^0). \tag{4d}$$

The same relations hold, of course, for the baryon octet, with the substitutions $\pi^0 \to \Sigma^0$, $\eta^0 \to \Lambda^0$. For the vector mesons, $\pi^0 \to \rho^0$, $\eta^0 \to \omega^0 \sin\theta_v - \phi^0 \cos\theta_v$, with $\sin\theta_v \approx \sqrt{\tfrac{1}{3}}$.

PROBLEM

An even more economical version of the quark model[4] assumes an especially strong di-quark binding in the symmetric $q \otimes q$ state,

$$q_2 = (q \otimes q)_6,$$

with the low-lying baryons given by

$$q \otimes q_2 = B_8 \oplus B_{10}.$$

Discuss the mesonic states resulting from the combinations $q_2 \otimes \overline{q_2}$.

---

[2] The terms in Equations (3) have, for their values at 20 GeV, ≈ 47, 39, 36.5, 31, and 26 mb, respectively.

[3] See Section 14.2, Equations (2′) through (2f).

[4] D. B. Lichtenberg, L. J. Tassie, and P. J. Kelemen, *Phys. Rev.*, *167:* 1535 (1968).

15.2 Introduction of Spin: *SU*(6)

So far, we have neglected the fact that the quarks have spin. Clearly, the assignment of spin $\frac{1}{2}$ to the quarks permits the simple construction of 0^- and 1^- mesons as $^1S_0$ and $^3S_1$ $q\bar{q}$ combinations, exactly as in the F–Y–S model, and of spin $\frac{1}{2}$ and $\frac{3}{2}$ baryons as qqq.

Taking into account the quark spin, there are six independent quark states, $q \equiv \{p_1, p_2, n_1, n_2, \lambda_1, \lambda_2\}$, where the subscripts 1 and 2 refer, respectively, to $m = \frac{1}{2}$ (spin up) and $m = -\frac{1}{2}$ (spin down). Assuming that the basic q–q and q–$\bar{q}$ interactions (the VSI) are invariant under rotations in ordinary space (i.e., behave as a scalar in spin space) as well as in t, U, and V space, the aforementioned sextet of quark states may be associated with the basic representation of the $SU(6)$ group. This is the "supermultiplet" model of Gürsey, Radicati, and Sakita, henceforth referred to as the G–R–S model.[5]

As applied to the mesons, there are 36 possible $q \otimes \bar{q}$ combinations,

$$q \otimes \bar{q} = 6 \otimes \bar{6} = 1 \oplus 35, \tag{5}$$

which divide into one completely symmetric spin and isospin singlet and a 35-plet of mixed symmetry. For the S-state $q\bar{q}$ combinations, these correspond to the 0^- singlet, η' or X_0^0, and the 0^- octet plus 1^- nonet ($8 \times 1 + 9 \times 3 = 35$). Thus, we obtain for the first time a reasonable explanation of the purity of the 0^- octet as compared to the 1^- nonet: the MSI, which leads to a mass fine structure among the mesons, is such that it also mixes the singlet and octet of the $SU(3)$ decomposition of the 35-plet meson representation

$$35 = 8_1 \oplus (1_3 \oplus 8_3). \tag{5a}$$

Since the members of the G–R–S sextet are the quarks of Gell-Mann and Zweig, the baryons may be taken as the $6^3 = 216$ qqq combinations,

$$q \otimes q \otimes q = 6 \otimes 6 \otimes 6 = 20 \oplus 56 \oplus 70 \oplus 70', \tag{6}$$

in which the wave functions corresponding to the 20 representation are antisymmetric, those of the 56 are symmetric, and those of the 70 and 70′ representations are of mixed symmetry with respect to permutations of the quark indices. The natural choice of the $SU(6)$ representation containing the baryon octet and decimet is the symmetrical 56, since this decomposes into just these

[5] F. Gürsey and L. A. Radicati, *Phys. Rev. Letters, 13:* 173 (1964); B. Sakita, *Phys. Rev., 136:* B1756 (1964). This model is the analogue of Wigner's supermultiplet theory of the nuclear forces [E. P. Wigner, *Phys. Rev., 51:* 105 (1937)] in which the spin invariance and isospin invariance of the nuclear forces are combined into an $SU(2) \otimes SU(2) = SU(4)$ invariance model; in the case of the elementary particles, the G–R–S model corresponds to $SU(3) \otimes SU(2) = SU(6)$. A given representarion of $SU(6)$ can, accordingly, be decomposed into a sum of $SU(3)$ multiplets of dimensions N, each carrying a definite spin value j [representation of $SU(2)$ of dimension $(2j+1)$], and symbolized by the notation N_{2j+1}.

two $SU(3)$ multiplets:[6]

$$56 = 8_2 \oplus 10_4. \tag{6a}$$

Accordingly, if we postulate a VSI between quarks which leads to a strong binding in the symmetric states, and either weak binding or repulsion in the others, we are led naturally to the model of the hadrons that is generally referred to as the *quark model.*

Table 15.2 lists the meson $q\bar{q}$ combinations and the baryon qqq combinations

Table 15.2 Spin and Isospin Combinations in the Quark Model

Particle[a]	Combination
(a) *Mesons*	
$\eta_0^{0\prime}(X_0^0)$	$\sqrt{\frac{1}{6}}\,(p_1\bar{p}_2 - p_2\bar{p}_1 + n_1\bar{n}_2 - n_2\bar{n}_1 + \lambda_1\bar{\lambda}_2 - \lambda_2\bar{\lambda}_1)$
η_0^0	$\sqrt{\frac{1}{12}}\,(p_1\bar{p}_2 - p_2\bar{p}_1 + n_1\bar{n}_2 - n_2\bar{n}_1 - 2\lambda_1\bar{\lambda}_2 + 2\lambda_2\bar{\lambda}_1)$
π_0^+	$\sqrt{\frac{1}{2}}\,(p_1\bar{n}_2 - p_2\bar{n}_1)$
π_0^0	$\frac{1}{2}\,(p_1\bar{p}_2 - p_2\bar{p}_1 - n_1\bar{n}_2 + n_2\bar{n}_1)$
π_0^-	$\sqrt{\frac{1}{2}}\,(n_1\bar{p}_2 - n_2\bar{p}_1)$
K_0^+	$\sqrt{\frac{1}{2}}\,(p_1\bar{\lambda}_2 - p_2\bar{\lambda}_1)$
K_0^0	$\sqrt{\frac{1}{2}}\,(n_1\bar{\lambda}_2 - n_2\bar{\lambda}_1)$
$\overline{K_0^0}$	$\sqrt{\frac{1}{2}}\,(\lambda_1\bar{n}_2 - \lambda_2\bar{n}_1)$
K_0^-	$\sqrt{\frac{1}{2}}\,(\lambda_1\bar{p}_2 - \lambda_2\bar{p}_1)$
$\phi_{\pm 1}^0$	$\lambda_{1,2}\bar{\lambda}_{1,2}$
ϕ_0^0	$\sqrt{\frac{1}{2}}\,(\lambda_1\bar{\lambda}_2 + \lambda_2\bar{\lambda}_1)$
$\omega_{\pm 1}^0$	$\sqrt{\frac{1}{2}}\,(p_{1,2}\bar{p}_{1,2} + n_{1,2}\bar{n}_{1,2})$
ω_0^0	$\frac{1}{2}\,(p_1\bar{p}_2 + p_2\bar{p}_1 + n_1\bar{n}_2 + n_2\bar{n}_1)$
$\rho_{\pm 1}^+$	$p_{1,2}\bar{n}_{1,2}$
ρ_0^+	$\sqrt{\frac{1}{2}}\,(p_1\bar{n}_2 + p_2\bar{n}_1)$
$\rho_{\pm 1}^0$	$\sqrt{\frac{1}{2}}\,(p_{1,2}\bar{p}_{1,2} - n_{1,2}\bar{n}_{1,2})$
ρ_0^0	$\frac{1}{2}\,(p_1\bar{p}_2 + p_2\bar{p}_1 - n_1\bar{n}_2 - n_2\bar{n}_1)$
$\rho_{\pm 1}^-$	$n_{1,2}\bar{p}_{1,2}$
ρ_0^-	$\sqrt{\frac{1}{2}}\,(n_1\bar{p}_2 + n_2\bar{p}_1)$
$K_{\pm 1}^{*+}$	$p_{1,2}\bar{\lambda}_{1,2}$
K_0^{*+}	$\sqrt{\frac{1}{2}}\,(p_1\bar{\lambda}_2 + p_2\bar{\lambda}_1)$
$K_{\pm 1}^{*0}$	$n_{1,2}\bar{\lambda}_{1,2}$
K_0^{*0}	$\sqrt{\frac{1}{2}}\,(n_1\bar{\lambda}_2 + n_2\bar{\lambda}_1)$
$\overline{K_{\pm 1}^{*0}}$	$\lambda_{1,2}\bar{n}_{1,2}$
$\overline{K_0^{*0}}$	$\sqrt{\frac{1}{2}}\,(\lambda_1\bar{n}_2 + \lambda_2\bar{n}_1)$
$K_{\pm 1}^{*-}$	$\lambda_{1,2}\bar{p}_{1,2}$
K_0^{*-}	$\sqrt{\frac{1}{2}}\,(\lambda_1\bar{p}_2 + \lambda_2\bar{p}_1)$

[a] In the symbol representing a particle state, the superscript is the particle's charge, while the subscript represents the z component of its spin, m.

[6] That the number of symmetrical qqq combinations is 56 may easily be seen by counting the possible symmetric combinations of the six quark indices ($i = 1, \cdots, 6$) taken three at a time:

$$\begin{aligned} iii &\rightarrow 6, \\ iij &\rightarrow 6 \times 5 = 30, \\ ijk &\rightarrow \frac{6 \times 5 \times 4}{6} = 20. \end{aligned} \tag{6a'}$$

Table 15.2 (continued)

Particle	Combination
(b) *Spin* $\frac{1}{2}^+$ *baryons* [b]	
$P_{1/2}$	$\sqrt{\frac{1}{18}}\,(2p_1p_1n_2 - p_1p_2n_1 - p_2p_1n_1 + \text{permutations})$
$N_{1/2}$	$\sqrt{\frac{1}{18}}\,(2n_1n_1p_2 - n_1n_2p_1 - n_2n_1p_1 + \text{permutations})$
$\Sigma^+_{1/2}$	$\sqrt{\frac{1}{18}}\,(2p_1p_1\lambda_2 - p_1p_2\lambda_1 - p_2p_1\lambda_1 + \text{permutations})$
$\Sigma^0_{1/2}$	$\frac{1}{6}\,(2p_1n_1\lambda_2 - p_1n_2\lambda_1 - p_2n_1\lambda_1 + \text{permutations})$
$\Sigma^-_{1/2}$	$\sqrt{\frac{1}{18}}\,(2n_1n_1\lambda_2 - n_1n_2\lambda_1 - n_2n_1\lambda_1 + \text{permutations})$
$\Lambda^0_{1/2}$	$\sqrt{\frac{1}{12}}\,(p_1n_2\lambda_1 - p_2n_1\lambda_1 - n_1p_2\lambda_1 + n_2p_1\lambda_1 + \text{permutations})$
$\Xi^0_{1/2}$	$\sqrt{\frac{1}{18}}\,(2p_2\lambda_1\lambda_1 - p_1\lambda_1\lambda_2 - p_1\lambda_2\lambda_1 + \text{permutations})$
$\Xi^-_{1/2}$	$\sqrt{\frac{1}{18}}\,(2n_2\lambda_1\lambda_1 - n_1\lambda_1\lambda_2 - n_1\lambda_2\lambda_1 + \text{permutations})$
(c) *Spin* $\frac{3}{2}^+$ *baryons* [b]	
$\Delta^{++}_{3/2}$	$p_1p_1p_1$
$\Delta^{++}_{1/2}$	$\sqrt{\frac{1}{3}}\,(p_1p_1p_2 + p_1p_2p_1 + p_2p_1p_1)$
$\Delta^+_{3/2}$	$\sqrt{\frac{1}{3}}\,(p_1p_1n_1 + p_1n_1p_1 + n_1p_1p_1)$
$\Delta^+_{1/2}$	$\frac{1}{3}\,(p_1p_1n_2 + p_1p_2n_1 + p_2p_1n_1 + \text{permutations})$
$\Delta^0_{3/2}$	$\sqrt{\frac{1}{3}}\,(p_1n_1n_1 + n_1p_1n_1 + n_1n_1p_1)$
$\Delta^0_{1/2}$	$\frac{1}{3}\,(p_2n_1n_1 + p_1n_1n_2 + p_1n_2n_1 + \text{permutations})$
$\Delta^-_{3/2}$	$n_1n_1n_1$
$\Delta^-_{1/2}$	$\sqrt{\frac{1}{3}}\,(n_1n_1n_2 + n_1n_2n_1 + n_2n_1n_1)$
${}_\Delta Y^+_{3/2}$	$\sqrt{\frac{1}{3}}\,(p_1p_1\lambda_1 + p_1\lambda_1p_1 + \lambda_1p_1p_1)$
${}_\Delta Y^+_{1/2}$	$\frac{1}{3}\,(p_1p_1\lambda_2 + p_1p_2\lambda_1 + p_2p_1\lambda_1 + \text{permutations})$
${}_\Delta Y^0_{3/2}$	$\sqrt{\frac{1}{6}}\,(p_1n_1\lambda_1 + n_1p_1\lambda_1 + \text{permutations})$
${}_\Delta Y^0_{1/2}$	$\sqrt{\frac{1}{18}}\,(p_1n_1\lambda_2 + p_1n_2\lambda_1 + p_2n_1\lambda_1 + \text{permutations})$
${}_\Delta Y^-_{3/2}$	$\sqrt{\frac{1}{3}}\,(n_1n_1\lambda_1 + n_1\lambda_1n_1 + \lambda_1n_1n_1)$
${}_\Delta Y^-_{1/2}$	$\frac{1}{3}\,(n_1n_1\lambda_2 + n_1n_2\lambda_1 + n_2n_1\lambda_1 + \text{permutations})$
${}_\Delta\Xi^0_{3/2}$	$\sqrt{\frac{1}{3}}\,(p_1\lambda_1\lambda_1 + \lambda_1p_1\lambda_1 + \lambda_1\lambda_1p_1)$
${}_\Delta\Xi^0_{1/2}$	$\frac{1}{3}\,(p_2\lambda_1\lambda_1 + p_1\lambda_2\lambda_1 + p_1\lambda_1\lambda_2 + \text{permutations})$
${}_\Delta\Xi^-_{3/2}$	$\sqrt{\frac{1}{3}}\,(n_1\lambda_1\lambda_1 + \lambda_1n_1\lambda_1 + \lambda_1\lambda_1n_1)$
${}_\Delta\Xi^-_{1/2}$	$\frac{1}{3}\,(n_2\lambda_1\lambda_1 + n_1\lambda_2\lambda_1 + n_1\lambda_1\lambda_2 + \text{permutations})$
$\Omega^-_{3/2}$	$\lambda_1\lambda_1\lambda_1$
$\Omega^-_{1/2}$	$\sqrt{\frac{1}{3}}\,(\lambda_1\lambda_1\lambda_2 + \lambda_1\lambda_2\lambda_1 + \lambda_2\lambda_1\lambda_1)$

[b] To obtain the wave functions for $-m$ from those corresponding to the spin component m, interchange the spin subscripts $1 \leftrightarrow 2$ of the quarks.

appropriate to the choices of $SU(6)$ meson and baryon representations made above. The symmetry properties of the $q\bar{q}$ combinations are obvious. For the baryons, it will be noted that all the wave functions are symmetrical with respect to all permutations of pairs. More important are the isospin and spin properties of the quark pairs. The isospin properties are, of course, precisely those discussed in connection with Table 15.1(c) and (d). As to the spin, it is evident that the $\frac{3}{2}^+$ baryon combinations require all possible pairs to be in the $j(\text{pair}) = 1$ state. For the $\frac{1}{2}^+$ baryons the situation is mixed, such that every isospin 0 pair combination is associated with a spin 0 pair combination, while isospin 1 and spin 1 go together, thereby insuring the symmetry of wave functions that have mixed symmetry with respect to either isospin or spin alone.

The spin $\frac{1}{2}$ baryon wave functions of Table 15.2 are most easily obtained as follows: For the proton with $m=\frac{1}{2}$, or $P_{1/2}$, which is a *ppn* combination, the two protons are perforce in the $t=1$ state, and must therefore also be in the $j=1$ state; then, we have

$$P_{1/2}=\sqrt{\tfrac{1}{3}}\,[\sqrt{\tfrac{2}{3}}\,(pp)_1^1 n_2-\sqrt{\tfrac{1}{3}}\,(pp)_1^0 n_1+\text{permutations}]$$
$$=\sqrt{\tfrac{1}{18}}\,[2p_1p_1n_2-p_1p_2n_1-p_2p_1n_1+\text{permutations}]. \qquad (7a)$$

By analogy,

$$\Sigma^0_{1/2}=\sqrt{\tfrac{1}{6}}\,[\sqrt{\tfrac{2}{3}}\,(pn+np)_1^1\lambda_2-\sqrt{\tfrac{1}{3}}\,(pn+np)_1^0\lambda_1+\text{permutations}], \qquad (7b)$$

and, by orthogonality,

$$\Lambda^0_{1/2}=\sqrt{\tfrac{1}{6}}\,[\sqrt{\tfrac{1}{2}}\,(pn-np)_0^0\lambda_1+\text{permutations}]. \qquad (7c)$$

That the choice of 56 for the baryons is the most natural may be seen by considering the $SU(3)$ decompositions of the other possibilities:

$$20=1_4\oplus 8_2, \qquad (6b)$$

$$70=1_2\oplus 8_2\oplus 8_4\oplus 10_2. \qquad (6c)$$

Other $SU(6)$ combinations are

$$6\otimes 6=15\oplus 21, \qquad (8a)$$

$$6\otimes 15=20\oplus 70, \qquad (8b)$$

$$6\otimes 21=56\oplus 70, \qquad (8c)$$

$$35\otimes 35=1\oplus 35\oplus 35'\oplus 189\oplus 280\oplus \overline{280}\oplus 405, \qquad (8d)$$

$$35\otimes 56=56\oplus 70\oplus 700\oplus 1134, \qquad (8e)$$

$$56\otimes 56=1\oplus 35\oplus 405\oplus 2695, \qquad (8f)$$

and some decompositions are

$$\begin{aligned}15&=\bar{3}_3\oplus 6_1,\\ 21&=\bar{3}_1\oplus 6_3.\end{aligned} \qquad (8g)$$

Note that[7] Equation (8d) permits heavy meson decays into two or more pseudoscalar and/or vector mesons; Equation (8e) permits decimet or octet → octet + meson; Equation (8f) allows the Yukawa $\bar{B}Bm$ interaction in $SU(6)$.

PROBLEM

Referring to the problem at the end of Section 15.1, we may now take

$$q_2=(q\otimes q)_{21}$$

for the quarks-with-spin model.

---

[7] A. Pais, *Phys. Rev. Letters, 13:* 175 (1965).

(a) Derive the eigenfunctions of

$$q \otimes q_2 = 56 \oplus 70.$$

(b) What are the mesonic states corresponding to $q_2 \otimes \overline{q_2}$ and their $SU(3)$ decompositions?

15.3 Hadron Properties Deriving from the Quark Model

Before embarking on this survey of quark model applications, we should emphasize once more that the quark model is primarily a handy and physically more transparent tool for deriving many of the consequences of $SU(6)$ symmetry and, when spin is not involved, of $SU(3)$, which is, of course, included in $SU(6)$. However, the quark model achieves special value insofar as it can suggest specific and useful mechanisms for $SU(6)$- and $SU(3)$-violating processes, and provide a relatively simple framework for computing the consequences of such violations.

15.3.1 Masses

The Baryons • The baryon mass formula [Section 14.3.1, Equation (9)], derived on the basis of the vector character in U space of the MSI, may be applied also to the individual $SU(3)$ submultiplets of the 56-plet $SU(6)$ baryon representation. Assuming that the symmetry-violating MSI behaves as a scalar in ordinary spin space, this relationship may be generalized to include all the members of the baryon octet and decimet, by the inclusion of one additional parameter,[8]

$$M = M_0 + A\mathcal{Y} + B\left[t(t+1) - \frac{\mathcal{Y}^2}{4}\right] + CS(S+1). \tag{9}$$

If we use the most accurately measured mass values ($\mathfrak{N}$, Λ, Σ, ${}_\Delta Y$, and ${}_\Delta \Xi$), the parameters deduced for Equation (9) are

$$\begin{aligned} M_0 &= 1066.6 \text{ MeV}/c^2, \\ A &= -196.1 \text{ MeV}/c^2, \\ B &= 38.8 \text{ MeV}/c^2, \\ C &= 65.3 \text{ MeV}/c^2. \end{aligned} \tag{9a}$$

These values have been used for the comparison, shown in Table 15.3, of the observed mass values with those predicted by Equation (9).

The Mesons • The 36 S-state $q\bar{q}$ combinations (Table 15.2) that represent the 0^- and 1^- mesons in $SU(6)$ are precisely those combinations postulated in the

[8] Generally, an MSI that violates $SU(6)$ but remains $SU(3)$-invariant will lead to additional mass terms involving the unitary spin **F** and its third component, F_3 (Section 14.5). However, in the case of the 56-plet representation, since the $SU(3)$ decomposition contains only 8 and 10, these terms may be incorporated into the last term of Equation (9). The second and third terms arise from the $SU(3)$-violating part of the MSI.

Table 15.3 Masses of the Baryons According to SU(6)

Baryon [a]	Observed mass (MeV/c^2) [b]	Computed mass
$\mathfrak{N}$	938.903	938.903
Λ	1115.58	1115.58
Σ	1193.16	1193.16
Ξ	1318.0	1331.05
Δ	1238.0	1251.2
$_\Delta Y$	1385.1	1389.1
$_\Delta \Xi$	1531.0	1527.0
Ω^-	1672.4	1664.9

[a] The mass of a given baryon is assumed to be the average of the masses of the members of the isospin multiplet.
[b] The underlined values are those used to compute the constants in the mass formula, Equations (9) and (9a); the average of the masses of $_\Delta Y$ and $_\Delta \Xi$ was used as the fourth input value.

F–Y–S model (Section 12.2.1, Table 12.2). However, in the quark model, the 0^- $\mathcal{Y} = t = 0$ singlet (η') is separated from the other 35 through being a member of a different $SU(6)$ representation. The remaining 35 belong to the same $SU(6)$ representation and should, accordingly, have masses that are connected by a single mass formula, whose form depends on the nature of the assumed $SU(6)$ symmetry-breaking MSI.

One of the simplest possible assumptions for the MSI postulates the following form:

$$O_{\mathrm{MSI}}^{(m^2)} = \tfrac{1}{2}Aj(j+1) + \Delta[\delta(q, \lambda) + \delta(\bar{q}, \bar{\lambda})], \tag{10}$$

in which the first term separates the pseudoscalar, $j = 0$, from the vector, $j = 1$, mesons, while the second term [$\delta(q, \lambda) = 1$ for the λ quark, 0 for the n or p quarks] gives rise to a mass splitting within the 0^- and 1^- multiplets through the different assumed (mass)^2 of the λ quark ($m_\lambda^2 = m_0^2 + \Delta$) as compared to the p and n quarks ($m_p^2 = m_n^2 = m_0^2$); all the other q–$\bar{q}$ interactions are assumed equal for the 35-plet group. Equation (10) leads immediately to the following values of the (mass)^2 of the mesons:

$$\begin{aligned} m_\eta^2 &= m_0^2 + \tfrac{4}{3}\Delta, \\ m_\pi^2 &= m_0^2, \\ m_K^2 &= m_0^2 + \Delta; \end{aligned} \tag{10a}$$

$$\begin{aligned} m_\phi^2 &= m_0^2 + A + 2\Delta = m_0'^2 + 2\Delta, \\ m_\omega^2 &= m_0'^2, \\ m_\rho^2 &= m_0'^2, \\ m_{K^*}^2 &= m_0'^2 + \Delta. \end{aligned} \tag{10b}$$

Equations (10a) give rise to the usual octet mass formula

$$4m_K^2 = 3m_\eta^2 + m_\pi^2, \tag{10a$'$}$$

which is satisfied by the observed pseudoscalar meson m^2's to within 6.5 percent.

For the vector mesons, Equations (10b) lead to a different set of relationships:

$$m_\omega^2 = m_\rho^2,$$
$$2m_\rho^2 - m_\omega^2 + m_\phi^2 = 2m_{K^*}^2. \tag{10b$'$}$$

Equations (10) contain just three parameters: m_0^2, A, and Δ. Starting with $m_0^2 = m_\pi^2 = 0.019\ (\text{GeV}/c^2)^2$, $A = m_\omega^2 - m_\pi^2 = 0.595$, we have four different ways of computing the third constant, Δ. The values obtained are compared in Table 15.4.

Finally, we note that the mass of the $\eta'(X_0^0)$ involves still another parameter, the "unperturbed" mass of the $SU(6)$ singlet, $m_0''^2$, in addition to the effect of the MSI, Equation (10):

$$m_{\eta'}^2 = m_0''^2 + \tfrac{2}{3}\,\Delta. \tag{10c}$$

Using the average value of Δ from Table 15.4, and the measured mass of the η', we obtain $m_0''^2 = 0.778\ (\text{GeV}/c^2)^2$. The large difference from the value $m_0^2 = 0.019$ is a measure of the difference between the VSI for the singlet and 35-plet $q\bar{q}$ combinations.

Table 15.4 SU(6) Symmetry-Breaking Parameter, Δ, as Computed from the Observed Meson Masses

Mass difference	$\Delta\ (\text{GeV}/c^2)^2$
$\eta - \pi$	0.212
$K - \pi$	0.227
$\phi - \omega$	0.213
$K^* - \omega$	0.188
	average = 0.210

EXAMPLE

General mass formula for a meson nonet. Using the special form of the MSI, Equation (10), we may derive a more general relationship between the masses of a given nonet of mesons of the same spin value j. Let

$$O^{(m^2)}|\psi_j^\mu\rangle = [O_{\text{VSI}}^{(m^2)} + \tfrac{1}{2}\,Aj(j+1)]|\psi_j^\mu\rangle = m_{j,\mu}^2|\psi_j^\mu\rangle \tag{11a}$$

represent the unperturbed mass of a member of one of the meson multiplets belonging to a singlet ($\mu = 1$) or octet ($\mu = 8$) of spin j. Let the corresponding wave functions be given by the (unperturbed) combinations

$$\psi_j^1(t=0) = \sqrt{\tfrac{1}{3}}\,(p\bar{p} + n\bar{n} + \lambda\bar{\lambda})\,J f_1(r),$$
$$\psi_j^8(t=0) = \sqrt{\tfrac{1}{6}}\,(p\bar{p} + n\bar{n} - 2\lambda\bar{\lambda})\,J f_8(r),$$
$$\psi_j^8(t=1)^+ = p\bar{n}\,J f_8(r), \qquad \text{etc.,}$$
$$\psi_j^8(t=\tfrac{1}{2})^+ = p\bar{\lambda}\,J f_8(r), \qquad \text{etc.,} \tag{11b}$$

where J is the appropriate combination of the q–$\bar{q}$ spins and $f_{1,8}(\mathbf{r})$ is the spatial dependence of the wave function, normalized to

$$\int f_{1,8}^2(\mathbf{r})\, d^3\mathbf{r} = 1. \tag{11c}$$

Assuming a mass-splitting perturbation of the form

$$O'^{(m^2)} = \Delta[\delta(q, \lambda) + \delta(\overline{q}, \overline{\lambda})], \tag{11d}$$

we obtain, for $O = O^{(m^2)} + O'^{(m^2)}$,

$$\begin{aligned} \langle\psi_j^{1*}|O\psi_j^1\rangle &= m_1^2 = m_{j,1}^2 + \tfrac{2}{3}\,\Delta, \\ \langle\psi_j^8(0)^*|O\psi_j^8(0)\rangle &= m_8^2 = m_{j,8}^2 + \tfrac{4}{3}\,\Delta, \\ \langle\psi_j^1(0)^*|O\psi_j^8(0)\rangle &= \langle\psi_j^8(0)^*|O\psi_j^1(0)\rangle = -\tfrac{2}{3}\sqrt{2}\mathcal{I}\Delta = m_{18}^2, \end{aligned} \tag{11e}$$

$$\begin{aligned} \langle\psi_j^8(1)^*|O\psi_j^8(1)\rangle &= m_{j,8}^2, \\ \langle\psi_j^8(\tfrac{1}{2})^*|O\psi_j^8(\tfrac{1}{2})\rangle &= m_{j,8}^2 + \Delta, \end{aligned} \tag{11f}$$

with

$$\mathcal{I} = \int f_1(\mathbf{r})\, f_8(\mathbf{r})\, d^3\mathbf{r} \le 1. \tag{11g}$$

Referring to the four states as η', η, π, K (as prototypes of the singlet and $t = 0, 1, \frac{1}{2}$ members of the octet, respectively), we note that the eigenvalues m_η^2 and $m_{\eta'}^2$ of the operator O are given by the equation

$$\begin{vmatrix} m_1^2 - \lambda & m_{18}^2 \\ m_{18}^2 & m_8^2 - \lambda \end{vmatrix} = 0. \tag{11h}$$

Taking advantage of the relationships (11f), we may reduce this to

$$(m_{\eta'}^2 - m_\pi^2)(m_\eta^2 - m_\pi^2) - \tfrac{4}{3}\Delta(m_{\eta'}^2 + m_\eta^2 - 2m_K^2) = \tfrac{8}{9}\Delta^2(1 - \mathcal{I}^2). \tag{11i}$$

Equation (11i) may be used to obtain $\mathcal{I}$, which is a measure of the overlap of the singlet and octet spatial distributions [Equation (11g)]. The values of this parameter, as well as the unperturbed mass values $m_{j,1}^2$ and $m_{j,8}^2$ are given in Table 15.5 for the 0^- and 1^- mesons, in which we have used as input values the observed masses. The difference between the 0^- and 1^- nonets is clearly observed, both in the greater derivation of $\mathcal{I}$ from unity and the larger difference between the unperturbed singlet and octet masses ($m_{j,\mu}^2$) in the former case.

PROBLEM

Using the values from Table 14.3 as input masses for the 2^+ nonet, compute the values of the unperturbed masses and the mixing parameter $\mathcal{I}$. Can you give a simple interpretation of the 2^+ nonet in terms of the quark model?

15.3.2 Hyperfine Mass Structure of Isospin Multiplets

We have previously considered, in Section 13.1, a model for the electromagnetic mass splittings within isospin multiplets, according to which the observed splittings can be ascribed to three effects: (1) intrinsic mass differences between the elementary constituents; (2) electrostatic energies of interaction

Table 15.5 Mixing Parameters for the Pseudoscalar and Vector-Meson Nonets

(a) *Input values*

Meson	m^2 (GeV/c^2)^2	Meson	m^2 (GeV/c^2)^2
η'	0.918	ϕ	1.039
η	0.301	ω	0.614
π	0.019	ρ	0.599
K	0.246	K^*	0.796
Δ	0.227	Δ	0.197

(b) *Computed parameters*

Parameter	0^-	1^-
$\mathcal{G}$	0.52	1.13
$m^2_{j,8}$	0.019	0.599
m^2_8	0.322	0.862
m^2_1	0.897	0.791
$m^2_{j,1}$	0.746	0.660
$-m^2_{18}$	0.111	0.209

between pairs of constituents; and (3) magnetostatic energies of interaction between pairs of constituents.

As applied to the quark model, these three effects give rise to electromagnetic self-energies (mass shifts) which can be computed directly as follows:

1. Assuming that the p quark has an intrinsic mass that differs from that of the n quark by the amount

$$\delta_1 = m_p - m_n = m_{\bar{p}} - m_{\bar{n}}, \tag{12}$$

we would have, for a given combination,

$$\delta M_1 = \delta_1 \sum_i \delta(q_i, p). \tag{12a}$$

We note that a naive model would ascribe the mass difference δ_1 to the charges of the quarks ($Q_p = \frac{2}{3}e$, $Q_n = -\frac{1}{3}e$, $Q_{\bar{q}} = -Q_q$),

$$\delta_1 \approx \left(\frac{4}{9} - \frac{1}{9}\right)\frac{e^2}{2R}, \tag{12$'$}$$

where R is a characteristic quark "size." However, we shall not prejudice the computation at this stage by excluding an internal quark structure, which could lead to values of δ_1 very different from (12′), e.g., even $\delta_1 < 0$.

2. The electrostatic *hfs* effect leads to mass shifts of the form

$$\delta M_2 = \sum_{i \neq j} Q_i Q_j \langle \frac{e^2}{r_{ij}} \rangle = \delta_2 \sum_{i \neq j} Q_i Q_j, \tag{13}$$

where the summation is over all quark pairs.

3. The quarks are assumed to have magnetic dipole moments proportional to their charges, $\boldsymbol{\mu}_q = Q_q \mu_q \boldsymbol{\sigma}_q$. Applying the S-state dipole-dipole interaction formula [Section 13.1, Equation (3a)], we have

$$\delta M_3 = K \sum_{i \neq j} Q_i Q_j \boldsymbol{\sigma}_i \cdot \boldsymbol{\sigma}_j |\psi_{ij}(0)|^2 = -\delta_3 \sum_{i \neq j} Q_i Q_j \boldsymbol{\sigma}_i \cdot \boldsymbol{\sigma}_j, \tag{14}$$

with

$$\begin{aligned} \boldsymbol{\sigma}_i \cdot \boldsymbol{\sigma}_j &= 1, && \text{for the triplet spin (1) combination} \\ &= -3, && \text{for the singlet.} \end{aligned} \tag{14a}$$

Baryons • Application of Equations (12) and (13) to the baryon combinations of Table 15.2 is completely straightforward. In applying Equation (14), however, it is important to note that, while all the qq pairs making up the $\frac{3}{2}^+$ baryons are in the $j = 1$ state, the $\frac{1}{2}^+$ baryons consist of a mixture of $j = 1$ and $j = 0$. In the case of the $\mathfrak{N}$ and Ξ, the like quark pair is in the $j = 1$ state, while the two unlike quark pairs have $j = 0$; for the Σ's, the nucleonic quark pairs have $j = 1$, while the $p\lambda$ and $n\lambda$ have $j = 0$; for the Λ^0, the pn pair has $j = 0$, while the $p\lambda$ and $n\lambda$ have $j = 1$. Table 15.6 summarizes the results of these computations for the baryons. Also shown in Table 15.6 are the measured masses (column 2) and the mass differences for which measured values exist (column 6).[9]

Table 15.6 Quark Model hfs Mass Splitting Among the Baryons

Particle	Mass (MeV/c^2)	$\delta M_1/\delta_1$	$\delta M_2/\delta_2$	$\delta M_3/\delta_3$	Differences	Measured (MeV/c^2)
P	938.26	2	0	$-\frac{16}{9}$	$\delta_1 + \frac{1}{3}(\delta_2 - \delta_3)$	(-1.2933 ± 0.0001)
N	939.55	1	$-\frac{1}{3}$	$-\frac{13}{9}$		
Σ^+	1189.43	2	0	$-\frac{16}{9}$		
Σ^0	1192.55	1	$-\frac{1}{3}$	$-\frac{1}{9}$	$2\delta_1 - \frac{1}{3}(\delta_2 + 7\delta_3)$	(-8.00 ± 0.18)
Σ^-	1197.42	0	$\frac{1}{3}$	$\frac{5}{9}$	$\delta_1 - \frac{2}{3}(\delta_2 + \delta_3)$	(-4.87 ± 0.07)
Λ^0	1115.57	1	$-\frac{1}{3}$	$-\frac{5}{9}$		
Ξ^0	1314.7	1	$-\frac{1}{3}$	$-\frac{13}{9}$	$\delta_1 - \frac{2}{3}(\delta_2 + 3\delta_3)$	(-6.6 ± 0.7)
Ξ^-	1321.3	0	$\frac{1}{3}$	$\frac{5}{9}$		
Δ^{++}	1236.0	3	$\frac{4}{3}$	$-\frac{4}{3}$		
Δ^+	—	2	0	0	$2\delta_1 + \frac{5}{3}(\delta_2 - \delta_3)$	(-0.45 ± 0.85)
Δ^0	—	1	$-\frac{1}{3}$	$\frac{1}{3}$	$3\delta_1 + \delta_2 - \delta_3$	(-7.9 ± 6.8)
Δ^-	—	0	$\frac{1}{3}$	$-\frac{1}{3}$		
${}_\Delta Y^+$	1382.2	2	0	0		
${}_\Delta Y^0$	—	1	$-\frac{1}{3}$	$\frac{1}{3}$	$2\delta_1 - \frac{1}{3}(\delta_2 - \delta_3)$	(-5.8 ± 3.1)
${}_\Delta Y^-$	1388.0	0	$\frac{1}{3}$	$-\frac{1}{3}$		
${}_\Delta \Xi^0$	1528.9	1	$-\frac{1}{3}$	$\frac{1}{3}$	$\delta_1 - \frac{2}{3}(\delta_2 - \delta_3)$	(-4.9 ± 2.2)
${}_\Delta \Xi^-$	1533.8	0	$\frac{1}{3}$	$-\frac{1}{3}$		
Ω^-	1672.4	0	$\frac{1}{3}$	$-\frac{1}{3}$		

[9] Values are from the Rosenfeld compilation (Table 2.1).

The predicted *hfs* mass shifts in Table 15.6 satisfy the $SU(3)$ mass relationships of Section 14.3.2, Equations (13) and (14). In addition, however, they provide the following relationships between the $\frac{1}{2}^+$ and $\frac{3}{2}^+$ mass shifts:

$$\tfrac{1}{3}(\Delta^{++}-\Delta^-)=(\Delta^+-\Delta^0)=({}_\Delta Y^+-{}_\Delta Y^0)=(P-N), \tag{15a}$$

$$(\Delta^0-\Delta^-)=({}_\Delta Y^0-{}_\Delta Y^-)=({}_\Delta\Xi^0-{}_\Delta\Xi^-)=(\Xi^--\Xi^0)-2(\Sigma^--\Sigma^0). \tag{15b}$$

However, instead of attempting a direct confrontation of Equations (15) with the data, which would require a certain amount of shuffling among values with large uncertainties, it is perhaps most illuminating to compute the three parameters δ_1, δ_2, δ_3 from the three most accurately known mass differences ($P-N$, $\Sigma^+-\Sigma^-$, $\Sigma^0-\Sigma^-$), and to use these to predict the values corresponding to the other observations. From the aforementioned data, we obtain

$$\begin{aligned}\delta_1&=-1.890\ \text{MeV}/c^2,\\ \delta_2&=3.138\ \text{MeV}/c^2,\\ \delta_3&=1.348\ \text{MeV}/c^2,\end{aligned} \tag{16}$$

which lead to the predictions that are compared to the experimental values in Table 15.7.

Table 15.7 Quark Model Predictions of Measured hfs Mass Splittings

Mass difference	Predicted	Measured (MeV/c^2)
$\Xi^--\Xi^0$	6.68	6.6 ± 0.7
$\Delta^--\Delta^{++}$	3.88	7.9 ± 6.8
$\Delta^0-\Delta^{++}$	−0.99	0.45 ± 0.85
${}_\Delta Y^--{}_\Delta Y^+$	4.38	5.8 ± 3.1
${}_\Delta\Xi^--{}_\Delta\Xi^0$	3.08	4.9 ± 2.2

How reasonable are the derived parameters, Equations (16)? Considering, first, the value of δ_2, which gives the mean electrostatic energy between two quarks [Equation (13)], we may derive the mean separation

$$\langle 1/r_{ij}\rangle=(0.42\ \text{f})^{-1}, \tag{13a}$$

which does not appear too unreasonable.

We next turn to the parameter δ_3, which [compare Equation (14) with Section 13.1, Equation (3a)] has the value

$$\delta_3=\frac{8\pi}{3}\,|\psi_{ij}(0)|^2\,\mu_q^2, \tag{14b}$$

where, as noted,

$$\boldsymbol{\mu}_i=Q_i\mu_q\boldsymbol{\sigma}_i. \tag{14c}$$

We may measure the dimensions of the i–j quark combination by a parameter $m\approx\langle r_{ij}\rangle^{-1}$, and taking

$$|\psi_{ij}(0)|^2 = \frac{m^3}{\pi}, \tag{14d}$$

we may compute the value of the intrinsic quark moment, μ_q, which yields the measured δ_3 for different values of the range parameter m. These are shown in Table 15.8. Note the sensitivity of μ_q to the assumed range.

Table 15.8 Intrinsic Quark Moment, in Units of $\mu_0 = e\hbar/2M_pc$, as a Function of Assumed Range $\langle r_{ij}\rangle = m^{-1}$ of the Quark-Quark Interaction

Range (fermis)	m/m_π	μ_q/μ_0
0.42	3.14	1.75
0.71	2.0	3.45
1.00	1.41	5.80

But the most surprising result is the value deduced for δ_1, the intrinsic p–n mass difference, which comes out to be both *negative and relatively small* — in fact, not too different from the physical P–N mass difference. Taken at its face value, this result would imply that the quarks themselves have some kind of internal structure.

Mesons • Application of Equations (12) through (14) to the meson combinations of Table 15.2 leads to the mass shifts summarized in Table 15.9. Among the *hfs* mass differences (column 6), only two have been determined with reasonable accuracy, $(\pi^\pm - \pi^0)$ and $(K^\pm - K^0)$. These lead to the following values of the parameters:

$$\begin{aligned} \delta_1 &= -7.01 \pm 0.13 \text{ MeV}, \\ \delta_2 + 3\delta_3 &= 9.208 \pm 0.008 \text{ MeV}. \end{aligned} \tag{16'}$$

Table 15.9 Quark Model hfs Mass Splittings Among the Mesons

Particle	Mass (MeV/c^2)	$\delta M_1/\delta_1$	$\delta M_2/\delta_2$	$\delta M_3/\delta_3$	Differences
$\pi^\pm$	139.578 ± 0.013	1	$\frac{2}{9}$	$\frac{2}{3}$	$\frac{1}{2}(\delta_2 + 3\delta_3)$
π^0	134.974 ± 0.013	1	$-\frac{5}{18}$	$-\frac{5}{6}$	(4.604 ± 0.004)
η^0	548.8 ± 0.6	$\frac{1}{3}$	$-\frac{1}{6}$	$-\frac{1}{2}$	
$K^\pm$	493.82 ± 0.11	1	$\frac{2}{9}$	$\frac{2}{3}$	$\delta_1 + \frac{1}{3}(\delta_2 + 3\delta_3)$
K^0	497.76 ± 0.16	0	$-\frac{1}{9}$	$-\frac{1}{3}$	(-3.94 ± 0.13)
η'	958.3 ± 0.8	$\frac{2}{3}$	$-\frac{2}{9}$	$-\frac{2}{3}$	
$\rho^\pm$	762 ± 8	1	$\frac{2}{9}$	$-\frac{2}{9}$	$\frac{1}{2}(\delta_2 - \delta_3)$
ρ^0	764 ± 11	1	$-\frac{5}{18}$	$\frac{5}{18}$	
ω^0	783.4 ± 0.7	1	$-\frac{5}{18}$	$\frac{5}{18}$	
ϕ^0	1019.5 ± 0.6	0	$-\frac{1}{9}$	$\frac{1}{9}$	
$K^{*\pm}$	891.4 ± 0.6	1	$\frac{2}{9}$	$-\frac{2}{9}$	$\delta_1 + \frac{1}{3}(\delta_2 - \delta_3)$
K^{*0}		0	$-\frac{1}{9}$	$\frac{1}{9}$	(-6.3 ± 4.1)

However, in order to predict the mass differences among the vector mesons, we require the combination (δ_2–δ_3). We shall attempt to estimate this as follows: we assume that the dimensions of the $q\bar{q}$ system are determined by a single parameter m, taking

$$\delta_2 = \left\langle \frac{e^2}{r_{ij}} \right\rangle \cong \left(\frac{m}{m_\pi} \right) \text{MeV} \tag{13b}$$

and

$$\delta_3 \cong \frac{2}{3} e^2 m \left(\frac{m}{M_P} \right)^2 \left(\frac{\mu_q}{\mu_0} \right)^2$$

$$= \frac{2}{3} \left(\frac{m_\pi}{M_P} \right)^2 \left(\frac{m}{m_\pi} \right)^3 \left(\frac{\mu_q}{\mu_0} \right)^2 \text{MeV.} \tag{14e}$$

We still require the intrinsic quark moment, μ_q/μ_0, which we shall arbitrarily set equal to $\mu_p/\mu_0 = 2.79$ (a choice that is not unreasonable on the basis of Table 15.8, and which we shall justify in Section 15.3.3). With this assumption, the value of $\delta_2 + 3\delta_3 = 9.208$ MeV [Equation (16′)] is obtained for $m/m_\pi = 2.61$ (range $= m^{-1} = 0.53$ f), giving

$$\begin{aligned} \delta_2 &= 2.61 \text{ MeV}, \\ \delta_3 &= 2.20 \text{ MeV}, \\ \delta_2 - \delta_3 &= 0.405 \text{ MeV}. \end{aligned} \tag{16'a}$$

These parameters predict $\rho^\pm - \rho^0 = 0.20$ MeV, and $K^{*\pm} - K^{*0} = -6.9$ MeV, which are not in disagreement with the observed masses.

However, the major disquieting aspect of these results[10] is the large, negative value of $\delta_1 = m_p - m_n$, which is not only in violent disagreement with the value obtained from our analysis of the baryon mass differences, Equation (16), but also serves to remind us that the large, negative $(K^\pm - K^0)$ mass difference continues to elude a reasonable explanation.

PROBLEM

Assume that the quarks $\{p, n, \lambda\}$ resemble the physical baryons $\{P, N, \Lambda\}$ in the following sense:

$\delta_1 \cong (\delta_P - \delta_N)$, [see Equation (12a)]

$\langle r_{ij} \rangle^{-1} \cong m_\pi \cong m$, [see Equations (13) and (14d)]

$$\left.\begin{aligned} \mu_p &= \mu_P \\ \mu_n &= \mu_N \\ \mu_\lambda &= \mu_\Lambda . \end{aligned}\right\} \quad \text{[see Equations (14)]}$$

Compute the consequent baryon and meson *hfs* mass differences and compare with the measured values.

[10] It is not unreasonable that the separation of the $q\bar{q}$ for the mesons should not be the same as that of the qq pairs in the baryons; hence, the differences in the values of δ_2 and δ_3 [Equations (16) and (16′a)] are not surprising.

15.3.3 Magnetic Moments

According to the simplest quark model, quark constituents of the combinations representing the 0^- and 1^- mesons, as well as the $\frac{1}{2}^+$ and $\frac{3}{2}^+$ baryons, are bound in relative S states. Correspondingly, the magnetic moments of the individual quarks are additive, and the magnetic-moment operator corresponding to a given particle may be represented as the sum of the individual quark moments

$$\boldsymbol{\mu} = \sum_i \boldsymbol{\mu}_i = \mu_q \sum_i Q_i \boldsymbol{\sigma}_i. \tag{17}$$

Thus, the matrix elements of the νth component of the magnetic moment, between two particles whose wave functions are represented in Table 15.2, may be obtained in straightforward fashion:

$$\mu_{ba}^{(\nu)} = \langle a^* | \sum_i \mu_i^{(\nu)} b \rangle \tag{17a}$$

Static Moments • The static moments are given by the diagonal matrix elements of the third component of $\boldsymbol{\mu}$,

$$\mu_a = \langle a^* | \sum_i \mu_i^{(3)} a \rangle = \mu_q \langle a^* | \sum_i Q_i 2m_i\, a \rangle, \tag{17a$'$}$$

evaluated in the state $m_j = j$. Hence the static magnetic moment of any particle may be derived in terms of the intrinsic quark moment μ_q. Let us evaluate the moments of the physical proton (P) and the neutron (N) according to Equation (17a′):

$$\mu_P = \tfrac{1}{6}\{4(\tfrac{2}{3} + \tfrac{2}{3} + \tfrac{1}{3}) + (\tfrac{2}{3} - \tfrac{2}{3} - \tfrac{1}{3}) + (-\tfrac{2}{3} + \tfrac{2}{3} - \tfrac{1}{3})\}\, \mu_q = \mu_q, \tag{18a}$$

$$\mu_N = \tfrac{1}{6}\{4(-\tfrac{1}{3} - \tfrac{1}{3} - \tfrac{2}{3}) + (-\tfrac{1}{3} + \tfrac{1}{3} + \tfrac{2}{3}) + (\tfrac{1}{3} - \tfrac{1}{3} + \tfrac{2}{3})\}\, \mu_q = -\tfrac{2}{3}\mu_q. \tag{18b}$$

Thus, we obtain the prediction

$$\frac{\mu_N}{\mu_P} = -\frac{2}{3}, \tag{18}$$

which is in amazingly good agreement with the experimental value (-0.68504 ± 0.00003). This prediction represents a major triumph of $SU(6)$.[11]

Equation (18a) also determines the value of the intrinsic quark moment:

$$\mu_q \cong 2.79 \frac{e\hbar}{2M_p c}. \tag{18a$'$}$$

If we were to interpret μ_q as representing the intrinsic moment of an elementary (Dirac) fermion,

$$\mu_q = \frac{e\hbar}{2M_q c}, \tag{18c}$$

[11] This result was first derived, on the basis of $SU(6)$ alone, by M. Beg, B. W. Lee, and A. Pais, *Phys. Rev. Letters, 13:* 514 (1964).

Equation (18a′) would yield for the quark mass

$$M_q \cong \frac{M_P}{2.79} = 336 \text{ MeV}/c^2, \tag{18c′}$$

a surprisingly small value. However, there is no a priori reason why the quarks should not have anomalous moments,[12] so that the failure to observe quarks of such a small mass need not be taken as a compelling argument against their reality.

Equation (17a′) may be applied to each of the quark combinations represented in Table 15.2. The results for the $\frac{1}{2}^+$ baryons are given in Table 15.10. Note that the relationships among the baryon moments are precisely those derived on the basis of $SU(3)$ (Section 14.3.2). For the $\frac{3}{2}^+$ baryons, as well as for the vector (1^-) mesons, the quark model yields a magnetic moment proportional to the particle's charge:

$$\mu_a = Q_a\mu_q = \left(\sum_i Q_i\right)_a \mu_q. \tag{18d}$$

For the pseudoscalar mesons, on the other hand, owing to the spin 0, the magnetic moments are all 0.

Table 15.10 Magnetic Moments of the $\frac{1}{2}^+$ Baryons According to the Quark Model or SU(6)

Baryon	μ/μ_q	μ/μ_0	Observed value
P	1	2.79	2.793
N	$-\frac{2}{3}$	−1.86	−1.913
Σ^+	1	2.79	2.6 ± 0.5
Σ^0	$\frac{1}{3}$	0.93	—
Σ^-	$-\frac{1}{3}$	−0.93	—
Λ^0	$-\frac{1}{3}$	−0.93	-0.73 ± 0.16
Ξ^0	$-\frac{2}{3}$	−1.86	—
Ξ^-	$-\frac{1}{3}$	−0.93	—

EXAMPLE

Effect of SU(6) breaking. The most general approach to the quark model moments would assume that the p, n, and λ moments are independent. We may express this[13] by the general form

$$\boldsymbol{\mu}_i = [\mu_1 Q_i + \mu_2 \mathcal{Y}_i + \mu_3 t_i(t_i + 1)]\,\boldsymbol{\sigma}_i, \tag{19}$$

which gives

---

[12] Indeed, we have noted in the previous section that the intrinsic mass difference between the quarks suggests a complex quark structure.

[13] S. B. Gerasimov, *Sov. Phys. — JETP, 23:* 1040 (1966).

$$\begin{aligned} \mu_p &= \tfrac{2}{3}\mu_1 + \tfrac{1}{3}\mu_2 + \tfrac{3}{4}\mu_3, \\ \mu_n &= -\tfrac{1}{3}\mu_1 + \tfrac{1}{3}\mu_2 + \tfrac{3}{4}\mu_3, \\ \mu_\Lambda &= -\tfrac{1}{3}\mu_1 - \tfrac{2}{3}\mu_2 . \end{aligned} \tag{19a}$$

(The μ_1 term alone corresponds to our original assumption which leads to the values in Table 15.10.) The resulting moments of the baryons are given in Table 15.11. Using the physical P, N, and Λ moments (Table 15.10, column 4) to evaluate the constants, these are

$$\begin{aligned} \frac{\mu_1}{\mu_0} &= 2.824, \\ \frac{\mu_2}{\mu_0} &= -0.315 \pm 0.24, \\ \frac{\mu_3}{\mu_0} &= 0.100 \pm 0.11. \end{aligned} \tag{19b}$$

Note the smallness of the correction terms. Their effects on the baryon moments are shown in column 4 of Table 15.11.

Table 15.11 Magnetic Moments of the Baryons on the Broken SU(6) Quark Model

Baryon	μ	μ/μ_0 (uncorrected)[a]	μ/μ_0 (corrected)[b]
P	$\mu_1 + \frac{1}{3}\mu_2 + \frac{3}{4}\mu_3$	2.793	2.793
N	$-\frac{2}{3}\mu_1 + \frac{1}{3}\mu_2 + \frac{3}{4}\mu_3$	−1.862	−1.913
Λ^0	$-\frac{1}{3}\mu_1 - \frac{2}{3}\mu_2$	−0.931	-0.73 ± 0.16
Σ^+	$\mu_1 + \frac{2}{3}\mu_2 + \mu_3$	2.793	2.71 ± 0.20
Σ^0	$\frac{1}{3}\mu_1 + \frac{2}{3}\mu_2 + \mu_3$	0.931	0.83 ± 0.20
Σ^-	$-\frac{1}{3}\mu_1 + \frac{2}{3}\mu_2 + \mu_3$	−0.931	-1.05 ± 0.20
Ξ^0	$-\frac{2}{3}\mu_1 - \mu_2 - \frac{1}{4}\mu_3$	−1.862	-1.59 ± 0.24
Ξ^-	$-\frac{1}{3}\mu_1 - \mu_2 - \frac{1}{4}\mu_3$	−0.937	-0.65 ± 0.24
Δ^{++}	$2\mu_1 + \mu_2 + \frac{9}{4}\mu_3$	5.586	5.56 ± 0.35
Δ^+	$\mu_1 + \mu_2 + \frac{9}{4}\mu_3$	2.793	2.73 ± 0.35
Δ^0	$\mu_2 + \frac{9}{4}\mu_3$	0	-0.09 ± 0.35
Δ^-	$-\mu_1 + \mu_2 + \frac{9}{4}\mu_3$	−2.793	-2.91 ± 0.35
${}_\Delta Y^+$	$\mu_1 + \frac{3}{2}\mu_3$	2.793	2.97 ± 0.17
${}_\Delta Y^0$	$\frac{3}{2}\mu_3$	0	0.15 ± 0.17
${}_\Delta Y^-$	$-\mu_1 + \frac{3}{2}\mu_3$	−2.793	-2.67 ± 0.17
${}_\Delta \Xi^0$	$-\mu_2 + \frac{3}{4}\mu_3$	0	0.39 ± 0.25
${}_\Delta \Xi^-$	$-\mu_1 - \mu_2 + \frac{3}{4}\mu_3$	−2.793	-2.43 ± 0.25
Ω^-	$-\mu_1 - 2\mu_2$	−2.793	-2.19 ± 0.48

[a] That is, assuming $\mu_2 = \mu_3 = 0$.
[b] The first three values are assumed.

Transition Moments • Electromagnetic transitions between particles a and b, $a \rightarrow b + \gamma$, corresponding to $\Delta j = 0$ or ± 1, no parity change ($0 \rightarrow 0$ forbidden), can occur via $M1$ photon emission, with the decay rate (width) determined by the matrix element of $\mu_{ba}^{(3)}$ (for $\Delta m = 0$) or $\mu_{ba}^{(\pm)}$ (for $\Delta m = \pm 1$) [see Equations (17)]. We have already considered, in Section 13.2.3, the rates for $M1$ transitions between vector and pseudoscalar mesons, on the basis of the F–Y–S model. The quark model also permits the direct computation of these, as well as of the $M1$ transitions between $\frac{3}{2}^+$ and $\frac{1}{2}^+$ baryons (e.g., $\Delta^+ \to P + \gamma$), and between members of the $\frac{1}{2}^+$ baryon octet ($\Sigma^0 \to \Lambda^0 + \gamma$). Thus, while relationships between these decay rates can be derived on the basis of $SU(3)$ symmetry and the vector-dominance hypothesis (Section 14.3.3), the quark model permits the prediction of the absolute rates of such decays in terms of the assumed quark moment, μ_q.

The rate (width) for $M1$ transitions from an initial state a_i is given by[14]

$$\Gamma = \sum_f \Gamma_{fi} = \frac{4}{3} k_\gamma^3 \sum_f \left\langle a_i^* \middle| \sum_j \mu_j^{(\nu)} b_f \right\rangle^2$$

$$= \frac{4}{3} \left(\frac{M_a^2 - M_b^2}{2M_a} \right)^3 \sum_f \langle \mu_{fi}^{(\nu)} \rangle^2$$

$$= 2.226 \left(\frac{M_a^2 - M_b^2}{M_a M_P} \right)^3 \sum_f \left\langle \frac{\mu_{fi}^{(\nu)}}{\mu_q} \right\rangle^2 \text{ (MeV).} \tag{20a}$$

The matrix elements and corresponding rates for the decays of interest are summarized and compared with the observed values in Table 15.12. It is most noteworthy that there are no significant disagreements between the quark model predictions and the observations.[15] In contrast, the F–Y–S model, whether the basic constituents of the mesons are the physical nucleons or their Dirac proto-

Table 15.12 M1 Transition Rates Based on the Quark Model

Transition	$\langle \mu^{(3)}/\mu_q \rangle$	$\langle \mu^{(\pm)}/\mu_q \rangle$	Γ_{calc} (MeV)[a]	Γ_{obs} (MeV)
$\omega^0 \to \pi^0 + \gamma$	1	1	1.19	1.13 ± 0.16
$\omega^0 \to \eta^0 + \gamma$	$\frac{1}{3}\sqrt{\frac{1}{3}}$	$\frac{1}{3}\sqrt{\frac{1}{3}}$	6.4×10^{-3}	< 0.18
$\rho \to \pi + \gamma$	$\frac{1}{3}$	$\frac{1}{3}$	0.127	< 0.6
$\rho^0 \to \eta^0 + \gamma$	$\sqrt{\frac{1}{3}}$	$\sqrt{\frac{1}{3}}$	0.054	—
$\phi^0 \to \pi^0 + \gamma$	0	0	0	—
$\phi^0 \to \eta^0 + \gamma$	$\frac{2}{3}\sqrt{\frac{2}{3}}$	$\frac{2}{3}\sqrt{\frac{2}{3}}$	0.30	< 0.3
$\phi^0 \to \eta'^0 + \gamma$	$-\frac{2}{3}\sqrt{\frac{1}{3}}$	$-\frac{2}{3}\sqrt{\frac{1}{3}}$	0.67×10^{-3}	—
$\eta'^0 \to \rho^0 + \gamma$	$\sqrt{\frac{2}{3}}$	$\sqrt{\frac{2}{3}}$	0.18	≤ 0.9
$\eta'^0 \to \omega^0 + \gamma$	$\frac{1}{3}\sqrt{\frac{2}{3}}$	$\frac{1}{3}\sqrt{\frac{2}{3}}$	0.019	—
$K^{*\pm} \to K^\pm + \gamma$	$\frac{1}{3}$	$\frac{1}{3}$	0.071	—
$K^{*0} \to K^0 + \gamma$	$-\frac{2}{3}$	$-\frac{2}{3}$	0.28	—
$\Sigma^0 \to \Lambda^0 + \gamma$	$\sqrt{\frac{1}{3}}$	$\sqrt{\frac{2}{3}}$	8.4×10^{-3}	$> 6.6 \times 10^{-8}$
$\Delta^+ \to P + \gamma$	$\frac{2}{3}\sqrt{2}$	$\frac{2}{3}$	0.407	0.58 ± 0.06
$\Delta^0 \to N + \gamma$	$-\frac{2}{3}\sqrt{2}$	$-\frac{2}{3}$	0.404	0.58 ± 0.10

[a] For the case of baryon decays ($B \to B' + \gamma$), Equation (20a) should be modified by multiplication by the factor $E_b/M_a = (M_a^2 + M_b^2)/2M_a^2$.

[14] Note, we are using a nonrationalized system of units, i.e., $e^2/\hbar c = e^2 = \frac{1}{137}$.

[15] However, the computed $\Delta \to \mathfrak{N} + \gamma$ decay rate is somewhat low; see R. H. Dalitz and D. G. Sutherland, *Phys. Rev.*, *146:* 1180 (1966).

types (Table 13.4), predicts values of the decay widths in marked disagreement with the observed values. We note that the relative values of the matrix elements are consistent with the $SU(3)$ predictions, Table 14.9.[16]

Note, also, that for the decays $B_{10} \to B_8 + \gamma$ ($\frac{3}{2}^+ \to \frac{1}{2}^+$) the quark model predicts the vanishing of the $E2$-transition matrix elements (otherwise permitted, see Section 13.2.3) since there are no orbital angular momenta contained in either the initial or final states; $E2$ transitions require $\Delta l = 2$.

A number of related electromagnetic processes can also be computed on the same basis. For example, the decay

$$\eta^0 \to \pi^+\pi^-\gamma \tag{21}$$

can be thought of as proceeding in two steps:

$$\begin{aligned} \eta^0 &\to \rho^0 + \gamma \\ &\quad \hookrightarrow \pi^+ + \pi^- . \end{aligned} \tag{21a}$$

However, owing to the small mass of the η^0, the intermediate ρ-meson must be produced with a mass very much less than its normal mass value — i.e., the $\pi^+\pi^-$ system is produced with a total energy relatively far removed from its resonance value, or far off the "mass shell." We outline below a straightforward estimate of the decay rate for this process, which yields the result

$$\Gamma(\eta^0 \to \pi^+\pi^-\gamma) \cong 0.2 \text{ keV}. \tag{21b}$$

EXAMPLES

1. *Estimate of rate of reaction (21a).* We assume the emission of a photon of momentum k_γ, together with a corresponding "ρ^0" of mass

$$m^2 = m_\eta^2 - 2m_\eta k_\gamma . \tag{22a}$$

In the decay of this "ρ^0" into $\pi^+\pi^-$, the momentum, q, of each pion in the ρ^0 rest frame is

$$4q^2 = m^2 - 4m_\pi^2 . \tag{22b}$$

We now assume that the probability of forming the "ρ^0" at the mass $m^2 \ll m_\rho^2$ is given by an expression of the Breit–Wigner form

$$dP(m^2) = \frac{N\, q^2\, dm^2}{(m_\rho^2 - m^2)^2 + m_\rho^2 \Gamma_\rho^2} \tag{22c}$$

with the normalization condition

$$\int_{4m_\pi^2}^{\infty} dP(m^2) = 1, \tag{22d}$$

---

[16] For comparison with the $SU(3)$ results, Table 14.9, let

$$-A = B = \sqrt{\tfrac{1}{2}}\, C = \tfrac{2}{3}; \qquad D = 0.$$

giving

$$N \cong \frac{4\Gamma_\rho m_\rho}{\pi(m_\rho^2 - 4m_\pi^2)}. \tag{22e}$$

As an approximation to the decay width, we assume

$$\Gamma(\eta^0 \to \pi^+\pi^-\gamma) = 4\langle\mu_{\rho\eta}\rangle^2 \int_{m^2=4m_\pi^2}^{m^2=m_\eta^2} k_\gamma^3 \, dP(m^2). \tag{20a$'$}$$

Equation (20a′) may be evaluated by use of Equations (22a) through (22e), Table 15.12, and a numerical integration, giving the aforementioned result, Equation (21b).

A more sophisticated computation[17] based on a field-theoretic model for reactions (21a) gives a width of 0.096 keV for (21b).

2. Another two-step process is the reaction

$$\eta^0 \to \pi^0 + \gamma + \gamma, \tag{23}$$

which may be assumed to proceed via two successive $M1$ emissions:

$$\eta^0 \to (\rho^0 \text{ or } \omega^0 \text{ or } \phi^0) + \gamma$$
$$\quad\quad\quad\quad\quad\quad \hookrightarrow \pi^0 + \gamma. \tag{23a}$$

In this case, a "semiclassical" estimate may be made by use of second-order perturbation theory, or one may resort to a more accurate field-theoretic computation;[18] in either case, a numerical integration is required over the intermediate photon energy, with the result

$$(\eta^0 \to \pi^0\gamma\gamma) \cong 0.5 \text{ eV}, \tag{23b}$$

a partial width smaller than that of the one-photon η decay by $\sim \alpha/\pi$. It is to be noted that although some earlier experiments indicated an appreciable relative strength of reaction (23), more recent results[19] (see Table 15.16) indicate a negligible branching ratio for $\eta^0 \to \pi^0\gamma\gamma$, in agreement with this estimate.

$q\bar{q}$ Annihilation Processes • The quark model permits a direct computation of the strength of the vector meson → photon transition process arising from $q\bar{q}$ annihilation, as depicted in Figure 15.3. The annihilation of a Dirac fermion and its antifermion is a well-studied process.[20] For annihilation at rest into a single photon, the $q\bar{q}$ must be in the $^3S_1$ state — i.e., parallel spins; the annihilation amplitude is given by

$$A(q_1\bar{q}_1 \to \gamma) = \frac{2Q_q\psi_{q\bar{q}}(0)}{m_{q\bar{q}}^{3/2}}, \tag{24a}$$

where $\psi_{q\bar{q}}(0)$ is the value of the $q\bar{q}$ wave function for zero separation. For a given

[17] Y. Nambu and J. J. Sakurai, *Phys. Rev. Letters, 8:* 79 (1962); also, A. Dar, private communication.
[18] R. Van Royen and V. F. Weisskopf, *Nuovo Cimento, 50A:* 617 (1967).
[19] Baltay, *et al., Phys. Rev. Letters, 19:* 1495 (1967).
[20] See W. Heitler, *The Quantum Theory of Radiation,* Clarendon Press, Oxford, England (1936).

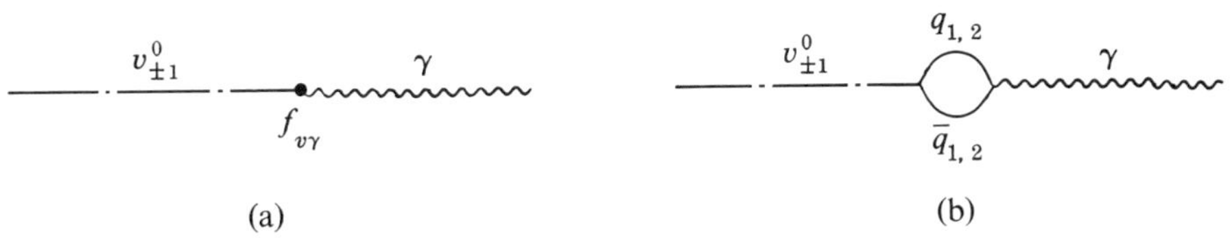

Figure 15.3 $v^0 \to \gamma$ process according to the quark model. (a) Vector dominance. (b) $q\bar{q}$ annihilation.

neutral vector meson it is necessary to sum the contributions of the different $q\bar{q}$ components in its wave function, giving

$$f_{v\gamma} = \frac{2Q_v \psi_v(0)}{m_v^{3/2}}, \tag{24b}$$

where

$$Q_v = \sum_i \langle q_{1i}\overline{q_{1i}} | Q_i v_1^0 \rangle. \tag{24c}$$

The values of Q_v for the ρ^0, ω^0, and ϕ^0 mesons, obtained by use of the wave functions in Table 15.2, are given in column 2 of Table 15.13. Note that

$$Q_\rho^2 : Q_\omega^2 : Q_\phi^2 = 9:1:2, \tag{24d}$$

precisely as predicted by $SU(3)$ under the (vector-dominance) assumption that the photon has the properties of the U_0^0 member of a vector octet (Section 14.3.2).

Table 15.13 Properties of $f_{v\gamma}$ According to the Quark Model

Process	Q_v/e	$f_{v\gamma}/e$	$9(m_\rho/m_\pi)^2 f_{v\gamma}^2/e^2$
$\rho^0 \to \gamma$	$\sqrt{\frac{1}{2}}$	m_π/m_ρ	9.0
$\omega^0 \to \gamma$	$\frac{1}{3}\sqrt{\frac{1}{2}}$	$m_\pi/3m_\omega$	0.99
$\phi^0 \to \gamma$	$-\frac{1}{3}$	$-\sqrt{2}\, m_\pi/3m_\phi$	1.17

However, the v–γ coupling strength, $f_{v\gamma}$, also depends on the value of $\psi_v(0)/m_v^{3/2}$. In the case of the ρ–γ coupling, we may estimate this constant by using the connection [21] between $f_{\rho\gamma}$ and the $\rho \to \pi\pi$ decay coupling, $f_{\rho\pi\pi}$, predicted by the vector-dominance hypothesis. This connection is easily obtained by consideration of the diagram, combining $f_{\rho\gamma}$ and $f_{\rho\pi\pi}$, which is, on the basis of the vector-dominance model, responsible for the pion's electric form factor, $F_\pi^E(k^2)$, Figure 15.4. On this basis

$$F_\pi^E(k^2) = f_{\rho\gamma} f_{\rho\pi\pi} \frac{m_\rho^2}{m_\rho^2 - k^2}. \tag{25a}$$

[21] M. Gell-Mann and F. Zachariesen, *Phys. Rev., 124:* 953 (1961); M. Gell-Mann, D. Sharp, and W. Wagner, *Phys. Rev. Letters, 8:* 261 (1962).

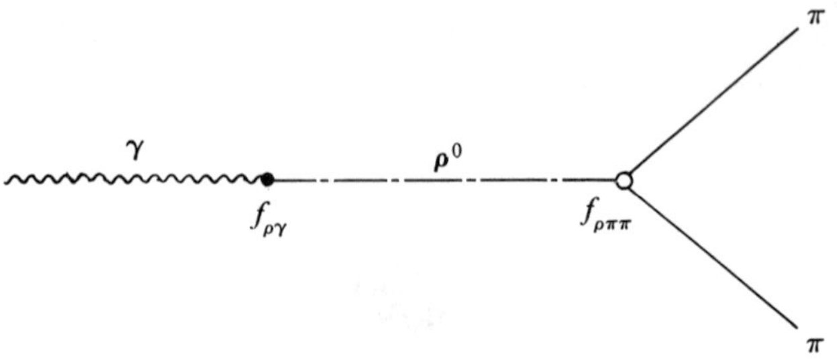

Figure 15.4 Pion form factor diagram for vector-dominance model.

Since the value of the form factor at zero-momentum transfer is simply the pion's charge

$$F_\pi^E(0) = e = f_{\rho\gamma} f_{\rho\pi\pi}, \tag{25b}$$

the desired connection [22] follows immediately, (25b).

The strong coupling constant $f_{\rho\pi\pi}$ is determined by the ρ-meson decay width

$$\Gamma(\rho^0 \to \pi^+\pi^-) = \frac{2}{3}\left(\frac{f_{\rho\pi\pi}^2}{4\pi}\right)\frac{q_\pi^3}{m_\rho^2}. \tag{25a$'$}$$

Using the ρ-decay constants,[23] we obtain

$$f_{\rho\pi\pi}^{-1} = 0.187 \cong \frac{m_\pi}{m_\rho} = 0.183. \tag{25b$'$}$$

Hence

$$\frac{f_{\rho\gamma}}{e} = \frac{\sqrt{2}\,\psi_\rho(0)}{m_\rho^{3/2}} \cong \frac{m_\pi}{m_\rho}. \tag{25c}$$

We shall *assume* that the (approximate) relation (25c) holds in general for all the vector mesons, i.e.,

$$\frac{\sqrt{2}\,\psi_v(0)}{m_v^{3/2}} = \frac{m_\pi}{m_v}, \qquad |\psi_v(0)|^2 = \frac{m_v}{m_\pi}\cdot\frac{m_\pi^3}{2}, \tag{25d}$$

which leads to the vector-meson–photon coupling henceforth assumed in our model

$$f_{v\gamma} = \frac{\sqrt{2}\,Q_v m_\pi}{m_v}. \tag{25}$$

Equation (25) yields the values listed in columns 3 and 4 of Table 15.13. Note

[22] The vector-dominance coupling strength is frequently defined in the literature through the constant $\gamma_v/e \equiv (2f_{v\gamma})^{-1}$.

[23] That is, $m_\rho = 764$ MeV/c^2, $\Gamma_\rho = 120$ MeV.

that the $v \rightarrow \gamma$ coupling strengths of Figure 15.3(a) and column 3 are accordingly modified from the $SU(3)$ values [Equation (24d)] to

$$f_{\rho\gamma}^2 : f_{\omega\gamma}^2 : f_{\phi\gamma}^2 = 9:1:1.17, \tag{24d'}$$

an effect that is also important for understanding the data on the photoproduction of vector mesons, to be discussed in Chapter 17.

A direct manifestation of the v–γ coupling occurs in the processes

$$v \rightarrow l^+ + l^-, \tag{26}$$

where l is a lepton (electron or muon) (see Figure 15.5) for which the theoretical decay width is[24]

$$\Gamma(v^0 \rightarrow l^+l^-) = \frac{4\pi}{3} e^2 f_{v\gamma}^2 m_v \left(1 - \frac{4m_l^2}{m_v^2}\right)^{1/2} \left(1 + \frac{2m_l^2}{m_v^2}\right)$$
$$\cong \frac{4\pi}{3} e^2 f_{v\gamma}^2 m_v. \tag{26a}$$

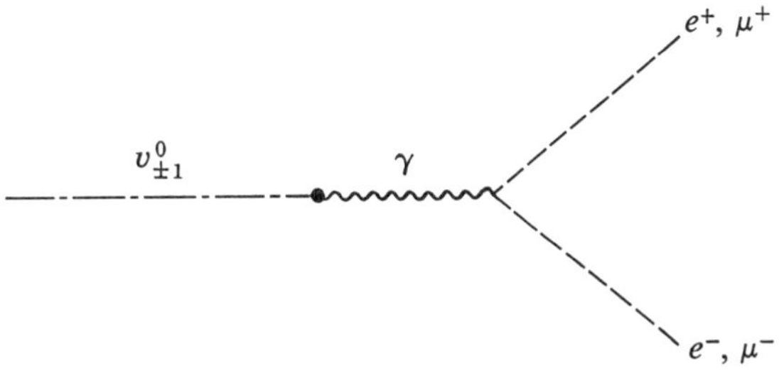

Figure 15.5 $v^0 \rightarrow l^+ + l^-$ decay diagram.

The widths computed on the basis of (26a) and Table 15.13 are compared with the measured widths in Table 15.14. The excellent agreement provides an empirical justification for the assumed expression for $f_{v\gamma}$, Equation (25).

Table 15.14 Comparison of Theory and Experiment[a] for $v^0 \rightarrow l^+l^-$

Decay	Γ_{calc} (keV)	Γ_{exp} (keV)
$\rho \rightarrow e^+e^-$	5.3	6.5 ± 0.8
$\rightarrow \mu^+\mu^-$		7.0 ± 1.4
$\omega \rightarrow e^+e^-$	0.59	0.74 ± 0.16
$\rightarrow \mu^+\mu^-$		< 4
$\phi \rightarrow e^+e^-$	0.90	1.5 ± 0.4
$\rightarrow \mu^+\mu^-$		$1.1 {+1.1 \atop -0.6}$

[a] See S. C. C. Ting, *Proceedings of the 16th International High Energy Conference*, Vienna (1968); also see Table 2.1.

[24] Gell-Mann, Sharp, and Wagner, *Phys. Rev. Letters, 8:* 261 (1962).

EXAMPLE

Angular distribution in the decay $v^0 \to l^+l^-$. Assuming the vector-dominance model, the vector-meson decay into two leptons, since it proceeds through the intermediary of a photon (Figure 15.5), has the angular distribution characteristic of decay from states of helicity ± 1 ($m = \pm 1$ along the line of flight of the vector meson). The decay into a pair of particles of spin 0 (e.g., $\rho \to 2\pi$) would in this case require orbital angular momentum 1 and would result in the angular distribution

$$W_{\rho \to 2\pi}(\theta) = |Y_1^{\pm 1}|^2 = \frac{3}{8\pi} \sin^2 \theta. \tag{27}$$

However, for the decay into two leptons, owing to the parity properties of the Dirac equation (Section 6.1.3), the final state is $^3S_1(m = \pm 1)$ which, however, despite the apparent absence of orbital angular momentum, leads to a decay angular distribution of the form

$$W_{\rho \to l^+l^-}(\theta) = \frac{3}{16\pi}(1 + \cos^2 \theta). \tag{28}$$

To understand the origin of this angular distribution, we consider the form of the wave function for the emission of a particle of spin $\frac{1}{2}$ in an S state

$$\psi_l = \begin{pmatrix} u \\ w \end{pmatrix}, \tag{28a}$$

where the large component,

$$u = \begin{Bmatrix} \alpha \\ \beta \end{Bmatrix} f(r), \tag{28b}$$

and the small component,

$$w = \left(\frac{\boldsymbol{\sigma} \cdot \mathbf{p}}{E + m}\right) u = a \begin{Bmatrix} \cos \theta \; \alpha + \sin \theta \; e^{i\varphi} \beta \\ \sin \theta \; e^{-i\varphi} \alpha - \cos \theta \; \beta \end{Bmatrix} f'(r), \tag{28c}$$

have the relative magnitude

$$\xi_l = \frac{2 \operatorname{Re} a}{1 + |a|^2} = \left(\frac{v}{c}\right)_l. \tag{28d}$$

Now, we consider a final-state l^+l^- wave function of the (parity-conserving) form

$$\begin{aligned}
\psi_1^{+1} &= u_{1/2}^+ u_{1/2}^- + w_{1/2}^+ w_{1/2}^- \\
&= \alpha_+\alpha_- - (a_+a_-)(\cos \theta_+ \alpha_+ + \sin \theta_+ e^{i\varphi_+} \beta_+)(\cos \theta_- \alpha_- + \sin \theta_- e^{i\varphi_-} \beta_-) \\
&= \alpha_+\alpha_-(1 + a_+a_- \cos^2 \theta) + \sqrt{\tfrac{1}{2}}\,(\beta_+\alpha_- + \beta_-\alpha_+)(a_+a_-)\sqrt{2} \sin \theta \cos \theta \, e^{i\varphi} \\
&\quad + \beta_+\beta_-(a_+a_-) \sin^2 \theta \, e^{2i\varphi},
\end{aligned} \tag{28e}$$

since

$$\begin{aligned}\theta &= \theta_+ = \pi - \theta_-,\\ \varphi &= \varphi_+ = \varphi_- + \pi,\\ \mathbf{p} &= \mathbf{p}_+ = -\mathbf{p}_-.\end{aligned} \tag{28f}$$

Then the angular distribution

$$W(\theta) = |\psi_1^1|^2 = 1 + \left(\frac{v}{c}\right)_l^2 \cos^2\theta \simeq 1 + \cos^2\theta \tag{28'}$$

follows directly from Equation (28e).

Having established the appropriate form of the v–γ annihilation amplitudes, we are now in a position to consider the pseudoscalar meson decays

$$\pi^0, \eta^0 \rightarrow \gamma + \gamma \tag{29}$$

in analogy to the two-photon annihilation of ${}^1S_0$ positronium. Figure 15.6 depicts these decays as a two-step process, in which the emission of the first photon

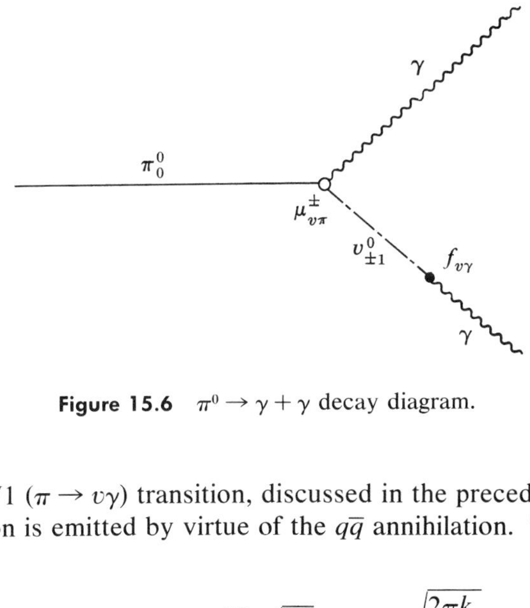

Figure 15.6 $\pi^0 \rightarrow \gamma + \gamma$ decay diagram.

occurs via the $M1$ ($\pi \rightarrow v\gamma$) transition, discussed in the preceding section, while the second photon is emitted by virtue of the $q\bar{q}$ annihilation. The decay matrix element is

$$A(\pi \rightarrow \gamma\gamma) = 2 \sum_v \sqrt{8\pi}\, \mu_{v\pi} f_{v\gamma} \sqrt{\frac{2\pi k_\gamma}{V}}, \tag{29a}$$

where the summation is over all possible intermediate vector-meson states, with the $M1$ matrix elements, $\mu_{v\pi}$, given by Table 15.12, and $f_{v\gamma}$, by Table 15.13. The decay widths (*note*: $k_\gamma = m_\pi/2$),

$$\Gamma(\pi \rightarrow \gamma\gamma) = 2\pi |A(\pi \rightarrow \gamma\gamma)|^2 \frac{2\pi V}{(2\pi)^3} k_\gamma^2 = \pi \left(\sum_v \mu_{v\pi} f_{v\gamma}\right)^2 m_\pi^3, \tag{29b}$$

obtained from Equation (29b) for π^0, η^0, and $\eta'^0 \to 2\gamma$ decays, are compared with the experimental values in Table 15.15. The agreement is only fair.

Table 15.15 Comparison of Theory and Experiment for psc$^0 \to \gamma\gamma$

Decay	Γ_{calc} (keV)	Γ_{exp} (keV)
$\pi^0 \to \gamma\gamma$	12.1×10^{-3}	$(7.8 \pm 1.6) \times 10^{-3}$
$\eta^0 \to \gamma\gamma$	0.36	0.88 ± 0.19
$\eta'^0 \to \gamma\gamma$	10.7	22^{+14}_{-12}

A number of possibilities exist for removing the discrepancies between the computed and observed values. On the one hand, the empirical relationship assumed for the values of $\psi_{q\bar{q}}(0)$, Equations (25d), may not be completely appropriate to the case where the intermediate state is a mixture of the various vector mesons. On the other hand, even the relatively slight mixing of the η_8 and η_1 (see Table 14.3) in the observed η and η' is sufficient to remove the discrepancy for the $\eta \to 2\gamma$ decay width.[25]

The 2γ decay is the principal η-decay mode. However, a number of other modes compete favorably, e.g., $\eta \to 3\pi$, while the $\pi^+\pi^-\gamma$ decay mode has, as we have previously seen, a non-negligible width. The $\pi^0\gamma\gamma$ mode, on the other hand, should be negligible according to our considerations. A comparison of the observed and computed η-decay widths is shown in Table 15.16.

Table 15.16 Decay Widths for the η-Decay Modes

Mode	Γ_{exp} (keV) [a]	Γ_{calc} (keV) [b]
$\gamma\gamma$	1 ± 0.2	~ 1
$3\pi^0$	0.88	—
$\pi^+\pi^-\pi^0$	0.56	—
$\pi^+\pi^-\gamma$	0.16	0.16
$\pi^0\gamma\gamma$	≤ 0.28	0.0005

[a] The partial widths for the modes other than $\gamma\gamma$ are obtained from the observed branching ratios [Baltay, *et al.*, *Phys. Rev. Letters, 19:* 1498 (1967)] and the assumption $\Gamma(\gamma\gamma) = 1$ keV. The uncertainties in the branching ratios are typically $\sim$ 10–15 percent. The computed value of $\Gamma(\gamma\gamma) \sim 1$ keV is corrected from the value in Table 15.15 to take into account the η–η' mixing angle of $\sim 10°$.

[b] We have not attempted to compute the widths for the 3π-decay modes, also presumably arising from electromagnetic effects. However, we note that the experimental ratio $\Gamma(\eta \to 3\pi^0)/\Gamma(\eta \to \pi^+\pi^-\pi^0) = 1.58 \pm 0.25$ is in excellent agreement with the assumption that the final 3π system is in the $t = 1$ state [see Section 7.4.1, Equation (29i')].

On the whole, then, we may conclude that $SU(3)$ and $SU(6)$ with, in particular, the specifications indicated by our quark model, provide a reasonable basis for understanding the observed photonic decays of the mesons and baryons.

[25] R. H. Dalitz and D. G. Sutherland, *Nuovo Cimento, 37:* 1777; *38:* 1945 (1965).

PROBLEMS

1. Using the F–Y–S model of the mesons, with $\{p, n, \lambda\}$ either the Dirac or the physical baryons, and the techniques developed in this section, compute the decay widths for $\pi^0, \eta \rightarrow 2\gamma$ and $\rho, \omega, \phi \rightarrow l^+l^-$; compare with the quark-model predictions.
2. The vector-dominance model may be used to compute the widths for the decay processes

$$\omega^0 \rightarrow 3\pi, \qquad \text{(a)}$$

$$\omega^0 \rightarrow \pi^0\gamma, \qquad \text{(b)}$$

$$\pi^0 \rightarrow 2\gamma, \qquad \text{(c)}$$

according to the diagrams of Figure 15.7. Using the values of $f_{\rho\pi\pi}$ and $f_{v\gamma}$ deduced above, compare the values of $f_{\omega\rho\pi}$ deduced from the experimental widths for these three decays.
3. Estimate the width for the (G-parity forbidden) decay

$$\omega^0 \rightarrow 2\pi \qquad \text{(d)}$$

by use of the diagram in Figure 15.7(d).
4. Discuss the η decays (Table 15.16) on the basis of the vector-dominance model and an assumed strong $\eta \rightarrow vv$ vertex.
5. Consider the decay $\eta' \rightarrow \pi\pi\gamma$. Assuming a $\rho\gamma$ intermediate state, estimate the decay width and compare with the experimental value.

15.3.4 The Strong Interactions

In this section, we inquire into the properties of the strong Yukawa interactions among baryons that follow from $SU(6)$ symmetry and, in particular, from application of the quark model. We begin by reviewing the properties of the Yukawa process corresponding to pseudoscalar meson exchange among the baryons, previously discussed in Sections 1.1 and 12.4.

In general, the charge-independent Yukawa emission and absorption of virtual mesons, e.g.,

$$\begin{aligned} P &\rightleftharpoons P\pi^0 - \sqrt{2}\, N\pi^+ \\ &\rightleftharpoons \Lambda K^+ \\ &\rightleftharpoons \sqrt{2}\, \Sigma^+K^0 - \Sigma^0K^+, \\ N &\rightleftharpoons -N\pi^0 + \sqrt{2}\, P\pi^-, \qquad \text{etc.,} \end{aligned} \tag{30}$$

may be described in terms of an interaction Lagrangian whose general form has been discussed in Section 12.4 [Equations (2), (3), (5), (8)]. Aside from the requirement of charge independence, which leads to the relative values of the numerical coefficients in Equations (30), the relative strengths of the various interactions are determined by the coupling constants

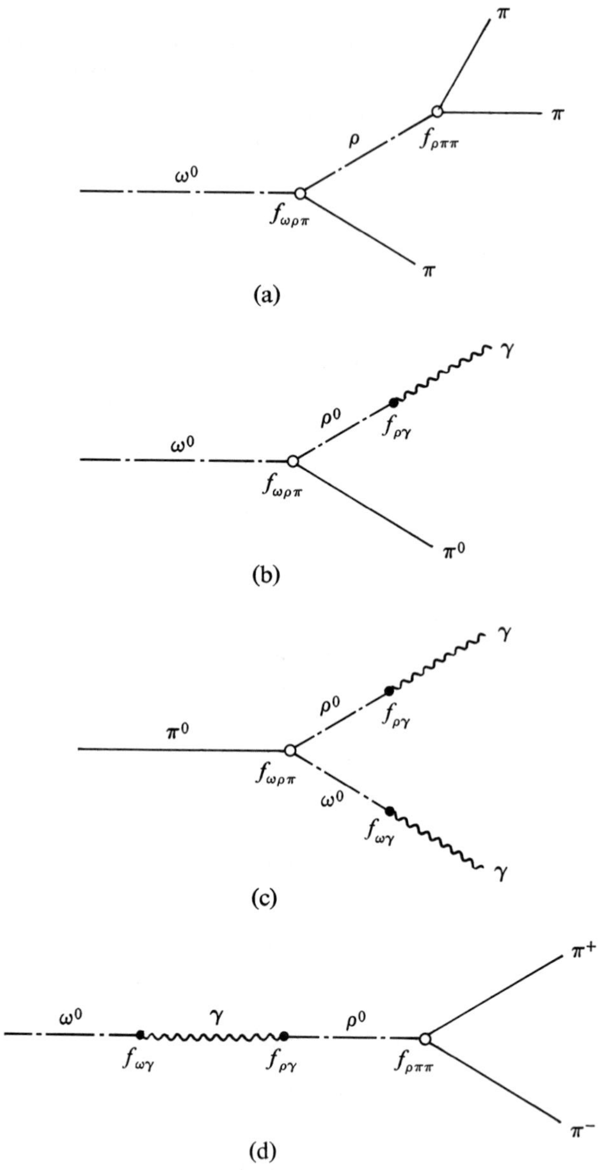

Figure 15.7 Vector-dominance diagrams for ω decay. (a) $\omega^0 \to 3\pi$. (b) $\omega^0 \to \pi^0\gamma$. (c) $\pi^0 \to 2\gamma$. (d) $\omega^0 \to 2\pi$.

$$\mathcal{G}_{BB'm} = \frac{2M_B}{M_m} f_{BB'm}, \tag{30a}$$

while the spin and space dependence is determined by the Dirac matrix γ_5 ($\rightarrow \boldsymbol{\sigma} \cdot \boldsymbol{\nabla}$ in the nonrelativistic limit of small-meson momenta). Thus, for example, the general form of the charge-independent Yukawa Lagrangian involving the meson emission and absorption processes described by Equations (30) would be

$$\mathcal{L}_{\mathfrak{N}} = \mathcal{G}_{\mathfrak{N}\mathfrak{N}\pi} \mathfrak{N}^\dagger \gamma_5 (\boldsymbol{\tau} \cdot \boldsymbol{\pi}) \mathfrak{N} + \mathcal{G}_{\mathfrak{N}\Lambda K} \mathfrak{N}^\dagger \gamma_5 \Lambda^0 K + \mathcal{G}_{\mathfrak{N}\Sigma K} \mathfrak{N}^\dagger \gamma_5 (\boldsymbol{\tau} \cdot \boldsymbol{\Sigma}) K + \text{hermitian conjugate}, \tag{30b}$$

in which all the symbols have been defined in Section 12.4.

Now, the assumption of a given interaction symmetry implies a precise set of relationships among the coupling constants $\mathcal{G}_{BB'm}$. Thus, if we adopt the octet model of $SU(3)$, in which we start with the basic $\frac{1}{2}^+$ baryon octet, $B(\mathfrak{N}, \Lambda, \Sigma, \Xi)$, and the 0^- meson octet, $\pi(K, \eta, \pi, \overline{K})$, the assumption of $SU(3)$ symmetry for the strong interactions implies a Lagrangian of the form

$$\mathcal{L}_8 = \sum_{i=1}^{8} \sum_j \sum_k \{\mathcal{G}_1 B_i^\dagger(x) \gamma_5 \mathfrak{D}_{ij,k}^{(1)} B_j(x) \pi_k(x) + \mathcal{G}_2 B_i^\dagger(x) \gamma_5 \mathfrak{D}_{ij,k}^{(2)} B_j(x) \pi_k(x) + \text{h.c.}\}, \tag{30c}$$

in which the $\mathfrak{D}_{ij,k}^{(\nu)}$'s are products of the isoscalar factors (de Swart coefficients, Appendix 6) and the appropriate Clebsch–Gordan coefficients, connecting the state $\overline{B}_i \times B_j$ with the meson octet state π_k; there are two sets of such coefficients ($\nu = 1$ and 2), arising from the presence of two octets in the product $\overline{8} \otimes 8$.[26]

The quark model being $SU(3)$-invariant [$SU(6) = SU(3) \times SU(2)$], the corresponding Lagrangian for the Yukawa processes between the B's and the π's generally will have the same form as Equation (30c). However, in the spirit of the quark model, we may explore the possibility of obtaining a simpler description of the VSI in terms of a set of basic Yukawa processes involving only the quarks themselves. In other words, we assume that the basic Yukawa reactions are the emission and absorption of pseudoscalar mesons by the quarks themselves, according to the $SU(3)$-invariant Lagrangian

$$\mathcal{L}_{qq\pi} = \mathcal{G}_0 \sum_{i=1}^{3} \sum_{j=1}^{3} \sum_{k=1}^{8} q_i^\dagger \gamma_5 d_{ij,k} q_j \pi_k + \mathcal{G}_0' \sum_{i=1}^{3} \sum_{j=1}^{3} q_i^\dagger \gamma_5 d_{ij,\eta'} q_j \eta' + \text{h.c.} \tag{31}$$

In this case, the components of the $d_{ij,k}$ are easily obtained by considering the combinations

$$\overline{q} \otimes q = 1 \oplus 8, \tag{31a}$$

[26] The associated matrices are usually denoted by $\mathfrak{D}_{ij,k}$ and $\mathfrak{F}_{ij,k}$; we could add another term to the Lagrangian

$$\mathcal{L}_8' = \mathcal{G}' \sum_i \sum_j B_i^\dagger \gamma_5 \mathfrak{D}_{ij,\eta'} B_j \eta', \tag{30c'}$$

corresponding to the combination $\overline{8} \otimes 8 = 1$.

(see Table 15.2). They are most conveniently represented by the 3×3 matrices:

$$d_{ij,k}\pi_k = \begin{pmatrix} (\pi^0 + \sqrt{\tfrac{1}{3}}\,\eta) & -\sqrt{2}\,\pi^+ & \sqrt{2}\,K^+ \\ \sqrt{2}\,\pi^- & (-\pi^0 + \sqrt{\tfrac{1}{3}}\,\eta) & \sqrt{2}\,K^0 \\ \sqrt{2}\,K^- & -\sqrt{2}\,\overline{K^0} & -\sqrt{\tfrac{4}{3}}\,\eta \end{pmatrix} \tag{31b}$$

$$d_{ij,\eta'}\eta' = \sqrt{\tfrac{2}{3}}\begin{pmatrix} \eta' & 0 & 0 \\ 0 & \eta' & 0 \\ 0 & 0 & \eta' \end{pmatrix}, \tag{31c}$$

in terms of which the appropriate Yukawa reactions become

$$(q) \equiv \begin{pmatrix} p \\ n \\ \lambda \end{pmatrix} \rightleftharpoons (d_{ij,k}\pi_k + d_{ij,\eta'}\eta')\begin{pmatrix} p \\ n \\ \lambda \end{pmatrix}. \tag{31d}$$

Before proceeding further, we note that the possibility of utilizing the Yukawa reaction in the form of Equation (31) for the description of the Yukawa processes among the physical baryons depends on the expectation that the Yukawa processes among the quarks are "low-energy" processes, in the sense that the momenta of the emitted and absorbed mesons are small (so as not to disrupt the *qqq* structure of the physical baryon involved); in this case, we may as well adopt a nonrelativistic description from the start, replacing γ_5 by the $\boldsymbol{\sigma} \cdot \boldsymbol{\nabla}$ operator. Furthermore, it will be more convenient for our purposes to utilize a Hamiltonian description for the strong interactions (see Section 1.1):

$$H_q = H_{ji} = -\sqrt{4\pi}\,\frac{f_0}{m_0}\,(\boldsymbol{\sigma} \cdot \boldsymbol{\nabla})\, d_{ij,k}\,\phi_k\,\Psi_i(x, \sigma_i), \tag{32}$$

where Ψ_i is a spinor representing the quark source, ϕ_k is a meson-creation operator, and m_0 is an appropriate normalizing mass.

Our first application of (32) will be to obtain the value of the coupling constant f_0. To do this, we compare the strength of the Yukawa pion emission from a real proton, *P*, as obtained by use of (32), with the conventional Yukawa reaction for a physical nucleon,

$$H_{\mathfrak{N}} = -\sqrt{4\pi}\,\frac{f}{m_\pi}\,(\boldsymbol{\sigma} \cdot \boldsymbol{\nabla})(\boldsymbol{\tau} \cdot \boldsymbol{\phi}_\pi)\,\psi_{\mathfrak{N}}(x, \sigma_{\mathfrak{N}}), \tag{32a}$$

for which the coupling constant $f^2 = 0.082$ [$\mathcal{G}^2 = 14.6$; see Equation (30a)] is derived from the low-energy pion-proton scattering and photoproduction experiments. We recall [Section 1.1, Equation (18)], letting

$$\psi_P(x, \tfrac{1}{2}) = P_{1/2}\,f(r), \tag{33a}$$

that

$$(\boldsymbol{\sigma} \cdot \boldsymbol{\nabla})(\boldsymbol{\tau} \cdot \boldsymbol{\phi}_\pi)\,\psi_P\left(x, \frac{1}{2}\right) = \sqrt{\frac{4\pi}{3}}\,[P_{1/2}\,\pi^0\,Y_1^0(\theta_\pi, \varphi_\pi) - \sqrt{2}\,P_{-1/2}\,\pi^0\,Y_1^1$$
$$-\sqrt{2}\,N_{1/2}\pi^+\,Y_1^0 + 2N_{-1/2}\pi^+\,Y_1^1(\theta_\pi, \varphi_\pi)]f'(r). \tag{33b}$$

Equation (33b) holds, as well, for the application of H_{ji}, Equation (32), on a p_1 quark, if we confine our attention to the pion-creation terms only. Thus, we may consider the effect of the sum of the individual quark operators on the physical proton, whose qqq wave function is given in Table 15.2, with the result

$$\sum_{i=1}^{3} (\boldsymbol{\sigma}_i \cdot \boldsymbol{\nabla})(\boldsymbol{\tau}_i \cdot \boldsymbol{\phi}_\pi) P_{1/2} f(r)$$
$$= \sqrt{\frac{4\pi}{3}}\,\{2\sqrt{2}\,\Delta^{++}_{3/2}\,\pi^- Y_1^{-1} - \frac{4}{3}\sqrt{3}\,\Delta^{++}_{1/2}\,\pi^- Y_1^0 + 2\sqrt{\frac{2}{3}}\,\Delta^{++}_{-1/2}\,\pi^- Y_1^1$$
$$-\frac{4}{3}\sqrt{3}\,\Delta^{+}_{3/2}\,\pi^0 Y_1^{-1} + \frac{4}{3}\sqrt{2}\,\Delta^{+}_{1/2}\,\pi^0 Y_1^0 - \frac{4}{3}\,\Delta^{+}_{-1/2}\,\pi^0 Y_1^1$$
$$+2\sqrt{\frac{2}{3}}\,\Delta^{0}_{3/2}\,\pi^+ Y_1^{-1} - \frac{4}{3}\,\Delta^{0}_{1/2}\,\pi^+ Y_1^0 + \frac{2\sqrt{2}}{3}\,\Delta^{0}_{-1/2}\,\pi^+ Y_1^1$$
$$+\frac{5}{3}(P_{1/2}\,\pi^0 Y_1^0 - \sqrt{2}\,P_{-1/2}\,\pi^0 Y_1^1 - \sqrt{2}\,N_{1/2}\,\pi^+ Y_1^0 + 2N_{-1/2}\,\pi^+ Y_1^1)\}f'(r). \tag{33c}$$

Comparison of (33b) with (33c) immediately yields the conclusion that, to obtain the observed Yukawa strength for $P \rightleftarrows \mathfrak{N}\pi$, we require

$$\frac{f_0}{m_0} = \frac{3}{5}\frac{f}{m_\pi}. \tag{33d}$$

Equation (33c) also indicates that we may use the quark model of $SU(6)$ to perform a direct computation of the matrix element for the strong decay $\Delta \to \mathfrak{N} + \pi$, and consequently of the decay rate, or the width of the Δ. We note that for the transition

$$\Delta^{++}_{3/2} \to P_{1/2}\,\pi^+, \tag{34a}$$

there is only one channel,[27] with the matrix element [see Equation (33c)]

$$\langle\ \rangle \equiv \langle \Delta^{++}_{3/2}\,\pi^- |\sum_q H_q P_{1/2}\rangle = \sqrt{4\pi}\,\frac{f_0}{m_0}\,\langle\sigma\tau\rangle\,\sqrt{\frac{4\pi}{3}}\,Y_1^{-1} f'(r)$$
$$= \sqrt{4\pi}\,\frac{f_0}{m_0}\,(2\sqrt{2})\,\sqrt{\frac{4\pi}{3}}\,Y_1^{-1}(\theta_\pi, \varphi_\pi) f'(r). \tag{34b}$$

[The matrix element $\langle\sigma\tau\rangle$ is simply the numerical coefficient of the appropriate term within the braces in Equation (33c).]

The decay rate is

---

[27] Of course, the same result is obtained by considering the sum of the decays $\Delta^{++}_{1/2} \to P_{1/2}\,\pi^+$ and $\Delta^{++}_{1/2} \to P_{-1/2}\,\pi^+$, since $(2\sqrt{2})^2 = (4/\sqrt{3})^2 + (\sqrt{8/3})^2$; or, for that matter, the sum of the transition rates from any given Δ state. By considering the transition (34a), the computation is simplified.

$$\Gamma = \int_{\theta=0}^{\pi} 2\pi \langle \ \rangle^2 \frac{V}{(2\pi)^3} 2\pi \sin\theta \, d\theta \frac{p^2 \, dp}{dE}$$

$$= \int (2\pi)^{-1} \langle \ \rangle^2 V \sin\theta \, d\theta \, pE_\pi \left(1 - \frac{E_\pi}{M_\Delta}\right). \tag{34c}$$

We now put $Y_1^{-1} = \sqrt{3/8\pi} \sin\theta \, e^{-i\varphi}$, $f(r) = (2E_\pi V)^{-1} e^{ipr}$, $(f_0/m_0) = \frac{3}{5}(f/m_\pi)$ with $f^2 = 0.082$, giving

$$\Gamma(\Delta \to \mathfrak{N}\pi) = 0.0197 \, (2\sqrt{2})^2 \left(\frac{p}{m_\pi}\right)^2 \left(1 - \frac{E_\pi}{M_\Delta}\right) p$$

$$= 2.70 \, (2\sqrt{2})^2 \left(\frac{p}{m_\pi}\right)^3 \left(1 - \frac{E_\pi}{M_\Delta}\right) \text{MeV}$$

$$= 80 \text{ MeV}, \tag{34d}$$

as compared to the experimental value of 120 ± 2 MeV.

Clearly, the same computation may be performed for the strong pionic decays of the other members of the $\frac{3}{2}^+$ decimet, using Equation (34d) with the appropriate values of the decay momentum and parent mass, and substituting the appropriate numerical coefficient for $\langle\sigma\tau\rangle = (2\sqrt{2})$. The results are summarized in Table 15.17. With the exception of the Δ-decay width, the agreement is excellent. We note that the relative values of the decay matrix elements are precisely those obtained by use of $SU(3)$ (see the last column of Table 14.4); however, in addition, the quark model provides a straightforward $SU(6)$-invariant means of specifying the strength of the strong interaction, so that there are no free parameters in the computation.

Table 15.17 Strong Decay Rates for $B_{10} \to B_8 + \pi$ Based on the Quark Model

Decay	$\langle\sigma\tau\rangle$	p (MeV/c)	M_{10} (MeV/c^2)	Γ_{calc} (MeV)	Γ_{exp} (MeV)
$\Delta^{++}_{3/2} \to P_{1/2}\pi^+$	$2\sqrt{2}$	231	1236	80	120 ± 2
${}_\Delta Y^{+}_{3/2} \to \Sigma^{+}_{1/2}\pi^0$	$-2\sqrt{\frac{1}{3}}$	117	1382	3.9	3.3 ± 1.1
$\to \Sigma^{0}_{1/2}\pi^+$	$2\sqrt{\frac{1}{3}}$				
$\to \Lambda^{0}_{1/2}\pi^+$	2	208	1382	31	34 ± 3
${}_\Delta \Xi^{0}_{3/2} \to \Xi^{0}_{1/2}\pi^0$	$-2\sqrt{\frac{1}{3}}$	145	1529	11.1	7.3 ± 1.7
$\to \Xi^{-}_{1/2}\pi^+$	$2\sqrt{\frac{2}{3}}$				

Another possible application of the quark-pion emission Hamiltonian, H_q, Equation (32), is in the decays of vector mesons through pion emission, e.g.,

$$\rho \to \pi\pi, \tag{35a}$$

$$K^* \to K\pi, \tag{35b}$$

The matrix elements $\langle\sigma\tau\rangle$ [the numerical coefficients resulting from the operation $\sum_i (\boldsymbol{\sigma}_i \cdot \nabla)(\boldsymbol{\tau}_i \cdot \boldsymbol{\phi}_\pi)$] are obtained exactly as previously discussed, and the decay widths are given by Equation (34d), with the appropriate value of $\langle \sigma\tau \rangle$ substituted for $(2\sqrt{2})$ and M_v substituted for M_Δ. The matrix elements and other parameters of interest are shown in Table 15.18(a).

A number of interesting questions immediately arise: With respect to the $\rho \to \pi\pi$ decay, there is an asymmetry in the treatment of the two pions; one is treated as the quantum of the Yukawa field, while the second is the spin-singlet $q\bar{q}$ compound resulting from the spin-flip, P-wave emission of a pion quantum by one of the quark members of the spin-triplet rho. It is this asymmetric treatment that is used[28] to justify the incoherent addition of the first two rows in Table 15.18(a) to obtain the total $\rho\pi\pi$ width. Even so, the computed value exceeds the experimental width by ~ 50–100 percent.

Table 15.18 Strong Decays $v \to ps + ps$ Based on the Quark Model

Decay	$\langle \sigma\tau \rangle$	p (MeV/c)	Γ_{calc} (MeV)	Γ_{obs} (MeV)
(a) $v \to ps + \pi$				
$\rho_1^+ \to \pi_0^+ \pi^0$	2	353	185	90 – 150
$\to \pi_0^0 \pi^+$	−2			
$K_1^{*+,0} \to K_0^{+,0} \pi^0$	1	288	48	49.6 ± 1.4
$\to K_0^{0,+} \pi^{+,-}$	$-\sqrt{2}$			
(b) $v \to ps + K$				
$K_1^{*+} \to \pi_0^0 K^+$	1	288	48	49.6 ± 1.4
$\to \pi_0^+ K^0$	$-\sqrt{2}$			
$\phi_1^0 \to K_0^+ K^-$	$\sqrt{2}$	125	4.1	1.73
$K_0^- K^+$	$\sqrt{2}$			
$\to K_0^0 \overline{K^0}$	$-\sqrt{2}$	107	2.6	1.44
$\overline{K_0^0} K^0$	$-\sqrt{2}$			
		(total ϕ_1^0)	6.7	3.2 ± 0.7

The estimated width for Yukawa pion emission of the K^* (rows 3, 4) turns out to be remarkably close to the observed value. However, any satisfaction with this success must be immediately tempered by the realization that Table 15.18(a) neglects the Yukawa kaon-emission processes

$$\lambda \rightleftharpoons \sqrt{2}\, pK^- - \sqrt{2}\, n\overline{K^0}, \tag{36}$$

which, assuming $SU(3)$ symmetry for the strong Yukawa reactions of the quarks, should be as important as the pion-emission processes previously considered. In fact, according to Equations (31) and (32), all meson-emission processes should be considered together, with the matrix element $\langle \sigma d \rangle$ substituted for $\langle \sigma\tau \rangle$ in the previous considerations. Of course, for pion emissions, the results

[28] R. Van Royen and V. F. Weisskopf, *Nuovo Cimento, 50A:* 617 (1967); also, C. Becchi and G. Morpurgo, *Phys. Rev., 149:* 1284 (1966).

are identical with those in Tables 15.17 and 15.18(a). However, in addition there are strong kaon-emission processes, and these lead, for example, to the decays

$$K^* \rightarrow \pi + K, \tag{36a}$$

$$\phi \rightarrow K + \overline{K}, \tag{36b}$$

whose properties are summarized in Table 15.18(b). Now note that the combined width computed for the $K^* \rightarrow K\pi$ reaction, (35b) and (36a), is about twice the observed, as is the width computed for the $\phi^0 \rightarrow KK$ decay.

Apparently the quark model predicts widths for the decays $v \rightarrow ps + ps$ which are universally $\sim$ 2 times too large. Whether this arises from a fundamental deficiency in the model, or perhaps as a result of the neglect of the difference in the spatial distributions of the vector and pseudoscalar meson states (overlap integrals $\sim \sqrt{\frac{1}{2}}$), or of "form factors" of some other origin, cannot be stated with any certainty. Of course, it should be noted that in a nonrelativistic Yukawa model, such as we have been using in the decay computations, the relatively large symmetry-breaking interactions, which lead to the large π–K mass difference, might also give rise to effects of the magnitude of the discrepancies in question.

However, if we consider the relativistic $qq\pi$ Lagrangian, in the form of Equation (31), we may use this to compare the values of the baryon-baryon-meson couplings appropriate to high energy where, presumably, they are less influenced by $SU(3)$-violating effects. The problem is to derive connections between the various baryon-baryon-meson coupling constants, as defined by the general Lagrangian, whose conventional form is

$$\begin{aligned}
\mathcal{L} = {} & \mathcal{G}_{\mathfrak{N}\mathfrak{N}\pi}\overline{\mathfrak{N}}\gamma_5\tau_\alpha\mathfrak{N}\pi_\alpha + \mathcal{G}_{\Xi\Xi\pi}\overline{\Xi}\gamma_5\tau_\alpha\Xi\pi_\alpha \\
& + \mathcal{G}_{\Lambda\Sigma\pi}(\overline{\Lambda}\gamma_5\Sigma_\alpha + \overline{\Sigma}_\alpha\gamma_5\Lambda)\pi_\alpha \\
& - i\mathcal{G}_{\Sigma\Sigma\pi}(\overline{\boldsymbol{\Sigma}} \times \gamma_5\boldsymbol{\Sigma}) \cdot \boldsymbol{\pi} \\
& + \mathcal{G}_{\mathfrak{N}\mathfrak{N}\eta}\overline{\mathfrak{N}}\gamma_5\mathfrak{N}\eta + \mathcal{G}_{\Xi\Xi\eta}\overline{\Xi}\gamma_5\Xi\eta + \mathcal{G}_{\Lambda\Lambda\eta}\overline{\Lambda}\gamma_5\Lambda\eta \\
& + \mathcal{G}_{\Sigma\Sigma\eta}\overline{\Sigma}_\alpha\gamma_5\Sigma_\alpha\eta \\
& + \mathcal{G}_{\mathfrak{N}\Lambda K}(\overline{\mathfrak{N}}K\gamma_5\Lambda + \overline{\Lambda}\gamma_5\overline{K}\mathfrak{N}) \\
& + \mathcal{G}_{\Xi\Lambda K}(\overline{\Xi}K_c\gamma_5\Lambda + \overline{\Lambda}\gamma_5\overline{K}_c\Xi) \\
& + \mathcal{G}_{\mathfrak{N}\Sigma K}(\overline{\Sigma}_\alpha\gamma_5\overline{K}\tau_\alpha\mathfrak{N} + \overline{\mathfrak{N}}\tau_\alpha K\gamma_5\Sigma_\alpha) \\
& + \mathcal{G}_{\Xi\Sigma K}(\overline{\Sigma}_\alpha\gamma_5\overline{K}_c\tau_\alpha\Xi + \overline{\Xi}\tau_\alpha K_c\gamma_5\Sigma_\alpha),
\end{aligned} \tag{37}$$

with

$$\mathfrak{N} = \begin{pmatrix} P \\ N \end{pmatrix}, \quad \Xi = \begin{pmatrix} \Xi^0 \\ \Xi^- \end{pmatrix}, \quad K = \begin{pmatrix} K^+ \\ K^0 \end{pmatrix}, \quad K_c = \begin{pmatrix} \overline{K^0} \\ -K^- \end{pmatrix}. \tag{37a}$$

[In Equation (37), all baryons are Dirac spinors and all mesons are pseudoscalars; $\mathfrak{N}$, Ξ, K are spinors in charge space, $\boldsymbol{\Sigma}$ and $\boldsymbol{\pi}$ are vectors, while Λ and η are isoscalars; a bar stands for hermitian conjugate. The manipulations among these functions have previously been discussed in Section 12.4].

What one does, of course, is to apply Equation (31) successively to the baryons, using the qqq wave functions of Table 15.2 and finally projecting out the different resulting baryon-meson states. The relative strengths obtained in this way correspond to the relative strengths of the coupling constants in Equation (37).

Thus, for example,[29] from the consideration of expansions such as

$$\begin{aligned}\sum_q \sigma_3\, d_{ij,k} P_{1/2} &= \sqrt{\tfrac{1}{18}} \sum_q \sigma_3\, d_{ij,k}(2p_1p_1n_2 - p_1p_2n_1 - p_2p_1n_1 + \text{permutations})\\ &= -\tfrac{4}{3}(\sqrt{3}\,\pi^- \Delta^{++}_{1/2} - \sqrt{2}\,\pi^0 \Delta^{+}_{1/2} + \pi^+ \Delta^0_{1/2})\\ &\quad + \tfrac{2}{3}\sqrt{2}\,(K^+\,{}_\Delta Y^0_{1/2} - \sqrt{2}\,K^0\,{}_\Delta Y^+_{1/2})\\ &\quad + \tfrac{5}{3}(\pi^0 P_{1/2} - \sqrt{2}\,\pi^+ N_{1/2}) + \sqrt{\tfrac{1}{3}}\,\eta P_{1/2}\\ &\quad + \tfrac{1}{3}(K^+ \Sigma^0_{1/2} - \sqrt{2}\,K^0 \Sigma^+_{1/2}) + \sqrt{3}\,K^+ \Lambda_{1/2},\end{aligned} \tag{38}$$

we derive the relative strengths of the coupling constants summarized in

Table 15.19 Relative $BB\pi_k$ Coupling Constants According to the $SU(6)$ Quark Model

Combination	$\mathcal{G}(BB\pi_k)/\mathcal{G}_0$
$\mathfrak{N}\mathfrak{N}\pi$	5/3
$\Sigma\Sigma\pi$	4/3
$\Lambda\Sigma\pi = \Sigma\Lambda\pi$	$-2\sqrt{3}/3$
$\Xi\Xi\pi$	$-1/3$
$\mathfrak{N}\mathfrak{N}\eta$	$\sqrt{3}/3$
$\Sigma\Sigma\eta$	$2\sqrt{3}/3$
$\Lambda\Lambda\eta$	$-2\sqrt{3}/3$
$\Xi\Xi\eta$	$-\sqrt{3}$
$\mathfrak{N}\Lambda K = -\Lambda\mathfrak{N}\overline{K}$	$\sqrt{3}$
$\mathfrak{N}\Sigma K = -\Sigma\mathfrak{N}\overline{K}$	1/3
$\Xi\Lambda\overline{K} = -\Lambda\Xi K$	$\sqrt{3}/3$
$\Xi\Sigma\overline{K} = -\Sigma\Xi K$	5/3

Table 15.19. Note that these coupling constants obey the $SU(3)$ relationships (derived on the basis of $8 \otimes \overline{8}$)

$$-\sqrt{3}\,\mathcal{G}(\Sigma\Lambda\pi) + \mathcal{G}(\Sigma\Sigma\pi) = 2\mathcal{G}(\mathfrak{N}\mathfrak{N}\pi) = 2\mathcal{G}(\Sigma\Sigma\pi) - 2\mathcal{G}(\Xi\Xi\pi), \tag{39a}$$

$$\mathcal{G}(\mathfrak{N}\Sigma K) + \sqrt{3}\,\mathcal{G}(\mathfrak{N}\Lambda K) = -2\mathcal{G}(\Sigma\Xi K) = 4\mathcal{G}(\mathfrak{N}\Sigma K) - 2\sqrt{3}\,\mathcal{G}(\Lambda\Xi K), \tag{39b}$$

$$\mathcal{G}(\Sigma\Sigma\eta) = -\mathcal{G}(\Lambda\Lambda\eta), \tag{39c}$$

$$\mathcal{G}(\mathfrak{N}\mathfrak{N}\eta) + \mathcal{G}(\Sigma\Sigma\eta) + \mathcal{G}(\Xi\Xi\eta) = 0, \tag{39d}$$

as well as the connecting relations

[29] For simplicity, we have substituted σ_3 for γ_5 in deriving Equation (38); we also need to consider the $\sigma_\pm$ terms to obtain the complete result.

$$\mathcal{G}(\mathfrak{N}\mathfrak{N}\pi) = -\mathcal{G}(\Sigma\Xi K) = \mathcal{G}, \tag{39e}$$

$$-\mathcal{G}(\Xi\Xi\pi) = \mathcal{G}(\mathfrak{N}\Sigma K) = (1-2\alpha)\mathcal{G}, \tag{39f}$$

$$\mathcal{G}(\Lambda\Sigma\pi) = \mathcal{G}(\Lambda\Lambda\eta) = -\mathcal{G}(\Sigma\Sigma\eta) = -\frac{2\sqrt{3}}{3}(1-\alpha)\mathcal{G}, \tag{39g}$$

$$\mathcal{G}(\Sigma\Sigma\pi) = 2\alpha\mathcal{G}, \tag{39h}$$

$$\mathcal{G}(\mathfrak{N}\mathfrak{N}\eta) = -\mathcal{G}(\Lambda\Xi K) = \sqrt{\tfrac{1}{3}}\,(4\alpha-1)\mathcal{G}, \tag{39i}$$

$$\mathcal{G}(\mathfrak{N}\Lambda K) = -\mathcal{G}(\Xi\Xi\eta) = \sqrt{\tfrac{1}{3}}\,(1+2\alpha)\mathcal{G}, \tag{39j}$$

where $\alpha/(1-\alpha)$ is the ratio between the independent $\mathfrak{D}$ and $\mathfrak{F}$ couplings. Comparing Table 15.19 and Equations (39e) through (39j) yields the connections

$$\mathcal{G} = \tfrac{5}{3}\mathcal{G}_0, \tag{39k}$$

$$\alpha = \tfrac{2}{3} \tag{39l}$$

between the $SU(3)$ and the $SU(6)$ quark-model strong coupling constants $\mathcal{G}$ and $\mathcal{G}_0$.

PROBLEMS

1. Derive the relative strengths of the strong couplings: $\mathcal{G}(\Delta\mathfrak{N}\pi)$, $\mathcal{G}({}_\Delta Y\Sigma\pi)$, $\mathcal{G}({}_\Delta Y\Lambda\pi)$, $\mathcal{G}({}_\Delta\Xi\Xi\pi)$, $\mathcal{G}(\Delta\Sigma K)$, $\mathcal{G}({}_\Delta Y\Xi K)$, $\mathcal{G}({}_\Delta Y\mathfrak{N}\overline{K})$, $\mathcal{G}({}_\Delta\Xi\Sigma K)$, $\mathcal{G}({}_\Delta\Xi\Lambda K)$, $\mathcal{G}(\Omega\Xi\overline{K})$, $\mathcal{G}({}_\Delta Y\Sigma\eta)$, $\mathcal{G}({}_\Delta\Xi\Xi\eta)$, and show that these obey the following relationships:

$$\mathcal{G}(\Delta\mathfrak{N}\pi) = -\sqrt{3}\,\mathcal{G}({}_\Delta Y\Sigma\pi) = -\sqrt{2}\,\mathcal{G}({}_\Delta Y\Lambda\pi) = \sqrt{2}\,\mathcal{G}({}_\Delta\Xi\Xi\pi),$$
$$\mathcal{G}(\Delta\Sigma K) = \sqrt{3}\,\mathcal{G}({}_\Delta Y\Xi K) = -\sqrt{3}\,\mathcal{G}({}_\Delta Y\mathfrak{N}\overline{K}) = \sqrt{2}\,\mathcal{G}({}_\Delta\Xi\Sigma K)$$
$$= -\sqrt{2}\,\mathcal{G}({}_\Delta\Xi\Lambda K) = \sqrt{\tfrac{1}{2}}\,\mathcal{G}(\Omega\Xi\overline{K}),$$
$$\mathcal{G}({}_\Delta Y\Sigma\eta) = \mathcal{G}({}_\Delta\Xi\Xi\eta).$$

2. Consider the decay $\omega \to \pi\pi\pi$, and assume this goes through the intermediate state "ρ"π, with the ρ off resonance (see the $\eta \to \pi^+\pi^-\gamma$ decay discussion of the previous section). Using the assumption for the matrix element

$$d|M(\omega \to \pi\pi\pi)|^2 = |M(\omega \to \rho\pi)|^2\, dP(m^2),$$

estimate the width of the ω.
3. How would you account for the $\eta' \to \eta\pi\pi$ and the $\eta \to 3\pi$ decays in terms of the strong and electromagnetic quark interactions discussed in this and the preceding sections? Estimate the corresponding decay widths.
4. Consider the decays $v \to 2\,ps$ (see Table 15.18). The agreement between the computed and observed widths may be improved by assuming (i) a spatial overlap integral, $R = \int R_v(r)\,R_{ps}(r)\,d^3\mathbf{r} \leq 1$, and (ii) a breakdown of $SU(3)$ invariance resulting in different values of the effective pion and kaon Yukawa couplings [f_0/m_0, Equation (32)] which we may express by introducing a difference in the normalizing masses, $m_{0\pi} \neq m_{0K}$. Can you find values of the two parameters (R and $m_{0\pi}/m_{0K}$) which will give agreement for all the decay

widths? Try doing this under the assumptions

(a) that the amplitudes for different field quanta, but the same final charge state, are superimposed incoherently;
(b) that they are added coherently.

[For the purposes of this problem, take $\Gamma_\rho \cong 120$ MeV.]

15.4 The Pursuit of the Quark

The striking successes of the quark model, in predicting the static properties of the elementary particles and many of the dynamical features of their interactions, suggests that the possibility of the existence of quarks must be given very serious consideration. If the quarks are real particles, what are their properties and under what circumstances can they be observed?

The most clearly different property of the quarks is their charge — $\frac{2}{3}e$ and $-\frac{1}{3}e$, respectively, for the p and n or λ. This fractional-integral charge is the basis of practically all of the attempts at their observation, to be discussed below. However, before going into the question of their experimental detection, it is useful to consider some of the other implications of the quark model. In particular, what can be said about the mass of the quarks, and about the statistical aspects of their combination?

Considering, first, the problem of the quark statistics, we are immediately presented with a serious dilemma. The 56-plet representation of $SU(6)$, which we have adopted as the symmetry group appropriate to the description of the observed baryon spin $\frac{1}{2}^+$ octet and spin $\frac{3}{2}^+$ decimet, requires that the three-quark combinations specific to the baryons (Table 15.2) shall be symmetric (even) with respect to permutations of the quark indices. However, this symmetry of these wave functions refers to the combination of spin and isospin. So far, nothing has been specified as to the symmetry properties of the space part of the qqq wave function. The most natural choice of space wave functions would be an antisymmetrical combination (e.g., pairs of quarks in a relative P state, with the third quark in an S state with respect to the center of mass of the total qqq system). Under this assumption, the total wave function would be antisymmetric (odd) with respect to q–q interchange, which would lead to the expected Fermi statistics for particles of spin $\frac{1}{2}$. However, such qqq wave functions would, in general, lead to magnetic moments, electromagnetic interactions, and form factors of the baryons that could be quite different from the predictions derived in Sections 15.3.2 and 15.3.3 on the basis of the assumption that all quark pairs in the qqq baryon wave functions are in relative S states.[30] Stated more positively: A large part of the success of the quark model is based on the assumption that all quark pairs are in relative S states, which would give rise to completely symmetric qqq wave functions for the baryons and hence imply that the quarks obey Bose–Einstein statistics, despite their spin of $\frac{1}{2}$.

There is a possible way out of this dilemma, in the assumption that the quarks

[30] See, however, G. Morpurgo, *Phys. Letters, 27B:* 378 (1968).

are governed by parastatistics,[31] which is a theoretically feasible (if drastic) means of circumventing the conventional connection between spin and statistics, hitherto found to be applicable to all the elementary particles.

But even accepting this solution to the dilemma of the quark statistics, the quark model, in the form in which it has been developed in this chapter, still is subject to some fundamental objections. These objections relate to the lack of relativistic (Lorentz) invariance of the model: Specifically, the quark model separates the spin and the space components of the $q\bar{q}$ or qqq wave functions used to describe the mesons or baryons. However, the total angular momentum of a multiquark system is not an invariant property of the system under the application of a Lorentz transformation; the total angular momentum of such a system becomes a complicated combination of spin and orbital angular momentum in a moving frame of reference.[32] Unfortunately, all attempts to provide a useful, relativistically invariant version of the $SU(6)$ symmetry have thus far been unsuccessful. The quark model remains, with the notable exceptions to be discussed in Chapter 17, a description whose usefulness is limited to the rest frame of the elementary particles under discussion.

But even in the particle rest frame, it is impossible to avoid some aspects of the relativity problem. This problem is intimately related to that of the mass of the quarks. If we were to accept the most naive interpretation of the quark magnetic moments (equal to $Q_q\mu_P$ according to Section 15.3.3), which ascribes these to the intrinsic moments of the quarks, the quark magneton should be

$$\frac{e\hbar}{2M_q c} \cong 2.8\,\frac{e\hbar}{2M_P c}, \tag{40}$$

implying a value of

$$M_q \cong \frac{M_p}{2.8} \cong 335\ \text{MeV}/c^2. \tag{40a}$$

However, all the experimental evidence yields a lower limit to the quark mass of $M_q \gtrsim 5\ \text{GeV}/c^2$ and, correspondingly, a rather large *anomalous* quark magnetic moment. Accepting this interpretation, we are faced with the problem of binding three such heavy quarks in a baryon of mass ~ 1 GeV, which means that the binding energy of the system is comparable to the mass of the quarks. This is a highly relativistic problem which, in the case of particles of spin $\frac{1}{2}$, obeying a Dirac equation, normally gives rise to significant P-wave ($l = 1$) mixing through the no longer "small components" of the wave functions describing the qqq mixtures. Such effects would severely limit the applicability of the assumption of the additivity of quark moments, on which is based the success of the fitting of the magnetic moments, transition matrix elements, and hyperfine mass splittings of the baryons.

---

[31] A. Messiah and O. W. Greenberg, *Phys. Rev.*, *136:* B248 (1964); *138:* B1155 (1965).

[32] The properties of the group product $SU(3) \otimes SU(2) \otimes \mathcal{L}$ ($\mathcal{L}$ = Lorentz group) are generally much more complicated than required or desired; particularly, most relativistic generalizations of $SU(6)$ require the association of the elementary particles with representations of infinite dimensions, which is not especially helpful.

However, large binding energies do not necessarily lead to large relativistic effects;[33] the binding energy depends both on the depth of the interaction potential and on its range. For an interaction of range R, the mean value of the particle's momentum is

$$\langle p^2 \rangle \approx \frac{\hbar^2}{R^2}. \tag{41a}$$

The condition for the nonrelativistic approximation to be useful is

$$\langle p^2 \rangle \ll M_q^2 c^2, \tag{41b}$$

or

$$R \gg \frac{\hbar}{M_q c} \lesssim 0.1 \text{ f} \qquad (\text{for } M_q \gtrsim 2 \text{ GeV}/c^2),$$

a condition that is presumably not too difficult to satisfy.

These arguments can be made more explicit by considering a special model[34] in which the quarks making up the nucleons are assumed to move in an average (self-consistent) potential $V(r)$, which is taken as a scalar for convenience. The Dirac equation for a quark then becomes

$$\{\gamma_0 E + i(\boldsymbol{\gamma} \cdot \nabla) - [M + V(r)]\}\psi = 0, \tag{42}$$

with

$$\gamma_0 = \begin{pmatrix} I & 0 \\ 0 & I \end{pmatrix}, \qquad \boldsymbol{\gamma} = \begin{pmatrix} 0 & \boldsymbol{\sigma} \\ -\boldsymbol{\sigma} & 0 \end{pmatrix}, \tag{42a}$$

where I is the unit 2×2 matrix and $\boldsymbol{\sigma}$ the Pauli spin matrices. The ground-state solution of Equation (42),

$$\psi_0 = \begin{pmatrix} f(r)\chi \\ ig(r)(\boldsymbol{\sigma} \cdot \mathbf{r})\chi \end{pmatrix}, \tag{42b}$$

is a 4-component wave function (χ is a Dirac spinor) whose large components represent a symmetric $S_{1/2}$ state, and whose small components correspond to a $P_{1/2}$ configuration; the ground-state energy per quark is

$$E_0 \cong \frac{M_P}{3} = 313 \text{ MeV}/c^2, \tag{42c}$$

and the total angular-momentum operator $\mathbf{J} = \frac{1}{2}\boldsymbol{\sigma} + \mathbf{L}$ has the eigenvalue $\frac{1}{2}$,

$$\langle \psi_0^\dagger | J_3 \psi_0 \rangle = \tfrac{1}{2}\langle \sigma_3 \rangle + \langle L_3 \rangle = \pm\tfrac{1}{2}. \tag{42d}$$

Letting

$$\langle L_3 \rangle_{1/2} = \delta \tag{43a}$$

---

[33] C. Becchi and G. Morpurgo, *Phys. Rev., 140:* B687 (1965).

[34] N. N. Bogolubov, *Ann. Inst. Henri Poincaré, 8:* 163 (1968); see also P. Horwitz, *Phys. Rev., 161:* 1415 (1967).

be a measure of the relative magnitude of the small components in Equation (42b), it may be shown that

$$\delta = \frac{\langle p^2 \rangle}{6E_0^2}, \tag{43b}$$

as anticipated by the qualitative arguments advanced in the preceding.

Equation (42) may be solved in the presence of a uniform magnetic field, $\mathbf{H} = H\mathbf{z}_0$, by the usual substitution

$$i\frac{\partial}{\partial x} \rightarrow i\frac{\partial}{\partial x} + eQ_q A_x(r), \tag{44a}$$

where $\mathbf{A}$ is the vector potential $\mathbf{H} = \nabla \times \mathbf{A}$. Taking for the magnetic interaction energy

$$\delta E_q = -\boldsymbol{\mu}_q \cdot \mathbf{H}, \tag{44b}$$

one obtains

$$\begin{aligned} \boldsymbol{\mu}_q &= Q_q \frac{e\hbar}{2E_0 c}(1-\delta)J_q \\ &= 2Q_q \mu_0 \frac{M_P}{E_0}(1-\delta)J_q, \end{aligned} \tag{44c}$$

with $\mu_0 = e\hbar/2M_P c$. Setting $M_P(1-\delta)/E_0 \simeq 3(1-\delta) \simeq 2.79$, we obtain[35] $\delta \simeq 0.1$.

The foregoing analysis still tells us nothing about the quark mass. Assuming the reality of quarks,[36] the evidence that $M_q > 5$ GeV/c^2 comes from thus far unsuccessful attempts to produce them at existing accelerators. However, the rate of production of quarks for a given bombarding energy depends as well on the quark-production cross section as on its mass. The same experiments that yield the lower limit of ~ 5 GeV/c^2 on the quark mass also yield an upper limit of ~ 10^{-11} barns (10^{-35} cm^2) for the cross section for their production in π–$\mathfrak{N}$ or $\mathfrak{N}$–$\mathfrak{N}$ interactions for a projectile energy of ~ 30 GeV, while a search for quarks produced by a 70-GeV proton beam on an Al target at the synchrotron of the Russian Institute for High-Energy Physics at Serpukhov, USSR, has established an upper limit of 3×10^{-39} cm^2 for the total cross section for production of quarks of charge $\frac{1}{3}e$ and mass less than 5 GeV/c^2.[37]

There have also been a number of attempts to observe quarks in the cosmic radiation (in which considerably higher energies are available, but very much

---

[35] Assuming $U(r) = M + V(r)$ for the scalar potential [Equation (42)] to be represented by a square well of infinite depth, one obtains, from Equation (43b) with $E_0 = M_P/3$, the values $\delta \simeq 0.17$ and $\langle r^2 \rangle_P = 0.43\, m_\pi^{-2} \cong (0.93\ \text{f})^2$. The value of δ is decreased somewhat for a finite quark mass ($\delta \simeq 0.16$ for $M_q = 6.4$ GeV/c^2) [E. E. Radescu, *Nuovo Cimento, 52A:* 1324 (1967)].

[36] For an admirable summary of the various experimental attempts at quark hunting, see L. Lederman, *Comments on Nuclear and Particle Physics, 1:* 155 (1967). See also R. H. Dalitz, *Proceedings of the 13th International Conference on High-Energy Physics,* University of California Press, Berkeley (1966), and G. Morpurgo, *Proceedings of the 14th International Conference on High-Energy Physics,* Vienna (1968).

[37] Yu. A. Antipov, *et al., IHEP Report,* 69–49 (1969).

smaller fluxes, than at accelerators). These attempts rely on the expectation that particles of charge $\frac{1}{3}e$ or $\frac{2}{3}e$ will ionize at a much smaller rate ($\propto Q^2$) than relativistic particles of normal charge $\pm e$. They also assume that at least one of the quarks will be relatively stable, with a mean life $\geq 10^{-7}$ sec. None of these attempts to date (end of 1968) has yielded a positive result; they establish an upper limit of $\sim 10^{-10}$ quarks/cm²/sterad/sec for the flux of quarks in the cosmic radiation.

Another type of experiment is based on the assumption that at least one of the quarks is stable against spontaneous decay, and that such quarks, if produced by the cosmic radiation, will be accumulated in ordinary matter, being captured into atomic orbits of very small radius (owing to their large mass) to produce ions of charge $\frac{1}{3}$ or $\frac{2}{3}e$. Searches utilizing geophysical-chemical techniques of high sensitivity, applied to samples of matter of widely differing cosmological origin, indicate an upper limit to the concentration of $\sim 10^{-24}$ quarks per nucleus of ordinary matter. Finally, an attempt to detect fractional charges in small grains of pyrolitic graphite[38] (the Milliken oil-drop experiment) yields an upper limit of 5×10^{-19} quarks per nucleon.

It should be noted that theoretical estimates of the cross section for the production of $q\bar{q}$ pairs in nucleon-nucleon collisions vary from ~ 1 μb (for a peripheral-interaction model) to $\sim 10^{-3}$–10^{-10} μb (for statistical models) for a quark mass of $\gtrsim 3$ GeV/c^2.

Despite the discouraging results to date, the hunting of the quark continues with ever improving experimental techniques and, especially, at new accelerators of higher energy as they become available. There is, however, a growing body of opinion among particle physicists that quarks never will be found — that they represent only a convenient mathematical device for obtaining a useful approximation to what will eventually turn out to be an appropriate theoretical description of the elementary particles and their interactions, a theory that will account for the observed symmetries of the particles and their interactions without the necessity of invoking these new and peculiar particles.

Of course, it will take very little to confound the advocates of this view — merely the observation of heavy baryonic particles of third-integral charge. But even if they should be found, we will still be faced with formidable conceptual problems: the quark statistics; the nature of q–q forces that only permit bound states containing multiples of three quarks, but allow binding in q–$\bar{q}$ combinations. Undoubtedly, such questions will be resolved once real quarks are observed and studied. But pending this, the questions of their existence and of the reasons for the remarkable successes of the quark model constitute perhaps the most intriguing mystery of contemporary particle physics.

---

[38] G. Gallinaro and G. Morpurgo, *Phys. Letters, 23:* 609 (1966).

16

The Quark Model with Orbital Angular Momentum

In the preceding chapter, we have been able to account for the main features of the spin 0^- and 1^- mesons as $q\bar{q}$ combinations, and of the spin $\frac{1}{2}^+$ and $\frac{3}{2}^+$ baryons as qqq combinations of members of a basic quark triplet (p, n, λ), all quark pairs being bound in relative S states. We have noted that the mesons may be assigned to the singlet and 35-plet representations of the $SU(6)$ group, with the $SU(3)$ decompositions 1_1 and $8_1 \oplus 1_3 \oplus 8_3$, while the baryons are assigned to the 56-plet representation with the decomposition $8_2 \oplus 10_4$. We now take up the question of the classification and properties of the excited mesonic and baryonic states.

The observed mass spectra of known hadronic states are plotted in Figure 16.1, in which the values are taken from the compilation of Rosenfeld, *et al.* (Table 2.1). The meson (mass)^2 spectra are shown in Figure 16.1(a) for the three isospin types, $t=0$ (η, ω, ϕ, η', etc.), $t=1$ (π, ρ, etc.), and $t=\frac{1}{2}$ (K, K^*, etc.); the notation beside each level is the value of j^{PC}. Note that, in addition to the low-lying pseudoscalar and vector nonets, the lowest excited states observed are essentially all of positive parity and spins 0, 1, 2. (The one exception appears to be the $t=0$, 0^{-+} E-meson.) Of the two uncertain levels in the $t=1$ spectrum (broken lines), the level between the δ- and the A_1-mesons probably corresponds to the $K\bar{K}$ decay mode of the 0^{++} δ-meson with the value of the observed resonance peak being shifted upward as a consequence of the energy threshold, 0.98 (GeV/c^2)^2 for the $K\bar{K}$ decay. The level slightly below that of the $t=1$, A_2 (2^{++}) presents a real puzzle: The experiments indicate a "dipole" shape for the A_2-meson mass distribution — i.e., a symmetrical resonance with a narrow dip at the center.[1] However, although the evidence favors such an interpretation,

[1] G. Chikovani, *et al.*, *Phys. Letters, 25B:* 44 (1967); also, W. Kienzle, *et al.*, *Proceedings of the University of Pennsylvania Conference on Meson Spectroscopy* (April 1968); D. J. Crennel, *et al.*, *Phys. Rev. Letters, 20:* 1318 (1968). The properties of a dipole or double-pole resonance are described in Appendix 7.

it cannot yet be excluded that the observed A_2 is a superposition of two close (noninterfering) resonances with different spin values.

The meson spectra of Figure 16.1(a) indicate the probable presence of four positive parity octets or nonets (0^{++}, 1^{++}, 1^{+-}, 2^{++}), although a number of the members with $t = 0$ still remain to be found. At higher mass values, one observes the beginnings of a set of multiplets of negative parity mesons with $j > 1$.

The spectra of baryon resonances, shown in Figure 16.1(b), fall into six categories: $\mathcal{N}(t = \frac{1}{2}, \mathcal{Y} = 1)$, $\Delta(t = \frac{3}{2}, \mathcal{Y} = 1)$, $\Lambda(t = 0, \mathcal{Y} = 0)$, $\Sigma(t = 1, \mathcal{Y} = 0)$, $\Xi(t = \frac{1}{2}, \mathcal{Y} = -1)$, and $\Omega(t = 0, \mathcal{Y} = -2)$. The low-lying levels correspond to the baryon $\frac{1}{2}^+$ octet ($\mathcal{N}$, Λ, Σ, Ξ) and $\frac{3}{2}^+$ decimet (Δ, ${}_\Delta\Sigma$, ${}_\Delta\Xi$, Ω^-). Among the excited baryon states, the dominating feature is the presence of a set of levels with negative parity and spins $\frac{1}{2}^-$, $\frac{3}{2}^-$, $\frac{5}{2}^-$, among which the $\frac{1}{2}^-$ and $\frac{3}{2}^-$ states put in multiple appearances; the presence of these levels has, as we shall see in the following discussion, a natural explanation in terms of the L-excitation quark model. In addition, a number of positive parity levels are evident, most of which may be reasonably explained as Regge recurrences of the $\frac{1}{2}^+$ octet and $\frac{3}{2}^+$ decimet. There are, however, at least two exceptions: the $\frac{1}{2}^+$ $\mathcal{N}(1470)$ resonance and the possible $\frac{5}{2}^+$ $\Delta(1910)$.[2]

In addition to the levels shown in Figure 16.1, there are a number of experimental indications of possible resonances corresponding to multiplets not provided for in the figure, both among the mesons ($t > 1$, multiply charged states) and among the baryons, none of which, however, with the possible exception of a $Z_0(1865)$ baryon with $\mathcal{Y} = +1$, is as yet capable of withstanding critical scrutiny.[3] Such resonances have been referred to as "exotic" or "far-out" states, and their presence or absence provides the most crucial tests of the models to be developed in this chapter.

There are two obvious approaches to the problem of classification of the excited states.[4] One approach attempts to account for the excited states in terms of the same $q\bar{q}$ meson and qqq baryon combinations, but with internal orbital angular momentum. The second approach invokes higher quark multiplicities for the excited states — e.g., $q\bar{q}q\bar{q}$ for the mesons and $qqqq\bar{q}$ for the baryons. We consider the second alternative first.

16.1 Combinations Containing More Than Three Quarks

In the case of the mesons, if we continue to assume binding in relative S states, the combinations $q\bar{q}q\bar{q}$ lead to states of positive parity ($0^- + 0^- \to 0^+$; $0^- + 1^- \to 1^+$; $1^- + 1^- \to 0^+, 1^+, 2^+$). As far as $SU(6)$ is concerned, the possible representations in which these states are contained arise from the products

[2] A number of additional positive-parity resonances have been conjectured as a consequence of phase-shift analyses of π–$\mathcal{N}$ scattering data [C. Lovelace, *Proceedings of the 1967 Heidelberg International Conference on Elementary Particles,* North-Holland Publishing Co., Amsterdam (1968), p. 79], but their confirmation awaits further independent evidence.

[3] A. H. Rosenfeld, *Proceedings of the University of Pennsylvania Conference on Meson Spectroscopy,* University of Pennsylvania, Philadelphia (1968).

[4] For an excellent summary, see R. H. Dalitz, *Proceedings of the 13th International Conference on High-Energy Physics,* University of California Press, Berkeley (1966).

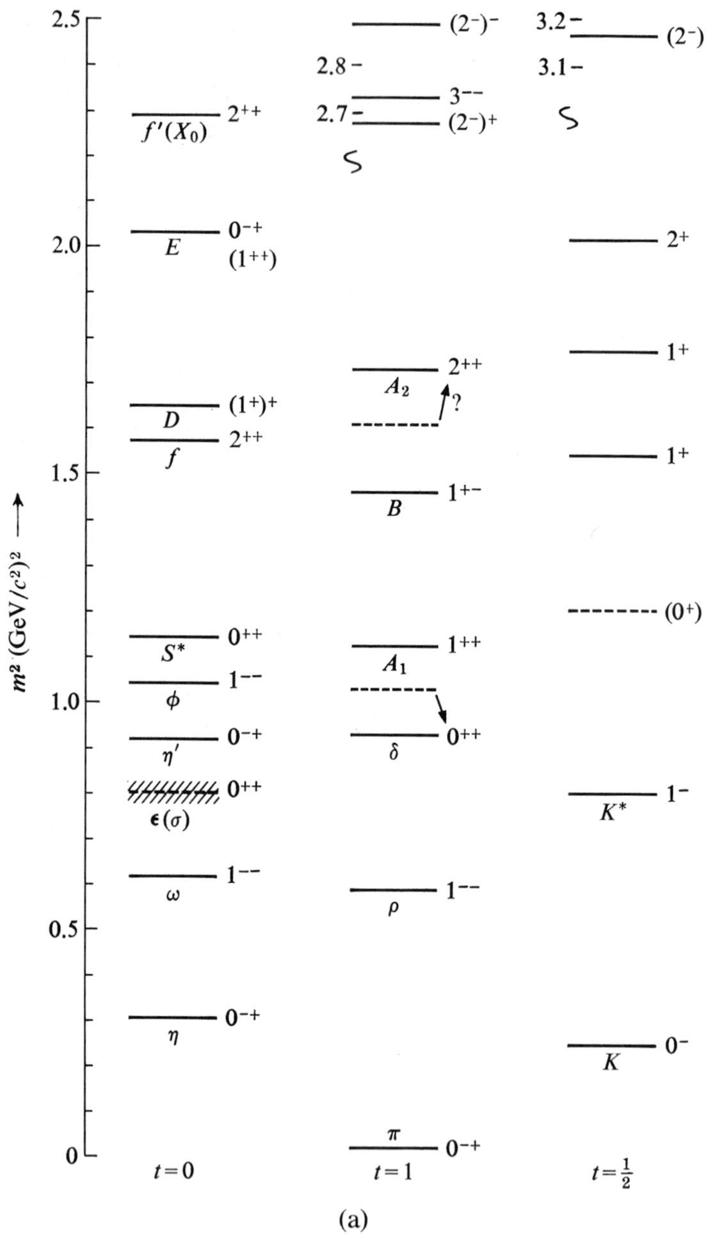

Figure 16.1 Observed hadronic mass spectra (September 1968). (a) Mesons. (b) Baryons.

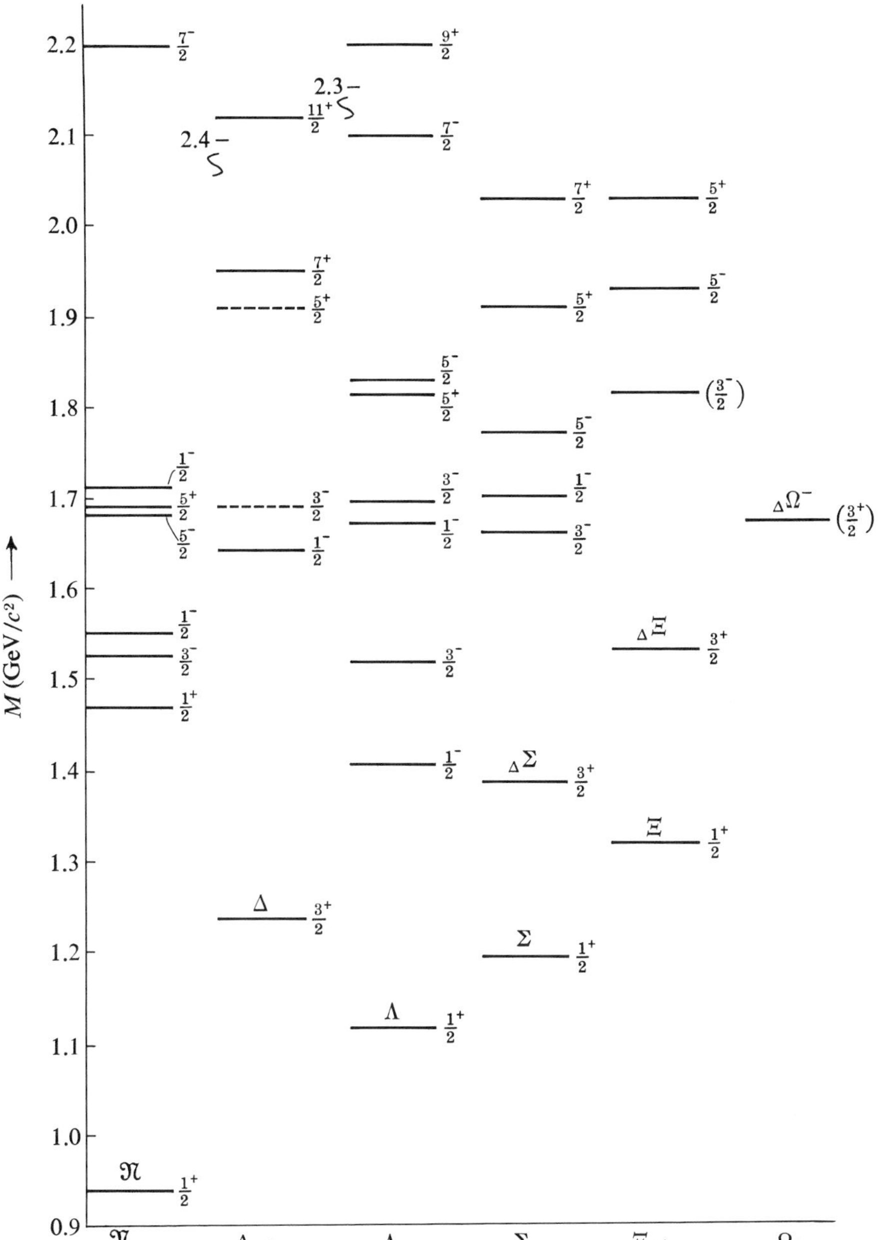

M (GeV/c^2) →
2.2
2.1
2.0
1.9
1.8
1.7
1.6
1.5
1.4
1.3
1.2
1.1
1.0
0.9
2.3 –
2.4 –
$\mathcal{N}$
Δ
Λ
Σ
Ξ
ΔΣ
ΔΞ
ΔΩ⁻
$\mathcal{N}_{1/2}$
$\Delta_{3/2}$
Λ_0
Σ_1
$\Xi_{1/2}$
Ω_0

(b)

$$1 \otimes 1 = 1, \tag{1a}$$

$$1 \otimes 35 = 35, \tag{1b}$$

$$35 \otimes 35 = 1 \oplus 35 \oplus 35' \oplus 189 \oplus 280 \oplus \overline{280} \oplus 405. \tag{1c}$$

The $SU(3)$ decompositions of these product representations are summarized in Table 16.1. We note that various possibilities exist for the observed mesons of positive parity. However, in particular, the existence of the 2^+ nonet $[A_2, f, f', K^*(1420)]$ implies the prospect of other positive parity multiplets belonging to the 10, $\overline{10}$, and 27 representations of $SU(3)$. There is no firm experimental evidence for any such meson groups.

Table 16.1 SU(3) Decomposition of the Products $q\bar{q}q\bar{q}$

$SU(3)$ \ $SU(6)$	1	35	189	280	405
27	—	—	0^+	1^+	$2^+, 1^+, 0^+$
$\overline{10}$	—	—	1^+	$1^+, 0^+$	1^+
10	—	—	1^+	$2^+, 0^+$	1^+
8	—	$0^+, 1^+$	$2^+, 1^+, 1^+, 0^+$	$2^+, 1^+, 1^+, 0^+$	$2^+, 1^+, 1^+, 0$
1	0^+	1^+	$2^+, 0^+$	1^+	$2^+, 0^+$

We turn now to the baryonic combinations $qqqq\bar{q}$: Always assuming S-state binding of pairs, the available states all have negative parity ($\frac{1}{2}^+ + 0^- \to \frac{1}{2}^-$; $\frac{1}{2}^+ + 1^- \to \frac{3}{2}^-, \frac{1}{2}^-$; $\frac{3}{2}^+ + 0^- \to \frac{3}{2}^-$; $\frac{3}{2}^+ + 1^- \to \frac{5}{2}^-, \frac{3}{2}^-, \frac{1}{2}^-$), and may be assigned to the $SU(6)$ representations

$$35 \otimes 56 = 56 \oplus 70 \oplus 700 \oplus 1134. \tag{2}$$

The $SU(3)$ decompositions of these representations are given in Table 16.2. Again, we note that the observation of a $\frac{5}{2}^-$ octet (Table 14.2) implies the possibility of many thus far undetected baryon groups with higher multiplicities. In addition, this approach requires quark combinations in numbers even greater than five to account for the observed states of $J > \frac{5}{2}$.

Table 16.2 SU(3) Decomposition of the Products $qqqq\bar{q}$

$SU(3)$ \ $SU(6)$	56	70	700	1134
35	—	—	$\frac{5}{2}^-, \frac{3}{2}^-$	$\frac{3}{2}^-, \frac{1}{2}^-$
27	—	—	$\frac{3}{2}^-, \frac{1}{2}^-$	$\frac{5}{2}^-, \frac{3}{2}^-, \frac{3}{2}^-, \frac{1}{2}^-, \frac{1}{2}^-$
$\overline{10}$	—	—	$\frac{1}{2}^-$	$\frac{3}{2}^-, \frac{1}{2}^-$
10	$\frac{3}{2}^-$	$\frac{1}{2}^-$	$\frac{5}{2}^-, \frac{3}{2}^-, \frac{1}{2}^-$	$\frac{5}{2}^-, \frac{3}{2}^-, \frac{3}{2}^-, \frac{1}{2}^-, \frac{1}{2}^-$
8	$\frac{1}{2}^-$	$\frac{1}{2}^-, \frac{3}{2}^-$	$\frac{3}{2}^-, \frac{1}{2}^-$	$\frac{5}{2}^-, \frac{3}{2}^-, \frac{3}{2}^-, \frac{3}{2}^-, \frac{1}{2}^-, \frac{1}{2}^-, \frac{1}{2}^-$
1	—	$\frac{1}{2}^-$	—	$\frac{3}{2}^-, \frac{1}{2}^-$

Thus, the possibility of accounting for the observed excited mesonic and baryonic states in terms of quark combinations with greater than three constituents requires the existence of meson and baryon multiplets other than those contained in Figure 16.1. The evidence against the existence of such "exotic" or "far-out" states [5] represents a persuasive argument against the applicability of this approach to the interpretation of the observed spectrum of hadronic states.

16.2 Excited States with Orbital Angular Momentum

Despite the problems of Lorentz invariance arising from any attempted treatment of orbital angular momentum within the context of the quark model (as discussed in Chapter 15), it is of interest to consider a nonrelativistic quark model in which the higher spin states of the hadrons arise from the introduction of an orbital angular momentum **l** associated with the $q\bar{q}$ or qq combinations involved in the basic meson and baryon configurations.

16.2.1 Mesons

We may attempt to assign other mesonic states, of masses greater than those of the corresponding members of the 0^- and 1^- nonets, to "rotational" states of the $q\bar{q}$ system. In this case, corresponding to the $SU(6)$ singlet η' or X^0 with $l=0$, $s=0$ (1_1), we have a multiplet with total angular momentum $j=l$, $s=0$ $(2l+1$ members), while the members of the 35-plet $(8_1 \oplus 8_3 \oplus 1_3)$ give rise to the following combinations: $8_1 \rightarrow 8(2l+1)$ members with $j=l$; $8_3 \rightarrow 24(2l+1)$ members in three states of total angular momentum $j=l-1, l, l+1$; $1_3 \rightarrow 3(2l+1)$ members, also in three states with $j=l-1$, l, $l+1$, for a total of $35(2l+1)$ substates.

All of these states have the same parity,

$$P=-(-1)^l, \tag{3a}$$

but the neutral members with $\mathcal{Y}=0$ have the charge-conjugation numbers

$$C=(-1)^{l+s}, \tag{3b}$$

while the corresponding G-parity quantum numbers of the $\mathcal{Y}=0$ mesons are

$$G=C(-1)^t=(-1)^{l+s+t}. \tag{3c}$$

These related multiplets may be said to comprise [6] a "supermultiplet," whose members are characterized by the values of their "good" quantum numbers $\mathcal{Y}$, t, j, l, s, as well as by the common $SU(6)$ group and its $SU(3)$ decomposition from which they originate. Within a given supermultiplet, the $\mathcal{Y}=0$ members with the same value of $j=l$ and the same isotopic spin t, but arising from different spin (s) multiplets, are distinguished on the basis of the opposite values of their

[5] A. H. Rosenfeld, *Proceedings of Univ. of Penna. Conf.*, 1968.

[6] In effect, they belong to representations of the combined group $SU(6) \otimes O(3)$, where $O(3)$ is the rotation group.

C and G quantum numbers; these quantum numbers manifest themselves in the selection rules governing the strong decays of these excited mesonic states (i.e., in the minimum number of pions into which they can decay). For the corresponding strange mesons ($\mathcal{Y}=\pm 1$), originating from the $K(s=0, j=l)$ and the $K^*(s=1, j=l)$, we must seek a different basis for their distinction; the strong decays do not help us too much here, since meson emission in the strong interactions (and photon emission as well) can lead both to spin flip and nonflip of the quark components.[7] Thus, we shall have to resort to the $SU(3)$ mass relationships to resolve ambiguities in the K-meson assignments.

The $l=1$ Supermultiplet • We can use such considerations to help classify all of the observed mesonic states of even parity as belonging to the $l=1$ supermultiplet arising from the excited $SU(6)$ 35-plet group of 0^- and 1^- mesons. Table 16.3 shows a tentative set of assignments of these states.[8] The first column lists the values of j, P, and C (for the neutral, nonstrange members); the values in parentheses are the accepted mass values in MeV/c^2. A question mark indicates some residual uncertainty in the resonance identification; those listed in brackets are of still unproved existence. The (mass)^2 spectra for these multiplets are compared with those of the $^1S_0$ (singlet + octet) and $^3S_1$ (nonet) in Figure 16.2.

Table 16.3 Even-Parity Mesonic States ($l=1$)

J^{PC}	$(t=1, \mathcal{Y}=0)$	$(\frac{1}{2}, \pm 1)$	Δ (GeV)^2	(0, 0)	(0, 0)
0^{++}	$\delta(962)=\pi_N(1016)$	$K_N(1100)$?	0.28	$S^*=\epsilon(700\text{–}1100)$?	[1210] [a]
1^{++}	$A_1(1070)$	$K_A(1230)$	0.36	[1020] [b]	$D(1285)$
1^{+-}	$B(1220)$	$K_A(1320)$	0.28	[1350] [c]	[[1550]] [d]
2^{++}	$A_2(1300)$	$K_N(1420)$	0.33	$f(1260)$	$f'(1514)$
$0^{-+}(^1S_0)$	π	K	0.23	η	$\eta'(X^0)$
$1^{--}(^3S_1)$	ρ	K^*	0.20	ω	φ

[a] Mass estimated on basis of nonet mass formula; main decay modes are $\pi\pi$, $K_1^0K_1^0$, and K^+K^-.
[b] Main decay modes are $K\bar{K}\pi$, $\pi\pi\eta$, $4\pi(\pi\pi\rho)$.
[c] Mass estimated on basis of octet mass formula; main decay modes are $3\pi(\pi\rho)$, $K\bar{K}\pi(\bar{K}K^*)$.
[d] Mass estimated on basis of assumed constant singlet-octet mass difference.

In Table 16.3, the identification of the $(t=1, \mathcal{Y}=0)$ mesons is unambiguous [once we have associated the $\pi_N(1016)$ with the $K\bar{K}$ decay mode of the δ]. Among the strange mesons, a number of problems arise — in particular, the problem of the assignment of the two $1^+(K_A)$ mesons. Here, we have based the assignments on the assumption of the approximate constancy of the value of the parameter

$$\Delta = m^2(t=\tfrac{1}{2}, \mathcal{Y}=\pm 1) - m^2(t=1, \mathcal{Y}=0), \tag{4a}$$

[7] However, the relative decay rates for different decay modes should show significant differences, arising from the different values of the combination coefficients for the final states.
[8] Similar assignments are arrived at by D. C. Peaslee, *Phys. Rev.*, *159:* 1335 (1967).

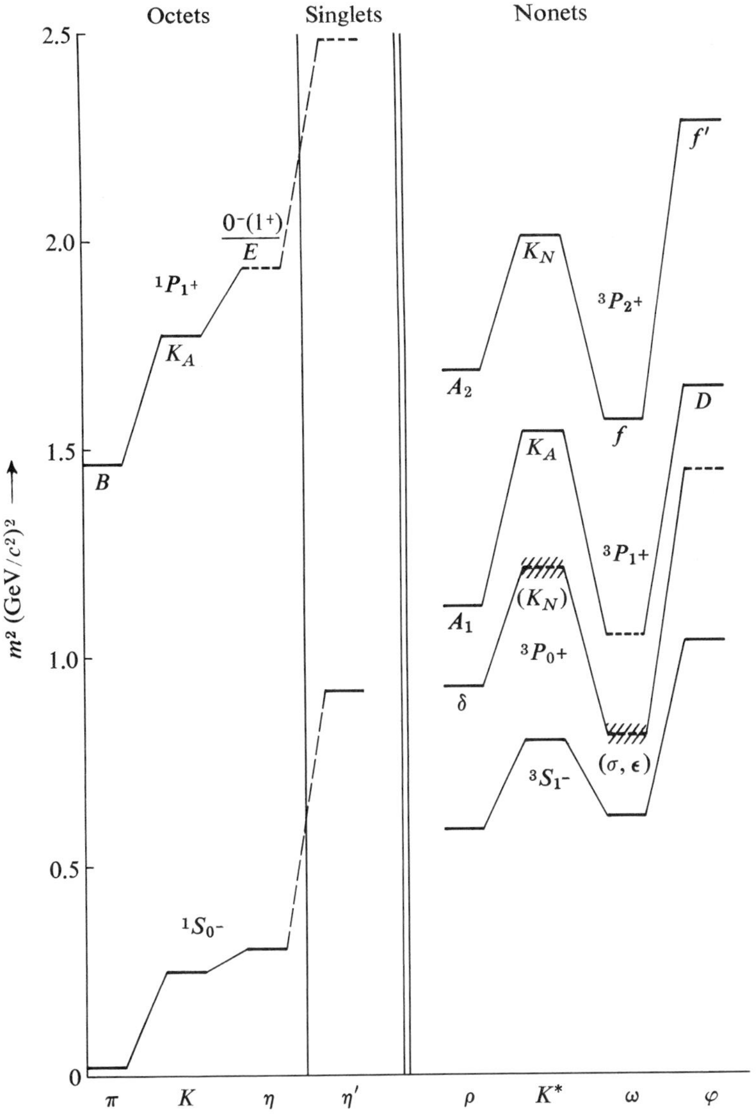

Figure 16.2 Spectrum of $l = 1$ mesonic states.

at least among multiplets originating from the same spin value, an assumption which, furthermore, is found to be roughly obeyed for the $^1S_0$ and $^3S_1$ multiplets. Even so, there is difficulty in fitting the masses of the two 1^+ multiplets, especially the 1^{++}, into the $SU(6)$ mass formulas as discussed in Section 15.3.1; however, recognizing that the two K_A-mesons perturb each other (so that the observed mesons are undoubtedly mixtures of the spin singlet and triplet), we have based our predictions of the masses of the unobserved ($t = 0$, $\mathcal{Y} = 0$) mesons on the following arguments: For the spin singlet (1^{+-}) we use the octet mass formula [$\mathcal{I}=0$ in Equation (11) of Chapter 15]:

$$m^2(t=1, \mathcal{Y}=0) + 3m^2(t=0, \mathcal{Y}=0) \cong 4m^2(t=\tfrac{1}{2}, \mathcal{Y}=\pm\tfrac{1}{2}); \tag{4b}$$

while for the three spin triplets we use the nonet formula [Equation (11), Chapter 15, with $\mathcal{I}=1$]:

$$m'^2(t=0) - m^2(t=1) \cong \frac{4}{3}\Delta\left\{\frac{m^2(t=0) - m^2(t=1) - 2\Delta}{m^2(t=0) - m^2(t=1) - 4\Delta/3}\right\}. \tag{4c}$$

Equation (4c) fits very well for the case of the 2^{++} nonet, the only case for which all four members are identified.[9]

For the 0^{++} nonet, we have assumed that the $S^*(1070)$ is the $K\overline{K}$ decay mode of a broad ($t=0$) resonance, $\epsilon(700\text{–}1100)$, for which we have arbitrarily adopted the central mass value of ≈ 900 MeV/c^2. The mass of the second $t=0$ member then follows from Equation (4c).

The assignment of the K_A-mesons in the 1^{++} nonet and 1^{+-} octet is, as noted, based on the assumed constancy of Δ (at least for the nonets). However, although an unperturbed value of ≈ 1200 MeV/c^2 would give better agreement for the 1^{++}, we note that such a shift could not arise from a mixing of the two K_A states.[10]

With respect to the 1^{++} nonet, it is of interest to consider the possibility that the $E(1420)$ might be the fourth member, although the experiments favor the spin assignment 0^- over 1^+. However, in this case, the masses would fit the octet mass formula, Equation (4b), rather than that of the nonet (4c) — i.e., no octet-singlet mixing — which would be in opposition to the assignment of this nonet as the $^3P_1$ member of the $l=1$ supermultiplet.[11]

As to the use of the relative decay rates for verifying the multiplet assignments, the only multiplet for which sufficient data exist is the 2^{++} nonet. A comparison of experiment with theory for these decay rates, corrected for phase-space and angular-momentum barrier effects, is reproduced in Table 16.4. In general, the reasonable agreement between theory and experiment may be taken as a demonstration of the potential utility of such comparisons for verifying and establishing multiplet assignments.

Aside from the mass splittings between members of a nonet of given j^{PC}, which can be described in terms of the Schwinger relationship [Chapter 15, Equation (11)], it is of interest to consider the origins of the differences between the unperturbed mass values, as characterized by the masses of the $t=1, \mathcal{Y}=0$ members of the four $l=1$ nonets listed in column 2 of Table 16.3. Such a mass fine structure would be expected to result from a spin-orbit interaction, which could be described by a perturbing potential of the form

$$V_{ls} = (\mathbf{s}_q + \mathbf{s}_{\bar{q}}) \cdot \mathbf{l} f(r), \tag{5a}$$

---

[9] Note, however, the problem of the "dipole" shape of the A_2 resonance.

[10] Level mixing can only increase the level separation from its unperturbed value.

[11] It cannot, of course, be assigned to the $^1P_1$ multiplet because of the observed evenness of the charge-conjugation quantum number, $C=+1$.

Table 16.4 Comparison of Theory and Experiment for the Relative Rates of Decay Modes of the 2^{++} Meson Nonet [a]

Decay mode	RELATIVE WIDTH [b] $SU(3)$	Four-quark model [c]	Experiment
(a) $2^+ \to 0^- + 0^-$			
$f \to 2\pi$	$\underline{100}$	$\underline{100}$	$\underline{100} \pm 14$
$\to K\overline{K}$	2.4	0	2.3 ± 0.6
$\to \eta\eta$	0.2	≈ 0.5	small
$f' \to \pi\pi$	1.7	0	$< 12 \pm 9$
$\to K\overline{K}$	31	53	$> 51 \pm 10$
$\to \eta\eta$	9	≈ 15	not seen
$A_2 \to K\overline{K}$	$\underline{6}$	0	3.1 ± 1
$\to \eta\pi$	11	≈ 30	2.3 ± 1.5
$K_v \to K\pi$	42	42	48 ± 5
$\to K\eta$	1.4	≈ 13	1.9 ± 2.8
(b) $2^+ \to 1^- + 0^-$			
$A_2 \to \rho\pi$	$\underline{75}$	$\underline{75}$	$\underline{75} \pm 7$
$K_v \to K^*\pi$	28.5	37.8	33 ± 3
$\to K\rho$	8.2	11.1	8.2 ± 4
$\to K\omega$	3	2.9	0.92 ± 1.5
$f' \to K^*\overline{K} + \overline{K^*}K$	18	31.8	$< 34 \pm 10$

[a] M. Elitzur, H. R. Rubinstein, H. Stern, and H. J. Lipkin, *Phys. Rev. Letters*, *17:* 420 (1966).
[b] Normalized to the underlined values.
[c] We have assumed that the η is the member of a pure $SU(3)$ octet — i.e., no singlet-octet mixing, or $\theta_{ps} = 0$.

which would lead to mass shifts characterized by

$$\Delta M(^3l_{l-1}):\Delta M(^3l_l):\Delta M(^1l_l):\Delta M(^3l_{l+1}) = -(l+1):-1:0:l. \tag{5b}$$

In the case of the $l = 1$ supermultiplet, such an interaction would give rise to equal spacing between the mass values under consideration.

Comparison of the mass values of the δ, A_1, B, and A_2 mesons indicates that this is approximately the case.[12] However, we have previously noted that the $s = 1$ and $s = 0$ mesons of the ground-state 35-plet (the vector and pseudoscalar mesons) require an appreciable spin-spin interaction term to account for the mass splitting between the π and the ρ (Section 15.3.1):

$$V_{ss} = (\boldsymbol{\sigma}_q \cdot \boldsymbol{\sigma}_{\bar{q}}) f'(r). \tag{6}$$

It is therefore natural to consider a mass formula for the $(t = 1, \mathcal{Y} = 0)$ mesons of the form

$$m^2 = m_l^2 + a_l(\boldsymbol{\sigma}_q \cdot \boldsymbol{\sigma}_{\bar{q}}) + \tfrac{1}{2} b_l(\boldsymbol{\sigma}_q + \boldsymbol{\sigma}_{\bar{q}}) \cdot \mathbf{l}. \tag{7}$$

The constants in Equation 7, characterizing the $l = 0$ and $l = 1$ meson supermultiplets, are given in the first two rows of Table 16.5. Note that, while the con-

[12] Both for the masses and for their squares.

Table 16.5 Meson Mass Relations (Quark Model) for l-Excited Multiplets (I spin = 1, strangeness = 0)

l	$m_l^2\,(\mathrm{GeV}/c^2)^2$	$a_l\,(\mathrm{GeV}/c^2)^2$	$b_l\,(\mathrm{GeV}/c^2)^2$
0	0.445	0.142	—
1	1.44	−0.008	0.269
2	2.78	0.031	−0.077

stants corresponding to $l = 0$ are simply computed from the π and ρ masses, those for $l > 0$ are overdetermined, since there are four mass values to be satisfied by just three constants. In the $l = 1$ case, the mass values computed from these constants for δ, A_1, B_1, and A_2 — 947, 1080, 1210, and 1305, respectively — are in reasonable accord with the accepted values, Table 16.3.

The smallness of the spin-spin parameter a_1 may be taken as an indication of the relatively short range of the spin-spin force, characterized by the shape function $f'(r)$ in Equation (6), both as compared to the range of the $SU(6)$-invariant VSI and of the $SU(6)$-violating spin-orbit interaction, Equation (5a).

Mesons with $l > 1$ • Our information concerning the meson supermultiplets with $l > 1$ comes from two sources. First, there are the results of the missing-mass spectrometer measurements of Maglic and co-workers,[13] in which the reaction

$$\pi^- + P \rightarrow P + (X)^- \tag{8}$$

is used to determine the invariant masses of the products $(X)^-$ through the momentum spectrum of the observed protons. They have observed a series of lines, corresponding to a sequence of heavy mesons, ranging from the ρ^- to a meson of mass ~ 2400 MeV/c^2.

In addition, there are a number of mesons, observed by more conventional techniques (see Figure 16.1 and Table 2.1), in the ~ 1600–1900 MeV/c^2 mass range. Such direct observations — for example, observation of the decay products in a hydrogen bubble chamber — have the advantage that they can determine the branching ratios for various decay modes (hence, the G-parity) and, under favorable circumstances, the meson spin and parity through the decay angular distributions. However, such resonances become increasingly difficult to detect and identify as the invariant mass increases.

Among the members of the $l = 1$ supermultiplet, the missing-mass spectrometer experiments observe only the δ and the A_2.[14] It is not clear why the A_1 and B are not observed, although their considerably larger widths may render them more difficult to observe by this technique.

---

[13] M. N. Focacci, W. Kienzle, B. Levrat, B. C. Maglic, and M. Martin, *Phys. Rev. Letters, 17:* 890 (1966).

[14] It is in these experiments that the splitting of the A_2 is most clearly observed, with a separation of ≈ 45 MeV/c^2 between components.

One possible interpretation of the series of peaks observed by Focacci, *et al.*, is that those of mass greater than that of the A_2 correspond to excited states of the $q\bar{q}$ system with $l = 2$, 3, 4, etc. If so, each of these lines should, under sufficiently high resolution, split into four, provided the energy differences exceed the resonance widths. In this case, the energy splittings should follow the predictions of Equation (7).

In the case of the presumed $l = 2$ peak, the R-mesons of mass $\sim$ 1700 MeV/c^2, the missing-mass spectrometer, with an experimental resolution of $\sim$ 15–20 MeV/c^2, observes a splitting into three peaks,[15] with mass values 1630, 1700, and 1748 MeV/c^2. In attempting to associate these with the ($t = 1, \mathcal{Y} = 0$) members of the $l = 2$ supermultiplet, with values of $j^{PC} = 1^{--}$, 2^{--}, 2^{-+}, and 3^{--}, we note (Table 2.1) that two resonances are observed in the region $m \approx$ 1630–1650 MeV/c^2, one of odd G-parity and "abnormal" spin-parity,[16] possibly the $2^{-+}(^1D_2)$, and the other probably the $3^{--}(^3D_3)$; another "abnormal" spin-parity resonance, but with even G-parity, is observed at $\approx$ 1700 MeV/c^2 (2^{--}?). We list the observed R-mesons in Table 16.6, together with our assignments and the mass values predicted on the basis of Equation (7) and the constants given in row 3 of Table 16.5.

It is interesting that, at least according to the assignments of Table 16.6, the order of levels in the $l = 2$ supermultiplet is inverted as compared to those with $l = 1$. If confirmed, this represents a very significant aspect of the $SU(6)$ symmetry-breaking $q\bar{q}$ forces.[17]

Table 16.6 Observed and Predicted Values for the ($t = 1$, $\mathcal{Y} = 0$) Members of the R-Meson ($l = 2$) Supermultiplet

	MASS (MeV/c^2)		
j^{PC}	From m–m spectrometer	From direct observation	Predicted
1^{--}	1748	—	1744
2^{--}	1700	1700 ± 20	1700
2^{-+} }	1630	1633 ± 9	1640
3^{--} }		1650 ± 20	1630

Concerning the rest of the members of this supermultiplet, only one member seems so far to have been observed — the K_A(1780) or L-meson, whose spin-parity is consistent with 2^-. We (tentatively) assign this to the $^3D_{2^-}$ multiplet on the basis of the corresponding value of $\Delta = 0.28$ [Equation (4a) and Table 16.3]; however, we must emphasize that, even assuming that this is the correct assignment of spin-parity, the observed 2^- K-mesons are likely to be mixtures of the $^1D_{2^-}$ and $^3D_{2^-}$ states. Nevertheless, purely for the purpose of rough, qualitative

[15] There is a possible additional weak peak reported at $\sim$ 1830 MeV/c^2.
[16] Normal spin-parity is defined as $P = (-1)^j$.
[17] Note also that, in addition to their opposite signs, $a_2 > |a_1|$, which would indicate that the range function $f'(r)$ in Equation (6), may also depend on the l-value, i.e., $f'(r) \rightarrow f'_l(r)$.

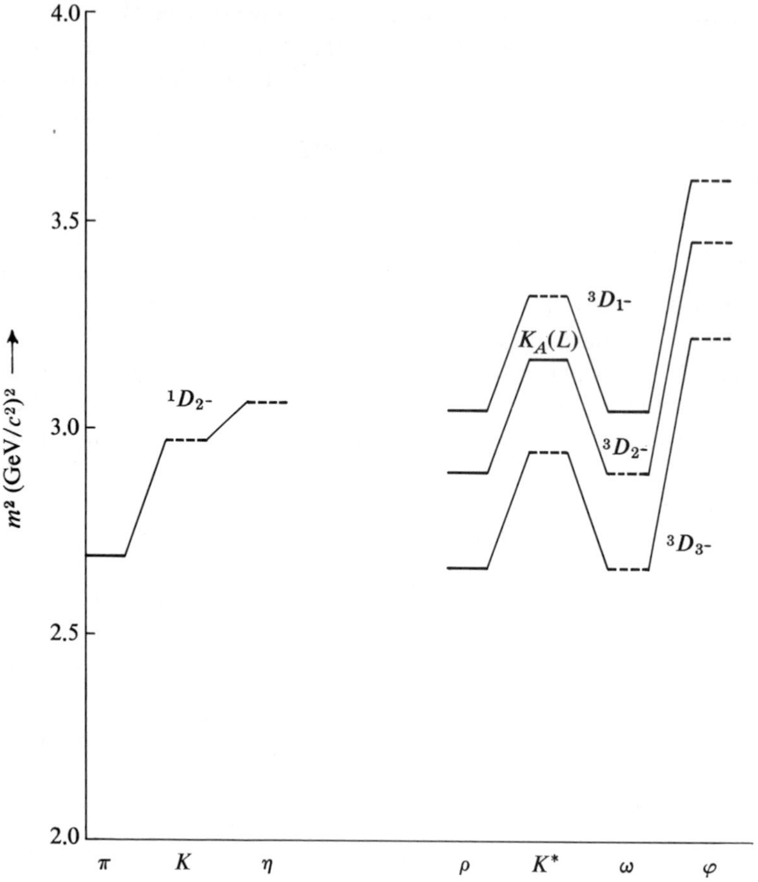

Figure 16.3 Conjectured spectrum of R-mesons ($l = 2$).

orientation, we have arbitrarily assumed the universality of the value $\Delta \cong 0.28$ $(\text{GeV}/c^2)^2$ to "predict" the spectrum of R-mesons shown in Figure 16.3. The predicted mass values are based on Equation (4b), in the case of the $^1D_2$ octet, and (4c) for the $^3D_{1,2,3}$ nonets with, however, in this case, the additional simplifying assumption

$$m^2(t=1, \mathcal{Y}=0) \approx m^2(t=0, \mathcal{Y}=0), \tag{4b'}$$

which is (very roughly) borne out by the nonet spectra for $l = 0$ and 1; see Figure 16.2.

In searching for the missing members of the $l = 2$ supermultiplet, it is useful to consider what will be the main (two-body) decay modes that follow as a consequence of the conservation of j, P, t, C, and G in their strong decays. These are summarized in Table 16.7.

We now turn to the question of the supermultiplets with $l > 2$: In considering the main unresolved peaks observed by the missing-mass technique, the authors point out an interesting linear relationship between the peak number and the

Table 16.7 Main Decay Modes of R(l = 2)-Mesons

j^{PC}	$t = 1$	$t = \frac{1}{2}$	$t = 0$
1^{--}	2π, $K\overline{K}(K_1^0K_2^0)$	$K\pi$	$K\overline{K}(K_1^0K_2^0)$, $\pi\rho$, 3π
2^{--}	$\overline{K}K^*$, $\pi\omega$, πA_2, $\rho\rho$	$K^*\pi$, $K\rho$	$\overline{K}K^*$, $\pi\rho$, 3π
2^{-+}	$\overline{K}K^*$, $\pi\rho$, πf	$K^*\pi$, $K\rho$	$\overline{K}K^*$, $\pi\omega$
3^{--}	2π, $K\overline{K}(K_1^0K_2^0)$	$K\pi$	$K\overline{K}(K_1^0K_2^0)$, $\pi\rho$, 3π

corresponding (mass)^2, as shown[18] in Figure 16.4. Since the centrifugal term in the binding energy corresponding to a central potential would have the form

$$\delta_l(m^2) = l(l+1)\left\langle\frac{1}{r^2}\right\rangle_l, \tag{9}$$

the potential that would lead to a linear (mass)^2 sequence must be such that

$$\left\langle\frac{1}{r^2}\right\rangle_l \propto \frac{1}{l}. \tag{9a}$$

Dalitz has noted[19] that an effective potential that is rather flat and open, such as that corresponding to a harmonic oscillator, would lead to a relationship of the form of Equation (9a).

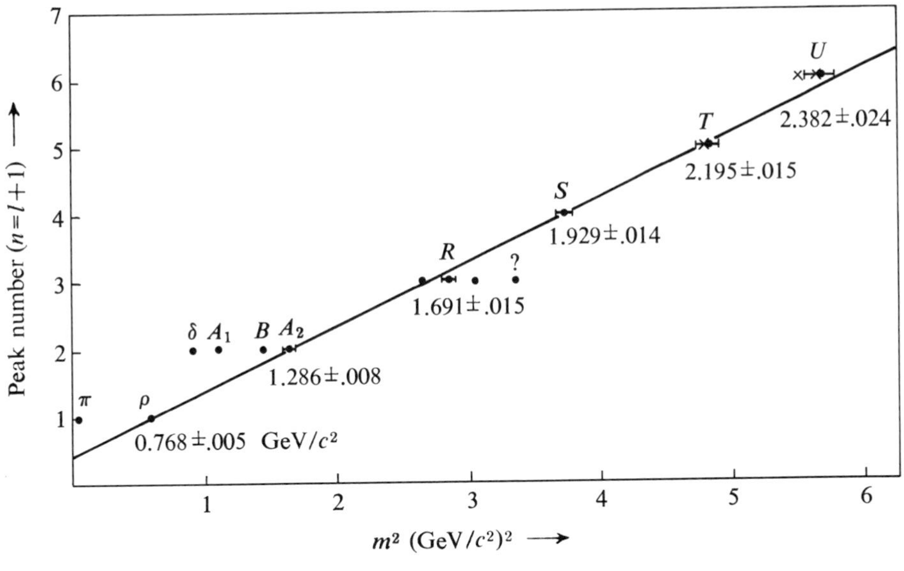

Figure 16.4 Plot of peak number versus (mass)^2 for the main peaks observed in the missing-mass spectrometer observations on the reaction

$$\pi^- + P \rightarrow P + (X^-).$$

[18] Focacci, *et al.*, *Phys. Rev. Letters, 17:* 890 (1966). Also shown (by crosses) are a number of resonances observed in $\mathfrak{N}\overline{\mathfrak{N}}$ interactions (Table 2.1).

[19] R. H. Dalitz, *Proceedings of the Berkeley Conference* (1966).

Figure 16.4 may be considered to be a plot of the Regge trajectory for mesonic states with $n=j=l+1$. [Actually, the straight line represents two almost coincident trajectories with opposite "signature," the ρ trajectory ($j=1^-, 3^-, 5^-, \ldots$) and the A_2 trajectory ($2^+, 4^+, 6^+, \ldots$).] The points corresponding to other meson trajectories — $\pi, B, \ldots$ (${}^1l_l$); $\delta({}^3l_{l-1})$ and $A_1({}^3l_l)$ — are also plotted in Figure 16.4, but we do not yet have enough information to specify the positions of the appropriate states for $l > 1$. However, the missing-mass experiment appears to indicate that the separation between the quartet of states for a given $l > 1$ becomes relatively small, which would be the case if the spin-orbit interaction range, $f(r)$ in Equation (5a), is significantly smaller than that of the VSI. In fact, the relative values of b_1 and b_2 (Table 16.5) seem to bear out this surmise.

There remains the problem of the rather small widths of the higher-mass resonances which, from the resolution of the missing-mass spectrometer, would appear to be $\lesssim$ 15–20 MeV. Such small widths are probably accounted for in terms of the high angular-momentum barriers associated with the most likely (2- and 3-meson) decay modes of the mesons under consideration. Decay via a cascade process $[l \rightarrow \pi + (l-1)]$ is probably relatively weak because of poor overlap between the radial wave functions of the initial and final states.[20] In any event, it should be noted that the missing-mass spectrometer would be unlikely to resolve high-mass states of large width, owing to the large background subtractions involved, so that the resolution of the width problem must await the development of more refined techniques.

PROBLEMS

1. Considering the quantum numbers (j, P, t, C, G) of members of the $l=1$ supermultiplet, show that their most important decay modes are as summarized below and use these to confirm or contradict the assignments suggested in Table 16.3.

Summary

State	$t=1$	$t=\frac{1}{2}$	$t=0$
0^{++}	$\pi\eta, K\bar{K}$	$K\pi, K\eta,$ $K^*\rho, K^*\omega$	$\pi\pi, K\bar{K}$
1^{++}	$3\pi, \pi\rho$	$K\rho, K^*\pi$	$K\bar{K}\pi, K\bar{K}\eta, \pi\pi\rho$
1^{+-}	$\pi\omega(\pi\phi)$	$K\rho, K^*\pi$	$\rho\pi, 3\pi, K\bar{K}, K^*\bar{K}$
2^{++}	$\pi\eta, K\bar{K},$ $3\pi, \pi\rho$	$K\pi, K^*\pi$ $K\rho, K\eta$	$2\pi, K\bar{K}$

2. Baltay, *et al.*[21] have observed two $t=1$ resonances:

$$R_1(G=-1),\ m_1 = 1630 \pm 10 \text{ MeV } (\Gamma_1 = 70 \pm 40 \text{ MeV}),$$
$$R_2(G=+1),\ m_2 = 1720 \pm 15 \text{ MeV } (\Gamma_2 = 100 \pm 35 \text{ MeV}).$$

[20] *Ibid.* Also see the problem at the end of Section 1.2.
[21] *Phys. Rev. Letters, 20:* 887 (1968).

Among the identified decay modes, they find the following branching ratios:

$$R_1 \begin{cases} \rho^0\pi^+ & < 20\% \\ f^0\pi^+ & 35 \pm 20\% \\ \eta^0\pi^+ & < 2\% \end{cases}$$

$$R_2 \begin{cases} \omega^0\pi^+ & 25 \pm 10\% \\ A_2^0\pi^+ & 40 \pm 20\% \end{cases}$$

(a) With the aid of Table 16.7, discuss the possible assignments of these resonances in the $l = 2$ supermultiplet.

(b) What would be the likely assignments if these resonances belonged to the $l = 3$ supermultiplet?

3. What sort of experiment(s) would you design to detect and identify the ${}^3D_1$, $\mathcal{Y} = 0$ members of the $l = 2$ supermultiplet?
4. Discuss the possible electromagnetic decays of the $l = 1$ mesons, estimating, where you can, the corresponding decay widths.

16.2.2 Baryons

Reference to Table 14.2 and Figure 16.1(b) indicates a relatively large concentration of baryon resonances of negative parity and low spin ($\frac{1}{2}$, $\frac{3}{2}$, $\frac{5}{2}$) in the $\sim$ 1400–1900 MeV/c^2 mass range. Thus, for example, among the isospin $\frac{1}{2}$ nucleonic states, there are four such resonances between 1525 and 1710 MeV/c^2, with the next negative-parity resonance (spin $\frac{7}{2}^-$) occurring at 2190 MeV/c^2. A similar situation pertains among the resonances with other values of $\mathcal{Y}$ and t; however, these have been less extensively explored than have the nucleon resonances.

We have previously noted the difficulties of associating the excited baryonic states with possible $qqqq\bar{q}$ combinations (see Table 16.2) since their lowest available $SU(6)$ representations, 56 and 70, cannot accommodate all the observed groups (e.g., a $\frac{5}{2}^-$ octet or a $\frac{3}{2}^-$ singlet), while the next higher-multiplicity representation, the 700, contains far too many unobserved multiplets, including many unobserved resonances of the "exotic" or "far-out" variety.

The alternative is to consider these as qqq states with internal orbital angular momentum, which is what we attempt in the following: If we assume attractive central forces between quark pairs, the ground state is completely symmetric, with orbital angular momentum $L = 0$; it belongs to the 56^+ representation of $SU(6)$, with the $SU(3)$ decomposition $8_2 \oplus 10_4$ (i.e., an octet of spin $\frac{1}{2}^+$ and a decimet of spin $\frac{3}{2}^+$ baryons). The sequence of excited states of such a quark triplet depends, of course, on the details of the q–q interaction. However, for the purposes of orientation, we may consider the excited states of a qqq system that would result from placing the quarks in a harmonic oscillator potential; these are shown in Figure 16.5. In this case, the first excited state has $L = 1$, negative parity, and belongs to the 70 representation of $SU(6)$.

That, indeed, it is entirely plausible that this should be the first excited state may be seen from relatively simple considerations of the qqq system in terms of

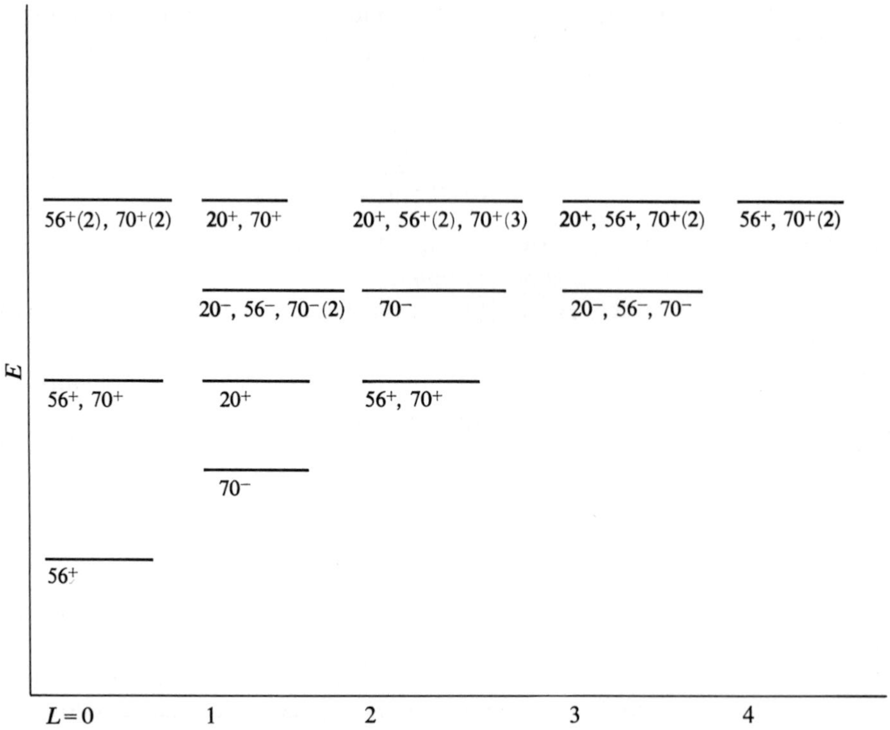

Figure 16.5 States of the *qqq* system in a harmonic oscillator potential.

the spatial configuration shown in Figure 16.6. Letting $\mathbf{l}=$ the angular momentum of the q_1–q_2 pair in its own *cm* and $\mathbf{l}'=$ the angular momentum of q_3 with respect to the *cm* of the total, then

$$\mathbf{L}=\mathbf{l}+\mathbf{l}'\,. \tag{10}$$

Assuming that the ground state has $l=l'=0$, the state of lowest excitation will have $l=1$, $l'=0$ or $l=0$, $l'=1$ (actually, an appropriate combination of the two), negative parity, $P=(-1)^{l+l'}$, and mixed spatial symmetry; accordingly, it must be associated with the *qqq* representation of mixed symmetry — namely, the 70-plet.

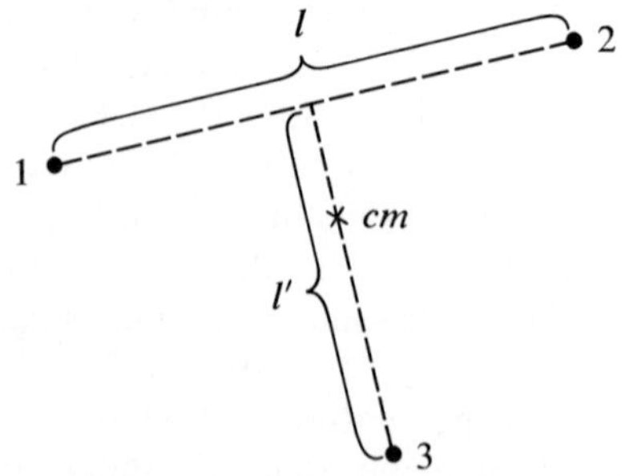

Figure 16.6 The *qqq* spatial configuration.

Now the $SU(3)$ decomposition of the 70-plet is $1_2 \oplus 8_2 \oplus 10_2 \oplus 8_4$. Hence, we expect the following negative-parity $SU(3)$ multiplets associated with the first excited qqq state: ${}^4P_{5/2,3/2,1/2}$ (three octets); ${}^2P_{3/2,1/2}$ (two singlets, two octets, and two decimets). Of these nine $SU(3)$ multiplets anticipated, there is empirical evidence for at least one member of each of the predicted multiplets, with the possible exception of one of the $\frac{3}{2}^-$ octets (see Table 16.8).

Table 16.8 Interpretation of the Mass Spectrum of Negative-Parity Baryons as Members of the L = 1, 70⁻ qqq Supermultiplet

(a) *Observed levels* [a]

		Mass (MeV/c^2)					
$SU(3)$ multiplet	Spin	$\mathcal{N}^*_{1/2}$	$\mathcal{N}^*_{3/2}$	Λ^*_0	Σ^*_1	$\Xi^*_{1/2}$	Ω^*_0
1_2	$\frac{1}{2}^-$			1405			
	$\frac{3}{2}^-$			1520			
8_2	$\frac{1}{2}^-$	1525		1670	(1615)	×	
	$\frac{3}{2}^-$	1515		1690	1660 [b]	1820 [b]	
10_2	$\frac{1}{2}^-$		1630		(1700)	×	×
	$\frac{3}{2}^-$		1670		×	×	×
8_4	$\frac{1}{2}^-$	1715		(1750)	×	×	
	$\frac{3}{2}^-$	(1730)		×	×	×	
	$\frac{5}{2}^-$	1675		1830	1765	1930	

[a] The mass values in this table differ slightly from those in Table 14.2; they have been taken from a more recent version of the Rosenfeld compilation (that of January 1969). The underlined mass values are those used in computing the unperturbed mass constants given in Equation (11b). Values in parentheses indicate uncertain identification. Crosses indicate missing members.

[b] These multiplet assignments are arbitrary; they could equally well belong to the 10_2, or even the 8_4, multiplet. In the case of the $\Sigma_1^*(1660)$ there is, in fact, some evidence that this level is a superposition of two [see P. Eberhard, *et al., Phys. Rev. Letters, 22:* 200 (1969)].

(b) *Unperturbed mass values computed from Equations (11) and (11a) using the constants of Equation (11b)*

		Mass (MeV/c^2)					
$SU(3)$ multiplet	Spin	$\mathcal{N}^*_{1/2}$	$\mathcal{N}^*_{3/2}$	Λ^*_0	Σ^*_1	$\Xi^*_{1/2}$	Ω^*_0
1_2	$\frac{1}{2}^-$			1540			
	$\frac{3}{2}^-$			1505			
8_2	$\frac{1}{2}^-$	1565		1709	1641	1819	
	$\frac{3}{2}^-$	1567		1711	1643	1821	
10_2	$\frac{1}{2}^-$		1632		1810	1988	2166
	$\frac{3}{2}^-$		1672		1850	2028	2206
8_4	$\frac{1}{2}^-$	1675		1820	1752	1930	
	$\frac{3}{2}^-$	1678		1823	1755	1933	
	$\frac{5}{2}^-$	1682		1827	1759	1937	

(c) *Proposed (tentative) spectrum, taking into account perturbations among levels with the same quantum numbers*[a]

		Mass (MeV/c^2)					
$SU(3)$ multiplet	Spin	$\mathcal{N}^*_{1/2}$	$\mathcal{N}^*_{3/2}$	Λ^*_0	Σ^*_1	$\Xi^*_{1/2}$	Ω^*_0
1_2	$\frac{1}{2}^-$			1405			
	$\frac{3}{2}^-$			1520			
8_2	$\frac{1}{2}^-$	1525		1670	1615	1790	
	$\frac{3}{2}^-$	1515		1690	1660	1835	
10_2	$\frac{1}{2}^-$		1630		1890	2070	2165
	$\frac{3}{2}^-$		1670		1900	2080	2205
8_4	$\frac{1}{2}^-$	1715		1995	1700	1880	
	$\frac{3}{2}^-$	1730		1830	1690	1865	
	$\frac{5}{2}^-$	1680		1825	1760	1935	

[a] Mass values have been rounded off to the closest unit of five. See text for procedure used in estimating the perturbations from the values in Table 16.8(b).

Mass Spectrum of the L = 1 Baryons • We may try to fit the observed masses by a generalization of the relationship [Chapter 15, Equation (9)] which was successful in accounting for the masses of the 8_2 and 10_4 members of the ground-state baryon 56-plet. In general form, this may be written as

$$M = M_0(\mathcal{Y}, t) + CS(S+1) + \tfrac{1}{6}DF^2 + (\alpha + \tfrac{1}{6}\beta F^2)\,\mathbf{S}\cdot\mathbf{L}, \tag{11}$$

in which the first term is the usual $SU(3)$ mass formula [which, we assume, accounts adequately for the $SU(3)$-violating terms of the MSI]:

$$M_0(\mathcal{Y}, t) = M_0 + A\mathcal{Y} + B\left[t(t+1) - \frac{\mathcal{Y}^2}{4}\right], \tag{11a}$$

while the remaining terms arise from $SU(6)$-violating, but presumably $SU(3)$-invariant, parts of the MSI. The first of these derives from a spin-spin interaction between quark pairs. The second comes from a possible dependence of the interaction on the "unitary spin," F, of the $SU(3)$ representation;[22] F^2 has the values 0, 6, and 12, respectively, for the 1, 8, and 10 representations of $SU(3)$ (see Section 14.5, especially Table 14.14). Also for the last term, arising from the quark spin-orbit interactions, we have assumed a general $SU(3)$-invariant form, which may also be unitary-spin dependent.

We summarize, in Table 16.8(a), the spectrum of negative-parity levels which we are attempting to interpret, and their tentative multiplet assignments.

There are two difficulties associated with any attempt to interpret this spectrum

[22] We omitted this term from Equation (9) of Chapter 15, since the splitting between the 8_2 and 10_4 multiplets required only a single new constant, and the introduction of two would have been redundant. However, strictly speaking, Equation (11) above should have been used; the introduction of the DF^2 term does not influence the fitting of the masses of the 56^+ multiplet, but it changes the interpretation of the numbers obtained in this fitting [Equation (9a) of Chapter 15], i.e., $M_0 \to M_0 + \frac{3}{4}D$, $C \to C + \frac{1}{3}D$. In this situation, it is not possible to assign unique values to M_0, C, and D for the ground-state baryons.

of observed negative-parity resonances in terms of Equation (11): First (and hopefully of only transitory importance), not all of the expected resonances have yet been observed, and the identification of some of those observed is still uncertain. Second (and conceptually more serious), we expect a certain mixing of states with identical quantum numbers, arising from the same $SU(3)$- and $SU(6)$-violating MSI that give rise to the mass equation (11). In particular, the $SU(3)$-violating terms will mix members of different $SU(3)$ multiplets — the 1_2 and 8_2 through mixing of the Λ_0^*'s, and the 8_2 and 10_2 through Σ_1^* and $\Xi_{1/2}^*$ mixing — but a central interaction would not mix $S=\frac{1}{2}$ and $S=\frac{3}{2}$. Any other spin dependence (aside from $\Sigma\, \boldsymbol{\sigma}_i \cdot \boldsymbol{\sigma}_j$), in particular the spin-orbit interaction, will not only violate $SU(6)$ but will mix particles of the same angular momentum (i.e., $\frac{1}{2}^-$ or $\frac{3}{2}^-$) between the 8_2 and 8_4 multiplets. Such mixings will not only shift entire groups from the mass positions predicted by Equation (11), but they may also lead to apparent violations of the Gell-Mann–Okubo mass formula, Equation (11a).

The importance of this last effect may be gauged by comparison of the $SU(3)$ mass-formula parameters (A and B) as computed for the three octets for which at least three members are identified — the $\frac{1}{2}^-[\mathfrak{N}^*(1525)]$ and $\frac{3}{2}^-[\mathfrak{N}^*(1515)]$, both presumably 8_2, and the $\frac{5}{2}^-[\mathfrak{N}^*(1675)]$, of necessity 8_4. This comparison is given in Table 16.9. It may be noted that the three sets, although quantitatively somewhat different, have the same qualitative features (large and negative A; relatively small and negative B). Of the three, the last pair ($\frac{5}{2}^-$) are the values that should be identified with Equation (11a), since the $\frac{5}{2}^-$ levels are unique within the $L=1$ supermultiplet and hence not perturbed by any nearby levels with the same good quantum numbers. On the other hand, we may conclude that the $\frac{1}{2}^-$ and $\frac{3}{2}^-$ members of 8_2 are perturbed, but probably not to an extent sufficient to confuse their identification.[23]

Table 16.9 SU(3) Mass Constants for Perturbed Octets Within the $70^-(L=1)$ Supermultiplet

Multiplet	Spin value	A (MeV/c^2)	B (MeV/c^2)
8_2	$\frac{1}{2}^-$	−131	−27.5
8_2 [a]	$\frac{3}{2}^-$	−167	−15
8_4 [b]	$\frac{5}{2}^-$	−127	−34

[a] The constants have been evaluated using the $\mathfrak{N}^*$, Λ^*, and Σ^* members only. These predict the mass value 1850 MeV/c^2 for the Ξ^*. If, on the other hand, the $\Xi^*(1820)$ were assumed to belong to the $10_2(\frac{3}{2}^-)$ multiplet, this would imply the value $(A+\frac{3}{2}B)=-75$. Almost the same value is obtained for the $10_2(\frac{1}{2}^-)$ constants, on the assignment of $\Sigma^*(1700)$ to this multiplet, which casts some doubt on both 10_2 assignments.

[b] In this case, all four masses being known, the constants are overdetermined. The fit is excellent, the $SU(3)$ mass relation $2(\mathfrak{N}^*+\Xi^*)=(3\Lambda^*+\Sigma^*)$ being satisfied to within approximately 0.5 percent.

Nevertheless, owing to the mixing of states with the same quantum numbers, most of the observed mass values cannot be used directly to determine the parameters in Equation (11). However, in principle, if all the levels of the supermultiplet were known, it would be possible to obtain a unique (indeed, overdetermined) fit to Equation (11), and a measure of the level perturbations as well.

[23] By the same token, in the main, their wave functions are probably relatively unmixed.

Thus, for example, the constants A and B [Equation 11(a)], plus a certain combination of the remaining constants, may be obtained from the masses of any three of the members of the 8_4 ($\frac{5}{2}^-$) octet, since these are unperturbed by the other members of the supermultiplet[24] (see Table 16.8). Two additional combinations may be obtained from either the $\mathcal{N}^*_{3/2}$ or the Ω^* members of the 10_2 ($\frac{1}{2}^-$ and $\frac{3}{2}^-$) since these are, again, unique.[25] All of these mass values yield, in total, five independent relations among the seven parameters in Equation (11). Another two equations may be obtained from the mean values of the masses of the two $\mathcal{N}^*_{1/2}$ states in the 8 ($\frac{1}{2}^-$) and 8 ($\frac{3}{2}^-$) multiplets since, for the case of perturbing levels, the sum of the perturbed masses is equal to the sum of the unperturbed values. Finally, if all three members of any of the remaining groups with identical quantum numbers were available, such a group would yield an additional relationship among the constants, using the rule of the equality of the sum of perturbed and unperturbed masses. Potentially, there are six of such triplets, so that — provided all the masses were known — we would be able to obtain thirteen relationships among the seven parameters of Equation (11).

However, as may be seen in Table 16.8(a), not all the levels are available. In fact, in order to obtain a minimum set for the analysis, we have had to use at least one mass value whose identification is uncertain.[26] Using the indicated masses, the parameters in Equations (11) and (11a) take on the values[27]

$$\begin{aligned} M_0 &= 1488 \text{ MeV}/c^2,\\ A &= -127 \text{ MeV}/c^2,\\ B &= -34 \text{ MeV}/c^2,\\ C &= 38 \text{ MeV}/c^2,\\ D &= 194 \text{ MeV}/c^2,\\ \alpha &= -23.3 \text{ MeV}/c^2,\\ \beta &= 25 \text{ MeV}/c^2. \end{aligned} \tag{11b}$$

The unperturbed level structure for the 70^- supermultiplet, based on the mass formula and constants of Equations (11), (11a), and (11b), is shown in Table

[24] We assume that the perturbations due to mixing with members of higher supermultiplets (e.g., 70^- with $L=3$) are negligible.

[25] Only one each of the 10_2 ($\frac{1}{2}^-$) and 10_2 ($\frac{3}{2}^-$) members is required; the other merely serves to check the value of the constant $(A+\frac{3}{2}B)$.

[26] Another possibility would have been to use, instead of the $\frac{3}{2}^-$-$\mathcal{N}^*_{1/2}$ doublet, the $\frac{1}{2}^-$ triplet of Λ_0^*'s. This choice leads to an inconsistent solution, in that it leads to predicted $\mathcal{N}^*_{1/2}$ mass values that violate the requirement that a pair of mutually perturbing levels must repel each other. We have, therefore, perforce, chosen those values underlined in Table 16.8(a) for this preliminary analysis.

[27] The corresponding values of the parameters for the ground state ($L=0$) 56^+ supermultiplet are

$$\begin{aligned} M_0+\tfrac{3}{4}D &= 1067 \text{ MeV}/c^2,\\ A &= -196 \text{ MeV}/c^2,\\ B &= 39 \text{ MeV}/c^2,\\ C+\tfrac{1}{3}D &= 65 \text{ MeV}/c^2. \end{aligned}$$

In this case, there is not enough information possible to permit a unique separation of M_0, C, and D, since there are only two $SU(3)$ multiplets, 8_2 ($\frac{1}{2}^+$) and 10_4 ($\frac{3}{2}^+$).

16.8(b), and plotted on the left-hand side of Figure 16.7.[28] It is worth reemphasizing that this analysis contains no redundancy and, further, that it is based on level identifications which are not always certain and on mass values that, at best, are inexact, so that the results are mainly illustrative at this stage. Nevertheless, it is worth noting that, on the basis of the constants of Equation (11b), all the conjectured $SU(6)$- and $SU(3)$-violating interactions are of more or less equal importance, amounting in each case to ~ 5–10 percent of the unperturbed mass value M_0. Correspondingly, the level shifts, among levels with the same j, t, and $\mathcal{Y}$, may be expected to be of the same order of magnitude.

We also give, in Table 16.8(c), estimates of the mass values of the remaining members of the 70^- supermultiplet. In the case of the unique Ω_0^* states, these follow immediately from Equation (11). In all the other cases [values not underlined in Table 16.8(a)] we have used the experimental values, together with the rule of constant sums, whenever possible. This has been possible for the Λ_0^* states (note the discrepancy between the uncertain experimental identification and the predicted mass for the $\frac{1}{2}^-$ 8_4 member) as well as for the $\frac{1}{2}^-$ Σ_1^*'s, although the latter estimate is based on two very uncertain identifications. In the case of the $\frac{3}{2}^-$ Σ_1^*'s, we have assumed a near degeneracy between levels at 1660 and 1690 MeV/c^2 [see footnote (b), Table 16.8(a)], thereby providing two of the three perturbed values.

In order to guess at the mass values of the Ξ^*'s, we have adopted the simple prescription that the shifts of the perturbed [Table 16.8(c)] values are, in every case, the same as those of the Σ^* members of the same multiplet. This prescription may not be unreasonable in view of the similarity of distribution of the Σ^*'s and Ξ^*'s among the multiplets of the 70^- supermultiplet. The effect is to move the $\frac{3}{2}^-$ 8_2 member away from agreement with the experimental value (of 1820 MeV/c^2), but by only 15 MeV/c^2, however; this is certainly not a serious discrepancy.

Our proposed mass spectrum is graphically illustrated in Figure 16.7, in which the level shifts from their unperturbed values are shown on the right-hand side of the figure, both for the Λ_0^* states and for the $\mathfrak{N}_{1/2}^*$ states [reduced to the same scale by subtracting $A + \frac{1}{2}B = -144$ MeV/c^2 from the corresponding values in Table 16.8(c)].

Since, at this stage, our analysis has no redundancies, it is only possible to conclude that the L-excitation interpretation provides a consistent picture of the negative-parity baryon resonances.

Further evidence, relating to the possible assignments of the negative-parity states in the 70^-, $L = 1$ supermultiplet, may be sought in the relative rates of decay into alternative decay modes of the resonances in question. Thus, for example, our original preference for the assignment of the $\frac{3}{2}^-$ $\Xi_{1/2}^*(1820)$ to the 10_2, rather than the 8_2, multiplet arose from the expectation of a $\Sigma\overline{K}/\Lambda\overline{K}$ decay ratio of ~ 0.3 for the former, as compared to ~ 10 for the latter assignment;[29] experimentally, this ratio (corrected for phase space) is observed to be $\lesssim 2$. However, it is important to note that the appreciable mixing of states, as discussed above, will

---

[28] We have plotted the masses of the Λ_0^* members of the multiplets; in the case of the 10_2, however, there being no Λ_0^* member, we have plotted the equivalent value of $M_0 + \frac{3}{4}C + 2D[-(\alpha + 2\beta)$ and $+\frac{1}{2}(\alpha + 2\beta)$ for the $\frac{1}{2}^-$ and $\frac{3}{2}^-$ level, respectively].

[29] A. Mitra and M. Ross, *Rutherford High Energy Laboratory Report* (August 1966).

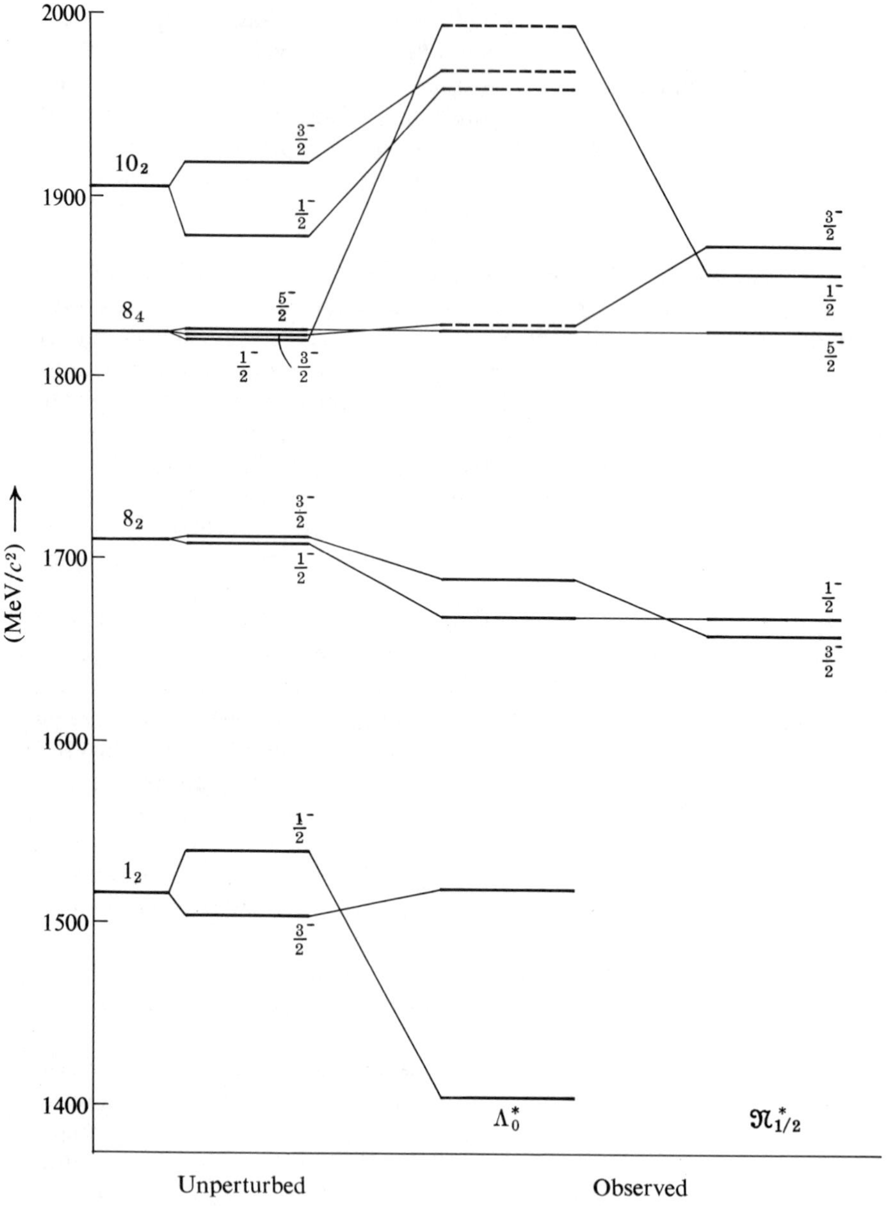

Figure 16.7 Comparison of unperturbed and observed (solid) or "predicted" (broken lines) spectra for the $L = 1$, qqq supermultiplet. The mass values plotted are, where necessary, corrected to remove the $\mathcal{Y}$ and t dependence [according to Equation (11a) and the constants A and B of Equation (11b)]. Note, in the case of the 10_2, that the masses shown as Λ_0^* are the corrected Σ_1^* predictions from Table 16.8(c).

result in a drastic alteration of the relative decay rates from those predicted on the basis of the $SU(3)$ assignments. Thus, the analysis of Mitra and Ross leads to a number of significantly different assignments from those indicated in Table 16.8(a) and would give rise to much more serious discrepancies from the pattern predicted by Equation (11).

An interesting observation by Moorhouse[30] tends to confirm the $\frac{5}{2}^-$ spin and 8_4 multiplet assignment of the $\mathfrak{N}^*_{1/2}(1675)$. He notes that the reaction

$$\gamma + P \rightarrow \mathfrak{N}^{*+}_{1/2}(\tfrac{5}{2}^-) \tag{12a}$$

is forbidden by the quark model, since $E3$ absorption is not permitted for a ${}^2S \rightarrow {}^4P$ transition, while the $M2$ transition matrix element happens to vanish for the quark-model assignments of the baryons in question. In fact, the photo-excitation of this resonance is not observed, while other resonances in the same mass range [e.g., $\mathfrak{N}^{*+}(\frac{3}{2}^-)$, $\mathfrak{N}^{*+}(\frac{5}{2}^+)$] are strongly excited by photons. However, the $M2$ matrix element is expected to be appreciable for the reaction

$$\gamma + N \rightarrow \mathfrak{N}^{*0}_{1/2}(\tfrac{5}{2}^-), \tag{12b}$$

but this reaction, as of December 1968, still has not been investigated in the appropriate energy range.

Baryons with $L > 1$ • The relatively plausible case, which we have been able to establish in the preceding section, for the interpretation of the $\frac{1}{2}^-, \frac{3}{2}^-, \frac{5}{2}^-$ baryon resonances as corresponding to the 70^- representation of $SU(6)$ arising from the lowest $L = 1$ excitation of the 56^+ qqq configuration (see Figure 16.5) encourages us to attempt to interpret the remaining observed baryon resonances [Tables 14.2 and 2.1 and Figure 16.1(b)] as belonging to qqq configurations with $L \geq 2$. However, the paucity of data on the properties of the higher-mass resonances does not permit the type of detailed analysis that we attempted for the $L = 1$ supermultiplet. Instead, we are forced to resort to an indirect approach, based on the Regge-pole conjecture.

According to this approach, we would expect the regular recurrence of the 56^+ ($L = 0$) ground state, but with $L = 2, 4, 6, \ldots$, with monotonically increasing mass values; correspondingly, the odd-parity 70^- supermultiplet should also be repeated at higher mass values, but with $L = 3, 5, 7, \ldots$.

On this basis, the $\mathfrak{N}^*_{1/2}(1688)$ of spin $\frac{5}{2}^+$ would be interpreted as the first of the Regge recurrences of the nucleon, the $\mathfrak{N}^*_{3/2}(1950)$ of spin $\frac{7}{2}^+$ as the first recurrence of the $\Delta_{3/2}(1236)$, the $\mathfrak{N}^*_{1/2}(2190)$, spin $\frac{7}{2}^-$, as the first recurrence of the $\frac{3}{2}^-$ $\mathfrak{N}^*_{1/2}(1520)$, etc. Such an interpretation is supported by Figures 16.8 and 16.9 in which the successive baryon isobars are shown on a Regge plot — i.e., the baryon $(\text{mass})^2$ values are plotted against their spin values. It is of great interest that, with very few exceptions (which will be discussed individually below), all the known baryons appear to lie on a set of approximately parallel, straight-line Regge trajectories.

It should be noted at the outset that the interpretation suggested by Figures

[30] R. G. Moorhouse, *Phys. Rev. Letters, 16:* 772 (1966).

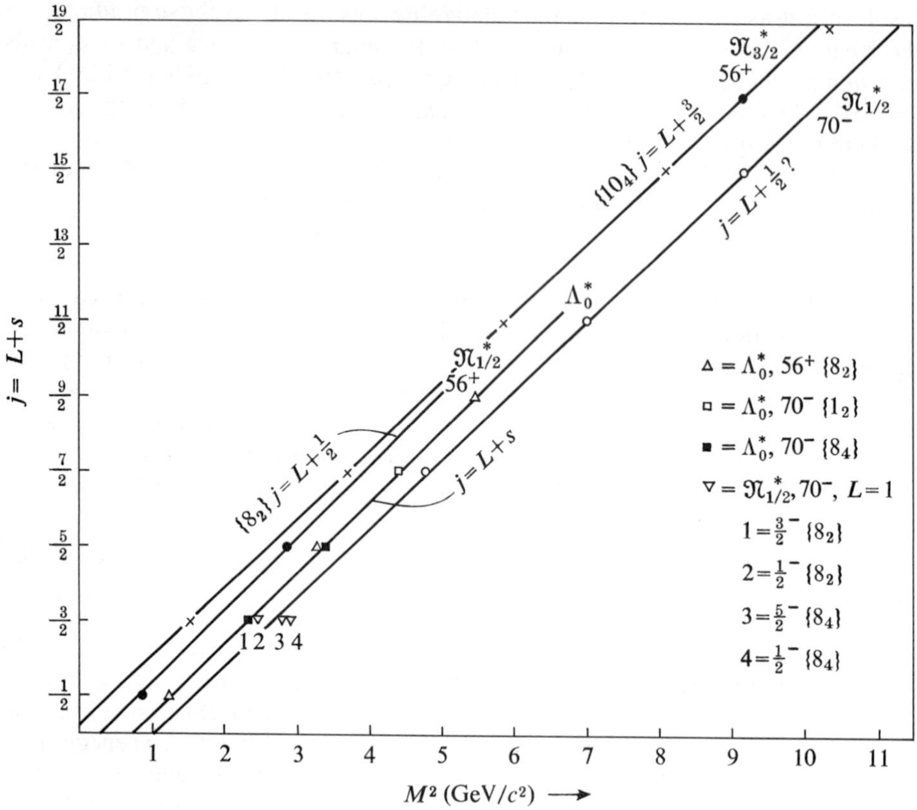

Figure 16.8 Regge trajectories for nucleonic and Λ_0^* resonances.

16.8 and 16.9 is not unique, since only one of the assignments of spin $> \frac{7}{2}$, that of $\frac{11}{2}^+$ for $\Delta(2420)$, has so far been experimentally verified; all other $\geq \frac{9}{2}$ values are, in fact, assigned on the basis of the Regge trajectories assumed in these figures. Thus, considering the conjectured $\mathfrak{N}^*_{3/2}$ trajectory of Figure 16.8, the two highest mass resonances are most simply interpreted as belonging to the 10_4 $SU(3)$ multiplet contained in the 56^+ representation of $SU(6)$, with $j = L$ (even) $+ \frac{3}{2}$, since on this interpretation they all lie on the straight-line trajectory determined by the $\frac{3}{2}^+$ ($L = 0$) and $\frac{7}{2}^+$ ($L = 2$) $\mathfrak{N}^*_{3/2}$ mass values. However, they could also belong to the corresponding $j = L + \frac{1}{2}$ trajectory, in which case their spins would be one unit less than assumed and they would fall on a lower, but parallel, straight line (which happens to coincide with the proposed 70^-, $\mathfrak{N}^*_{1/2}$, $j = L + \frac{1}{2}$ trajectory). Or they could have $j = L - \frac{1}{2}$, or even $j = L - \frac{3}{2}$, in which case the appropriate trajectories would still be parallel to that conjectured, but displaced still further downward.

However, if any of these possibilities should in fact be true, and assuming the validity of the L-excitation interpretation of the excited baryon states, it would appear strange that none of the other members of the $L \geq 2$, $\mathfrak{N}^*_{3/2}$ multiplets has as yet been observed. A somewhat more attractive hypothesis is that the spin-orbit splittings for $L \geq 2$ tend to be small, owing to the short-range character of the spin-orbit interaction potential (as compared, say, to the VSI) so that the quartet of $\mathfrak{N}^*_{3/2}$ (56^+, 10_4) levels are experimentally unresolved (the observed widths of the higher $\mathfrak{N}^*_{3/2}$ levels are $\approx$ 200–400 MeV). On this interpretation, there should be a quartet of parallel 56^+, $\mathfrak{N}^*_{3/2}$ trajectories, with the three not shown in Figure 16.8 starting at $j = \frac{5}{2}$, $\frac{3}{2}$, and $\frac{1}{2}$, respectively, but with masses deviating only slightly from that of the $\frac{7}{2}^+$ level. Clearly, in this case, it is most economical to plot a single trajectory, which we could do by letting the ordinate be $L + \frac{3}{2}$ rather than j. On such a plot, all four 10_4, 56^+ trajectories would coincide for large L values, but they might well separate somewhat for the lower L values.

The same problem arises in the case of the nucleon trajectory (56^+, 8_2) for which only two states are available — the nucleon and the $\frac{5}{2}^+$, presumably $L = 2$, with $j = L + \frac{1}{2}$. Here again, assuming a decreasing spin-orbit splitting with increasing L, the two trajectories corresponding to 8_2 would merge into a single trajectory if plotted against $L + \frac{1}{2}$ rather than j.

Now, *on the basis of only two points*, the $\mathfrak{N}^*_{1/2}$ trajectory corresponding to the 56^+ supermultiplet appears to have a significantly different slope from that of the $\mathfrak{N}^*_{3/2}$. If the slopes of trajectories within the same supermultiplet should be significantly different, this would indicate a strong L dependence of the constants C and D of Equation (11). However, it is also possible that this trajectory eventually merges with that of the $\mathfrak{N}^*_{3/2}$. Thus, if the (spin-parity unknown) $\mathfrak{N}^*_{1/2}(3030)$ had spin $\frac{17}{2}^+$ ($L = 8$ member of 56^+, 8_2, with $j = L + \frac{1}{2}$), it would fall on the $\mathfrak{N}^*_{3/2}$ line. [The $\mathfrak{N}^*_{1/2}(2650)$ is supposed to have negative parity, which assigns it to a 70^- supermultiplet.]

The trajectory for the $\mathfrak{N}^*_{1/2}$ corresponding to odd L (or the 70^- supermultiplets) is, as previously noted, parallel to that of the $\mathfrak{N}^*_{3/2}$ and displaced by exactly one unit of spin. However, it should be noted that its position is entirely determined by the assignment of spin $\frac{7}{2}^-$ to the $\mathfrak{N}^*_{1/2}(2190)$. For example, if this resonance were to have spin $\frac{9}{2}^-$, the appropriate trajectory might very well correspond to $J = L + \frac{3}{2}$, with the (unmeasured) spins of the two highest-mass states being $\frac{13}{2}$ and $\frac{17}{2}$, rather than the conjectured $\frac{11}{2}$ and $\frac{15}{2}$; in this case, the lowest point on the trajectory would correspond to the $\frac{5}{2}^-$ member of the 8_4 ($L = 1$), which, in fact, fits rather better on the straight line than does the $\frac{3}{2}^-$ level indicated by "1" on Figure 16.8. On the other hand, for a $\frac{5}{2}^-$ spin assignment of $\mathfrak{N}^*_{1/2}(2190)$, we could equally well have assigned the trajectory to either the 8_2 or 10_4 multiplets with $j = L - \frac{1}{2}$. Since only one $\mathfrak{N}^*_{1/2}$ state of the $L = 3$ supermultiplet is so far identified, it is impossible to decide whether or not all the 70^- trajectories become coincident (for an appropriate choice of ordinates).

Turning to the Λ^*_0 trajectories, also plotted in Figure 16.8, we note that the 56^+, 8_2 and the 70^-, 1_2 trajectories, both $j = L + \frac{1}{2}$, appear to be coincident; in addition, the 70^-, 8_4 ($\frac{5}{2}^-$), i.e., $j = L + \frac{3}{2}$, mass falls on the same trajectory. On the other hand, although the $\Lambda^*_0(\frac{1}{2}^-)$ corresponding to the 1_2 and both the $\frac{1}{2}^-$ and $\frac{3}{2}^-$ of the 8_2, $L = 1$ multiplets deviate significantly from this line, it is not possible to tell whether they lie on parallel trajectories in the absence of determination of the masses of the corresponding members of the $L = 3$ supermultiplet. Finally, we note that the $\Lambda_0^*(2350)$ mass falls right on the straight line if its spin is $\frac{9}{2}$, which would identify it as the $j=L+\frac{1}{2}$ member of the 56^+ supermultiplet with $L=4$. However, if the spin-orbit splitting decreases rapidly with L, it could also have $j=\frac{7}{2}^+$, or be a superposition of both $\frac{7}{2}^+$ and $\frac{9}{2}^+$.

The situation with respect to the Σ_1^* baryons is much more uncertain, owing to the paucity of identified levels. However, as indicated in Figure 16.9, the trajectories appear to exhibit a rather simple pattern. Thus, on the basis of only two members each, the $j=L+\frac{3}{2}$, 10_4 and $j=L+\frac{1}{2}$, 8_2 members of the 56^+ supermultiplet appear to lie on trajectories parallel to that of the $\mathfrak{N}_{3/2}^*$, 56^+. Furthermore, if we identify the $\Sigma_1^*(2250)$ as one of the members of the 70^- supermultiplet with $L=3$ (of which there are expected to be eight — two sets of ${}^2F_{5/2,7/2}$, corresponding to 8_2 and 10_2, and a quartet, ${}^4F_{3/2,5/2,7/2,9/2}$, corresponding to 8_4), it falls on a third parallel trajectory. However, although we have plotted it at $j=\frac{7}{2}$ for convenience, the indicated positions of the three identified members of the $L=1$, 70^- group demonstrate that it could equally well have been associated with the trajectories for which $\frac{1}{2}$ or $\frac{5}{2}$ are the lowest spin values. Finally, the placing of the two highest-mass resonances is entirely conjectural, although they are not inconsistent with the assignments $j=\frac{9}{2}$, $L=4$ and $j=\frac{11}{2}$, $L=4$ of the 56^+, 8_2 and 10_4, respectively.

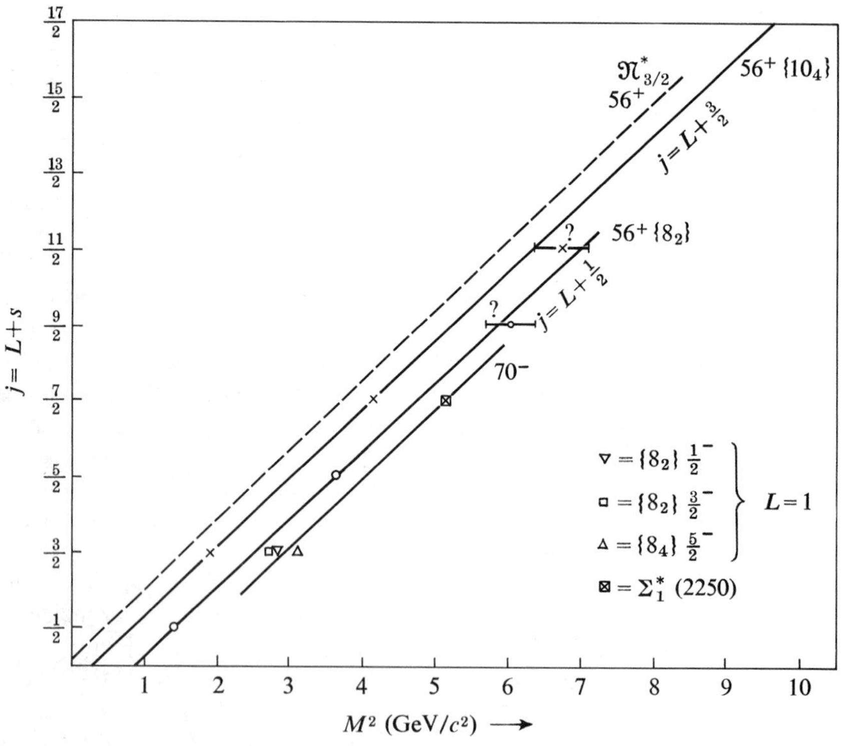

Figure 16.9 Possible Regge trajectories for Σ_1^* resonances.

Thus, with the aid of the assumption that members of the L-excited 56^+ and 70^- supermultiplets lie on straight-line (and, with the possible exception of that corresponding to the nucleon, apparently parallel) trajectories, one can find plausible identifications for all the observed baryon resonances with but one [or perhaps two, if we take seriously the $\frac{5}{2}^+$ $\Delta^*(1910)$ assignment] exception. Only the $\mathfrak{N}^*_{1/2}(1470)$, $\frac{1}{2}^+$ isobar eludes simple interpretation in terms of the model developed in the preceding. It has been conjectured [31] that it may be one of the members of the 20^+ $SU(6)$ qqq configuration corresponding to the first excited $L = 1$ $(l = l' = 1)$ configuration (see Figures 16.5 and 16.6). Since this $SU(6)$ group has the $SU(3)$ decomposition $1_4 \oplus 8_2$, the $\mathfrak{N}^*_{1/2}(1470)$ would correspond to the $j = L - \frac{1}{2}$ nucleonic member of the octet which, for some reason associated with the completely antisymmetric form of its qqq wave function with respect to both its $SU(6)$ and its space indices, may have its mass depressed by the MSI to a value far below those of the other members of this supermultiplet.

Once the spin values and other relevant quantum numbers of the resonances with $j > \frac{7}{2}$ have been experimentally determined, it will become clearer whether this and the other conjectures developed in the foregoing correspond to the realities of baryon spectroscopy.

PROBLEMS

1. Referring to the diquark-quark model of Lichtenberg, *et al.* (see Problems, Sections 15.1 and 15.2), how could you interpret the lowest lying even- and odd-parity baryons of $j \leq \frac{5}{2}$ in terms of $q \otimes q_2$? Derive the mass spectrum in terms of $M(q)$, $M(q_2)$, and their interactions.
2. Assuming the 56^+ and the 70^- multiplets can be described as the lowest $L = 0$ and $L = 1$ qqq configurations in an effective harmonic oscillator potential,

   (a) compare the matrix elements for various possible $70^- \rightarrow 56^+ + \gamma$ (electromagnetic) decays;
   (b) do the same for $70^- \rightarrow 56^+ + \pi$ or K (strong Yukawa) decays.

3. Derive the qqq wave functions for members of the 20^+ $(L = 1)$ supermultiplet.
4. Consider three levels with the same quantum numbers, which mutually perturb each other. Can you derive any simple relationship(s) for obtaining the unperturbed energy values in terms of the observed (perturbed) ones? Can such relationships be used to obtain a less ambiguous interpretation of the mass spectrum of the 70^- supermultiplet than the one given in the text?

---

[31] R. H. Dalitz, *Proceedings of the Berkeley Conference* (1966).

17

High-Energy Interactions and the Quark Model

The assumption of a compound model of observed hadrons suggests the possibility of interpreting their interactions in terms of the interactions between their constituents (Section 13.3.3). The validity of such an interpretation is not at all obvious, however, in the case of strongly interacting particles, since there is no guarantee that the constituent elements exhibit the same properties in their various compound states; nor can one discard out of hand the possibility of significant many-particle forces.

Nevertheless, such an independent particle approach has proved highly successful in the interpretation of nuclear reactions, even though its theoretical justification came considerably after the empirical demonstration of its utility. A similar independent particle approach, based on the quark model of the hadrons, appears to be capable of predictions that are usually in excellent accord with the observations, as will be indicated in this chapter.

It should be emphasized that while many, although by no means all, of the results of this application of the quark model reproduce relationships derivable from various relevant symmetry schemes — particularly $SU(6)$ and some of the attempts at its relativistic generalization — the quark model of high-energy interactions goes beyond these insofar as it provides a basis for the introduction of an interaction dynamics. Thus, we shall observe that the quark model provides a conceptual basis for some of the assumptions underlying such general approaches as the optical models or that of Regge (Chapter 11).

17.1 Forward Scattering Amplitudes and Total Cross Sections

Since forward elastic scattering involves no transfer of momentum, the application of the independent particle approximation to forward scattering is the least risky of such applications. Given the forward elastic scattering amplitude, the optical theorem leads immediately to the total cross section of the particles involved:

$$\sigma_{\text{tot},aA}(s) = \frac{4\pi}{k_a} \text{Im } T_{aA \to aA}(s, t=0). \tag{1}$$

Thus, using the suggestion of Okun and Lipkin that the forward scattering amplitude for the interaction of two hadrons can be approximated by the sum of the amplitudes of all possible quark pairs among their constituents, Levin and Frankfurt, Lipkin and Scheck, and Anisovich demonstrated that this approach does, indeed, lead to relationships in good accord with the observations.[1]

To demonstrate the approach, let us first consider the asymptotic high-energy limit, assuming that all quark-quark scattering amplitudes tend towards the same spin and isotopic-spin independent value [i.e., $SU(6)$ invariance of the forward elastic amplitudes]:

$$\langle q_i q_j | q_i q_j \rangle \cong \langle q_i \bar{q}_j | q_i \bar{q}_j \rangle \cong a, \tag{2}$$

with $i, j = 1, \cdots 6$. In this case, all meson-baryon forward scattering amplitudes become

$$\begin{aligned} \langle aA | aA \rangle &= \langle (q_i \bar{q}_j)(q_l q_m q_n) | (q_i \bar{q}_j)(q_l q_m q_n) \rangle \\ &= \sum_{l=1}^{3} \langle q_i q_l | q_i q_l \rangle + \sum_{l=1}^{3} \langle \bar{q}_j q_l | \bar{q}_j q_l \rangle \\ &\cong 6a, \end{aligned} \tag{2a}$$

while all baryon-baryon amplitudes become

$$\begin{aligned} \langle AB | AB \rangle &= \langle (q_i q_j q_k)(q_l q_m q_n) | (q_i q_j q_k)(q_l q_m q_n) \rangle \\ &\cong 9a, \end{aligned} \tag{2b}$$

or

$$\begin{aligned} \langle \bar{A}B | \bar{A}B \rangle &= \langle (\bar{q}_i \bar{q}_j \bar{q}_k)(q_l q_m q_n) | (\bar{q}_i \bar{q}_j \bar{q}_k)(q_l q_m q_n) \rangle \\ &\cong 9a. \end{aligned} \tag{2c}$$

Hence, in the "Pomeranchuk limit," this model yields the following relationships among the observable (total) cross sections:

$$\begin{aligned} \sigma(\pi^\pm P) &\cong \sigma(\pi^\pm N) \cong \sigma(K^\pm P) \cong \sigma(K^\pm N) \cong \tfrac{2}{3}\sigma(PP) \cong \tfrac{2}{3}\sigma(NP) \\ &\cong \tfrac{2}{3}\sigma(\Lambda P) \cong \tfrac{2}{3}\sigma(\bar{P}P) \cong \tfrac{2}{3}\sigma(\bar{N}P). \end{aligned} \tag{2d}$$

Referring to Figure 13.1, we obtain, for the values of the known cross sections at the highest available incident momentum of ≈ 20 GeV/c (with typical uncertainties of $\approx$ 1–2 mb),

---

[1] E. M. Levin and L. L. Frankfurt, *JETP Lett., 2:* 65 (1965); H. J. Lipkin and F. Scheck, *Phys. Rev. Letters, 16:* 71 (1965); V. V. Anisovich, *JETP Lett. 2:* 439 (1965).

$$\left.\begin{aligned}\sigma(\pi^- P) &\cong 25 \text{ mb}\\ \sigma(\pi^+ P) &\cong 23.5 \text{ mb}\\ \sigma(K^- P) &\cong 21 \text{ mb}\\ \sigma(K^- N) &\cong 20 \text{ mb}\\ \sigma(K^+ N) &\cong \sigma(K^+ P) \cong 17.5 \text{ mb}\end{aligned}\right\} \text{av.} = 21 \text{ mb}, \tag{2e}$$
$$\left.\begin{aligned}\sigma(\bar{P}N) &\cong 49 \text{ mb}\\ \sigma(\bar{P}P) &\cong 47.5 \text{ mb}\\ \sigma(PP) &\cong \sigma(NP) \cong 39 \text{ mb}\end{aligned}\right\} \frac{2}{3}\text{ av.} = 29 \text{ mb}.$$

Equations (2d) are clearly not too well satisfied. There are a number of rather obviously plausible possibilities for explaining the failure of Equations (2d): An incident momentum of 20 GeV/c [$s \approx 40$ (GeV)^2] is probably still significantly below the energy at which the Pomeranchuk limit prevails; thus, for example, at this energy, $\sigma(\pi^- P)$ and $\sigma(\pi^+ P)$ are still separated by ~ 1.5 mb, although the other pairs are closer. Furthermore, as is immediately observable in Figure 17.1 (which is a summary of the detailed data shown in Figure 13.1), the $\bar{\mathfrak{N}}\mathfrak{N}$ and $\mathfrak{N}\mathfrak{N}$ cross sections are still quite widely separated — by ≈ 10 mb. Thus, not only is 20 GeV/c still clearly considerably below the Pomeranchuk limit, but it is not yet obvious, from the available data, that the Pomeranchuk theorem is asymptotically valid. This question has been studied in detail by Lindenbaum [2] who suggests, as an appropriate expression for extrapolating the observed cross sections into the asymptotic region,

$$\sigma_{\text{tot}} = a + \frac{b}{p^n}, \tag{2f}$$

with the parameters shown in Table 17.1 (p is the incident *lab* momentum in GeV/c). Considering the values of a from the table ($\frac{2}{3}a_{\mathfrak{N}\mathfrak{N}} = 25.4$ mb) and taking some mean of the values of σ_{K^-P} and σ_{K^+P} from Equation (2e), as representing a good approximation to the asymptotic $K\mathfrak{N}$ cross sections, we conclude that Equations (2d) are probably not even asymptotically satisfied.

However, there is really no a priori reason why all quark pairs must exhibit the same forward scattering amplitude. Thus, Figure 17.1 would appear to indicate that there is an appreciable difference between the scattering amplitude for nucleonic quarks (p or n) on nucleonic quarks and the scattering amplitude for nucleonic quarks on the λ quark, as well as between nucleonic quarks on nucleonic quarks and nucleonic quarks on antinucleonic quarks. Such differences are not surprising, in view of the differences between the quark masses and quark bindings required to account for the $SU(3)$-violating mass differences between hadrons in the same $SU(3)$ multiplet, and the difference between the qq and $q\bar{q}$ bindings required to account for the scale of baryon and meson masses.

[2] S. J. Lindenbaum, *Proceedings of the Conference on $\pi\mathfrak{N}$ Scattering,* University of California, Irvine (December 1967). Lindenbaum refers to the still remote region, at which the Pomeranchuk theorem is presumably satisfied, as "asymptopia," and estimates that its achievement requires an incident *lab* energy of $\gtrsim$ 20,000 GeV.

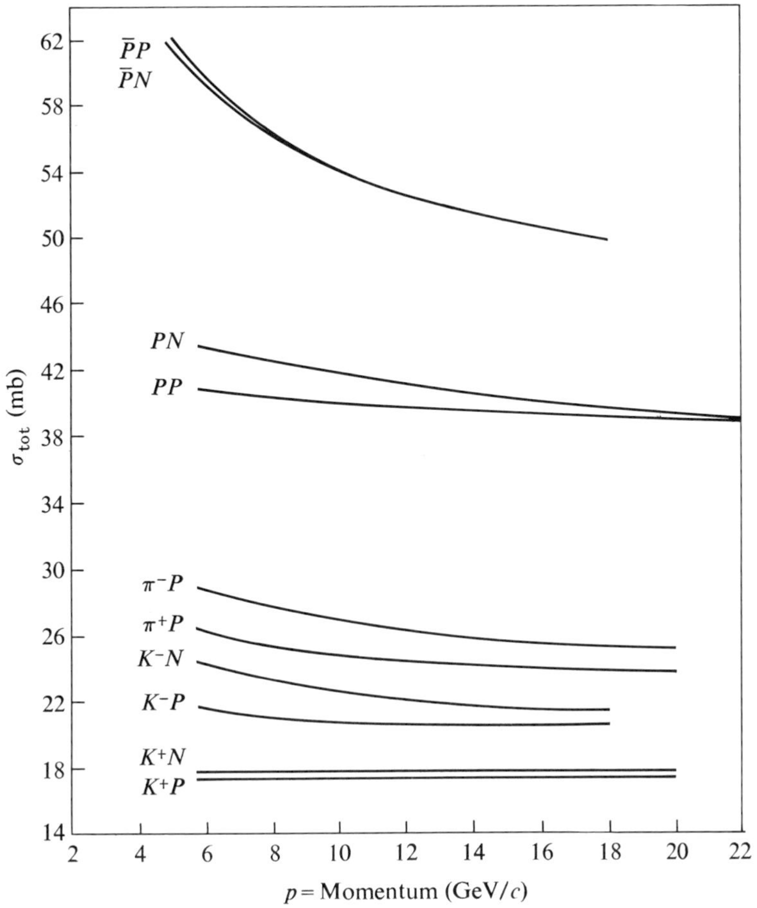

Figure 17.1 σ_{tot} for hadron-hadron interactions.

Table 17.1 Parameters[a] for Extrapolating σ_{tot} to Infinite p, According to $\sigma_{tot} = a + b/p^n$

Incident particles	a (mb)	b [in mb (GeV/c)^n]	n
π^-P	22.72	20.33	0.697
π^+P	22.72	28.99	1.128
$\bar{P}P$	38.15	91.5	0.74
PP	38.15	14.16	0.92

[a] After Lindenbaum, *Proceedings of the Conference on $\pi\mathfrak{N}$ Scattering,* University of California, Irvine (December 1967).

17.1.1 Charge-Independent Approximation

We may take into account the possibility of differences among the quark scattering properties by assigning different amplitudes to the different qq combinations while preserving, however, the consequences of isotopic-spin invariance (charge independence), which requires the p and n quarks to behave as members of an isotopic doublet. The most general [3] set of forward qq scattering amplitudes under this condition (and also satisfying the conditions of charge-conjugation invariance) is:

$$\langle pp|pp\rangle = \langle nn|nn\rangle = \langle \overline{pp}|\overline{pp}\rangle = \langle \overline{nn}|\overline{nn}\rangle = a, \tag{3a}$$

$$\langle pn|pn\rangle = \langle np|np\rangle = \tfrac{1}{2}(a+b), \tag{3b}$$

$$\langle pn|np\rangle = \langle np|pn\rangle = \tfrac{1}{2}(a-b), \tag{3c}$$

$$\langle p\lambda|p\lambda\rangle = \langle n\lambda|n\lambda\rangle = c, \tag{3d}$$

$$\langle p\overline{\lambda}|p\overline{\lambda}\rangle = \langle n\overline{\lambda}|n\overline{\lambda}\rangle = \overline{c}, \tag{3e}$$

$$\langle p\lambda|\lambda p\rangle = \langle n\lambda|\lambda n\rangle = c', \tag{3f}$$

$$\langle \overline{p}n|\overline{p}n\rangle = \langle \overline{n}p|\overline{n}p\rangle = \overline{a}, \tag{3g}$$

$$\langle \overline{p}p|\overline{p}p\rangle = \langle \overline{n}n|\overline{n}n\rangle = \tfrac{1}{2}(\overline{a}+\overline{b}), \tag{3h}$$

$$\langle \overline{p}p|\overline{n}n\rangle = \langle \overline{n}n|\overline{p}p\rangle = -\tfrac{1}{2}(\overline{a}-\overline{b}), \tag{3i}$$

$$\langle \lambda\lambda|\lambda\lambda\rangle = d, \tag{3j}$$

$$\langle \overline{\lambda}\lambda|\overline{\lambda}\lambda\rangle = \overline{d}, \tag{3k}$$

$$\langle \overline{p}p|\overline{\lambda}\lambda\rangle = \langle \overline{n}n|\overline{\lambda}\lambda\rangle = \overline{e}. \tag{3l}$$

The quark amplitudes defined in Equations (3a)–(3l), taken in conjunction with the Okun–Lipkin *ansatz*, lead to the forward scattering amplitudes for the observable hadron-hadron reactions summarized in column 2 of Table 17.2. In deriving these amplitudes, we have assumed the quark combinations for hadrons given in Table 15.2. Thus, for example, considering the reaction $\pi^-P \to \pi^-P$, we have

$$\begin{aligned}\langle \pi^-P|\pi^-P\rangle &= \langle (n\overline{p})(ppn)|(n\overline{p})(ppn)\rangle \\ &= 2\,\langle np|np\rangle + \langle nn|nn\rangle + 2\,\langle \overline{p}p|\overline{p}p\rangle + \langle \overline{p}n|\overline{p}n\rangle \\ &= (a+b) + a + (\overline{a}+\overline{b}) + \overline{a} \\ &= 2(a+\overline{a}) + (b+\overline{b}).\end{aligned} \tag{4}$$

---

[3] Since, at this stage, we are considering elastic amplitudes only, we are omitting the possibility of spin-flip processes, and therefore neglecting completely the possible spin dependence of the scattering amplitudes. This will be taken into account at a later stage, when we consider inelastic reactions. By the same token, charge or hypercharge exchange amplitudes, such as (3c, f, i, l), will not play any role in the evaluation of the forward elastic scattering amplitudes and corresponding total cross sections. We also neglect those quark exchange amplitudes that require the exchange of two units of strangeness, e.g., $\langle \lambda\overline{\lambda}|\overline{\lambda}\lambda\rangle \approx 0$, or of two units of baryon number, e.g., $\langle \overline{pn}|\overline{np}\rangle \approx 0$.

Table 17.2 Forward Elastic Scattering Amplitudes for Observable Hadron-Hadron Interactions According to the Quark Model

Process	Forward amplitude	Lipkin's hypothesis
$\langle \pi^+ P \vert \pi^+ P \rangle$	$\frac{5}{2}(a+\bar{a})+\frac{1}{2}(b+\bar{b})$	$6P+A$
$\langle \pi^- P \vert \pi^- P \rangle$	$2(a+\bar{a})+(b+\bar{b})$	$6P+2A$
$\langle \pi^- P \vert \pi^0 N \rangle$	$(\sqrt{2}/4)(a+\bar{a}-b-\bar{b})$	$-\sqrt{\frac{1}{2}}A$
$\langle K^+ P \vert K^+ P \rangle$	$\frac{5}{2}a+\frac{1}{2}b+3\bar{c}$	$6P-3S \cong 6P-A$
$\langle K^+ N \vert K^+ N \rangle$	$2a+b+3\bar{c}$	$6P-3S \cong 6P-A$
$\langle K^+ N \vert K^0 P \rangle$	$\frac{1}{2}(a-b)$	0
$\langle K^- N \vert K^- N \rangle$	$\frac{5}{2}\bar{a}+\frac{1}{2}\bar{b}+3c$	$6P+A-3S \cong 6P$
$\langle K^- P \vert K^- P \rangle$	$2\bar{a}+\bar{b}+3c$	$6P+2A-3S \cong 6P+A$
$\langle K^- P \vert \overline{K^0} N \rangle$	$\frac{1}{2}(\bar{a}-\bar{b})$	$-A$
$\langle PP \vert PP \rangle$	$7a+2b$	$9P$
$\langle PN \vert PN \rangle$	$\frac{13}{2}a+\frac{5}{2}b$	$9P$
$\langle PN \vert NP \rangle$	$\frac{1}{2}(a-b)$	0
$\langle \bar{P}N \vert \bar{P}N \rangle$	$7\bar{a}+2\bar{b}$	$9P+4A$
$\langle \bar{P}P \vert \bar{P}P \rangle$	$\frac{13}{2}\bar{a}+\frac{5}{2}\bar{b}$	$9P+5A$
$\langle \bar{P}P \vert \bar{N}N \rangle$	$-\frac{1}{2}(\bar{a}-\bar{b})$	A
$\langle \Lambda P \vert \Lambda P \rangle$	$\frac{9}{2}a+\frac{3}{2}b+3c$	$9P-3S \cong 9P-A$
$\langle \rho^0 P \vert \rho^0 P \rangle$, $\langle \omega^0 P \vert \omega^0 P \rangle$	$\frac{3}{4}(3a+b+3\bar{a}+\bar{b})$	$6P+\frac{3}{2}A$
$\langle \phi^0 P \vert \phi^0 P \rangle$	$3c+3\bar{c}$	$6P-6S \cong 6P-2A$

Considering the forward scattering amplitudes (or, for given k_a, the total cross sections) exhibited in column 2, we may attempt to find relationships among the total cross sections for the hadrons involved. These are of two types:

1. Connections among average cross sections, which are the generalization for the quark model of the asymptotic relations (2):

$$\Sigma(\pi P) \equiv \sigma(\pi^+ P) + \sigma(\pi^- P) = \tfrac{1}{3}[\sigma(PP) + \sigma(\bar{P}P) + \sigma(PN) + \sigma(\bar{P}N)]$$
$$= \tfrac{1}{3}[\Sigma(PP) + \Sigma(PN)], \qquad \text{(5a)}$$

and

$$\Sigma(PP) \equiv \sigma(PP) + \sigma(\bar{P}P) = \tfrac{3}{2}[\sigma(\pi^+ P) + \sigma(\pi^- P)] + \tfrac{1}{2}[\sigma(K^+ P) - \sigma(K^+ N)]$$
$$+ \tfrac{1}{2}[\sigma(K^- P) - \sigma(K^- N)]$$
$$= \tfrac{3}{2}\Sigma(\pi P) + \tfrac{1}{2}[\Sigma(KP) - \Sigma(KN)], \qquad \text{(5b)}$$

where, by definition,

$$\Sigma(AB) \equiv \sigma(AB) + \sigma(\bar{A}B). \qquad \text{(5c)}$$

Comparisons between the two sides of Equations (5a) and (5b) over the energy range 5–20 GeV are shown in Figure 17.2(a). Although the agreement is still only fair, the discrepancies at the highest energy (~ 15–20 percent) are appreciably less than the $\gtrsim 30$ percent differences previously indicated by the values of (2e).

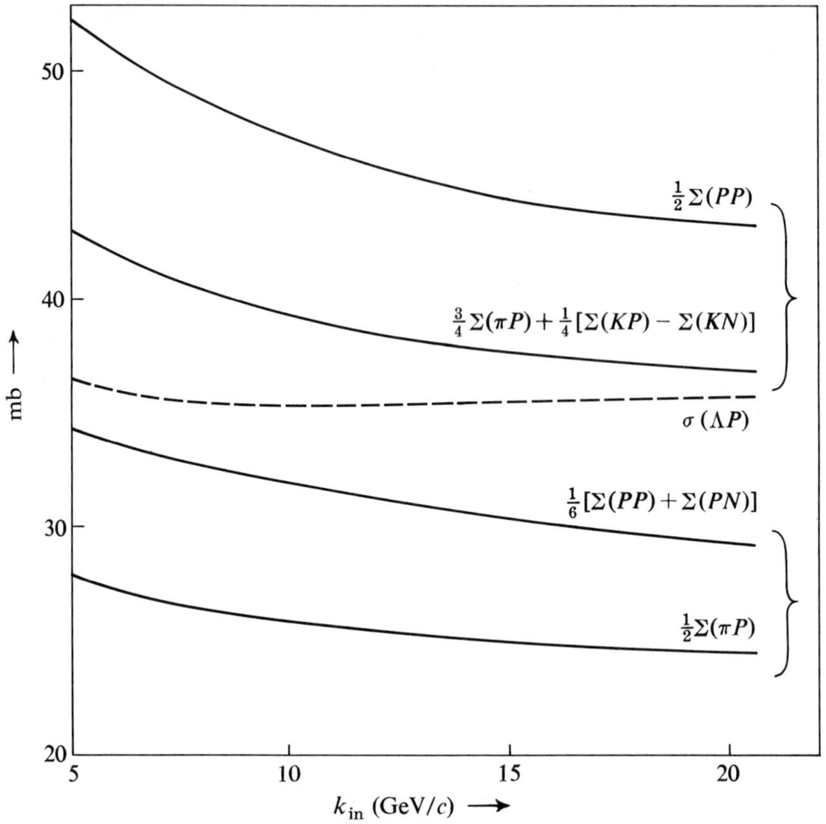

50
40
30
20
mb →
$\frac{1}{2}\Sigma(PP)$
$\frac{3}{4}\Sigma(\pi P)+\frac{1}{4}[\Sigma(KP)-\Sigma(KN)]$
$\sigma(\Lambda P)$
$\frac{1}{6}[\Sigma(PP)+\Sigma(PN)]$
$\frac{1}{2}\Sigma(\pi P)$
5
10
15
20
k_{in} (GeV/c) →

(a)

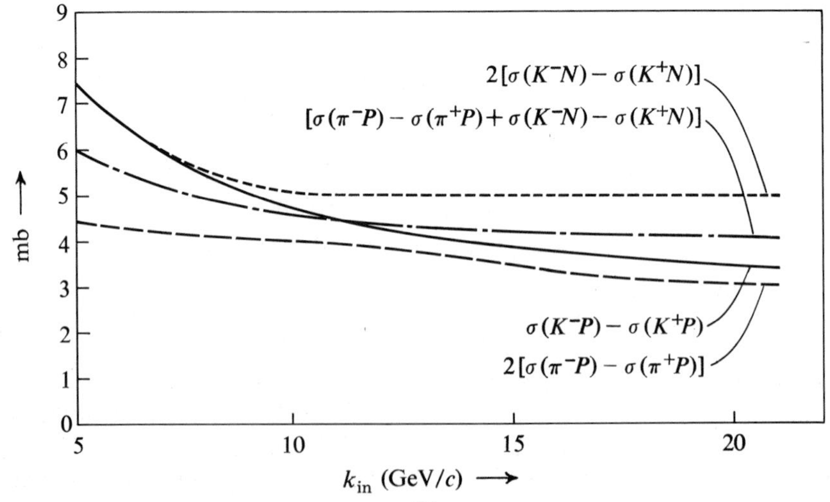

9
8
7
6
5
4
3
2
1
0
mb →
$2[\sigma(K^-N)-\sigma(K^+N)]$
$[\sigma(\pi^-P)-\sigma(\pi^+P)+\sigma(K^-N)-\sigma(K^+N)]$
$\sigma(K^-P)-\sigma(K^+P)$
$2[\sigma(\pi^-P)-\sigma(\pi^+P)]$
5
10
15
20
k_{in} (GeV/c) →

(b)

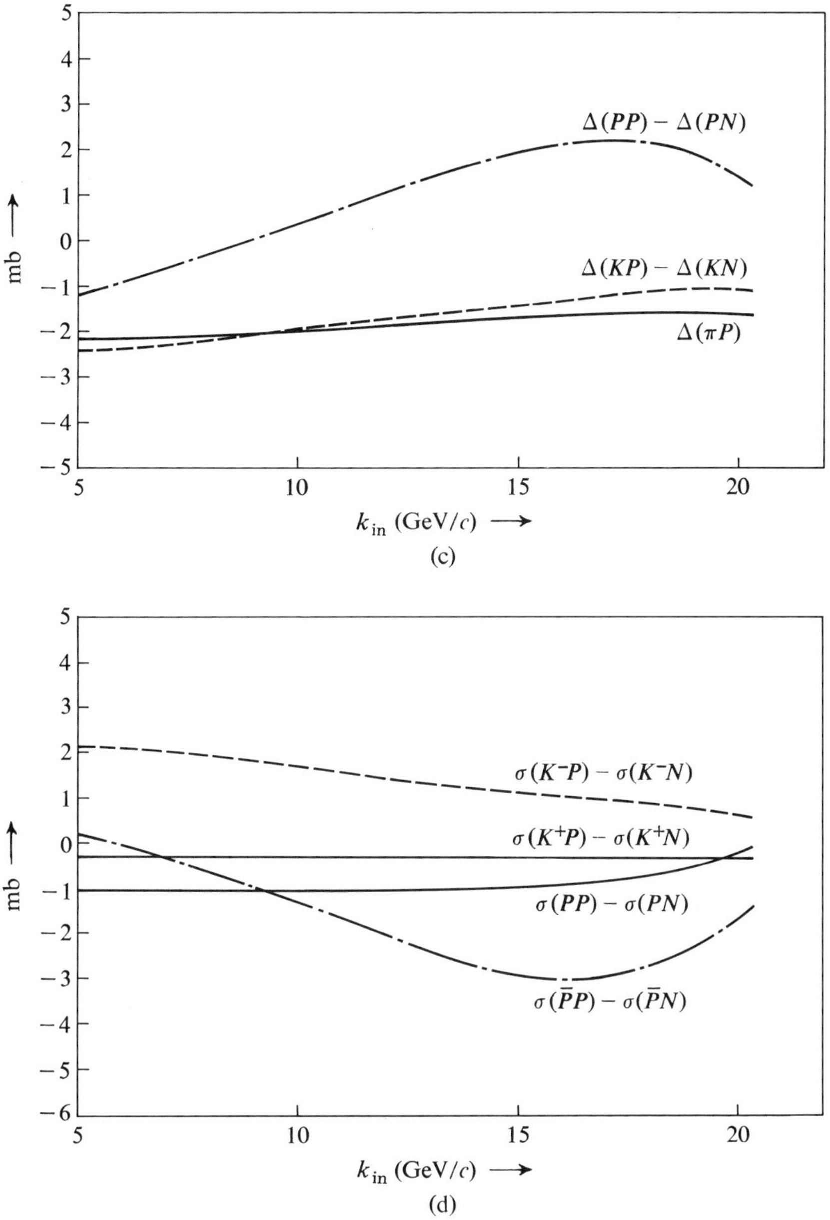

Figure 17.2 Comparison between quark-model predictions and experiments for total hadron-hadron cross sections. (a) Relations among average cross sections [Equations (5a) and (5b)]. Also shown is the value of the predicted ΛP cross section [Equation (7)]. (b) Relations among meson-nucleon cross sections [Equation (6a)], compared to the $SU(6)$ (Johnson–Treiman) predictions [Equations (6c) and (6d)]. (c) Relations among cross section differences [Equations (6a) and (6b)]. (d) $\Delta(K\mathfrak{N})$, $\Delta(\pi P)$, and $\Delta(P\mathfrak{N})$ comparison [Equations (6e) and (6f)].

2. Connections between cross-section differences:

$$\Delta(\pi P) = \sigma(\pi^+P) - \sigma(\pi^-P) = \sigma(K^+P) - \sigma(K^-P) - \sigma(K^+N) + \sigma(K^-N)$$
$$= \Delta(KP) - \Delta(KN), \tag{6a}$$

and

$$\Delta(\pi P) = \sigma(PP) - \sigma(\bar{P}P) - \sigma(PN) + \sigma(\bar{P}N) = \Delta(PP) - \Delta(PN), \tag{6b}$$

with

$$\Delta(AB) \equiv \sigma(AB) - \sigma(\bar{A}B). \tag{6c}$$

Equation (6a) also can be obtained from the sum of two relationships (the Johnson–Treiman relationships) derivable as a consequence of unbroken $SU(6)$ symmetry:

$$\Delta(KP) = 2\Delta(KN) = 2\Delta(\pi P), \tag{6d}$$

neither of which, alone, follows from Table 17.2. Comparison of the experimental values of $\sigma(K^-P) - \sigma(K^+P)$ with the predictions of Equations (6a) and (6d) is shown in Figure 17.2(b), while the predictions of the quark model, Equations (6a) and (6b), are compared with experiment in Figure 17.2(c).

We note that all the relations involving meson-nucleon reactions — both the quark model result (6a) and the $SU(6)$, Johnson–Treiman relations (6d) — agree quite well[4] with the experiments, while the relation involving the baryon cross sections (6b) does not do so well. This observation is borne out by comparison with experiment of the two other quark-model predictions

$$\sigma(K^+P) - \sigma(K^+N) = \sigma(PP) - \sigma(PN), \tag{6e}$$

$$\sigma(K^-P) - \sigma(K^-N) = \sigma(\bar{P}P) - \sigma(\bar{P}N), \tag{6f}$$

as shown in Figure 17.2(d). It would appear from Figure 17.2(d) that the main problems are associated with the $(\mathfrak{N}\mathfrak{N})$ cross sections. Whether these deficiencies, as well as the discrepancies in the experimental comparisons with Equations (5a), (5b), and (6b), will disappear with further experiments, especially at higher energies, is a matter of conjecture. However, the good agreement between experiment and the Johnson–Treiman relations, Equations (6d) and Figure 17.2(b), indicate that the generalized quark model may be unnecessarily unconstrained. We consider in the following section a more restrictive approach, due to Lipkin, in which some features of $SU(3)$ invariance are taken into account.

However, before concluding consideration of the unrestricted approach, it is worth noting a few other relations that may be deduced from Table 17.2, column 2. Thus, on the same basis, we may derive expressions for the total cross sections of any two hadrons belonging to either the $SU(6)$ 35-plet meson or 56-plet baryon representations (Table 15.2). Among the baryon-baryon cross

---

[4] We recall that the experimental uncertainties are ~ 1–2 mb.

sections, $\sigma(\Lambda P)$ is amenable to experimental investigation. The quark model predicts

$$\sigma(\Lambda P) = \sigma(PP) + \sigma(K^-N) - \sigma(\pi^+P), \tag{7}$$

and the predicted values of $\sigma(\Lambda P)$ are shown in Figure 17.2(a). In addition, still assuming spin independence, an assumption that will be examined in a later section, we may predict the values of the vector-meson–nucleon cross sections:

$$\sigma(\rho^\pm\mathfrak{N}) = \sigma(\pi^\pm\mathfrak{N}), \tag{8a}$$

$$\sigma(\rho^0\mathfrak{N}) = \sigma(\omega^0\mathfrak{N}) = \tfrac{1}{2}[\sigma(\pi^+\mathfrak{N}) + \sigma(\pi^-\mathfrak{N})] = \tfrac{1}{2}\Sigma(\pi\mathfrak{N}), \tag{8b}$$

$$\sigma(\phi^0P) = \tfrac{1}{2}[\Sigma(KP) + \Sigma(KN) - \Sigma(\pi P)], \tag{8c}$$

$$\sigma(K^*\mathfrak{N}) = \sigma(K\mathfrak{N}). \tag{8d}$$

17.1.2 Broken *SU*(3): Lipkin's Approximation

Short of the extreme assumption of complete $SU(3)$ symmetry for the scattering amplitudes, which leads to the asymptotic relationships explored in Equations (2a) through (2f), we may consider the possibility of an approximate $SU(3)$ symmetry, broken only in ways that are consistent with those leading to the mass differences within $SU(3)$ multiplets. Thus, for example, if we assume[5] $c \cong \bar{c}$ in Equations (3d) and (3e), this leads (Table 17.2) to the additional relationship

$$3[\Delta(KP) + \Delta(KN)] = \Delta(PP) + \Delta(PN). \tag{9}$$

Comparison of Equation (9) with experiment, Figure 17.3(a), indicates rather poor agreement in the intermediate energy range. However, as in the case of the discrepancies encountered in the relationship (6f), Figure 17.2(d), it is likely that the observed differences stem from the experimental problems associated with the measurement of $\sigma(\bar{P}N)$.

The Pomeranchuk theorem leads to the expectation that, at sufficiently high energy, the differences between a and b, and $\bar{a}$ and $\bar{b}$, should tend toward zero (vanishing of the charge-exchange amplitudes); however, the problem of the isotopic-spin dependence of the qq amplitudes is different from that of the $q\bar{q}$ since, in the case of the latter, there is the additional annihilation channel ($p\bar{p} \to n\bar{n}$ or $\lambda\bar{\lambda}$, etc.) whose presence can give rise to differences between $\bar{a}$, $\bar{b}$, and $\bar{d}$ [Equations (3g), (3h), and (3k)]. The difference between a and $\bar{a}$ or b and $\bar{b}$, on the other hand, arise in addition from the same interaction differences that lead to the differences in binding between the qq and $q\bar{q}$ combinations.

In the circumstance, it is useful to resort to the empirical evidence on the scattering cross sections for the resolution of the questions posed in the previous paragraph. One of the outstanding features (see Figure 17.1) of the observations is the relatively small difference over the entire energy range between

[5] U-spin invariance ($n \longleftrightarrow \lambda$) within the quark triplet would lead to the relationships $c = \frac{1}{2}(a + b)$ and $\bar{c} = \bar{a}$. However, since it is precisely the U-spin violating MSI that give rise to the mass splittings, this is not a reasonable set of connections to adopt.

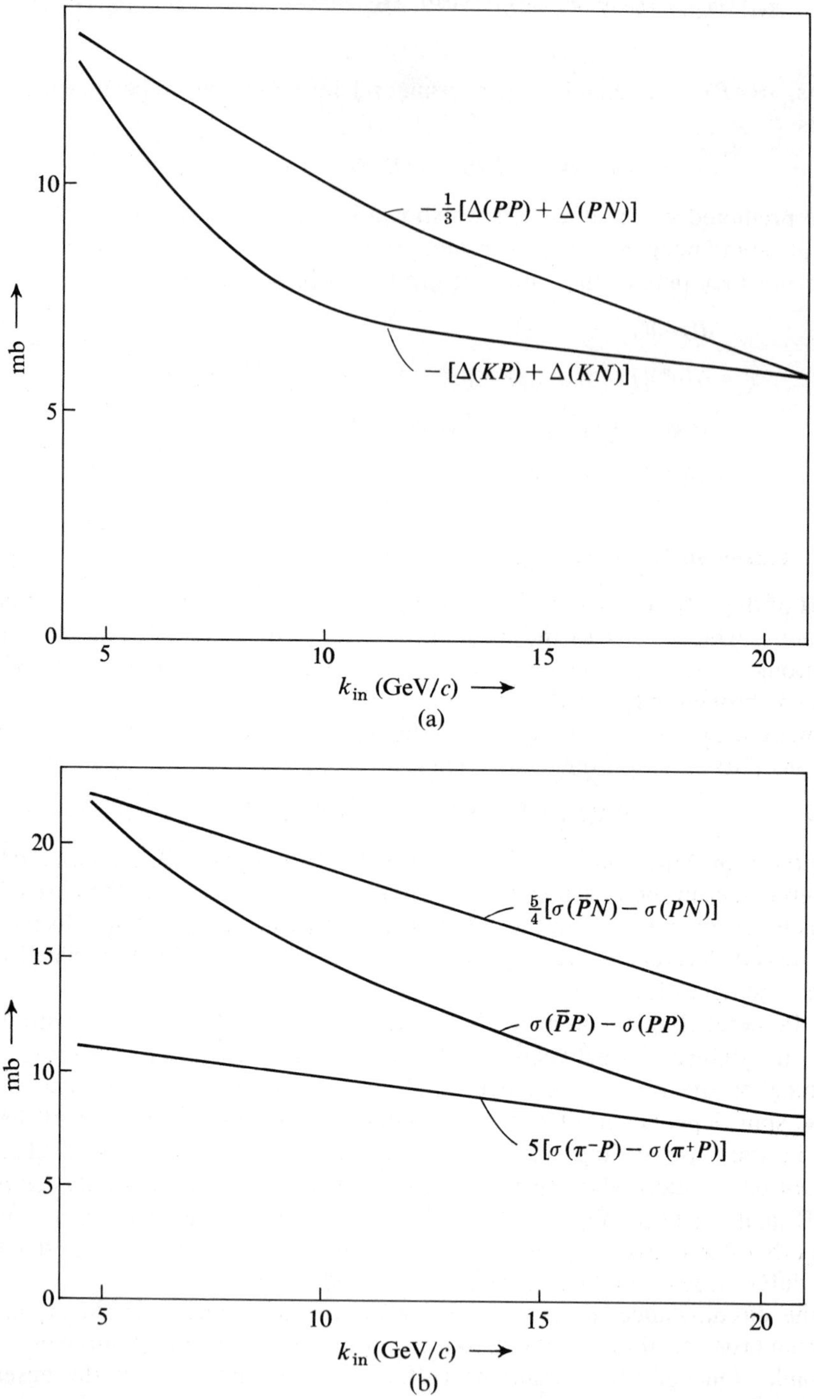

Figure 17.3 Comparison between restricted quark-model predictions (Lipkin's approximation) and experiment for total hadron-hadron cross sections. (a) $\Delta(P\mathfrak{N})$ and $\Delta(K\mathfrak{N})$ [Equation (9)]. (b) Relations between $\pi^{\pm}\mathfrak{N}$ and $\mathfrak{N}\mathfrak{N}$, $\overline{\mathfrak{N}}\mathfrak{N}$ cross sections [Equation (10)].

$\sigma(K^+P)$ and $\sigma(K^+N)$, as well as between $\sigma(PN)$ and $\sigma(PP)$. Since both these differences are equal to $\frac{1}{2}(b-a)$, see Table 17.2, we may take, as a good first approximation, $b \cong a$. Combining this assumption with the assumption $\bar{c} \cong c$, we may now invoke the success of the Johnson–Treiman relations, Equations (6d) and Figure 17.2(b), to arrive at an additional empirical relationship, $a \cong \bar{a}$. Taken all together, this evidence is consistent with the assumption that the universal $qq = q\bar{q}$ asymptotic interaction is moderated by a slight reduction for the case when one (or more) of the quarks is λ, and by a difference in the $q\bar{q}$ annihilation channel, which is assumed to affect the isoscalar amplitude only.

This set of connections between the qq and $q\bar{q}$ forward scattering amplitudes, empirically arrived at through the considerations of the preceding paragraph, comprises Lipkin's approximation, which may be expressed in terms of three parameters, P, A, and S.

$$\langle pp|pp\rangle = \langle nn|nn\rangle = P, \tag{3a'}$$

$$\langle pn|pn\rangle = \langle np|np\rangle = P, \tag{3b'}$$

$$\langle pn|np\rangle = \langle np|pn\rangle = 0, \tag{3c'}$$

$$\langle p\lambda|p\lambda\rangle = \langle n\lambda|n\lambda\rangle = P - S, \tag{3d'}$$

$$\langle p\bar{\lambda}|p\bar{\lambda}\rangle = \langle n\bar{\lambda}|n\bar{\lambda}\rangle = P - S, \tag{3e'}$$

$$\langle p\lambda|\lambda p\rangle = \langle n\lambda|\lambda n\rangle \approx 0, \tag{3f'}$$

$$\langle \bar{p}n|\bar{p}n\rangle = \langle \bar{n}p|\bar{n}p\rangle = P, \tag{3g'}$$

$$\langle \bar{p}p|\bar{p}p\rangle = \langle \bar{n}n|\bar{n}n\rangle = P + A, \tag{3h'}$$

$$\langle \bar{p}p|\bar{n}n\rangle = \langle \bar{n}n|\bar{p}p\rangle = A, \tag{3i'}$$

$$\langle \lambda\lambda|\lambda\lambda\rangle = \frac{(P-S)^2}{P} \approx P - 2S, \tag{3j'}$$

$$\langle \bar{\lambda}\lambda|\bar{\lambda}\lambda\rangle = \frac{(P+A)(P+S)^2}{P^2} \approx P - 2S + A, \tag{3k'}$$

$$\langle \bar{p}p|\bar{\lambda}\lambda\rangle = \langle \bar{n}n|\bar{\lambda}\lambda\rangle = \frac{A(P-S)}{P}. \tag{3l'}$$

The consequences of Equations (3a′) through (3l′) for the forward scattering amplitudes (total cross sections) of observable processes are shown in column 3 of Table 17.2. These naturally lead to all the relationships obtained in the preceding, including the Johnson–Treiman relations. In addition, we obtain the relation

$$\Delta(\pi P) = \tfrac{1}{5}\Delta(PP) = \tfrac{1}{4}\Delta(PN), \tag{10}$$

which is compared with the experiments in Figure 17.3(b).

Finally, we take note of another empirical relationship,

$$\sigma(\pi^- P) - \sigma(K^- N) \cong 2[\sigma(K^- N) - \sigma(K^+ P)], \tag{10a}$$

which holds to within $\lesssim$ 10 percent over the entire 5–20 GeV/c energy range. This suggests an additional relationship among the Lipkin parameters,

$$A \cong 3S, \tag{10b}$$

whose consequences are also indicated in Table 17.2.

EXAMPLE

Formal theory:[6] The results derived in the preceding section, and summarized in Table 17.2, may be expressed formally in terms of the sums and differences of the forward quark-quark scattering amplitudes (or their equivalents, $\sigma_{\text{tot},qq}$):

$$(\Sigma, \Delta)_{ij} = \langle q_i q_j | q_i q_j \rangle \pm \langle \bar{q}_i q_j | \bar{q}_i q_j \rangle. \tag{11a}$$

Letting n_i^A be the number of q_i in A, etc. ($i, j = p, n, \lambda$), the quark model, with the assumption of additivity of amplitudes, gives

$$(\Sigma, \Delta)_{AB} = \sum_{i,j} (n_i^A \pm n_{\bar{i}}^A)(n_j^B \pm n_{\bar{j}}^B)(\Sigma, \Delta)_{ij}, \tag{11b}$$

or

$$(\Sigma, \Delta)_{AB} = \sum_{\nu=1}^{3} (\rho, \lambda)_\nu (s, d)_\nu^A (s, d)_\nu^B, \tag{11c}$$

where $(\rho, \lambda)_\nu$ are the eigenvalues of the $(\Sigma, \Delta)_{ij}$ matrices

$$(\rho, \lambda)_1 = (\Sigma, \Delta)_{pp} - (\Sigma, \Delta)_{pn}, \tag{11d}$$

$$(\rho, \lambda)_{2,3} = \tfrac{1}{2}\{(\Sigma, \Delta)_{pp} + (\Sigma, \Delta)_{pn} + (\Sigma, \Delta)_{\lambda\lambda} \pm \sqrt{[(\Sigma, \Delta)_{pp} + (\Sigma, \Delta)_{pn} - (\Sigma, \Delta)_{\lambda\lambda}]^2 + 8(\Sigma, \Delta)_{p\lambda}^2}; \tag{11e, f}$$

$(s, d)_\nu^A$ are the quark "charges" of the hadron A, etc.,

$$(s, d)_\nu^A = \sum_i C_{\nu i}(n_i^A \pm n_{\bar{i}}^A); \tag{11g}$$

and C_{ij} is the orthogonal matrix

$$\sqrt{2}\, C_{ij} = \begin{pmatrix} 1 & -1 & 0 \\ x & x & -\sqrt{2}\, y \\ y & y & \sqrt{2}\, x \end{pmatrix}, \tag{11h}$$

with

$$x = \left\{\frac{1}{2} + \frac{[(\Sigma, \Delta)_{pp} + (\Sigma, \Delta)_{pn} - (\Sigma, \Delta)_{\lambda\lambda}]}{2\sqrt{[(\Sigma, \Delta)_{pp} + (\Sigma, \Delta)_{pn} - (\Sigma, \Delta)_{\lambda\lambda}]^2 + 8(\Sigma, \Delta)_{p\lambda}^2}}\right\}^{1/2}, \tag{11i}$$

$$y = (1 - x^2)^{1/2}. \tag{11j}$$

Equations (11b), (11c), etc., contain all the results previously derived. They are very significantly simplified for certain special assumptions concerning the

[6] H. J. Lipkin, *Z. Physik, 202:* 345 (1967); J. Daboul, *Nuovo Cimento, 50A:* 850 (1967).

qq scattering amplitudes. For example, assuming $\Delta_{p\lambda} = 0$ [see Equations (3d′) and (3e′)], we get

$$\lambda_1 = \Delta_{pp} - \Delta_{pn}, \tag{11d′}$$

$$\lambda_2 = \Delta_{pp} + \Delta_{pn}, \tag{11e′}$$

$$\lambda_3 = \Delta_{\lambda\lambda}, \tag{11f′}$$

and, correspondingly,

$$x = 1, \tag{11i′}$$

$$y = 0. \tag{11j′}$$

17.1.3 Photoproduction of Vector Mesons; Justification of the Vector-Dominance Model

We have previously developed, in Sections 14.3.2 and 15.3.3, the vector-dominance model and suggested its utility in describing the photoproduction of vector mesons. According to this model [see Figure 17.4(a)], the forward amplitude for the production of vector mesons by photons is given by

$$\langle \gamma P | v^0 P \rangle = \sqrt{4\pi}\, f_{v\gamma}\, \langle v^0 P | v^0 P \rangle. \tag{12a}$$

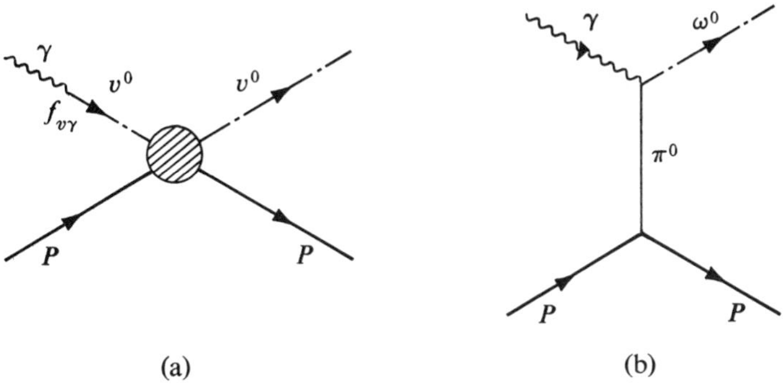

Figure 17.4 Diagrams for vector-meson photoproduction. (a) Diffraction via the vector-dominance model. (b) One-pion exchange for ω^0 production.

Since the optical theorem gives [7]

$$\langle v^0 P | v^0 P \rangle = \frac{k_\gamma}{4\pi} \sigma_{\text{tot}}(v^0 P), \tag{12b}$$

we have for the differential cross section in the forward direction

$$\begin{aligned} \frac{d\sigma}{dt}(\gamma P \to v^0 P)_{\theta=0} &= \frac{\pi}{k_\gamma^2} \frac{d\sigma}{d\Omega}(\gamma P \to v_0 P)_{\theta=0} \\ &= \tfrac{1}{4} f_{v\gamma}^2\, \sigma_{\text{tot}}^2(v^0 P). \end{aligned} \tag{12c}$$

[7] Assuming a purely imaginary forward amplitude.

Now, the values of $f_{v\gamma}$ are given by the vector-dominance model, Table 15.13,

$$f_{v\gamma} = (\sqrt{2}\, Q_v)\left(\frac{m_\pi}{m_v}\right), \tag{12d}$$

while the values of $\sigma_{\text{tot}}(v^0P)$ are predicted by our quark model, Equations (8b) and (8c), thus permitting the computation of $(d\sigma/dt)(\gamma P \to v^0P)_0$. These predictions are compared with the observed values in Table 17.3.

Generally speaking, the observed $\gamma \to v^0$ cross sections are given, at least for small t, by the expression

$$\frac{d\sigma}{dt}(\gamma \to v^0) = A\; e^{at}. \tag{12e}$$

It is the values of A in Table 17.3(b) which are to be compared with the predictions in Table 17.3(a).[8] From Equation (12a), we expect that $a(\gamma \to v^0)$ should be the same as $a(v^0 \to v^0)$, which, according to the quark model, should be essentially the same as $a(\pi \to \pi) \approx 8\ (\text{GeV}/c)^{-2}$, at least for the photoproduction of ρ^0 and ω^0. This is indeed found to be the case. For φ^0 production, on the other hand, the measured values of $a(\gamma \to \varphi^0)$ turn out to be rather smaller, although the significance of this result, both experimentally and theoretically, is not yet clear.

Assuming Equation (12e), the total cross section for vector-meson production becomes

$$a\;\sigma(\gamma \to v^0) \cong A\; e^{-|at|_{\min}}. \tag{12f}$$

This is consistent with the results given in Table 17.3(b).

We note that the "mystery" of the small ϕ^0 photoproduction is now essentially resolved; it originates in part from the reduction of $f_{\phi\gamma}$ due to the larger value of m_ϕ, but mainly from the reduced ϕP scattering cross section due to the smaller scattering amplitude for λ quarks.

Another prediction of the vector-dominance model is that the total $\gamma \to v^0$ cross section, being a diffraction scattering effect, should be essentially energy inde-

Table 17.3 Comparison of Predicted and Observed Cross Sections for Photoproduction of Vector Mesons

(a) *Predictions of the Quark Model*

$k_{\gamma,lab}$ (GeV/c)	$\sigma_{\text{tot}}(v^0P)$ (mb)		$\frac{d\sigma}{dt}(\gamma P \to v^0P)_{\theta=0}$ (μb/GeV²)		
	$v^0 = \rho^0$ or ω^0	φ^0	$v^0 = \rho^0$	ω^0	φ^0
5	27.7	13.7	110	11.7	3.4
10	25.7	13.0	94	10.1	3.1
15	24.8	13.5	88	9.4	3.3
20	24.3	13.7	84	9.0	3.4

[8] Strictly speaking, it is $A\,e^{-|at|_{\min}}$, but $|at|_{\min} \ll 1$ for the photon energies under consideration.

Table 17.3 *(continued)*

(b) *Some Experimental Results* [a]

$k_{\gamma,lab}$ (GeV/c)	A (μb/GeV^2)	a (GeV^{-2})	$\sigma_{tot}(\gamma \to v_0)$ (μb)
(i) $\gamma \to \rho^0$			
$2 - 5.8$ [b]			$(18.2 \pm 1.7)\, E_\gamma^{-0.08\pm0.07}$
$3.2 - 4.4$ [c]	125 ± 15	8.1 ± 1.5	14.6 ± 1.8
$2.5 - 6.0$ [d]			16 ± 1.6
$2.5 - 3.5$ [b]	147 ± 13	6.9 ± 0.4	17.8 ± 2.0
$3.5 - 4.5$ [b]	149 ± 18	8.1 ± 0.7	16.4 ± 2.0
$4.5 - 5.8$ [b]	130 ± 16	7.9 ± 0.7	16.0 ± 2.0
4.3 [e]			14.0 ± 2.0
5.2 [e]			16.0 ± 2.5
6.5 [e]	146 ± 50	10.0 ± 1.5 (3.7 ± 1.3)	
7.5 [e]			14.4 ± 2.5
$11.5 - 17.8$ [e]	82 ± 13	8.2 ± 0.6 (1.7 ± 0.6)	
(ii) $\gamma \to \omega^0$			
$2.1 - 5.8$ [b]			$(18.4 \pm 5.8)\, E_\gamma^{-1.6} + (1.9 \pm 0.9)\, E_\gamma^{-0.08}$
$2.5 - 3.5$ [b] }			4.8 ± 0.8
$3.5 - 4.5$ [b] }	28.4 ± 5.2	7.6 ± 1.2	3.6 ± 0.6
$4.5 - 5.8$ [b] }			3.1 ± 0.7
$2.5 - 6.0$ [d]			2.4 ± 0.5
(iii) $\gamma \to \varphi^0$			
$2.5 - 3.5$ [b] }	1.6 ± 0.6	3.5 ± 0.9	0.41 ± 0.14
$3.5 - 5.8$ [b] }			0.45 ± 0.13
5.2 [f]	2.7 ± 0.5		
$9 - 15$ [e]		~ 5	< 1.2

[a] See report of S. C. C. Ting, *Proceedings of the 14th International Conference on High-Energy Physics*, Vienna (September 1968). Constants refer to the expression $d\sigma/dt(\gamma \to v_0) = A\, e^{at+bt^2}$ with the values of b, when measured, given in parentheses in column 3.
[b] DESY Bubble Chamber Group; see, for example, *Proceedings of Stanford Conference on Photon and Electron Interactions* (1967).
[c] DESY Spark Chamber Group, *DESY Report* F32/4 (1968).
[d] CEA Bubble Chamber Group, *Phys. Rev., 146:* 994 (1966).
[e] SLAC Counter Group; Tsai, *et al., Phys. Rev. Letters, 19:* 915 (1967); Boyarski, *et al., Phys. Rev. Letters, 20:* 877 (1968); Ballam, *et al., Bull. Am. Phys. Soc., 13:* 1442 (1968).
[f] DESY-MIT Counter Group; see, for example, J. G. Asbury, *et al., Phys. Rev. Letters, 20:* 227 (1968).

pendent. This is strikingly confirmed by the values in the table for the $\gamma \to \rho^0$ process. In the case of ω^0 photoproduction, however, it should be noted that there is an appreciable contribution, which decreases rapidly with increasing photon energy, which can be ascribed to a one-pion exchange process,[9] Figure 17.4(b). Assuming a diffraction contribution to the total $\gamma \to \omega^0$ cross section of $\approx 2\mu$b,

[9] According to the quark-model predictions for the strength of the $v\pi\gamma$ vertices, Table 15.12, the OPE contribution to the other vector-meson photoproduction cross sections should be negligible.

we note that Equation (12f) gives $A(\gamma \to \omega^0) \approx (15 \pm 7)\ \mu b/GeV^2$, which is not inconsistent with the predictions.

Further confirmation of the model is provided by Asbury, *et al.*,[10] who reverse the procedure used above to obtain $\sigma_{tot}(v^0\mathfrak{N})$ from the observed coherent photoproduction of vector mesons on complex nuclei, by comparing the production of vector mesons from a series of nuclei of different atomic weight (from Be to Pb), using an optical model to take into account the attenuation of the vector mesons on traversing nuclear matter. They obtain[11] (in the $k_\gamma = 2$–5 GeV/c energy range)

$$\sigma_{tot}(\rho^0\mathfrak{N}) = (30.7 \pm 5.3) \text{ mb}, \qquad (12g)$$

$$\sigma_{tot}(\phi^0\mathfrak{N}) = (12.0 \pm 3.9) \text{ mb}, \qquad (12h)$$

in excellent agreement with the quark-model predictions summarized in Table 17.3(a).

PROBLEMS

1. It is now possible to measure the scattering cross sections on nucleons of all the relatively stable hadrons (i.e., those which decay *via* the weak interactions). Predict the $B\mathfrak{N}$ total cross sections for $B = \Lambda^0, \Sigma^{+,-}, \Xi^{0,-}$, and Ω^-, and derive relationships among them, using the quark model according to

   (a) the unrestricted, charge-independent approximation;
   (b) Lipkin's approximation.

2. With the availability of storage rings, associated with high-energy accelerators, it should eventually become possible to measure the cross sections for π–π, π–K, and K–K collisions. Using the quark model and the available total cross sections in the 5–20 GeV energy range,

   (a) determine the range of energies of colliding beams over which it is possible to make cross-section predictions;
   (b) predict the total cross sections for the above-mentioned interactions.

3. Consider coherent vector-meson photoproduction from the complex nucleus $_ZA^N$. Assume that the distribution of nucleons in the nucleus is given by

$$\rho(\mathfrak{N}) = \text{const}, \qquad \text{for } r \le R,$$
$$\rho(\mathfrak{N}) = 0, \qquad \text{for } r > R,$$

   with

$$R = r_0 A^{1/3} \text{ fermis.}$$

   Assume, further, that $\sigma_{tot}(v^0P) = \sigma_{tot}(v^0N)$ (charge symmetry), and that any vector meson that interacts inside the nucleus goes undetected in an experiment that observes only those vector mesons produced in the strictly forward direction. Derive an expression for

---

[10] J. G. Asbury, *et al.*, *Phys. Rev. Letters, 20:* 227 (1968).

[11] Using a more complete method of analysis, which takes into account the incoherent and double scattering effects, Margolis (CERN–TH. 875, 1968) obtains, from the same data, $\sigma_{tot}(\rho^0\mathfrak{N}) = 26 \pm 3$, in even better agreement with the quark-model prediction.

$$\frac{d\sigma}{d\Omega}(\gamma A \to v^0 A)_{\theta=0}$$

as a function of A, assuming the vector-dominance model and using the eikonal approximation (see Chapter 11).

17.2 Inelastic Two-Body Amplitudes

Emboldened by the successes of the assumption of additivity of quark amplitudes in predicting the forward hadron-hadron scattering amplitudes, we may inquire into the possibility of applying the same model to the inelastic two-body processes resulting from charge- and strangeness-exchange qq interactions [Equations (3c), (3f), (3i), (3l)]. In attempting such an application of the quark-additivity approximation, however, it should be noted that even for the case of forward qq scattering, we are dealing with inelastic processes, in which appreciable momentum may be exchanged among the hadrons involved (owing to their mass differences). Accordingly, the model is on much shakier ground than in the applications of the previous section. Furthermore, we shall need to take into account these momentum transfers, both kinematically and through the introduction of appropriate dynamical corrections, which we may attempt to express in terms of multiplicative (form) factors associated with the qq amplitudes.

17.2.1 Spin-Independent Approximation

For the time being, we continue to neglect spin-flip amplitudes. Then, straightforward application to the hadron quark structures, summarized in Table 15.2, of the techniques developed in the preceding sections, using the unrestricted, charge-independent approximation, yields the amplitudes for inelastic processes summarized in Table 17.4. In addition, of course, the results for elastic scattering, given in Table 17.2, continue to apply in this approximation.

Besides the expected relationships that follow from isotopic-spin conservation, e.g.,

$$\langle K^-P|\pi^-\Sigma^+\rangle + \langle K^-P|\pi^+\Sigma^-\rangle + 2\langle K^-P|\pi^0\Sigma^0\rangle = 0, \tag{13a}$$

a number of additional general relationships emerge. Thus, for example, we obtain a general equality between $\Lambda^0(\overline{\Lambda^0})$ and $\Sigma^0(\overline{\Sigma^0})$ production amplitudes,

$$\langle aP(\overline{P})|a'\Lambda^0(\overline{\Lambda^0})\rangle = -\sqrt{3}\,\langle aP(\overline{P})|a'\Sigma^0(\overline{\Sigma^0})\rangle, \tag{13b}$$

as well as the triangular equality

$$\langle K^-P|\eta^0\Lambda^0\rangle + \sqrt{2}\,\langle K^-P|X_0^0\Lambda^0\rangle = \sqrt{3}\,\langle K^-P|\pi^0\Lambda^0\rangle. \tag{13c}$$

Equations (13a) through (13c) are consequences of $SU(3)$ invariance, of course.

Additional relationships among the forward reaction amplitudes follow from the specific assumptions of Lipkin on the qq amplitudes [Equations (3a′)–(3l′)], summarized in column 3 of Table 17.4.

Table 17.4 Forward Reaction Amplitudes for Observable Hadron-Hadron Two-Body Inelastic Interactions According to the Spin-Independent Quark Model

Process	Forward amplitude	Lipkin's approximation
$\langle\pi^- P\|\eta^0 N\rangle$	$\frac{1}{2}\sqrt{\frac{1}{6}}\,(a-b-\bar{a}+\bar{b})$	$\sqrt{\frac{1}{6}}\,A$
$\langle\pi^- P\|X^0 N\rangle$	$\frac{1}{2}\sqrt{\frac{1}{3}}\,(a-b-\bar{a}+\bar{b})$	$\sqrt{\frac{1}{3}}\,A$
$\langle\pi^+ P\|K^+\Sigma^+\rangle$	$\bar{e}$	$A(P-S)/P \cong A(1-A/3P)$
$\langle\pi^- P\|K^0\Sigma^0\rangle$	$\sqrt{\frac{1}{2}}\,\bar{e}$	$\sqrt{\frac{1}{2}}\,A(P-S)/P$
$\langle\pi^- P\|K^+\Sigma^-\rangle$ [a]	0	0
$\langle\pi^- P\|K^0\Lambda^0\rangle$ [b]	$-\sqrt{\frac{3}{2}}\,\bar{e}$	$-\sqrt{\frac{3}{2}}\,A(P-S)/P$
$\langle K^- P\|\pi^0\Sigma^0\rangle$ [b]	$-\frac{1}{2}c'$	0
$\langle K^- P\|\pi^-\Sigma^+\rangle$	c'	0
$\langle K^- P\|\eta^0\Lambda^0\rangle$	$-\bar{e}+\frac{1}{2}c'$	$-A(P-S)/P$
$\langle K^- P\|X^0\Lambda^0\rangle$	$\sqrt{\frac{1}{2}}\,(\bar{e}+c')$	$\sqrt{\frac{1}{2}}\,A(P-S)/P$
$\langle\bar{N}P\|\overline{\Sigma^0}\Sigma^+\rangle$	$\sqrt{\frac{1}{2}}\,\bar{e}$	$\sqrt{\frac{1}{2}}\,A(P-S)/P$
$\langle\bar{N}P\|\overline{\Sigma^-}\Sigma^0\rangle$	$-\sqrt{\frac{1}{2}}\,\bar{e}$	$-\sqrt{\frac{1}{2}}\,A(P-S)/P$
$\langle\bar{P}P\|\overline{\Sigma^0}\Sigma^0\rangle$	$-\frac{1}{2}\bar{e}$	$-\frac{1}{2}\,A(P-S)/P$
$\langle\bar{P}P\|\overline{\Sigma^+}\Sigma^+\rangle$	$\bar{e}$	$A(P-S)/P$
$\langle\bar{P}P\|\overline{\Lambda^0}\Lambda^0\rangle$	$-\frac{3}{2}\bar{e}$	$-\frac{3}{2}\,A(P-S)/P$
$\langle\Lambda^0 P\|\Sigma^+ N\rangle$	0	0
$\langle\Lambda^0 P\|P\Sigma^0\rangle$	$-(\sqrt{3}/2)\,c'$	0
$\langle\Lambda^0 P\|N\Sigma^+\rangle$	$(\sqrt{6}/2)\,c'$	0

[a] All amplitudes $\langle aP|a'\Sigma^-\rangle = 0$, since there is no possibility for exchange of two units of charge, as long as we neglect double quark-scattering effects.

[b] Generally, the amplitudes for Λ^0 and Σ^0 production are simply related, according to Equation (13b). Hence we have connections such as

$$\langle\bar{P}P|\overline{\Lambda^0}\Lambda^0\rangle = -\sqrt{3}\,\langle\bar{P}P|\overline{\Lambda^0}\Sigma^0\rangle = 3\langle\bar{P}P|\overline{\Sigma^0}\Sigma^0\rangle.$$

17.2.2 Introduction of Spin

The introduction of spin doubles the number of independent qq amplitudes [Equations (3a)–(3l)], since for each combination we must distinguish between scattering in the triplet and singlet spin states. Thus, for example, we have

$$\langle p_1p_1|p_1p_1\rangle = a_1, \tag{14a}$$

$$\langle p_1p_2|p_1p_2\rangle = \tfrac{1}{2}(a_1+a_0), \tag{14b}$$

$$\langle p_1p_2|p_2p_1\rangle = \tfrac{1}{2}(a_1-a_0), \tag{14c}$$

$$\langle p_1n_1|p_1n_1\rangle = \tfrac{1}{2}(a_1+b_1), \tag{14d}$$

$$\langle p_1n_1|n_1p_1\rangle = \tfrac{1}{2}(a_1-b_1), \tag{14e}$$

$$\langle p_1n_2|p_1n_2\rangle = \tfrac{1}{4}(a_1+a_0+b_1+b_0), \tag{14f}$$

$$\langle p_1n_2|p_2n_1\rangle = \tfrac{1}{4}(a_1-a_0+b_1-b_0), \tag{14g}$$

$$\langle p_1n_2|n_1p_2\rangle = \tfrac{1}{4}(a_1+a_0-b_1-b_0), \tag{14h}$$

$$\langle p_1n_2|n_2p_1\rangle = \tfrac{1}{4}(a_1-a_0-b_1+b_0), \tag{14i}$$

and so on. In general, the introduction of spin dependence leads to connections between all the members of the meson 36-plet and baryon 56-plet representations of $SU(6)$, whose wave functions are summarized in Table 15.2. Thus, for example, the possibility of quark spin-flip leads to finite values of amplitudes like $\langle \pi^+P|\pi^0\Delta^{++}\rangle$, $\langle \pi^-P|\rho^0N\rangle$, etc., with the additional complication that the amplitudes are generally different for the different possible combinations of the helicities of the particles concerned. However, for the purpose of comparison with most experiments, in which the initial particles are unpolarized and the product particle polarizations are not detected,[12] it is sufficient to consider a sum over final helicity states and average over the initial helicities. When this is done, for example, the results of Section 17.1.1, relating to elastic amplitudes, are reproduced.

Since consideration of the general case gives rise to a vast variety of amplitudes, both elastic and inelastic, we shall not attempt to list them all here. Instead, we confine ourselves to a subset of such relationships where either the mesons (a and a') or the baryons (A and A') are treated as "elementary" particles, the quark structure being taken into account for only a pair of members of the incident (a, A) and product (a' A') set. In this way, we may reduce the large set of spin-dependent amplitudes [Equations (14a)–(14i)] to somewhat more manageable subsets. Thus, for the pion-quark amplitudes,[13] we may write

$$\langle \pi^+p_1|\pi^+p_1\rangle = \langle \pi^-n_1|\pi^-n_1\rangle = \alpha_3, \tag{15a}$$

$$\langle \pi^+p_1|\pi^+p_2\rangle = \langle \pi^-n_1|\pi^-n_2\rangle = \beta_3, \tag{15b}$$

$$\langle \pi^-p_1|\pi^-p_1\rangle = \langle \pi^+n_1|\pi^+n_1\rangle = \tfrac{1}{3}\alpha_3 + \tfrac{2}{3}\alpha_1, \tag{15c}$$

$$\langle \pi^-p_1|\pi^-p_2\rangle = \langle \pi^+n_1|\pi^+n_2\rangle = \tfrac{1}{3}\beta_3 + \tfrac{2}{3}\beta_1, \tag{15d}$$

$$\langle \pi^-p_1|\pi^0n_1\rangle = \langle \pi^+n_1|\pi^0p_1\rangle = \frac{\sqrt{2}}{3}(\alpha_3 - \alpha_1), \tag{15e}$$

$$\langle \pi^-p_1|\pi^0n_2\rangle = \langle \pi^+n_1|\pi^0p_2\rangle = \frac{\sqrt{2}}{3}(\beta_3 - \beta_1), \tag{15f}$$

$$\langle \pi^-p_1|\eta^0n_1\rangle = -\langle \pi^+n_1|\eta^0p_1\rangle = \gamma, \tag{15g}$$

$$\langle \pi^-p_1|\eta^0n_2\rangle = -\langle \pi^+n_1|\eta^0p_2\rangle = \delta, \tag{15h}$$

$$\langle \pi^-p_1|K^0\lambda_1\rangle = -\langle \pi^+n_1|K^+\lambda_1\rangle = \xi, \tag{15i}$$

$$\langle \pi^-p_1|K^0\lambda_2\rangle = -\langle \pi^+n_1|K^+\lambda_2\rangle = \eta. \tag{15j}$$

Using these π–q amplitudes, we may derive the amplitudes for the variety of resulting $\pi^\pm$–P reactions shown in Table 17.5. These amplitudes are not all independent, since they are constrained [by the assumption of isospin invariance inherent in the basic amplitudes, Equations (15a) through (15j)] to conform to

[12] For observations on the angular correlations in the decay of unstable products, however, final-state helicities must be taken into consideration, of course.

[13] We leave to the reader the problem of deriving the connections between α, β, . . . and a_1, a_0, ... We also consider, for simplicity, only pseudoscalar meson products.

Table 17.5 Forward Reaction Amplitudes for $\pi^{\pm}$–P Reactions, Taking into Account Spin Dependence

Process	Amplitude	Process	Amplitude
$\langle \pi^+ P_{1/2} \| \pi^+ P_{1/2} \rangle$	$\frac{1}{3}(7\alpha_3 + 2\alpha_1)$	$\langle \pi^+ P_{1/2} \| \eta^0 \Delta^{++}_{3/2} \rangle$	$-\sqrt{2}\,\delta$
$\langle \pi^- P_{1/2} \| \pi^- P_{1/2} \rangle$	$\frac{1}{3}(5\alpha_3 + 4\alpha_1)$	$\langle \pi^- P_{1/2} \| \eta^0 \Delta^0_{3/2} \rangle$	$-\sqrt{\frac{2}{3}}\,\delta$
$\langle \pi^- P_{1/2} \| \pi^0 N_{1/2} \rangle$	$(\sqrt{2}/3)(\alpha_3 - \alpha_1)$	$\langle \pi^{\pm} P_{1/2} \| \eta^0 \Delta_{1/2} \rangle$	0
$\langle \pi^+ P_{1/2} \| \pi^+ P_{-1/2} \rangle$	$\frac{1}{9}(11\beta_3 - 2\beta_1)$	$\langle \pi^+ P_{1/2} \| \eta^0 \Delta^{++}_{-1/2} \rangle$	$\sqrt{\frac{2}{3}}\,\delta$
$\langle \pi^- P_{1/2} \| \pi^- P_{-1/2} \rangle$	$\frac{1}{9}(\beta_3 + 8\beta_1)$	$\langle \pi^- P_{1/2} \| \eta^0 \Delta^0_{-1/2} \rangle$	$(\sqrt{2}/3)\,\delta$
$\langle \pi^- P_{1/2} \| \pi^0 N_{-1/2} \rangle$	$(5\sqrt{2}/3)(\beta_3 - \beta_1)$	$\langle \pi^+ P_{1/2} \| K^+ \Sigma^+_{1/2} \rangle$	$-\xi$
$\langle \pi^+ P_{1/2} \| \pi^+ \Delta^+_{3/2} \rangle$	$-\frac{2}{3}\sqrt{\frac{2}{3}}(\beta_3 - \beta_1)$	$\langle \pi^- P_{1/2} \| K^0 \Sigma^0_{1/2} \rangle$	$-\sqrt{\frac{1}{2}}\,\xi$
$\langle \pi^+ P_{1/2} \| \pi^0 \Delta^{++}_{3/2} \rangle$	$\frac{2}{3}(\beta_3 - \beta_1)$	$\langle \pi^- P_{1/2} \| K^+ \Sigma^-_{1/2} \rangle$	0
$\langle \pi^- P_{1/2} \| \pi^- \Delta^+_{3/2} \rangle$	$\frac{2}{3}\sqrt{\frac{2}{3}}(\beta_3 - \beta_1)$	$\langle \pi^+ P_{1/2} \| K^+ \Sigma^+_{-1/2} \rangle$	$\frac{1}{3}\eta$
$\langle \pi^- P_{1/2} \| \pi^0 \Delta^0_{3/2} \rangle$	$-\frac{2}{3}\sqrt{\frac{1}{3}}(\beta_3 - \beta_1)$	$\langle \pi^- P_{1/2} \| K^0 \Sigma^0_{-1/2} \rangle$	$\frac{1}{3}\sqrt{\frac{1}{2}}\,\eta$
$\langle \pi^- P_{1/2} \| \pi^+ \Delta^-_{3/2} \rangle$	0	$\langle \pi^- P_{1/2} \| K^+ \Sigma^-_{-1/2} \rangle$	0
all $\langle \pi^{\pm} P_{1/2} \| \pi \Delta_{1/2} \rangle$	0	$\langle \pi^- P_{1/2} \| K^0 \Lambda^0_{1/2} \rangle$	$\sqrt{\frac{3}{2}}\,\xi$
$\langle \pi^+ P_{1/2} \| \pi^+ \Delta^+_{-1/2} \rangle$	$(2\sqrt{2}/9)(\beta_3 - \beta_1)$	$\langle \pi^- P_{1/2} \| K^0 \Lambda^0_{-1/2} \rangle$	$-\sqrt{\frac{3}{2}}\,\eta$
$\langle \pi^+ P_{1/2} \| \pi^0 \Delta^{++}_{-1/2} \rangle$	$-\frac{2}{3}\sqrt{\frac{1}{3}}(\beta_3 - \beta_1)$	$\langle \pi^+ P_{1/2} \| K^+ {}_\Delta Y^+_{3/2} \rangle$	$-\sqrt{\frac{2}{3}}\,\eta$
$\langle \pi^- P_{1/2} \| \pi^- \Delta^+_{-1/2} \rangle$	$-(2\sqrt{2}/9)(\beta_3 - \beta_1)$	$\langle \pi^- P_{1/2} \| K^0 {}_\Delta Y^0_{3/2} \rangle$	$-\sqrt{\frac{1}{3}}\,\eta$
$\langle \pi^- P_{1/2} \| \pi^0 \Delta^0_{-1/2} \rangle$	$\frac{2}{9}(\beta_3 - \beta_1)$	all $\langle \pi^- P_{1/2} \| K^+ {}_\Delta Y^-_m \rangle$	0
$\langle \pi^- P_{1/2} \| \pi^+ \Delta^-_{-1/2} \rangle$	0	all $\langle \pi^{\pm} P_{1/2} \| K_\Delta Y_{1/2} \rangle$	0
$\langle \pi^- P_{1/2} \| \eta^0 N_{1/2} \rangle$	γ	$\langle \pi^+ P_{1/2} \| K^+ {}_\Delta Y^+_{-1/2} \rangle$	$(\sqrt{2}/3)\,\eta$
$\langle \pi^- P_{1/2} \| \eta^0 N_{-1/2} \rangle$	$\frac{5}{3}\delta$	$\langle \pi^- P_{1/2} \| K^0 {}_\Delta Y^0_{-1/2} \rangle$	$\frac{1}{3}\eta$

the isotopic-spin conservation requirements

$$\langle \pi^+ P_{1/2} | \pi^+ P_m \rangle - \langle \pi^- P_{1/2} | \pi^- P_m \rangle = \sqrt{2}\, \langle \pi^- P_{1/2} | \pi^0 N_m \rangle, \tag{16a}$$

$$\begin{aligned} 2\langle \pi^- P_{1/2} | \pi^- \Delta^+_m \rangle &+ \sqrt{2}\, \langle \pi^- P_{1/2} | \pi^0 \Delta^0_m \rangle \\ &= \langle \pi^- P_{1/2} | \pi^- \Delta^+_m \rangle - \sqrt{\tfrac{1}{3}}\, \langle \pi^- P_{1/2} | \pi^+ \Delta^-_m \rangle \\ &= -\langle \pi^+ P_{1/2} | \pi^+ \Delta^+_m \rangle = \sqrt{\tfrac{2}{3}}\, \langle \pi^+ P_{1/2} | \pi^0 \Delta^{++}_m \rangle, \end{aligned} \tag{16b}$$

$$\langle \pi^+ P_{1/2} | \eta^0 \Delta^{++}_m \rangle = \sqrt{3}\, \langle \pi^- P_{1/2} | \eta^0 \Delta^0_m \rangle, \tag{16c}$$

$$\langle \pi^+ P_{1/2} | K^+ \Sigma^+_m \rangle - \langle \pi^- P_{1/2} | K^+ \Sigma^-_m \rangle = \sqrt{2}\, \langle \pi^- P_{1/2} | K^0 \Sigma^0_m \rangle, \tag{16d}$$

$$\langle \pi^+ P_{1/2} | K^+ {}_\Delta Y^+_m \rangle - \langle \pi^- P_{1/2} | K^+ {}_\Delta Y^-_m \rangle = \sqrt{2}\, \langle \pi^- P_{1/2} | K^0 {}_\Delta Y^0_m \rangle. \tag{16e}$$

Most of the specific consequences of the quark model on the cross sections (summed over spin states) for the set of reactions under consideration follow from Equations (16a) through (16e) combined with the vanishing of amplitudes corresponding to the exchange of two units of charge. Thus, the result

$$\langle \pi^- P_{1/2} | \pi^+ \Delta^-_m \rangle = 0 \tag{16b$'$}$$

leads directly, from Equation (16b), to the relationship among the squares of the amplitudes

$$\sigma(\pi^+P|\pi^0\Delta^{++}) : \sigma(\pi^+P|\pi^+\Delta^+) : \sigma(\pi^-P|\pi^-\Delta^+) : \sigma(\pi^-P|\pi^0\Delta^0) : \sigma(\pi^-P|\pi^+\Delta^-) = 3 : 2 : 2 : 1 : 0, \quad (16b'')$$

while

$$\langle \pi^-P_{1/2}|K^+\Sigma^-_m\rangle = \langle \pi^-P_{1/2}|K^+{}_\Delta Y^-_m\rangle = 0 \quad (16d')$$

leads to

$$\sigma(\pi^+P|K^+\Sigma^+) : \sigma(\pi^-P|K^0\Sigma^0) : \sigma(\pi^-P|K^+\Sigma^-) = 2 : 1 : 0, \quad (16d'')$$

$$\sigma(\pi^+P|K^+{}_\Delta Y^+) : \sigma(\pi^-P|K^0{}_\Delta Y^0) : \sigma(\pi^-P|K^+{}_\Delta Y^-) = 2 : 1 : 0, \quad (16e')$$

all of which are, of course, implicitly contained in the amplitudes given in Table 17.5.

The above relationships among the spin sums of the amplitudes (squared) apply, strictly speaking, only to the differential cross sections for forward meson emission. We shall attempt, in the following section, to relate these to the differential cross sections at off-forward angles for the reactions under consideration. In the meantime, the symbol $\sigma(aA|a'A')$ may be regarded as a shorthand notation for the corresponding $\Sigma_m|\langle aA_{1/2}|a'A'_m\rangle|^2$.

Short of the possibility of observations that can distinguish between different helicity states of the product baryons, the amplitudes contained in Table 17.5 yield only a few additional relationships susceptible of comparison with experiment. Thus, for example, we have

$$3\sigma(\pi^-P|\eta^0\Delta^0) \le \tfrac{24}{25}\sigma(\pi^-P|\eta^0N), \quad (17a)$$

the equality holding in the case of the vanishing of the spin-nonflip $\pi^- \to \eta^0$ amplitude [γ of Equation (15g)]. Similarly, owing to the effect of the spin-flip $\pi^- \to K^0$ amplitude [η of Equation (15j)], the general result of the spin-independent approximation, Equation (13b), is modified for the spin-dependent case

$$3\sigma(\pi^-P|K^0\Sigma^0) \le \sigma(\pi^-P|K^0\Lambda^0) \le 27\sigma(\pi^-P|K^0\Sigma^0). \quad (17b)$$

There is, however, one equality that follows from Table 17.5, namely,

$$3\sigma(\pi^-P|K^0{}_\Delta Y^0) = \sigma(\pi^-P|K^0\Lambda^0) - 3\sigma(\pi^-P|K^0\Sigma^0). \quad (17c)$$

In a fashion similar to that discussed above, we may consider the set of relationships where the initial and final baryons (A and A') are considered "elementary," while the projectile (meson or baryon), a, and the product, a', are decomposed into their quark constituents according to Table 15.2. Since the procedures are entirely analogous to those described above, we simply quote some of the more interesting results: [14]

$$\sigma(\pi^-P|K^0\Lambda^0) = \tfrac{9}{4}\sigma(\overline{P}P|\overline{\Sigma^0}\Lambda^0) - \tfrac{1}{12}\sigma(\overline{P}P|\overline{\Lambda^0}\Lambda^0), \quad (18a)$$

$$\sigma(\overline{P}P|\overline{\Lambda^0}\Lambda^0) = 3\sigma(\overline{P}P|\overline{\Sigma^0}\Lambda^0) + 3\sigma(\overline{P}P|{}_\Delta\overline{Y^0}\Lambda^0), \quad (18b)$$

$$\sigma(\pi^-P|K^{*0}\Lambda^0) = \tfrac{9}{4}\sigma(\overline{P}P|{}_\Delta\overline{Y^0}\Lambda^0), \quad (18c)$$

---

[14] H. J. Lipkin, F. Scheck, and H. Stern, *Phys. Rev., 152:* 1375 (1967); see also D. P. Dare, *Nuovo Cimento, 52A:* 1015 (1967) and K. J. Sebastian, *Phys. Rev., 167:* 1523 (1968).

$$\sigma(\overline{P}P|\overline{\Sigma^+}\Sigma^+) = \sigma(\pi^+P|K^+\Sigma^+) + \tfrac{1}{9}\sigma(\pi^+P|K^{*+}\Sigma^+), \tag{18d}$$

$$\sigma(\pi^+P|K^{*+}\Sigma^+) = \tfrac{9}{8}\sigma(\overline{P}P|_{\Delta}\overline{Y^+}\Sigma^+), \tag{18e}$$

$$\sigma(PP|N\Delta^{++}) = \sigma(K^+P|K^0\Delta^{++}) + \tfrac{25}{9}\sigma(K^+P|K^{0*}\Delta^{++}), \tag{18f}$$

$$\sigma(K^+P|K^{0*}\Delta^{++}) = \tfrac{9}{8}\sigma(PP|\Delta^0\Delta^{++}), \tag{18g}$$

$$\sigma(K^-P|\rho^0\Lambda^0) = \sigma(K^-P|\omega^0\Lambda^0). \tag{18h}$$

Additional relationships may be obtained if one assumes connections among the basic amplitudes [i.e., Equations (15a)–(15j)], such as, for example, those imposed by $SU(3)$ symmetry (see footnote 14).

Another approach[15] is to assume that the quark-quark scattering amplitudes are determined by the Regge trajectories which may be exchanged in the t-channel (Chapter 11). We summarize in Table 17.6 the most important trajectories involved in the various qq amplitudes. The trajectories corresponding to the different values of the quantum numbers (t, C) exchanged may be singled out by considering appropriate combinations of qq scattering amplitudes. In addition, the signatures corresponding to the different trajectories determine the sign of their corresponding contributions to the amplitudes for $\overline{q}q$ as compared to qq scattering. Thus (see Example in Section 11.2.2), the contributions of the vector-meson trajectories to the forward scattering amplitudes may be isolated by considering appropriate sums and differences between total cross sections. Recalling the definitions $\Delta(a\mathfrak{N}) \equiv \sigma(a\mathfrak{N}) - \sigma(\overline{a}\mathfrak{N})$, $\Sigma(a\mathfrak{N}) \equiv \sigma(a\mathfrak{N}) + \sigma(\overline{a}\mathfrak{N})$, we note that the amplitude corresponding to $C=-1$, $t=1$ (ρ) exchange is given by $\Delta(\pi P)$ or

Table 17.6 Regge Trajectories Exchanged in the t-Channel for Quark-Quark Scattering Processes

Amplitude	Trajectory[a] $t=1, C=+1$	$t=1, C=-1$	$t=0, C=+1$	$t=0, C=-1$	$t=\frac{1}{2}, \mathcal{Y}=\pm 1$
$\langle pp\|pp\rangle$	$\pi, \delta, A_1, \underline{A_2}$	$\underline{\rho}, B$	$\underline{P}, \eta, \underline{f}, \underline{f'}$	$\underline{\omega}$	—
$\langle pn\|pn\rangle$	"	"	"	"	—
$\langle pn\|np\rangle$	"	"	—	—	—
$\langle \overline{p}n\|\overline{p}n\rangle$	"	"	$\underline{P}, \eta, \underline{f}, \underline{f'}$	$\underline{\omega}$	—
$\langle \overline{p}p\|\overline{p}p\rangle$	"	"	"	"	—
$\langle \overline{p}p\|\overline{n}n\rangle$	"	"	—	—	—
$\langle \overline{p}p\|\overline{\lambda}\lambda\rangle$	—	—	—	—	K, K^*
$\langle \overline{\lambda}\lambda\|\overline{\lambda}\lambda\rangle$	—	—	$\underline{P}, \eta, \underline{f}, \underline{f'}$	$\underline{\phi}$	—
$\langle p\lambda\|p\lambda\rangle$	—	—	"	"	—
$\langle p\overline{\lambda}\|p\overline{\lambda}\rangle$	—	—	"	"	—
$\langle p\lambda\|\lambda p\rangle$	—	—	—	—	K, K^*

[a] The underlined are those trajectories which, because they lie highest on an α versus t plot, are expected to dominate at high energies.

[15] H. J. Lipkin, *Proceedings of the International Conference on Elementary Particles,* Heidelberg (1967); P. G. O. Freund, *Phys. Rev. Letters, 15:* 929 (1965); F. Scheck, *CERN Report* Th. 890 (1968).

$[\Delta(KP)-\Delta(KN)]$ or $[\Delta(PP)-\Delta(PN)]$, while the $C=-1, t=0$ (ω) trajectories are responsible for the combinations $\frac{1}{3}[\Delta(KP)+\Delta(KN)]$ or $\frac{1}{9}[\Delta(PP)+\Delta(PN)]$.

In addition, it is to be noted that only $\bar{q}q$ combinations give rise to annihilation in the s-channel, which can lead to differences in $\bar{q}q$ and qq scattering amplitudes for processes in which the same Regge trajectories are exchanged in the t-channel, e.g., $\langle pp|pp\rangle$ and $\langle\bar{p}p|\bar{p}p\rangle$. Finally, comparison of the trajectories associated with the different qq scattering amplitudes can be used to justify approximations, such as that of Lipkin, for relationships among these amplitudes. Thus, in the formal treatment, developed in Section 17.1.2, for the forward scattering amplitudes, [see Equations (11a)–(11j′)], the eigenamplitudes resulting from the assumption $\Delta_{p\lambda}=0$ correspond to the exchange of single vector-meson trajectories:

$$\lambda_1=\Delta_{pp}-\Delta_{pn}=2\lambda_\rho, \tag{11d''}$$

$$\lambda_2=\Delta_{pp}+\Delta_{pn}=2\lambda_\omega, \tag{11e''}$$

$$\lambda_3=\Delta_{\lambda\lambda}=\lambda_\varphi. \tag{11f''}$$

17.2.3 Application to Two-Body Reaction Cross Sections

So far, the amplitudes for the hadron reactions $a+A\rightarrow a'+A'$, derived on the assumption of the additivity of the pairwise qq scattering amplitudes, have been assumed to hold only when the product hadrons are emitted in the forward direction ($t\cong 0$). However, we may loosen this restriction somewhat and attempt to apply the same approximation to processes involving small momentum transfers, at least for those (two-body) processes in which the quarks constituting the hadrons are sufficiently strongly bound so that, for sufficiently small t-values, the hadrons will recoil as a unit, rather than be dissociated. Since the differential cross sections for two-body reactions at high energies are almost universally observed to fall off very rapidly with increasing $|t|$, the region of validity of such an approximation may generally be assumed to cover essentially the entire range of t-values over which the differential cross section has an appreciable value. In this case, the relationships among reaction amplitudes may be extended to the reaction cross sections as well.

Elastic Scattering • We consider, first, the consequences of such an assumption for hadron-hadron elastic scattering, following the approach of Kokkedee and Van Hove.[16] Let

$$T_{ij}(s,t)=\langle q_iq_j|q_iq_j\rangle \tag{19a}$$

be the quark-quark scattering amplitudes, and $f_i^a(t)$ and $f_j^A(t)$ be form factors relating to the individual quark distributions in the hadrons a and A, respectively. Then the additivity assumption implies, for the amplitude $\langle aA|aA\rangle$,

$$\langle aA|aA\rangle=T_{aA}(s,t)=\sum_{i,j}f_i^a(t)f_j^A(t)\,T_{ij}(s,t). \tag{19b}$$

[16] J. J. J. Kokkedee and L. Van Hove, *Nuovo Cimento, 42:* 711 (1966).

Now, generally, the $T_{ij}(s, t)$ may be different for different $q_i q_j$ combinations, so that Equation (19b) would be a complicated function of s and t, different for each aA combination.[17] However, if we assume that, in the limit of large s and small t, all the qq amplitudes approach a common, $SU(3)$-invariant form,

$$T_{ij}(s \to \infty, t \text{ small}) \cong i\beta(s)\, g(t), \tag{19c}$$

then Equation (19b) becomes

$$T_{aA}(s, t) \to i\beta(s)\, g(t) \left[\sum_i f_i^a(t)\right]\left[\sum_j f_j^A(t)\right] = i\beta(s)\, g(t)\, F_a(t)\, F_A(t), \tag{19d}$$

in which the contributions of the quarks in each hadron give rise to a factorizable form factor characteristic of the hadron in question. Equation (19d) provides a justification, in terms of the quark model, of the factorizability of scattering amplitudes which follows in the Regge pole approximation from the assumption of the asymptotic dominance of the Pomeranchuk trajectory (Chapter 11). Generally, then, assuming $SU(3)$ invariance for the qq amplitudes, the hadron-hadron scattering cross sections are given in terms of a small number of universal functions of t. In particular, we may consider two extreme assumptions on the form of the quark amplitudes:

1. The t dependence is dominated by the strong falling-off of $g(t)$ with $-t$. Then we may take

$$f_i^a(t) \cong f_j^A(t) \cong f(0) = 1, \tag{20a}$$

and Equation (19d) becomes, for this case,

$$T_{aA}(s, t) \cong iN_a N_A \beta(s)\, g(t), \tag{20b}$$

where N equals the number of quarks constituting the hadron in question. In this extreme,

$$\begin{aligned}\frac{d\sigma}{dt}(qq|qq) = |T_{qq}(s,t)|^2 &\cong \frac{1}{81}\frac{d\sigma}{dt}(\mathfrak{N}\mathfrak{N}|\mathfrak{N}\mathfrak{N}) \cong \frac{1}{81}\frac{d\sigma}{dt}(\overline{\mathfrak{N}}\mathfrak{N}|\overline{\mathfrak{N}}\mathfrak{N}) \\ &\cong \frac{1}{36}\frac{d\sigma}{dt}(\pi\mathfrak{N}|\pi\mathfrak{N}) \cong \frac{1}{36}\frac{d\sigma}{dt}(K\mathfrak{N}|K\mathfrak{N}),\end{aligned} \tag{20c}$$

and, by the optical theorem,

$$\sigma(qq) \cong \tfrac{1}{9}\sigma(\mathfrak{N}\mathfrak{N}) \cong \tfrac{1}{9}\sigma(\overline{\mathfrak{N}}\mathfrak{N}) \cong \tfrac{1}{6}\sigma(\pi\mathfrak{N}) = \tfrac{1}{6}(K\mathfrak{N}), \tag{20d}$$

so that the quarks may be regarded as relatively transparent objects of a size

---

[17] There is the additional problem of the relationship of the total *cm* energy of the two quarks to the s-value of the $a + A$ combination. Clearly, this depends on the quark masses and bindings in the various hadrons, and is simply resolved only in the case of lightly bound, light quarks. We assume that, for whatever reasons, this is effectively the case, and treat the system in the simplest possible fashion. Actually, for elastic scattering, the high-energy cross sections are not very strongly s-dependent, and we are probably justified in assuming that this is also the case for the qq amplitudes.

comparable to that of the nucleon. Equations (20c) and (20d), of course, are the usual asymptotic relations corresponding to a quark model with $SU(3)$ invariance for the quark amplitudes.

2. At the other extreme, we may take the quarks to be very small objects so that the t dependence is now dominated by the hadron form factors $F_{a,A}(t)$. Taking

$$g(t) \cong g(0) \tag{21a}$$

leads to

$$T_{aA}(s,t) \cong i\beta(s)\, g(0)\, F_a(t)\, F_A(t). \tag{21b}$$

The quarks in this case, while small (as compared to the baryons), are relatively strongly absorbing since [recall $F_{a,A}(0) = N_{a,A}$] Equation (20d) still holds, but $d\sigma/dt$ falls off much more slowly for qq than for $\mathfrak{N}\mathfrak{N}$ scattering.

Furthermore, if the $F_{a,A}(t)$ are associated with the distribution of scattering material in the hadrons, we might generally assume that they are essentially the same as the electric form factors of the hadrons in question, e.g.,

$$F_{\mathfrak{N}}(t) \cong G_P^E(t). \tag{21c}$$

In this case, we have the interesting relationship

$$\frac{d\sigma}{dt}(\mathfrak{N}\mathfrak{N}) \cong \left(\frac{d\sigma}{dt}\right)_0 [G_P^E(t)]^4, \tag{21d}$$

previously conjectured (Section 11.1.3) on the basis of the eikonal scattering approximation.

Since the t dependences of all measured hadron-hadron scattering cross sections, although similar, are not identical, we may assume that the second extreme is probably a somewhat more reasonable approximation than the first.

EXAMPLE

On the basis of this approximation, we may use the observed properties of πP, PP, and $\bar{P}P$ scattering to predict the characteristics of the $\pi\pi$ scattering cross section.[18] Thus, let

$$T_{PP}(s,t) = [3G_P(t)]^2\, T_{qq}(s,t), \tag{22a}$$

$$T_{\bar{P}P} = [3G_P(t)]^2\, T_{q\bar{q}}, \tag{22b}$$

$$T_{\pi P} = 3G_\pi(t)\, G_P(t)\, [T_{qq} + T_{q\bar{q}}]. \tag{22c}$$

Then, assuming $T_{qq} \cong T_{q\bar{q}}$, we would have

$$T_{\pi\pi} = \frac{2}{3}\frac{G_\pi(t)}{G_P(t)}\, T_{\pi P}. \tag{22d}$$

[18] E. Shrauner, *Phys. Rev. Letters, 20:* 1258 (1968).

Now, since

$$\frac{d\sigma_i}{dt} = |T_i(s, t)|^2 \cong A_i e^{a_i t}, \tag{22e}$$

$$\sigma_i \cong \frac{A_i}{a_i} = \frac{4\pi}{k_i} \operatorname{Im} T_i(s, t=0), \tag{22f}$$

we may use the observed high-energy parameters

$$\begin{aligned} \sigma_{PP} &\cong 38 \text{ mb}, & a_{PP} &\cong 9\text{–}10\,(\text{GeV}/c)^{-2}, \\ \sigma_{\bar{P}P} &\cong 48 \text{ mb}, & a_{\bar{P}P} &\cong 11\text{–}12\,(\text{GeV}/c)^{-2}, \\ \sigma_{\pi P} &\cong 25 \text{ mb}, & a_{\pi P} &\cong 8\text{–}9\,(\text{GeV}/c)^{-2}, \end{aligned} \tag{22g}$$

to derive the $\pi\pi$ scattering values

$$\sigma_{\pi\pi} \cong 14 \text{ mb}, \qquad a_{\pi\pi} \cong 5.8\,(\text{GeV}/c)^{-2}, \tag{22h}$$

$$G_\pi(t) \cong \frac{0.87}{[1 - t/0.57\,(\text{GeV}/c)^2]} \tag{22i}$$

[based on a dipole form for $G_P(t)$ (see Chapter 9)], and

$$\langle r^2 \rangle_\pi = 6\, \frac{(dG_\pi/dt)_{t=0}}{G_\pi(0)} \cong (0.65 \text{ f})^2. \tag{22j}$$

Aside from the (small) violation of the requirement that $G_\pi(0) = 1$, the $\pi\pi$ scattering parameters [Equations (22h) through (22j)] derived on this basis appear to be quite reasonable.

Inelastic Reactions • Before we attempt any direct comparisons between experiments and the quark-model predictions for inelastic two-body reactions, even in the forward direction, it is necessary to apply certain kinematical corrections to take into account the differences in masses between the particles involved in the reactions being compared. It is conventional [19] to compare related reactions between different particles at a common value of the available *cm* energy, or Q-value (see Section 13.3.3):

$$Q = s^{1/2} - M_{a'} - M_{A'}. \tag{23a}$$

Thus, the incident *cm* momentum, k_a, and product *cm* momentum, $k_{a'}$, as well as the *cm* energy, $s^{1/2}$, and 4-momentum transfer, t, will necessarily be different for the reactions in question. We correct for the resulting differences in incident flux and product phase space by dividing the experimental cross section by the correction factor [20]

$$\mathfrak{F}_1 = \frac{k_{a'}}{s k_a}. \tag{24a}$$

However, the equal Q-value prescription is not obviously the best one for com-

[19] S. Meshkov, G. A. Snow, and G. B. Yodh, *Phys. Rev. Letters, 12:* 87 (1964).

[20] In terms of the invariant amplitudes $A_i(s, t)$, the cross section is $d\sigma_i/dt = \mathfrak{F}_{1,i}|A_i(s, t)|^2$.

paring different reactions. Another possibility,[21] which leads to improved results for the comparison of total cross sections (forward elastic scattering amplitudes), is to compare reactions for the same value of the relative quark velocities in the incident *cm*,

$$\frac{s_{aA}-m_a^2-m_A^2}{m_a m_A}=\frac{s_{ij}-m_i^2(a)-m_j^2(A)}{m_i(a)\,m_j(A)}, \tag{23b}$$

where $m_i(a)$ and $m_j(A)$ are, respectively, the masses of the quarks i and j in the projectile (a) and target (A) hadrons. Assuming constant and equal quark masses, we obtain from Equation (23b) the prescription for comparing the reactions $a+A$ and $b+B$:

$$\frac{s_{aA}-m_a^2-m_A^2}{s_{bB}-m_b^2-m_B^2}=\frac{m_a m_A}{m_b m_B}. \tag{23c}$$

In any case, whatever the prescription for determining the equivalent values of s, the observed cross sections must be corrected by the factor (24a) to obtain the reaction amplitudes appropriate for comparison of the quark-model predictions.

A second correction introduces a "structure factor" to account for the bound-state quark distributions in the physical hadrons. In the $SU(3)$ limit of equal qq scattering amplitudes [Equation (19d)], this factor would simply be

$$\mathfrak{F}_2=F_a^2(t)\,F_A^2(t). \tag{24b}$$

More generally, assuming a much weaker t dependence of the quark scattering and reaction amplitudes than of the quark form factors [approximation (2) on p. 419], the factorization of Equation (21b) may be assumed to hold also for inelastic processes in the forward direction,[22] and Equation (24b) may be applied to such inelastic processes, giving for the total correction factor to be used in the comparison of the forward inelastic cross sections (at either the same Q-value or the same relative quark velocity)

$$\mathfrak{F}(a+A\to a'+A')=\mathfrak{F}_1\cdot\mathfrak{F}_2=\frac{k_{a'}}{sk_a}\,F_a^2(t)\,F_A^2(t). \tag{25}$$

Thus, the cross section relations of Equations (18a) through (18h) are to be compared with the corrected experimental values, at the energies appropriate for the comparison,

$$\bar{\sigma}(a+A\to a'+A')\to\frac{\sigma_{\exp}}{\mathfrak{F}(a+A\to a'+A')}. \tag{25a}$$

---

[21] P. B. James and H. D. D. Watson, *Phys. Rev. Letters, 18:* 179 (1967).

[22] The structure factor has the same origin as the Debye–Waller factor for X-ray scattering by bound systems, or the Mössbauer factor in the scattering of photons by bound nuclei. Let $\Delta\mathbf{k}=\mathbf{k}-\mathbf{k}'$ be the *cm* momentum change of the reacting quark bound in the particle X. Then the form factor of X is given by

$$F_X(\Delta\mathbf{k})=\langle\psi_f^X|e^{i\Delta\mathbf{k}\cdot\mathbf{x}}|\psi_i^X\rangle, \tag{24c}$$

where ψ_i^X and ψ_f^X are the initial and final bound state wave functions and $\mathbf{x}$ is the coordinate of the interacting quark in X. The reaction amplitude is thus multiplied by the factor $F_a(\Delta\mathbf{k})\cdot F_A(\Delta\mathbf{k})$, and the cross section by its square. In the relativistic case, the 3-momentum transfer is replaced by $t^{1/2}$; see H. J. Lipkin, F. Scheck, and H. Stern, *Phys. Rev., 152:* 1375 (1967).

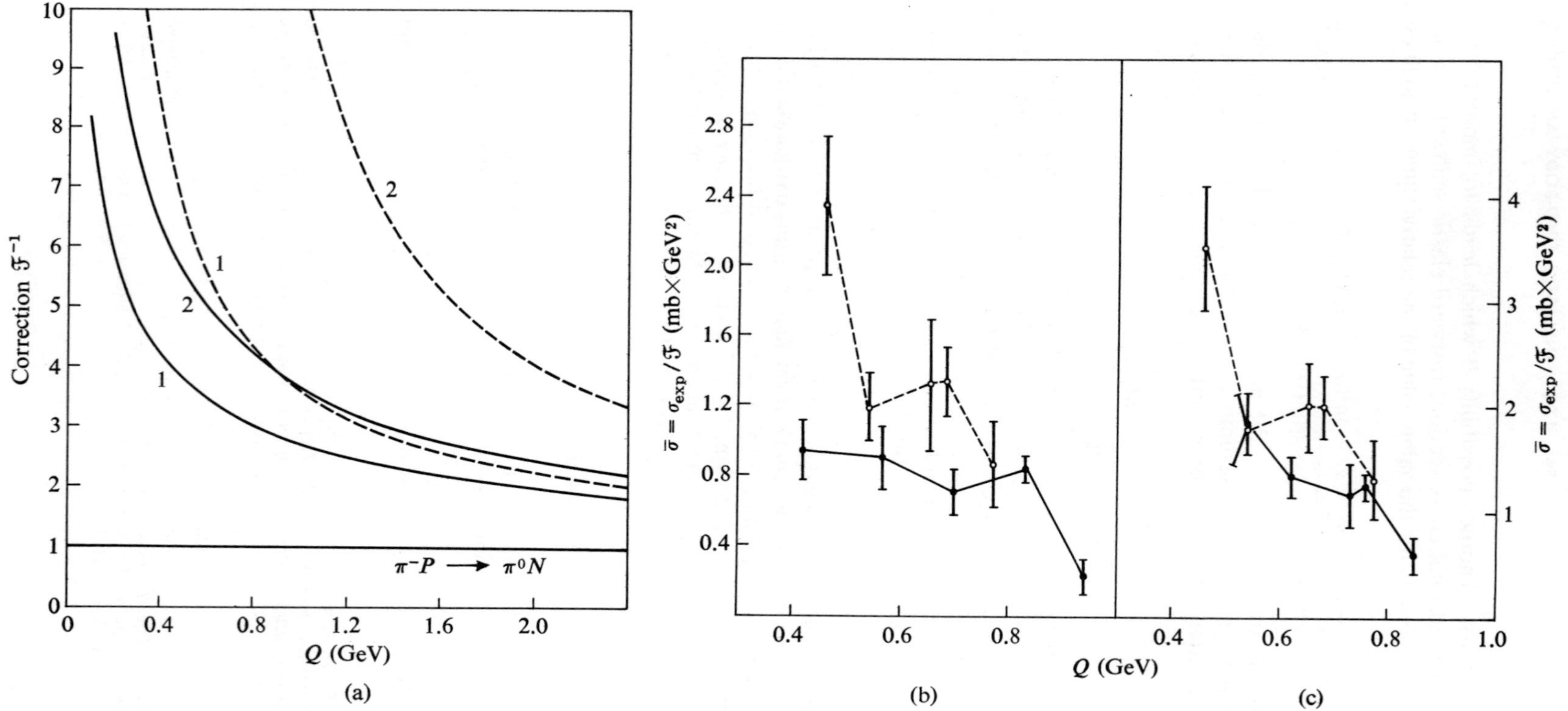

Figure 17.5 (a) Correction factors $\mathfrak{F}^{-1}$ for some $\overline{P}P$ reactions with (dashed lines) and without (solid lines) the form factor correction $\mathfrak{F}_2$. Curves 1 are for $\overline{P}P \to \overline{\Lambda}\Lambda$ and curves 2 for $\overline{P}P \to {}_{\Delta}\overline{Y}\Sigma$. The factors $\mathfrak{F}$ shown are divided by $\mathfrak{F}(\pi^- P \to \pi^0 N)$. (b) Experimental test of the relation (18a′) for the reaction cross sections in the forward direction. The solid circles correspond to $\sigma(\pi^- P|K^0\Lambda^0)$ and the open circles to $2\sigma(\overline{P}P|\overline{\Sigma^0}\Lambda^0)$. (c) Experimental test of the relation (18b′) for the reaction cross sections in the forward direction. The solid circles correspond to $\sigma(\overline{P}P|\overline{\Lambda^0}\Lambda^0)$ and the open circles to $3\sigma(\overline{P}P|\overline{\Sigma^0}\Lambda^0)$. [From Lipkin, Scheck, and Stern, *Phys. Rev.*, *152*: 1375 (1967).]

For large s and not-too-large t, we assume that the differential elastic cross sections are dominated by the form factors [approximation (2) on p. 419], all of which exhibit an exponential t dependence, e^{at}. Hence, we assume the general form

$$F_X(t) \cong e^{a_X t/2} \tag{24d}$$

and use the observed hadron-hadron scattering observations to obtain the required coefficients in

$$\mathfrak{F}_2 \cong e^{(a_a + a_A)t}. \tag{24e}$$

The values we adopt[23] are

$$\begin{aligned} a_{\pi^+} + a_P &= 8.6 + 2.1t\ (\mathrm{GeV}/c)^{-2}, \\ a_{\pi^-} + a_P &= 9.4 + 2.7t\ (\mathrm{GeV}/c)^{-2}, \\ a_{K^+} + a_P &= 6.4 + 1.25t\ (\mathrm{GeV}/c)^{-2}, \\ a_{K^-} + a_P &= 9.0 + 2.8t\ (\mathrm{GeV}/c)^{-2}, \\ a_P + a_P &= 9.2 + 2.0t\ (\mathrm{GeV}/c)^{-2}, \\ a_{\overline{P}} + a_P &= 12.6\ (\mathrm{GeV}/c)^{-2}. \end{aligned} \tag{24f}$$

Owing to the sparsity of reliable data on the cross sections in question, confrontation of relations such as Equations (18a) through (18h) with experiment usually lead to equivocal results. A number of such comparisons have been attempted by Lipkin, Scheck, and Stern.[24] We reproduce in Figure 17.5 their analysis as applied to the observed differential cross sections for forward scattering in the reactions (18a) and (18b). In making this comparison, they have neglected $\sigma(\overline{P}P|_\Delta \overline{Y}^0\Lambda^0)$ in (18b), since the experimental indications are that it is much smaller than the other cross sections involved, thus reducing the two relations to

$$\overline{\sigma}(\pi^- P|K^0\Lambda^0) \cong 2\overline{\sigma}(\overline{P}P|\overline{\Sigma}^0\Lambda^0), \tag{18a$'$}$$

$$\overline{\sigma}(\overline{P}P|\overline{\Lambda}^0\Lambda^0) \cong 3\overline{\sigma}(\overline{P}P|\overline{\Sigma}^0\Lambda^0). \tag{18b$'$}$$

They conclude: "Both relations are in rough agreement with experiment, but clearly more data at higher Q-values are needed."

Finally, we note that since many related reactions at high energy exhibit the same t dependence of their differential cross sections (at least for small t-values which, owing to the rapid decrease of most $d\sigma/dt$ with increasing $|t|$, contribute the bulk of the total cross section), the relationships among the total cross sections for such reactions should follow approximately from those of the forward cross sections [Equations (18a) through (18h)], always corrected according to Equation (25a). We would especially expect this to be the case among reactions that originate from the same set of qq amplitudes, or the same t-channel exchange

[23] A. Wetherell, *Proceedings of the 13th International Conference on High-Energy Physics*, University of California Press, Berkeley (1966). Note that we include a slight t^2 dependence of the observed "Gaussian" form factors.

[24] *Phys. Rev., 152:* 1375 (1967). Note that they compute the factor $\mathfrak{F}_1$ at equal Q-values [Equation (23a)].

processes. Assuming this to be the case for reactions (17c) and (18a) through (18c), we exhibit in Figure 17.6 the comparison of the experimental total cross sections[25] for these reactions, compared at the same Q-values.

PROBLEMS

1. Derive the following relationships for inelastic vector-meson interactions:

$$\langle \rho^+P|\rho^+P\rangle = \tfrac{1}{2}(5a + b + 5\bar{a} + \bar{b}),$$
$$\langle \rho^0P|\rho^+N\rangle = \tfrac{1}{2}\sqrt{\tfrac{1}{2}}\,(a - b + \bar{a} - \bar{b}) = \langle \rho^-P|\rho^0N\rangle,$$
$$\langle \rho^-P|\rho^-P\rangle = 2a + b + 2\bar{a} + \bar{b},$$
$$\langle \rho^0P|\omega^0P\rangle = \tfrac{1}{4}(a - b - \bar{a} + \bar{b}),$$
$$\langle \rho^-P|\omega^0N\rangle = -\tfrac{1}{2}\sqrt{\tfrac{1}{2}}\,(a - b - \bar{a} + \bar{b}),$$
$$\langle \rho^+P|K^{*+}\Sigma^+\rangle = \bar{e},$$
$$\langle \rho^0P|K^{*+}\Sigma^0\rangle = \tfrac{1}{2}\bar{e} = -\langle \omega^0P|K^{*+}\Sigma^0\rangle,$$
$$\langle \rho^0P|K^{*0}\Sigma^+\rangle = \tfrac{1}{2}\bar{e} = \langle \omega^0P|K^{*0}\Sigma^+\rangle = \langle \rho^-P|K^{*0}\Sigma^0\rangle,$$
$$\langle \phi^0P|K^{*+}\Sigma^0\rangle = -\sqrt{\tfrac{1}{2}}\,c' = -\sqrt{\tfrac{1}{2}}\,\langle \phi^0P|K^{*0}\Sigma^+\rangle.$$

2. Assume that the qq and $\bar{q}q$ scattering amplitudes are given by the Regge expressions (see Section 11.2.2). Taking for the exchanged trajectories those underlined in Table 17.6, derive expressions for the differential cross sections, $(d\sigma/dt)_{\text{ex}}$, for charge-exchange scattering in the following cases:

   (a) $NP \to PN$,

   (b) $\bar{P}P \to \bar{N}N$,

   (c) $\pi^-P \to \pi^0N$,

   (d) $K^-P \to \overline{K^0}N$,

   (e) $K^+N \to K^0P$.

   Compare with the available data (see footnote 25).

3. It has been empirically observed that the following reactions appear to be dominated by the one-pion-exchange (OPE) mechanism:

$$\pi P \to \rho P,$$
$$\pi P \to \rho \mathfrak{N}^*,$$
$$KP \to K^*\mathfrak{N},$$
$$NP \to PN,$$
$$PP \to \mathfrak{N}^*\mathfrak{N}^*,$$
$$\bar{P}P \to \overline{\mathfrak{N}^*}\mathfrak{N}^*.$$

[25] Comparison of the great variety of available high-energy reaction cross section measurements is greatly facilitated by the existence of two sets of extensive data compilations:

(a) P. K. Williams, D. M. LeVine, and J. A. Koschik, *References and Some Two-Body Data for High Energy Reactions,* University of Michigan, Ann Arbor (1967).

(b) H. Kanada, T. Kobayashi, and Y. Sumi, eds., "Experimental Data on Hadron Interactions in GeV Region," *Suppl. Progr. Theoret. Phys.* (Japan), *41* and *42* (1967).

Assuming a spin-independent qq interaction model, with only those amplitudes contributing that can interact *via* pion exchange (column 2 of Table 17.6), derive a set of relationships among the scattering amplitudes for the above reactions.

4. In Figures 13.1 and 17.1, the total cross sections for hadron-hadron interactions are compared at the same projectile (*lab*) momenta. Repeat this comparison using, however, the corrected cross sections, $\mathfrak{F}^{-1}\sigma_{\text{tot}}$,

   (a) at the same Q-values,
   (b) at the same values of the relative qq (*cm*) velocities.

5. Assuming Lipkin's approximation for the isotopic-spin dependence of the qq and $\bar{q}q$ scattering amplitudes, but also a spin dependence of the form

$$a_{ij} = \alpha_{ij} + \beta_{ij}\mathbf{s}_i \cdot \mathbf{s}_j,$$

derive expressions for the forward reaction amplitudes for vector-meson production by pions

$$\pi P \rightarrow vB$$

(averaged over initial and summed over final m-values). Relate these to the cross sections for pion and kaon scattering, derived under the same assumptions.

17.3 Some Other Applications

17.3.1 Nucleon-Antinucleon Annihilation

One of the useful applications of the quark model is in the prediction of the distribution of mesons resulting from nucleon-antinucleon annihilation, on the basis of the simplest and most direct set of possible assumptions. According to the model of Rubinstein and Stern,[26] the annihilation process is described by projecting, out of the set of constituent nucleon quarks and antinucleon antiquarks, all possible pairings of three sets of mesonic ($q\bar{q}$) states, $b_{\xi,\eta,\zeta}$:

$$\mathfrak{N}_\alpha(q_iq_jq_k) + \overline{\mathfrak{N}}_\beta(\bar{q}_l\bar{q}_m\bar{q}_n) \rightarrow \sum_\gamma w_{\alpha\beta\gamma}\rho_\gamma[b_\xi(q_i\bar{q}_l) + b_\eta(q_j\bar{q}_m) + b_\zeta(q_k\bar{q}_n)], \quad (26)$$

the $w_{\alpha\beta\gamma}$ being the projected weights, using the quark-model wave functions of Table 15.2, of the possible combinations $\gamma = \xi, \eta, \zeta$, and the ρ_γ being the relative phase-space factors for the combinations under consideration.

The results of this simple model are summarized in Table 17.7 (from Rubinstein and Stern). Even without reference to the table, however, a number of qualitative conclusions may be drawn from the model:

1. Two-meson final states are forbidden, the lowest final-state multiplicity being three pions. Larger-pion multiplicities arise from the decay of the heavier members of the pseudoscalar and vector-meson nonets.

[26] H. R. Rubinstein and H. Stern, *Phys. Letters, 21:* 447 (1966).

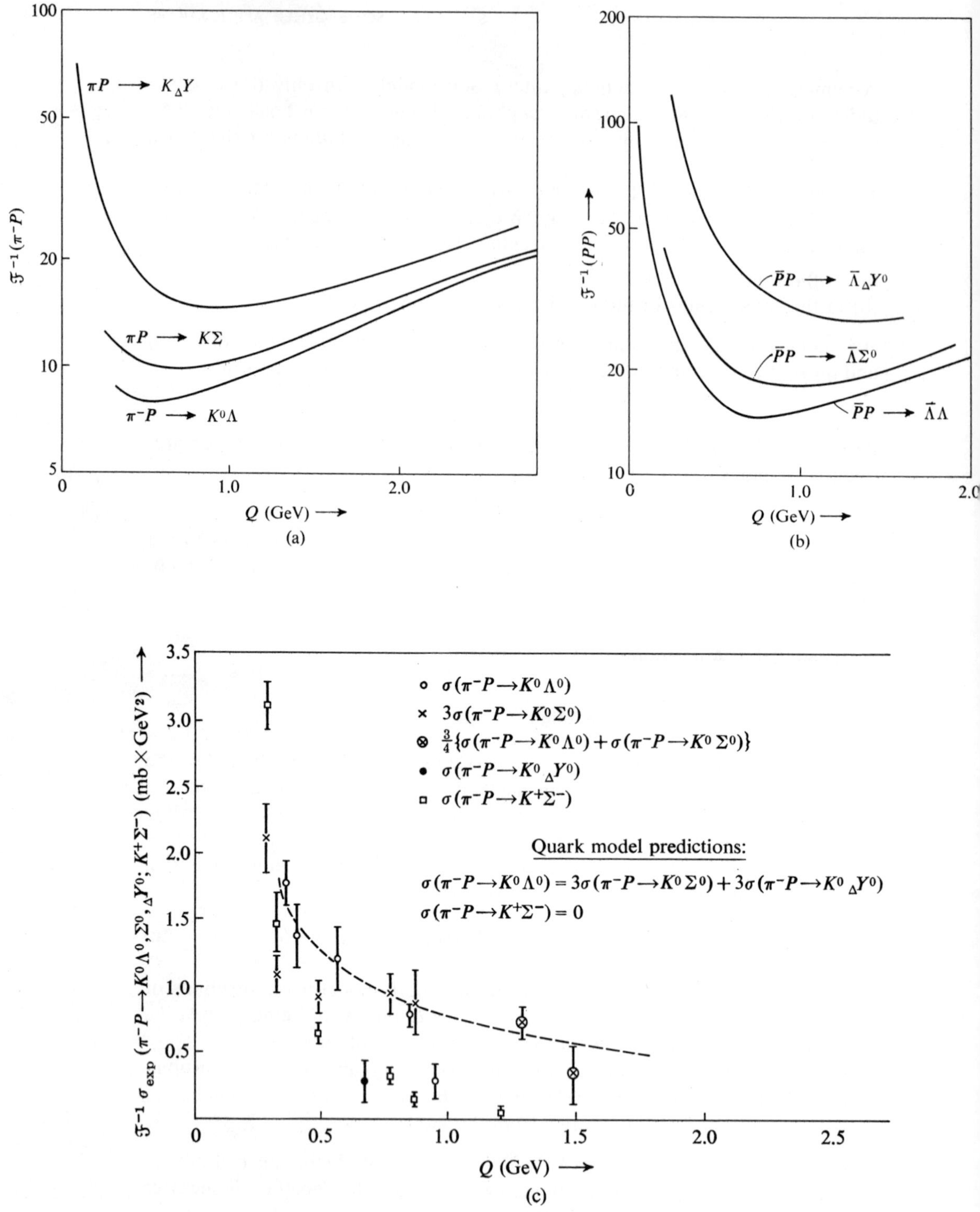

Figure 17.6 Comparison of quark model predictions with experiment for *total* cross sections: (a) Correction factors for $\pi P \to K\Lambda$, Σ. ${}_\Delta Y$ reactions. (b) Correction factors for $\bar{P}P \to \bar{\Lambda}\Lambda$, Σ, ${}_\Delta Y$ reactions. (c) Test of prediction (17c). (d) Test of predictions (18b) and (18c). (e) Test of prediction (18a). (The curves are drawn for convenience of following the trends only.)

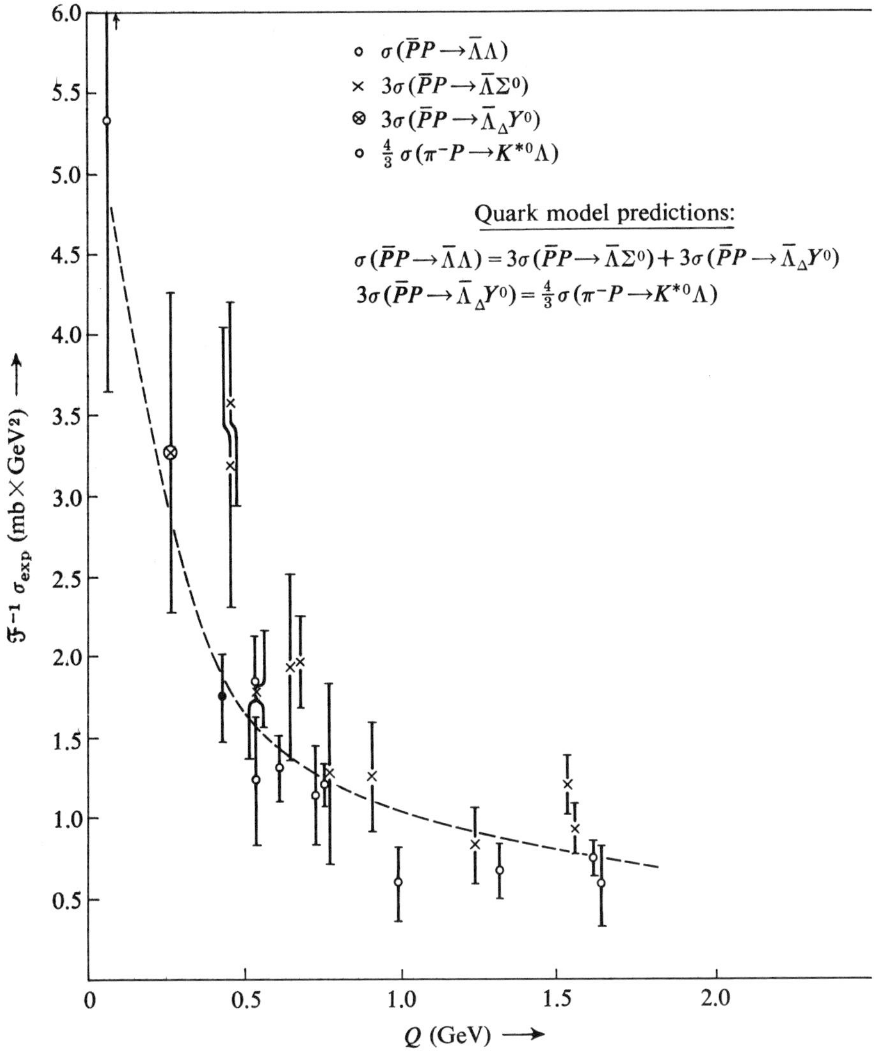

$\circ$ $\sigma(\bar{P}P \to \bar{\Lambda}\Lambda)$
$\times$ $3\sigma(\bar{P}P \to \bar{\Lambda}\Sigma^0)$
$\otimes$ $3\sigma(\bar{P}P \to \bar{\Lambda}_\Delta Y^0)$
$\circ$ $\frac{4}{3}\sigma(\pi^- P \to K^{*0}\Lambda)$
Quark model predictions:
$\sigma(\bar{P}P \to \bar{\Lambda}\Lambda) = 3\sigma(\bar{P}P \to \bar{\Lambda}\Sigma^0) + 3\sigma(\bar{P}P \to \bar{\Lambda}_\Delta Y^0)$
$3\sigma(\bar{P}P \to \bar{\Lambda}_\Delta Y^0) = \frac{4}{3}\sigma(\pi^- P \to K^{*0}\Lambda)$
$\mathfrak{F}^{-1}\sigma_{exp}$ (mb × GeV²) ⟶
Q (GeV) ⟶
6.0
5.5
5.0
4.5
4.0
3.5
3.0
2.5
2.0
1.5
1.0
0.5
0
0.5
1.0
1.5
2.0

(d)

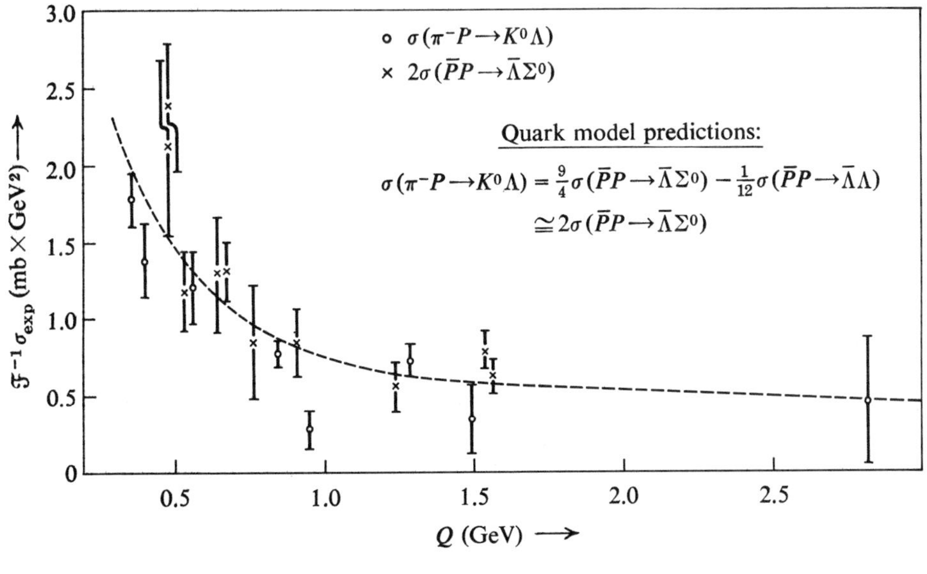

$\circ$ $\sigma(\pi^- P \to K^0\Lambda)$
$\times$ $2\sigma(\bar{P}P \to \bar{\Lambda}\Sigma^0)$
Quark model predictions:
$\sigma(\pi^- P \to K^0\Lambda) = \frac{9}{4}\sigma(\bar{P}P \to \bar{\Lambda}\Sigma^0) - \frac{1}{12}\sigma(\bar{P}P \to \bar{\Lambda}\Lambda)$
$\cong 2\sigma(\bar{P}P \to \bar{\Lambda}\Sigma^0)$
$\mathfrak{F}^{-1}\sigma_{exp}$ (mb × GeV²) ⟶
Q (GeV) ⟶
3.0
2.5
2.0
1.5
1.0
0.5
0
0.5
1.0
1.5
2.0
2.5

(e)

Table 17.7 Properties of $P\overline{P}$ Annihilation Predicted by the Quark-Rearrangement Model

Final state	Resulting pion combination	Branching ratio	$w_{\alpha\beta\gamma}$ $S(\alpha+\beta)=0$	$w_{\alpha\beta\gamma}$ $S(\alpha+\beta)=1$	FRACTION Rest	FRACTION 2.8 GeV
$\pi^+\pi^-\pi^0$	$\pi^+\pi^-\pi^0$	1.00	$\frac{9}{32}$	0	0.08	0.04
$3\pi^0$	$3\pi^0$	1.00	$\frac{27}{64}$	0	0.12	0.06
$\rho^+\pi^-\pi^0$	$\pi^+\pi^-2\pi^0$	1.00	0	$\frac{3}{32}$	0.01	0.01
$\rho^-\pi^+\pi^0$	$\pi^+\pi^-2\pi^0$	1.00	0	$\frac{3}{32}$	0.01	0.01
$\rho^0\pi^+\pi^-$	$2\pi^+2\pi^-$	1.00	0	$\frac{75}{32}$	0.25	0.17
$\rho^0 2\pi^0$	$\pi^+\pi^-2\pi^0$	1.00	0	$\frac{27}{64}$	0.045	0.03
$\eta^0\pi^+\pi^-$	$2\pi^+2\pi^-\pi^0$	0.25	$\frac{9}{32}$	0	0.01	0.00
$\eta^0 2\pi^0$	$\pi^+\pi^-3\pi^0$	0.25	$\frac{9}{64}$	0	0.005	0.00
$\omega^0\pi^+\pi^-$	$2\pi^+2\pi^-\pi^0$	0.88	0	$\frac{75}{32}$	0.28	0.19
$\omega^0 2\pi^0$	$\pi^+\pi^-3\pi^0$	0.88	0	$\frac{75}{64}$	0.14	0.095
$\rho^+\rho^-\pi^0$	$\pi^+\pi^-3\pi^0$	1.00	$\frac{75}{32}$	$\frac{27}{16}$	0.06	0.08
$\rho^0\rho^0\pi^0$	$2\pi^+2\pi^-\pi^0$	1.00	$\frac{27}{64}$	0	0.01	0.008
$\rho^0\omega^0\pi^0$	$2\pi^+2\pi^-2\pi^0$	0.88	$\frac{1}{32}$	0	0.00	0.026
$\rho^+\omega^0\pi^-$	$2\pi^+2\pi^-2\pi^0$	0.88	$\frac{3}{32}$	0	0.005	0.065
$\rho^-\omega^0\pi^+$	$2\pi^+2\pi^-2\pi^0$	0.88	$\frac{3}{32}$	0	0.005	0.065
$\rho^+\eta^0\pi^-$	$2\pi^+2\pi^-2\pi^0$	0.25	0	$\frac{3}{32}$	0.00	0.037
$\rho^-\eta^0\pi^+$	$2\pi^+2\pi^-2\pi^0$	0.25	0	$\frac{3}{32}$	0.00	0.037
$\rho^0\eta^0\pi^0$	$2\pi^+2\pi^-2\pi^0$	0.25	0	$\frac{3}{32}$	0.00	0.037
$\rho^+\rho^-\rho^0$	$2\pi^+2\pi^-2\pi^0$	1.00	$\frac{27}{16}$	$\frac{189}{32}$	0.00	0.00
$\rho^0\rho^0\rho^0$	$3\pi^+3\pi^-$	1.00	0	$\frac{45}{8}$	0.00	0.00
$X^0\pi^+\pi^-$	$3\pi^+3\pi^-\pi^0$	0.19	$\frac{9}{32}$	0	0.00	0.002
$X^0\pi^0\pi^0$	$2\pi^+2\pi^-3\pi^0$	0.19	$\frac{9}{64}$	0	0.00	0.001
$\eta^0\eta^0\pi^0$	$2\pi^+2\pi^-3\pi^0$	0.06	$\frac{9}{64}$	0	0.00	0.00
$\omega^0\omega^0\pi^0$	$2\pi^+2\pi^-3\pi^0$	0.77	$\frac{75}{64}$	0	0.00	0.032
$\omega^0\eta^0\pi^0$	$2\pi^+2\pi^-3\pi^0$	0.22	0	$\frac{3}{32}$	0.00	0.00
$\rho^+\rho^-\eta^0$	$2\pi^+2\pi^-3\pi^0$	0.25	$\frac{75}{32}$	$\frac{27}{16}$	0.00	0.00
$\rho^0\rho^0\eta^0$	$3\pi^+3\pi^-\pi^0$	0.25	$\frac{75}{64}$	0	0.00	0.00
$\rho^+\rho^-\omega^0$	$2\pi^+2\pi^-3\pi^0$	0.88	$\frac{27}{16}$	$\frac{189}{32}$	0.00	0.00
$\rho^0\rho^0\omega^0$	$3\pi^+3\pi^-\pi^0$	0.88	0	$\frac{37}{8}$	0.00	0.00
$X^0\rho^+\pi^-$	$3\pi^+3\pi^-2\pi^0$	0.19	0	$\frac{3}{32}$	0.00	0.00
$X^0\rho^-\pi^+$	$3\pi^+3\pi^-2\pi^0$	0.19	0	$\frac{3}{32}$	0.00	0.00
$X^0\rho^0\pi^0$	$3\pi^+3\pi^-2\pi^0$	0.19	0	$\frac{3}{32}$	0.00	0.00
$\rho^0\eta^0\omega^0$	$3\pi^+3\pi^-2\pi^0$	0.22	$\frac{3}{32}$	0	0.00	0.00
$\rho^0\eta^0\eta^0$	$3\pi^+3\pi^-2\pi^0$	0.06	0	$\frac{75}{64}$	0.00	0.00
$\rho^0\omega^0\omega^0$	$3\pi^+3\pi^-2\pi^0$	0.77	0	$\frac{189}{32}$	0.00	0.00

2. Strange particles cannot be directly produced owing to the absence of λ and $\overline{\lambda}$ quarks from the initial $\mathfrak{N}$ and $\overline{\mathfrak{N}}$ states. Although $K\overline{K}$ pairs would result from the decay of the ϕ-meson, its production is also forbidden to the extent that the ϕ is a pure $\lambda\overline{\lambda}$ state. By the same token, η-meson production is severely limited.

3. The mean pion multiplicity $\overline{n}$ is expected to increase slowly with increasing

energy owing to the increase in the phase-space factor corresponding to the production of the heavier mesons. For annihilation at rest, Table 17.7 predicts

$$\bar{n}(\text{rest}) = 4.4, \tag{26a}$$

which is to be compared with the experimental value of 5.0 ± 0.2. At higher incident energies, Rubinstein and Stern predict

$$\bar{n}(2.8 \text{ GeV}) = 4.7, \tag{26b}$$

$$\bar{n}(12 \text{ GeV}) = 6.4. \tag{26c}$$

Since one would expect the observed mean pion multiplicities to exceed those predicted, as a result of the possibility of Yukawa pion emission during the quark rearrangement process, the difference between the computed result (26a) and the experimental value is not surprising.

Obviously, the model of Rubinstein and Stern is unnecessarily simple, in that it neglects the possibility of charge exchange, spin-flip, and strangeness exchange in the $q\bar{q}$ interactions. However, the amplitudes for such processes are generally small as compared to those for elastic $q\bar{q}$ scattering, and we would therefore not expect that taking them into account will greatly alter the results given in Table 17.7. Thus, for example, although we expect some production of strange meson pairs through the reaction $\langle p\bar{p}|\lambda\bar{\lambda}\rangle$, this amplitude is predicted to be much smaller than the competing elastic $\langle p\bar{p}|p\bar{p}\rangle$ amplitude; thus, on the basis of Equations (3l′) and (3h′) and the observed elastic scattering cross sections, we estimate $\langle p\bar{p}|\lambda\bar{\lambda}\rangle / \langle p\bar{p}|p\bar{p}\rangle \approx \frac{1}{6}$ which, combined with the smaller phase space available to combinations including two strange mesons, accounts for the very small fraction of strange mesons observed in $\mathfrak{N}\bar{\mathfrak{N}}$ annihilation.

While the gross features of the predictions of Rubinstein and Stern — i.e., the values of $\bar{n}$ and the distribution of meson multiplicities for $n \geq 3$ — are roughly borne out by the observations, some of the details do not fare nearly so well when confronted with the experimental facts. Thus, although it is observed that the $\pi^+\pi^-\pi^0$ final state accounts for (6.9 ± 0.4) percent of the $P\bar{P}$ annihilations at rest,[27] these measurements also indicate that a large proportion of the observed 3π distribution arises from two-body final states (≈ 55 percent from $\rho^\pm\pi^\mp$ and ≈ 3.5 percent from $f^0\pi^0$), which are expected to be relatively unimportant on the basis of the quark-rearrangement model.

On the other hand, the existence of appreciable cross sections for the reactions $\pi^\pm P \to \rho^\pm P$ (involving ω^0 exchange in the t-channel) implies an appreciable s-channel amplitude for $P\bar{P} \to \pi^\pm\rho^\mp$, an effect which is not taken into account in the model of Rubinstein and Stern.

Clearly, a comprehensive theory of the $P\bar{P}$ annihilation process, even on the basis of the quark model, must eventually take such two-body processes into account. Pending the evaluation of all such effects, the predictions of Table 17.7 must be regarded as a crude first approximation.

---

[27] Foster, *et al.*, *Nucl. Phys.*, *B6:* 107 (1968); compare this figure with the prediction of 8 percent, row 1, Table 17.7.

17.3.2 More on the Vector-Dominance Model

In Section 17.1.3, we have used the vector-dominance model, in combination with the spin-independent quark scattering approximation [i.e., $SU(3)$ invariance], to explain the observed features of the photoproduction of vector mesons (Table 17.3). The same approach may be applied to the photoproduction of pions.

Consider, for example, the reaction

$$\gamma + P \rightarrow \pi^+ + N. \tag{27a}$$

According to the vector-dominance model, the main contributions to this reaction would be expected to arise from the two diagrams shown in Figure 17.7(a). Accordingly, the reaction amplitude is given by

$$\begin{aligned}\langle \gamma P|\pi^+N\rangle &= \sqrt{4\pi}\sum_v f_{v\gamma}\langle v^0P|\pi^+N\rangle_{\lambda=\pm1}\\ &= \sqrt{4\pi}\sum_v f_{v\gamma}\langle \pi^+N|v^0P\rangle_{\lambda=\pm1}\\ &= \sqrt{4\pi}\sum_v f_{v\gamma}\langle \pi^-P|v^0N\rangle_{\lambda=\pm1},\end{aligned} \tag{27b}$$

in which the successive steps follow, respectively, as a consequence of time-reversal and isotopic-spin invariance. The qualification ($\lambda=\pm1$) on the $\langle \pi\mathfrak{N}|v^0\mathfrak{N}'\rangle$ amplitudes indicates that the vector mesons in Figure 17.7(a) are produced in states of helicity ±1 only. Owing to the relative strengths of the $\gamma \rightarrow v^0$ vertices involved, reaction (27a) is expected to be dominated by the first of the two diagrams. If we neglect the $\gamma \rightarrow \omega^0$ contribution, the *cm* cross section for (27a) may be obtained in terms of the measurable cross section for the reaction

$$\pi^- + P \rightarrow \rho^0 + N \tag{27c}$$

through

$$\frac{d\sigma}{d\Omega}(\gamma P \rightarrow \pi^+N) \cong 4\pi f_{\rho\gamma}^2 \left(\frac{k_\pi}{k_\gamma}\right)^2 \rho_{11}^{(\rho)} \frac{d\sigma}{d\Omega}(\pi^-P \rightarrow \rho^0N). \tag{27d}$$

The factor $(k_\pi/k_\gamma)^2$ is a kinematical correction permitting the reactions to be compared at the same *cm* energy; the factor $\rho_{11}^{(\rho)}$ is the density matrix element corresponding to the $\lambda=\pm1$ helicity requirement on the product ρ in reaction (27c).

In the case of the reaction

$$\gamma + P \rightarrow \pi^0 + P, \tag{28a}$$

the processes involved are shown in Figure 17.7(b). In this case, the prediction of the cross section involves knowledge of the reactions

$$\pi^0 + P \rightarrow v^0 + P, \tag{28b}$$

which, although not directly measurable, follow from the application of charge independence to the measurable reactions

$$\pi^\pm P \rightarrow v\mathfrak{N}. \tag{28c}$$

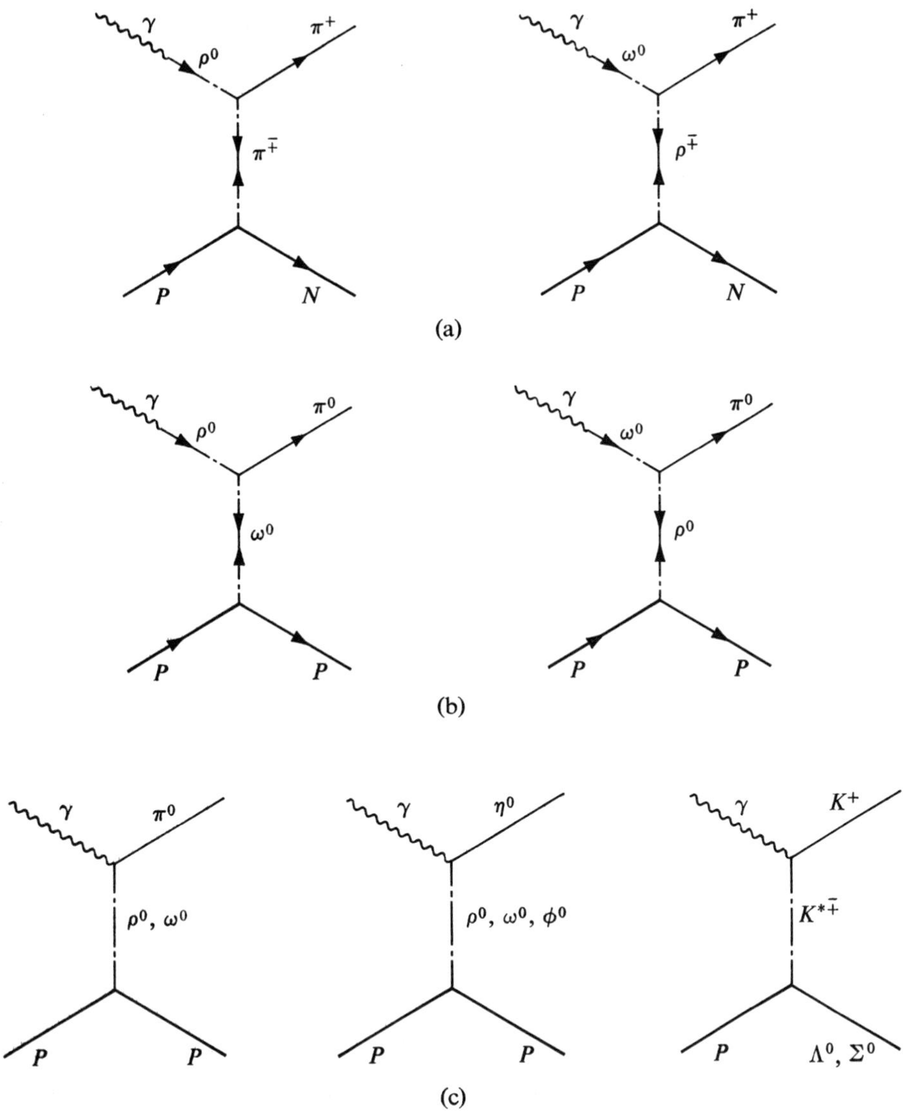

Figure 17.7 Diagrams for photopion production according to the vector-dominance model. (a) $\gamma P \rightarrow \pi^+ N$. (b) $\gamma P \rightarrow \pi^0 P$. (c) Direct diagrams for pseudoscalar meson photoproduction.

In particular, owing to the relative strengths of the $\gamma \rightarrow v^0$ vertices involved, we expect the ω^0-exchange process to dominate in π^0 photoproduction.

This approach has been applied successfully to reactions (27a) and (28a) by a number of authors.[28] In addition, through a similar series of arguments, and also

[28] A. Dar, V. F. Weisskopf, C. A. Levinson, and H. J. Lipkin, *Phys. Rev. Letters, 20:* 1261 (1968); C. Iso and H. Yoshii, *Ann. Phys.* (New York), *47:* 424 and *48:* 237 (1968).

utilizing the quark-model [or $SU(6)$-symmetry] properties of the mesons, Dar and Weisskopf[29] are able to relate the cross section for the photoproduction of η-mesons to that for the reaction $(\pi^+ N \to \omega^0 P)$, which involves predominantly ρ-meson exchange.

Finally, vector dominance may be used to relate the total $\gamma\mathfrak{N}$ cross section to observable cross sections for vector-meson photoproduction in the forward direction, by use of the diagram of Figure 17.8 and the arguments developed in Section 17.1.3, using

$$\begin{aligned}\langle\gamma\mathfrak{N}|\gamma\mathfrak{N}\rangle &= \sqrt{4\pi}\sum_i f_{v_i\gamma}\langle\gamma\mathfrak{N}|v_i^0\mathfrak{N}\rangle \\ &= 4\pi\sum_i f_{v_i\gamma}^2\langle v_i^0\mathfrak{N}|v_i^0\mathfrak{N}\rangle, \qquad (12a')\end{aligned}$$

together with the optical theorem. On this basis, a total γP cross section of $\approx$ 110–140 μb, essentially constant over the 1–10 GeV/c energy range, is predicted, in excellent agreement with the observations.[30]

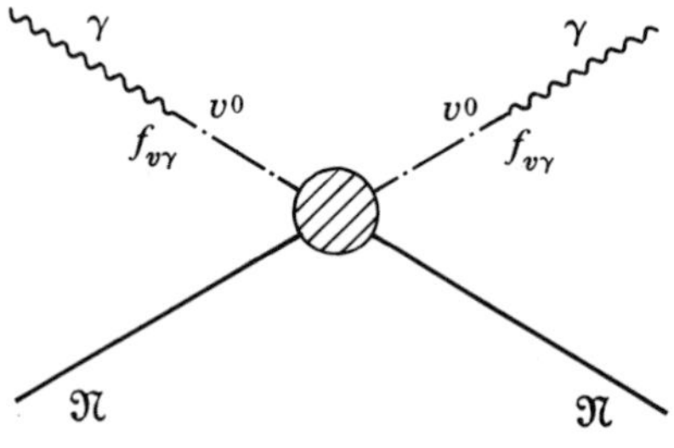

Figure 17.8 Photon Compton scattering according to the vector-dominance model.

17.3.3 Quark Model with the Assumption of Factorizability

An interesting, and surprisingly fruitful conjecture concerning the hadron-hadron scattering amplitudes for finite momentum transfer has been put forward by Kawaguchi, Sumi, and Yokomi.[31] They assume that the amplitude for scattering of two hadrons through the (cm) angle θ is made up out of the contributions of terms relating to the scattering of the individual quarks, either through the angle θ or $\pi-\theta$, with each contribution being proportional to the *product* of the individual quark scattering amplitudes. In some sense, this amounts to a quark "rearrangement" model for the scattering process, with the assumption of

---

[29] A. Dar and V. F. Weisskopf, *Phys. Rev. Letters, 20:* 762 (1968). For a striking confirmation of their predictions, see Bellenger, *et al., Phys. Rev. Letters, 21:* 1205 (1968).

[30] S. C. C. Ting, *Proceedings of the 14th International Conference on High-Energy Physics,* Vienna (September 1968).

[31] M. Kawaguchi, Y. Sumi, and H. Yokomi, *Progr. Theoret. Phys.* (Japan), *38:* 1178 and 1183 (1967); *Phys. Rev., 168:* 1556 (1968). The model has been extended to inelastic two-body reactions by M. Ikeda, M. Kawaguchi, and H. Yokomi, *Progr. Theoret. Phys.* (Japan), *40:* 594 (1968).

multiplicative probabilities for the individual quark rearrangement processes (i.e., deflection through the *cm* angle θ), and with the further assumption that the amplitude for a given hadron scattering process is proportional to the net (i.e., product) probability that the appropriate quark combinations will emerge in the appropriate directions.

We may illustrate the procedure for computing the hadron-hadron reaction amplitudes in terms of the individual quark-rearrangement amplitudes, by considering the case of PP scattering and the rearrangement diagrams of Figure 17.9. Let $g(\theta)$ be the multiplicative factor corresponding to the deflection of a p or n quark through the angle θ. Diagram (a) then corresponds to all six quarks being deflected through the angle θ. Diagram (b) represents an exchange of one quark between the two P's (i.e., two quark deflections through the angle $\pi-\theta$); there are five possible combinations — four for the exchange of a p quark and one for the n quark. The same holds true for the two-quark exchange process, diagram (c). Finally, all six quarks can be deflected through $\pi-\theta$ (complete exchange) as in (d). Hence, the scattering amplitude becomes [32]

$$\begin{aligned}\langle PP|PP\rangle(\theta) &= g^6(\theta) + 5g^4(\theta)\, g^2(\pi-\theta) + 5g^2(\theta)\, g^4(\pi-\theta) + g^6(\pi-\theta)\\ &= g^6(\theta)[1 + 5r^2(\theta) + 5r^4(\theta) + r^6(\theta)]\\ &= g^6(\theta)\,(1 + 4r^2 + r^4)\,(1 + r^2), \qquad (29a)\end{aligned}$$

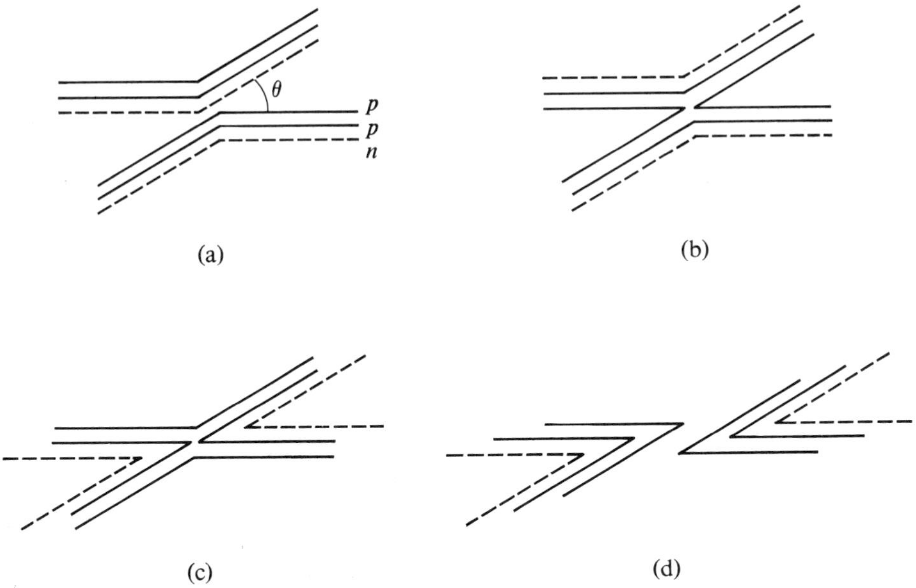

Figure 17.9 Contributions to P–P scattering according to the factorizability model of Kawaguchi, Sumi, and Yokomi. (a) $g^6(\theta)$. (b) $5g^4(\theta)\, g^2(\pi-\theta)$. (c) $5g^2(\theta)\, g^4(\pi-\theta)$. (d) $g^6(\pi-\theta)$.

[32] We absorb all kinematic factors into $g(\theta)$.

where

$$r(\theta) \equiv \frac{g(\pi-\theta)}{g(\theta)}. \tag{29b}$$

In such fashion, Ikeda, Kawaguchi, Sumi, and Yokomi have computed the amplitudes for various possible elastic and inelastic two-body reactions between hadronic members of the pseudoscalar meson and baryon octets, in terms of the assumed (spin and isotopic-spin independent) rearrangement amplitudes

$$\langle p|p\rangle = \langle n|n\rangle = \langle \bar{p}|\bar{p}\rangle = \langle \bar{n}|\bar{n}\rangle = g(\theta), \tag{30a}$$

$$\langle \lambda|\lambda\rangle = \langle \bar{\lambda}|\bar{\lambda}\rangle = g'(\theta), \tag{30b}$$

and the annihilation (i.e., charge and hypercharge exchange) amplitudes

$$\langle \bar{p}p|\bar{p}p\rangle = \langle \bar{n}n|\bar{n}n\rangle = \langle \bar{p}p|\bar{n}n\rangle = h_1^2(\theta), \tag{30c}$$

$$\langle \bar{p}p|\bar{\lambda}\lambda\rangle = \langle \bar{n}n|\bar{\lambda}\lambda\rangle = h_2^2(\theta). \tag{30d}$$

The results, summarized in Table 17.8, are somewhat simplified by the further assumption

$$r'(\theta) = \frac{g'(\pi-\theta)}{g'(\theta)} = r(\theta). \tag{29b$'$}$$

The total cross sections for hadron-hadron processes are obtained from the forward ($\theta = 0$) elastic scattering amplitudes via the optical theorem. Although the relations obtained from the amplitudes contained in Table 17.8 are consistent with the Johnson–Treiman relations, Equations (6a) and (6d), assuming $g' = g$, the simple relations among mB and BB cross sections derived from the additivity model, Equations (6b), (6e), (6f), no longer obtain for the factorizability model.

However, the amplitudes of Table 17.8 yield another type of relationship, e.g.,

$$\frac{\sigma_{\text{tot}}(\pi^+P)}{\sigma_{\text{tot}}(\pi^-P)} = \frac{\sigma_{\text{tot}}(K^+P)}{\sigma_{\text{tot}}(K^+N)} \cdot \frac{\sigma_{\text{tot}}(K^-N)}{\sigma_{\text{tot}}(K^-P)}, \tag{31a}$$

and

$$\frac{\sigma_{\text{tot}}(K^+P)}{\sigma_{\text{tot}}(K^+N)} \cong \frac{\sigma_{\text{tot}}(PP)}{\sigma_{\text{tot}}(PN)}, \tag{31b}$$

[the latter resulting from the neglect of higher powers of $|r^2(\theta = 0)| \ll 1$], which stand up quite well on comparison with the observations.

The relationship (31a) also applies to the differential scattering cross sections, or amplitudes squared, at all values of the 4-momentum transfer $-t$. Other connections between values of $d\sigma/dt$, which can be derived from the amplitudes of Table 17.8, include[33]

$$\frac{d\sigma(K^-P \to \pi^-\Sigma^+)}{d\sigma(K^-P \to K^-P)} = \frac{d\sigma(PN \to NP)}{d\sigma(PN \to PN)} = |r^2(\theta)|^2, \tag{31c}$$

[33] Note that $\langle PN|NP\rangle = g^6r^2(1 + 4r^2 + r^4)$ by letting $\theta \to \pi - \theta$ in the expression for $\langle PN|PN\rangle$.

Table 17.8 Hadron-Hadron Reaction Amplitudes Based on the Factorizability Model of Ikeda, Kawaguchi, Sumi, and Yokomi

Process	Amplitude
(a) $m + B \to m' + B'$	
$\pi^+P \to \pi^+P$	$g^3(\theta)\,[g^2(\theta) + h_1^2(\theta)]\,[1 + 2r^2(\theta)]$
$\to K^+\Sigma^+$	$g^3(\theta)\,h_2^2(\theta)\,[1 + 2r^2(\theta)]$
$\pi^-P \to \pi^-P$	$g^3(g^2 + 2h_1^2)\,(1 + r^2)$
$\to \pi^0N$	$\sqrt{\frac{1}{2}}\,g^3(r^2g^2 - h_1^2)$
$\to \eta^0N$	$(1/\sqrt{6})\,g^3(r^2g^2 + h_1^2 + 2r^2h_1^2)$
$\to K^0\Lambda$	$-\sqrt{\frac{3}{2}}\,g^3h_2^2\,(1 + r^2)$
$\to K^0\Sigma^0$	$-(1/\sqrt{2})\,g^3h_2^2(1 + r^2)$
$\to K^+\Sigma^-$	$-g^3r^2h_2^2$
$K^+P \to K^+P$	$g^4g'(1 + 2r^2)$
$K^+N \to K^+N$	$g^4g'(1 + r^2)$
$K^-P \to K^-P$	$g^2g'(g^2 + 2h_1^2)$
$\to \overline{K^0}N$	$g^2g'h_1^2$
$\to K^+\Xi^-$	$-2g^2g'r^2h_2^2$
$\to K^0\Xi^0$	$-g^2g'r^2h_2^2$
$\to \pi^+\Sigma^-$	$-g^2g'r^2h_1^2$
$\to \pi^0\Lambda$	$-(\sqrt{3}/2)\,g^2g'r^2(g^2 + h_1^2)$
$\to \pi^0\Sigma^0$	$-\frac{1}{2}g^2g'r^2(g^2 + 3h_1^2)$
$\to \eta^0\Lambda$	$-\frac{1}{2}g^2g'(r^2g^2 + r^2h_1^2 - 2h_2^2)$
$\to \eta^0\Sigma^0$	$-(1/2\sqrt{3})\,g^2g'(r^2g^2 - r^2h_1^2 - 2h_2^2)$
$\to \pi^-\Sigma^+$	$g^2g'r^2(g^2 + 2h_1^2)$
$K^-N \to K^-N$	$g^2g'(g^2 + h_1^2)$
(b) $B_1 + B_2 \to B_1' + B_2'$	
$PP \to PP$	$g^6(1 + 4r^2 + r^4)\,(1 + r^2)$
$PN \to PN$	$g^6(1 + 4r^2 + r^4)$
$\overline{P}P \to \overline{P}P$	$(g^4 + 4g^2h_1^2 + h_1^4)\,(g^2 + h_1^2)$
$\to \overline{N}N$	$h_1^2(g^2 + h_1^2)^2$
$\to \overline{\Sigma^+}\Sigma^+$	$h_2^2(g^4 + 4g^2h_1^2 + h_1^4)$
$\to \overline{\Lambda}\Lambda$	$\frac{3}{2}h_2^2(g^2 + h_1^2)^2$
$\to \overline{\Lambda}\Sigma^0$ or $\overline{\Sigma^0}\Lambda$	$(\sqrt{3}/2)\,h_2^2(g^2 + h_1^2)^2$
$\to \overline{\Sigma^0}\Sigma^0$	$\frac{1}{2}h_2^2(g^2 + h_1^2)^2$
$\to \overline{\Sigma^-}\Sigma^-$	$h_1^2h_2^2(g^2 + h_1^2)$
$\to \overline{\Xi^-}\Xi^-$	$h_2^4(g^2 + h_1^2)$
$\overline{P}N \to \overline{P}N$	$g^2(g^2 + 2h_1^2)^2$

$$\frac{d\sigma(K^-P \to K^+\Xi^-)}{d\sigma(K^-P \to \pi^+\Sigma^-)} = \frac{4d\sigma(\overline{P}P \to \overline{\Lambda}\Lambda)}{9d\sigma(\overline{P}P \to \overline{N}N)} = \frac{d\sigma(\overline{P}P \to \overline{\Xi^-}\Xi^-)}{d\sigma(\overline{P}P \to \overline{\Sigma^-}\Sigma^-)} = \left|\frac{h_2^2}{h_1^2}\right|^2, \tag{31d}$$

$$\frac{d\sigma(\pi^+P \to K^+\Sigma^+)}{d\sigma(\pi^+P \to \pi^+P)} = \frac{d\sigma(\overline{P}P \to \overline{\Sigma^+}\Sigma^+)}{d\sigma(\overline{P}P \to \overline{P}P)} = \frac{d\sigma(\overline{P}P \to \overline{\Sigma^-}\Sigma^-)}{d\sigma(\overline{P}P \to \overline{N}N)}$$

$$= \left|\frac{h_2^2}{g^2 + h_1^2}\right|^2 = \left|\frac{h_2^2}{h_1^2}\right|^2 \frac{d\sigma(K^-P \to \overline{K^0}N)}{d\sigma(K^-P \to K^-P)}. \tag{31e}$$

Such relationships, and others, can be used to obtain numerical values of the parameters involved in the factorizability model. Thus, applying Equations (31b) and (31c) to the PN and PP scattering observations yields (over the incident nucleon energy range $\sim$ 2–10 GeV/c)

$$r^2(0) \cong -0.1, \tag{32a}$$

the choice of the minus sign deriving from the observation (see Figures 13.1 and 17.1)

$$\frac{\sigma_{\text{tot}}(K^+P)}{\sigma_{\text{tot}}(K^+N)} = \frac{[1 + 2r^2(0)]}{[1 + r^2(0)]} < 1. \tag{31f}$$

Likewise, the annihilation parameter

$$\left|\frac{h_1^2(0)}{g^2(0)}\right| \leq 0.1 \tag{32b}$$

follows, over the same energy range, on the basis of the observed value of the ratio $d\sigma(K^-P \to \overline{K^0}N)/d\sigma(K^-P \to K^-P)$, while the ratio

$$\left|\frac{h_2^2(0)}{h_1^2(0)}\right| \cong 0.3 \tag{32c}$$

is obtained from the ratio $d\sigma(\overline{P}P \to \overline{\Lambda}\Lambda)/d\sigma(\overline{P}P \to \overline{N}N)$ in the forward direction. Finally,

$$\frac{g'(\theta)}{g(\theta)} \cong 0.8\text{–}0.9 \tag{32d}$$

is derived from the observed ratio $d\sigma(K^-P \to K^-P)/d\sigma(\pi^-P \to \pi^-P)$.

However, knowledge of the ratios of the quark-rearrangement amplitudes at $\theta = 0°$ [Equations (32a) through (32d)] is not sufficient to specify their dependence on θ or t and particularly their values for large 4-momentum transfers, at which the factorizability model is most interesting. Thus, for example, at $\theta = \pi/2$ we have $r(\pi/2) = 1$, by definition; and, indeed, most of these ratios appear to increase with increasing $|t|$, at least for small values of the momentum transfer.

We may obtain the value of $x_1^2 \equiv h_1^2/g^2)_{\theta=\pi/2}$ by comparing the appropriate differential scattering cross sections $d\sigma(aP)/d\sigma(bP)$, as shown in Table 17.9. We note that the meson-baryon results indicate $x_1^2 \cong 1$, but that the B–P scattering observations do not agree, the $PP/\overline{P}P$ comparison favoring a value of $x_1^2 \sim 0.2$, while the PP/PN ratio should have the value of 4, independent of x_1, instead of the observed value of ≈ 1.

Of particular interest are the backward-to-forward ratios

$$R \equiv \frac{d\sigma(\pi)}{d\sigma(0)}. \tag{33}$$

Generally, these depend on the ratios

$$r_1 = \frac{h_1^2(\pi)}{h_1^2(0)} \tag{33a}$$

Table 17.9 Comparison Between Observed Ratios of Cross Sections at 90° (cm) and the Predictions of the Factorizability Model

RATIO	PREDICTED VALUE $x_1^2=0$	$\frac{1}{4}$	$\frac{1}{2}$	1	OBSERVED VALUE k_{in} (GeV/c)	Ratio
$PP/\bar{P}P$ [a]	144	22	5.2	1	5.9	~ 35
PP/PN [b]	4	4	4	4	3	1.4 ± 0.2
					5	1.0 ± 0.4
					7	0.6 ± 0.3
					3–7	0.9 ± 0.1
π^+P/π^-P [c]	$\frac{9}{4}$	1.56	1.27	1	~ 1.5	~ 2
					2	~ 1
					4	~ 1
K^+P/K^-P [d]	9	4	$\frac{9}{4}$	1	1.2	1.0 ± 0.1
					2.0	1.2 ± 0.5
					3–3.5	~ 0.5–1

[a] C. W. Akerlof, *et al.*, *Phys. Rev.*, *159:* 1138 (1967); R. Rubinstein, *et al.*, *CERN Conference on High Energy Hadron Collisions*, 1968 (private communication).
[b] C. W. Akerlof, *et al.*, *Phys. Rev.*, *159:* 1138 (1967); M. N. Kreisler, *et al.*, *Phys. Rev. Letters*, *16:* 1217 (1966); J. Cox, *et al.*, *Phys. Rev. Letters*, *21:* 641 (1968).
[c] W. R. Frisken, *et al.*, *Phys. Rev. Letters*, *15:* 313 (1965).
[d] V. Cook, *et al.*, *Phys. Rev.*, *129:* 2743 (1963); W. Chinowsky, *et al.*, *Phys. Rev.*, *139:* B1411 (1965); J. Banaigs, *et al.*, *Phys. Letters*, *24B:* 317 (1967); W. R. Holley, *et al.*, *Phys. Rev.*, *154:* 1273 (1967); L. Sodickson, *et al.*, *Phys. Rev.*, *133:* B757 (1964); R. Crittenden, *et al.*, *Phys. Rev. Letters*, *12:* 429 (1964).

and

$$r_2 = \frac{h_2^2(\pi)}{h_2^2(0)}, \tag{33b}$$

on which there is only very scanty experimental information. Using an estimate of $|r_2|^2 \simeq \frac{1}{5}$, derived from the observed

$$R(\pi^-P \to K^0\Lambda) = \left| r(0)\,\frac{h_2^2(\pi)}{h_2^2(0)} \right|^2 \simeq \frac{1}{50}, \tag{33c}$$

together with the assumption $|r_1| \cong |r_2|$, as well as the values of the other ratios previously estimated [see Equations (32a) through (32d)], Ikeda, Kawaguchi, and Yokomi[34] have compared the predicted and observed values of R for a variety of two-body reactions. This comparison is reproduced in Table 17.10. On the whole, the agreement is excellent.

As a final application of the factorizability model, we consider the values of R for the elastic scattering reactions. Among these (see Table 17.8), the values $R(NP)$, $R(K^+P)$, and $R(K^+N)$ depend only on the backward-to-forward ratios of the quark-rearrangement amplitudes, for which we assume $|r(0)| \cong |r'(0)|$. The others depend, as well, on the ratios h_1^2/g^2 ($\theta = 0$ and $\theta = \pi$), which we assume to be negligible [see Equations (32a) through (32d)]. The observed cross-section

[34] *Progr. Theoret. Phys.* (Japan), *40:* 594 (1968).

Table 17.10 Backward-to-Forward Ratio of the Differential Reaction Cross Sections for Various Two-Body Processes[a]

	PREDICTION (4 GeV/c)		EXPERIMENT		
PROCESS	R	Peak	R	Peak	k_{in} (GeV/c)
$\pi^+P \to K^+\Sigma^+$	$\frac{1}{10}$	forward	$\frac{1}{6}$	forward	4
$\pi^-P \to K^0\Lambda$	$\frac{1}{40}$	forward	$\frac{1}{40}$	forward	4
$\pi^-P \to K^0\Sigma^0$	$\frac{1}{40}$	forward	$\frac{1}{120}$	forward	4
$\pi^-P \to K^+\Sigma^-$	2.5	backward	13	backward	4
$K^-P \to K^+\Xi^-$	2.5	backward	$\frac{3}{0}$	backward	6
$K^-P \to \pi^+\Sigma^-$		backward	2.5	backward	2.24
$\pi^+P \to \pi^+P$	4×10^{-3}	forward	5×10^{-3}	forward	4
$\pi^-P \to \pi^-P$	10^{-3}	forward	6×10^{-4}	forward	4
$K^+P \to K^+P$	4×10^{-3}	forward	3×10^{-3}	forward	3.55
$K^-P \to K^-P$	10^{-5}	forward	$< 4 \times 10^{-5}$	forward	3.55
$K^-P \to \pi^-\Sigma^+$	$\frac{1}{10}$	forward	$\frac{1}{20}$	forward	2.24
$K^-P \to \pi^0\Lambda$	$\frac{1}{10}$	forward	$\frac{1}{8}$	forward	6
$K^-P \to \overline{K^0}N$		forward	$\frac{0}{50}$	forward	6

[a] See Ikeda, Kawaguchi, and Yokomi, *Progr. Theoret. Phys.* (Japan), *40:* 594 (1968).

ratios are plotted in Figure 17.10, as a function of the incident particle (*lab*) momentum, k_{in}, while the values of $|r^2(0)|$, deduced from the smooth curves connecting the data points, are compared in Table 17.11. The values derived from the different elastic scattering reactions agree[35] to within a factor of ~ 2.

Figure 17.10 indicates a very strong energy dependence of $|r^2(0)|$. However, the relative shapes of the momentum dependences of the different $R(aA)$ curves appear to follow quite well the predictions shown in Table 17.11.

Similarly, the factorizability model predicts a constant value of $\simeq 4$ for the ratio $d\sigma(\pi^+P)/d\sigma(\pi^-P)$ in the backward direction ($\theta = \pi$) which is borne out by the available measurements. The backward ratio $4d\sigma(K^-P)/d\sigma(K^+P) \simeq |r^2(0)|^2$, on the other hand, is expected to decrease with energy, roughly like $R(NP)$ in Figure 17.10(a), while the ratio of baryon-baryon backward scattering is predicted to be $d\sigma(\overline{P}P)/d\sigma(NP) \simeq |r^2(0)|^4$. Both these predictions are not in disagreement with the very meager experimental information.

The success of the factorizability model seems to imply that, at least for

[35] In fact, if we compare the values of R at the same value of the *cm* quark momentum, an incident momentum $k_{in} = 8$ GeV/c for NP scattering would correspond to $k_{in} = 3.6$ GeV/c for $\pi^{\pm}P$ scattering, and the corresponding values of $|r^2(0)|$ deduced from π^+P [Figure 17.10(a)] and π^-P [Figure 17.10(b)] scattering would be 0.14 and 0.10, respectively.

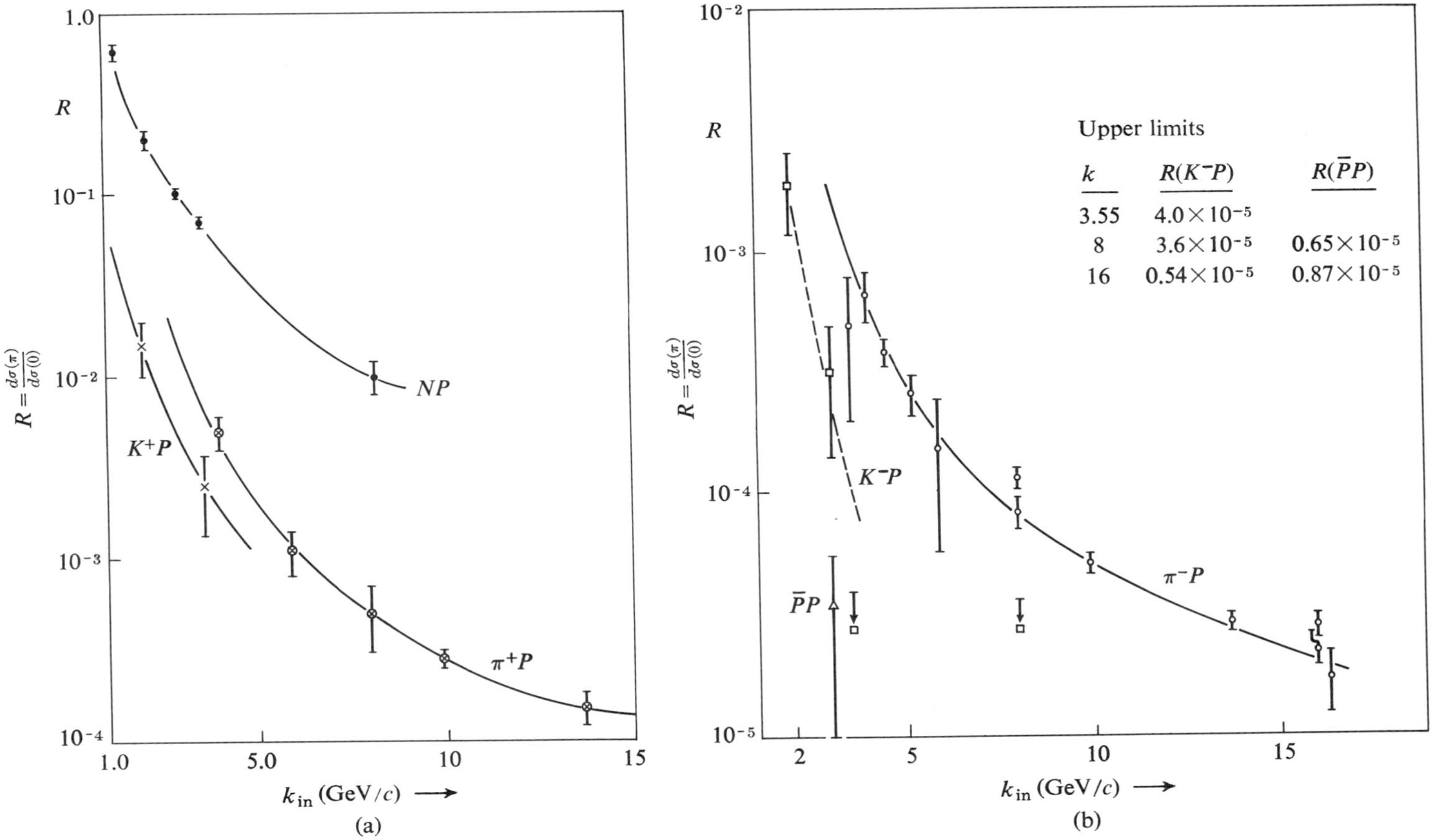

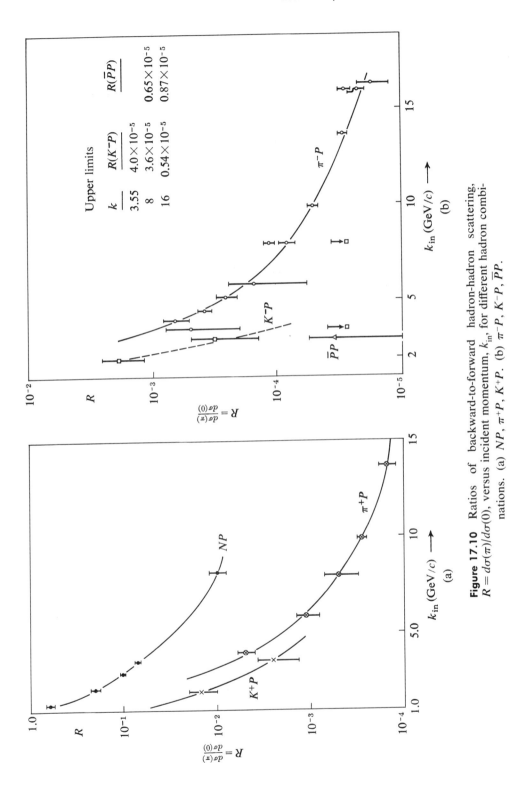

Figure 17.10 Ratios of backward-to-forward hadron-hadron scattering, $R = d\sigma(\pi)/d\sigma(0)$, versus incident momentum, k_{in}, for different hadron combinations. (a) NP, π^+P, K^+P. (b) π^-P, K^-P, $\bar{P}P$.

Table 17.11 Predictions of the Factorizability Model for the Ratio of Backward-to-Forward Hadron-Hadron Scattering Cross Sections

Process	$R = d\sigma(\pi)/d\sigma(0)$	$\lvert r^2(0)\rvert$ ($k_{\text{in}} = 8$ GeV/c)
$NP \to NP$	$\lvert r^2(0)\rvert^2$	0.10
$\pi^+P \to \pi^+P$, $K^+P \to K^+P$	$4\lvert r^2(0)\rvert^3 \cdot \dfrac{\lvert 1+\frac{1}{2}r^2(0)\rvert^2}{\lvert 1+2r^2(0)\rvert^2}$	0.053
$\pi^-P \to \pi^-P$, $K^+N \to K^+N$	$\lvert r^2(0)\rvert^3$	0.046
$K^-P \to K^-P$, $K^-N \to K^-N$	$\lvert r^2(0)\rvert^5$	—
$\overline{P}P \to \overline{P}P$	$\lvert r^2(0)\rvert^6$	—

scatterings involving appreciable momentum transfer, the individual quark-rearrangement probabilities (amplitudes) may be thought of as being statistically independent, so that a given reaction requires the coincidence of independent quark deflections through the appropriate angle for all the quarks involved. In a very crude sense, this model would seem to imply relatively weak quark bindings and, correspondingly, relatively small quark masses. However, it is dangerous to draw such a mechanistic conclusion from what might well be a coincidental set of empirical relationships.

PROBLEMS

1. Consider a model in which the 0^+, 1^+, and 2^+ mesons (m^+) are taken to be $q\bar{q}q\bar{q}$ compounds belonging to the 189-plet representation of $SU(6)$; see Table 16.1.
   Adopting the quark-rearrangement model for $\overline{P}P$ annihilations at rest, derive the relative strengths of the possible $\overline{P}P \to m_{35}m^+$ final states.
2. Consider the reactions

$$\gamma P \to K^+\Lambda^0$$
$$\to K^+\Sigma^0.$$

   (a) What is the Feynman diagram corresponding to these reactions according to the vector-dominance model (see Figure 17.7)?
   (b) Predict the ratio of the two cross sections, on the assumption that the relative strengths of the $PK\Lambda^0/PK\Sigma^0$ vertices are determined by the relative values of the $SU(3)$ combination coefficients.
   (c) Consider the "direct" process as depicted in Figure 17.7(c). How does this affect the previous considerations?
   (d) Compare your predictions with the available experimental values of the cross sections under consideration.

3. Derive the relationships among the reactions

$$\pi^- P \rightarrow v\mathfrak{N}$$

on the basis of the factorizability model.

4. Recent measurements on backward ρ^- production in the reactions [36]

$$\pi^- P \rightarrow P\rho^-$$

yield the following values of the parameters used in fitting the differential cross section $d\sigma/du = Ae^{au}$.

k_π (GeV/c)	A [mb (GeV)$^{-2}$]	a (GeV)$^{-2}$
8	7.6 ± 0.6	5.8 ± 0.6
16	1.4 ± 0.2	4.4 ± 0.6

Discuss these from the point of view of the factorizability model.

---

[36] H. R. Bleiden, *et al., Bull. Am. Phys. Soc., 13:* 1442 (1968).

18

The Weak Interactions

We have previously outlined, in Section 2.2, the main characteristics of the weak interactions and the consequent weak decays — leptonic (into electrons, muons, and neutrinos only), semileptonic (leptons plus hadrons), and nonleptonic (hadrons only).[1] The kinematical features of decay processes have been discussed in Chapters 3 through 8, including the consequences of angular momentum conservation and parity nonconservation (Section 6.1.3), isotopic-spin conservation and the $\Delta t = \frac{1}{2}$ selection rule (Section 7.4.3), and the peculiar aspects of the K_1^0–K_2^0 conversion and decay phenomena (Chapter 8). In this chapter, we consider the relationships among the different weak decay processes, mainly in terms of some useful models of hadron structure and of the symmetries that can be built into the phenomenological Lagrangian used to describe the weak interactions. Finally, we describe some consequences of recently developed techniques for elucidating the relationships among the weak, electromagnetic, and strong interactions.

18.1 Review of Fermi Theory of β Decay [2]

The most useful approach to the computation of the properties of the weak interactions is a generalization of the prescription originally given by Fermi, in which the observed 4-fermion interactions (Figure 2.1) are described in terms

[1] The measured parameters associated with the weak decays of the elementary particles are given in Table 2.1. Also see Appendix 8 for the best available values of the parameters of the *CP*-violating K_L^0 decays.

[2] E. Fermi, *Z. Physik, 88:* 161 (1934). In preparing this chapter, we have leaned heavily on recent reviews by T. D. Lee and C. S. Wu, *Ann. Rev. Nucl. Sci., 15:* 381 (1965) and *16:* 471 (1966), and by N. Cabibbo, *Proceedings of the XIII International Conference on High-Energy Physics,* University of California Press, Berkeley (1966). The reader is also referred to a number of illuminating discussions on current problems in the new journal *Comments on Nuclear and Particle Physics,* Gordon and Breach, New York.

of a phenomenological Lagrangian

$$\mathcal{L}_w = \frac{G_w}{\sqrt{2}} \{l_\lambda l_\lambda^* + J_\lambda l_\lambda + J_\lambda^* l_\lambda^*\} + \mathcal{L}_{wh}. \tag{1}$$

The constant G_w (of dimensions M^{-2})[3] is a universal (Fermi) coupling constant. The first term gives rise to the leptonic interactions, l_λ being the leptonic current; J_λ is a hadronic current, so that the next two terms represent the semileptonic weak interactions. Finally, $\mathcal{L}_{wh}$ represents the nonleptonic (purely hadronic) weak interactions. Assuming the universal β-decay tetrahedron [Figure 2.1(b)], we would expect

$$\mathcal{L}_{wh} = \frac{G_w}{\sqrt{2}} J_\lambda J_\lambda^*, \tag{1a}$$

but there are special problems, associated with the strong interactions, to which we shall return, which make it less convenient to treat the nonleptonic weak decays in precisely this form.

The prescription of Fermi specifies that the matrix elements of $\mathcal{L}_w$ between the various possible initial and final states (involving, in general, a total of four fermions) are to be computed by the use of first-order perturbation theory, ignoring the fact that the application of conventional field theory to the computation of higher-order terms generally gives rise to divergent results. However, even ignoring this aspect of the phenomenological theory, we cannot expect to be able to ignore the effects of the strong (hadronic) interactions in modifying the form of the weak hadronic current, J_λ, and in complicating the computation of the semileptonic and nonleptonic decays. For the leptonic decay term, the simple prescription of Fermi can be carried through in a straightforward fashion.

18.1.1 Leptonic Decays

The form of the leptonic current term is particularly simple:

$$l_\lambda = l_{\mu\lambda} + l_{e\lambda} = \bar{\psi}_\mu \gamma_\lambda (1+\gamma_5)\psi_{\nu_\mu} + \bar{\psi}_e \gamma_\lambda (1+\gamma_5)\psi_{\nu_e}, \tag{2}$$

in which the ψ_l are Dirac spinors,[4] and the γ's are the conventional Dirac matrices. This corresponds to an interaction[5] which is an equal combination of the vector (γ_λ) and axial vector ($-\gamma_\lambda\gamma_5$) types, with opposite phases, or $V-A$. Thus, the product $l_\lambda l_\lambda^*$ gives rise to two types of terms: (1) $l_{\mu\lambda} l_{e\lambda}^* + l_{\mu\lambda}^* l_{e\lambda}$, responsible for the decays

$$\mu^\pm \to e^\pm + \binom{\nu_e}{\bar{\nu}_e} + \binom{\bar{\nu}_\mu}{\nu_\mu}, \tag{2a}$$

[3] In conventional cgs units, G_w has the dimensions ergs cm³; the combination $G_w M^2 c/\hbar^3$ ($G_w M^2$ in the natural system of units) is dimensionless.

[4] $\bar{\psi}_l \equiv i\psi_l \gamma_4$.

[5] R. Feynman and M. Gell-Mann, *Phys. Rev., 109:* 193 (1958); R. E. Marshak and E. C. G. Sudarshan, *Phys. Rev., 109:* 1860 (1958).

as well as to neutrino-induced reactions like

$$\nu_\mu + e^- \rightarrow \nu_e + \mu^-, \tag{2b}$$

and (2) $l_{\mu\lambda} l^*_{\mu\lambda} + l_{e\lambda} l^*_{e\lambda}$, which does not lead to decays but, rather, to scattering and annihilation processes like

$$\mu + \nu_\mu \rightarrow \mu + \nu_\mu, \tag{3a}$$

$$e^+ + e^- \rightarrow \nu_e + \bar{\nu}_e \tag{3b}$$

(which are, as yet, experimentally unobserved, but important in astrophysical theories).

The details of the decays (2a) have been discussed in Section 6.1.3. From the measured mean life of the muon, using the computed value (including the lowest-order electromagnetic correction)

$$\tau_\mu^{-1} = \frac{G_\mu^2 m_\mu^5}{192\pi^3}\left[1 - \frac{\alpha}{2\pi}\left(\pi^2 - \frac{25}{4}\right)\right], \tag{4}$$

one obtains

$$G_\mu = (1.4350 \pm 0.0011) \times 10^{-49} \text{ erg cm}^3 \tag{4a}$$

or

$$G_\mu M_P^2 = 1.03 \times 10^{-5}. \tag{4b}$$

The cross section for the lepton-exchange reaction (2b) likewise can be computed in a straightforward fashion. The scattering is pure S wave, with

$$\sigma = \frac{4}{\pi}(G_\mu p_{0\nu})^2. \tag{5a}$$

The most interesting aspect of this result is that it sets an upper limit on the value of the *cm* neutrino momentum, $p_{0\nu,\max}$, above which the Fermi prescription cannot be valid, since the unitarity requirement limits the S-wave scattering cross section to [6]

$$\sigma \leq \frac{\pi \lambda\!\!\!^{-}{}_\nu^2}{2} = \frac{\pi}{2p_{0\nu}^2}. \tag{5b}$$

Combining (4b), (5a), and (5b), we obtain

$$p_{0\nu} \leq 300 \text{ GeV}/c = p_{0\nu,\max} \tag{5c}$$

as an upper limit to the validity of the Fermi weak-interaction theory. Stated in other words, the 4-fermion point interaction must exhibit a nonlocality for distances of closest approach less than

---

[6] Note that $\sigma_l^{(\max)} = (2j+1)\pi\lambda\!\!\!^{-2}/(2s_1+1)(2s_2+1)$ in general. For the neutrino, however, $(2s_2+1) \rightarrow 1$ since only one helicity state is permitted.

$$\Lambda \lesssim \frac{\hbar c}{p_{0\nu,\max}} = 0.66 \times 10^{-16} \text{ cm}. \tag{5d}$$

Such a nonlocal interaction could result from an intermediate weak-interaction boson of mass $M_W \approx 300$ GeV/c^2, which is still considerably greater than the lower limit of $\gtrsim 2$ GeV/c^2 set by other experimental observations (see Section 2.2.8). It should also be noted that other considerations — in particular, of the weak-interaction origins of the K_1^0–K_2^0 mass difference — seem to set a much larger value, $\sim 0.5 \times 10^{-14}$ cm ($p_{0\nu,\max} \sim 4$ GeV/c), on the limit of validity of Fermi weak-interaction theory.[7]

As noted above, $l_{l\lambda} l^*_{l\lambda}$ terms in the weak-interaction Lagrangian can give rise to elastic ν_l–l scattering or to l–$\bar{l}$ annihilation into ν_l–$\bar{\nu}_l$. Although there is no experimental confirmation of the necessity for the presence of such terms in the phenomenological $\mathcal{L}_w$, the intermediate-boson theory would require their presence, however. In this case, the scattering processes would arise from the diagrams shown in Figure 18.1, with the resulting elastic scattering cross sections (in the limit $M_W \to \infty$)

$$\frac{d\sigma}{dt}(l^-\bar{\nu}_l) = \frac{G_\mu^2}{\pi}\left(1 + \frac{t}{2m_l p_\nu}\right), \tag{6a}$$

$$\frac{d\sigma}{dt}(l^-\nu_l) = \frac{G_\mu^2}{\pi}, \tag{6b}$$

where p_ν is the *lab* momentum of the incident neutrino and t is the (4-momentum transfer)^2 to the scattered electron or muon, l, of *lab* energy E,

$$-t = 2m_l(E - m_l). \tag{6c}$$

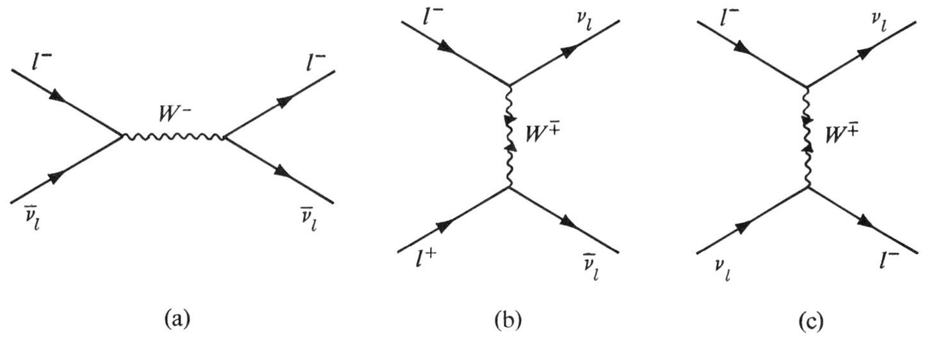

Figure 18.1 Intermediate boson exchange diagrams for ν_l–l scattering. (a) s-channel, $\bar{\nu}_l + l^- \to \bar{\nu}_l + l^-$. (b) t-channel, $l^+ + l^- \to \bar{\nu}_l + \nu_l$. (c) u-channel, $\nu_l + l^- \to \nu_l + l^-$.

[7] B. L. Ioffe and E. P. Shubalin, *Journal of Physics* (USSR), *6:* 828 (1967); F. E. Low, *Comments on Nuclear and Particle Physics, 2:* 33 (1968).

18.1.2 Semileptonic Decays

Nuclear β Decay • The weak hadronic current, J_λ, has been most extensively investigated for the case of nuclear β decay, arising from the fundamental processes

$$P \rightarrow N + e^+ + \nu_e, \tag{7a}$$

$$N \rightarrow P + e^- + \bar{\nu}_e, \tag{7b}$$

in terms of the β-decay Lagrangian[8]

$$\mathcal{L}_\beta = \frac{G_\beta}{\sqrt{2}} (J_{\mathfrak{N}\lambda}\, l_{e\lambda} + J^*_{\mathfrak{N}\lambda}\, l^*_{e\lambda}). \tag{7c}$$

The form of $J_{\mathfrak{N}\lambda}$ is specified by the $V-A$ interaction (which has been accurately verified)

$$J_{\mathfrak{N}\lambda} = \bar{\psi}_P \gamma_\lambda (1 + a_\beta \gamma_5) \psi_N \tag{8a}$$

in which the constant

$$a_\beta = \frac{G^A_\beta}{G^V_\beta} e^{i\varphi} \tag{8b}$$

represents a modification of the $(1+\gamma_5)$ form of the leptonic current, resulting from the different renormalization corrections to the vector and axial vector weak-decay vertices, arising from the strong interactions. Experimentally,

$$\frac{G^A_\beta}{G^V_\beta} = 1.18 \pm 0.025, \tag{8b$'$}$$

$$\varphi = (0 \pm 8)^0. \tag{8b$''$}$$

The determination of the coupling constant $G_\beta = G^V_\beta$ depends on an accurate knowledge of nuclear matrix elements — which introduces some uncertainties — as well as on the calculation of the electromagnetic corrections, about which there remain some unresolved theoretical questions. The currently accepted best value (without radiative corrections) is

$$G_\beta = (1.4149 \pm 0.0022) \times 10^{-49} \text{ erg cm}^3, \tag{9}$$

which differs by $\approx$ 1.2 percent from the (uncorrected) value of G_μ [Equations (4), (4a), (4b)]; the radiative corrections appear to raise this difference to $\approx$ 2.2 percent, still a very small difference indeed.

This (near) equality of G_μ and G^V_β led Gerstein and Zeldovich, and Feynman and Gell-Mann,[9] to propose the hypothesis of the conserved vector current (or CVC). According to CVC, the vector (i.e., γ_λ) part of the weak-interaction

---

[8] The $(J_{\mathfrak{N}\lambda}\, l_{\mu\lambda} + J^*_{\mathfrak{N}\lambda}\, l^*_{\mu\lambda})$ terms are responsible for μ-capture processes, e.g.,

$$\mu^- + P \rightarrow N + \nu_\mu. \tag{7a$'$}$$

[9] S. S. Gerstein and J. B. Zeldovich, *JETP* (USSR), *29:* 698 (1955); R. Feynman and M. Gell-Mann, *Phys. Rev., 109:* 193 (1958).

currents shares the property of the electromagnetic current of being divergence-free. In other words, if we separate the weak current into a vector and axial vector part

$$J_\lambda = V_\lambda - A_\lambda, \tag{10a}$$

then the 4-divergence of V_λ vanishes:[10]

$$\frac{\partial V_\lambda}{\partial x_\lambda} = 0. \tag{10b}$$

In addition to the consequence that the weak coupling constant G_β^V will be unchanged by the effects of virtual strong interactions, CVC, in the form proposed by Feynman and Gell-Mann, gives rise to a small correction, proportional to the difference between the proton and neutron anomalous magnetic moments, to the nuclear β-decay matrix elements (referred to as "weak magnetism").[11] This correction to the vector current,

$$V'_{\mathfrak{N}\lambda} = \bar{\psi}_P \left(\frac{\bar{\mu}_P - \bar{\mu}_N}{M_P + M_N}\right) \not{p}_\mu \, \sigma_{\mu\lambda} \, \psi_N, \tag{11a}$$

with $\bar{\mu}_P = \mu_P - 1 \cong 1.79$, $\bar{\mu}_N = \mu_N \cong -1.91$ and

$$\sigma_{\mu\lambda} = \frac{i}{2}(\gamma_\mu\gamma_\lambda - \gamma_\lambda\gamma_\mu), \tag{11b}$$

gives rise, among other effects, to a small difference between the β-decay spectra of mirror nuclei. Its presence has been strikingly verified[12] in a careful comparison of the β^- spectrum of B^{12} with the β^+ spectrum of N^{12}.

Pionic β Decay • In principle, the pion may be regarded — by virtue of its strong Yukawa interaction — as an $\mathfrak{N}$–$\bar{\mathfrak{N}}$ combination in the ${}^1S_0$ state, and therefore the β decay of the pion

$$\pi^\pm \to l^\pm + \begin{pmatrix} \nu_l \\ \bar{\nu}_l \end{pmatrix} \tag{12}$$

could be thought of as proceeding through a two-stage process, as depicted in Figure 18.2(a). Since the pion is coupled to the $\mathfrak{N}$–$\bar{\mathfrak{N}}$ pair through a gradient interaction [relativistically, the pion field, φ_π, is proportional to $\sqrt{4\pi}\, g_s^\pi \bar{\psi}_{\mathfrak{N}} \gamma_5 \psi_{\mathfrak{N}}$, with $(g_s^\pi)^2/4\pi = 15.7 \pm 1.8$], the matrix element for weak pion annihilation is

---

[10] More specifically, Feynman and Gell-Mann proposed that V_λ and V_λ^* transform, respectively, like the $t_3 = +1$ and $t_3 = -1$ components of an isotriplet ($t = 1$) vector current, for which the $t_3 = 0$ component is taken to be proportional to the isovector part of the electromagnetic current, $V_{\lambda 0} = (G_\beta^V/e)J_\lambda^{\text{em}}$ ($t = 1$). This assumption automatically leads to CVC, as well as to the other consequences discussed in the following.

[11] M. Gell-Mann, *Phys. Rev.*, *111:* 362 (1958). Other predictions of the isotriplet vector current hypothesis — the decay rate of $\pi^+ \to \pi^0 + e^+ + \nu_e$, and the vanishing of the vector contribution to $\Sigma^\pm \to \Lambda^0 + e^\pm + \begin{pmatrix} \nu_e \\ \bar{\nu}_e \end{pmatrix}$ — have also been verified experimentally.

[12] Y. K. Lee, L. W. Mo, and C. S. Wu, *Phys. Rev. Letters*, *10:* 253 (1963).

proportional to the matrix element of the gradient of the weak hadron current, i.e.,

$$\langle \text{vacuum}\, |J_\lambda|\pi^+\rangle \propto \left\langle N \left| \frac{\partial J_\lambda}{\partial x_\lambda} \right| P \right\rangle = \left\langle N \left| \frac{\partial A_\lambda}{\partial x_\lambda} \right| P \right\rangle, \tag{13}$$

the last step resulting by virtue of the vanishing of the 4-divergence of V_λ [Equation (10b)]. Hence, the pion decays (12) depend only on the axial vector part of the weak hadronic current, in particular on the divergence of A.

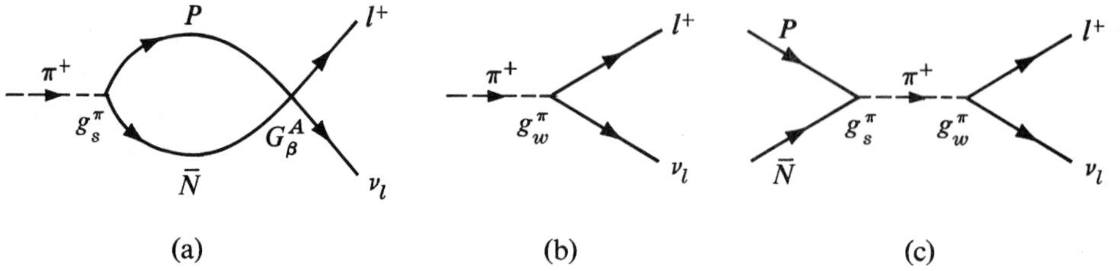

Figure 18.2 Feynman diagrams associated with the decays $\pi^+ \to l^+ + \nu_l$. (a) Two-stage approximation. (b) Direct coupling approximation. (c) Single pion pole approximation for the axial vector β-decay term.

In practice, however, it is more convenient to treat the pion decay phenomenologically, as arising from a direct coupling to the leptonic current, l_λ [Figure 18.2(b)], with the coupling constant g_w^π (of dimensions m^{-1}) defined[13] by the Lorentz-invariant annihilation matrix element

$$\langle \text{vacuum}\, |J_\lambda(A)|\pi\rangle = \frac{i g_w^\pi p_{\pi\lambda}}{(2\epsilon_\pi)^{1/2}}\, e^{i\mathbf{p}_\pi \cdot \mathbf{r}}\,. \tag{13a}$$

---

[13] The weak pion coupling constant has almost as many definitions as there are independent investigators in the field, and the usage is as much a question of fashion as logic. Thus, it is frequently preferred to express it in terms of the weak Fermi interaction strength:

$$g_w^\pi = f_\pi G_\beta^V. \tag{13a$'$}$$

In this case, f_π has the dimensions of a mass. Alternatively, one may define a dimensionless coupling strength, $f_0^\pi \equiv f_0$:

$$g_w^\pi = G_\beta^V \frac{m_\pi}{2 f_0^\pi}. \tag{13a$''$}$$

From the weak-decay constants, we have

$$f_0^\pi = \frac{m_\pi}{2 f_\pi} \cong 0.8. \tag{13c$'$}$$

Note also that the strong coupling strength is frequently described in terms of another dimensionless constant:

$$f_s^\pi \equiv f = \frac{m_\pi}{2 M_{\mathfrak{N}}} g_s^\pi \cong 1.0, \tag{13c$''$}$$

derived from the low-energy pion-nucleon scattering and photoproduction data

$(f^2/4\pi = 0.081 \pm 0.002)$.

Application of (13a) to the pion decays (12) in the rest frame of the pion ($\mathbf{p}_\pi = 0$, $\epsilon_\pi = \not{p}_{0\pi} = m_\pi$) leads to the decay rate

$$\tau_{\pi l2}^{-1} = \tau^{-1}\left(\pi^\pm \to l^\pm + \frac{\nu_l}{\bar{\nu}_l}\right) = \frac{|g_w^\pi|^2 m_l^2}{4\pi m_\pi^3}(m_\pi^2 - m_l^2)^2, \tag{13b}$$

which yields, for $\tau_{\pi\mu 2} = (2.604 \pm 0.007) \times 10^{-8}$ sec,

$$|g_w^\pi|^2 m_\pi^2 = (2.2 \pm 0.02) \times 10^{-14}. \tag{13c}$$

We may now invert the argument and, assuming that the axial vector term of the nucleonic weak current is dominated by the single pion intermediate state (or pion pole term), as illustrated in Figure 18.2(c), derive a simple connection between the axial vector β-decay coupling constant G_β^A and the strong and weak pion coupling constants g_s^π and g_w^π (or f_π). The matrix element associated with Figure 18.2(c) is

$$\begin{aligned}\left\langle N \left| \frac{\partial A_\lambda}{\partial x_\lambda} \right| P \right\rangle &= \sqrt{2}\,\frac{g_w^\pi g_s^\pi K(t)\, m_\pi^2}{m_\pi^2 - t}\,\bar{\psi}_N \gamma_5 \psi_P\, e^{-i\mathbf{p}_\pi\cdot\mathbf{r}} \\ &= \sqrt{\tfrac{1}{2}}(M_P + M_N)\, G_\beta^A \bar{\psi}_N \gamma_5 \psi_P\, e^{-i\mathbf{p}_\pi\cdot\mathbf{r}},\end{aligned} \tag{14}$$

in which the last expression[14] is derived directly from the 4-fermion interaction Lagrangian, Equation (7c); $K(t)$ is a pion-nucleon (strong) interaction form factor, which modifies the strong interaction coupling for momentum transfers differing appreciably from those corresponding to the static limit, $-t = m_\pi^2$. By definition, $K(-m_\pi^2) = 1$. In the case of nucleon β decay, for which $t \to 0$ [the pion is virtual in Figure 18.2(c)], Equation (14) leads directly to the well-known Goldberger–Treiman relation[15]

$$G_\beta^A = \frac{2 g_w^\pi g_s^\pi K(0)}{M_P + M_N} = \frac{g_s^\pi f_\pi G_\beta^V K(0)}{M_{\mathfrak{N}}} = \frac{f_s^\pi}{f_0^\pi} K(0)\, G_\beta^V. \tag{14a}$$

The degree of numerical agreement, between the value of

$$\frac{G_\beta^A/G_\beta^V}{K(0)} \cong 1.3\text{–}1.4 \tag{14b}$$

derived from pion β decay and the nuclear β-decay value of $G_\beta^A/G_\beta^V = 1.2$ [Equation (8b′)], indicates that the form factor $K(t)$ is slowly varying for small t; the success of the numerical comparison may be taken as a measure of the validity of the approximations — mainly the single pion pole approximation for the axial current, Figure 18.2(c) — used in the derivation of the Goldberger–Treiman relation.

---

[14] We have neglected an additional term, proportional to the 4-momentum (squared) transfer, t, arising from an "induced pseudoscalar" interaction. This term is important in β-decay processes involving appreciable momentum, since its effective coupling is ~ 7 times as strong as that of the conventional axial vector coupling.

[15] M. L. Goldberger and S. B. Treiman, *Phys. Rev.*, *110:* 1178 (1958). Actually, Goldberger and Treiman used the two-step pion decay mechanism, Figure 18.2(a), together with dispersion theory techniques, in their original derivation.

The relationships discussed above give rise to two further comments:

1. We have previously compared (in Section 6.1.3) the experimental decay rates

$$\frac{\lambda(\pi_{e2}^{\pm})}{\lambda(\pi_{\mu 2}^{\pm})} = (1.21 \pm 0.07) \times 10^{-4} \tag{15a}$$

with the theoretical value[16]

$$\frac{\lambda(\pi_{e2}^{\pm})}{\lambda(\pi_{\mu 2}^{\pm})} = \frac{m_e^2(m_\pi^2 - m_e^2)^2}{m_\mu^2(m_\pi^2 - m_\mu^2)^2} \times 0.965 = 1.23 \times 10^{-4} \tag{15b}$$

derived from Equation (13b) on the assumption of the equality of the pion-lepton coupling constants $(g_w^\pi)^e = (g_w^\pi)^\mu$. The agreement between (15a) and (15b) attests again to the universality of the β-decay coupling, at least as between the μ–ν_μ, e–ν_e, and $\mathfrak{N}$–$\overline{\mathfrak{N}}$ vertices.

2. The very existence of the $\pi_{l2}^{\pm}$ decays requires that the 4-divergence of the axial vector weak nucleonic current must be nonvanishing, in contrast to the CVC hypothesis for the vector current, Equation (10b). The approximate validity of the Goldberger–Treiman relation suggests that the 4-divergence of the axial vector current may be simply related to the pion field φ_π through the strong Yukawa interaction [see Equation (14)]. The suggested relationship[17]

$$\frac{\partial A_\lambda^i(x)}{\partial x_\lambda} = m_\pi^2 f_\pi \varphi_\pi^i(x) = \left(\frac{m_\pi}{2f_0^\pi}\right) m_\pi^2 \varphi_\pi^i(x) \tag{16}$$

is known as the partially conserved axial vector current hypothesis, or PCAC[18]; its use permits the derivation of a number of other interesting connections between the weak and the strong interactions, by use of the techniques of current algebra, which will be discussed in a subsequent section of this chapter.

Finally, we remark briefly on the $\pi_{e3}^{\pm}$ decays

$$\pi^\pm \to \pi^0 + e^\pm + \begin{pmatrix} \nu_e \\ \bar{\nu}_e \end{pmatrix}. \tag{17}$$

Since the matrix elements

$$\langle \pi^0 | A_\lambda | \pi^\pm \rangle = 0 \tag{17a}$$

vanish by virtue of parity conservation,[19] these decays result entirely from the vector part of the weak nucleon current

$$\langle \pi^0 | V_\lambda | \pi^\pm \rangle = \frac{p_{\pi\lambda}}{\epsilon_\pi} G_\beta^V, \tag{17b}$$

---

[16] The factor 0.965 arises from a radiative correction.

[17] M. Gell-Mann and M. Levy, *Nuovo Cimento, 16:* 705 (1960); K. C. Chou, *JETP* (USSR), *39:* 703 (1960). Note φ_π is an isotopic vector, with components φ_π^i, $i = 1, 2, 3$.

[18] It is also known as "pion dominance in the divergence of the axial current," or PDDAC.

[19] Both the vector and the axial vector terms in the weak-interaction Lagrangian [Equations (7c), (8a)] are individually parity conserving. It is, of course, their simultaneous presence that leads to parity nonconservation, which is mainly manifested in the interference between them.

for which the coupling strength, G_{β}^{V}, follows from the CVC hypothesis of Feynman and Gell-Mann. The predicted decay rate

$$\frac{\lambda(\pi^+ \to \pi^0 + e^+ + \nu_e)}{\lambda(\pi^+ \to \mu^+ + \nu_\mu)} = 1.07 \times 10^{-8} \tag{17c}$$

is in excellent agreement with the experimental value [20] of $(1.12 \pm 0.08) \times 10^{-8}$.

Kaon β-Decay • The K-mesons are similar to the pions; they also may be treated in most respects as $^1S_0$ baryon-antibaryon combinations. However, in the case of the kaons, at least one of the components must also carry the attribute of strangeness. Unlike the pions, which have isotopic spin 1, the kaons have isospin $\frac{1}{2}$, the (K^+, K^0) pair having strangeness (and hypercharge $\mathcal{Y}$) + 1 while the $(\overline{K^0}, K^-)$ pair, being their antiparticles, have strangeness -1. All four kaons exhibit appreciable leptonic decays [21] (see Table 2.1).

According to the hypothesis of the universal β-decay tetrahedron (see Figure 2.1), decays involving baryon-antibaryon pairs with $S = \pm 1$ can be described in terms of a weak current, $S_\lambda = V_\lambda^S + A_\lambda^S$, with properties analogous to those of the weak nucleonic current, $J_\lambda = V_\lambda + A_\lambda$, discussed in the preceding section. For example, a strangeness-carrying current of the form

$$S_\lambda = \overline{\psi}_P \gamma_\lambda (1 + a_\beta^S \gamma_5) \psi_\Lambda \tag{18}$$

can be used to describe both the Λ decays,

$$\Lambda \to P + l^- + \overline{\nu}_l, \tag{18a}$$

and the K_{l2} decays,

$$K^- \to l^- + \overline{\nu}_l. \tag{18b}$$

As in the case of the pions, the K_{l2} decay (18b) may also be treated as a direct process, with the coupling constant g_w^K, leading to a decay rate given by Equation (13b), with the substitutions $g_w^\pi \to g_w^K$ and $m_\pi \to m_K$. One consequence, assuming the identical coupling of A_λ^S to the e and μ currents, is the predicted ratio [see Equation (15b)]

$$\frac{K_{e2}^\pm}{K_{\mu 2}^\pm} = 2.5 \times 10^{-5}. \tag{18c}$$

This prediction is borne out by the experimental value of $(1.95 \pm 0.63) \times 10^{-5}$ for the ratio (18c).

In the case of the $K_{\mu 2}$ decays, the measured decay rate

$$\tau_{K_{\mu 2}^\pm}^{-1} = (5.11 \pm 0.06) \times 10^7 \text{ sec}^{-1} \tag{18d}$$

leads to

$$|g_w^K|^2 m_K^2 = (2.03 \pm 0.02) \times 10^{-14}, \tag{18e}$$

---

[20] See T. D. Lee and C. S. Wu, *Ann. Rev. Nucl. Sci., 15:* 381 (1965), p. 470 and ref. 184.

[21] Among the pions, the β-decay modes of the π^0 are not observed owing to the overwhelming probability of the electromagnetic $\pi^0 \to 2\gamma$ decay mode.

or, using (13c) and the known masses,

$$\frac{|g_w^K|^2}{|g_w^\pi|^2} = (7.39 \pm 0.10) \times 10^{-2} \simeq \frac{m_\pi^2}{m_K^2} = 7.8 \times 10^{-2}. \tag{18f}$$

Assuming that the Goldberger–Treiman relationship holds also for the kaon decays (i.e., one-kaon pole dominance for the strange hadron current A_λ^S) the difference between g_w^K and g_w^π could be ascribed to a difference either between the strong (relativistic) Yukawa couplings g_s^K and g_s^π or between the axial vector coupling constants G_β^A and $G_{S\beta}^A$. The evidence from the strong interactions (Section 15.3.4) indicates approximate equality of g_s^K and g_s^π, so that the ratio (18f) appears to be the consequence of a comparable value of $(G_{S\beta}^A/G_\beta^A)^2$. Accordingly, we must tentatively reject the assumption of universality of the couplings between the vertices of the Dallaporta, Gell-Mann, Puppi tetrahedron (Figure 2.1).

The same conclusion is reached for the vector coupling constants by consideration of the K_{l3} decays:

$$K^\pm \to \pi^0 + l^\pm + \binom{\nu_l}{\bar{\nu}_l}. \tag{19}$$

From the matrix element [22]

$$\langle \pi^0 | V_\lambda^S | K^+ \rangle = \frac{1}{2(\epsilon_K \epsilon_\pi)^{1/2}} [(p_{K\lambda} + p_{\pi\lambda}) f_+(t) + (p_{K\lambda} - p_{\pi\lambda}) f_-(t)]\, e^{iq_\lambda x_\lambda} \tag{19a}$$

(p_λ are the components of the 4-momenta, $q_\lambda = p_{K\lambda} - p_{\pi\lambda}$, $-t = q_\lambda q_\lambda = \not{q}^2$; note that $\not{q}$ is the 4-momentum of the lepton pair), it is possible to derive the details of the decay spectrum, lepton polarization, etc., in terms of the two (in general, complex) form factors $f_\pm(t)$. Thus, for the K_{e3} decay (neglecting m_e), the decay distribution is given by

$$\frac{d^2N(K_{e3})}{dt\, d(\cos\alpha)} = \frac{P_\pi^2}{16\pi^3} |f_+(t)|^2 \sin^2\alpha, \tag{19b}$$

where α is the angle between the e and π^0 in the e–ν rest frame and P_π is the pion momentum in the K rest frame,

$$t = -\not{q}^2 = m_K^2 + m_\pi^2 - 2m_K(P_\pi^2 + m_\pi^2)^{1/2}. \tag{19c}$$

Comparison of (17b) and (19a) indicates that the form factor $f_+(0)$ may be associated with the vector coupling constant for strangeness-changing β decay, $G_{S\beta}^V$. The experimental decay rates for K_{l3} and π_{l3} yield the value

$$\left(\frac{G_{S\beta}^V}{G_\beta^V}\right)^2 \approx 5.2 \times 10^{-2}, \tag{19d}$$

which is probably not significantly different from the ratio of the axial vector coupling constants (18f). In addition, the details of the spectra and polarization

[22] See Equation (17b) for the simpler $\pi_{e3}^\pm$ case. For a complete discussion, see Lee and Wu, *Ann. Rev. Nucl. Sci., 15:* 381 (1965); *16:* 471 (1966).

measurements indicate

$$f_+(t) \cong f_-(t) \cong \text{constant}. \tag{19e}$$

Similar considerations may be applied to the K^0_{l3} and $\overline{K^0_{l3}}$ decays. However, rather than go into the details, we shall resort to a simple model from which the outstanding features of these decays may be derived in a straightforward manner. This model starts from the observation that, according to the isotriplet vector current hypothesis (CVC), the mechanism for the $\pi^\pm_{l3}$ decays may be conceived of as a two-stage process,

$$\pi^\pm \to \pi^0 + \rho^\pm \\ \hookrightarrow l^\pm + \binom{\nu_l}{\bar{\nu}_l}, \tag{20a}$$

since $\rho^\pm$ are the charged members of an isotriplet of vector mesons. By analogy [or on the basis of $SU(3)$ or the quark model] the K_{l3} decays may correspondingly be visualized as proceeding through an intermediate (strong) step involving the vector K^*-mesons, i.e.,

$$K^+ \to \pi^0 + K^{*+} \\ \hookrightarrow l^+ + \nu_l, \tag{20b}$$

$$K^- \to \pi^0 + K^{*-} \\ \hookrightarrow l^- + \bar{\nu}_l, \tag{20c}$$

$$K^0 \to \pi^- + K^{*+} \\ \hookrightarrow l^+ + \nu_l, \tag{20d}$$

$$\overline{K^0} \to \pi^+ + K^{*-} \\ \hookrightarrow l^- + \bar{\nu}_l. \tag{20e}$$

Equations (20b) through (20e) imply the $\Delta S = \Delta Q$ rule. They also give rise to the prediction of $\sqrt{2}$ for the ratio of the neutral-to-charged K_{l3} decay amplitudes (or the ratio 2 for the rates), owing to the requirement that the intermediate (πK^*) states have the same isospin $(\frac{1}{2})$ as the K's. However, the test of this last prediction is somewhat more subtle, since the K^0_{l3} and $\overline{K^0_{l3}}$ decays are only observed in the decay of the long-lived K^0_2 combination[23] (see Chapter 8):

$$K^0_2 = \sqrt{\tfrac{1}{2}}\,(K^0 - \overline{K^0}). \tag{21}$$

Since, from (20d) and (21),

$$\langle K^0_2 |\, \mathcal{L}_w | \pi^- l^+ \nu_l \rangle = \sqrt{\tfrac{1}{2}}\, \langle K^0 |\, \mathcal{L}_w | \pi^- l^+ \nu_l \rangle = \langle K^+ |\, \mathcal{L}_w | \pi^0 l^+ \nu_l \rangle \tag{21a}$$

and, from (20e) and (21),

$$\langle K^0_2 |\, \mathcal{L}_w | \pi^+ l^- \bar{\nu}_l \rangle = \sqrt{\tfrac{1}{2}}\, \langle \overline{K^0} |\, \mathcal{L}_w | \pi^+ l^- \bar{\nu}_l \rangle = \langle K^- |\, \mathcal{L}_w | \pi^0 l^- \bar{\nu}_l \rangle, \tag{21b}$$

we obtain

$$\lambda(K^0_2 \to \pi^+ + l^- + \bar{\nu}_l) + \lambda(K^0_2 \to \pi^- + l^+ + \nu_l) = 2\lambda(K^\pm \to \pi^0 + l^\pm + \nu). \tag{21c}$$

[23] We neglect here the very small effects of the CP-violating term on the K^0_2 decays.

The experimental ratios between the neutral K_2^0 and charged $K^{\pm}$ decay rates are (2.12 ± 0.17) and (2.08 ± 0.27) for the K_{e3} and $K_{\mu 3}$ decays, respectively.

Hadronic β Decays; Cabibbo Theory • We have already presented, in the preceding section, evidence that argues against the equality of the coupling constants governing the strange and the nonstrange hadronic semileptonic decays, both in the case of the vector [see Equation (19d)] and the axial vector [Equation (18f)] interactions. This conclusion is strikingly reinforced by consideration of the observed branching ratios for the decays

$$\frac{\Lambda \to P + e^- + \bar{\nu}_e}{\Lambda \to \mathfrak{N} + \pi} \cong 0.8 \times 10^{-3} \tag{22a}$$

and

$$\frac{\Sigma^- \to N + e^- + \bar{\nu}_e}{\Sigma^- \to N + \pi^-} \cong 1.1 \times 10^{-3}, \tag{22b}$$

for which the assumption of a universal coupling constant would yield 0.014 and 0.051, respectively. The discrepancies, by factors of ~ 20 and 50, are so large that they foreclose the possibility of preserving the concept of the universal tetrahedron [see Figure 2.1(b)] by means of some minor modification.

The problem of universality is, furthermore, not confined to the strange ($K^{\pm}$-like) vertex alone. The observed rate for the $\Delta S = 0$ decay,

$$\Sigma^- \to \Lambda + e^- + \bar{\nu}_e, \tag{23}$$

is only ~ 0.3 of that which would be predicted on the basis of a common strength for all the $\pi^{\pm}$-like baryon current couplings.[24] Hence, we are forced to reconsider the concept of universality, at least insofar as it relates to the components of the currents that involve the strange hadrons. However, as we shall demonstrate in the following, far from having to discard the concept of universality, it is possible, following Cabibbo,[25] to enlarge its meaning by taking into account the intimate relationships among all the baryons that follow from the $SU(3)$ symmetry scheme of Gell-Mann and Ne'eman (see Chapter 14).

According to Cabibbo, there is a single universal weak hadronic current, which includes all appropriate combinations of the members of the baryon octet $(\mathfrak{N}, \Lambda, \Sigma, \Xi)$,

$$J_\lambda = \cos\theta \, J_\lambda^{(0)} + \sin\theta \, J_\lambda^{(1)}, \tag{24a}$$

and which is universally coupled to the leptonic currents according to Equation (1). In Equation (24a), θ is an empirical parameter that determines the relative strengths of the nonstrange $(S = 0)$ current, $J_\lambda^{(0)}$, and the strangeness-carrying $(S = 1)$ current, $J_\lambda^{(1)}$. Both currents consist of a vector (γ_λ) and an axial vector $(-\gamma_\lambda \gamma_5)$ component,

---

[24] The factor ~ 0.3 is predicated on the assumption that, as required by CVC, the $\Sigma^{\pm}$–$\bar{\Lambda}$ component of the hadronic current is purely axial vector.

[25] N. Cabibbo, *Phys. Rev. Letters, 10:* 531 (1963).

$$J_\lambda^{(i)} = V_\lambda^{(i)} - A_\lambda^{(i)}, \tag{24b}$$

which, in the case of the vector components, transform, respectively for $i=0$ and 1, under $SU(3)$ operations like the ρ^+ and K^{*+} members of the vector meson octet.[26] Thus, the currents involving the baryon-antibaryon combination $B\bar{A}$ (e.g., $P\bar{N}$, $\Lambda\bar{\Sigma}^-$, $\Xi^0\bar{\Xi}^-$ for $i=0$; $P\bar{\Lambda}$, $N\bar{\Sigma}^-$, $\Sigma^0\bar{\Xi}^-$ for $i=1$) have the form

$$J_\lambda^{(i)} = \bar{\psi}_A \gamma_\lambda \overline{C}_1^{B\bar{A}} D\, \gamma_5\, \psi_B + \bar{\psi}_A \gamma_\lambda \overline{C}_2^{B\bar{A}} (1 + F\gamma_5)\, \psi_B . \tag{24c}$$

The two terms in Equation (24c) result from the fact that the $SU(3)$ decomposition of the product of two $SU(3)$ octets $(B \otimes \bar{A})$ contains two independent octets,[27] 8_1 and 8_2, of which the first transforms like a purely antisymmetric tensor under the exchange of the $SU(3)$ indices and, therefore, has vanishing matrix elements of $V_\lambda^{(i)}$. The parameters F and D are renormalization constants arising from the effects of the strong interactions,[28] while the $\overline{C}_{1,2}^{B\bar{A}}$ are proportional to the $SU(3)$ combination coefficients (de Swart's isoscalar factors) for $8 \otimes 8 \to 8_1$ and 8_2 corresponding to the combinations $B\bar{A} \to \pi^+(\rho^+)$ or $K^+(K^{*+})$ for $i=0$ or 1, respectively. In order that the nuclear β-decay current have the form of Equation (8a), we must take, for the normalization constants of the $\overline{C}_{1,2}^{B\bar{A}}$, the values of the combination coefficients (see Appendix 6) for the $P\bar{N} \to \pi^+(\rho^+)$ component of $B_8 \otimes \bar{B}_8$,

$$\overline{C}_1^{B\bar{A}} = \frac{C_1^{B\bar{A}}}{C_1^{P\bar{N}}} = -\sqrt{\frac{10}{3}}\, C_1^{B\bar{A}}, \tag{25a}$$

$$\overline{C}_2^{B\bar{A}} = \frac{C_2^{B\bar{A}}}{C_2^{P\bar{N}}} = -\sqrt{6}\, C_2^{B\bar{A}}, \tag{25b}$$

as well as the (experimental) requirement

$$D + F = a_\beta = 1.18. \tag{25c}$$

Furthermore, the assumption of universal weak current-current coupling [Equation (1)] yields the condition

$$G_\beta = G_\beta^V = G_\mu \cos\theta, \tag{26}$$

from which we obtain, using the values of the constants given in the preceding

---

[26] Specifically, we may postulate an octet of currents [see M. Gell-Mann and Y. Ne'eman, *The Eightfold Way*, W. A. Benjamin, New York (1964)] $J_\lambda^{j=1-8}$, of which the first three are equivalent to the isospin operators and the second three to the U-spin operators; in terms of these,

$$J_\lambda^{(0)} = J_\lambda^1 + iJ_\lambda^2, \tag{24b$'$}$$

$$J_\lambda^{(1)} = J_\lambda^4 + iJ_\lambda^5, \tag{24b$''$}$$

and the $t=1$, $t_3=0$ (isovector electromagnetic current) component is

$$J_\lambda^{\text{em}} = J_\lambda^3 + \sqrt{\tfrac{1}{3}}\, J_\lambda^8 . \tag{24b$'''$}$$

[27] We follow the notation of de Swart; see Appendix 6 and *Rev. Mod. Phys., 35:* 916 (1963).

[28] It is assumed, following the CVC hypothesis, that the vector coupling constant is not affected by the strong interactions.

sections, including the best available estimates of the radiative corrections,[29]

$$\begin{aligned} 1 - \cos\theta &= 0.022 \pm 0.005, \\ \sin\theta &= 0.210 \pm 0.016. \end{aligned} \tag{26a}$$

This value is, incidentally, completely consistent with the value obtained from the experimental ratio [see Equation (19d)]:

$$\frac{\lambda(K_{l3})}{\lambda(\pi_{l3})} = \tan^2\theta. \tag{26b}$$

However, the main test of the Cabibbo theory is its ability to yield the observed leptonic decay rates of the strange baryons. The forms of the weak currents corresponding to the various observable decays, obtained by application of Equations (25a) and (25b) in Equation (24c), are summarized in Table 18.1.

Table 18.1 The Weak Hadronic Currents, $J_\lambda^{(0,1)}$, for Baryonic β Decay According to the Cabibbo Theory, Equation (24c)

Decay	$J_\lambda^{(i)}$
$N \to P + e^- + \bar{\nu}_e$	$\cos\theta\,\gamma_\lambda\,[1 + (D+F)\gamma_5]$ [a]
$\Sigma^\mp \to \Lambda + e^\mp + \begin{pmatrix}\bar{\nu}_e \\ \nu_e\end{pmatrix}$	$-\cos\theta\,\gamma_\lambda\,\sqrt{\tfrac{2}{3}}\,D\gamma_5$
$\Sigma^\mp \to \Sigma^0 + e^\mp + \begin{pmatrix}\bar{\nu}_e \\ \nu_e\end{pmatrix}$	$\pm\cos\theta\,\gamma_\lambda\,\sqrt{2}\,(1 + F\gamma_5)$
$\Xi^- \to \Xi^0 + e^- + \bar{\nu}_e$	$\cos\theta\,\gamma_\lambda\,[-1 + (D-F)\gamma_5]$
$\Lambda^0 \to P + l^- + \bar{\nu}_l$	$\sin\theta\,\gamma_\lambda\,[\sqrt{\tfrac{3}{2}} + \sqrt{\tfrac{1}{6}}\,(D+3F)\gamma_5]$
$\Sigma^- \to N + l^- + \bar{\nu}_l$	$\sin\theta\,\gamma_\lambda\,[-1 + (D-F)\gamma_5]$
$\Xi^- \to \Lambda + l^- + \bar{\nu}_l$	$\sin\theta\,\gamma_\lambda\,[-\sqrt{\tfrac{3}{2}} + \sqrt{\tfrac{1}{6}}\,(D-3F)\gamma_5]$
$\Xi^- \to \Sigma^0 + l^- + \bar{\nu}_l$	$\sin\theta\,\gamma_\lambda\,\sqrt{\tfrac{1}{2}}\,[1 + (D+F)\gamma_5]$
$\Xi^0 \to \Sigma^+ + l^- + \bar{\nu}_l$	$-\sin\theta\,\gamma_\lambda\,[1 + (D+F)\gamma_5]$

[a] This value of $J_\lambda^{(0)}$ follows from the definitions of the $\overline{C}_{1,2}^{B\bar{A}}$, Equations (25a) and (25b).

EXAMPLE

We illustrate, here, the use of de Swart's isoscalar factors in computing the expressions in the table.

(a) $\Sigma^- \to \Lambda^0 + l^- + \bar{\nu}_l$: We require the values of $C_{1,2}^{\Lambda\overline{\Sigma^-}}$ (i.e., the combination with $\mathcal{Y} = 0$, $t = 1$). These are

$$C_1^{\Lambda\overline{\Sigma^-}} = \sqrt{\tfrac{1}{5}}; \qquad \overline{C}_1^{\Lambda\overline{\Sigma^-}} = -\sqrt{\tfrac{1}{5}} \times \sqrt{\tfrac{10}{3}} = -\sqrt{\tfrac{2}{3}}; \tag{27a}$$

$$\overline{C}_2^{\Lambda\overline{\Sigma^-}} = 0 = C_2^{\Lambda\overline{\Sigma^-}}. \tag{27b}$$

[29] The uncertainty in the value of $\sin\theta$ arises mainly from the uncertainty in the radiative correction applicable to β decay.

(b) $\Sigma^- \rightarrow N + l^- + \bar{\nu}_l$: The required combination $N\overline{\Sigma^-}$ has $\mathcal{Y} = 1$, $t = \frac{1}{2}$, with $t_3 = \frac{1}{2}$; hence,[30]

$$C_1 = -\frac{3\sqrt{5}}{10} \times \sqrt{\frac{2}{3}}; \qquad \bar{C}_1 = \frac{-3\sqrt{5}}{10} \times \sqrt{\frac{2}{3}} \times -\sqrt{\frac{10}{3}} = 1; \tag{28a}$$

$$C_2 = \tfrac{1}{2} \times \sqrt{\tfrac{2}{3}}; \qquad \bar{C}_2 = \tfrac{1}{2} \times \sqrt{\tfrac{2}{3}} \times -\sqrt{6} = -1. \tag{28b}$$

Since the currents $J_\lambda^{(0)}$ and $J_\lambda^{(1)}$ carry the isospin values $t = 1$ and $\frac{1}{2}$, respectively, the Cabibbo currents automatically yield the isospin selection rules $\Delta t = 1$ for $S = 0$ and $\Delta t = \frac{1}{2}$ for the $S = \pm 1$ semileptonic decays. Furthermore, the fact that $J_\lambda^{(1)}$ carries $S = +1$ together with $Q = +1$, with $S = Q = -1$ for $J_\lambda^{(1)*}$, provides a guarantee of the $\Delta S = \Delta Q$ law.

The phenomenal success of the Cabibbo theory in fitting the observations is demonstrated in Table 18.2. The values quoted in the table were compiled

Table 18.2 Comparison of Observed Baryon β-decay Rates and Predictions of Cabibbo Theory[a]

DECAY	BRANCHING RATIO ($\times 10^3$) Predicted	Observed
$\Lambda \rightarrow Pe^-\bar{\nu}_e$	0.82	0.80 ± 0.07
$\rightarrow P\mu^-\bar{\nu}_\mu$	0.14	0.135 ± 0.06
$\Sigma^- \rightarrow Ne^-\bar{\nu}_e$	1.01	1.08 ± 0.06
$\rightarrow N\mu^-\bar{\nu}_\mu$	0.49	0.48 ± 0.06
$\rightarrow \Lambda e^-\bar{\nu}_e$	0.064	0.061 ± 0.007
$\Sigma^+ \rightarrow \Lambda e^+\nu_e$	0.019	0.020 ± 0.005
$\Xi^- \rightarrow \Lambda e^-\bar{\nu}_e$	0.55 }	$0.68^{+0.18}_{-0.27}$
$\rightarrow \Sigma^0 e^-\bar{\nu}_e$	0.08 }	
$\rightarrow \Lambda\mu^-\bar{\nu}_\mu$	0.10	
$\Xi^0 \rightarrow \Sigma^+ e^-\bar{\nu}_e$	0.25	
$\rightarrow \Sigma^+\mu^-\bar{\nu}_\mu$	0.0020	

[a] *Proceedings of the 14th International Conference on High-Energy Physics,* Vienna (September 1968).

by the Heidelberg group; the predictions are based on the matrix elements of Table 18.1, with the constants

$$a_\beta = D + F = 1.23 \pm 0.02, \tag{29a}$$

$$D = 0.735 \pm 0.021, \tag{29b}$$

$$F = 0.495 \pm 0.021, \tag{29c}$$

$$\alpha = \frac{D}{(D+F)} \cong 0.60, \tag{29d}$$

[30] The last factor, $\sqrt{\frac{2}{3}}$, is the Clebsch–Gordan coefficient, $C^{1/2,1/2}_{1/2,-1/2;\,1,1}$, for the isospin combination $(t = \frac{1}{2},\ t_3 = -\frac{1}{2}) + (t = 1,\ t_3 = 1) \rightarrow (t = \frac{1}{2},\ t_3 = \frac{1}{2})$.

$$\frac{D}{F} \cong 1.5, \tag{29e}$$

$$\theta = 0.227 \pm 0.006. \tag{29f}$$

However, it should be noted that the data are also amenable to a slightly different interpretation, still in the spirit of the Cabibbo approach: Just as the strong interaction effects lead to a difference from unity in the value of $(D+F)$, it is also possible that the strong interactions will alter the relative strengths of $V_\lambda^{(1)}$ and $A_\lambda^{(1)}$ as compared to $V_\lambda^{(0)}$ and $A_\lambda^{(0)}$. Such an effect will be manifested by a different value of the parameter θ for the vector and the axial vector currents — i.e., $\theta_A \neq \theta_V = \theta$. If, in fact, we interpret the ratio of $K_{\mu 2}$ and $K_{\pi 2}$ decay rates [see Equations (13) and (18)] as

$$\frac{\lambda(K_{\mu 2})}{\lambda(\pi_{\mu 2})} = \frac{m_K}{m_\pi} \tan^2 \theta_A, \tag{29g}$$

we obtain the value

$$\sin \theta_A = 0.264 \pm 0.002, \tag{29h}$$

which differs significantly[31] from (26a). Thus, in interpreting the hadronic decay data within the framework of the Cabibbo theory, one may introduce, in general, three unknown parameters: $\theta = \theta_V$, θ_A, and $\alpha = D/(D+F)$, the values of $G_\beta = G_\mu \cos\theta$ and $D + F = a_\beta$ being taken from the experiments on muon and nuclear β decay. A recent detailed analysis of the available data[32] has obtained an excellent fit on this basis (i.e., $\theta_A \neq \theta_V$), with the best values of these parameters being

$$\sin \theta_V = 0.210 \pm 0.004, \tag{29i}$$

$$\sin \theta_A = 0.265 \pm 0.001, \tag{29j}$$

$$\alpha = 0.665 \pm 0.018, \left(\frac{D}{F} \cong 2.0\right), \tag{29k}$$

$$a_\beta = D + F = 1.18 \pm 0.03. \tag{29l}$$

At the present stage, it is not possible to choose between the two approaches, but the success of both attest to the basic validity of the Cabibbo theory of the semi-leptonic baryon decays.

Quark Model of β Decay • In view of the successes of the quark model in reproducing most of the strong and electromagnetic interaction properties of the hadrons (see Chapters 15–17), it is of interest to consider a model of the β-decay interactions in which the basic hadronic currents are carried by the appropriate combinations of the three quarks (p, n, λ). The most straightforward

[31] It is interesting that the ratio $\theta_A/\theta_V = 1.26 \pm 0.03$ is not significantly different from $(D+F) = G_\beta^A/G_\beta^V = 1.23 \pm 0.03$. However, the meaning of this near equality is not clear.

[32] N. Brene, L. Veje, M. Roos, and C. Cronström, *Phys. Rev., 149:* 1288 (1966).

assumption,[33] in the spirit of the Cabibbo approach, is to take for the weak quark current

$$J^q_\alpha = \cos\theta\ \bar{\psi}_p \gamma_\alpha(1 + a_q\gamma_5)\psi_n + \sin\theta\ \bar{\psi}_p\gamma_\alpha(1 + a_q\gamma_5)\psi_\lambda \tag{30}$$

with, again, the universal coupling of J^q_α to the leptonic current, l_α,

$$G_q = G_\mu, \tag{30a}$$

i.e.,

$$G^V_q = G_\mu \cos\theta_V, \tag{30b}$$

$$G^A_q = G_\mu a_q \cos\theta_A. \tag{30c}$$

Since the quark model is also $SU(3)$ invariant, we need not be surprised that it reproduces the main results of the Cabibbo theory with, however, somewhat less leeway in the choice of the constants (i.e., the ratio D/F is fixed) owing to the added requirement of $SU(6)$ symmetry for the quark model.[34]

The matrix elements for the various hadronic decays are obtained by summing the contributions over the quark constituents in the appropriate hadronic wave functions of Table 15.2 (qqq combinations for the baryons; $q\bar{q}$ combinations for the 0^- and 1^- mesons). A number of interesting conclusions follow:

1. Considering the nucleonic β decay, $P \to N + e^- + \bar{\nu}_e$, the matrix element[35] is

$$\left\langle P\left|\sum_q V^q_\alpha\right|N\right\rangle = \langle P|V^{(0)}_\alpha|N\rangle \tag{31a}$$

by definition, whence

$$G^V_q = G^V_\beta, \tag{31b}$$

as anticipated in Equation (30b); on the other hand,

$$\left\langle P\left|\sum_q A^q_\alpha\right|N\right\rangle = \frac{5}{3}\langle P|A^{(0)}_\alpha|N\rangle, \tag{32a}$$

so that, in order to fit the observed $V - 1.18A$ nucleonic β-decay current, we require

$$a_q = \tfrac{3}{5}a_\beta = 0.71 \pm 0.02. \tag{32b}$$

---

[33] R. Van Royen and V. F. Weisskopf, *Nuovo Cimento, 50A:* 617 (1967); A. Dar, *MIT (LNS) Report* (1967).

[34] That is, $3 \otimes \bar{3} = 1 \oplus 8$, so that the quark model yields only one octet of axial vector currents, instead of the two independent octets of the Cabibbo theory.

[35] The computation of the matrix elements of $\Sigma_q V^q_\alpha$ between two physical hadronic states is completely equivalent to the application of the generalized isotopic-spin operator $\Sigma_q d^+_{ij,k}$, which was defined in Section 15.3.4, Equations (31) through (31d), in connection with the strong interactions. Correspondingly, the matrix elements of $\Sigma_q A^q_\alpha$ are the same as those of $\Sigma_q d^+_{ij,k}\gamma_5$ which reduce, in the nonrelativistic limit, to $\Sigma_q d^+_{ij,k}\sigma^+_q$ (or to $\Sigma_q \tau^+_q \sigma^+_q$ for states involving only the p and n quarks). It is therefore no surprise that the numerical factor $\frac{3}{5}$, between the axial quark coupling and the axial nucleon coupling [Equation (32b) in the present chapter], should be the same as that between the quark Yukawa coupling and the nucleon Yukawa coupling [Chapter 15, Equation (33d)]. Likewise, the D/F ratio corresponding to the strong $\bar{B}B\pi_k$ Lagrangian given by the quark model (Table 15.19) is the same as that found for the weak Lagrangian [Equation (33d) in the present chapter].

2. Comparison of the matrix elements for the decays $\Sigma^- \to \Sigma^0 + l^- + \bar{\nu}_l$ and $\Sigma^- \to \Lambda + l^- + \bar{\nu}_l$ leads to a determination of the ratio D/F corresponding to the quark model (see Table 18.1). As expected from the CVC hypothesis,[36]

$$\left\langle \Lambda \left| \sum_q V_\alpha^q \right| \Sigma^- \right\rangle = 0. \tag{33a}$$

On the other hand, for the axial vector matrix elements,

$$\frac{\left\langle \Lambda \left| \sum_q A_\alpha^q \right| \Sigma^- \right\rangle}{\left\langle \Sigma^0 \left| \sum_q A_\alpha^q \right| \Sigma^- \right\rangle} = \frac{\sqrt{3}}{2}, \tag{33b}$$

while, from Table 18.1,

$$\frac{\langle \Lambda | A_\alpha^{(0)} | \Sigma^- \rangle}{\langle \Sigma^0 | A_\alpha^{(0)} | \Sigma^- \rangle} = \sqrt{\frac{1}{3}} \frac{D}{F}. \tag{33c}$$

Hence, we obtain

$$\frac{D}{F} = \frac{3}{2}; \; \alpha = \frac{D}{D+F} = 0.60 \tag{33d}$$

for the quark model, in beautiful agreement with the results of the empirical analysis,[37] Equations (29d) and (29e).

3. Direct computation of the $K_{\mu 2}/\pi_{\mu 2}$ decay rates, which derive from the axial vector parts of the quark currents, as well as from the $q\bar{q}$ annihilation probability, yields

$$\frac{\lambda(K_{\mu 2})}{\lambda(\pi_{\mu 2})} = \frac{|\psi_K(0)|^2}{|\psi_\pi(0)|^2} \tan^2 \theta_A, \tag{34a}$$

where the $\psi_{K,\pi}(0)$ are the mesonic $q\bar{q}$ wave functions for zero separation. Comparison of Equations (34a) and (29g) yields the requirement

$$\frac{|\psi_K(0)|^2}{m_K} = \frac{|\psi_\pi(0)|^2}{m_\pi}, \tag{34b}$$

a relationship that we have previously adopted (on an *ad hoc* basis) to account for the electromagnetic annihilation properties of vector mesons (Section 15.3.3 and Section 17.1.3). The same conclusion [Equation (34b)] may be drawn from consideration of the K_{l3} decay rates.[38]

---

[36] According to the CVC, the matrix element $\langle \Lambda^0 | V_\alpha^{(0)} | \Sigma^\pm \rangle$ is proportional to the isovector electric current matrix element $\langle \Lambda^0 | J_\alpha^{\text{el}}(t=1) | \Sigma^0 \rangle$. Since $J_\alpha^{\text{el}} = J_\alpha^{(0)} t_3 + J_\alpha^{(1)} \mathcal{Y}/2$, the isovector component (or first term) vanishes for the matrix element in question, at least in the limit of small 4-momentum transfer. [See Lee and Wu, *Ann. Rev. Nucl. Sci., 15:* 381 (1965), p. 405.]

[37] Note, however, the alternative corresponding to the two-angle analysis, Equation (29k).

[38] R. Van Royen and V. F. Weisskopf, *Nuovo Cimento, 50A:* 617 (1967).

PROBLEMS

1. Starting from the definitions of the Dirac γ matrices, such that

$$\gamma_\lambda \not{p}_\lambda u = mu$$

is the Dirac equation for a free spin $\frac{1}{2}$ particle of mass m,[39] show that

$$\bar{u}_1 \gamma_\lambda \gamma_5 u_2 = \frac{-i\not{P}_\lambda}{m_1 - m_2} \cdot \bar{u}_1 \gamma_5 u_2 + \frac{\bar{u}_1(\mathsf{Q}\,\gamma_\lambda - \gamma_\lambda\,\mathsf{Q})\,\gamma_5 u_2}{2(m_1 - m_2)},$$

$$\bar{u}_1 \gamma_5 u_2 = \frac{2\bar{u}_1\,\mathsf{Q}\,\gamma_5 u_2}{m_1 + m_2},$$

where

$$\not{P} = \not{p}_1 + \not{p}_2,$$
$$\not{Q} = \not{p}_1 - \not{p}_2,$$

and

$$\mathsf{Q} = -i\gamma_\lambda \not{Q}_\lambda .$$

2. Consider the decay of a vector meson,

$$W \to \mu + \nu,$$

with the decay matrix element

$$T_{\mathrm{fi}} = g\epsilon_\lambda\, \bar{u}_\mu\, \gamma_\lambda (1 + \gamma_5)\, u_\nu,$$

where ϵ_λ are the components of the 4-vector polarization of the W,

$$p\epsilon_{1,2,3} = (\mathbf{s} \cdot \mathbf{p})_{-,+,0},$$
$$\not{p} \cdot \not{\epsilon} = 0,$$
$$\not{\epsilon} \cdot \not{\epsilon} = 1.$$

Find the relative amplitudes for emission of a μ with helicity $+1$ and -1.

3. The phenomenological Lagrangian for π–$l2$ or K–$l2$ decay may be written

$$\mathcal{L}_{\pi,K} = \frac{g_w^{\pi,K}\, J_\lambda^{\pi,K}\, l_\lambda}{\sqrt{2}},$$

with

$$J_\lambda^{\pi,K} = \not{p}_{\lambda\,\pi,K}$$

(since $\not{p}$ is the only available 4-vector for a pseudoscalar meson). Evaluate the matrix elements for $J_\lambda l_\lambda = \bar{u}_l \not{p}_\lambda \gamma_\lambda (1 + \gamma_5)\, u_\nu$ and use their sum over final states to obtain the decay rates, Equation (13b).

[39] See J. D. Bjorken and S. D. Drell, *Relativistic Quantum Mechanics,* McGraw-Hill, New York (1964).

4. Using de Swart's tables of isoscalar factors (Appendix 6), derive the entries in column 2 of Table 18.1.
5. Using Equation (30) for the weak quark currents, compute the matrix elements for

$$q\bar{q} \rightarrow l\nu_l$$

and use these to derive Equation (34a).

18.2 Nonleptonic Decays

Within the framework of the current-current interaction description of the weak decays, the nonleptonic (hadronic) decays derive from the term [see Equations (1a) and (24a)]

$$\mathcal{L}_{wh} = \frac{G_w}{\sqrt{2}} J_\lambda J_\lambda^* = \frac{G_\mu}{\sqrt{2}} [\cos\theta J_\lambda^{(0)} + \sin\theta J_\lambda^{(1)}][\cos\theta J_\lambda^{(0)} + \sin\theta J_\lambda^{(1)}]^*. \quad (35)$$

Effects of the nonstrange product $J_\lambda^{(0)} J_\lambda^{(0)*}$ are being sought[40] in parity-violating properties of nuclear levels and their nucleonic or electromagnetic decays, but such effects are expected to be relatively extremely small owing to the smallness of G_w^2. The terms $(J_\lambda^{(0)} J_\lambda^{(1)*} + J_\lambda^{(1)} J_\lambda^{(0)*})$ give rise to weak nonleptonic decays of the strange hadrons, with the selection rule $\Delta S = \pm 1$. This selection rule is satisfied to a high order of accuracy (for example, the small value of the K_2^0–K_1^0 mass difference, Chapter 8).[41]

A difficulty arises, however, with respect to the isotopic-spin selection rule $\Delta t = \frac{1}{2}$ which is satisfied to a relatively high degree of accuracy (Section 7.4.3). Since $J_\lambda^{(0)}$ carries $t = 1$, $t_3 = 1$, while $J_\lambda^{(1)*}$ carries $t = \frac{1}{2}$, $t_3 = -\frac{1}{2}$, the products in question will give rise to decays with both $\Delta t = \frac{1}{2}$ and $\Delta t = \frac{3}{2}$ (but $\Delta t_3 = \pm\frac{1}{2}$) and there is, indeed, no apparent reason why the magnitude of the latter should not be comparable to that of the former. The problem, then, is to modify the simple theory [Equation (35)] in such a way as to suppress the $\Delta t = \frac{3}{2}$ decays.

One possibility is to add a neutral current term, $N_\lambda N_\lambda^*$, with a structure appropriate to guarantee $\Delta t = \frac{1}{2}$. However, there is absolutely no evidence for neutral leptonic currents, so that such a term would have to be an exclusive feature of the weak hadronic Lagrangian (the problem of universality). Other suggestions depend on dynamical effects to suppress the $\Delta t = \frac{3}{2}$ contributions.[42] While the origins of the $\Delta t = \frac{1}{2}$ rule remain obscure, we shall nevertheless assume its validity in the discussion that follows.

---

[40] L. B. Okun, *Comments on Nuclear and Particle Physics, 1:* 181 (1967).

[41] However, the possibility is not experimentally excluded that a "superweak" interaction, which might account for the *CP* violation in the $K_L^0 \rightarrow 2\pi$ decays, may permit direct $\Delta S = \pm 2$ processes (see Appendix 8).

[42] For example, since J_λ is assumed to have the transformation properties of an $SU(3)$ octet, the product $J_\lambda J_\lambda^*$ will contain terms that transform like the products of $8 \otimes 8$; in particular, they will include 27-plet terms as well as octets, the former being responsible for the $\Delta t = \frac{3}{2}$ decay contributions. Hence if, for dynamical reasons, these could be suppressed, the result would yield predominantly $\Delta t = \frac{1}{2}$. This is the basis of the "octet dominance" models.

18.2.1 Kaon Decays

The analysis of the $K_{\pi 2}$ and $K_{\pi 3}$ decays, in Section 7.4.3, has demonstrated the degree of validity of the $\Delta t = \frac{1}{2}$ selection rule. In the case of the $K_{\pi 2}$ decays, the relative strength of the $K^{\pm} \to \pi^{\pm}\pi^{0}$ decay, as compared to $K_1^0 \to 2\pi$, yields a quantitative measure of the degree of its violation. Assuming the violation corresponds mainly to a $\Delta t = \frac{3}{2}$ transition [i.e., $A(\Delta t = \frac{5}{2}) \ll A(\Delta t = \frac{3}{2}) \ll A(\Delta t = \frac{1}{2})$], we may use the experimental decay rates to yield, for the ratio of the amplitudes,

$$\left[\frac{\lambda(K^{\pm} \to \pi^{\pm}\pi^{0})}{\lambda(K_1^0 \to 2\pi)}\right]^{1/2} = \frac{3}{4}\left|\frac{A(\Delta t = \frac{3}{2})}{A(\Delta t = \frac{1}{2})}\right| = 0.0385$$

$$\cong \frac{m_{\pi^{\pm}}^2 - m_{\pi^0}^2}{2m_{\pi^0}^2} = 0.035. \tag{36}$$

Although there is as yet no convincing derivation[43] of the second line of relationship (36), it is generally presumed that the breakdown of the $\Delta t = \frac{1}{2}$ law, as well as the $\pi^{\pm}$–π^{0} mass difference, is electromagnetic in origin.

As concerns the $K_{\pi 3}$ decays, the $\Delta t = \frac{1}{2}$ rule is very accurately obeyed, as illustrated in Table 18.3, in which the observed decay rates and spectral-shape parameters are compared for the four observable decay modes

$$K^{\pm} \to \pi^{\pm}\pi^{\pm}\pi^{\mp}, \tag{37a}$$

$$K^{\pm} \to \pi^{0}\pi^{0}\pi^{\pm}, \tag{37b}$$

$$K_2^0 \to \pi^{+}\pi^{-}\pi^{0}, \tag{37c}$$

$$K_2^0 \to \pi^{0}\pi^{0}\pi^{0}. \tag{37d}$$

The decay rates [(λ/Ω), row 3] depend on the decay amplitudes $A_{ijk}(\not{A}_i, \not{A}_j, \not{A}_k)$

Table 18.3 Properties of $K_{\pi 3}$ Decays: Comparison of Experiment and Theory

Decay	$K^{\pm} \to \pi^{+}\pi^{-}\pi^{\pm}$	$K^{\pm} \to \pi^{0}\pi^{0}\pi^{\pm}$	$K_2^0 \to \pi^{+}\pi^{-}\pi^{0}$	$K_2^0 \to \pi^{0}\pi^{0}\pi^{0}$
$\lambda \times 10^{-6}$ (sec^{-1})	4.51 ± 0.03	1.38 ± 0.04	2.29 ± 0.09	4.81 ± 0.41
Relative phase-space factor, Ω	1	1.246	1.228	1.496
$(\lambda/\Omega) \times 10^{-6}$	4.51 ± 0.03	1.11 ± 0.03	1.87 ± 0.07	3.21 ± 0.27
Theory relative	4	1	2	3
Shape parameter, ξ	0.093 ± 0.011	-0.25 ± 0.02	-0.24 ± 0.02	0
Theory relative	1	−2	−2	0
absolute	0.113	−0.226	−0.226	0

[43] Most computations yield, for the ratio of the amplitudes, $\approx (m_{\pi^{\pm}}^2 - m_{\pi^0}^2)/m_K^2$, which is too small by a factor of ≈ 7.

through the relationship

$$\lambda_{ijk} = \frac{1}{16(2\pi)^5 m_K} \int \frac{d^3q_1\, d^3q_2\, d^3q_3}{\epsilon_1 \epsilon_2 \epsilon_3} \delta^4(\not{p} - \not{q}_1 - \not{q}_2 - \not{q}_3)\, |A_{ijk}|^2$$
$$= \frac{1}{64\pi^3 m_K} \int d\epsilon_1\, d\epsilon_2 |\bar{A}_{ijk}|^2. \tag{37e}$$

The shape parameters of the table (row 5) are defined in terms of the deviations of the spectra of the odd (third) pions from the shape predicted by pure phase space (uniform density of decays in the Dalitz plot) fitted to a linear dependence of the decay amplitudes on the kinetic energy, κ, of the odd pion,

$$A_{ijk} = \bar{A}_{ijk} \left\{ 1 - \frac{\xi_{ijk}}{m_\pi^2} (s_3 - \bar{s}) \right\}, \tag{37f}$$

with

$$s_3 = (\not{p}_K - \not{p}_{\pi 3})^2 = m_K^2 + m_\pi^2 - 2m_K \epsilon_{\pi 3} = (m_K - m_\pi)^2 - 2m_K \kappa_{\pi 3} \tag{37g}$$

and

$$\bar{s} = \frac{m_K^2}{3} + m_\pi^2 . \tag{37h}$$

It should be noted that the theoretical predictions, quoted in rows 4 and 6 of Table 18.3, are based on the assumption that the parity-conserving $K_{\pi 3}$ decays proceed predominantly through the final three-pion $t = 1$ state with $l = l' = 0$ (l = relative orbital angular momentum of the two like pions, ij, and l' = the orbital angular momentum of the odd pion, k, with respect to the *cm* of ijk), while the deviations from the pure phase-space distribution arise from a (small) admixture of $l = l' \geq 1$ final states; the relative strength of the admixture is an arbitrary parameter, although the final isotopic spin in each case is assumed to be predominantly $t = 1$ for the three pions.

On the basis of the assumption that the emission of the odd pion can be treated in the limit of zero 4-momentum ($m_\pi \to 0$, or "soft pion" approximation[44]) the PCAC hypothesis permits[45] the prediction of the amplitudes for the $K_{\pi 3}$ decay modes in terms of the $K_1^0 \to 2\pi$ amplitude

$$|A(K_1^0 \to 2\pi)|^2 = \frac{16\pi m_K^2}{3[(m_K^2/4) - m_\pi^2]^{1/2}} \lambda(K_1^0) \tag{38}$$

as follows:

$$\sqrt{2}\, A_{\pi^\pm \pi^\pm \pi^\mp} = \frac{A(K_1^0 \to 2\pi)}{2f_\pi} \left(\frac{m_K^2 + m_\pi^2 - s_3}{m_K^2 - m_\pi^2} \right), \tag{38a}$$

---

[44] See Section 18.3.2.

[45] C. Itzykson, M. Jacob, and G. Mahoux, *Suppl. Nuovo Cimento, 5:* 978 (1967); see also G. C. Wick, *Ann. Phys.* (New York), *18:* 65 (1962).

$$\sqrt{2}\,A_{\pi^0\pi^0\pi^\pm} = A_{\pi^+\pi^-\pi^0} = \frac{A(K_1^0 \to 2\pi)}{2f_\pi}\left(\frac{s_3 - m_\pi^2}{m_K^2 - m_\pi^2}\right), \tag{38b}$$

$$\sqrt{6}\,A_{\pi^0\pi^0\pi^0} = \frac{A(K_1^0 \to 2\pi)}{2f_\pi}\left(\frac{m_K^2}{m_K^2 - m_\pi^2}\right). \tag{38c}$$

Equations (38a) through (38c) lead to predictions that are not only in excellent accord with the average values of A_{ijk} (at $s_3 = \bar{s}$), row 3 of Table 18.3, but also with the spectral shape parameters — see Equation (37f) and the last row of the table.

18.2.2 Hyperon Decays

In our previous discussion of the nonleptonic hyperon decays (Sections 6.1.3 and 7.4.3), we have seen that the observed decay amplitudes, symbolized[46] by Y_j^i, and the parameters characterizing the polarization of the product baryons (Tables 6.6 and 6.5) satisfy a particularly simple set of interconnecting relationships. Considering the amplitudes as vectors in a plane, with the x component proportional to the amplitude for S-wave ($l = 0$) decay, and the y component to the amplitude for P-wave ($l = 1$) decay,

$$\mathbf{Y}_j^i = S(Y_j^i)\,\mathbf{x}_0 + P(Y_j^i)\,\mathbf{y}_0, \tag{39}$$

then the $\Delta t = \frac{1}{2}$ rule (which must also hold separately for the S- and P-wave components) is expressed by the vector sum rules (see Table 7.9)

$$\Lambda_-^0 + \sqrt{2}\,\Lambda_0^0 = 0, \tag{39a}$$

$$\sqrt{2}\,\Sigma_0^+ + \Sigma_+^+ - \Sigma_-^- = 0, \tag{39b}$$

$$\sqrt{2}\,\Xi_0^0 - \Xi_-^- = 0, \tag{39c}$$

$$\Omega_-^- + \sqrt{2}\,\Omega_0^- = 0. \tag{39d}$$

In addition, we have noted the empirical relationships

$$S(\Sigma_+^+) \cong P(\Sigma_-^-) \cong 0 \tag{39e}$$

and

$$\sqrt{3}\,\Sigma_0^+ \cong 2\,\Xi_-^- - \Lambda_-^0, \tag{39f}$$

this last being known as the Lee–Sugawara rule. The degree of validity of the relationships (39b), (39e), and (39f) is demonstrated in Figure 18.3.

We have also noted that the Ω^- decays must be treated separately, although still satisfying the $\Delta t = \frac{1}{2}$ rule, Equation (39d), since angular-momentum conservation (the Ω^- has spin $\frac{3}{2}^+$) requires that the parity-violating decay be to a $D_{3/2}$ final $\Xi\pi$ state, while the parity-conserving decay is to a $P_{3/2}$ state. In addition, the

[46] Y is the parent hyperon, of charge i, decaying into a pion of charge j, with the selection rule $\Delta S = 1$, e.g., Λ_-^0 is the amplitude for $\Lambda^0 \to P + \pi^-$, Ξ_-^- for $\Xi^- \to \Lambda^0 + \pi^-$, etc.

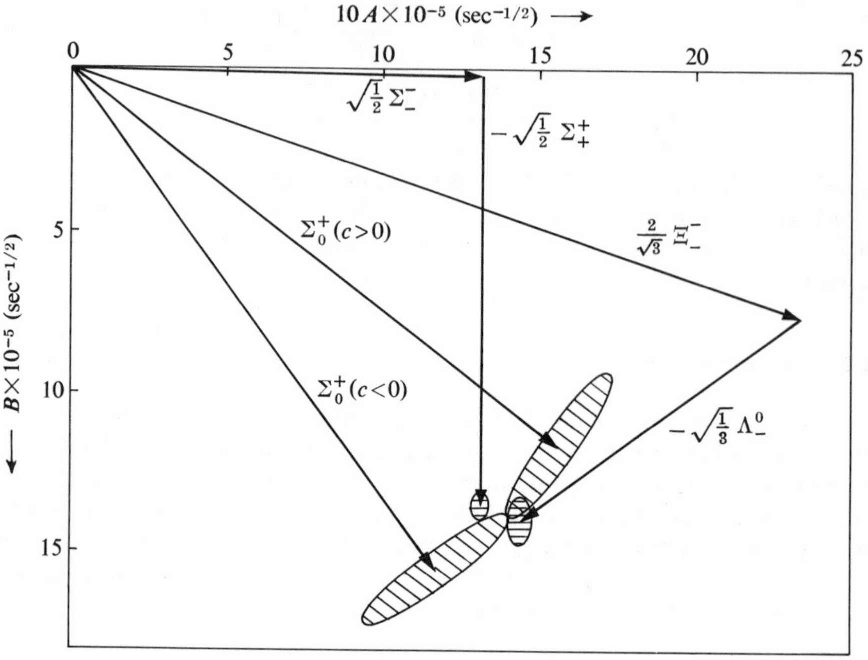

Figure 18.3 Demonstration of the relations among the hyperon nonleptonic decay amplitudes:

$$-\sqrt{\tfrac{1}{2}}\,(\Sigma_+^+ - \Sigma_-^-) \cong \Sigma_0^+ \cong \sqrt{\tfrac{1}{3}}\,(2\Xi_-^- - \Lambda_-^0).$$

Note the two possible solutions for Σ_0^+, not yet experimentally resolved, coincide if $S(\Sigma_0^+) = P(\Sigma_0^+)$. [After Berge, *Proceedings of the XIII Conference on High-Energy Physics*, Berkeley (1966).]

decay mode $\Omega^- \to \Lambda^0 + K^-$ (amplitude $\Omega_{K^-}^-$), satisfying the $\Delta S = 1$ requirement, is also energetically permitted.

Aside from the $\Delta t = \frac{1}{2}$ rule [Equations (39a) through (39d)], whose possible origins have been discussed in the preceding, the remarkable simplicity of the connections (39e) and (39f) cries out for a simple physical explanation. The remainder of this section is devoted to some possibilities that have been proposed toward this end.

Quark Model of Nonleptonic Hyperon Decays • The quark model of the hadrons offers a straightforward approach to the understanding of the S-wave (parity-nonconserving) components of the hyperon, as well as the kaon, decays.[47] On this model, the basic decay, as illustrated in Figure 18.4(a), is of the λ quark into a nucleon quark plus a pion (with orbital angular momentum $l = 0$). It is assumed that the λ decay obeys the $\Delta t = \frac{1}{2}$ selection rule

$$\lambda \to \sqrt{2}\, p\pi^- - n\pi^0\,, \qquad (40a)$$

[47] S. Badier, *Phys. Letters, 24B:* 157 (1967); see also F. C. Chan, *Nuovo Cimento, 45A:* 236 (1966).

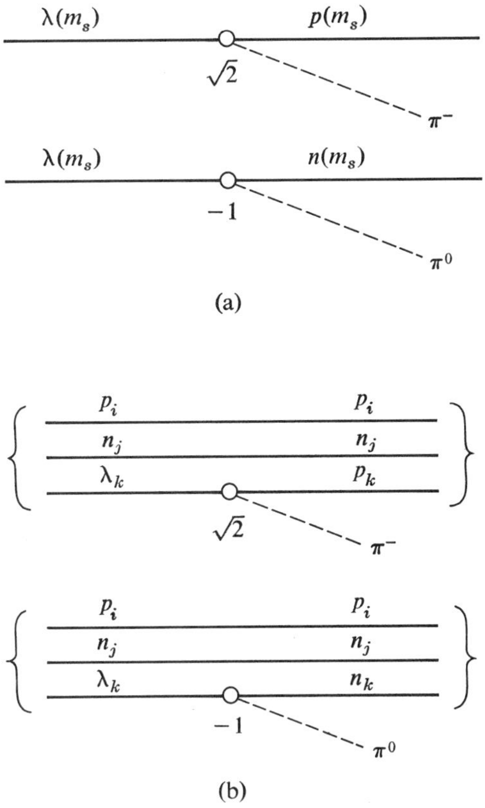

Figure 18.4 Quark model of the S-wave decay processes of hadrons: (a) The basic decays. (b) Diagrams leading to Λ^0 or Σ^0 decays.

while the orientation of the quark spin (m_s) remains unchanged in the decay process. Accordingly, the parity-nonconserving decay of a Λ^0 or Σ^0 hyperon proceeds through the processes illustrated in Figure 18.4(b). Thus, starting with the baryon qqq combinations of Table 15.2, and superimposing the decay amplitudes corresponding to the components of these wave functions, we arrive directly at the relative S-wave amplitudes given in column 2 of Table 18.4. The calculation may be symbolized by the expression

$$S(Y_j^i) = \sum_q \langle B_f(\Sigma\, q_i' q_j' q_k')\pi_j | \mathcal{O}(\lambda_{ijk})\, Y_i(\Sigma\, q_i q_j q_k)\rangle, \tag{40b}$$

where the final quark combinations $q_i'q_j'q_k'$ differ from the initial ones by the (single) substitution of a p or n quark for a λ quark, since the operator $\mathcal{O}(\lambda)$ performs the transformation (40a) on one of the constituent λ quarks of Y_i.

This model immediately suggests an explanation for the result $S(\Sigma_+^+) = 0$; the conversion of the Σ^+ quark combinations ($pp\lambda$) to the N combinations (pnn) would require the simultaneous transformation of two quarks. [Another description of the same effect is that the basic λ-decay process, Equation (40a), cannot

Table 18.4 Relative[a] Hadron Nonleptonic Decay Amplitudes According to the Quark Model

Decay	S	P_a	P_b	P_c	$P=\Sigma P_i$
Λ^0_-	$\sqrt{3}$	$\sqrt{3}/2$	$\sqrt{3}/5$	$3\sqrt{3}/10$	$\sqrt{3}$
Λ^0_0	$-\sqrt{3/2}$	$-\sqrt{3/8}$	$-\sqrt{3/50}$	$-3\sqrt{3/200}$	$-\sqrt{3/2}$
Σ^+_+	0	$\sqrt{1/2}$	$\sqrt{1/2}$	0	$\sqrt{2}$
Σ^+_0	1	$-1/2$	$-2/5$	$-1/10$	-1
Σ^-_-	$\sqrt{2}$	0	$\sqrt{2}/10$	$-\sqrt{2}/10$	0
Ξ^0_0	$\sqrt{3/2}$	$2\sqrt{3/200}$	$\sqrt{3/200}$	$\sqrt{3/200}$	$2\sqrt{3/50}$
Ξ^-_-	$\sqrt{3}$	$\sqrt{3}/5$	$\sqrt{3}/10$	$\sqrt{3}/10$	$2\sqrt{3}/5$
Ω^-_-	—	$-3\sqrt{2}/5$	0	$-3\sqrt{2}/5$	$-6\sqrt{2}/5$
Ω^-_0	—	$3/5$	0	$3/5$	$6/5$
$\Omega_{\bar{K}^-}$	—	$3\sqrt{3}/5$	$3\sqrt{3}/5$	0	$6\sqrt{3}/5$
$K^0_{1\,\pm\mp}$	$\sqrt{2}$	0	0	0	0
$K^0_{1\,00}$	-1	0	0	0	0
$K^\pm_{\pm 0}$	0	0	0	0	0

[a] Normalized to $S(\Sigma^+_0) = -P(\Sigma^+_0) = 1$.

give rise to the emission of a π^+.][48] We also note that, according to this model, the parity-nonconserving amplitudes for the Ω^- decays are all zero, since a spin-nonflip pion (or kaon) emission process cannot convert a member of the $\frac{3}{2}^+$ decimet to one of the $\frac{1}{2}^+$ octet [no D-wave pion emission is possible in the process (40a)]; hence, the quark model predicts a pure $P_{3/2}$ (parity-conserving) decay for the Ω^-.

The results for the $K_{\pi 2}$ decays (last three rows of Table 18.4) are quite remarkable; not only does the model yield the $\Delta t = \frac{1}{2}$ selection rule,[49] but a computation of the relative value of the decay amplitude, e.g., as compared to $S(\Lambda^0_-)$, yields a value in excellent agreement with the observed decay rate, on the assumption that the relative rates are given by $|S|^2$ times a two-body phase-space factor.[50]

Finally, it is to be noted that the S-wave amplitudes of Table 18.4 obey the Lee–Sugawara rule, Equation (39f), and accordingly agree very well with the experimental values summarized in Table 6.6.

---

[48] Generally speaking, since $\Sigma^+ \to N$ requires $\Delta t_3 = \frac{3}{2}$, any interaction Hamiltonian that is linear in the $SU(3)$ operators [i.e., that leads only to transitions between neighboring members of $SU(3)$ multiplets] will automatically yield $\Sigma^+_+ = 0$.

[49] This is, in itself, not remarkable, since $\Delta t = \frac{1}{2}$ is built into the basic decay process (40a), and consequently the $\Delta t = \frac{1}{2}$ rule emerges for all the decays, Equations (39a) through (39d). In the case of the K^0 and $\bar{K}^0$ decays, the charged pion emission ($\bar{\lambda} \to \bar{p}\pi^+$ and $\lambda \to p\pi^-$, respectively) converts the K^0 or $\bar{K}^0$ to a π^- or π^+, and these two final states combine *incoherently* in the K^0_1 decay; for the K^0 or $\bar{K}^0 \to 2\pi^0$, on the other hand, the final $2\pi^0$ states combine coherently; the $K^\pm \to \pi^\pm\pi^0$ decays vanish as a result of a cancellation of the amplitudes corresponding to charged and neutral pion emission. However, a pure $SU(3)$ octet current times octet current model of the $K_{\pi 2}$ decays predicts, also, the vanishing of the $K^0_{1\,\pi 2}$ amplitudes. The difference is that the quark model treats the two decay pions in an asymmetric way — one is the residual octet member $K \to \pi$, while the other is treated as the quantum of a field emission process (40a). It is only in the symmetrization of the final 2π wave function that the two are treated on an equal footing.

[50] S. Badier, *Phys. Letters, 24B:* 157 (1967).

The P-wave (parity-conserving) decays present a more difficult problem. The simplest parity-conserving $\Delta t = \frac{1}{2}$, $\Delta S = 1$ quark decay is via the weak decay process

$$\lambda_i(\bar{\lambda}_i) \to n_i(-\bar{n}_i), \tag{41}$$

in which the quark spin state (i) is unaltered by the transition. However, this transition must, in the physical case, be accompanied by a P-wave pion (or kaon) emission, to conserve parity, energy, and momentum. This emission process could occur simultaneously with the quark conversion process, but it can also occur separately as a consequence of the strong Yukawa interactions among the quarks (see Section 15.3.4). Since the latter assumption corresponds to the simplest form of the weak, parity-conserving decay interaction, and since the strong Yukawa processes are well understood, it is of interest to consider a two-stage [weak, via Equation (41), plus strong Yukawa] model for the parity-conserving hyperon decays.

For such a model, there are three possible sequences: (1) Weak $\lambda \to n$ decay followed by strong pion emission (kaon emission in the case of the $\Omega^-_{K^-}$ decay) by one of the quark constituents of the hadron in question (not necessarily the n quark resulting from the $\lambda \to n$ decay). (2) Strong pion (kaon) emission by one of the quarks, followed by the weak $\lambda \to n$ conversion. (3) Strong kaon emission from a λ quark ($\lambda \to p + K^-$ or $n + \overline{K^0}$) followed by weak $\overline{K} \to \pi$ conversion through a $\lambda \to n$ conversion in the strongly emitted $\overline{K}$. This last process (see Table 15.2) gives, for the weak $\overline{K}$-decay strengths,

$$K^- \to \pi^-, \tag{41a}$$

$$\overline{K^0} \to -\sqrt{\tfrac{1}{2}}\,\pi^0. \tag{41b}$$

Diagrams illustrating each of these three sequences for the case of the Σ_0^+ decay are shown in Figure 18.5. Note that the strong decay processes (solid circles in Figure 18.5) result in either isospin and/or spin-flip or nonflip processes according to the properties of the $\boldsymbol{\sigma}_i\boldsymbol{\tau}_i$ operator that governs the strong Yukawa interactions [see Section 1.1, Equation (18)]. Application of this operator plus (41) to the hadronic qqq wave functions results in the relative P-wave decay amplitudes shown in Table 18.4; their sum is given in the last column.

Since both the strong interaction and the assumed weak interaction obey the $\Delta t = \frac{1}{2}$ rule, the P-wave decay amplitudes — for each possible sequence (columns 3–5) and in their sum (column 6) — also satisfy this selection rule, i.e., Equations (39a) through (39d). On the other hand, while the weak-strong sequence yields $P_a(\Sigma_-^-) = 0$ [the initial $nn\lambda$ state decays, via $\lambda \to n$ without spin-flip, into an nnn state of spin $\frac{1}{2}^+$, which is not permitted by $SU(6)$ symmetry considerations], the two other possible decay sequences yield $P_{b,c}(\Sigma_-^-) \neq 0$; however, assuming $SU(3)$ symmetry for the strong interaction constants, we note that the sum $P(\Sigma_-^-)$ does indeed vanish, which corresponds to the experimental situation, Equation (39e).

Unhappily for this simple approach, the other predictions do not fare nearly so well when compared to the observations. Thus, only the amplitudes P_c obey the

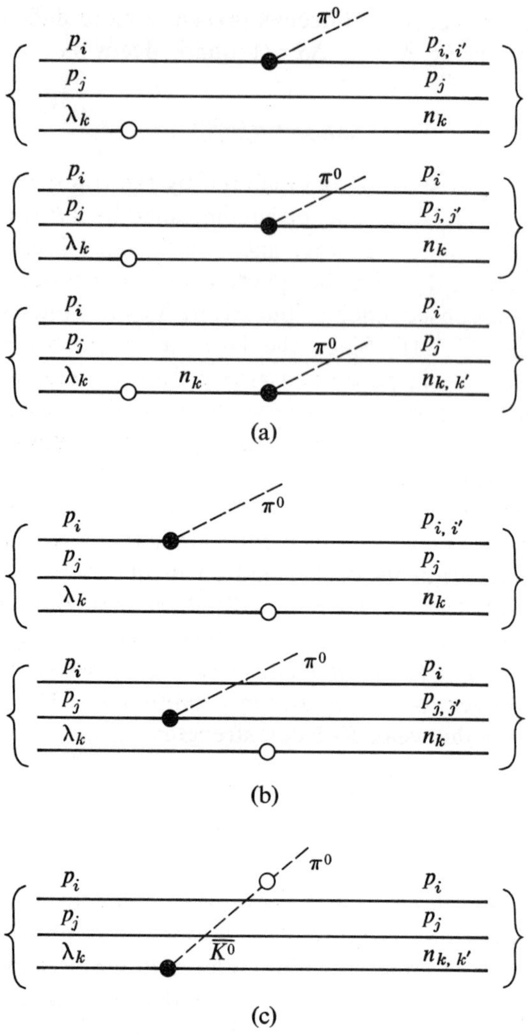

Figure 18.5 Weak P-wave hadronic decay sequences for $\Sigma^+ \to P\pi^0$, according to the two-stage quark model: (a) Weak-strong sequences. (b) Strong-weak sequences. (c) $\overline{K} \to \pi$ sequence.

Lee–Sugawara rule [Equation (39f)], and even in this case, as well as for the other sequences and for the sum, the signs of the $P(\Xi)$ are the same as those of the $S(\Xi)$, and opposite to the experimental values [see the negative sign of the asymmetry parameters, $a(\Xi)$, in Table 6.5].

In addition, the relative magnitude of the $P(\Lambda_-^0)$ amplitude, predicted in column 6 of Table 18.4, is $\sim$ 2–3 times larger than observed (Table 6.6). Finally, the relative rates of the Ω^- decays also are predicted to be much larger than observed,[51] by a factor of ~ 5. Thus, aside from its success in predicting $P(\Sigma_-^-)=0$, the two-stage quark model of the parity-conserving nonleptonic hadronic decays leaves much to be desired.

Alternative Approaches; Pole Models A variety of approaches has been proposed to describe the hadronic currents leading to the nonleptonic decays. Generally, those that incorporate the $\Delta t = \frac{1}{2}$ rule plus some form of $SU(3)$ symmetry into the description (including our quark model) have succeeded in reproducing the salient features of the parity-violating (S-wave) decays — namely, the vanishing of $S(\Sigma_+^+)$ and the Lee–Sugawara rule, Equation (39f). The problems always arise in respect to the P-wave decays that involve, in addition to the vector part of the hadron current, the strong (Yukawa) interactions as well.

A modified version[52] of $SU(6)$-symmetric theory invokes the assumption that the symmetry is violated in the hadronic decays in a special way — i.e., that the interaction is symmetric under the $SU(6)_W$ group, a restricted subgroup of $SU(6)$. The resulting relationships among the $Y(\frac{1}{2}^+)$ decays are the same as for the quark model (Table 18.4, column 6):

$$-\sqrt{2}\,P(\Sigma_+^+) = 3P(\Sigma_0^+) + \sqrt{\tfrac{1}{3}}\,P(\Lambda_-^0) = \tfrac{10}{3}[P(\Sigma_0^+) + \sqrt{\tfrac{1}{3}}\,P(\Xi_-^-)]; \tag{42a}$$

while the predictions for the Ω^- decays,

$$5P(\Omega_0^-) = 2\sqrt{3}\,[P(\Sigma_+^+) + 5P(\Sigma_-^-)], \tag{42b}$$

$$5P(\Omega_{K^-}^-) = 6P(\Sigma_+^+), \tag{42c}$$

reduce the discrepancy between the observed and predicted Ω^--decay rates, but only by the factor 1.5.

One of the main deficiencies of the quark model is its failure to provide a proper kinematical treatment of the pion emission vertices (i.e., the $Y\mathfrak{N}\pi$ vertices of Figures 18.4 and 18.5) — for example, effects of the mass differences between the baryons involved [which are $SU(3)$-violating effects] are disregarded. This deficiency is corrected in the "pole" models,[53] in which the parity-violating vertex is associated with the divergence of the strange hadronic axial vector current of Cabibbo, $A_\lambda^{(1)}$ [see Section 18.1.2, Equation (24c)].[54]

In computing the matrix elements of $\partial A_\lambda^{(1)}/\partial x_\lambda$ by use of the pole models, we assume, further, that the PDDAC (PCAC) hypothesis (Section 18.1.2) may be

---

[51] But with an experimental uncertainty of ~ 50 percent.

[52] D. Horn, *et al., Phys. Rev. Letters, 14:* 717 (1965); R. Gatto, *et al., Phys. Rev., 139B:* 1294 (1965).

[53] H. Sugawara, *Phys. Rev. Letters, 15:* 870 and 997 (1965); M. Suzuki, *Phys. Rev. Letters, 15:* 986 (1965); Y. Haru, Y. Nambu, and J. Schechter, *Phys. Rev. Letters, 16:* 380 (1966); L. S. Brown and C. M. Sommerfield, *Phys. Rev. Letters, 17:* 751 (1966); M. L. Good and M. M. Nieto, *Phys. Rev. Letters, 20:* 624 (1968).

[54] However, in order to fit the observations, it may be necessary to include an additional term, corresponding to the $t = \frac{1}{2}$ elements of the 27-plet resulting from the $8 \otimes \overline{8}$ baryon combination [see Good and Nieto, *Phys. Rev. Letters, 20:* 624 (1968)].

extended to the strange $BB'\pi$ vertex, with the coupling constant given by the Goldberger–Treiman relation [Equation (14a)]. This assumption leads directly to a set of S-wave decay amplitudes in excellent agreement with the observed values.

In order to compute the P-wave amplitudes, it is necessary to make additional assumptions relating to the treatment of the divergence of the strange vector current, $V_\lambda^{(1)}$, leading to the $\overline{Y}$ annihilation vertices (see Figure 18.5), as well as to take into account in a consistent fashion the strong Yukawa P-wave pion emission. The most successful pole models are based on the assumption that the vector and axial vector currents are connected through a set of commutation relationships postulated in the current-algebra approach of Gell-Mann (see the following section), while the Yukawa pion-emission process is generally treated in the Born approximation. These assumptions result in effective weak hadronic nonleptonic decay matrix elements of the form

$$\langle Y|\mathfrak{N}\pi\rangle = -\frac{1}{2\sqrt{2}f_\pi}\,\overline{\psi}(Y)\,\psi(\mathfrak{N})\,(A + kB), \tag{43}$$

where k is a kinematical factor,

$$k = \left[\frac{(M_Y - M_{\mathfrak{N}})^2 - m_\pi^2}{(M_Y + M_{\mathfrak{N}})^2 - m_\pi^2}\right]^{1/2}, \tag{43a}$$

and the S- and P-wave amplitudes (A and B, respectively) contain contributions from the 8_1, 8_2 [and possibly $27(t=\frac{1}{2})$] components of the $8 \otimes \overline{8}$ decomposition. The usual (Cabibbo) choice of hadronic current parameters leads[55] to a set of P-wave amplitudes that obey the Lee–Sugawara rule — i.e., the correct sign of $P(\Xi)$ — but which are uniformly too small by a factor of ≈ 2. However, by inclusion of an appropriate recipe for the $(t=\frac{1}{2})$ contribution from the 27-plet, Good and Nieto obtain[56]

$$\frac{P}{S}(\Sigma_0^+) = -0.97\ (\alpha = -1.00), \tag{43b}$$

$$\frac{P}{S}(\Lambda_-^0) = 0.71\ (\alpha = 0.94), \tag{43c}$$

$$\frac{P}{S}(\Xi_-^-) = -0.20\ (\alpha = -0.38), \tag{43d}$$

in quite good accord with experiment (see Tables 6.5 and 6.6). Nevertheless, it should be stressed that the assumptions, and the computational approximations employed, contain sufficient ambiguities so that the theory of the weak, nonleptonic hadron decays still cannot be said to be on a really firm footing.[57]

---

[55] Brown and Sommerfield, *Phys. Rev. Letters, 17:* 751 (1966).
[56] *Phys. Rev. Letters, 20:* 624 (1968).
[57] S. Okubo, *Ann. Phys.* (New York), *47:* 351 (1968).

PROBLEMS

1. Consider the decays

$$K \rightarrow \pi_1 \pi_2$$

with the assumed matrix element

$$T_{\text{fi}} = \frac{g}{(8E_K E_1 E_2)^{1/2}} \frac{\not{p}_K \cdot (\not{p}_1 + \not{p}_2)}{M_K}.$$

(a) Why is this the most reasonable form for $T_{\text{fi}}(K \rightarrow 2\pi)$?

(b) Compute the decay rate and, using the experimental values (see Table 2.1), determine and compare the values of g for
   (i) K_1^0,
   (ii) $K^{\pm}$,
   (iii) K_2^0.

(c) Let

$$R = \frac{\lambda(K_2^0 \rightarrow 2\pi)}{\lambda(K_1^0 \rightarrow 2\pi)} \cong R_0 + ap_K(lab)$$

represent the experimental observations over the range of $K^0(lab)$ momenta $\sim$ 1–10 GeV/c, with $R_0 = (2.0 \pm 0.1) \times 10^{-3}$, $a \approx (2 \pm 3) \times 10^{-5}$ (GeV/c)$^{-1}$.[58] Discuss the implications of the establishment of a finite value of $|a|$ in terms of the invariance principles involved.

2. The parity-conserving $K_{\pi 3}$ decays may be thought of as proceeding through the following possible sequences (s = strong, w = weak):

$$K \underset{w}{\rightarrow} \pi \underset{s}{\rightarrow} \pi\rho, \qquad \rho \underset{s}{\rightarrow} \pi\pi,$$

$$K \underset{s}{\rightarrow} \pi K^*, \qquad K^* \underset{w}{\rightarrow} \rho \underset{s}{\rightarrow} \pi\pi.$$

(a) Draw the diagrams corresponding to these decays according to the quark model and derive the amplitudes in terms of the basic ($\lambda \rightarrow n$) quark amplitude.

(b) Using the techniques discussed in Chapter 15, estimate the decay rate $\lambda(K_2^0 \rightarrow 3\pi)$. [You will need some independent source for obtaining the $\lambda \rightarrow n$ weak coupling constant.]

18.3 Recent Developments

The relative simplicity of the form of the weak interactions, describable in terms of leptonic and hadronic currents coupled universally to each other, with the hadronic currents exhibiting the transformation properties of members of

[58] X. de Bouard, *et al.*, *Nuovo Cimento*, *52A*: 662 (1967).

$SU(3)$ octets, has inspired a number of recent theoretical attempts to generalize these concepts to include all of the hadronic interactions — weak, electromagnetic, and strong — within a uniform and broader theoretical framework. These attempts have given rise to the development of new and powerful techniques (approximations) for treating the hadronic interactions and for elucidating relationships among the various coupling constants, masses, widths, etc., previously regarded as following from the more or less accidental values of the set of apparently independent empirical parameters employed in a variety of phenomenological theories. Although such attempts are, at this time, still very much in the exploratory stage, the connections and insights that have emerged give promise of yielding, in due time, a more comprehensive approach to a theory of the elementary particles. In this section we outline some of the most promising of these new approaches and mention some of their most interesting results.

18.3.1 Algebra of Currents

We have observed in Section 18.1.2 that the components of the weak nucleonic vector current $V_\lambda^{(0)}$ have the properties of the components of an isotopic-spin vector ($\tau^\pm$) which, together with the isovector component of the electromagnetic current ($\propto \tau_3$), form a divergence-free 4-vector (CVC); and that the components of the weak nucleonic axial vector current $A_\lambda^{(0)}$ may be associated with the pion field through the PCAC or PDDAC hypothesis [59] (Section 18.1.2).

Now, as far as isotopic spin is concerned, the properties of the $\boldsymbol{\tau} = \tau_i (i = 1, 2, 3)$ operators are completely described by specification of the commutation relations obeyed by the components

$$[\tau_i, \tau_j] = \tau_i \tau_j - \tau_j \tau_i = i\epsilon_{ijk} \tau_k , \tag{45a}$$

where $\epsilon_{ijk} = 1$ for all cyclical sequences of ijk and $\epsilon_{ijk} = -1$ for odd permutations. We may define an isotopic 4-current $\mathfrak{J}_{i\lambda}$, where

$$\tau_i = -i \int \mathfrak{J}_{i4}\, d^3x. \tag{45b}$$

[59] In the same way as the PDDAC hypothesis gives rise to the Goldberger–Treiman relation [Equations (13) and (14)] one may postulate [J. J. Sakurai, *Ann. Phys.* (New York), *11:* 1 (1960)] that the isospin vector current matrix elements are dominated by the π-meson pole

$$\langle \text{vacuum} | \tau_\lambda^{(i)} | \rho \rangle = f_\rho m_\rho^2 \phi_\rho^{(i)}, \tag{44a}$$

which leads, through analogous arguments, to the relationship

$$1 = 2 f_\rho g_s^{\rho\mathfrak{N}\mathfrak{N}} \equiv \frac{g_s^{\rho\mathfrak{N}\mathfrak{N}}}{\gamma_\rho}. \tag{44b}$$

Sakurai notes that the postulate of a universal ρ coupling,

$$g_s^{\rho\mathfrak{N}\mathfrak{N}} = g_s^{\rho\pi\pi}, \tag{44c}$$

yields the experimentally observed ρ width, as well as an understanding of the low-energy pion-nucleon scattering phase shifts (Section 1.1). It also provides a basis for the ρ-dominance model of the electromagnetic-hadronic interactions.

Isospin invariance (charge independence) is then guaranteed by the divergence-free nature of $\mathfrak{I}_{i\lambda}$,

$$\dot{\tau}_i \equiv \frac{d\tau_i}{dt} = \int \frac{\partial \mathfrak{I}_{i\lambda}}{\partial x_\lambda} d^3x = 0, \tag{45c}$$

since

$$\frac{\partial \mathfrak{I}_{i\lambda}}{\partial x_\lambda} = 0. \tag{45d}$$

The isospin current elements also exhibit a simple commutation relation

$$[\mathfrak{I}_{i4}(\mathbf{x}, t), \mathfrak{I}_{j4}(\mathbf{y}, t)] = -i\epsilon_{ijk}\mathfrak{I}_{k4}(\mathbf{x}, t)\,\delta(\mathbf{x}-\mathbf{y}). \tag{45e}$$

Since the components of the weak nonstrange vector currents $V_{i\lambda}^{(0)}$ have the same transformation properties as the $\mathfrak{I}_{i\lambda}$, they obey the same commutation rule (45e).

Gell-Mann has proposed [60] that such commutation relations may be a general feature of the vector and axial vector hadronic currents. Thus, considering the nonstrange axial currents, $A_{i\lambda}^{(0)}$, we may define [see Equation (45b)]

$$\mathfrak{A}_i(t) = -i \int A_{i4}^{(0)}\, d^3x, \tag{46a}$$

such that

$$[\tau_i, \mathfrak{A}_j] = [\mathfrak{A}_i, \tau_j] = i\epsilon_{ijk}\mathfrak{A}_k, \tag{46b}$$

and we may close the chain by assuming

$$[\mathfrak{A}_i, \mathfrak{A}_j] = i\epsilon_{ijk}\tau_k. \tag{46c}$$

The relations (45) and (46) define a set (algebra) of equal-time commutation relations among the components of the weak, nonstrange hadronic currents which is closed under the isospin group operations,[61] $SU(2) \times SU(2)$,

$$[V_{i4}^{(0)}(\mathbf{x}, t), A_{j4}^{(0)}(\mathbf{y}, t)] = -i\epsilon_{ijk}A_{k4}^{(0)}(\mathbf{x}, t)\,\delta(\mathbf{x}-\mathbf{y}), \tag{47a}$$

$$[A_{i4}^{(0)}(\mathbf{x}, t), A_{j4}^{(0)}(\mathbf{y}, t)] = -i\epsilon_{ijk}V_{k4}^{(0)}(\mathbf{x}, t)\,\delta(\mathbf{x}-\mathbf{y}), \tag{47b}$$

$$[V_{i4}^{(0)}(\mathbf{x}, t), V_{j4}^{(0)}(\mathbf{y}, t)] = -i\epsilon_{ijk}V_{k4}^{(0)}(\mathbf{x}, t)\,\delta(\mathbf{x}-\mathbf{y}). \tag{47c}$$

Since the weak hadronic currents, $J_{i\lambda} = \cos\theta\, J_{i\lambda}^{(0)} + \sin\theta\, J_{i\lambda}^{(1)}$, transform like members of an $SU(3)$ octet, Gell-Mann has proposed that they may form a closed algebra under $SU(3) \times SU(3)$ [or an extended $SU(6)$ algebra]. Defining

$$\mathfrak{V}_i^{(0,1)}(t) = -i \int V_{i4}^{(0,1)}\, d^3x \tag{48a}$$

---

[60] M. Gell-Mann, *Phys. Rev.*, *125:* 1067 (1962); *Physics*, *1:* 63 (1964).

[61] The property of invariance under $SU(2) \times SU(2)$ (or the "chiral" group) is referred to as chiral invariance.

[$\mathcal{V}_i^{(0)}$ transforms like τ_i, Equations (45)], we may generalize Equations (45a), (46b), (46c):

$$[\mathcal{V}_i^{(0,1)}(t), \mathcal{A}_j^{(0,1)}(t)] = if_{ijk}\,\mathcal{A}_k^{(0,1)}(t), \tag{48b}$$

$$[\mathcal{A}_i^{(0,1)}(t), \mathcal{A}_j^{(0,1)}(t)] = if_{ijk}\,\mathcal{V}_k^{(0,1)}(t), \tag{48c}$$

$$[\mathcal{V}_i^{(0,1)}(t), \mathcal{V}_j^{(0,1)}(t)] = if_{ijk}\mathcal{V}_k^{(0,1)}(t), \tag{48d}$$

where the f_{ijk} are the unitary-spin permutation coefficients appropriate to the $SU(3)$ transformation properties (see Section 14.5). The elements of the currents,[62] $V_{i\lambda}$ and $A_{i\lambda}$, then obey the (closed) set of equal-time commutation relations

$$[\mathcal{V}_i(t), V_{j\lambda}(\mathbf{x}, t)] = if_{ijk}V_{k\lambda}(\mathbf{x}, t), \tag{49a}$$

$$[\mathcal{V}_i(t), A_{j\lambda}(\mathbf{x}, t)] = if_{ijk}A_{k\lambda}(\mathbf{x}, t), \tag{49b}$$

$$[\mathcal{A}_i(t), V_{j\lambda}(\mathbf{x}, t)] = if_{ijk}A_{k\lambda}(\mathbf{x}, t), \tag{49c}$$

$$[\mathcal{A}_i(t), A_{j\lambda}(\mathbf{x}, t)] = if_{ijk}V_{k\lambda}(\mathbf{x}, t). \tag{49d}$$

The closed sets of commutation relations [Equations (47), (48), (49)] postulated by Gell-Mann form the basis of the current-algebra approach to the hadronic interactions. Many applications have been made to a variety of strong, electromagnetic, and weak interaction processes. Generally, such applications consist of the evaluation of a matrix element of some current component between two well-defined hadronic states (a and b), advantage being taken of the cloture property

$$\langle a|[A, B]|b\rangle = \sum_n \{\langle a|A|n\rangle\langle n|B|b\rangle - \langle a|B|n\rangle\langle n|A|b\rangle\}, \tag{50}$$

where n represents the complete set of intermediate hadronic states accessible to a and b through the operations A and B. In some cases, it may be assumed that the summation over n is "saturated" by some finite group of intermediate states which, by physical argument or theoretical conjecture, is believed to dominate the interaction in question.[63] The evaluation of the matrix elements of both sides of a given commutation relation, Equation (50), then leads to a "sum rule" or relationship among the physical constants involved.

However, in general, the computation of the required summations [Equation (50)] is an arduous process, for which special and elegant techniques have been devised by Fubini and others.[64]

---

[62] Since the relationships under consideration involve all the components of $J_{i\lambda}$, we henceforth drop the superfluous superscript $^{(0,1)}$.

[63] For example, it is sometimes assumed that the strong pion-nucleon interaction is dominated by the (3, 3) resonance $\mathfrak{N}^*_{3/2}(1238)$.

[64] For example, S. Fubini, *Nuovo Cimento, 43:* 475 (1966); S. Fubini and G. Furlan, *Physics, 1:* 229 (1965); K. Johnson and F. E. Low, *Suppl. Progr. Theoret. Phys.* (Japan), *37* and *38:* 74 (1966).

18.3.2 Some Applications

The Adler–Weisberger Relationship • One of the most interesting applications has been the computation,[65] by Adler and Weisberger, of the renormalization constant of the nucleon axial vector β-decay strength

$$a_\beta = \frac{G_\beta^A}{G_\beta^V} \tag{51a}$$

[see Section 18.1.2, Equations (8a) and (8b)]. In the following, we summarize the main steps in this computation, without reproducing the (formidable) computational details: The computation starts from a special form of relationship (46c)

$$[\mathcal{A}^+(t), \mathcal{A}^-(t)] = 2\tau_3, \tag{51b}$$

where

$$\mathcal{A}^\pm = \mathcal{A}_1 \pm i\mathcal{A}_2, \tag{51c}$$

and utilizes two relationships, discussed in the preceding,

$$\langle \mathcal{N}(\not{q})|J^{(0)}|\mathcal{N}(\not{q})\rangle = \left(\frac{M_\mathcal{N}}{q_0}\right) G_\beta^V \overline{\psi}_\mathcal{N}(\not{q})\,\gamma_\lambda\,(1 + a_\beta\gamma_5)\,\tau^+\,\psi_\mathcal{N}(\not{q}), \tag{51d}$$

which defines a_β, and PCAC [Equations (14) and (16)] in the form

$$-i\frac{d}{dt}\int d^3x\,A_4^\pm = \frac{d}{dt}\mathcal{A}^\pm = \frac{\sqrt{2}M_\mathcal{N}\,m_\pi^2\,a_\beta}{g_s^\pi\,K(0)}\int d^3x\,\phi_{\pi^\pm} \tag{51e}$$

(note that $\int d^3x\,\phi_{\pi^\pm} \propto e^{iq_0t}$). We now equate the matrix elements of both sides of Equation (51b) between two proton states, using

$$\langle P(\not{q})|2\tau_3|P(\not{q}')\rangle = (2\pi)^3\,\delta(\mathbf{q} - \mathbf{q}') \tag{51f}$$

for the right-hand side, and Equation (50) for the left. The resulting summation contains two types of intermediate states — states containing just a single neutron, for which utilization of Equation (51d) gives the contribution

$$\sum_{n=N}\Big\{\quad\Big\} = (2\pi)^3\,\delta(\mathbf{q} - \mathbf{q}')\,a_\beta^2\left(1 - \frac{M_N^2}{q_0^2}\right), \tag{51g}$$

and intermediate states containing one or more pions, for which PCAC [Equation (51e)] gives, in a typical case,

$$\begin{aligned}\langle P(\not{q})|\mathcal{A}^\pm|n\rangle &= -i\,\frac{\langle P(\not{q})|\dot{\mathcal{A}}^\pm|n\rangle}{E_p - E_n}\\ &= \frac{\sqrt{2}M_\mathcal{N}\,m_\pi^2\,a_\beta}{g_s^\pi\,K(0)}\int d^3x\,\frac{\langle P(\not{q})|\phi_\pm(x)|n\rangle}{E_p - E_n}.\end{aligned} \tag{51h}$$

---

[65] W. I. Weisberger, *Phys. Rev. Letters, 25:* 1047 (1965); S. L. Adler, *Phys. Rev. Letters, 25:* 1051 (1965).

Combining these results, we obtain the sum rule

$$\frac{1}{a_\beta^2}=1-\left(\frac{M_N}{E_P}\right)^2+\left(\frac{\sqrt{2}M_{\mathfrak{N}}\,m_\pi^2}{g_s^\pi\,K(0)}\right)^2\int d^3x\sum_n\{\quad\}, \tag{51i}$$

in which the { } in the integral is a complicated sum over products of matrix elements of one-pion emission between a proton and a given intermediate state. The evaluation of this integral is difficult and requires some approximations, but the main point of the computation is that the products of the matrix elements involved may be associated with the matrix elements for the scattering of (single) pions by a proton and thus, through the optical theorem, with the total $\pi^\pm$–P cross sections, $\sigma^\pm$, giving, eventually, in the limit of $E_P \gg M_N$,

$$1-\frac{1}{a_\beta^2}=\frac{2M_{\mathfrak{N}}^2}{\pi(g_s^\pi)^2\,K^2(0)}\int_{(M_P+m_\pi)^2}^{\infty}ds\,\frac{[\sigma^+(s,0)-\sigma^-(s,0)]}{s-M_N^2}, \tag{51j}$$

where s is the total *cm* energy squared. There is, however, a final complication in that the cross sections, $\sigma^\pm(s,\ t=0)$, correspond to those of an (unphysical) zero-mass pion, while experiment gives $\sigma^\pm(s, -m_\pi^2)$. The required extrapolation introduces some ambiguity into the evaluation of the integral, and has resulted in a range of predictions[66] for a_β. Thus Adler obtained[67]

$$a_\beta^{\rm th}\cong 1.24, \tag{51k}$$

while the simple approximation

$$\frac{\sigma^\pm(s,0)}{K^2(0)}=\sigma^\pm(s,-m_\pi^2) \tag{51l}$$

yields

$$a_\beta^{\rm th'}\cong 1.16. \tag{51m}$$

Experiment [Equations (8b)] gives

$$a_\beta^{\rm exp}=1.18\pm 0.03. \tag{51n}$$

Considering the approximations and assumptions involved, the result may be regarded as an important verification of the usefulness of this approach.

In a similar application,[68] starting from the commutation relations among the isospin current densities, Equation (45e), in terms of which one may define the electric dipole moment operators

$$\mathbf{D}_i=\int d^3x\,\mathfrak{J}_{i4}\,\mathbf{x} \tag{52a}$$

which give rise to the absorption of "isovector" photons, Cabibbo and Radicati have derived the sum rule

---

[66] In any case, it is not sufficient to consider the effects of the (3, 3) resonance only.

[67] A more recent attempt, following the method of Adler but with presumably more reliable experimental information, yields $a_\beta = 1.175$ [G. Höhler and R. Strauss, preprint (1968)].

[68] N. Cabibbo and L. A. Radicati, *Phys. Letters, 19:* 697 (1966).

$$\left(\frac{\mu_P - \mu_N}{2M_{\mathfrak{N}}}\right)^2 + \frac{1}{2\pi^2\alpha}\int \frac{d\omega}{\omega}\,[2\sigma^v_{1/2}(\omega) - \sigma^v_{3/2}(\omega)] = \frac{1}{3}\,\langle r^2\rangle^v_{\mathfrak{N}}\,. \tag{52b}$$

In Equation (52b), σ^v_t are the total cross sections for proton absorption of isovector photons into states of total isotopic spin $t = \frac{1}{2}$ and $\frac{3}{2}$, while

$$\frac{1}{6}\,\langle r^2\rangle^v_{\mathfrak{N}} = -\frac{dG^V_E}{dq^2} + \frac{1}{8M^2_{\mathfrak{N}}} \tag{52c}$$

is the mean-square nucleon charge radius relating to the isovector charge form factor of the nucleons (see Chapter 9). The integral over the photoproduction cross sections in Equation (52b) may be estimated in terms of a phenomenological decomposition of observed γP cross sections, yielding the approximate prediction

$$\mu_P - \mu_N \approx 5.5\mu_0\,, \tag{52d}$$

which is to be compared with the experimental value of 4.70.

"Soft" Pion Theorems • The commutator relationships and the PCAC assumption, discussed in the preceding section, may be used to deduce some properties relating to pion emission and scattering in the limit of vanishing pion 4-momentum, $\not{q}_\pi = 0$ (i.e., $m_\pi \to 0$, $\mathbf{q}_\pi = 0$). Insofar as the pion mass may be considered small in comparison with the momentum transfers important in the process concerned (i.e., smooth and small extrapolation from $t = 0$ to $|t|^{1/2} = m_\pi$), such relationships may be expected to be reasonably accurate.[69]

Soft pion theorems may be derived from the following approach: Define

$$M^j_\mu = i\int d^4x\; e^{iq_\lambda x_\lambda}\,\theta(x_0)\,\langle b|[A^j_\mu(x), B(0)]|a\rangle, \tag{53a}$$

where B is any current element and a and b are the initial and final states. Integration by parts yields

$$\begin{aligned} -iq_\mu M^j_\mu = {} & i\int d^4x\; e^{iq_\lambda x_\lambda}\,\theta(x_0)\left\langle b\left|\left[\frac{\partial A^j_\mu}{\partial x_\mu}(x), B(0)\right]\right|a\right\rangle \\ & + i\int d^4x\; e^{iq_\lambda x_\lambda}\,\delta(x_0)\,\langle b|[A^j_4(x), B(0)]|a\rangle. \end{aligned} \tag{53b}$$

Thus, in the limit $\not{q} \to 0$, Equation (53b) yields a connection between one of the field components, expressed in terms of the commutator contained in the second term on the right-hand side, and the commutator $[\phi^j_\pi(x), B(0)]$ obtained from the first term by use of PCAC. Appropriate choice of the current component $B(0)$ and the initial and final states then permits a connection to be derived between some physical process $a \to b$, and the process $a \to b + \pi$ *in the limit* $\not{q}_\pi = 0$.

Thus, for example, Callan and Treiman[70] were able to derive relationships

[69] Note that in the limit of $m_\pi \to 0$, the axial vector current, like the vector current, is divergence-free (i.e., CAC); see Equation (16).

[70] C. G. Callan and S. B. Treiman, *Phys. Rev. Letters, 16:* 153 (1966); see also S. Weinberg, *Phys. Rev. Letters, 17:* 336 (1966).

between the parameters (amplitudes, form factors) of K_{l2} and K_{l3} decays, K_{l3} and K_{l4} decays, as well as the nonleptonic kaon decays (Section 18.2.1).

Similarly, Weinberg[71] has derived a series of soft pion theorems relating to the strong emission and scattering of pions in the $m_\pi \to 0$ limit. For example, through the connection between the (scattering) amplitude M,

$$\langle b, \not{q}_{\pi f}|M|a, \not{q}_{\pi i}\rangle,$$

evaluated between an initial $a\pi_i$ state and a final $b\pi_f$ state, and the commutator

$$\left\langle b\left|\left[\frac{\partial A^f_\mu}{\partial x_\mu}(x), \frac{\partial A^i_\nu}{\partial x_\nu}(y)\right]\right|a\right\rangle,$$

using PCAC, Weinberg obtains a general expression for the low-energy (S-wave) scattering length of soft pions by any hadronic target of isospin t and mass M_t, in the state of total isospin T,

$$a_T = -\Lambda\left(1+\frac{m_\pi}{M_t}\right)^{-1}[T(T+1)-t(t+1)-2], \tag{54a}$$

where Λ is a scale-setting length

$$\Lambda = \frac{(G^V_\beta)^2 m_\pi}{8\pi f_\pi^2} \cong \frac{[g_s^\pi K(0)]^2 m_\pi a_\beta^2}{8\pi M_{\mathfrak{N}}^2} = 0.11 m_\pi^{-1}. \tag{54b}$$

For the low-energy S-wave pion-nucleon scattering lengths, Equations (54a) and (54b) give

$$m_\pi a_{1/2} = 0.20 \qquad (0.171 \pm 0.005), \tag{54c}$$

$$m_\pi a_{3/2} = -0.10 \qquad (-0.088 \pm 0.004), \tag{54d}$$

$$a_{1/2} + 2a_{3/2} = 0. \tag{54e}$$

(The values in parentheses are the experimental numbers.)

Weinberg also has obtained values for the π–π S-wave scattering lengths a_0 and a_2, but here the soft pion extrapolation is clearly much trickier and more suspect. The values obtained,

$$a_0 = \tfrac{7}{4}\Lambda = 0.20 m_\pi^{-1}, \tag{54f}$$

$$a_2 = -\tfrac{1}{2}\Lambda = -0.06 m_\pi^{-1}, \tag{54g}$$

are rather smaller (at least the value of a_0) than those deduced (indirectly) from the experimental indications.

Other applications of soft pion techniques lead to the derivation[72] of some interesting sum rules that connect hadron masses and coupling constants. Finally,

---

[71] S. Weinberg, *Phys. Rev. Letters, 16:* 879; *17:* 616 (1966).

[72] S. Weinberg, *Phys. Rev. Letters, 18:* 507 (1967); T. Das, V. S. Mathur, and S. Okubo, *Phys. Rev. Letters, 18:* 761; *19:* 470 (1967); S. L. Glashow, H. Schnitzer, and S. Weinberg, *Phys. Rev. Letters, 19:* 139 and 205 (1967).

it should be noted that the soft pion approximation may be improved by computing the relevant matrix elements in the limit $\not{q}_\pi^2 \to 0$ (instead of $\not{q}_\pi \to 0$), since the extrapolation to the physical range $|t| \geq m_\pi^2$ then becomes much closer.[73]

Superconvergence Relations • One consequence of commutation relations among currents relating to strongly interacting particles is that for certain of the hadron-hadron scattering amplitudes, $A(s, t)$, it is possible to derive a simple sum rule of the form

$$\int \operatorname{Im} A(\nu, t)\, d\nu = 0. \tag{55a}$$

[It is convenient, in considering the s dependence of reactions dominated by t-channel exchanges, to adopt the energy variable $\nu = \frac{1}{2}(s-u)$; for fixed t, s and u are related through $s+u+t=\Sigma m_i^2$, so that, as $s \to \infty$, for t finite, $u \to -s$.] Moreover, it has been shown[74] that the relation (55a) is a general property of amplitudes whose asymptotic s dependence is given by

$$A(s, 0) \to s^\alpha, \tag{55b}$$

with

$$\alpha < -1. \tag{55c}$$

Equation (55b) has precisely the form of the Regge amplitudes,

$$R(\nu, t) = \frac{\beta(t)}{\Gamma(\alpha+1)} \frac{[\mp 1 - e^{i\pi\alpha(t)}]}{\sin \pi\alpha(t)} \left(\frac{\nu}{\nu_0}\right)^{\alpha(t)}, \tag{55d}$$

which, for processes involving a total spin of j in the t-channel, must be multiplied by factors $\nu^{-(0,1,\ldots j)}$, depending on the particular helicity states in question.[75] Hence, the sum rule (55a), generally referred to as a "superconvergence" relation, is applicable to a large number of scattering processes.

Thus, DeAlfaro, *et al.*, applying these considerations to the $\pi\rho$ scattering process at $t=0$ (assuming ρ exchange in the isospin 1 t-channel, ω and ϕ exchange in the isospin 0 u-channel) derived the following set of relationships among the strong coupling constants (see footnote 74):

$$m_\rho^2(g_{\omega\rho\pi}^2 + g_{\varphi\rho\pi}^2) - 4g_{\rho\pi\pi}^2 = 0, \tag{55e}$$

$$(\nu_\omega + m_\rho^2)\, g_{\omega\rho\pi}^2 + (\nu_\varphi + m_\rho^2)\, g_{\varphi\rho\pi}^2 - 4g_{\rho\pi\pi}^2 = 0, \tag{55f}$$

with

$$\nu_{\omega,\varphi} = \tfrac{1}{2}(m_{\omega,\varphi}^2 - m_\rho^2 - m_\pi^2). \tag{55g}$$

Since $\nu_\omega \approx 0$, Equations (55e) and (55f) require $g_{\varphi\rho\pi}^2/g_{\omega\rho\pi}^2 \ll 1$, and consequently

---

[73] S. Okubo, R. E. Marshak, and V. S. Mathur, *Phys. Rev. Letters, 19:* 407 (1967).

[74] V. DeAlfaro, S. Fubini, G. Rossetti, and G. Furlan, *Phys. Letters, 21:* 576 (1966). [Note that the meson-meson-meson coupling constants g_i, as defined in this paper and used in Equations (55e) and (55f), are not dimensionless.] See also F. E. Low, *Comments on Nuclear and Particle Physics, 1:* 125 (1967).

[75] For example, in $\pi\mathfrak{N}$ scattering, if the nonflip amplitude $A(\nu, 0) \sim \nu^\alpha$, then the spin-flip amplitude $B(\nu, 0) \sim \nu^{\alpha-1}$, since νB has the same asymptotic behavior as A.

yield $m_\rho g_{\omega\rho\pi} \cong 2g_{\rho\pi\pi}$, both of which are in good accord with the observations on the strong vector-meson decays and production reactions.

Another important application of the superconvergence relations has been the demonstration by Harari [76] that they may be used to compute some of the dispersion integrals (i.e., those terms corresponding to $\Delta t = 2$) involved in estimating the electromagnetic self-energies leading to the mass differences between members of a given isotopic-spin multiplet, thereby not only providing a firmer basis for some of the successful hyperfine mass-difference computations, but also greatly clarifying the reasons for the failure of such computations in certain cases.

The superconvergence relation (55a) has been shown [77] to lead to a general set of sum rules, called finite energy sum rules (FESR), obeyed by all scattering amplitudes,

$$S_n(\bar{\nu}) = \frac{1}{\bar{\nu}^{n+1}} \int_0^{\bar{\nu}} \nu^n \operatorname{Im} A(\nu, t)\, d\nu = \sum_i \frac{\beta_i(t)\, \bar{\nu}^{\alpha_i(t)}}{(\alpha_i + n + 1)\Gamma(\alpha_i + 1)}, \tag{55h}$$

where $\bar{\nu}$ corresponds to an arbitrary value of the energy, while the summation is taken over all the Regge trajectories, i, which contribute by t-channel exchange to the scattering in question; it is only assumed that the scattering amplitude can be reasonably well approximated, for energies $\nu > \bar{\nu}$, by a summation over Regge amplitudes, R_i, of the form (55d).

The FESR can be applied in a number of strikingly useful fashions. Thus, for example, for processes in which one Regge pole predominates, the properties of the corresponding Regge trajectory determine the low-energy behavior in the s-channel including, presumably, the effects of s-channel resonances. Conversely, the observed s-channel cross section at low energies can be used to determine the parameters relevant to the trajectory in question, which is assumed to dominate for high-energy scattering. These properties of the FESR have been demonstrated [78] in the case of the charge-exchange reaction, $\pi^- P \to \pi^0 N$, assumed to be dominated by the ρ pole. In addition, the FESR have been used [79] to obtain an estimate, in reasonable accord with the observed value, of the electromagnetic mass difference of the K-mesons, which is dominated by the contribution of the $\Delta t = 1$ dispersion integral, for which the condition (55c) for the applicability of the superconvergence relation (55a) is not satisfied.[80]

Since it turns out that the FESR yield a very good approximation to the average [81] scattering cross section at low energies, we have the remarkable effect that the exchange of Regge poles in the t-channel (e.g., ρ exchange in $\pi^- P \to \pi^0 N$) already leads to the main contributions of s-channel resonances (presumably

---

[76] H. Harari, *Phys. Rev. Letters, 17:* 1303 (1966); *18,* 319 (1967); see also S. D. Drell, *Comments on Nuclear and Particle Physics, 1:* 94 (1967).

[77] R. Dolen, D. Horn, and C. Schmid, *Phys. Rev., 166:* 1768 (1968); also, A. Logunov, L. D. Soloviev, and A. N. Tavkhelidze, *Phys. Letters, 24B:* 181 (1967); K. Igi and S. Matsuda, *Phys. Rev. Letters, 18:* 625 (1967).

[78] Dolen, Horn and Schmid, *Phys. Rev., 166:* 1768 (1968).

[79] B. V. Struminsky and G. M. Zinovjev, *Report* E2–5853, Joint Institute for Nuclear Research, Dubna, USSR (1968).

[80] See H. Harari, *Phys. Rev. Letters, 17:* 1303 (1966).

[81] By average, we mean the smooth curve obtained by averaging over (not subtracting!) s-channel resonance contributions.

$\mathfrak{N}^*_{1/2}$ and $\mathfrak{N}^*_{3/2}$ in the reaction in question); to consider such cross sections as a superposition of amplitudes due to s-channel resonances and to t-channel Regge exchanges, as has frequently been done, is to count the resonances twice!

In certain particular cases, as for example in π–π scattering, s- and t-channel exchanges involve the same particles (i.e., ρ, f, g, etc., in this case), and one may use the property of the FESR, of expressing the parameters of the t-channel trajectories in terms of those of the s-channel resonances, to derive a set of consistency conditions on these parameters, which serves to determine them uniquely.[82] This type of computation is known as a "bootstrap," for obvious reasons. One of the most important applications of the FESR is to provide a basis for such bootstrap calculations.

18.3.3 Phenomenological Lagrangians

A powerful approach, based on an assumed dynamical origin of the chiral $SU(2) \times SU(2)$ symmetry [applicable also to extended chiral $SU(3) \times SU(3)$] — in contrast to the kinematical basis of the current-algebra assumptions discussed above — has been developed by Schwinger.[83] This approach starts from a phenomenological Lagrangian, describing the meson and nucleon fields and their interactions, with interaction strengths (coupling constants) introduced as arbitrary parameters whose values are to be determined by experimental observations, but with consistency relations that are derived from the assumption of invariance of the Lagrangian under the transformations of the chiral group.

1. For simplicity, we start by considering an $SU(2) \times SU(2)$ invariant Lagrangian involving only pions and nucleons which, following Schwinger, has the general form (if we include only the nucleon and pion fields and their derivatives)

$$\begin{aligned}\mathcal{L}_{\mathfrak{N}\pi} = &-\frac{1}{2}\left(\frac{\partial \phi_\pi}{\partial x_\mu}\right)^2 - \frac{1}{2} m_\pi \phi_\pi^2 - \overline{\psi}_{\mathfrak{N}}\left(-\gamma^\mu i \frac{\partial}{\partial x_\mu} + M\right)\psi_{\mathfrak{N}} \\ &+ \left(\frac{f}{m_\pi}\right)\overline{\psi}_{\mathfrak{N}} i\gamma^\mu \gamma_5 \boldsymbol{\tau} \cdot \psi_{\mathfrak{N}} \frac{\partial \boldsymbol{\phi}_\pi}{\partial x_\mu} \\ &- \left(\frac{f_0}{m_\pi}\right)^2 \overline{\psi}_{\mathfrak{N}} \gamma^\mu \boldsymbol{\tau} \cdot \psi_{\mathfrak{N}} \boldsymbol{\phi}_\pi \times \frac{\partial \boldsymbol{\phi}_\pi}{\partial x_\mu}.\end{aligned} \tag{56a}$$

In (56a) the first two terms represent the free pion field, the third the free nucleon field, while the fourth and fifth terms represent, respectively, the P-wave and

[82] C. Schmid, *Phys. Rev. Letters, 20:* 628 (1968). A formula for the Regge amplitude that provides simultaneously for s-, t-, and u-channel exchange of Regge trajectories, while satisfying automatically the "crossing-symmetry" requirements, has been suggested recently by G. Veneziano [*Nuovo Cimento, 57A:* 190 (1968)].

[83] J. Schwinger, *Phys. Letters, 24B:* 473 (1967); *Phys. Rev. Letters, 18:* 923 (1967); see also S. Weinberg, *Phys. Rev. Letters, 18:* 188 (1967), who introduced a similar technique as a device for circumventing some of the computational difficulties of the algebra of currents as applied to soft pion processes.

S-wave pion-nucleon interactions. The dimensionless coupling constants may be determined empirically:

$$\frac{2M_{\mathfrak{N}}}{m_\pi} f = g_s^\pi, \tag{56b}$$

giving

$$f \cong 1.0, \left(\frac{f^2}{4\pi} = 0.081\right) \tag{56b$'$}$$

and

$$\frac{2f_0}{m_\pi} = f_\pi^{-1}, \tag{56c}$$

giving

$$f_0 \cong 0.8 \tag{56c$'$}$$

(see Section 18.1.2). We then note (without giving the details of the derivations [84]) that the assumption of invariance under the infinitesimal chiral group transformations

$$\boldsymbol{\phi}_\pi \to \boldsymbol{\phi}_\pi + \delta\boldsymbol{\phi} + \left(\frac{f_0}{m_\pi}\right)^2 [2\,\boldsymbol{\phi}_\pi\,\delta\boldsymbol{\phi}\cdot\boldsymbol{\phi}_\pi - \delta\boldsymbol{\phi}\,\phi_\pi^2], \tag{56d}$$

$$\psi_{\mathfrak{N}} \to \left[1 + i\left(\frac{f_0}{m_\pi}\right)^2 \boldsymbol{\tau}\cdot\boldsymbol{\phi}_\pi \times \delta\boldsymbol{\phi}\right]\psi_{\mathfrak{N}}, \tag{56e}$$

leads to the relation for the (conventionally defined) axial vector current, $A_\mu^{(0)}$,

$$\frac{\partial A_\mu^{(0)}}{\partial x_\mu} = \left(\frac{m_\pi}{2f_0}\right) m_\pi^2\,\phi_\pi \quad \text{(PCAC)}, \tag{56f}$$

with the additional condition

$$\frac{G_\beta^A}{G_\beta^V} = a_\beta = \frac{f}{f_0} = \sqrt{\frac{1}{2}} \times \frac{5}{3} = 1.18 \tag{56g}$$

(see the Adler–Weisberger relation) in agreement with both the weak interactions and the experimental observations on π–$\mathfrak{N}$ scattering [Equations (56b′) and (56c′)]. Note that, of the terms in the phenomenological Lagrangian (56a), only the second or pion mass term violates chiral invariance, so that the results of the application of the chiral transformations [Equations (56d) and (56e)] apply in the soft pion limit $m_\pi \to 0$.

2. Now, if additional terms are added to the phenomenological Lagrangian, corresponding to the free ρ-meson field and the ρ–$\pi\pi$ and ρ–$\mathfrak{N}\overline{\mathfrak{N}}$ interactions,

[84] J. Schwinger, *Phys. Letters, 24B:* 473 (1967); *Phys. Rev. Letters, 18:* 923 (1967).

$$\mathcal{L}_\rho = -\frac{1}{2}\,\phi_\rho^{\mu\nu}\cdot\left(\frac{\partial\phi_{\rho\nu}}{\partial x_\mu}-\frac{\partial\phi_{\rho\mu}}{\partial x_\nu}\right)+\frac{1}{4}\,\phi_\rho^{\mu\nu}\cdot\phi_{\rho\mu\nu}-\frac{1}{2}\,m_\rho^2\,\phi_\rho^\mu\cdot\phi_{\rho\nu}$$

$$+\,g_\rho\,\phi_\rho^\mu\cdot\left(\boldsymbol{\phi}_\pi\times\frac{\partial\boldsymbol{\phi}_\pi}{\partial x_\mu}+\frac{1}{2}\,\overline{\psi}_{\mathfrak{N}}\,\gamma_\mu\,\boldsymbol{\tau}\,\psi_{\mathfrak{N}}\right), \tag{57a}$$

the chiral transformation invariance condition leads to the relation

$$\frac{g_\rho}{2m_\rho}=\sqrt{\frac{1}{2}}\,\frac{f_0}{m_\pi} \tag{57b}$$

as well as to the CVC condition on the 4-divergence of the vector current $V_\mu^{(0)}$,

$$\frac{\partial V_\mu^{(0)}}{\partial x_\mu}=0. \tag{57c}$$

3. The coupling of hadrons to the electromagnetic field is assumed to be dominated by the U-spin scalar, vector-meson combination (vector-dominance model, Section 14.3.2); correspondingly, the electromagnetic interactions are introduced into the phenomenological Lagrangian through the substitutions

$$\phi_{\rho^0}^\mu \to \left(\frac{e}{g_\rho}\right)A^\mu, \tag{58a}$$

$$\phi_{\omega^0}^\mu \to \frac{1}{3}\left(\frac{e}{g_\rho}\right)\left(\frac{m_\rho}{m_\omega}\right)A^\mu, \tag{58b}$$

$$\phi_{\phi^0}^\mu \to -\frac{\sqrt{2}}{3}\left(\frac{e}{g_\rho}\right)\left(\frac{m_\rho}{m_\phi}\right)A^\mu. \tag{58c}$$

The coupling with an external magnetic field then leads to the following predictions for the baryon magnetic moments:

$$\mu_P=\frac{5}{3}\,\frac{e}{2m_\rho}+\frac{1}{3}\,\frac{e}{2m_\omega}, \tag{58d}$$

$$\mu_N=-\frac{5}{3}\,\frac{e}{2m_\rho}+\frac{1}{3}\,\frac{e}{2m_\omega}, \tag{58e}$$

which yields, for $m_\rho \cong m_\omega$, the famous $SU(6)$ ratio

$$\frac{\mu_P}{\mu_N}=-\frac{3}{2}, \tag{58f}$$

although the absolute values predicted are ~ 15 percent less than the observed. For the hyperon magnetic moments, the Schwinger model gives

$$\mu_\Lambda=-\frac{1}{3}\,\frac{e}{m_\phi}, \tag{58g}$$

$$\mu_{\Sigma^\pm}=\pm\frac{2}{3}\,\frac{e}{m_\rho}+\mu_{\Sigma^0}, \tag{58h}$$

$$\mu_{\Sigma^0} = \frac{2}{9}\frac{e}{m_\omega} + \frac{1}{9}\frac{e}{m_\phi}, \tag{58i}$$

predicting

$$\mu_\Lambda = -0.614 \qquad (-0.73 \pm 0.16), \tag{58j}$$

$$\mu_{\Sigma^+} = 2.362 \qquad (2.3 \pm 0.6), \tag{58k}$$

in nuclear magnetons, which compare well with the experimental values (in parentheses). Finally, the use of the vector-dominance hypothesis with Schwinger's phenomenological Lagrangian leads to predictions for the mesonic electromagnetic decay widths:

$$\Gamma(\omega^0 \to \pi^0\gamma) = 0.96 \text{ MeV} \qquad (1.2 \pm 0.2), \tag{58l}$$

$$\Gamma(\pi^0 \to \gamma\gamma) = 7.4 \text{ eV} \qquad (7.4 \pm 1.5), \tag{58m}$$

again in excellent accord with the experimental values.

4. Schwinger has applied his approach — in which the properties of the fields are intimately associated with those of the sources at which the field quanta are created and annihilated — to a variety of situations, including the strong and electromagnetic fields,[85] the gravitational field (transmitted by the graviton, a spin 2, massless quantum),[86] and to the problems of electrodynamics with magnetic charges.[87] The interest in magnetic charges stems from the work of Dirac,[88] who showed that the introduction of an elementary magnetic charge, of (dimensionless) strength g, leads to a quantization of electric charge, in units of $e = (137)^{-1/2}$, through

$$ge = 2n, \tag{59a}$$

with n integral.

The large value of the magnetic coupling,

$$g^2(n=1) = \frac{4}{e^2} = 4 \times 137, \tag{59b}$$

would render such magnetic poles very easy to observe, if they exist as free charges; but it would, on the other hand, lead to a very strong binding of opposite magnetic charges to form magnetically neutral matter, which is all that is ever observed.

Schwinger, in his phenomenological theory of magnetic charges, considered the conditions under which such elementary magnetic poles could also carry electric charge, e'; he notes that this is possible, provided

$$e' = \frac{e}{N}, \tag{59c}$$

[85] J. Schwinger, *Phys. Rev., 152:* 1219 (1966); *158:* 1391 (1967).
[86] *Phys. Rev., 173:* 1264 (1968).
[87] *Phys. Rev., 173:* 1536 (1968).
[88] P. A. M. Dirac, *Proc. Roy. Soc.* (London), *A133:* 60 (1931); *Phys. Rev., 74:* 817 (1948).

with $N \geq 3$ if the magnetically charged particles are fermions. The simplest of such systems consists of a triplet of fermions, with magnetic charges $\{2g, -g, -g\}$, each having the possibility of three electric charges $\{\frac{2}{3}e, -\frac{1}{3}e, -\frac{1}{3}e\}$, a situation that is very suggestive indeed.[89]

18.3.4 Bootstraps

As we have developed different models of the hadrons and their internal structure, it has become increasingly evident that one cannot single out just a few among the observed particles as the elementary building blocks out of which all the rest may be constructed. For example, adopting the $SU(3)$ symmetry scheme, which has proved to be so fruitful, it is really quite irrelevant which baryon multiplet is taken as elementary or basic. Gell-Mann and Ne'eman took the baryon octet, B_8, from which mesons may be obtained by $m = B_8 \otimes \overline{B_8}$, and excited baryons through $B^* = B_8 \otimes m_8$. But it is easy to show[90] that all the usual baryon and meson multiplets (and even slightly less than the usual excess) may be obtained by starting with B_{10} through $m = B_{10} \otimes \overline{B_{10}}$, $B^* = B_{10} \otimes m_8$.

Clearly, the distinction between the basic and the derived (or excited) multiplets, B and B^*, is entirely arbitrary. Indeed, not the least of the attractive features of the quark model is that it adopts an unobserved (and simple) triplet as the basic representation, and thereby permits *all the observed* hadrons to be treated on the same basis — as compounds of quarks. Many people feel, therefore, that the observation of quarks would destroy one of the more attractive "symmetries" that now appears to hold among the particles — the symmetry of "particle democracy."

However, the thesis that all particles are equally elementary — i.e., that every particle is a compound of all of the others (consistent, of course, with all the relevant laws of conservation and invariance) — is more than just a statement of philosophy; it has the operational consequence that, in principle, the properties of any one of the particles, or of its interaction in any combination, must derive from consideration of the properties of all the so-called elementary particles and particle (resonant) states, and their interactions. In its extreme form,[91] this approach denies the validity of any field-theoretic formulation of the theory of particle interactions, since such an approach implies the dominance of the elementary sources and carriers (quanta) of the fields; rather, the approach of complete particle democracy recognizes only the S-matrix, subject to certain physical restraints — such as Lorentz invariance, analyticity (i.e., mathematical continuity) of its elements, and unitarity (conservation of probability) of its reaction amplitudes — as being capable of representing the real (observable) world of stable and unstable particles.

Philosophy notwithstanding, however, the implied approach has led to the

---

[89] A related approach, leading to many similar conclusions, but starting from electric charges with a second type of coupling, has been developed by P. C. M. Yock (private communications, 1968).

[90] This is left as the last exercise for the reader.

[91] See G. F. Chew and S. C. Frautschi, *Phys. Rev. Letters, 7:* 394 (1961).

development of useful techniques for computing certain of the properties of observed particles and their interactions, by insisting that these properties must follow as a consequence of the mutual interactions among all the particles, themselves included, to which they are connected. Since none of the particle or interaction properties is postulated in advance, the method of deducing these properties through the requirement of internal consistency of all of their mutual relationships — in effect, of lifting oneself up by one's own bootstraps — is generally referred to as the "bootstrap" method. We outline, in the following, some examples of the applicability of this technique.[92]

A Classic Example • Since, in principle, all particles are assumed to be connected to all others, the applications of the bootstrap method should generally require the solution of a very large (possibly infinite) set of coupled equations. In practice, however, owing to the physical (observed) dominance of certain particle states and interactions, the number of components involved in the self-consistent computation may be very significantly reduced.

We have, in fact, already made use of a very crude prototype of a bootstrap computation, in the "pion atomic model" of the low-energy pion-nucleon scattering process (see Section 12.3.1). In this approximation, the field-theoretic approach of Yukawa (Sections 1.1 and 1.2) is used to derive an approximate static pion-nucleon potential,

$$V_{\pi\mathfrak{N}}(r) = \left(\frac{f^2_{\pi\mathfrak{N}}}{4\pi}\right)(\boldsymbol{\tau}_{\mathfrak{N}} \cdot \boldsymbol{\phi}_{\pi})(\boldsymbol{\sigma}_{\mathfrak{N}} \cdot \boldsymbol{\nabla})\,\frac{e^{-\kappa r}}{r}. \tag{60}$$

It being observed that this interaction leads to a strong attraction in the state of spin and isospin $\frac{3}{2}$, the $\mathfrak{N}^*_{3/2,3/2}$ state, Equation (60) can be used to compute the observed energy and width of the π–$\mathfrak{N}$ scattering resonance in this state, in terms of the parameters of $V_{\pi\mathfrak{N}}$ — i.e., $f^2_{\pi\mathfrak{N}}$ and $\kappa = m_\pi$. However, since the Yukawa field theory can be used to predict the π–$\mathfrak{N}$ scattering properties, including resonant scattering in the $\frac{3}{2}$, $\frac{3}{2}$ state, as well as a number of other low-energy pion-nucleon interaction phenomena — e.g., $\mathfrak{N}\mathfrak{N} \to \mathfrak{N}\mathfrak{N}$, $\gamma\mathfrak{N} \to \pi\mathfrak{N}$ — in terms of the same parameters, $f_{\pi\mathfrak{N}}$ and κ, we have a consistency check on the constants that go into the theory.

Strictly speaking, the above amounts to a bootstrap computation using the reactions depicted by the diagrams shown in Figure 18.6. Although, generally speaking, considering the crudeness of the approximations used, the results of the different approaches to the computation of the pion-nucleon coupling constant (the pion mass, κ, is used to set the scale of length and energy) are in gratifyingly good accord with each other, it is difficult to close the circle in the bootstrap

[92] For more complete discussions, see, e.g., R. E. Cutkosky in *Particle Symmetries,* M. Chretien and S. Deser, eds., *2:* 97, Gordon and Breach, New York (1966); F. Zachariasen and S. Frautschi, "Lectures Given at the Pacific International Summer School in Physics," Honolulu, Hawaii (August 1965) in *Recent Developments in Particle Physics,* Gordon and Breach, London (1966).

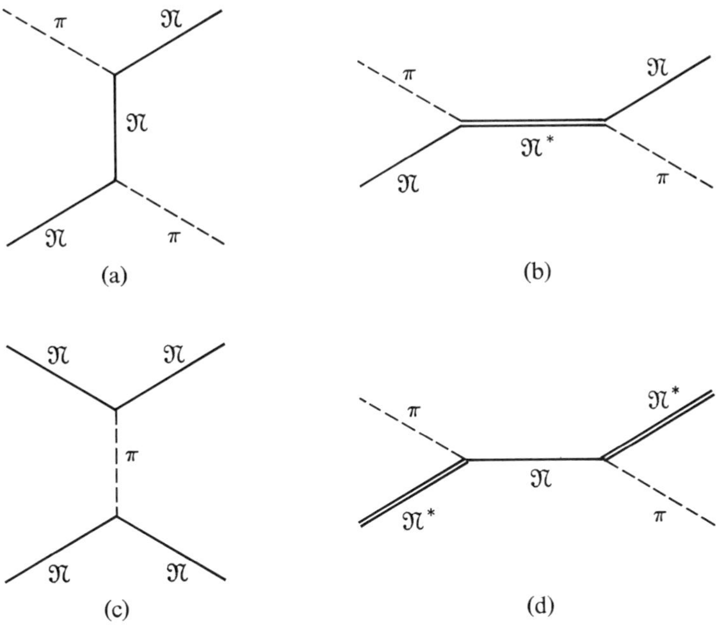

Figure 18.6 Some diagrams involved in the π–$\mathfrak{N}$ bootstrap: (a) Basic Yukawa $\pi\mathfrak{N} \rightleftharpoons \mathfrak{N}$ reaction. (b) π–$\mathfrak{N}$ scattering through the $\mathfrak{N}^*_{3,3}$ resonance. (c) $\mathfrak{N}$–$\mathfrak{N}$ scattering. (d) A neglected diagram.

computation, owing to the absence of empirical information on the properties of such relevant scattering diagrams[93] as Figure 18.6(d).

Because of the complexity of the π–$\mathfrak{N}$ bootstrap, it is more fruitful, as an illustration of the method, to consider the much simpler system involved in the π–π interaction in the state of isotopic spin $t=1$ (as a consequence of Bose statistics and parity conservation, the intermediate states involved must have j odd and negative parity). As a first approximation, we may assume that the dominant π–π scattering diagram is that involving the intermediate (s-channel) ρ-meson resonance, as shown in Figure 18.7. Accordingly, the π–π ($t=1$) scattering amplitude may be described in terms of the parameters corresponding to the s-channel formation of the ρ-meson resonance, i.e., the resonance width $\Gamma_{\rho\pi\pi}$, through which one may determine the coupling strength, $f_{\rho\pi\pi}$ (see Section 15.3.3), and the resonance energy, $m_\rho = s_r^{1/2}$. Thus, the scattering amplitude has the form

$$F_{\pi\pi}(s) = \frac{1}{k}\, e^{i\delta(s)} \sin \delta(s), \tag{61a}$$

[93] Thus, in a complete bootstrap, the coupling $f_{\mathfrak{N}\mathfrak{N}^*\pi}$, or the $\mathfrak{N}^*$ decay width, would be left as free parameters, rather than being derived on the basis of an assumed model of the $\pi\mathfrak{N}$ resonance (i.e., assumed $f_{\mathfrak{N}\mathfrak{N}\pi}$). This leads to a considerably larger number of coupled equations through which the parameters must be simultaneously determined by the bootstrap.

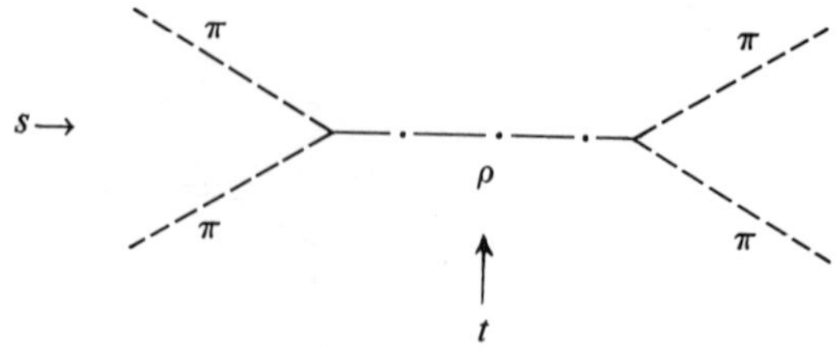

Figure 18.7 Dominating diagram in the π–π ($t=1$) scattering state.

with

$$\tan \delta = \frac{2m_\rho \Gamma_{\rho\pi\pi}}{m_\rho^2 - s}, \tag{61b}$$

and the width given by[94]

$$\Gamma_{\rho\pi\pi} = \frac{2}{3}\left(\frac{f_{\rho\pi\pi}^2}{4\pi}\right)\frac{q_\pi^3}{m_\rho^2}. \tag{61c}$$

Now, the interaction between two pions may be assumed to be mediated by the exchange of vector mesons, according to the vector-dominance theory of the strong interactions as developed by Sakurai,[95] and illustrated, for the case of the ($t=1$) π–π scattering, by the (t-channel) ρ exchange of Figure 18.7. The Lagrangian corresponding to this interaction is

$$\mathcal{L}_{\rho\pi} = -f_{\rho\pi\pi}\boldsymbol{\chi}_\rho \cdot \mathbf{J}_\pi, \tag{61d}$$

where $\boldsymbol{\chi}_\rho$ is the vector (ρ) current of positive G-parity,

$$G\boldsymbol{\chi}_\rho G^{-1} = \boldsymbol{\chi}_\rho, \tag{61e}$$

and the pion current is given by

$$\mathbf{J}_\pi = \boldsymbol{\phi}_\pi \times \frac{\partial \boldsymbol{\phi}_\pi}{\partial x_\mu}. \tag{61f}$$

The ρ exchange, corresponding to the Lagrangian (61d), is shown by Sakurai to lead (in the static approximation, i.e., infinite π mass, which is not very realistic) to a "static" potential of the form

$$V_{\pi\pi}(r) \approx -\left(\frac{f_{\rho\pi\pi}^2}{4\pi}\right)\frac{e^{-m_\rho r}}{r}, \tag{61g}$$

where the minus sign (attraction of the π–π force in the $t=1$ state) arises from the negative value of the $\boldsymbol{\tau}_\pi \cdot \boldsymbol{\tau}_\pi = -1$ isospin factor in the interaction Hamiltonian derived from the Lagrangian (61d). The most significant aspect of the resulting approximate potential, Equation (61g), is the attractive nature (minus sign). In

[94] Generally speaking, given an arbitrary scattering amplitude, $F(s)$, the resonance energy, s_r, is defined by the condition Re $F(s_r) = 0$, and the width, Γ, by $-2s_r^{1/2}\Gamma\,(d/ds)$ Re $F)_{s_r} =$ Im $F(s_r)$.
[95] J. J. Sakurai, *Ann. Phys.* (New York), *11:* 1 (1960).

principle, this should lead to a bound π–π state of $t = 1$, which is presumably the ρ-meson, whose mass and width would be determined by the solution of, e.g., the Schroedinger equation with the potential of Equation (61g), in terms of the parameters $f_{\rho\pi\pi}$ and m_ρ. The requirement, that the resulting resonant energy, m_ρ, and width, Equation (61c), be the same as those observed in the s-channel resonant scattering amplitude, Equation (61a), constitutes the bootstrap calculation of the $\pi\pi\rho$ interaction parameters.

The performance of a realistic computation is, however, much more difficult, owing to the complete inadequacy of the static potential, Equation (61g), for describing the π–π interaction. The first relatively successful π–π bootstrap was achieved by Zachariasen,[96] who used a dispersion relation approach to estimate the s-channel scattering amplitude resulting from the t-channel ρ-meson exchange potential; the values of the resonance energy and width, corresponding to this amplitude function, represent the self-consistent solution for the ρ-meson mass and coupling constant, for which the values obtained were

$$m_\rho \approx 950 \text{ MeV} \qquad (\approx 760 \text{ MeV}), \tag{61h}$$

$$\frac{f^2_{\rho\pi\pi}}{4\pi} \approx 2.8 \qquad (\approx 1), \tag{61i}$$

to be compared to the experimental values shown in parentheses.

One problem associated with the use of the exchange diagram of Figure 18.7 is its neglect of the exchange of higher-spin resonant states, with $j = 3^-, 5^-$, etc. These may be taken into account by associating the "ρ-meson" in the figure with that Regge trajectory which includes the "natural parity" $[(-1)^j]$ mesons of odd spin, and correspondingly using the appropriate Regge amplitude (see Section 11.2.2). Particularly, a natural technique for carrying out the bootstrap calculation involves taking advantage of the finite energy sum rules[97] (FESR, Section 18.3.2), which relate an integral over the low-energy s-channel resonances to the properties of the t-channel Regge exchange amplitudes appropriate to a high-energy description of the scattering amplitude for large s and small t.

At the same time, Schmid has been able to relate, through the bootstrap procedure outlined above, the low-energy π–π scattering in the $t = 0$ channel to the properties of the natural parity trajectory with even spin (0^+, $2^+ = f$, or f' . . .) through an appropriate FESR, while the scattering in the $t = 2$ state, which does not involve any known Regge-meson trajectory, may be bootstrapped by use of the superconvergence relation [Equation (55a)].

Other Bootstrap Applications • The requirement of self-consistency, which is the basis of the bootstrap approach, gives rise to a variety of applications. These generally fall into two categories: (1) the specification of the (relative) magnitudes of related parameters or reaction amplitudes, as a result of require-

[96] F. Zachariasen, *Phys. Rev. Letters, 7:* 112 (1961); see also F. Zachariasen and C. Zemach, *Phys. Rev., 128:* 849 (1962).
[97] C. Schmid, *Phys. Rev. Letters, 20:* 628 (1968).

ments of self-consistency such as those discussed in the foregoing; and (2) the demonstration of the inevitability of some of the observed symmetry (group) properties of observed hadronic states and their interactions. We outline below some interesting examples of such applications of the bootstrap method.

THE LINEAR MATRIX APPROACH: Dashen and Frautschi[98] and collaborators have developed a series of applications of the bootstrap method in the first category. The basis of their approach is the derivation of a set of linear equations relating appropriate matrix elements of the hadronic currents

$$\langle a|J^{\nu}|b\rangle = J^{\nu}_{ab}(t) = \sum_{cd} X_{ab,cd} J^{\nu}_{cd}(t) + D^{\nu}_{ab}(t), \tag{62a}$$

through use of dispersion relations, where the $X_{ab,cd}$ are the elements of a mixing matrix, whose properties are determined by the specific form of the dynamical reaction between the initial (ab) and final (cd) states, taking into account the symmetry properties of the interaction Lagrangian, while the (driving) terms D^{ν}_{ab} are, in general, subtraction constants required in order to render the appropriate dispersion integrals convergent.

Without attempting, at this stage, to specify the physical quantities in question, let us assume that the elements $J^{\nu}_{ab} = \delta J_i$ represent symmetry-violating matrix elements of an interaction whose main characteristics are summarized by the matrix $X_{i,j}$, the elements of which follow from an assumed dynamical symmetry scheme [e.g., $SU(6)$ symmetry]. Equation (62a) may be symbolically written as

$$\delta J_i = \sum X_{ij} \delta J_j + D_i, \tag{62b}$$

whose solution, again symbolically, has the form

$$\delta J_i = \sum_j (1 - X_{ij})^{-1} D_i. \tag{62c}$$

It is clear from Equation (62c) that the solutions for δJ_i will be dominated by those eigenstates of the matrix X_{ij} whose eigenvalues approach most closely to the value 1; correspondingly, the eigenvectors [solutions of (62b)] for the δJ_i will be dominated by those eigenvectors of X_{ij} which correspond to the eigenvalues closest to unity. Furthermore, assuming that only one (or very few) of the eigenvalues of X_{ij} is close to 1, the relative values of the symmetry-violating matrix elements, δJ_i, may be determined without knowledge of the values of the driving terms, D_i [see Equation (62c)].

Among a number of applications of this technique, one of the most interesting is the successful computation of the relative amplitudes for the parity-violating nonleptonic weak decays of the baryons.[99] In this computation, the elements of the parity-violating matrix X_{ij} have been determined by the requirement of self-

---

[98] R. F. Dashen and S. C. Frautschi, *Phys. Rev., 143:* 1171; *145,* 1287 (1966).

[99] R. F. Dashen, S. C. Frautschi, and D. H. Sharp, *Phys. Rev. Letters, 13:* 777 (1966). The attempts by the same authors to use these techniques to derive the relative amplitudes of the parity-conserving weak nonleptonic decays are, as are essentially all other such attempts (see Section 18.2.2), less fruitful.

consistency (bootstrap conditions) for the diagrams (a) and (b) shown in Figure 18.8, while the "driving" terms are assumed to arise from diagrams such as (c).

Dashen, *et al.*, have also applied this technique to the derivation of the strong coupling constants and mass shifts resulting from the symmetry-breaking strong and electromagnetic interactions. In this case, it is necessary to solve a set of coupled linear equations among the coupling constant shifts, δg_i, and mass shifts, δM_i, but the techniques are essentially the same. The results are in general in relatively reasonable accord with the observations.

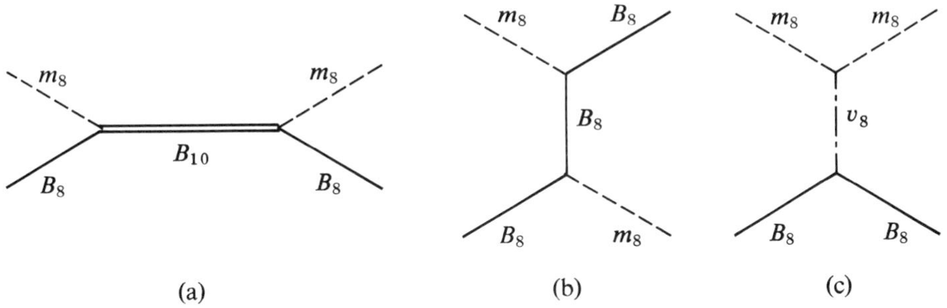

Figure 18.8 Bootstrap diagrams for the parity-violating nonleptonic decays of the baryons: (a) Direct decay diagram. (b) Exchange diagram. (c) "Driving" diagram.

A related, but algebraically more complicated, bootstrap has been considered [100] by Pais and by Cabibbo, in the context of $SU(3)$ symmetry. They start from a nonlinear equation of the form

$$y_i = \sqrt{3}\, d_{ijk}\, y_j\, y_k + a_i, \tag{62d}$$

in which the y_i ($i = 1, 2, \ldots 8$) are the generators of the octet representation of $SU(3)$ and the d_{ijk} are the elements of the symmetric strong-interaction matrix connecting 8 with $8 \otimes 8$; the driving force terms, a_i, are assumed to arise from the electromagnetic and weak interaction couplings to t_3 and $\mathcal{Y}$ (i.e., only a_3 and a_8 differ from zero; see Chapter 14). Starting from (62d), Pais and Cabibbo explore the possibility of self-consistent solutions corresponding to different coupling strengths for the strangeness-conserving and the strangeness-violating weak interactions — i.e., to a finite value of the Cabibbo angle θ. Although such solutions appear to be possible, they were unable to demonstrate the uniqueness of θ on the basis of (62d) alone.

SYMMETRY BOOTSTRAPS: An interesting generalization of the π–$\mathfrak{N}$ bootstrap, discussed as the first example in this section (see Figure 18.6), has been carried out by Capps and by Belinfante and Cutkosky.[101] As noted, the diagrams of the

[100] A. Pais, *Phys. Rev., 173:* 1587 (1968); N. Cabibbo in *Proceedings of the Fifth Coral Gables Conference on Symmetry Principles at High Energy,* W. A. Benjamin, New York (1968), p. 339.
[101] R. H. Capps, *Phys. Rev. Letters, 14:* 31 (1965); J. G. Belinfante and R. E. Cutkosky, *Phys. Rev. Letters, 14:* 33 (1965); see also G. L. Kane and W. F. Palmer, *Phys. Rev., 172:* 1648 (1968), for a bootstrap calculation relating to the vector-meson–nucleon couplings.

type of Figure 18.6(a) can, in principle, be used to determine the π–$\mathfrak{N}$ interaction potential which, if sufficiently strongly attractive, can give rise to new resonant states, as indicated in Figure 18.6(b). However, such resonances will, in general, when included in the bootstrap through diagrams such as in Figure 18.6(d), give rise to further resonances, which call for additional diagrams, *ad infinitum.* The question is: Under what circumstances, if any, will the bootstrap close on itself and give rise to a finite, self-consistent set of states?

Consider the set of baryonic states generated by an octet of mesons interacting [via an $SU(3)$-invariant set of Yukawa couplings] with an octet of baryons

$$m_8 \otimes B_8 = B_1 \oplus B_8 \oplus B_{8'} \oplus B_{10} \oplus B_{\overline{10}} \oplus B_{27}. \tag{63a}$$

In general, all of the states on the right-hand side of Equation (63a) could "resonate," in which case they all need to be taken into account in the bootstrap, giving rise to further resonances via combinations like $m_8 \otimes B_{27}$, etc. In fact, this bootstrap does not close on itself.

However, the aforementioned authors have shown that, starting with the $SU(6)$-invariant meson 35-plet and baryon 56-plet, for which

$$m_{35} \otimes B_{56} = B_{56} \oplus B_{70} \oplus B_{700} \oplus B_{1134}, \tag{63b}$$

the forces (potentials) generated by all possible meson exchanges are such that only the 56-plet of baryons is bound. (The potential is repulsive for the B_{70} and B_{1134}, and only very weakly attractive — presumably too weak for binding — for the B_{700}.) Consequently, only one diagram [see Figure 18.6(a), with $\pi \to m_{35}$ and $\mathfrak{N} \to B_{56}$] is required for a consistent bootstrap; i.e., the $m_{35} \otimes B_{56}$ forms a closed system, without any other baryonic $SU(6)$ multiplets playing any significant role. This is a striking confirmation of the relevance of $SU(6)$ as the symmetry group governing the strong-interaction Lagrangian.

In a variation on this theme, Belinfante and Cutkosky [102] have considered the set of couplings of $m_{35} \otimes B_{56}$ to the electromagnetic currents, which give rise to the baryon magnetic moments. They assume (see the pion atomic model, Section 13.2.1) that the baryon moments have the form of a sum of contributions from an intrinsic moment, $\boldsymbol{\mu}_B$, and a meson-cloud contribution, $\boldsymbol{\mu}_m$, and look for a self-consistent solution (i.e., where the μ_B are the final set of moments of the members of the B_{56}). It then turns out that the transformation properties of

$$\boldsymbol{\mu} = \boldsymbol{\mu}_B + \boldsymbol{\mu}_m \tag{64}$$

must be the same as those of μ_m (i.e., of the 35-plet representation) which gives rise to the set of $SU(6)$ relations previously derived (Section 15.3.3), e.g.,

$$\frac{\mu_P}{\mu_N} = -\frac{3}{2}. \tag{64a}$$

As applied to internal symmetries among the strongly interacting particles (hadrons), the bootstrap approach has, in fact, very wide applicability. Thus,

[102] *Phys. Rev. Letters, 14:* 33 (1965).

e.g., Abers, Zachariasen, and Zemach [103] have demonstrated that isotopic-spin invariance follows generally from arguments of internal consistency among the interactions that mutually bind together sets of particles with common extrinsic properties (spin, baryon number, etc.) while Zachariasen and Zemach [104] have given a plausible argument on how parity conservation might follow as a consequence of self-consistency requirements among the strong hadronic interactions.

MULTIPERIPHERAL BOOTSTRAP: Our final example [105] is from a recent work by Chew and Pignotti, in which they attempt to estimate the relative cross sections for multiple meson production in hadron-hadron collisions by consideration of diagrams of the form of Figure 18.9. For simplicity, they consider only two types of intermediate t-channel exchanges: a Pomeranchuk and a generalized (average) meson trajectory, and only pion emission at the intermediate vertices.

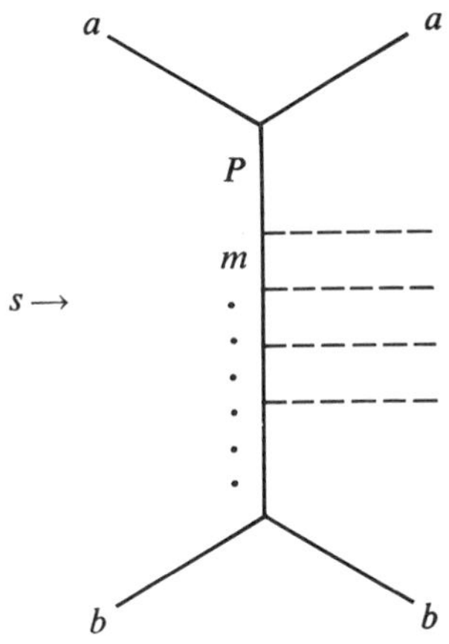

Figure 18.9 Diagram used in the multiperipheral bootstrap model of Chew and Pignotti.

The requirement that the total cross section (sum of inelastic cross sections over all meson multiplicities) be energy independent, and that it be related to the forward elastic scattering amplitude (i.e., properties of the Pomeranchuk trajectory exchange) through the optical theorem (or unitarity condition), together with the values of the inelastic and elastic cross sections, serve to determine all but one of the parameters — namely, the average values of the $\alpha(t)$ for the two trajectories and their coupling strengths at all possible vertices. The remaining parameter may then be adjusted to fit observed meson multiplicities (or the average multiplicity) at a given incident projectile energy.

---

[103] E. Abers, F. Zachariasen, and C. Zemach, *Phys. Rev., 132:* 1831 (1963).
[104] F. Zachariasen and C. Zemach, *Phys. Rev., 138:* B441 (1965).
[105] H. F. Bali, G. F. Chew, and A. Pignotti; *Phys. Rev., 163:* 1572 (1967); also, G. F. Chew and A. Pignotti, *Proceedings of the 14th International Conference on High-Energy Physics,* Vienna (September 1968).

The model gives rise to a cross section, for the production of n mesons, of the form

$$\sigma_n^{ab} \cong \sigma_{\text{tot, inel}}^{ab} \frac{(g_m^2 X_0)^n}{n!} e^{-g_m^2 X_0}, \tag{65}$$

where the parameter g_m^2 represents the mean strength of the meson-meson-pion vertex, and $X_0 \propto s$ is proportional to the total cm energy of the reaction. The mean multiplicity, according to Equation (65), is $\propto \ln s$, which is in accord with one of the long-known empirical facts of high-energy hadron-hadron interactions.

In addition, the model of Chew and Pignotti indicates $\overline{\alpha_p} \approx 1$, with a relatively small slope, and $\overline{\alpha_\pi} \approx 0.5$ [average value of α(small t) for the most important meson trajectories], both of which are quite reasonable on the basis of independent information — all in all, a considerable amount of information arising only from the bootstrap self-consistency requirements.

18.4 L'Envoi

The considerations of this last chapter indicate that the goal of a unified theory of the elementary particles and their interactions may not be unattainable. From a number of directions, new techniques and new insights are being developed, many tending to illuminate and extend the relationships between domains of particle phenomena which, until recently, appeared to be quite unrelated. This is a trend that we may certainly expect to see continued.

The various models considered in Chapters 12 through 18 have all been useful, in their respective domains of application, for indicating what the main features of an eventual unified theory will need to contain and explain. The $SU(3)$ symmetry will certainly play a dominant role; whether $SU(6)$, and particularly the quark model, will eventually emerge as more than a useful calculation device still remains an open question, ultimately to be decided by recourse to experiment. In any event, we now have at our disposal a number of powerful empirical tools for correlating and predicting the results of experimental observations involving the strong, electromagnetic, and the weak interactions among hadrons, photons, and leptons — at least in the energy range up to the maximum energy readily available until now, i.e., projectiles of energy $\lesssim 30$ GeV.

We must certainly look forward to new insights and surprises as a result of experiments at higher energies (~ 75 GeV now available in the U.S.S.R. and, eventually, ~ 2–300 GeV in both Europe and the U.S.A.).

Nevertheless, at this time (end of 1968), the situation in elementary particle physics appears strikingly reminiscent of the situation of atomic physics in the early part of this century. At that time, the speculations of Bohr concerning the role of the quantum of action in determining the properties of atomic energy levels and the transitions between them were providing a powerful framework for the empirical understanding of atomic phenomena; but the theoretical basis for Bohr's model — the quantum mechanics — did not emerge until more than a decade later.

Presumably, considering the accelerated pace of contemporary developments in physics, and assuming that efforts in this field will continue to be supported by society at a level commensurate with the capabilities of its practitioners, we shall not have so long to wait before a new dynamical theory of elementary particle interactions emerges, which will explain and consolidate our current gropings. By then, of course, the problems and puzzles will look very different. In any case, whatever may or may not develop in the directions discussed in this book, we may be certain of one historical extrapolation — that new experiments in unexplored energy domains will unfold new surprises, so that the never-ending quest for the understanding of observed natural phenomena will continue to challenge to the limit the ingenuity and creativity of succeeding generations of physicists.

Appendix 1

Clebsch–Gordan Coefficients

Table A1.1 $C^{j,m}_{j_1,m_1;\ 1/2,m_2}$

j	$m_2 = \frac{1}{2}$	$m_2 = -\frac{1}{2}$
$j_1 + \frac{1}{2}$	$\left(\frac{j_1 + m + \frac{1}{2}}{2j_1 + 1}\right)^{1/2}$	$\left(\frac{j_1 - m + \frac{1}{2}}{2j_1 + 1}\right)^{1/2}$
$j_1 - \frac{1}{2}$	$-\left(\frac{j_1 - m + \frac{1}{2}}{2j_1 + 1}\right)^{1/2}$	$\left(\frac{j_1 + m + \frac{1}{2}}{2j_1 + 1}\right)^{1/2}$

Table A1.2 $C^{j,m}_{j_1,m_1;\ 1,m_2}$

j	$m_2 = 1$	$m_2 = 0$	$m_2 = -1$
$j_1 + 1$	$\sqrt{\frac{(j_1 + m)(j_1 + m + 1)}{(2j_1 + 1)(2j_1 + 2)}}$	$\sqrt{\frac{(j_1 - m + 1)(j_1 + m + 1)}{(2j_1 + 1)(j_1 + 1)}}$	$\sqrt{\frac{(j_1 - m)(j_1 - m + 1)}{(2j_1 + 1)(2j_1 + 2)}}$
j_1	$-\sqrt{\frac{(j_1 + m)(j_1 - m + 1)}{2j_1(j_1 + 1)}}$	$\frac{m}{\sqrt{j_1(j_1 + 1)}}$	$\sqrt{\frac{(j_1 - m)(j_1 + m + 1)}{2j_1(j_1 + 1)}}$
$j_1 - 1$	$\sqrt{\frac{(j_1 - m)(j_1 - m + 1)}{2j_1(2j_1 + 1)}}$	$-\sqrt{\frac{(j_1 - m)(j_1 + m)}{j_1(2j_1 + 1)}}$	$\sqrt{\frac{(j_1 + m + 1)(j_1 + m)}{2j_1(2j_1 + 1)}}$

Note: Additional tables of Clebsch–Gordan coefficients are given in E. U. Condon and G. H. Shortley, *The Theory of Atomic Spectra*, Cambridge University Press, Cambridge, England (1935), pp. 76–78; see also M. A. Melvin and N. V. V. J. Swamy, *Phys. Rev., 107:* 186 (1957).

Table A1.3 $C^{j,m}_{j_1,m_1;\,3/2,m_2}$

j	$m_2 = \frac{3}{2}$	$m_2 = \frac{1}{2}$
$j_1 + \frac{3}{2}$	$\left\{\frac{(j_1+m-\frac{1}{2})(j_1+m+\frac{1}{2})(j_1+m+\frac{3}{2})}{(2j_1+1)(2j_1+2)(2j_1+3)}\right\}^{1/2}$	$\left\{\frac{3(j_1+m+\frac{1}{2})(j_1+m+\frac{3}{2})(j_1-m+\frac{3}{2})}{(2j_1+1)(2j_1+2)(2j_1+3)}\right\}^{1/2}$
$j_1 + \frac{1}{2}$	$-\left\{\frac{3(j_1+m-\frac{1}{2})(j_1+m+\frac{1}{2})(j_1-m+\frac{3}{2})}{2j_1(2j_1+1)(2j_1+3)}\right\}^{1/2}$	$-(j_1-3m+\frac{3}{2})\left\{\frac{j_1+m+\frac{1}{2}}{2j_1(2j_1+1)(2j_1+3)}\right\}^{1/2}$
$j_1 - \frac{1}{2}$	$\left\{\frac{3(j_1+m-\frac{1}{2})(j_1-m+\frac{1}{2})(j_1-m+\frac{3}{2})}{(2j_1-1)(2j_1+1)(2j_1+2)}\right\}^{1/2}$	$-(j_1+3m-\frac{1}{2})\left\{\frac{j_1-m+\frac{1}{2}}{(2j_1-1)(2j_1+1)(2j_1+2)}\right\}^{1/2}$
$j_1 - \frac{3}{2}$	$-\left\{\frac{(j_1-m-\frac{1}{2})(j_1-m+\frac{1}{2})(j_1-m+\frac{3}{2})}{2j_1(2j_1-1)(2j_1+1)}\right\}^{1/2}$	$\left\{\frac{3(j_1+m-\frac{1}{2})(j_1-m-\frac{1}{2})(j_1-m+\frac{1}{2})}{2j_1(2j_1-1)(2j_1+1)}\right\}^{1/2}$
	$m_2 = -\frac{1}{2}$	$m_2 = -\frac{3}{2}$
$j_1 + \frac{3}{2}$	$\left\{\frac{3(j_1+m+\frac{3}{2})(j_1-m+\frac{1}{2})(j_1-m+\frac{3}{2})}{(2j_1+1)(2j_1+2)(2j_1+3)}\right\}^{1/2}$	$\left\{\frac{(j_1-m-\frac{1}{2})(j_1-m+\frac{1}{2})(j_1-m+\frac{3}{2})}{(2j+1)(2j_1+2)(2j_1+3)}\right\}^{1/2}$
$j_1 + \frac{1}{2}$	$(j_1+3m+\frac{3}{2})\left\{\frac{j_1-m+\frac{1}{2}}{2j_1(2j_1+1)(2j_1+3)}\right\}^{1/2}$	$\left\{\frac{3(j_1+m+\frac{3}{2})(j_1-m-\frac{1}{2})(j_1-m+\frac{1}{2})}{2j_1(2j_1+1)(2j_1+3)}\right\}^{1/2}$
$j_1 - \frac{1}{2}$	$-(j_1-3m-\frac{1}{2})\left\{\frac{j_1+m+\frac{1}{2}}{(2j_1-1)(2j_1+1)(2j_1+2)}\right\}^{1/2}$	$\left\{\frac{3(j_1+m+\frac{1}{2})(j_1+m+\frac{3}{2})(j_1-m-\frac{1}{2})}{(2j_1-1)(2j_1+1)(2j_1+2)}\right\}^{1/2}$
$j_1 - \frac{3}{2}$	$-\left\{\frac{3(j_1+m-\frac{1}{2})(j_1+m+\frac{1}{2})(j_1-m-\frac{1}{2})}{2j_1(2j_1-1)(2j_1+1)}\right\}^{1/2}$	$\left\{\frac{(j_1+m-\frac{1}{2})(j_1+m+\frac{1}{2})(j_1+m+\frac{3}{2})}{2j_1(2j_1-1)(2j_1+1)}\right\}^{1/2}$

The Associated Legendre Polynomials

Definitions ($x \equiv \cos\theta$)

$$P_n(x) = \frac{1}{2^n n!}\frac{d^n}{dx^n}(x^2-1)^n,$$

$$P_n^m(x) = (1-x^2)^{m/2}\frac{d^m P_n(x)}{dx^m}, \qquad P_n^{-m} = (-1)^m P_n^m,$$

$$Y_n^0 = \sqrt{\frac{2n+1}{4\pi}}\,P_n(x),$$

$$Y_n^m(x) = \sqrt{\left(\frac{2n+1}{4\pi}\right)\frac{(n-|m|)!}{(n+|m|)!}}\,P_n^m(x)\,e^{im\varphi}, \qquad \int_0^{2\pi} d\varphi \int_{-1}^{1} dx\, Y_n^m\, Y_{n'}^{*m'} = \delta_{m,m'}\,\delta_{n,n'}\,.$$

Recursion Relations $[P_n'(x) \equiv dP_n(x)/dx]$

$$(n+1)P_{n+1}(x) - (2n+1)\,xP_n(x) + nP_{n-1}(x) = 0,$$
$$P_{n+1}'(x) - xP_n'(x) = (n+1)P_n(x),$$
$$(x^2-1)P_n'(x) = nxP_n(x) - nP_{n-1}(x).$$

Values for $n \leq 3$

$$Y_0^0 = \sqrt{\frac{1}{4\pi}},$$

$$\begin{cases} Y_1^0 = \sqrt{\dfrac{3}{4\pi}}\,x, \\ Y_1^{\pm 1} = \mp\sqrt{\dfrac{3}{8\pi}}\,(1-x^2)^{1/2}\,e^{\pm i\varphi}, \end{cases}$$

$$\begin{cases} Y_2^0 = \sqrt{\dfrac{5}{16\pi}}\,(3x^2 - 1), \\ Y_2^{\pm 1} = \mp \sqrt{\dfrac{15}{8\pi}}\, x(1 - x^2)^{1/2}\, e^{\pm i\varphi}, \\ Y_2^{\pm 2} = \sqrt{\dfrac{15}{32\pi}}\,(1 - x^2)\, e^{\pm 2i\varphi}, \end{cases}$$

$$\begin{cases} Y_3^0 = \sqrt{\dfrac{7}{16\pi}}\, x(5x^2 - 3), \\ Y_3^{\pm 1} = \mp \sqrt{\dfrac{21}{64\pi}}\,(1 - x^2)^{1/2}(5x^2 - 1)\, e^{\pm i\varphi}, \\ Y_3^{\pm 2} = \sqrt{\dfrac{7 \times 15}{32\pi}}\, x(1 - x^2)\, e^{\pm 2i\varphi}, \\ Y_3^{\pm 3} = \mp \sqrt{\dfrac{35}{64\pi}}\,(1 - x^2)^{3/2}\, e^{\pm 3i\varphi}. \end{cases}$$

Addition Theorem of Spherical Harmonics

Let (θ, φ) and (θ', φ') be the directions of two unit vectors, making the angle α with each other:

$$\cos\alpha = \cos\theta\cos\theta' + \sin\theta\sin\theta'\cos(\varphi - \varphi').$$

Then

$$\left(\frac{2n+1}{4\pi}\right) P_n(\cos\alpha) = \sum_{m=-n}^{n} Y_n^m(\theta, \varphi)\, Y_n^{*m}(\theta', \varphi').$$

The Vector Spherical Harmonics

Starting from the definition

$$\sqrt{l(l+1)}\,\mathbf{X}_{l,m}(\theta,\varphi) = -i(\mathbf{r}_0 \times \boldsymbol{\nabla})\,Y_{l,m}(\theta,\varphi),$$

we obtain

$$\begin{cases} \mathbf{X}_{1,0} = i\sqrt{\dfrac{3}{8\pi}}\sin\theta\,\boldsymbol{\varphi}_0, \\ \mathbf{X}_{1,\pm1} = \sqrt{\dfrac{3}{16\pi}}(\boldsymbol{\theta}_0 \pm i\cos\theta\,\boldsymbol{\varphi}_0)\,e^{\pm i\varphi}, \end{cases}$$

$$\begin{cases} \mathbf{X}_{2,0} = i\sqrt{\dfrac{15}{8\pi}}\cos\theta\sin\theta\,\boldsymbol{\varphi}_0, \\ \mathbf{X}_{2,\pm1} = \sqrt{\dfrac{5}{16\pi}}\{\cos\theta\,\boldsymbol{\theta}_0 \pm i(2\cos^2\theta - 1)\,\boldsymbol{\varphi}_0\}\,e^{\pm i\varphi}, \\ \mathbf{X}_{2,\pm2} = \mp\sqrt{\dfrac{5}{16\pi}}(\boldsymbol{\theta}_0 \pm i\cos\theta\,\boldsymbol{\varphi}_0)\sin\theta\,e^{\pm 2i\varphi}, \end{cases}$$

$$\begin{cases} \mathbf{X}_{3.0} = i\sqrt{\dfrac{21}{64\pi}}(5\cos^2\theta - 1)\sin\theta\,\boldsymbol{\varphi}_0, \\ \mathbf{X}_{3,\pm1} = \dfrac{1}{2}\sqrt{\dfrac{7}{64\pi}}\{(5\cos^2\theta - 1)\,\boldsymbol{\theta}_0 \pm i(15\cos^2\theta - 11)\cos\theta\,\boldsymbol{\varphi}_0\}\,e^{\pm i\varphi}, \\ \mathbf{X}_{3,\pm2} = \mp\sqrt{\dfrac{35}{32\pi}}\left\{\cos\theta\,\boldsymbol{\theta}_0 \pm i\left(\dfrac{3}{2}\cos^2\theta - \dfrac{1}{2}\right)\boldsymbol{\varphi}_0\right\}\sin\theta\,e^{\pm 2i\varphi}, \\ \mathbf{X}_{3,\pm3} = \dfrac{1}{2}\sqrt{\dfrac{105}{64\pi}}(\boldsymbol{\theta}_0 \pm i\cos\theta\,\boldsymbol{\varphi}_0)\sin^2\theta\,e^{\pm 3i\varphi}. \end{cases}$$

Defining the Poynting vector as

$$Z_{l,m} = \mathbf{X}_{l,m} \cdot \mathbf{X}^*_{l,m},$$

we have

$$\begin{cases} Z_{1,0} = \dfrac{3}{8\pi} \sin^2 \theta, \\ Z_{1,\pm 1} = \dfrac{3}{16\pi} (1 + \cos^2 \theta), \end{cases}$$

$$\begin{cases} Z_{2,0} = \dfrac{15}{32\pi} \sin^2 2\theta, \\ Z_{2,\pm 1} = \dfrac{15}{48\pi} (4 \cos^4 \theta - 3 \cos^2 \theta + 1), \\ Z_{2,\pm 2} = \dfrac{15}{48\pi} (1 - \cos^4 \theta), \end{cases}$$

$$\begin{cases} Z_{3,0} = \dfrac{21}{64\pi} (5 \cos^2 \theta - 1) \sin^2 \theta, \\ Z_{3,\pm 1} = \dfrac{21}{768\pi} (1 + 111 \cos^2 \theta - 305 \cos^4 \theta + 225 \cos^6 \theta), \\ Z_{3,\pm 2} = \dfrac{105}{384\pi} (1 - 3 \cos^2 \theta + 11 \cos^4 \theta - 9 \cos^6 \theta), \\ Z_{3,\pm 3} = \dfrac{105}{256\pi} (1 + \cos^2 \theta) \sin^4 \theta. \end{cases}$$

Some Properties of the Rotation Matrices $d^j_{\lambda\mu}$

Integral $j = l$

$$d^l_{m0}(\theta) = (-1)^m\, d^l_{0m}(\theta) = \left(\frac{4\pi}{2l+1}\right)^{1/2} \mathcal{P}^m_l(\theta) = \left[\frac{(l-m)!}{(l+m)!}\right]^{1/2} P^m_l(\cos\theta).$$

Thus

$$d^l_{00}(\theta) = P_l(\cos\theta),$$
$$d^l_{10}(\theta) = -[l(l+1)]^{-1/2} \sin\theta\, P'_l(\cos\theta),$$
$$d^l_{20}(\theta) = [(l-1)l(l+1)(l+2)]^{-1/2}[2P'_{l-1}(\cos\theta) - l(l-1)P_l(\cos\theta)].$$

In general,

$$d^l_{\lambda,\mu\pm1}(\theta) = [(l\pm\mu+1)(l\mp\mu)]^{-1/2}\left\{\frac{-\lambda}{\sin\theta} + \mu\cot\theta \mp \frac{\partial}{\partial\theta}\right\} d^l_{\lambda\mu},$$

$$\begin{aligned} 2[(l+\mu)(l+\mu-1)]^{1/2}\, d^l_{\lambda\mu}(\theta) = {} & [(l+\lambda)(l+\lambda-1)]^{1/2}(1+\cos\theta)\, d^{l-1}_{\lambda-1,\mu-1} \\ & + 2(l^2-\lambda^2)^{1/2} \sin\theta\, d^{l-1}_{\lambda,\mu-1} \\ & + [(l-\lambda)(l-\lambda-1)]^{1/2}(1-\cos\theta)\, d^{l-1}_{\lambda+1,\mu-1}. \end{aligned}$$

Half Integral $j = l + \frac{1}{2}$

$$d^j_{1/2,1/2}(\theta) = (l+1)^{-1} \cos\frac{\theta}{2}\,(P'_{l+1} - P'_l),$$

$$d^j_{-1/2,1/2}(\theta) = (l+1)^{-1} \sin\frac{\theta}{2}\,(P'_{l+1} + P'_l),$$

$$d^j_{1/2,3/2}(\theta) = (l+1)^{-1} \sin\frac{\theta}{2}\left\{\sqrt{\frac{l}{l+2}}\,P'_{l+1} + \sqrt{\frac{l+2}{l}}\,P'_l\right\},$$

$$d^j_{-1/2,3/2}(\theta) = (l+1)^{-1} \cos\frac{\theta}{2}\left\{-\sqrt{\frac{l}{l+2}}\,P'_{l+1} + \sqrt{\frac{l+2}{l}}\,P'_l\right\}.$$

In general,

$$d^j_{\lambda,1/2} = \left(j+\frac{1}{2}\right)^{-1/2}\left[(j+\lambda)^{1/2}\, d^{j-1/2}_{\lambda-1/2,0}(\theta)\cos\frac{\theta}{2} + (j-\lambda)^{1/2}\, d^{j-1/2}_{\lambda+1/2,0}(\theta)\sin\frac{\theta}{2}\right].$$

Product of Two d's

$$d^j_{\lambda\mu}\, d^{j'}_{\lambda'\mu'} = \sum_l C^{l,\lambda-\lambda'}_{j,\lambda;\; j',-\lambda'} \cdot C^{l,\mu-\mu'}_{j,\mu;\; j',-\mu'} \cdot (-1)^{\lambda'-\mu'}\, d^l_{\lambda-\lambda',\mu-\mu'}.$$

Differential Cross Sections of $a + A \to a' + A'$ for Particles with Spin

Conventional Representation

Let $\mathbf{S} = \mathbf{S}_a + \mathbf{S}_A$, $\mathbf{S}' = \mathbf{S}_{a'} + \mathbf{S}_{A'}$ be the incoming and outgoing channel spins. For initial and final polarizations $\langle S_z \rangle = m$, $\langle S'_z \rangle = m'$ (taking the z axis along the direction of the projectile a), the differential cross section is

$$\frac{d\sigma}{d\Omega}(\theta, \phi; S, m; S', m') = \frac{2\pi}{k^2}\Bigg| \sum_{l,l',j} \left(l + \frac{1}{2}\right)^{1/2} C^{j,m}_{l,0;\ S,m} \cdot C^{j,m}_{l',\Delta m;\ S',m'} \cdot T^{S,j,S'}_{l,l'}(E) \cdot Y^{\Delta m}_{l'}(\theta, \phi)\Bigg|^2,$$

where $\mathbf{j} = \mathbf{l} + \mathbf{S} = \mathbf{l}' + \mathbf{S}'$; $\Delta m = m - m'$. There is an additional limitation on the possible values of l and l', given by the parity condition

$$\pi_a \pi_A (-1)^l = \pi_{a'} \pi_{A'} (-1)^{l'}.$$

The total $d\sigma/d\Omega$ is obtained by summing over final m' and S' and averaging over the initial polarization states and channel spins; for unpolarized projectile and target, this gives

$$\frac{d\sigma}{d\Omega} = \frac{1}{(2S_a + 1)(2S_A + 1)} \sum_{S,S'} \sum_{m,m'} \frac{d\sigma}{d\Omega}(\theta, \phi; S, m; S', m').$$

The results, for the following illustrative combinations, follow:

1. $S_a = 0^-$, $S_A = \frac{1}{2}^+$ $\quad (\pi + \mathfrak{N}, K + \mathfrak{N})$
   (a) $S_{a'} = 0^-$, $S_{A'} = \frac{1}{2}^+$ $\quad (\pi + \mathfrak{N}, K + \Lambda, \overline{K} + \Xi$, etc.)
   (b) $S_{a'} = 0^+$, $S_{A'} = \frac{1}{2}^+$
   (c) $S_{a'} = 0^-$, $S_{A'} = \frac{3}{2}^+$

(d) $S_{a'} = 0^-$, $S_{A'} = \frac{5}{2}^+$
(e) $S_{a'} = 1^-$, $S_{A'} \leq \frac{3}{2}$

2. $S_a = \frac{1}{2}^+$, $S_A = \frac{1}{2}^+$ $\quad(\mathfrak{N} + \mathfrak{N}, \overline{\mathfrak{N}} + \mathfrak{N}, \Lambda + \mathfrak{N}$, etc.)

(a) $S_{a'} = \frac{1}{2}^+$, $S_{A'} = \frac{1}{2}^+$
(b) $S_{a'} = \frac{1}{2}^+$, $S_{A'} = \frac{3}{2}^+$

Results

1. $S_a = 0^-$, $S_A = \frac{1}{2}^+$

(a) $S_{a'} = 0^-$, $S_{A'} = \frac{1}{2}^+$

(i) $$4k^2 \frac{d\sigma}{d\Omega}\left(\theta, \phi; \frac{1}{2}, \frac{1}{2}; \frac{1}{2}, \frac{1}{2}\right) = \left| \sum_l \{(l+1)\, T_{l,l}^{l+1/2}(E) + l\, T_{l,l}^{l-1/2}(E)\}\, P_l(\cos\theta) \right|^2.$$

(ii) $$4k^2 \frac{d\sigma}{d\Omega}\left(\theta, \phi; \frac{1}{2}, \frac{1}{2}; \frac{1}{2}, -\frac{1}{2}\right) = \left| \sum_l \{T_{l,l}^{l+1/2} - T_{l,l}^{l-1/2}\} \sin\theta\, P_l'(\cos\theta)\, e^{i\phi} \right|^2.$$

(iii) $\frac{d\sigma}{d\Omega}\left(\theta, \phi; \frac{1}{2}, -\frac{1}{2}; \frac{1}{2}, \frac{1}{2}\right)$; same as (ii).[a]

(iv) $\frac{d\sigma}{d\Omega}\left(\theta, \phi; \frac{1}{2}, -\frac{1}{2}; \frac{1}{2}, -\frac{1}{2}\right)$; same as (i).

(b) $S_{a'} = 0^+$, $S_{A'} = \frac{1}{2}^+$

(i) $$4k^2 \frac{d\sigma}{d\Omega}\left(\theta, \phi; \frac{1}{2}, \frac{1}{2}; \frac{1}{2}, \frac{1}{2}\right) = \left| \sum_l \left\{(l+1)\, T_{l,l+1}^{l+1/2} P_{l+1} + l\, T_{l,l-1}^{l-1/2} P_{l-1}\right\} \right|^2.$$

(ii) $$4k^2 \frac{d\sigma}{d\Omega}\left(\theta, \phi; \frac{1}{2}, \frac{1}{2}; \frac{1}{2}, -\frac{1}{2}\right) = \left| \sum_l \left\{T_{l,l+1}^{l+1/2} P_{l+1}' - T_{l,l-1}^{l-1/2} P_{l-1}'\right\} \sin\theta\, e^{i\phi} \right|^2.$$

(iii) same as (ii).[a]

(iv) same as (i).

Note that, formally, case (b) reduces to case (a) on the substitutions $l - 1 \to l$ for $j = l - \frac{1}{2}$ and $l + 1 \to l$ for $j = l + \frac{1}{2}$, respectively. (The $T_{l,l'}^j$ appear different, of course, since $l' = l \pm 1$ for case (b); however, since the T's are undetermined parameters, this apparent difference is undetectable in the expressions for the angular distribution.) The inability of angular distributions to distinguish between the different parity possibilities for the same spins — sometimes referred to as the Minami ambiguity — is a general feature of reaction angular distributions.

[a] Except $e^{i\phi} \leftrightarrow e^{-i\phi}$.

As a consequence, we shall give expressions for only one of each of the four possible parity combinations associated with the reactants.

(c) $S_{a'} = 0^-$, $S_{A'} = \frac{3}{2}^+$

(i) $$4k^2 \frac{d\sigma}{d\Omega}\left(\theta, \phi; \frac{1}{2}, \frac{1}{2}; \frac{3}{2}, \frac{3}{2}\right) = \Bigg|\sum_l \Bigg\{ \sqrt{\frac{(l+1)^2}{(2l+3)(2l+4)}}\, T^{l+1/2}_{l,l+2} P'_{l+2} + \sqrt{\frac{3(l+1)^2}{(2l+3)2l}}\, T^{l+1/2}_{l,l} P'_l + \sqrt{\frac{3l^2}{(2l-1)(2l+2)}}\, T^{l-1/2}_{l,l} P'_l + \sqrt{\frac{l^2}{(2l-2)(2l-1)}}\, T^{l-1/2}_{l,l-2} P'_{l-2} \Bigg\} \sin\theta\, e^{-i\phi}\Bigg|^2.$$

(ii) $$4k^2 \frac{d\sigma}{d\Omega}\left(\theta, \phi; \frac{1}{2}, \frac{1}{2}; \frac{3}{2}, \frac{1}{2}\right) = \Bigg|\sum_l \Bigg\{ \sqrt{\frac{3(l+1)^2(l+2)}{2(2l+3)}}\, T^{l+1/2}_{l,l+2} P_{l+2} - \sqrt{\frac{l(l+1)^2}{2(2l+3)}}\, T^{l+1/2}_{l,l} P_l + \sqrt{\frac{(l+1)l^2}{2(2l-1)}}\, T^{l-1/2}_{l,l} P_l - \sqrt{\frac{3(l-1)l^2}{2(2l-1)}}\, T^{l-1/2}_{l,l-2} P_{l-2} \Bigg\}\Bigg|^2.$$

(iii) $$4k^2 \frac{d\sigma}{d\Omega}\left(\theta, \phi; \frac{1}{2}, \frac{1}{2}; \frac{3}{2}, -\frac{1}{2}\right) = \Bigg|\sum_l \Bigg\{ \sqrt{\frac{3(l+1)^2}{2(l+2)(2l+3)}}\, T^{l+1/2}_{l,l+2} P'_{l+2} - \sqrt{\frac{(l+3)^2}{2l(2l+3)}}\, T^{l+1/2}_{l,l} P'_l - \sqrt{\frac{(l-2)^2}{(2l+2)(2l-1)}}\, T^{l-1/2}_{l,l} P'_l + \sqrt{\frac{3l^2}{(2l-2)(2l-1)}}\, T^{l-1/2}_{l,l-2} P'_{l-2} \Bigg\} \sin\theta\, e^{i\phi}\Bigg|^2.$$

(iv) $$4k^2 \frac{d\sigma}{d\Omega}\left(\theta, \phi; \frac{1}{2}, \frac{1}{2}; \frac{3}{2}, -\frac{3}{2}\right) = \Bigg|\sum_l \Bigg\{ \sqrt{\frac{1}{2(2l+3)(l+2)}}\, T^{l+1/2}_{l,l+2} P''_{l+2} + \sqrt{\frac{3}{2l(2l+3)}}\, T^{l+1/2}_{l,l} P''_l - \sqrt{\frac{3}{(2l-1)(2l+2)}}\, T^{l-1/2}_{l,l} P''_l - \sqrt{\frac{1}{(2l-1)(2l-2)}}\, T^{l-1/2}_{l,l-2} P''_{l-2} \Bigg\} \sin^2\theta\, e^{2i\phi}\Bigg|^2.$$

(v) $\frac{d\sigma}{d\Omega}\left(\theta, \phi; \frac{1}{2}, -\frac{1}{2}; \frac{3}{2}, \frac{3}{2}\right)$; same as (iv).[b]

[b] Except $e^{2i\phi} \leftrightarrow e^{-2i\phi}$.

(vi) $\frac{d\sigma}{d\Omega}\left(\theta, \phi; \frac{1}{2}, -\frac{1}{2}; \frac{3}{2}, \frac{1}{2}\right)$; same as (iii).[a]

(vii) $\frac{d\sigma}{d\Omega}\left(\theta, \phi; \frac{1}{2}, -\frac{1}{2}; \frac{3}{2}, -\frac{1}{2}\right)$; same as (ii).

(viii) $\frac{d\sigma}{d\Omega}\left(\theta, \phi; \frac{1}{2}, -\frac{1}{2}; \frac{3}{2}, -\frac{3}{2}\right)$; same as (i).[a]

(d) $S_{a'} = 0^-$, $S_{A'} = \frac{5}{2}^+$

(i) $4k^2 \frac{d\sigma}{d\Omega}\left(\theta, \phi; \frac{1}{2}, \frac{1}{2}; \frac{5}{2}, \frac{5}{2}\right)$

$$
\begin{aligned}
&= \Bigg|\sum_l \Bigg\{ \sqrt{\frac{5(l+1)^2}{(2l+6)(2l+4)(2l+3)(2l+1)}}\, T^{l+1/2}_{l,l+2} P''_{l+2} \\
&+ \sqrt{\frac{10(l+1)^2}{(2l+4)(2l+3)(2l)(2l-1)}}\, T^{l+1/2}_{l,l} P''_{l} \\
&+ \sqrt{\frac{(l+1)^2}{(2l+1)2l(2l-1)(2l-2)}}\, T^{l+1/2}_{l,l-2} P''_{l-2} \\
&+ \sqrt{\frac{l^2}{(2l+4)(2l+3)(2l+2)(2l+1)}}\, T^{l-1/2}_{l,l+2} P''_{l+2} \\
&+ \sqrt{\frac{10l^2}{(2l+3)(2l+2)(2l-1)(2l-2)}}\, T^{l-1/2}_{l,l} P''_{l} \\
&+ \sqrt{\frac{5l^2}{(2l+1)(2l-1)(2l-2)(2l-4)}}\, T^{l-1/2}_{l,l-2} P''_{l-2} \Bigg\} \sin^2\theta\, e^{-2i\phi} \Bigg|^2 .
\end{aligned}
$$

(ii) $4k^2 \frac{d\sigma}{d\Omega}\left(\theta, \phi; \frac{1}{2}, \frac{1}{2}; \frac{5}{2}, \frac{3}{2}\right)$

$$
\begin{aligned}
&= \Bigg|\sum_l \Bigg\{ \frac{(l+1)(3l+4)}{\sqrt{(2l+6)(2l+4)(2l+3)(2l+1)}}\, T^{l+1/2}_{l,l+2} P'_{l+2} \\
&- \frac{(l+2)(l+1)}{\sqrt{l(2l-1)(2l+3)(2l+4)}}\, T^{l+1/2}_{l,l} P'_{l} \\
&- \frac{\sqrt{5}\,(l+1)l}{\sqrt{(2l+1)(2l)(2l-1)(2l-2)}}\, T^{l+1/2}_{l,l-2} P'_{l-2} \\
&+ \frac{\sqrt{5}\,(l+1)l}{\sqrt{(2l+1)(2l+2)(2l+3)(2l+4)}}\, T^{l-1/2}_{l,l+2} P'_{l+2} \\
&+ \frac{l(l-1)}{\sqrt{(2l+3)(l+1)(2l-1)(2l-2)}}\, T^{l-1/2}_{l,l} P'_{l} \\
&- \frac{l(3l-1)}{\sqrt{(2l+1)(2l-1)(2l-2)(2l-4)}}\, T^{l-1/2}_{l,l-2} P'_{l-2} \Bigg\} \sin\theta\, e^{-i\phi} \Bigg|^2 .
\end{aligned}
$$

[a] Except $e^{i\phi} \leftrightarrow e^{-i\phi}$.

$$\text{(iii)}\ 4k^2 \frac{d\sigma}{d\Omega}\left(\theta, \phi; \frac{1}{2}, \frac{1}{2}; \frac{5}{2}, \frac{1}{2}\right) = \left|\sum_l \left\{\sqrt{\frac{(l+3)(l+2)(l+1)^2}{2(2l+3)(2l+1)}}\, T^{l+1/2}_{l,l+2} P_{l+2} - \frac{2l(l+2)(l+1)}{\sqrt{(2l+4)(2l+3)(2l)(2l-1)}}\, T^{l+1/2}_{l,l} P_l + \frac{\sqrt{10}\, l(l+1)(l-1)}{\sqrt{(2l+1)(2l)(2l-1)(2l-2)}}\, T^{l+1/2}_{l,l-2} P_{l-2} + \frac{\sqrt{10}\, (l)(l+1)(l+2)}{\sqrt{(2l+4)(2l+3)(2l+2)(2l+1)}}\, T^{l-1/2}_{l,l+2} P_{l+2} - \frac{2l(l-1)(l+1)}{\sqrt{(2l+3)(2l+2)(2l-1)(2l-2)}}\, T^{l-1/2}_{l,l} P_l + \frac{\sqrt{2}\, l(l-1)(l-2)}{\sqrt{(2l-4)(2l+1)(2l-1)(2l-2)}}\, T^{l-1/2}_{l,l-2} P_{l-2}\right\}\right|^2.$$

$$\text{(iv)}\ 4k^2 \frac{d\sigma}{d\Omega}\left(\theta, \phi; \frac{1}{2}, \frac{1}{2}; \frac{5}{2}, -\frac{1}{2}\right) = \left|\sum_l \left\{\frac{\sqrt{2}\,(l-2)(l+1)}{\sqrt{(2l+6)(2l+4)(2l+3)(2l+1)}}\, T^{l+1/2}_{l,l+2} P'_{l+2} - \frac{2(l-2)(l+2)}{\sqrt{(2l+4)(2l+3)(2l)(2l-1)}}\, T^{l+1/2}_{l,l} P'_l + \frac{\sqrt{10}\, l(l+1)}{\sqrt{(2l+1)(2l)(2l-1)(2l-2)}}\, T^{l+1/2}_{l,l-2} P'_{l-2} - \frac{\sqrt{10}\, l(l+1)}{\sqrt{(2l+4)(2l+3)(2l+2)(2l+1)}}\, T^{l-1/2}_{l,l+2} P'_{l+2} + \frac{2(l+3)(l-1)}{\sqrt{(2l+3)(2l+2)(2l-1)(2l-2)}}\, T^{l-1/2}_{l,l} P'_l - \frac{\sqrt{2}\, l(l+3)}{\sqrt{(2l+1)(2l-1)(2l-2)(2l-4)}}\, T^{l-1/2}_{l,l-2} P'_{l-2}\right\} \sin\theta\, e^{i\phi}\right|^2.$$

$$\text{(v)}\ 4k^2 \frac{d\sigma}{d\Omega}\left(\theta, \phi; \frac{1}{2}, \frac{1}{2}; \frac{5}{2}, -\frac{3}{2}\right) = \left|\sum_l \left\{\frac{(3l-1)}{\sqrt{(2l+6)(2l+4)(2l+3)(2l+1)}}\, T^{l+1/2}_{l,l+2} P''_{l+2} - \frac{(l+7)}{\sqrt{(2l+4)(2l+3)(l)(2l-1)}}\, T^{l+1/2}_{l,l} P''_l - \frac{\sqrt{5}\,(l+1)}{\sqrt{(2l+1)(2l)(2l-1)(2l-2)}}\, T^{l+1/2}_{l,l-2} P''_{l-2} - \frac{\sqrt{5}\, l}{\sqrt{(2l+4)(2l+3)(2l+2)(2l+1)}}\, T^{l-1/2}_{l,l+2} P''_{l+2}\right.\right.$$

$$- \frac{(l-6)}{\sqrt{(2l+3)(l+1)(2l-1)(2l-2)}} T_{l,l}^{l-1/2} P_l''$$

$$\left. + \frac{(3l+4)}{\sqrt{(2l+1)(2l-1)(2l-2)(2l-4)}} T_{l,l-2}^{l-1/2} P_{l-2}'' \right\} \sin^2 \theta \, e^{2i\phi} \Bigg|^2 .$$

(vi) $4k^2 \dfrac{d\sigma}{d\Omega}\left(\theta, \phi; \frac{1}{2}, \frac{1}{2}; \frac{5}{2}, -\frac{5}{2}\right)$

$$= \Bigg| \sum_l \Bigg\{ \frac{\sqrt{5}}{\sqrt{(2l+6)(2l+4)(2l+3)(2l+1)}} T_{l,l+2}^{l+1/2} P_{l+2}'''$$

$$+ \frac{\sqrt{10}}{\sqrt{(2l+3)(2l+4)(2l-1)(2l)}} T_{l,l}^{l+1/2} P_l'''$$

$$+ \frac{1}{\sqrt{(2l+1)(2l)(2l-1)(2l-2)}} T_{l,l-2}^{l+1/2} P_{l-2}'''$$

$$- \frac{1}{\sqrt{(2l+4)(2l+3)(2l+2)(2l+1)}} T_{l,l+2}^{l-1/2} P_{l+2}'''$$

$$- \frac{\sqrt{10}}{\sqrt{(2l+3)(2l+2)(2l-1)(2l-2)}} T_{l,l}^{l-1/2} P_l'''$$

$$\left. - \frac{\sqrt{5}}{\sqrt{(2l+1)(2l-1)(2l-2)(2l-4)}} T_{l,l-2}^{l-1/2} P_{l-2}''' \right\} \sin^3 \theta \, e^{3i\phi} \Bigg|^2 .$$

(vii) $\dfrac{d\sigma}{d\Omega}\left(\theta, \phi; \frac{1}{2}, -\frac{1}{2}; \frac{5}{2}, \frac{5}{2}\right)$; same as (vi).[c]

(viii) $\dfrac{d\sigma}{d\Omega}\left(\theta, \phi; \frac{1}{2}, -\frac{1}{2}; \frac{5}{2}, \frac{3}{2}\right)$; same as (v).[b]

(ix) $\dfrac{d\sigma}{d\Omega}\left(\theta, \phi; \frac{1}{2}, -\frac{1}{2}; \frac{5}{2}, \frac{1}{2}\right)$; same as (iv).[a]

(x) $\dfrac{d\sigma}{d\Omega}\left(\theta, \phi; \frac{1}{2}, -\frac{1}{2}; \frac{5}{2}, -\frac{1}{2}\right)$; same as (iii).

(xi) $\dfrac{d\sigma}{d\Omega}\left(\theta, \phi; \frac{1}{2}, -\frac{1}{2}; \frac{5}{2}, -\frac{3}{2}\right)$; same as (ii).[a]

(xii) $\dfrac{d\sigma}{d\Omega}\left(\theta, \phi; \frac{1}{2}, -\frac{1}{2}; \frac{5}{2}, -\frac{5}{2}\right)$; same as (i).[b]

(e) $S_{a'} = 1^-$, all $S_{A'}$

In these cases, there are generally three final channel spins: $S' = S_{A'} + 1$, $S_{A'}$, $S_{A'} - 1$ (except for $S_{A'} = \frac{1}{2}$, where $S' = \frac{3}{2}$ and $\frac{1}{2}$ only). The differential cross

[a] Except $e^{i\phi} \leftrightarrow e^{-i\phi}$.
[b] Except $e^{2i\phi} \leftrightarrow e^{-2i\phi}$.
[c] Except $e^{3i\phi} \leftrightarrow e^{-3i\phi}$.

section, for a given combination of m and m', is an incoherent superposition (sum over amplitudes squared) of the corresponding terms previously given for the simpler cases $S_{a'}=0$, $S_{A'}=S'$.

2. $S_a = S_A = \frac{1}{2}^+$

In this case there are two independent incident channel spins, $S=0$ and $S=1$, so that, generally, for a given outgoing channel spin S', we have

$$\frac{d\sigma}{d\Omega}(\theta, \phi; m=0, m') = \frac{d\sigma}{d\Omega}(\theta, \phi; 0, 0; S', m') + \frac{d\sigma}{d\Omega}(\theta, \phi; 1, 0; S', m')$$

and

$$\frac{d\sigma}{d\Omega}(\theta, \phi; m=\pm 1, m') = \frac{d\sigma}{d\Omega}(\theta, \phi; 1, \pm 1; S', m')$$

with, for unpolarized projectile and target baryons,

$$\frac{d\sigma}{d\Omega}(\theta, \phi) = \frac{1}{4} \sum_{S', m'} \left\{ \frac{d\sigma}{d\Omega}(\theta, \phi; 0, m') + \frac{d\sigma}{d\Omega}(\theta, \phi; 1, m') + \frac{d\sigma}{d\Omega}(\theta, \phi; -1, m') \right\}.$$

Generally, when $S_a = S_A$, and also for the case $S_{a'} = S_{A'}$, we must distinguish the possibility that the incident and product baryons are identical (indistinguishable) from the case in which either the incident or product particles, or both, are different (e.g., $\mathfrak{N} + \mathfrak{N} \to \mathfrak{N} + \mathfrak{N}$ versus $\mathfrak{N} + \mathfrak{N} \to \mathfrak{N}^* + \mathfrak{N}$ or $\Lambda + \mathfrak{N} \to \Lambda + \mathfrak{N}$). For the case of two nucleons, the Pauli principle requires that for $S=0$, which is odd under particle interchange, the rest of the wave function be even; for two identical nucleons ($P+P$ or $N+N$), the isospin wave function ($t=1$, since $t_3 = \pm 1$) being even, the space wave function must also be even, i.e., l-even; for the $P+N$ state, both $t=1$ and $t=0$ are possible, and hence both even and odd l-values are possible. For $S=1$, on the other hand, the rest of the wave function must be odd under particle interchange. In any event, for a given isospin state, the summation over orbital angular momenta can include only every second value, either l-even or l-odd.

As a consequence, for reactions involving identical particles the summations over l and/or l' contain only every other term; in addition, there may be further selection rules, i.e., $S = S'$, $S' \pm 2, \ldots$ only, for the elastic scattering of identical baryons. However, the expressions for $d\sigma/d\Omega$, given below, treat the baryons as distinguishable, it being left to the reader to omit those terms forbidden by the Pauli principle in the circumstances where either the incident or product particles are identical.

(a) $S_{a'} = S_{A'} = \frac{1}{2}^+$ ($S' = 0^+$ and 1^+)

(i) $$4k^2 \frac{d\sigma}{d\Omega}(\theta, \varphi; 0, 0; 0, 0) = \left| \sum_l (2l+1) T_{l,l}^{0,l,0} P_l \right|^2,$$

$$\frac{d\sigma}{d\Omega}(\theta, \varphi; 0, 0; 1, 0) = 0 = \frac{d\sigma}{d\Omega}(\theta, \varphi; 1, 0; 0, 0),$$

$$4k^2 \frac{d\sigma}{d\Omega}(\theta, \varphi; 1, 0; 1, 0) = \left| \sum_l \left\{ \sqrt{(l+1)(l+2)}\, T^{1,l+1,1}_{l,l+2} P_{l+2} - (l+1)\, T^{1,l+1,1}_{l,l} P_l - l T^{1,l-1,1}_{l,l} P_l + \sqrt{l(l-1)}\, T^{1,l-1,1}_{l,l-2} P_{l-2} \right\} \right|^2 .$$

(ii) $$4k^2 \frac{d\sigma}{d\Omega}(\theta, \varphi; 1, 1; 0, 0) = \left| \sum_l \frac{(2l+1)}{\sqrt{2l(l+1)}} T^{1,l,0}_{l,l} P'_l \sin\theta\, e^{i\varphi} \right|^2 ,$$

$$4k^2 \frac{d\sigma}{d\Omega}(\theta, \varphi; 1, 1; 1, 0) = \left| \sum_l \left\{ \sqrt{\frac{(l+1)}{2(l+2)}}\, T^{1,l+1,1}_{l,l+2} P'_{l+2} - \frac{(l+2)}{\sqrt{2}\,(l+1)} T^{1,l+1,1}_{l,l} P'_l + \frac{(2l+1)}{\sqrt{2}\, l(l+1)} T^{1,l,1}_{l,l} P'_l + \frac{(l-1)}{\sqrt{2}\, l} T^{1,l-1,1}_{l,l} P'_l - \sqrt{\frac{l}{2(l-1)}}\, T^{1,l-1,1}_{l,l-2} P'_{l-2} \right\} \sin\theta\, e^{i\varphi} \right|^2 .$$

(iii) $\frac{d\sigma}{d\Omega}(\theta, \varphi; 1, -1; S', 0)$; same as (ii).[a]

(iv) $$4k^2 \frac{d\sigma}{d\Omega}(\theta, \varphi; 0, 0; 1, 1) = \left| \sum_l \frac{(2l+1)}{\sqrt{2l(l+1)}} T^{0,l,1}_{l,l} P'_l \sin\theta\, e^{-i\varphi} \right|^2 ,$$

$$4k^2 \frac{d\sigma}{d\Omega}(\theta, \varphi; 1, 0; 1, 1) = \left| \sum_l \left\{ \sqrt{\frac{(l+1)}{2(l+2)}}\, T^{1,l+1,1}_{l,l+2} P'_{l+2} + \sqrt{\frac{1}{2}}\, T^{1,l+1,1}_{l,l} P'_l - \sqrt{\frac{1}{2}}\, T^{1,l-1,1}_{l,l} P'_l - \sqrt{\frac{l}{2(l-1)}}\, T^{1,l-1,1}_{l,l-2} P'_{l-2} \right\} \sin\theta\, e^{-i\varphi} \right|^2 .$$

(v) $\frac{d\sigma}{d\Omega}(\theta, \varphi; S, 0; 1, -1)$; same as (iv).[a]

---

[a] Except $e^{i\phi} \leftrightarrow e^{-i\phi}$.

$$\text{(vi)}\ 4k^2\frac{d\sigma}{d\Omega}(\theta,\varphi;1,1;1,1)=4k^2\frac{d\sigma}{d\Omega}(\theta,\varphi;1,-1;1,-1)$$
$$=\left|\sum_l\left\{\frac{1}{2}\sqrt{(l+1)(l+2)}\,T^{1,l+1,1}_{l,l+2}P_{l+2}+\frac{1}{2}(l+2)\,T^{1,l+1,1}_{l,l}P_l+\frac{1}{2}(2l+1)\,T^{1,l,1}_{l,l}P_l+\frac{1}{2}(l-1)\,T^{1,l-1,1}_{l,l}P_l+\frac{1}{2}\sqrt{l(l-1)}\,T^{1,l-1,1}_{l,l-2}P_{l-2}\right\}\right|^2.$$

$$\text{(vii)}\ 4k^2\frac{d\sigma}{d\Omega}(\theta,\varphi;1,1;1,-1)=\left|\sum_l\left\{\frac{1}{2\sqrt{(l+1)(l+2)}}T^{1,l+1,1}_{l,l+2}P''_{l+2}+\frac{1}{2(l+1)}T^{1,l+1,1}_{l,l}P''_l-\frac{(2l+1)}{2l(l+1)}T^{1,l,1}_{l,l}P''_l+\frac{1}{2l}T^{1,l-1,1}_{l,l}P''_l+\frac{1}{2\sqrt{l(l-1)}}T^{1,l-1,1}_{l,l-2}P''_{l-2}\right\}\sin^2\theta\, e^{2i\varphi}\right|^2.$$

$$\text{(viii)}\ \frac{d\sigma}{d\Omega}(\theta,\varphi;1,-1;1,1);\ \text{same as (vii).}^{b}$$

(b) $S_{a'}=\frac{1}{2}^+$, $S_{A'}=\frac{3}{2}^+$ ($S'=1^+$ and 2^+)

For the case $S'=1$, the expressions for $d\sigma/d\Omega\ (\theta,\phi;S,m;1,m')$ are the same as those for case (a) above. For $S'=2$, we have

$$\text{(i)}\ 4k^2\frac{d\sigma}{d\Omega}(\theta,\varphi;0,0;2,0)=\left|\sum_l\left\{\sqrt{\frac{3(l+1)(l+2)(2l+1)}{2(2l+3)}}T^{0,l,2}_{l,l+2}P_{l+2}-\sqrt{\frac{l(l+1)(2l+1)^2}{(2l-1)(2l+3)}}T^{0,l,2}_{l,l}P_l+\sqrt{\frac{3(l-1)l(2l+1)}{2(2l-1)}}T^{0,l,2}_{l,l-2}P_{l-2}\right\}\right|^2,$$

$$\frac{d\sigma}{d\Omega}(\theta,\varphi;1,0;2,0)=0.$$

$$\text{(ii)}\ 4k^2\frac{d\sigma}{d\Omega}(\theta,\varphi;1,1;2,0)=\left|\sum_l\left\{\sqrt{\frac{3}{2(l+2)(l+3)}}T^{1,l+1,2}_{l,l+2}P'_{l+2}-\sqrt{\frac{3(l+2)}{2l(l+1)^2}}T^{1,l+1,2}_{l,l}P'_l\right.\right.$$

[b] Except $e^{2i\phi}\leftrightarrow e^{-2i\phi}$.

$$+\sqrt{\frac{3l(2l+1)}{4(l+2)(2l+3)}}\, T^{1,l,2}_{l,l+2}\, P'_{l+2}$$

$$+\frac{(2l+1)[3-l(l+1)]}{l(l+1)\sqrt{2(2l-1)(2l+3)}}\, T^{1,l,2}_{l,l}\, P'_{l}$$

$$+\sqrt{\frac{3(l+1)(2l+1)}{4(l-1)(2l-1)}}\, T^{1,l,2}_{l,l-2}\, P'_{l-2}$$

$$+\sqrt{\frac{3(l-1)}{2l^2(l+1)}}\, T^{1,l-1,2}_{l,l}\, P'_{l}$$

$$\left.-\sqrt{\frac{3}{2(l-1)(l-2)}}\, T^{1,l-1,2}_{l,l-2}\, P'_{l-2}\right\} \sin\theta\, e^{i\varphi}\Bigg|^2.$$

(iii) $\frac{d\sigma}{d\Omega}(\theta, \varphi;\ 1, -1;\ 2, 0)$; same as (ii).[a]

(iv) $$4k^2\frac{d\sigma}{d\Omega}(\theta, \varphi;\ 0, 0;\ 2, 1) = \Bigg|\sum_l\Bigg\{\sqrt{\frac{(l+1)(2l+1)}{(l+2)(2l+3)}}\, T^{0,l,2}_{l,l+2}\, P'_{l+2}$$

$$-\sqrt{\frac{3(2l+1)^2}{2l(l+1)(2l-1)(2l+3)}}\, T^{0,l,2}_{l,l}\, P'_{l}$$

$$\left.-\sqrt{\frac{l(2l+1)}{(l-1)(2l-1)}}\, T^{0,l,2}_{l,l-2}\, P'_{l-2}\right\} \sin\theta\, e^{-i\varphi}\Bigg|^2,$$

$$4k^2\frac{d\sigma}{d\Omega}(\theta, \varphi;\ 1, 0;\ 2, 1) = \Bigg|\sum_l\Bigg\{\frac{(l+1)}{\sqrt{2(l+2)(l+3)}}\, T^{1,l+1,2}_{l,l+2}\, P'_{l+2}$$

$$-\sqrt{\frac{(l+2)}{2l}}\, T^{1,l+1,2}_{l,l}\, P'_{l}$$

$$-\sqrt{\frac{(l-1)}{2(l+1)}}\, T^{1,l-1,2}_{l,l}\, P'_{l}$$

$$\left.+\frac{l}{\sqrt{2(l-1)(l-2)}}\, T^{1,l-1,2}_{l,l-2}\, P'_{l-2}\right\} \sin\theta\, e^{-i\varphi}\Bigg|^2.$$

(v) $\frac{d\sigma}{d\Omega}(\theta, \varphi;\ S, 0;\ 2, -1)$; same as (iv).[a]

(vi) $$4k^2\frac{d\sigma}{d\Omega}(\theta, \varphi;\ 1, 1;\ 2, 1) = 4k^2\frac{d\sigma}{d\Omega}(\theta, \varphi;\ 1, -1;\ 2, -1)$$

$$= \Bigg|\sum_l\Bigg\{\frac{1}{2}\sqrt{(l+2)(l+3)}\, T^{1,l+1,2}_{l,l+2}\, P_{l+2}$$

$$-\frac{1}{2}\sqrt{l(l+2)}\, T^{1,l+1,2}_{l,l}\, P_{l}$$

$$+\sqrt{\frac{l(l+2)(2l+1)}{2(2l+3)}}\, T^{1,l,2}_{l,l+2}\, P_{l+2}$$

[a] Except $e^{i\phi} \leftrightarrow e^{-i\phi}$.

$$+\frac{(2l+1)}{2}\sqrt{\frac{3}{(2l-1)(2l+3)}}\,T^{1,l,2}_{l,l}\,P_l$$
$$-\sqrt{\frac{(l-1)(l+1)(2l+1)}{2(2l-1)}}\,T^{1,l,2}_{l,l-2}\,P_{l-2}$$
$$+\frac{1}{2}\sqrt{(l-1)(l+1)}\,T^{1,l-1,2}_{l,l}\,P_l$$
$$\left.-\frac{1}{2}\sqrt{(l-1)(l-2)}\,T^{1,l-1,2}_{l,l-2}\,P_{l-2}\Big\}\right|^2.$$

(vii)
$$4k^2\frac{d\sigma}{d\Omega}(\theta,\varphi;1,1;2,-1) = \left|\sum_l\Big\{\frac{(l-1)}{2(l+1)\sqrt{(l+2)(l+3)}}\,T^{1,l+1,2}_{l,l+2}\,P''_{l+2}\right.$$
$$-\frac{(l+4)}{2(l+1)\sqrt{l(l+2)}}\,T^{1,l+1,2}_{l,l}\,P''_l$$
$$-\sqrt{\frac{l(2l+1)}{(l+1)^2(l+2)(2l+3)}}\,T^{1,l,2}_{l,l+2}\,P''_{l+2}$$
$$+\frac{3(2l+1)}{2l(l+1)}\sqrt{\frac{3}{(2l-1)(2l+3)}}\,T^{1,l,2}_{l,l}\,P''_l$$
$$+\sqrt{\frac{(l+1)(2l+1)}{2l^2(l-1)(2l-1)}}\,T^{1,l,2}_{l,l-2}\,P''_{l-2}$$
$$+\frac{(l-3)}{2l\sqrt{(l-1)(l+1)}}\,T^{1,l-1,2}_{l,l}\,P''_l$$
$$\left.-\frac{(l+2)}{2l\sqrt{(l-1)(l-2)}}\,T^{1,l-1,2}_{l,l-2}\,P''_{l-2}\Big\}\sin^2\theta\, e^{2i\varphi}\right|^2.$$

(viii) $\frac{d\sigma}{d\Omega}(\theta,\varphi;1,-1;2,1)$; same as (vii).[b]

(ix)
$$4k^2\frac{d\sigma}{d\Omega}(\theta,\varphi;0,0;2,2) = \left|\sum_l\Big\{\sqrt{\frac{(2l+1)}{4(l+1)(l+2)(2l+3)}}\,T^{0,l,2}_{l,l+2}\,P''_{l+2}\right.$$
$$+\sqrt{\frac{3(2l+1)^2}{2l(l+1)(2l-1)(2l+3)}}\,T^{0,l,2}_{l,l}\,P''_l$$
$$\left.+\sqrt{\frac{(2l+1)}{4l(l-1)(2l-1)}}\,T^{0,l,2}_{l,l-2}\,P''_{l-2}\Big\}\sin^2\theta\, e^{-2i\varphi}\right|^2,$$

$$4k^2\frac{d\sigma}{d\Omega}(\theta,\varphi;1,0;2,2) = \left|\sum_l\Big\{\frac{1}{\sqrt{2(l+2)(l+3)}}\,T^{1,l+1,2}_{l,l+2}\,P''_{l+2}\right.$$
$$+\frac{1}{\sqrt{2l(l+2)}}\,T^{1,l+1,2}_{l,l}\,P''_l$$
$$-\frac{1}{\sqrt{2(l-1)(l+1)}}\,T^{1,l-1,2}_{l,l}\,P''_l$$
$$\left.+\frac{1}{\sqrt{(l-1)(l-2)}}\,T^{1,l-1,2}_{l,l-2}\,P''_{l-2}\Big\}\sin^2\theta\, e^{-2i\varphi}\right|^2.$$

[b] Except $e^{2i\phi} \leftrightarrow e^{-2i\phi}$.

(x) $\dfrac{d\sigma}{d\Omega}(\theta, \varphi; S, 0; 2, -2)$; same as (ix).[b]

(xi)
$$4k^2 \frac{d\sigma}{d\Omega}(\theta, \varphi; 1, 1; 2, 2) = \Bigg|\sum_l \Bigg\{\frac{1}{2}\sqrt{\frac{(l+2)}{(l+3)}}\, T^{1,l+1,2}_{l,l+2} P'_{l+2} + \frac{1}{2}\sqrt{\frac{(l+2)}{l}}\, T^{1,l+1,2}_{l,l} P'_l + \frac{1}{2}\sqrt{\frac{l(2l+1)}{2(l+2)(2l+3)}}\, T^{1,l,2}_{l,l+2} P'_{l+2} + \frac{1}{2}\sqrt{\frac{3(2l+1)^2}{(2l-1)(2l+3)}}\, T^{1,l,2}_{l,l} P'_l + \frac{1}{2}\sqrt{\frac{(l+1)(2l+1)}{2(l-1)(2l-1)}}\, T^{1,l,2}_{l,l-2} P'_{l-2} + \frac{1}{2}\sqrt{\frac{(l-1)}{(l+1)}}\, T^{1,l-1,2}_{l,l} P'_l + \frac{1}{2}\sqrt{\frac{(l-1)}{(l-2)}}\, T^{1,l-1,2}_{l,l-2} P'_{l-2}\Bigg\} \sin\theta\, e^{-i\varphi}\Bigg|^2.$$

(xii) $\dfrac{d\sigma}{d\Omega}(\theta, \varphi; 1, -1; 2, -2)$; same as (xi).[a]

(xiii)
$$4k^2 \frac{d\sigma}{d\Omega}(\theta, \varphi; 1, 1; 2, -2) = \Bigg|\sum_l \Bigg\{\frac{1}{2(l+1)\sqrt{(l+2)(l+3)}}\, T^{1,l+1,2}_{l,l+2} P'''_{l+2} + \frac{1}{2(l+1)\sqrt{l(l+2)}}\, T^{1,l+1,2}_{l,l} P'''_l - \frac{1}{2(l+1)}\sqrt{\frac{(2l+1)}{2l(l+2)(2l+3)}}\, T^{1,l,2}_{l,l+2} P'''_{l+2} - \frac{(2l+1)}{2l(l+1)}\sqrt{\frac{3}{(2l-1)(2l+3)}}\, T^{1,l,2}_{l,l} P'''_l - \frac{1}{2l}\sqrt{\frac{(2l+1)}{2(l-1)(l+1)(2l-1)}}\, T^{1,l,2}_{l,l-2} P'''_{l-2} + \frac{1}{2l\sqrt{(l-1)(l+1)}}\, T^{1,l-1,2}_{l,l} P'''_l + \frac{1}{2l\sqrt{(l-1)(l-2)}}\, T^{1,l-1,2}_{l,l-2} P'''_{l-2}\Bigg\} \sin^3\theta\, e^{3i\varphi}\Bigg|^2.$$

(xiv) $\dfrac{d\sigma}{d\Omega}(\theta, \varphi; 1, -1; 2, 2)$; same as (xiii).[c]

---

[a] Except $e^{i\phi} \leftrightarrow e^{-i\phi}$.
[b] Except $e^{2i\phi} \leftrightarrow e^{-2i\phi}$.
[c] Except $e^{3i\phi} \leftrightarrow e^{-3i\phi}$.

Helicity Representation

In the helicity representation, the polarization states of all the particles are quantized along their directions of motion. For a given combination of helicity states, the differential cross section is

$$k^2 \frac{d\sigma}{d\Omega}(\theta, \varphi; \lambda_a, \lambda_A; \lambda_{a'}, \lambda_{A'}) = \left| \sum_j \left(j+\frac{1}{2}\right) T^j_{\lambda_{a'},\lambda_{A'};\, \lambda_a,\lambda_A}(E)\, e^{i(\lambda-\mu)\varphi}\, d^j_{\lambda\mu}(\theta, \varphi) \right|^2,$$

where $\lambda = \lambda_a - \lambda_A$, $\mu = \lambda_{a'} - \lambda_{A'}$, while the differential cross section for a given physical situation is obtained by summing over final helicities and averaging over initial helicity values. However, not all the $T^j_{\lambda_i}$'s are independent, since symmetry requirements give rise to relationships between various different combinations, e.g., $T^j_{\lambda_i} = T^j_{-\lambda_i}$. Some consequences of such requirements are considered in the specific examples quoted below. Once again, for initially unpolarized projectile and target, we have

$$\frac{d\sigma}{d\Omega} = \frac{1}{(2S_a+1)(2S_A+1)} \sum_{\lambda_A,\lambda_a} \sum_{\lambda_{A'},\lambda_{a'}} \frac{d\sigma}{d\Omega}(\theta, \varphi; \lambda_a, \lambda_A; \lambda_{a'}, \lambda_{A'}).$$

1. $S_a = S_{a'} = 0$, $S_A = S_{A'} = \frac{1}{2}$

Defining[d]

$$kf_{l\pm} \equiv i(T^j_{0,\pm 1/2;\, 0,\pm 1/2} \pm T^j_{0,\pm 1/2;\, 0,\mp 1/2}),$$

$$f_1 \equiv \sum_l (f_{l+} P'_{l+1} - f_{l-} P'_{l-1}),$$

$$f_2 \equiv \sum_l (f_{l+} - f_{l-}) P'_l,$$

we have

$$\frac{d\sigma}{d\Omega} = \frac{1}{2} \sum_j |f_j|^2,$$

with, for the amplitudes f_j (written in the form of a 2×2 matrix),

$$f_j = (f_1 + f_2)\cos\frac{\theta}{2} + i(f_1 - f_2)\sin\frac{\theta}{2}(\cos\varphi\,\sigma_y - \sin\varphi\,\sigma_x).$$

Note that the angles θ, φ characterize the *cm* direction of the scattered particles, with respect to the projectile direction, while the spin of the scattered baryon is referred to a set of axes rotated from the conventional one through the angles θ, φ (i.e., new z axis along the direction of the scattered baryon).

2. $S_a = S_{a'} = S_A = S_{A'} = \frac{1}{2}$

The complications, in this case, arise in the case of identical particles in the initial and/or final states. Observing that the states

$$|J, M; \tfrac{1}{2}, \tfrac{1}{2}\rangle$$

$$\sqrt{\tfrac{1}{2}}\,[|J, M; \tfrac{1}{2}, -\tfrac{1}{2}\rangle + |J, M; -\tfrac{1}{2}, \tfrac{1}{2}\rangle]$$

$$|J, M; -\tfrac{1}{2}, -\tfrac{1}{2}\rangle$$

---

[d] M. Jacob and G. C. Wick, *Ann. Phys.* (New York), *7:* 404 (1959).

belong to the triplet ($S = 1$), while

$$\sqrt{\tfrac{1}{2}}\,[|J, M; \tfrac{1}{2}, -\tfrac{1}{2}\rangle - |J, M; -\tfrac{1}{2}, \tfrac{1}{2}\rangle]$$

goes with the singlet ($S = 0$), we may write the parity eigenstates as

$$|J, M; a\rangle = \sqrt{\tfrac{1}{2}}\,[|J, M; \tfrac{1}{2}, \tfrac{1}{2}\rangle + |J, M; -\tfrac{1}{2}, -\tfrac{1}{2}\rangle],$$
$$|J, M; b\rangle = \sqrt{\tfrac{1}{2}}\,[|J, M; \tfrac{1}{2}, -\tfrac{1}{2}\rangle + |J, M; -\tfrac{1}{2}, \tfrac{1}{2}\rangle],$$

which have orbital parity $(-1)^{J-1}$, and

$$|J, M; c\rangle = \sqrt{\tfrac{1}{2}}\,[|J, M; \tfrac{1}{2}, \tfrac{1}{2}\rangle - |J, M; -\tfrac{1}{2}, -\tfrac{1}{2}\rangle],$$
$$|J, M; d\rangle = \sqrt{\tfrac{1}{2}}\,[|J, M; \tfrac{1}{2}, -\tfrac{1}{2}\rangle - |J, M; -\tfrac{1}{2}, \tfrac{1}{2}\rangle],$$

with orbital parity $(-1)^J$. Accordingly, the amplitudes corresponding to the (even) $t = 1$ isospin combination may be classified as follows:

$T^J_{a,a}$	even J, odd parity,
$T^J_{b,b}$	even J, odd parity,
$T^J_{c,c}$	even J, even parity,
$T^J_{d,d}$	odd J, odd parity,
$T^J_{a,b} = T^J_{b,a}$	even J, odd parity.

The (odd) $t = 0$ isospin combination then inverts the odd-evenness of the J-parity choices for the above combinations.

In describing nucleon-nucleon scattering, therefore, the helicity analysis is most conveniently made in terms of these combinations.

$SU(3)$ Combination Coefficients

Tables are given here[a] for the weights (isoscalar factors) of the combinations of two $SU(3)$ multiplets, decomposed into the product representations. Included are

Table A6.1	$8 \otimes 8 = 1 \oplus 8_1 \oplus 8_2 \oplus 10 \oplus \overline{10} \oplus 27,$
Table A6.2	$8 \otimes 10 = 8 \oplus 10 \oplus 27 \oplus 35,$
Table A6.3	$8 \otimes 27 = 8 \oplus 10 \oplus \overline{10} \oplus 27_1 \oplus 27_2 \oplus 35 \oplus \overline{35} \oplus 64,$
Table A6.4	$10 \otimes 10 = \overline{10} \oplus 27 \oplus 28 \oplus 35,$
Table A6.5	$10 \otimes \overline{10} = 1 \oplus 8 \oplus 27 \oplus 64.$

Table A6.1 Isoscalar factors for {8} ⊗ {8}. Given are the isoscalar factors

$$\left(\begin{matrix} 8 & 8 \\ I_1 Y_1 & I_2 Y_2 \end{matrix}\middle| \begin{matrix} \mu_\gamma \\ I\,Y \end{matrix}\right)$$

for the CG series $\{8\} \otimes \{8\} = \{27\} \oplus \{10\} \oplus \{10^*\} \oplus \{8\}_1 \oplus \{8\}_2 \oplus \{1\}.$

$Y=2 \quad I=1$

$I_1, \ Y_1; \ I_2, \ Y_2$	27	μ_γ
$\frac{1}{2}, \ 1; \ \frac{1}{2}, \ 1$	1	

$Y=2 \quad I=0$

$I_1, \ Y_1; \ I_2, \ Y_2$	10*	μ_γ
$\frac{1}{2}, \ 1; \ \frac{1}{2}, \ 1$	−1	

Note: For additional tables of $SU(3)$ combination coefficients, see P. McNamee and F. Chilton, "Tables of Clebsch–Gordan Coefficients of SU_3," *Rev. Mod. Phys., 36:* 1005 (1964).

[a] From J. J. de Swart, *Rev. Mod. Phys., 35:* 916 (1963); *37:* 326 (1965). Reprinted with permission of the author and the American Institute of Physics.

Table A6.1 (continued)

$Y=1 \quad I=\frac{3}{2}$

I_1, Y_1; I_2, Y_2	27	10	μ_γ
$\frac{1}{2}$, 1; 1, 0	$\sqrt{2}/2$	$-\sqrt{2}/2$	
1, 0; $\frac{1}{2}$, 1	$\sqrt{2}/2$	$\sqrt{2}/2$	

$Y=1 \quad I=\frac{1}{2}$

I_1, Y_1; I_2, Y_2	27	8_1	8_2	10*	μ_γ
$\frac{1}{2}$, 1; 1, 0	$\sqrt{5}/10$	$3\sqrt{5}/10$	1/2	−1/2	
1, 0; $\frac{1}{2}$, 1	$-\sqrt{5}/10$	$-3\sqrt{5}/10$	1/2	−1/2	
$\frac{1}{2}$, 1; 0, 0	$3\sqrt{5}/10$	$-\sqrt{5}/10$	1/2	1/2	
0, 0; $\frac{1}{2}$, 1	$3\sqrt{5}/10$	$-\sqrt{5}/10$	−1/2	−1/2	

$Y=0 \quad I=2$

I_1, Y_1; I_2, Y_2	27	μ_γ
1, 0; 1, 0	1	

$Y=0 \quad I=1$

I_1, Y_1; I_2, Y_2	27	8_1	8_2	10	10*	μ_γ
$\frac{1}{2}$, 1; $\frac{1}{2}$, −1	$\sqrt{5}/5$	$-\sqrt{30}/10$	$\sqrt{6}/6$	$-\sqrt{6}/6$	$\sqrt{6}/6$	
$\frac{1}{2}$, −1; $\frac{1}{2}$, 1	$\sqrt{5}/5$	$-\sqrt{30}/10$	$-\sqrt{6}/6$	$\sqrt{6}/6$	$-\sqrt{6}/6$	
1, 0; 1, 0	0	0	$\sqrt{6}/3$	$\sqrt{6}/6$	$-\sqrt{6}/6$	
1, 0; 0, 0	$\sqrt{30}/10$	$\sqrt{5}/5$	0	1/2	1/2	
0, 0; 1, 0	$\sqrt{30}/10$	$\sqrt{5}/5$	0	−1/2	−1/2	

$Y=0 \quad I=0$

I_1, Y_1; I_2, Y_2	27	8_1	1	8_2	μ_γ
$\frac{1}{2}$, 1; $\frac{1}{2}$, −1	$\sqrt{15}/10$	$\sqrt{10}/10$	1/2	$\sqrt{2}/2$	
$\frac{1}{2}$, −1; $\frac{1}{2}$, 1	$-\sqrt{15}/10$	$-\sqrt{10}/10$	−1/2	$\sqrt{2}/2$	
1, 0; 1, 0	$-\sqrt{10}/20$	$-\sqrt{15}/5$	$\sqrt{6}/4$	0	
0, 0; 0, 0	$3\sqrt{30}/20$	$-\sqrt{5}/5$	$-\sqrt{2}/4$	0	

$Y=-1 \quad I=\frac{3}{2}$

I_1, Y_1; I_2, Y_2	27	10*	μ_γ
$\frac{1}{2}$, −1; 1, 0	$\sqrt{2}/2$	$-\sqrt{2}/2$	
1, 0; $\frac{1}{2}$, −1	$\sqrt{2}/2$	$\sqrt{2}/2$	

$Y=-1 \quad I=\frac{1}{2}$

I_1, Y_1; I_2, Y_2	27	8_1	8_2	10	μ_γ
$\frac{1}{2}$, −1; 1, 0	$-\sqrt{5}/10$	$-3\sqrt{5}/10$	1/2	1/2	
1, 0; $\frac{1}{2}$, −1	$\sqrt{5}/10$	$3\sqrt{5}/10$	1/2	1/2	
$\frac{1}{2}$, −1; 0, 0	$3\sqrt{5}/10$	$-\sqrt{5}/10$	−1/2	1/2	
0, 0; $\frac{1}{2}$, −1	$3\sqrt{5}/10$	$-\sqrt{5}/10$	1/2	−1/2	

$Y=-2 \quad I=1$

I_1, Y_1; I_2, Y_2	27	μ_γ
$\frac{1}{2}$, −1; $\frac{1}{2}$, −1	1	

$Y=-2 \quad I=0$

I_1, Y_1; I_2, Y_2	10	μ_γ
$\frac{1}{2}$, −1; $\frac{1}{2}$, −1	1	

Table A6.2 Isoscalar factors for $\{8\} \otimes \{10\}$. *Given are the isoscalar factors*

$$\begin{pmatrix} 8 & 10 & \mu_\gamma \\ I_1 Y_1 & I_2 Y_2 & I\ Y \end{pmatrix}$$

for the CG series $\{8\} \otimes \{10\} = \{35\} \oplus \{27\} \oplus \{10\} \oplus \{8\}$.

$Y=2 \quad I=2$

I_1, Y_1; I_2, Y_2	35
$\frac{1}{2}$, 1; $\frac{3}{2}$, 1	1

$Y=2 \quad I=1$

I_1, Y_1; I_2, Y_2	27
$\frac{1}{2}$, 1; $\frac{3}{2}$, 1	−1

$Y=1 \quad I=\frac{5}{2}$

I_1, Y_1; I_2, Y_2	35
1, 0; $\frac{3}{2}$, 1	1

$Y=1 \quad I=\frac{3}{2}$

I_1, Y_1; I_2, Y_2	35	27	10
1, 0; $\frac{3}{2}$, 1	$-1/4$	$-\sqrt{5}/4$	$\sqrt{10}/4$
0, 0; $\frac{3}{2}$, 1	$\sqrt{5}/4$	$-3/4$	$-\sqrt{2}/4$
$\frac{1}{2}$, 1; 1, 0	$\sqrt{10}/4$	$\sqrt{2}/4$	$1/2$

$Y=1 \quad I=\frac{1}{2}$

I_1, Y_1; I_2, Y_2	27	8
1, 0; $\frac{3}{2}$, 1	$\sqrt{5}/5$	$-2\sqrt{5}/5$
$\frac{1}{2}$, 1; 1, 0	$-2\sqrt{5}/5$	$-\sqrt{5}/5$

$Y=0 \quad I=2$

I_1, Y_1; I_2, Y_2	35	27
1, 0; 1, 0	$\sqrt{3}/2$	$1/2$
$\frac{1}{2}$, −1; $\frac{3}{2}$, 1	$1/2$	$-\sqrt{3}/2$

$Y=0 \quad I=1$

I_1, Y_1; I_2, Y_2	35	27	10	8
1, 0; 1, 0	$-\sqrt{3}/6$	$-3\sqrt{5}/10$	$\sqrt{3}/3$	$\sqrt{30}/15$
0, 0; 1, 0	$\sqrt{2}/2$	$-\sqrt{30}/10$	0	$-\sqrt{5}/5$
$\frac{1}{2}$, 1; $\frac{1}{2}$, −1	$\sqrt{3}/3$	$\sqrt{5}/5$	$\sqrt{3}/3$	$\sqrt{30}/15$
$\frac{1}{2}$, −1; $\frac{3}{2}$, 1	$-\sqrt{3}/6$	$\sqrt{5}/10$	$\sqrt{3}/3$	$-2\sqrt{30}/15$

The column heads 35, 27, 10, 8 refer to μ_γ.

Table A6.2 (continued)

$Y=0 \quad I=0$

$I_1, \; Y_1; \; I_2, \; Y_2$	27	8	μ_γ
$1, \; 0; \; 1, \; 0$	$\sqrt{10}/5$	$-\sqrt{15}/5$	
$\frac{1}{2}, \; 1; \; \frac{1}{2}, \; -1$	$-\sqrt{15}/5$	$-\sqrt{10}/5$	

$Y=-1 \quad I=\frac{3}{2}$

$I_1, \; Y_1; \; I_2, \; Y_2$	35	27	μ_γ
$1, \; 0; \; \frac{1}{2}, \; -1$	$\sqrt{2}/2$	$\sqrt{2}/2$	
$\frac{1}{2}, \; -1; \; 1, \; 0$	$\sqrt{2}/2$	$-\sqrt{2}/2$	

$Y=-1 \quad I=\frac{1}{2}$

$I_1, \; Y_1; \; I_2, \; Y_2$	35	27	10	8	μ_γ
$1, \; 0; \; \frac{1}{2}, \; -1$	$-1/4$	$-7\sqrt{5}/20$	$\sqrt{2}/4$	$\sqrt{5}/5$	
$0, \; 0; \; \frac{1}{2}, \; -1$	$3/4$	$-3\sqrt{5}/20$	$\sqrt{2}/4$	$-\sqrt{5}/5$	
$\frac{1}{2}, \; 1; \; 0, \; -2$	$\sqrt{2}/4$	$3\sqrt{10}/20$	$1/2$	$\sqrt{10}/5$	
$\frac{1}{2}, \; -1; \; 1, \; 0$	$-1/2$	$\sqrt{5}/10$	$\sqrt{2}/2$	$-\sqrt{5}/5$	

$Y=-2 \quad I=1$

$I_1, \; Y_1; \; I_2, \; Y_2$	35	27	μ_γ
$1, \; 0; \; 0, \; -2$	$1/2$	$\sqrt{3}/2$	
$\frac{1}{2}, \; -1; \; \frac{1}{2}, \; -1$	$\sqrt{3}/2$	$-1/2$	

$Y=-2 \quad I=0$

$I_1, \; Y_1; \; I_2, \; Y_2$	35	10	μ_γ
$0, \; 0; \; 0, \; -2$	$\sqrt{2}/2$	$\sqrt{2}/2$	
$\frac{1}{2}, \; -1; \; \frac{1}{2}, \; -1$	$-\sqrt{2}/2$	$\sqrt{2}/2$	

$Y=-3 \quad I=\frac{1}{2}$

$I_1, \; Y_1; \; I_2, \; Y_2$	35	μ_γ
$\frac{1}{2}, \; -1; \; 0, \; -2$	1	

Table A6.3 Isoscalar factors for {8} ⊗ {27}. Given are the isoscalar factors

$$\begin{pmatrix} 8 & 27 & \mu_\gamma \\ I_1 Y_1 & I_2 Y_2 & I\ Y \end{pmatrix}$$

for the CG series $\{8\} \otimes \{27\} = \{64\} \oplus \{35\} \oplus \{35^*\} \oplus \{27\}_1 \oplus \{27\}_2 \oplus \{10\} \oplus \{10^*\} \oplus \{8\}$.

$Y = 3 \quad I = \frac{3}{2}$

I_1, Y_1; I_2, Y_2	64	μ_γ
$\frac{1}{2}$, 1; 1, 2	1	

$Y = 3 \quad I = \frac{1}{2}$

I_1, Y_1; I_2, Y_2	35*	μ_γ
$\frac{1}{2}$, 1; 1, 2	−1	

$Y = 2 \quad I = 2$

I_1, Y_1; I_2, Y_2	64	35	μ_γ
$\frac{1}{2}$, 1; $\frac{3}{2}$, 1	$\sqrt{6}/3$	$-\sqrt{3}/3$	
1, 0; 1, 2	$\sqrt{3}/3$	$\sqrt{6}/3$	

$Y = 2 \quad I = 1$

I_1, Y_1; I_2, Y_2	64	35*	27_1	27_2	μ_γ
$\frac{1}{2}$, 1; $\frac{3}{2}$, 1	$\sqrt{14}/21$	$-2/3$	$\sqrt{70}/14$	$\sqrt{6}/6$	
$\frac{1}{2}$, 1; $\frac{1}{2}$, 1	$2\sqrt{70}/21$	$\sqrt{5}/6$	$-\sqrt{14}/28$	$\sqrt{30}/12$	
1, 0; 1, 2	$-\sqrt{21}/21$	$-\sqrt{6}/6$	$-\sqrt{105}/14$	$1/2$	
0, 0; 1, 2	$\sqrt{14}/7$	$-1/2$	$-\sqrt{70}/28$	$-\sqrt{6}/4$	

$Y = 2 \quad I = 0$

I_1, Y_1; I_2, Y_2	35*	10*	μ_γ
$\frac{1}{2}$, 1; $\frac{1}{2}$, 1	$-\sqrt{30}/6$	$-\sqrt{6}/6$	
1, 0; 1, 2	$\sqrt{6}/6$	$-\sqrt{30}/6$	

$Y = 1 \quad I = \frac{5}{2}$

I_1, Y_1; I_2, Y_2	64	35	μ_γ
$\frac{1}{2}$, 1; 2, 0	$\sqrt{3}/3$	$-\sqrt{6}/3$	
1, 0; $\frac{3}{2}$, 1	$\sqrt{6}/3$	$\sqrt{3}/3$	

$Y = 1 \quad I = \frac{3}{2}$

I_1, Y_1; I_2, Y_2	64	35	35*	27_1	27_2	10	μ_γ
$\frac{1}{2}$, 1; 2, 0	$\sqrt{7}/21$	$-1/12$	$-\sqrt{5}/6$	$5\sqrt{42}/56$	$\sqrt{10}/8$	$-5\sqrt{2}/12$	
$\frac{1}{2}$, 1; 1, 0	$5\sqrt{7}/21$	$-5/12$	$\sqrt{5}/6$	$-3\sqrt{42}/56$	$\sqrt{10}/8$	$-\sqrt{2}/12$	
1, 0; $\frac{3}{2}$, 1	$-\sqrt{21}/63$	$7\sqrt{3}/36$	$-\sqrt{15}/9$	$-5\sqrt{14}/56$	$\sqrt{30}/8$	$5\sqrt{6}/36$	
1, 0; $\frac{1}{2}$, 1	$5\sqrt{42}/63$	$5\sqrt{6}/18$	$\sqrt{30}/18$	$\sqrt{7}/7$	0	$\sqrt{3}/9$	
0, 0; $\frac{3}{2}$, 1	$\sqrt{105}/21$	$-\sqrt{15}/12$	$-\sqrt{3}/3$	$\sqrt{70}/56$	$-\sqrt{6}/8$	$\sqrt{30}/12$	
$\frac{1}{2}$, −1; 1, 2	$\sqrt{35}/21$	$\sqrt{5}/6$	$-1/3$	$-\sqrt{210}/28$	$-\sqrt{2}/4$	$-\sqrt{10}/6$	

Table A6.3 (continued)

$Y=1 \quad I=\frac{1}{2}$

I_1, Y_1; I_2, Y_2	64	35*	27_1	27_2	10*	8	μ_γ
$\frac{1}{2}$, 1; 1, 0	$\sqrt{35}/21$	$-\sqrt{10}/6$	$3\sqrt{105}/70$	$1/2$	$-1/3$	$2\sqrt{5}/15$	
$\frac{1}{2}$, 1; 0, 0	$2\sqrt{35}/21$	$\sqrt{10}/6$	$-\sqrt{105}/70$	$1/2$	$1/3$	$\sqrt{5}/15$	
1, 0; $\frac{3}{2}$, 1	$-\sqrt{42}/63$	$\sqrt{3}/9$	$-\sqrt{14}/7$	0	$-\sqrt{30}/9$	$2\sqrt{6}/9$	
1, 0; $\frac{1}{2}$, 1	$-\sqrt{210}/63$	$-5\sqrt{15}/36$	$-19\sqrt{70}/280$	$\sqrt{6}/8$	$7\sqrt{6}/36$	$\sqrt{30}/45$	
0, 0; $\frac{1}{2}$, 1	$\sqrt{210}/21$	$-\sqrt{15}/12$	$-13\sqrt{70}/280$	$-\sqrt{6}/8$	$-\sqrt{6}/12$	$-\sqrt{30}/15$	
$\frac{1}{2}$, −1; 1, 2	$-2\sqrt{7}/21$	$\sqrt{2}/12$	$-\sqrt{21}/28$	$\sqrt{5}/4$	$-\sqrt{5}/6$	$-2/3$	

$Y=0 \quad I=3$

I_1, Y_1; I_2, Y_2	64	μ_γ
1, 0; 2, 0	1	

$Y=0 \quad I=2$

I_1, Y_1; I_2, Y_2	64	35	35*	27_1	27_2	μ_γ
$\frac{1}{2}$, 1; $\frac{3}{2}$, −1	$2\sqrt{21}/21$	$-\sqrt{3}/3$	$\sqrt{3}/6$	$-\sqrt{210}/28$	$\sqrt{2}/4$	
$\frac{1}{2}$, −1; $\frac{3}{2}$, 1	$2\sqrt{21}/21$	$\sqrt{3}/6$	$-\sqrt{3}/3$	$-\sqrt{210}/28$	$-\sqrt{2}/4$	
1, 0; 1, 0	$\sqrt{210}/21$	$\sqrt{30}/12$	$\sqrt{30}/12$	$\sqrt{21}/14$	0	
1, 0; 2, 0	0	$\sqrt{2}/4$	$-\sqrt{2}/4$	0	$\sqrt{3}/2$	
0, 0; 2, 0	$\sqrt{7}/7$	$-1/2$	$-1/2$	$\sqrt{70}/14$	0	

$Y=0 \quad I=1$

I_1, Y_1; I_2, Y_2	64	35	35*	27_1	27_2	10	10*	8	μ_γ
$\frac{1}{2}$, 1; $\frac{3}{2}$, −1	$2\sqrt{35}/63$	$-1/9$	$-5/18$	$3\sqrt{14}/28$	$\sqrt{30}/12$	$-2\sqrt{5}/9$	$-\sqrt{5}/9$	$4/9$	
$\frac{1}{2}$, −1; $\frac{3}{2}$, 1	$-2\sqrt{35}/63$	$5/18$	$1/9$	$-3\sqrt{14}/28$	$\sqrt{30}/12$	$-\sqrt{5}/9$	$-2\sqrt{5}/9$	$-4/9$	
$\frac{1}{2}$, 1; $\frac{1}{2}$, −1	$10\sqrt{7}/63$	$-\sqrt{5}/9$	$2\sqrt{5}/9$	$-3\sqrt{70}/70$	$\sqrt{6}/6$	$-1/9$	$4/9$	$2\sqrt{5}/45$	
$\frac{1}{2}$, −1; $\frac{1}{2}$, 1	$10\sqrt{7}/63$	$2\sqrt{5}/9$	$-\sqrt{5}/9$	$-3\sqrt{70}/70$	$-\sqrt{6}/6$	$-4/9$	$1/9$	$2\sqrt{5}/45$	
0, 0; 1, 0	$5\sqrt{7}/21$	$-\sqrt{5}/6$	$-\sqrt{5}/6$	$-\sqrt{70}/70$	0	$1/3$	$-1/3$	$-2\sqrt{5}/15$	
1, 0; 0, 0	$10\sqrt{7}/63$	$2\sqrt{5}/9$	$2\sqrt{5}/9$	$4\sqrt{70}/70$	0	$2/9$	$-2/9$	$-\sqrt{5}/45$	
1, 0; 1, 0	0	$\sqrt{30}/12$	$-\sqrt{30}/12$	0	$1/2$	$\sqrt{6}/6$	$\sqrt{6}/6$	0	
1, 0; 2, 0	$-\sqrt{14}/63$	$\sqrt{10}/36$	$\sqrt{10}/36$	$-\sqrt{35}/14$	0	$5\sqrt{2}/18$	$-5\sqrt{2}/18$	$2\sqrt{10}/9$	

Table A6.3 (continued)

$Y=0 \quad I=0$

I_1, Y_1; I_2, Y_2	64	27_1	27_2	8	μ_γ
$\frac{1}{2}$, 1; $\frac{1}{2}$, −1	$2\sqrt{21}/21$	$\sqrt{210}/70$	$\sqrt{2}/2$	$2\sqrt{15}/15$	
$\frac{1}{2}$, −1; $\frac{1}{2}$, 1	$-2\sqrt{21}/21$	$-\sqrt{210}/70$	$\sqrt{2}/2$	$-2\sqrt{15}/15$	
1, 0; 1, 0	$-\sqrt{21}/21$	$-4\sqrt{210}/70$	0	$2\sqrt{15}/15$	
0, 0; 0, 0	$2\sqrt{7}/7$	$-4\sqrt{70}/70$	0	$-\sqrt{5}/5$	

$Y=-1 \quad I=\frac{5}{2}$

I_1, Y_1; I_2, Y_2	64	35*	μ_γ
$\frac{1}{2}$, −1; 2, 0	$\sqrt{3}/3$	$-\sqrt{6}/3$	
1, 0; $\frac{3}{2}$, −1	$\sqrt{6}/3$	$\sqrt{3}/3$	

$Y=-1 \quad I=\frac{3}{2}$

I_1, Y_1; I_2, Y_2	64	35*	35	27_1	27_2	10*	μ_γ
$\frac{1}{2}$, −1; 2, 0	$-\sqrt{7}/21$	1/12	$\sqrt{5}/6$	$-5\sqrt{42}/56$	$\sqrt{10}/8$	$-5\sqrt{2}/12$	
$\frac{1}{2}$, −1; 1, 0	$5\sqrt{7}/21$	−5/12	$\sqrt{5}/6$	$-3\sqrt{42}/56$	$-\sqrt{10}/8$	$\sqrt{2}/12$	
1, 0; $\frac{3}{2}$, −1	$\sqrt{21}/63$	$-7\sqrt{3}/36$	$\sqrt{15}/9$	$5\sqrt{14}/56$	$\sqrt{30}/8$	$5\sqrt{6}/36$	
1, 0; $\frac{1}{2}$, −1	$5\sqrt{42}/63$	$5\sqrt{6}/18$	$\sqrt{30}/18$	$\sqrt{7}/7$	0	$-\sqrt{3}/9$	
0, 0; $\frac{3}{2}$, −1	$\sqrt{105}/21$	$-\sqrt{15}/12$	$-\sqrt{3}/3$	$\sqrt{70}/56$	$\sqrt{6}/8$	$-\sqrt{30}/12$	
$\frac{1}{2}$, 1; 1, −2	$\sqrt{35}/21$	$\sqrt{5}/6$	−1/3	$-\sqrt{210}/28$	$\sqrt{2}/4$	$\sqrt{10}/6$	

Table A6.3 (continued)

$Y=-1 \quad I=\frac{1}{2}$

I_1, Y_1; I_2, Y_2	64	35	27_1	27_2	10	8	μ_γ
$\frac{1}{2}$, −1; 1, 0	$-\sqrt{35}/21$	$\sqrt{10}/6$	$-3\sqrt{105}/70$	1/2	−1/3	$-2\sqrt{5}/15$	
$\frac{1}{2}$, −1; 0, 0	$2\sqrt{35}/21$	$\sqrt{10}/6$	$-\sqrt{105}/70$	−1/2	−1/3	$\sqrt{5}/15$	
1, 0; $\frac{3}{2}$, −1	$-\sqrt{42}/63$	$\sqrt{3}/9$	$-\sqrt{14}/7$	0	$\sqrt{30}/9$	$2\sqrt{6}/9$	
1, 0; $\frac{1}{2}$, −1	$\sqrt{210}/63$	$5\sqrt{15}/36$	$19\sqrt{70}/280$	$\sqrt{6}/8$	$7\sqrt{6}/36$	$-\sqrt{30}/45$	
0, 0; $\frac{1}{2}$, −1	$\sqrt{210}/21$	$-\sqrt{15}/12$	$-13\sqrt{70}/280$	$\sqrt{6}/8$	$\sqrt{6}/12$	$-\sqrt{30}/15$	
$\frac{1}{2}$, 1; 1, −2	$2\sqrt{7}/21$	$-\sqrt{2}/12$	$\sqrt{21}/28$	$\sqrt{5}/4$	$-\sqrt{5}/6$	2/3	

$Y=-2 \quad I=2$

I_1, Y_1; I_2, Y_2	64	35*	μ_γ
$\frac{1}{2}$, −1; $\frac{3}{2}$, −1	$\sqrt{6}/3$	$-\sqrt{3}/3$	
1, 0; 1, −2	$\sqrt{3}/3$	$\sqrt{6}/3$	

$Y=-2 \quad I=0$

I_1, Y_1; I_2, Y_2	35	10	μ_γ
$\frac{1}{2}$, −1; $\frac{1}{2}$, −1	$\sqrt{30}/6$	$-\sqrt{6}/6$	
1, 0; 1, −2	$\sqrt{6}/6$	$\sqrt{30}/6$	

$Y=-2 \quad I=1$

I_1, Y_1; I_2, Y_2	64	35	27_1	27_2	μ_γ
$\frac{1}{2}$, −1; $\frac{3}{2}$, −1	$-\sqrt{14}/21$	2/3	$-\sqrt{70}/14$	$\sqrt{6}/6$	
$\frac{1}{2}$, −1; $\frac{1}{2}$, −1	$2\sqrt{70}/21$	$\sqrt{5}/6$	$-\sqrt{14}/28$	$-\sqrt{30}/12$	
1, 0; 1, −2	$\sqrt{21}/21$	$\sqrt{6}/6$	$\sqrt{105}/14$	1/2	
0, 0; 1, −2	$\sqrt{14}/7$	−1/2	$-\sqrt{70}/28$	$\sqrt{6}/4$	

$Y=-3 \quad I=\frac{3}{2}$

I_1, Y_1; I_2, Y_2	64	μ_γ
$\frac{1}{2}$, −1; 1, −2	1	

$Y=-3 \quad I=\frac{1}{2}$

I_1, Y_1; I_2, Y_2	35	μ_γ
$\frac{1}{2}$, −1; 1, −2	1	

Table A6.4 Isoscalar factors for {10} ⊗ {10}. Given are the isoscalar factors

$$\begin{pmatrix} 10 & 10 & \mu_\gamma \\ I_1 Y_1 & I_2 Y_2 & I\ Y \end{pmatrix}$$

for the CG series $\{10\} \otimes \{10\} = \{35\} \oplus \{28\} \oplus \{27\} \oplus \{10^*\}$.

$Y=2 \quad I=3$

I_1,	Y_1;	I_2,	Y_2	28	μ_γ
$\frac{3}{2}$,	1;	$\frac{3}{2}$,	1	1	

$Y=1 \quad I=\frac{5}{2}$

I_1,	Y_1;	I_2,	Y_2	28	35	μ_γ
$\frac{3}{2}$,	1;	1,	0	$\sqrt{2}/2$	$\sqrt{2}/2$	
1,	0;	$\frac{3}{2}$,	1	$\sqrt{2}/2$	$-\sqrt{2}/2$	

$Y=2 \quad I=2$

I_1,	Y_1;	I_2,	Y_2	35	μ_γ
$\frac{3}{2}$,	1;	$\frac{3}{2}$,	1	-1	

$Y=1 \quad I=\frac{3}{2}$

I_1,	Y_1;	I_2,	Y_2	35	27	μ_γ
$\frac{3}{2}$,	1;	1,	0	$-\sqrt{2}/2$	$-\sqrt{2}/2$	
1,	0;	$\frac{3}{2}$,	1	$-\sqrt{2}/2$	$\sqrt{2}/2$	

$Y=2 \quad I=1$

I_1,	Y_1;	I_2,	Y_2	27	μ_γ
$\frac{3}{2}$,	1;	$\frac{3}{2}$,	1	1	

$Y=1 \quad I=\frac{1}{2}$

I_1,	Y_1;	I_2,	Y_2	27	10*	μ_γ
$\frac{3}{2}$,	1;	1,	0	$\sqrt{2}/2$	$\sqrt{2}/2$	
1,	0;	$\frac{3}{2}$,	1	$\sqrt{2}/2$	$-\sqrt{2}/2$	

$Y=2 \quad I=0$

I_1,	Y_1;	I_2,	Y_2	10*	μ_γ
$\frac{3}{2}$,	1;	$\frac{3}{2}$,	1	-1	

$Y=0 \quad I=2$

I_1,	Y_1;	I_2,	Y_2	28	35	27	μ_γ
$\frac{3}{2}$,	1;	$\frac{1}{2}$,	-1	$\sqrt{5}/5$	$\sqrt{2}/2$	$\sqrt{30}/10$	
$\frac{1}{2}$,	-1;	$\frac{3}{2}$,	1	$\sqrt{5}/5$	$-\sqrt{2}/2$	$\sqrt{30}/10$	
1,	0;	1,	0	$\sqrt{15}/5$	0	$-\sqrt{10}/5$	

Table A6.4 (continued)

$Y=0 \quad I=1$

I_1,	Y_1;	I_2,	Y_2	35	27	10*	μ_γ
$\frac{3}{2}$,	1;	$\frac{1}{2}$,	−1	$-\sqrt{6}/6$	$-\sqrt{2}/2$	$-\sqrt{3}/3$	
$\frac{1}{2}$,	−1;	$\frac{3}{2}$,	1	$-\sqrt{6}/6$	$\sqrt{2}/2$	$-\sqrt{3}/3$	
1,	0;	1,	0	$-\sqrt{6}/3$	0	$\sqrt{3}/3$	

$Y=0 \quad I=0$

I_1,	Y_1;	I_2,	Y_2	27	μ_γ
1,	0;	1,	0	1	

$Y=-1 \quad I=\frac{3}{2}$

I_1,	Y_1;	I_2,	Y_2	28	35	27	10*	μ_γ
$\frac{3}{2}$,	1;	0,	−2	$\sqrt{5}/10$	1/2	$3\sqrt{5}/10$	1/2	
0,	−2;	$\frac{3}{2}$,	1	$\sqrt{5}/10$	−1/2	$3\sqrt{5}/10$	−1/2	
1,	0;	$\frac{1}{2}$,	−1	$3\sqrt{5}/10$	1/2	$-\sqrt{5}/10$	−1/2	
$\frac{1}{2}$,	−1;	1,	0	$3\sqrt{5}/10$	−1/2	$-\sqrt{5}/10$	1/2	

$Y=-1 \quad I=\frac{1}{2}$

I_1,	Y_1;	I_2,	Y_2	35	27	μ_γ
1,	0;	$\frac{1}{2}$,	−1	$-\sqrt{2}/2$	$-\sqrt{2}/2$	
$\frac{1}{2}$,	−1;	1,	0	$-\sqrt{2}/2$	$\sqrt{2}/2$	

$Y=-2 \quad I=1$

I_1,	Y_1;	I_2,	Y_2	28	35	27	μ_γ
1,	0;	0,	−2	$\sqrt{5}/5$	$\sqrt{2}/2$	$\sqrt{30}/10$	
0,	−2;	1,	0	$\sqrt{5}/5$	$-\sqrt{2}/2$	$\sqrt{30}/10$	
$\frac{1}{2}$,	−1;	$\frac{1}{2}$,	−1	$\sqrt{15}/5$	0	$-\sqrt{10}/5$	

$Y=-2 \quad I=0$

I_1,	Y_1;	I_2,	Y_2	35	μ_γ
$\frac{1}{2}$,	−1;	$\frac{1}{2}$,	−1	−1	

$Y=-3 \quad I=\frac{1}{2}$

I_1,	Y_1;	I_2,	Y_2	28	35	μ_γ
$\frac{1}{2}$,	−1;	0,	−2	$\sqrt{2}/2$	$\sqrt{2}/2$	
0,	−2;	$\frac{1}{2}$,	−1	$\sqrt{2}/2$	$-\sqrt{2}/2$	

$Y=-4 \quad I=0$

I_1,	Y_1;	I_2,	Y_2	28	μ_γ
0,	−2;	0,	−2	1	

Table A6.5 Isoscalar factors for {10} ⊗ {10}. Given are the isoscalar factors*

$$\left(\begin{matrix}10 & 10^* \\ I_1Y_1 & I_2Y_2\end{matrix}\middle|\begin{matrix}\mu_\gamma \\ I\,Y\end{matrix}\right)$$

for the CG series $\{10\} \otimes \{10^*\} = \{64\} \oplus \{27\} \oplus \{8\} \oplus \{1\}$.

$Y=3 \quad I=\frac{3}{2}$

I_1,	Y_1;	I_2,	Y_2	64
$\frac{3}{2}$,	1;	0,	2	1

$Y=2 \quad I=2$

I_1,	Y_1;	I_2,	Y_2	64
$\frac{3}{2}$,	1;	$\frac{1}{2}$,	1	1

$Y=2 \quad I=1$

I_1,	Y_1;	I_2,	Y_2	64	27
$\frac{3}{2}$,	1;	$\frac{1}{2}$,	1	$\sqrt{21}/7$	$2\sqrt{7}/7$
1,	0;	0,	2	$2\sqrt{7}/7$	$-\sqrt{21}/7$

$Y=1 \quad I=\frac{5}{2}$

I_1,	Y_1;	I_2,	Y_2	64
$\frac{3}{2}$,	1;	1,	0	1

$Y=1 \quad I=\frac{3}{2}$

I_1,	Y_1;	I_2,	Y_2	64	27
$\frac{3}{2}$,	1;	1,	0	$\sqrt{14}/7$	$\sqrt{35}/7$
1,	0;	$\frac{1}{2}$,	1	$\sqrt{35}/7$	$-\sqrt{14}/7$

$Y=1 \quad I=\frac{1}{2}$

I_1,	Y_1;	I_2,	Y_2	64	27	8
$\frac{3}{2}$,	1;	1,	0	$\sqrt{7}/7$	$4\sqrt{35}/35$	$\sqrt{10}/5$
1,	0;	$\frac{1}{2}$,	1	$2\sqrt{7}/7$	$\sqrt{35}/35$	$-\sqrt{10}/5$
$\frac{1}{2}$,	−1;	0,	2	$\sqrt{14}/7$	$-3\sqrt{70}/35$	$\sqrt{5}/5$

$Y=0 \quad I=3$

I_1,	Y_1;	I_2,	Y_2	64
$\frac{3}{2}$,	1;	$\frac{3}{2}$,	−1	1

$Y=0 \quad I=2$

I_1,	Y_1;	I_2,	Y_2	64	27
$\frac{3}{2}$,	1;	$\frac{3}{2}$,	−1	$\sqrt{7}/7$	$\sqrt{42}/7$
1,	0;	1,	0	$\sqrt{42}/7$	$-\sqrt{7}/7$

(Each table's header row ends with μ_γ over the column labels.)

Table A6.5 (continued)

$Y=0 \quad I=1$

I_1, Y_1; I_2, Y_2	64	27	8	μ_γ
$\frac{3}{2}$, 1; $\frac{3}{2}$, −1	$\sqrt{21}/21$	$\sqrt{14}/7$	$\sqrt{6}/3$	
1, 0; 1, 0	$\sqrt{210}/21$	$3\sqrt{35}/35$	$-2\sqrt{15}/15$	
$\frac{1}{2}$, −1; $\frac{1}{2}$, 1	$\sqrt{210}/21$	$-4\sqrt{35}/35$	$\sqrt{15}/15$	

$Y=-1 \quad I=\frac{1}{2}$

I_1, Y_1; I_2, Y_2	64	27	8	μ_γ
1, 0; $\frac{3}{2}$, −1	$\sqrt{7}/7$	$4\sqrt{35}/35$	$\sqrt{10}/5$	
$\frac{1}{2}$, −1; 1, 0	$2\sqrt{7}/7$	$\sqrt{35}/35$	$-\sqrt{10}/5$	
0, −2; $\frac{1}{2}$, 1	$\sqrt{14}/7$	$-3\sqrt{70}/35$	$\sqrt{5}/5$	

$Y=0 \quad I=0$

I_1, Y_1; I_2, Y_2	64	27	8	1	μ_γ
$\frac{3}{2}$, 1; $\frac{3}{2}$, −1	$\sqrt{35}/35$	$\sqrt{210}/35$	$\sqrt{10}/5$	$\sqrt{10}/5$	
1, 0; 1, 0	$2\sqrt{105}/35$	$\sqrt{70}/14$	0	$-\sqrt{30}/10$	
$\frac{1}{2}$, −1; $\frac{1}{2}$, 1	$3\sqrt{70}/35$	$-\sqrt{105}/35$	$-\sqrt{5}/5$	$\sqrt{5}/5$	
0, −2; 0, 2	$2\sqrt{35}/35$	$-3\sqrt{210}/70$	$\sqrt{10}/5$	$-\sqrt{10}/10$	

$Y=-2 \quad I=2$

I_1, Y_1; I_2, Y_2	64	μ_γ
$\frac{1}{2}$, −1; $\frac{3}{2}$, −1	1	

$Y=-1 \quad I=\frac{5}{2}$

I_1, Y_1; I_2, Y_2	64	μ_γ
1, 0; $\frac{3}{2}$, −1	1	

$Y=-2 \quad I=1$

I_1, Y_1; I_2, Y_2	64	27	μ_γ
$\frac{1}{2}$, −1; $\frac{3}{2}$, −1	$\sqrt{21}/7$	$2\sqrt{7}/7$	
0, −2; 1, 0	$2\sqrt{7}/7$	$-\sqrt{21}/7$	

$Y=-1 \quad I=\frac{3}{2}$

I_1, Y_1; I_2, Y_2	64	27	μ_γ
1, 0; $\frac{3}{2}$, −1	$\sqrt{14}/7$	$\sqrt{35}/7$	
$\frac{1}{2}$, −1; 1, 0	$\sqrt{35}/7$	$-\sqrt{14}/7$	

$Y=-3 \quad I=\frac{3}{2}$

I_1, Y_1; I_2, Y_2	64	μ_γ
0, −2; $\frac{3}{2}$, −1	1	

Properties of a Dipole or Double-Pole Resonance

Breit–Wigner Resonance

Let $x = (E - E_r)$, $\gamma = \Gamma/2$. The amplitude is

$$A(E, E_r, \Gamma) = \frac{1}{2i}\left(\frac{x - i\gamma}{x + i\gamma} - 1\right) = -\frac{\gamma}{x + i\gamma} = \frac{1}{2i}(e^{2i\delta} - 1), \qquad \text{(A7.1)}$$

where δ is the phase shift

$$\tan\delta = \frac{\operatorname{Im} A}{\operatorname{Re} A} = -\frac{\gamma}{x}. \qquad \text{(A7.2)}$$

The characteristics of such a resonance are most simply described in terms of the Argand diagram, which is a plot of Im A versus Re A (see Figure A7.1). An elastic resonance ($\Gamma_{el} = \Gamma$) is described by a circle of unit diameter on the Argand diagram, in which the circle is traversed in a counterclockwise direction with increasing energy E.

The shape of the resonance

$$\operatorname{Im} A = |A|^2 \qquad \text{(A7.3)}$$

is plotted in Figure A7.2, while the value of Re A is shown in Figure A7.3.

Double-Pole Resonance

The amplitude for a double pole is given by

$$A' = \frac{1}{2i}\left\{\left(\frac{x - i\gamma}{x + i\gamma}\right)^2 - 1\right\}. \qquad \text{(A7.4)}$$

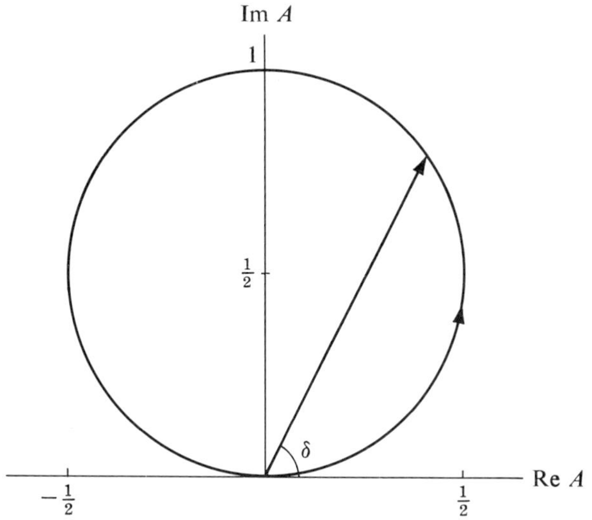

Figure A7.1 Argand diagram for an elastic Breit–Wigner resonance.

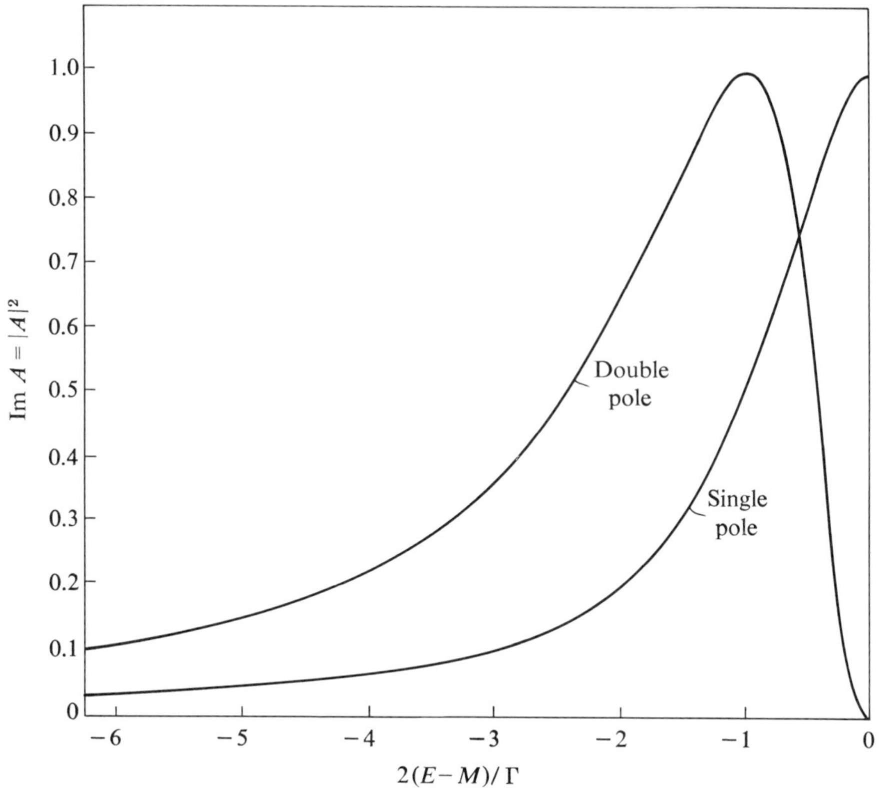

Figure A7.2 Im $A = |A|^2$ versus x/γ for a single- and double-pole Breit–Wigner resonance.

The shapes of Im A' and Re A' are plotted in Figures A7.2 and A7.3, respectively. Note that in the Argand diagram (Figure A7.1) for a double pole, the circle is traversed at twice the rate as for the ordinary Breit–Wigner resonance — i.e., one complete traversal is completed as the energy increases from 0 to $E_r = M$, and the pattern is repeated in going from $E = E_r$ to $E \to \infty$.

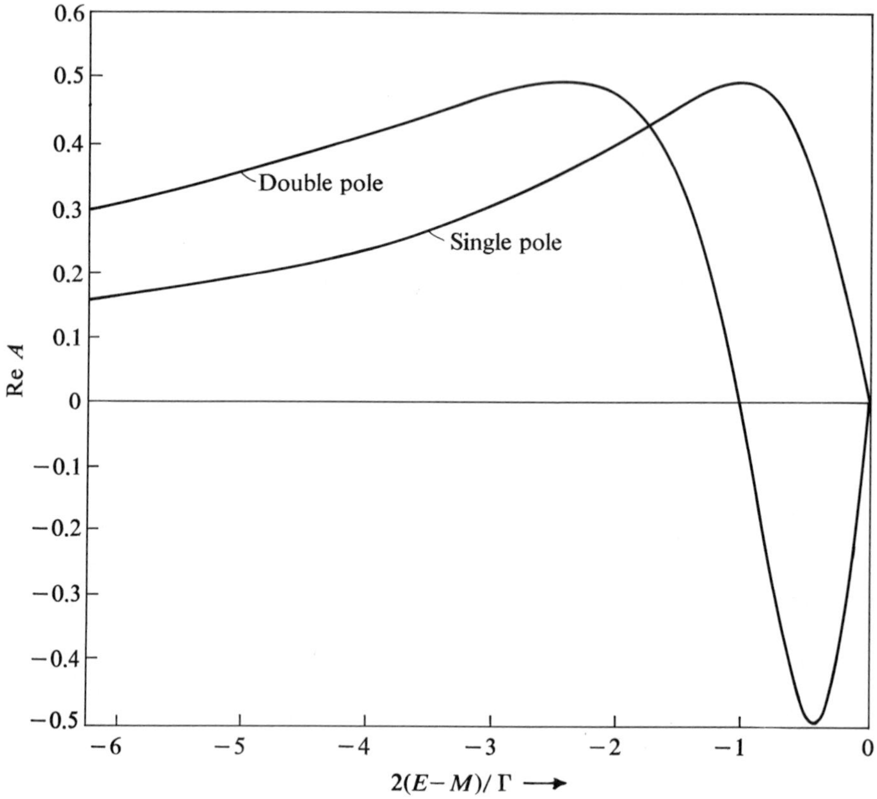

Figure A7.3 Re A versus x/γ for Breit–Wigner single- and double-pole resonances.

Dipole Resonance

The shape of a dipole resonance, for which

$$A_2(E, E_r, \Gamma_1, \Gamma_2) = A(E, E_r, \Gamma_1) - A(E, E_r, \Gamma_2) \qquad \text{(A7.5)}$$

is very similar to that of the double pole, except that whereas, in the case of the double pole, the ratio of the half-width of the total resonance to that of the central dip is fixed at $(\sqrt{2}+1)/(\sqrt{2}-1)$, the corresponding ratio for the dipole varies with the value of Γ_2/Γ_1, as shown in Figure A7.4.

The difference between a dipole (or double-pole) resonance and two overlapping resonances of different spin-parity values is that, in the case of the former, the amplitudes add coherently, while the overlapping, independent resonances do not interfere. The two cases can be distinguished on the basis of the shape of the resonance, provided the experimental energy resolution is sufficient.

Another possibility for a double peak is that of two closely spaced, independent (overlapping) resonances that happen to have the same spin-parity values; in this case, however, the phases and relative strengths of the resonances are arbitrary, and the result will resemble a dipole resonance only by accident.

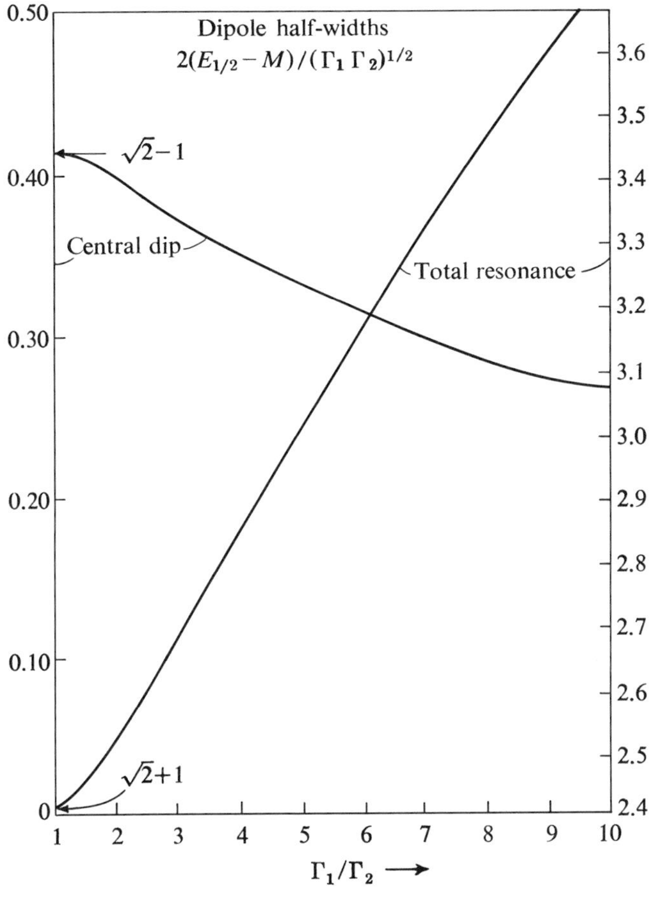

Figure A7.4 Half-width of resonance and of central dip for a dipole resonance versus Γ_1/Γ_2.

Present Status of Experimental Results Relating to *CP* Violation[a]

by Jack Steinberger

A Conference on the weak interaction was held at CERN during January.[b] Although the experimental situation concerning *CP* violation is not yet as clear as one would like, the results reported to the Conference, as well as other recent experimental results, have produced some clarification.

CP violation has been seen in three reactions: (1) the decay of the long-lived neutral kaon, K_L, into two charged pions; (2) the decay of K_L into two neutral pions, and (3) in the reactions $K_L \rightarrow \text{lepton} + \text{pion} + \text{neutrino}$ where a small charge asymmetry is observed. The results of these measurements are the following:

$$\eta_{+-} = \frac{\langle \pi^+\pi^- | T | K_L \rangle}{\langle \pi^+\pi^- | T | K_S \rangle} = (1.9 \pm 0.05) \times 10^{-3}\, e^{i(40\pm6)^\circ},$$

$$\eta_{00} = \frac{\langle \pi^0\pi^0 | T | K_L \rangle}{\langle \pi^0\pi^0 | T | K_S \rangle} = (2.5 \pm 0.7) \times 10^{-3}\, e^{i(17\pm31)^\circ},$$

$$\delta = \frac{N_+ - N_-}{N_+ + N_-} = (2.7 \pm 0.3) \times 10^{-3}.$$

η_{+-} and η_{00} are, roughly speaking, the *CP*-violating amplitudes in $K \rightarrow 2\pi$ decay and δ is the charge asymmetry in leptonic decay. All effects are of the order of 2×10^{-3}. Attempts to observe *CP* violation in other reactions have not been convincingly successful and have therefore established only upper limits.

---

[a] Reprinted from *Comments on Nuclear and Particle Physics, 3:* 73–4 (1969) with permission of Professor Steinberger and the publisher.

[b] CERN Topical Conference on Weak Interactions, Geneva, 1969.

The dominant question of the structure of the *CP*-violating interaction is not yet resolved, although the new data permit some progress. The data are now in agreement with the so-called superweak model. This model postulates a *CP*-violating interaction which is very weak (the strength is 10^{-9} times the strength of the ordinary weak interaction) and which connects states which differ in strangeness by two units. It predicts that *CP*-violating effects other than those already observed should be so small as to be practically unobservable. Furthermore it has the commendable property that all *CP*-violating effects can be written in terms of a single parameter, so that the predictions are very definite. These predictions are:

(1) $\eta_{+-} = \eta_{00}$,

(2) $\arg \eta = \tan^{-1} 2(m_L - m_S)/(\Gamma_L + \Gamma_S) = (42 \pm 1)^\circ$,

(3) $\delta = 2 \operatorname{Re} \eta_{+-} = 2 \operatorname{Re} \eta_{00}$.

Here m_L, m_S and Γ_L, Γ_S are the masses and widths of the long- and short-lived neutral kaons. As can be seen, these predictions are in good agreement with the experimental results.

Other models exist, the so-called milliweak models, in which the *CP* violation is the result of a term of the order of 10^{-3} in the strong or weak interaction Lagrangians.

These models make similar, but not identical, predictions as the superweak for the three observed processes. Furthermore, there are many ways of introducing a milliweak interaction and the predictions depend on this choice. With the present accuracy, discrimination between milliweak and superweak is not possible; however, a ten-fold improvement in accuracy should be sufficient for this. Such an experimental improvement seems possible in the near future.

The suggestion has also been made that *C* violation in the electromagnetic interaction is responsible. Attempts to find other effects of such a *C* violation have not yielded a convincing positive result, although a high sensitivity has been achieved, especially in the measurement of the neutron electric-dipole moment. However, the *C*-violating term in electrodynamics can be proposed in a variety of ways, and the calculations, especially in the case of the neutron dipole moment, cannot be unambiguously performed. At present the model cannot be ruled out.

Author Index

NOTE: This index contains the names of the authors of works cited in the footnotes. In many citations, papers by more than one author are identified by giving the name of the first-listed author (for example, A. Aaron, *et al.*). However, in such cases, all the authors are included in the index.

When there is more than one such footnote on a page, the footnote referred to is given in parentheses after the page number. If a particular footnote has more than one citation, the name of the identifying author is also given.

General Index

A B C D E F G H I J 5 4 3 2 1 7 0 6 9

General Atomic and Nuclear Constants

$$N = 6.02252 \times 10^{23} \text{ mole}^{-1} \text{ (based on } A_{C12} = 12)$$
$$c = 2.997925 \times 10^{10} \text{ cm sec}^{-1}$$
$$e = 4.80298 \times 10^{-10} \text{ esu} = 1.60210 \times 10^{-19} \text{ coulomb}$$
$$1 \text{ Mev} = 1.60210 \times 10^{-6} \text{ erg}$$
$$\hbar = 6.5819 \times 10^{-22} \text{ Mev sec}$$
$$= 1.05449 \times 10^{-27} \text{ erg sec}$$
$$\hbar c = 1.9732 \times 10^{-11} \text{ Mev cm} = 197.32 \text{ Mev fermi}$$
$$k = 8.6171 \times 10^{-11} \text{ Mev deg}^{-1} \text{ (Boltzmann const.)}$$
$$\alpha = e^2/\hbar c = 1/137.0388$$
$$m_e = 0.511006 \text{ MeV}/c^2 = 1/1836.10\ m_p$$
$$m_p = 938.256 \text{ MeV}/c^2 = 1836.10\ m_e = 6.721\ m_{\pi^\pm}$$
$$= 1.00727663\ m_1 \text{ (where } m_1 = 1 \text{ amu} = \tfrac{1}{12} m_{C12} = 931.478 \text{ MeV}/c^2)$$
$$r_e = e^2/m_e c^2 = 2.81777 \text{ fermi (1 fermi} = 10^{-13} \text{ cm)}$$
$$\lambda\!\!\!^{-}_e = \hbar/m_e c = r_e \alpha^{-1} = 3.86144 \times 10^{-11} \text{ cm}$$
$$a_{\infty \text{ Bohr}} = \hbar^2/m_e e^2 = r_e \alpha^{-2} = 0.529167 \text{ A (1 A} = 10^{-8} \text{ cm)}$$
$$\sigma_{\text{Thompson}} = \tfrac{8}{3}\pi r_e^2 = 0.66516 \times 10^{-24} \text{ cm}^2 = 0.66516 \text{ barn}$$
$$R_\infty = m_e e^4/2\hbar^2 = m_e c^2 \alpha^2/2 = 13.60535 \text{ eV (Rydberg)}$$

Hydrogen-like atom (non-rel., μ = reduced mass)

$$E_n = \mu z^2 e^4/2(n\hbar)^2; \quad a_{n=1} = \hbar^2/\mu z e^2; \quad v/c_{\text{rms}} = ze^2/n\hbar c$$
$$\mu_{\text{Bohr}} = e\hbar/2m_e c = 0.578817 \times 10^{-14} \text{ MeV gauss}^{-1}$$
$$\mu_{\text{nucl}} = e\hbar/2m_p c = 3.1524 \times 10^{-18} \text{ MeV gauss}^{-1}$$
$$\tfrac{1}{2}\omega_{\text{cyclotron}} \begin{cases} = e/2m_e c = 8.79404 \times 10^6 \text{ rad sec}^{-1} \text{ gauss}^{-1} \\ = e/2m_p c = 4.7895 \times 10^3 \text{ rad sec}^{-1} \text{ gauss}^{-1} \end{cases}$$
$$\sigma_{\text{natural}} = \pi(\hbar/m_{\pi^\pm} c)^2 = 62.768 \text{ mb}$$

Note: These constants are based mainly on E. R. Cohen and J. W. M. DuMond, *Rev. Mod. Phys.*, *37*: 537 (1965).